Physics

L. PAUL ELLIOTT

Late Professor of Physical Sciences
University of Florida

AND

WILLIAM F. WILCOX

Assistant Professor of Physics
Eastern Michigan College

Editorial Consultant

IRVING ORFUSS

Physics Instructor
New York City Public Schools

Physics

A MODERN APPROACH

New York
THE MACMILLAN COMPANY

© THE MACMILLAN COMPANY 1957

All rights reserved—no part of this book may be reproduced in any form without permission in writing from the publisher, except by a reviewer who wishes to quote brief passages in connection with a review written for inclusion in magazine or newspaper.

Printed in the United States of America

Cover and title page photograph reproduced with permission of Boeing Airplane Co. and Ewing Galloway.

Contents

Unit 1 The Beginning of Physics

Chapter 1 Falling Bodies

How a scientific controversy involving falling bodies led to the beginning of experimental physics. — 1

Chapter 2 The Method of Science: The Challenge of Our Age

How various methods have been employed in seeking truth and how the scientific method overcomes the defects of other methods. — 6

Chapter 3 The Role of Measurement in Science

How the need for a scientific system of measurement arose and how the English and metric systems compare. — 14

Chapter 4 The Role of Mathematics in Science

How some basic mathematical tools—formulas, ratios, proportions, and graphs—are used by the scientist. — 23

Chapter 5 Force, Gravity, Weight, Mass, Density, and Friction

How some commonly misused terms are precisely defined by scientists. — 30

Unit 2 Forces in Water and Other Liquids

Chapter 6 Liquid Forces in Open Vessels

How liquid forces act in open containers and how fluid pressure is measured. — 43

Chapter 7 Specific Gravity and Archimedes' Principle

How a basic principle of liquid forces can be applied in determining specific gravity, density, and the ability of a body to float. — 55

Chapter 8 Machines Which Transmit Forces through Liquids: Hydraulic Machines

How Pascal's Law explains a wide variety of applications of fluid pressure.   65

Unit 3 Forces in Air and Other Gases

Chapter 9 Forces Caused by the Earth's Atmosphere

How atmospheric forces are measured and utilized for practical purposes.   77

Chapter 10 Compression and Expansion in Gases

How a fundamental relationship between the pressure and volume of a gas is developed and how the behavior of gases is applied in several devices.   90

Chapter 11 Forces in High-Speed Liquids and Gases

How a single principle explains such diverse phenomena as the "curve" of a pitched ball and supersonic flight.   99

Unit 4 Forces and the Equilibrium of Bodies

Chapter 12 How to Combine and Control Forces

How an understanding of the composition and resolution of forces may save you work and may protect you from injury.   109

Chapter 13 Levers, Moment of Force, Center of Gravity, and Stability of Bodies

How the conditions necessary to hold a body in equilibrium are determined.   119

Unit 5 The Riddle of Motion

Chapter 14 Distance, Velocity, Time, and Acceleration

How the relationships among these factors enable us to derive some basic equations on accelerated motion.   133

Chapter 15 A Further Study of Falling Bodies

How an experimental determination of g enables us to broaden our understanding of the motion of falling bodies.   144

Chapter 16 Newton's Laws of Motion

How three basic laws explain the forces causing certain kinds of motion.   154

Chapter 17 **Circular and Rotary Motion**

How several applications of centrifugal force and rotary motion are explained.   170

Chapter 18 **Projectile Motion**

How some problems of concern to the track star and the prospective interplanetary traveler are analyzed.   180

Unit 6 Work and Machines

Chapter 19 **Work, Power, and Energy**

How the physicist distinguishes among these key terms and measures each of them.   193

Chapter 20 **Simple Machines**

How the simple machines operate and how their efficiency is determined.   205

Unit 7 Concerning the Nature of Matter

Chapter 21 **Molecular Physics**

How the molecular theory of matter explains a variety of physical phenomena and leads to the development of the kinetic theory of matter.   219

Unit 8 The Universe of Heat

Chapter 22 **What Are Heat and Temperature?**

How a controversy on the nature of heat was resolved and how temperature is measured.   231

Chapter 23 **Expansion**

How solids and liquids expand and how the practically uniform behavior of all gases enables us to formulate a general gas law.   239

Chapter 24 **Measurement of Heat**

How heat phenomena are measured and applied in our daily living.   251

Chapter 25 **The Transference of Heat**

How the three methods of heat transfer are both used and avoided.   264

Chapter 26   Work and Heat

    How the mechanical equivalent of heat is measured, how the heat of combustion is computed, and how the various heat engines operate.   275

Unit 9   Weather and Climate

Chapter 27   Humidity and Weather

    How the factors that determine our weather are analyzed and how weather predictions are made.   291

Unit 10   Sound

Chapter 28   The Nature of Sound

    How sound as a form of wave motion is produced and transmitted.   311

Chapter 29   Musical Sounds

    How the physicist interprets the world of music.   325

Unit 11   Static Electricity

Chapter 30   What Is Electricity?

    How the elektron *of the ancient world was revived to explain the behavior of charged bodies.*   341

Chapter 31   The Electron Theory versus the Atomic Theory of Matter

    How these two theories of matter explain electrical conductivity and electric current.   351

Chapter 32   How Does the Electron Theory Explain Leyden Jars, Condensers, and Lightning?

    How a "shocking" device led scientists to conduct some dangerous experiments to probe the nature of static electricity.   363

Unit 12   Magnetism

Chapter 33   What Is Magnetism?

    How the characteristic behavior of magnets is explained by the electron theory.   375

Chapter 34   What Is the Connecting Link between Magnetism and Electricity?

    How a new era began with the discovery of a simple relationship.   385

Unit 13   *Production of Electric Current and Electrical Measurement*

Chapter 35   **The Production of Electric Current by Chemicals**

How an experiment with a dead frog has had some rather far-reaching consequences.   399

Chapter 36   **How Oersted's Discovery Opened the Way for Measuring Electricity**

How one effect of an electric current is employed to measure electric currents.   412

Unit 14   *Electric Circuits*

Chapter 37   **Laws Governing Electric Circuits**

How series and parallel wiring of resistors may be analyzed and compared quantitatively.   427

Unit 15   *Electric Machines*

Chapter 38   **How an Electromotive Force Is Produced by Mechanical Means**

How Faraday's discovery is applied in generators and motors.   441

Chapter 39   **Induction Coils and Transformers**

How the ability to change a magnetic field electrically is applied in power transmission and in communication.   455

Unit 16   *Alternating Current*

Chapter 40   **Alternating Current**

How alternating current is measured and how its phase relations are analyzed.   467

Unit 17   *The Riddle of Light*

Chapter 41   **What Is Light?**

How two theories of light were advanced and how each explains reflection and refraction.   483

Chapter 42   **Interference, Polarization, and the Speed of Light**

How the wave theory gains additional support, but the measurement of the speed of light poses new problems.   496

Chapter 43 **Image Formation and Mirrors**
How the laws of reflection apply to the images formed by the various kinds of mirrors. 507

Chapter 44 **Lenses and Images**
How the laws of reflection and refraction explain image formation with lenses. 520

Chapter 45 **Optical Instruments**
How the principles of image formation by lenses are applied in several optical instruments. 531

Chapter 46 **The Eye**
How the human eye forms images and how visual defects are corrected. 540

Chapter 47 **Illumination and Better Seeing**
How light is measured and how your sight can be conserved. 551

Chapter 48 **The Riddle of Color**
How the color of objects is determined and how color is and should be used. 559

Chapter 49 **Spectra and the Emission and Absorption of Light**
How spectra are analyzed and how the discovery of the photoelectric effect led to a modified version of the corpuscular theory. 571

Unit 18   Electricity in Communication

Chapter 50 **Radio Communication**
How radio waves are generated, transmitted, and received. 587

Chapter 51 **Sound Movies, Television, and Radar**
How electrons provide us with entertainment and protection. 601

Unit 19   Nuclear Physics (Atomic Energy)

Chapter 52 **The Conquest of Atomic Energy**
How the equivalence of matter and energy was proved. 613

Chapter 53 **The Atom Is Harnessed and Civilization Is Challenged**
How the energy released by fission and fusion poses problems for all mankind. 627

Appendix 639

Index 645

Preface

Physics—A Modern Approach is your introduction to the study of physics, a subject with a very broad range. It will deal with a great many practical problems that you have undoubtedly wondered about—what lifts an airplane, how a boat sails into the wind, why a baseball pitcher "winds up" and "follows through," what causes glare and rainbows, and a host of others. In addition, you will study such recent developments as rocket propulsion, transistors, color television, and Geiger counters. But more important than the practical problems or the various technological developments, this book will concentrate on developing the fundamental principles of physics that will enable you to solve practical problems involving physical principles and to keep abreast of new scientific developments.

A Scientific Presentation. You will find that this book presents scientific principles in a way that is designed to help you understand the "whys" of physics. Each chapter starts with a problem whose outcome is unknown to you. As you read the problem, you will find that you may have asked yourself the same question or considered a similar situation.

Then you will follow the discussion as various scientific "guesses," or hypotheses, are proposed to explain a particular phenomenon. After analyzing each of the "guesses" logically and relating them to past observations or experiences, the most plausible "guess" will be tested by experiment. If the experiment confirms the hypothesis, the hypothesis becomes established tentatively as a theory or principle to explain a certain set of facts. If it does not confirm it, a new hypothesis must be proposed and tested by logic, observation, and experiment. This method of solving problems is called the scientific method. Needless to say, it offers an interesting way to learn how scientists come to grips with real problems and formulate conclusions. By following this procedure, you will be discovering the basic principles of physics for yourself, much as a scientist does.

Functional Use of Color. Another unique feature of this book is the use of a second color both in the text and in the line drawings. Important principles, laws, and formulas to be mastered are printed in red. To aid you in visualizing the dynamic aspects of the innumerable teaching diagrams, the motion of forces, the movement of electrons, and paths of light rays are shown in red.

Sample Problems. Scattered throughout the text are numerous problems and solutions. These solved problems appear immediately after an important principle or formula has been developed. In those cases where the subject matter warrants it, unsolved problems follow the illustrative examples to help you in checking your understanding.

Summaries and Conclusions at chapter ends will help you in reviewing the important points of the chapters. They also restate as conclusions the principles developed experimentally. The *Questions for Review* will check your understanding of the principles learned and your ability to apply those principles to new situations.

Problems. Particularly valuable in checking your mastery of the subject matter is the wide variety of problems. The problems are graded in difficulty from the simple to the complex. The first few problems in each set may involve substitution in a formula, while later problems of a given type may require the application of several principles. Remember that the more problems you solve, the more complete will be your understanding of the fundamental principles. To refresh your basic mathematical skills in using formulas, Chapter 4, "The Role of Mathematics in Science," will prove to be an invaluable aid. Mastery of the basic mathematical tools described there will give you a head start in your problem work.

Projects and Readings. To give you first-hand experience in demonstrating or applying principles, there are various projects at the ends of most chapters. Some of these projects are very simple and can be performed in a few minutes. Others are more challenging and will require you to improvise equipment. *Reading You Will Enjoy* suggests selections that will extend your scientific horizons as well as provide additional source material for projects and demonstrations.

The Adventure of Physics. As you explore this book, you will notice that the preliminary definition of the subject matter of physics is broadened by your contact with the various areas of physics. Not only will you discover many basic principles and applications, but you will also see that there are problems in many areas of physics that scientists have not yet completely solved. By studying some famous scientific controversies of the past, you can see how scientists at the frontiers of knowledge have solved important problems. There is a challenge in realizing that the expanding scientific frontier brings new problems to be solved by scientists of the future.

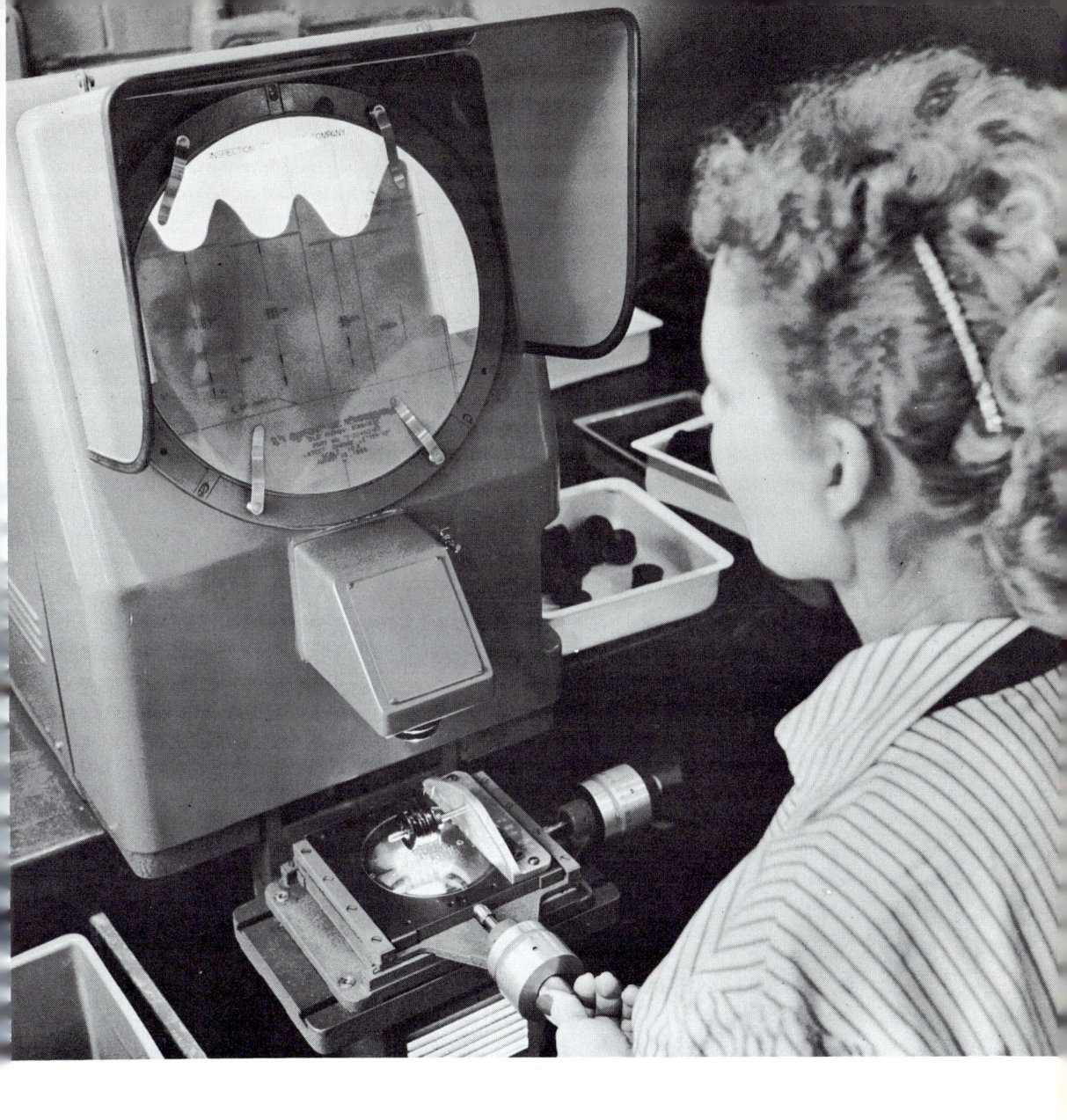

Unit 1

The Beginning of Physics

Modern industry, like physics, is built upon a solid foundation of accurate measurement. In the photograph on the preceding page, the technician is using a specially constructed gauge to measure the depth of grooves of rollers employed in the rayon yarn process. Each roller groove must be made to a range of accuracy, or tolerance, of a hundredth of an inch. Many industrial processes require even greater degrees of accuracy.

In this unit you will learn about some of the factors that contribute to making physics an exact science. Of paramount importance is the method used by scientists in solving a problem. You will also discover how this method can be applied to problems in your daily life. Then you will see how measurement is really scientific comparison and why different measurements are expressed in certain units. Finally, you will see how some simple tools of mathematics permit physicists to express a variety of physical relationships in shorthand form.

1. FALLING BODIES
2. THE METHOD OF SCIENCE — THE CHALLENGE OF OUR AGE
3. THE ROLE OF MEASUREMENT IN SCIENCE
4. THE ROLE OF MATHEMATICS IN SCIENCE
5. FORCE, GRAVITY, WEIGHT, MASS, DENSITY, AND FRICTION

Unit Photograph Courtesy du Pont "Better Living"

Chapter 1

Falling Bodies

The problem. You are all familiar with the old saying, "The bigger they come, the harder they fall." This is a favorite remark used by football coaches to encourage the small players to tackle the big fellows. And certainly your own experiences cause you to agree that heavy bodies fall harder than light ones.

You can imagine what would happen to you if you fell from the top of a 50-foot building to the ground. Yet perhaps you have seen a squirrel fall this far, hit the ground with a thud, and scamper off with no apparent injury. A mouse can fall fifty feet with little likelihood of injury, whereas a 50-pound dog would be crushed by the impact. Why is there so much difference? Why does a heavy body fall harder than a light one?

Some people will say it is because heavy bodies fall faster than light ones. "Do not stones, iron balls, and pieces of lead fall faster than feathers, leaves, and snowflakes?" they ask. Others will disagree, arguing that many light bodies will fall as fast as heavy ones. "Does not a pebble fall as fast as a large heavy stone?" they ask. So the argument goes, but it proves very little. It indicates, however, that if we are to find out why a heavy body falls harder than a light one, it would be wise to discover which one of them, if either, falls faster.

Aristotle's attempt to determine whether a light or a heavy body falls faster. About 2400 years ago Aristotle (384-322 B. C.), a Greek scholar, attempted to settle this argument. But instead of dropping a light ball and a heavy one together and observing their motion, as you would probably do, Aristotle reasoned that the speed of a falling body varies directly as its weight, and that therefore a two-pound ball falls twice as fast as a one-pound ball.

At that time few people, if any, were interested enough to question Aristotle's conclusion. As his reputation as a scholar grew, it became almost sacrilegious to question his word on any subject. And as late as A. D. 1500, it is said, "To be a scholar one had to know Aristotle by heart; to understand him was unimportant; to doubt him was blasphemy."

Galileo Galilei questions Aristotle's conclusion. Galileo Galilei (1564-1642), a young professor at the University of Pisa in Italy, was the first to really test Aristotle's conclusion. By experiment he found that a musket ball would fall as fast as a cannon ball. But when Galileo announced his discovery to his learned associates, most of whom were followers of Aristotle,

THE BEGINNING OF PHYSICS

Fig. 1. Galileo demonstrated that a light body falls as fast as a heavy body.

they refused to listen. Instead they ridiculed Galileo and asked, "What right has this young upstart to challenge the teachings of the great Aristotle?"

Partly to discredit his enemies but principally to prove them wrong, one morning before the assembled students and professors, Galileo climbed to the top of the now famous Leaning Tower of Pisa and simultaneously dropped a large cannon ball and a small musket ball. Together they fell and together they hit the ground. But still his opponents were not convinced, because what they saw was contrary to the teachings of Aristotle. With the exception of one professor, the whole teaching staff, as well as the heads of the University, turned against this young rebel.

Some historians question whether this experiment was performed under such impressive and dramatic circumstances, but they are quite certain that Galileo actually did perform it and that it set off a bitter controversy. The tower was an ideal place for the experiment because it leaned enough so that there was little danger of the balls striking its sides, and it was tall enough (183 feet high) so that the results of the test would be convincing. Because of this epochal experiment Galileo has been called the *father of experimental physics*.

Testing Galileo's results. Unless you prefer to be like Aristotle's followers, and not question what you are told, then you will want to compare for yourselves the speeds at which a heavy and a light body fall through air. To do this, take a small iron ball and a large iron ball and drop them together from a second or third story to the ground. The longer the fall, the more exacting the test. Have two or more observers on the ground to note which, if either, lands first. Why would it be well to repeat this experiment several times?

The guinea-and-feather experiment. Galileo's experiment proved that a heavy cannon ball does not fall faster than a light musket ball, but it did not explain why a stone falls faster than a feather. Galileo explained that the difference in speed is due to air resistance: air offers more resistance to a falling feather, in proportion to its weight, than to a stone. This *hypothesis,* an unproved explanation of facts, could be proved or disproved only by the dropping of a stone and a feather together in a vacuum.

Your school laboratory probably contains both an exhaust pump and a "vacuum" tube. Inside the tube are a feather and a metal disk. Early tubes of this type contained a feather and an English coin known as a guinea.

When the tube is exhausted of air, held vertically, and quickly inverted, the metal disk and the feather fall together. If the tube is full of air, the feather falls more slowly than the disk. Thus, as Galileo predicted, it appears that except for air resistance, an object as light as thistledown falls as fast as a ball of solid lead.

When the air and other resistance is completely absent or is negligible, so that only the force of gravity acts on a falling body, its motion is called *free fall*. Experimental tests show that for streamlined bodies falling from rest, the air resistance is almost negligible for the first 600 feet and hence the motion for this distance approximates free fall.

In conclusion, we may say that it is not necessarily difference in speeds that causes heavy bodies to fall harder than light ones. Suffice it to say that this question, with others concerning falling bodies, involves knowledge which is beyond the scope of this chapter. All will be considered later.

What do we study in physics? Many beginners enter physics with fear and trembling because they have a mistaken notion that it deals with things that are completely out of their world. Perhaps, though, by now you are beginning to realize that this is not true, because so far we have studied only things in everyday life.

In reality we have dealt with two things: matter and motion. *Matter includes air, water, stones, cannon balls, and other things which occupy space and have weight. Motion is continuous change of position.* Hence, in the light of our study so far, we can say that *physics is a study of matter and motion.*

Many may disagree with this definition because they know that physics includes machines, heat, sound, light, electricity, radio, and several related subjects. Can all these phenomena be reduced to mere matter and motion, as implied by the preceding definition of physics?

This question we could answer for you, but to do so would not be in keeping with the spirit of physics. The physicist works much like a detective; proposing and testing new ideas are part of his fun. So, as we progress in our studies, we should be continually on the lookout for any evidence which disagrees with the above definition. And in case we find such evidence, it will be our duty to redefine physics so that the new definition agrees with both the old and new evidence.

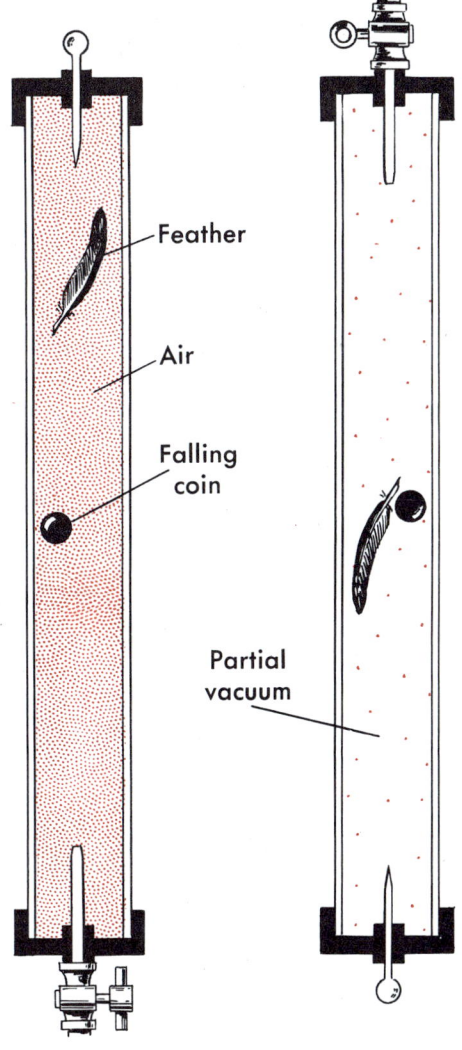

Fig. 2. In a vacuum, the feather and the lead ball fall freely at the same rate.

Courtesy Department of Defense

Fig. 3 The U. S. Navy "Pogo Stick," which is capable of taking off and landing in the position shown, is an excellent example of applied physics research in the study of motion. Experiments with vertical flight are being carried on to develop planes that can take off and land in a limited amount of space.

Fig. 4. Technicians are shown removing spent uranium fuel elements from an atomic reactor. This giant reactor is largely used by atomic scientists in basic research on the nature of matter.

Courtesy Brookhaven National Laboratory

QUESTIONS FOR REVIEW

1. What is one fundamental difference between the method used by Aristotle and that used by Galileo for finding truth?
2. What is matter? Motion? Give three examples of matter.
3. How have we defined physics thus far?

PROJECTS

1. Cut out two pieces of paper of the same size and weight, crumple one into a compact ball, and then drop them together. Account for the results. What do they tend to prove?
2. Place a small piece of paper on top of a coin which is held flat and then drop the coin so that it does not turn over or tip. Account for the results.
3. Which will coast downhill the faster, a soapbox cart containing one boy or one with two boys in it? Test your answer by experiment.
4. If one of two metal balls is heavier than the other, both have the same diameter, and both sink in water, will they fall together in water as they do in air? Test your answer by experiment and explain the results.

READING YOU WILL ENJOY

1. Galileo, *Two New Sciences,* pp. 61-67. Northwestern University Press, Evanston, Illinois, 1950 Edition. Tells in dialogue of the controversy between Galileo and his opponents concerning the nature of the motion of falling bodies.
2. De Harasanyi, Zsolt, *The Star Gazer*. G. P. Putnam's Sons, New York, 1939. An excellent modern story of Galileo of interest to both students and teachers.
3. Wilson, Grove, *Great Men of Science*. Garden City Publishing Company, Inc., Garden City, New York, 1929. Not only gives an interesting account of Galileo but includes short stories about Roger Bacon, Copernicus, and Kepler, whose discoveries and thinking pointed the way for Galileo.

Chapter 2

The Method of Science: The Challenge of Our Age

The challenge. Carved in the white walls of the Riverside Church on the banks of the Hudson River in New York City are the figures of six hundred great men of the ages. In one panel are the figures of fourteen scientists spanning the centuries from Hippocrates, who died about 370 B.C., to Albert Einstein, who was chosen from among the modern scientists.

Why Einstein is represented there in preference to other modern scientists, few of the thousands who worship every week in that great cathedral would know. In other words, what has really been going on in modern science for over 400 years, and particularly during the past 50 years, is almost unknown except by a few. The gadgets and luxuries produced by science have been eagerly accepted by all, but the spirit, attitudes, ways of thinking, and the responsibility in thought and action needed to live with modern science are yet to be learned and accepted by most people. This condition is most unfortunate. For as Einstein said, *"Restricting the body of knowledge to a small group deadens the philosophical spirit of a people and leads to spiritual poverty."*

Why the spirit of science and scientific ways of acting and thinking have not been developed and eagerly accepted is difficult to understand when we stop to consider that in terms of the hundreds of centuries that man has inhabited the earth it was only a few seconds ago that man was still dreaming, like his ancestors in the distant past, of flying machines; of horseless carriages; of boats which he would not have to row; and of machines with which he could flash messages around the earth, to the moon, or to other heavenly bodies. Electric lights, atomic energy, talking pictures, and television were hardly thought of. Today all these things are realities. Since the time of Galileo, in fact during the past fifty years, science has progressed more than during all previous time. And today science is marching forward at an ever-swifter pace.

Socially, in certain respects, we seem to be going backward. War, rather than peace, seems to be the natural state of affairs. This is tragic, but perhaps no more so than the fact that in America, during World War II and the wars which followed, the death toll caused by automobiles exceeded that caused by war. Also, during these same years there was a steady increase each year in juvenile delinquency, robbery, sex crimes, murder, and divorce, all of which were already at all-time highs.

And when there occurred very early in the morning of July 5, 1945, at a remote spot on the desert sands of Alamogordo, New Mexico, an enormous man-made atomic explosion, the social lag was increased more than ever.

As a result of the discovery of atomic energy, radar, electronics, jet propulsion, and rocket ships, we now stand on the threshold of a new age, the Atomic Age. Science has set the stage and put into our hands a tool with which we can either create a good life or completely destroy ourselves. Which shall we do? This is the challenge which science presents to our age.

But why, you ask, have other fields of thought not kept pace with science? Why have the method and spirit of science not been widely and universally accepted? What methods, other than the scientific method, has man used to solve problems, and what makes modern science so productive?

Perhaps we can answer these questions by making a study of the most important methods which man has used and still uses to solve problems and find dependable knowledge or truth.

Appeal to authority. When we were children, it seemed that our curiosities could never be satisfied; we wanted to know about everything. To learn, we asked questions of our parents or others in whom we had confidence, and generally we accepted without question what we were told.

If we turn back the pages of history, we find that this was the chief method used by primitive people. But often questions arose which the elder people felt themselves incompetent to answer. These were taken to the medicine man, who was supposed to possess powers and knowledge not possessed by ordinary men. This method of

Alan W. Richards

Fig. 1. The late Albert Einstein, whose research in physics provided the theoretical foundations for the development of the atomic bomb.

solving problems and finding truth is known as *appeal to authority*.

Today, a variation of appeal to authority is used by the palmist who reads your past and future by examining the lines in the palm of your hand. It is also used by the bearded and turbaned crystal gazer who can foretell, by consulting a crystal ball, everything from one's future love life to the ups and downs of the stock market.

Besides these "authorities" there are the astrologers who can predict your lucky and unlucky days by reading the stars. Also there is the water "witch" who can locate underground streams of water or oil, or veins of gold and other valuable metal ores, by interpreting the behavior of a peach limb when it is held in his hands. Then there are those who look to a rabbit foot, a horseshoe, or certain numbers such as seven or eleven to bring good luck.

Fig. 2. If any of the above influence your actions, you are appealing to authority.

The shortcomings of the method of appeal to authority are that it makes us entirely dependent upon others for knowledge and it provides within itself no test of truth, no test of what we are told. Everything must be taken on faith. As a consequence it does not train us to become the independent learners and thinkers that we must be if we are to live full, intelligent lives in a scientific and democratic world. However, since it is impossible to learn everything at first hand by ourselves, we are forced on many occasions to resort to authority. Granted this is true, our problem becomes one of knowing dependable authority. Whose writings do you say are the better authority on falling bodies, Galileo's or Aristotle's? Why?

Reasoning. Another method of finding truth is reasoning. Perhaps you already know that if you agree to, let us say, two basic ideas or assumptions, then in consequence you have to agree to a third idea. For example, if you agree that all normal boys have two hands and that Tom Smith is a normal boy, then you must agree that Tom Smith has two hands.

From the foregoing it is evident that if we take the proper steps, we can start with a few basic truths and from them derive many others. It should be noted, though, that two basic requirements must be met if we are to obtain truth by reasoning. First, the thinking must be straight; that is, each step must follow logically from the step which precedes it. For example, we might say that all normal boys have two hands and that Jo has two hands. But we cannot logically say therefore that Jo is a boy, because we have not said that *only* boys have two hands. Jo may stand for Josephine as well as for Joseph.

Second, even with the best of logic, the final results of reasoning will seldom be more truthful than the beliefs or assumptions from which the reasoning starts. For example, we may assume that the sun rises only because our neighbor's rooster crows every morning just before sunrise. Therefore we may conclude that if the rooster dies, the sun will never rise again.

This conclusion is false, but its falsity is not due to faulty reasoning. The error was in our assuming that the rooster caused the sun to rise. The conclusion was based on a false assumption. But unless the reasoning is faulty, the method of reasoning furnishes virtually no way for us to know whether either the assumption or the conclusion is correct. In spite of its faults, however, the ability to reason is one of man's most prized assets.

Observation. Another method that has been used to obtain truth and to answer questions is observation. According to advocates of this method, truth is what one tastes, touches, smells, hears, and sees; that is, what one observes. The hardboiled skeptical advocates of this doctrine put no faith in ideas obtained by revelation, dreaming, armchair theorizing, or by imagination. "To find truth," they say, "look to material things—to nature."

They say the duties of the scientist should be confined to observing, recording, and classifying facts. Once this is done, facts speak for themselves. Imagination, reasoning, and theorizing have no

THE METHOD OF SCIENCE: THE CHALLENGE OF OUR AGE

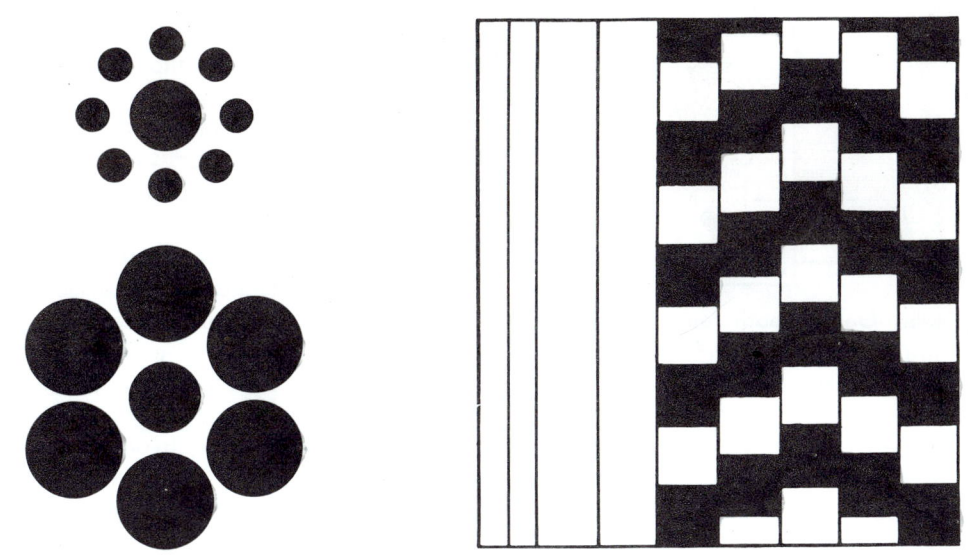

Fig. 3. Are the circles in the center equal in size? Are all the lines parallel? What do these drawings suggest to you about the reliability of our powers of observation?

place in finding truth, because the true scientist does not formulate truth. Instead he uncovers it much as one finds the kernel in a hard-shelled nut.

Opponents of the method of observation point out its weakness when they argue, "To our sense of sight the sun is as small as a pumpkin and the stars look like a rash on the sky." Also they say, "A baboon can hear, see, feel, taste, and smell better than a man; therefore a baboon is better fitted to judge truth than a sage."

Hypothesis and experiment—the method of science. Galileo applied the method of science—hypothesis and experiment—to the problem of falling bodies. So let us make a detailed study of Galileo's method and compare it with Aristotle's.

You will recall that Aristotle proposed the hypothesis that the heavier a body is, the faster it falls, and that therefore a two-pound ball falls twice as fast as a one-pound ball. Then Galileo showed by experiment that when a heavy cannon ball and a light musket ball are dropped together, they fall together. But still there remained the indisputable fact that a heavy stone falls faster than a feather, which tended to support Aristotle's hypothesis. Certainly not all the evidence supported either side.

Aristotle arrived at his conclusion chiefly by reasoning from assumption. Galileo arrived at his conclusion both by reasoning and by experiment. The followers of Aristotle, however, would not accept experimental results. They would accept only logical proof.

So in order to test by means of logic (reason) both his own and Aristotle's

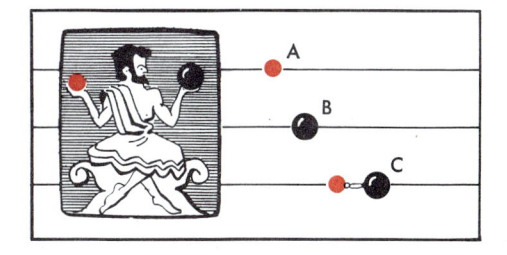

Fig. 4. Aristotle reasoned that C would fall three times as fast as A. Why did Galileo reason that this was not true?

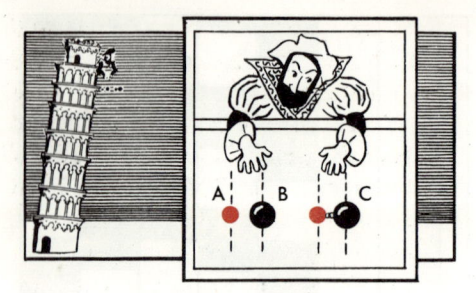

Fig. 5. Galileo both reasoned and demonstrated that A, B, and C would fall at the same rate.

hypothesis, Galileo considered the logical consequences of each; what other ideas would logically have to be true if either hypothesis were true. Aristotle's hypothesis meant that a two-pound ball would fall twice as fast as a one-pound ball, and if the two balls were tied together they would fall three times as fast as the one-pound ball alone.

On the other hand, when the two balls were tied together, it was just as logical to reason that since the one-pound ball would not fall as fast as the two-pound ball, then the one-pound ball would retard the two-pound ball so that the three-pound combination would not fall three times as fast as the one-pound ball alone. Thereby Galileo showed that there were at least two logical consequences of Aristotle's hypothesis, one as logical as the other, that were in total disagreement with each other. He also showed that, except for one or two instances, the logical consequences of Aristotle's hypothesis did not agree with experimental results or observation.

Next Galileo considered the logical consequences of his own hypothesis. It meant that a one-pound ball and a two-pound ball would fall together when dropped together, and that if the two were tied together the three-pound combination would fall with the same speed as either of the two balls alone. Not only did the logical consequences of Galileo's hypothesis agree with each other, they also agreed with observation and experiment. Everything, except for the fact that a stone falls faster than a feather, was in agreement. And for this exception Galileo had a very logical explanation.

Further analysis of the method of hypothesis and experiment. Thus we see that Galileo started with a problem which arose because there was a conflict between Aristotle's hypothesis and observation. To solve the problem Galileo set about formulating a new hypothesis that would agree with what he observed. Then he predicted the logical consequences of both hypotheses and tested these consequences experimentally. From Aristotle's hypothesis he deduced several conflicting possibilities, most of which did not happen when tested experimentally. From his own hypothesis he deduced several logical consequences, all of which were confirmed by experiment.

Finally Galileo rejected one hypothesis and accepted the other one because it brought into agreement three basic factors: an imagined hypothesis, reasoned consequences, and experimental outcome.

The steps may be listed as follows:

1. Recognition of a problem.
2. Formulation of one or more tentative hypotheses based upon assumption and the available known facts.
3. Prediction of the natural events which would logically have to happen if each hypothesis were true.
4. Performance of experiments which determine whether the predicted natural events actually happen.
5. Formulation of the *simplest* possible conclusion which brings into agreement three basic factors: an imagined hypothesis, reasoned consequences, and experimental outcome.

In case the experimental results agree with the reasoned consequences deduced from a given hypothesis, the hypothesis is strengthened. But in case they disagree, doubt is cast upon the hypothesis and it must be revised or totally rejected and the last four steps must be repeated until a satisfactory hypothesis is formulated.

"Science proceeds," said Sir James Jeans, the great English physicist, "by building up hypotheses, each of which covers more phenomena than its predecessor, but each of which may have to give place to another hypothesis in due course. Strictly speaking, the time for replacing a hypothesis by a claim to certainty never arrives."

The plan of this book. In writing this book, the authors hope to help its readers conduct for themselves scientific studies of problems which lie in the general field of high school physics. Such studies, if they are to be scientific, must therefore *begin* with problems and *end* with conclusions. And between the beginning and end of each study you should expect to find the formulation of hypotheses and the testing of these hypotheses by observation, past experience, and experiment. Do not expect, as you often find in "science" textbooks, to have questions answered for you as soon as they are asked. Genuinely scientific studies are not like that. Furthermore, even though you may believe that your teacher or your textbook writer knows the answer, you can hardly consider yourself a scientific thinker unless you think your own way through each and every problem, always questioning every conclusion and demanding both logical and experimental proof.

By dividing the book into units and the units into chapters, we take bigger problems and divide them up into smaller ones, the solution to each smaller problem contributing in turn to the final solution of the larger one. But you should recognize also that the units are related to one another, and that ideally your study of each subsequent unit should, and perhaps will, definitely modify and enrich the ideas you have developed in each and all previous units.

Moreover, your study of physics as a whole should contribute to the ideas you have developed in other courses, scientific and otherwise. And the ideas developed in other courses should modify those of physics. Try to develop a wide outlook on life which is in agreement and harmony in all phases. Only by resolving the conflicts in our daily lives and carrying this principle over to the solution of state, national, and international problems can we meet the challenge of modern science.

QUESTIONS FOR REVIEW

1. Choose the correct answer:

A. If you wanted to purchase a new car in a given price range, whose advice would you value most highly in making the final decision: (a) one expressed in an advertisement, (b) that of a salesman who tries to sell you a car, (c) that of a man who owns one in this price range, (d) that of a mechanic with years of experience in repairing the makes of cars considered? Give reasons for your choice.

B. If you wanted to know weather conditions twenty-four hours in advance, which would you consult: (a) a fortune teller, (b) an almanac, (c) the latest weather report and map, (d) a neighbor who tells by his rheumatism when a storm is coming? Give reasons for your answer.

C. Which of the following would carry the most weight if you were deciding whether or not an idea is true: (a) the reputation of the person advocating it, (b) the loudness and conviction with which it is proposed, (c) the number of people who believe it, (d) whether or not you wish it to be true, (e) the length of time it has been believed to be true,

(f) the fact that all its logical consequences have been verified by widely repeated experiment?

D. A scientific theory may be said to be entirely satisfactory if (a) it accounts for over half of the observed facts, (b) it is based upon common sense, (c) almost everybody agrees with it, (d) most of the leading scientists agree with it, (e) it has been believed for a long time, (f) it accounts for every bit of the known evidence.

2. What are the chief shortcomings of obtaining knowledge from authority? How must the authority obtain his knowledge if it is to be accepted by a scientist?

3. If truth is to be found by reasoning, what two requirements must be satisfied?

4. Study each of the following and, if possible, state whether (1) the basic ideas (assumptions) are adequate, (2) the reasoning is accurate, (3) the conclusion is true:

(a) Jack is a "good fellow" and is well liked. Therefore he should make a good captain of the football team.

(b) Only Boy Scouts are to be admitted free to the football game next Saturday. Jack is not a Boy Scout. He will not be admitted free.

(c) Statistics show that few people ever die past the age of 90. Mr. Jones is 95 years old. Therefore he will live for a long time.

(d) Statistics show that the number of arrests for crime increases as the number of policemen is increased. This proves that police cause crime.

(e) Ann uses X brand of soap. Ann is a beautiful girl. All girls who want to be beautiful should use X brand of soap.

5. Can a scientific hypothesis be of value even though it is later abandoned? Explain.

PROJECTS

1. Study the reasoning of your friends, advertisements, and editorials. Bring samples to class and discuss the assumptions on which the conclusions were based. Also decide whether the assumptions were true, the reasoning was good, and the conclusions were correct.

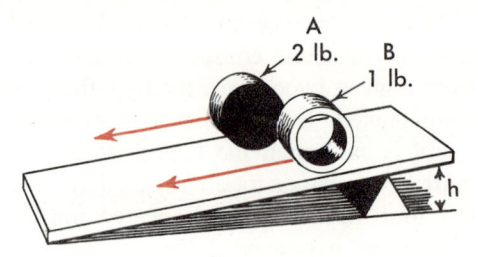

2. Discuss the differences between the ways in which a scientist and a propagandist use facts in reaching a conclusion and the difference between their attitudes.

3. Suppose that nothing happens when you turn on your flashlight. Write out, following the steps of the scientific method, how you would determine what was wrong with it. Assume that you have available a new battery, new bulb, and other replacement parts. Propose at least three hypotheses and explain how you would test each experimentally.

4.* As shown in Fig. 6, allow a 2-pound cylinder of solid metal and a 1-pound hollow cylinder to roll down an inclined plane (start them from rest). Using the scientific method, explain how you would find the true cause of the observed results. You may need to formulate and test several hypotheses. The intended solution does not involve knowledge of energy or other concepts not yet studied.

5. With the help of your teacher and others, organize a science club in your school. Suggestions that can be used in programs will be given among the projects and experiments in the chapters that follow.

READING YOU WILL ENJOY

1. *The Divining Rod, A History of Water Witching.* Water Supply Paper 416, U. S. Government.

*This problem is of special importance. It is referred to later.

2. Fielding, William J., *Strange Superstitions and Magical Practices*. The Blakiston Company, Inc., New York, 1945. Tells of many past and present superstitions.

3. Kellock, Harold, *Houdini, His Life Story*. Harcourt, Brace and Company, New York, 1928. Houdini was probably the greatest magician that has ever lived and certainly one of the greatest showmen. His magic feats were perfected through his vigorous self-training and his practical application of scientific knowledge. He detested fakery and claims of others that they possessed mystical and miraculous powers not possessed by other people. By the use of scientific principles Houdini exposed the false claims of many such quacks and charlatans.

4. Oreon, Keeslar, "The Elements of Scientific Method." *Science Education,* Vol. 29, No. 5, p. 273, 1945.

5. Standen, Anthony, *Science Is a Sacred Cow*. E. P. Dutton and Company, Inc., New York, 1950. This book is amusing and interestingly written. It should be read by every science teacher. The chapter "Physics, Science at Its Best" is especially good.

Chapter 3

The Role of Measurement in Science

The problem. To gain some notion of the problem of measurement, let us suppose that you own and operate a lumber yard at an Eastern seaport and that you import and export fine grades of lumber which have to be measured and have their values computed.

In this country lumber is measured by the *board foot*. A board foot is one foot long, one foot wide, and one inch thick. With pencil, paper, and simple arithmetic you can easily compute the number of board feet in almost any pile of lumber.

One day you make a trip into Virginia to buy some fine walnut logs for an importer in France. But when you figure the board feet, you have to use a whole new system because the logs are round. This done, you pay for the logs and arrange to have them shipped by rail to the seaport. Then you discover that logs are shipped by the hundredweight, so much per mile. The number of board feet is not taken into consideration.

When the logs arrive at the seaport they are loaded onto a ship. Again you have to pay the freight, but this time you are charged by the ton, so much per mile. But the mile at sea, called the nautical mile, is 6076.097 feet long instead of 5280 feet, the length of the mile used by landlubbers.

Regardless of these differences, your logs are landed in France. Here you have to pay dock rent. By the board foot? Not at all, but by the area which they take up on the wharf. And how do you suppose the area is computed, in square feet or square yards? In neither; it is computed in square meters.

Finally, the Frenchman to whom you sold the logs comes to measure them but board feet mean nothing to him. His country uses the metric system. He computes the amount of wood in cubic meters and pays you. In dollars? No, in francs.*

Naturally those who are scientifically minded want to know why there is so much chaos in measurement. For example, why does a mile on land differ from a mile at sea? For measuring weight, why do we have a metric system, a troy system, an avoirdupois system, and an apothecary system? Why do the French people use the metric system instead of the English system which we commonly use? Has a scientific international system of measurement been devised? Which system, the metric or the English, if either, meets the needs of scientists?

*The above passage has been adapted from Jeanne Bendick, *How Much and How Many*, by permission of the publisher, McGraw-Hill Book Company, Inc.

To answer these questions, we must study measurement further.

What is measurement? Can you explain exactly what it is that we do when we find the length of a room? Or can you explain what is meant when we say that Mary is four feet tall?

Measurement is really scientific comparison. *It is the comparison of an unknown quantity with a known fixed unit quantity.* If Mary is four feet tall, it means that her height is four times the length of a standard unit length known as one foot. What is meant when we say that a lake is four miles wide? Or that John weighs 150 pounds?

What are the characteristics of scientific measurement? We have already mentioned inches, feet, and miles for measuring length. Why use so many different units? Why not measure all lengths in terms of one of them?

To answer these questions, why not express a few known lengths in various units? The circumference of the earth is about 25,000 miles or 1,584,000,000 inches. The latter is a sizable number. The width of a box might be 6 inches or $\frac{1}{10,560}$ part of a mile. The latter is quite difficult to comprehend and certainly would cause difficulty in computation. Hence we see that any system of measurement should possess appropriate units for measuring quantities of various sizes.

But what about the relationships between the units? Is twelve, for example, a wise choice for the number of inches in a foot? Why not six, eight, or ten? To answer these questions, let us first change 283 inches to feet by dividing by twelve. This gives 283/12 or 23 7/12 feet. Now let us suppose there are ten inches in a foot. This time we divide 283.0 by ten. We do this by moving the decimal point one place to the left, which gives 28.3 feet. Change 283 cents to dollars and explain how it is done.

Would it be easier to change inches to feet and feet to inches if there were ten or if there were twelve inches in a foot? Explain.

Another thing which we must consider about measurement is whether the units shall be allowed to vary from day to day and from community to community. To some this may appear to be a ridiculous question. Nevertheless, as late as the middle of the eighteenth century, in Italy alone, as many as two hundred different lengths were called a foot.

Imagine the chaos which would follow if today we suddenly began using two hundred different lengths for the foot, and hence for the inch, in, say, the mass production of an airplane engine whose pistons are made in Wichita, Kansas, engine block in Detroit, and other parts in Los Angeles, all of which are shipped to Asia and assembled there into an airplane whose parts in some cases must fit to $\frac{1}{100,000}$ of an inch, so perfectly that the plane can be flown in non-stop flight around the earth in a few hours.

Fig. 1. Precision is the watchword of modern industry. A toolsetter is using a micrometer to check parts produced by a machine that is adjusted to a tolerance of 3/10,000 of an inch.

Courtesy Du Pont Better Living

16 THE BEGINNING OF PHYSICS

In conclusion, it is evident that if a system of measurement is to be scientific then it must have the following:

1. A standard unit for measuring each different kind of quantity.
2. Several different units, derived from the standard.
3. Units that are related to the standard by the ratio of 1 to 10, 1 to 100, and 1 to 1000. That is, the system should be a decimal system, the same as our number system.
4. Units that are not allowed to vary from day to day or from community to community and, if possible, that can be reproduced with a high degree of exactness even though the first copy is lost or destroyed.

In physics, only three basic standard units are needed. These are *length, time,* and *mass*. The latter is measured in the same units as weight is measured in. All other units, such as units of area, volume, and speed, are derived from the standard units. For example, the square yard and cubic yard are derived from the yard.

The English system—Is it scientifically designed? The English system originated in England. The English, however, have been wise enough, particularly in industry, not to use it. On the other hand they are still coping with a money system of pounds, shillings, and pence which we had enough foresight not to adopt.

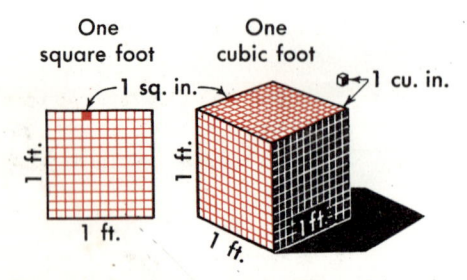

Fig. 2. Square and cubic measures compared.

The standard units of the English system are the *yard* for measuring length, the *pound* for measuring mass and weight, and the *second* for measuring time.

ENGLISH UNITS OF MEASUREMENT

Units of length
1 yard (yd.) = 3 feet (ft.)
1 foot (ft.) = 12 inches (in.)
1 mile (mi.) = 5280 ft.
1 mi. = 1760 yd.

Units of area
1 square foot (sq. ft.) = 144 sq. in.
1 sq. yd. = 9 sq. ft.

Units of volume
1 cubic foot (cu. ft.) = 1728 cu. in.
1 cu. yd. = 27 cu. ft.

Units of volume—liquid measure
1 gallon (gal.) = 4 quarts (qt.)
1 gal. = 231 cu. in.

Units of weight and mass
1 pound (lb.) = 16 ounces (oz.)
1 ton = 2000 lb.

Does this system meet the requirements of a scientific system as listed above? Explain your answer.

The development of the metric system. Previous to the French Revolution, measurement on the continent in Europe was in great confusion. Virtually every port, town, and local government had its own system. As a result, trade, travel, and communication were all difficult to carry on.

Since it was the plan of the French revolutionists to start a new scientific, social, and economic system, one not having any ties to the past, a group of scientists was selected to develop a new system of measurement. This was the *metric system*.

The metric units of length. The *meter,* which is a little over a yard long (see Fig. 3) and which was originally supposed to be one ten-millionth part of the distance from the North Pole to the Equator measured on a meridian through Paris, France, was chosen as the standard unit of length. Later it was discovered that the meter was

THE ROLE OF MEASUREMENT IN SCIENCE   17

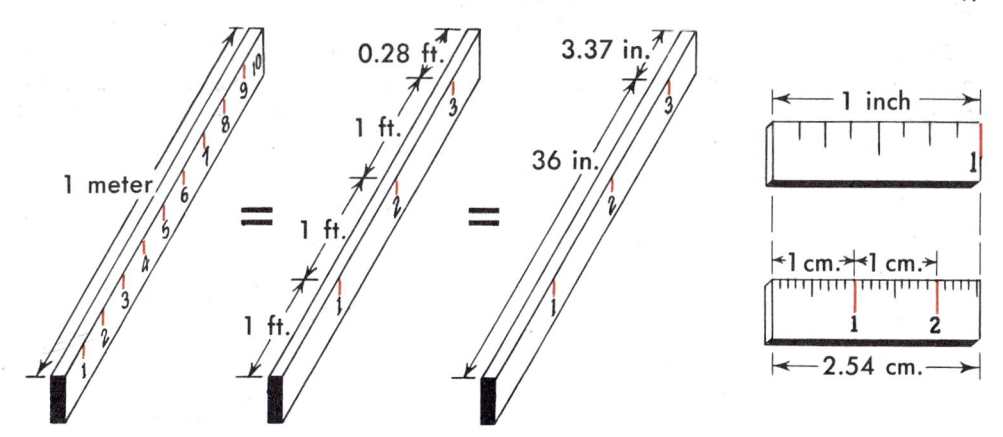

Fig. 3. English equivalents of the meter and a metric equivalent of the inch.

not exactly this amount. But since the new system had been accepted in several other European countries, no attempt was made to rectify the error. Strangely, the French people were among the last on the continent to put the system into common use.

On a meter stick the smallest division is the *millimeter*. Ten of these make a *centimeter*, ten centimeters make a *decimeter*, ten decimeters make a *meter*, and one thousand meters make a *kilometer*.

There are six prefixes that can be attached to any standard basic unit such as a meter, and each of these prefixes signifies a number. Four are most common:

Milli means $\frac{1}{1000} = .001$

Centi means $\frac{1}{100} = .01$

Deci means $\frac{1}{10} = .1$

Kilo means $1000 = 1000$

Not all of these are new to you because you know that a *mill* is

$$\frac{1}{1000} \text{ dollar}$$

and a *cent* is

$$\frac{1}{100} \text{ dollar}$$

In a dollar there are how many mills? Cents? Dimes? In a meter there are how many millimeters? Centimeters? Decimeters?

The following should be memorized:

METRIC UNITS OF LENGTH

.001 meter (m.) = 1 millimeter (mm.)
.01 meter (m.) = 1 centimeter (cm.)
.1 meter (m.) = 1 decimeter (dm.)
1000 meters (m.) = 1 kilometer (km.)

Find the length of this page in centimeters; in millimeters; in meters. What is the length of your desk in centimeters? Meters? Kilometers? What is the symbol for meter? Millimeter? Centimeter? Kilometer?

The metric units for measuring volume. The metric unit of volume is the *liter*. It was originally derived from the meter and was made equivalent to the volume of a cube which is $\frac{1}{10}$ meter or 10 cm. on each edge. This volume is 10 cm. × 10 cm. × 10 cm. or 1000 cubic centimeters. The liter is slightly larger than the liquid quart (see Fig. 4). One liter equals approximately 1.06 quarts.

METRIC UNITS OF VOLUME

1 liter (l.) = 1000 cubic centimeters (cc. or cm.³)
1 liter (l.) = 1000 milliliters (ml.)

THE BEGINNING OF PHYSICS

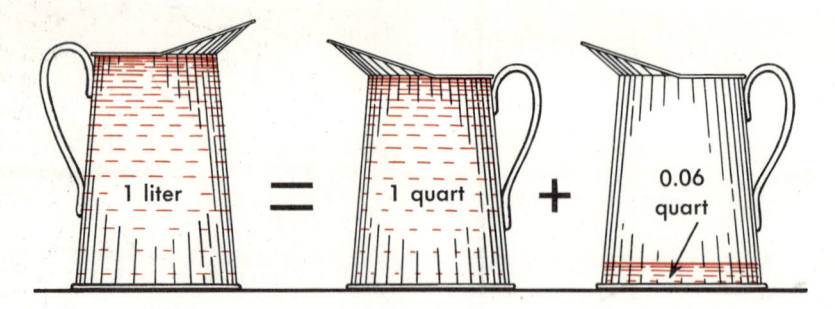

Fig. 4. Comparison of metric and English units of volume.

How many cubic centimeters in one milliliter? One liter? 1.06 quarts? One quart? Give the symbol for liter. Cubic centimeter.

The metric units for measuring weight and mass. Mass refers to the *quantity of matter in a body*. Usually mass is determined by "weighing" (see Fig. 5) and for this reason mass and weight are often confused. Furthermore, to make for still more confusion, both weight and mass are measured in the same units, such as pounds, ounces, grams, kilograms, and so on. Further distinction between mass and weight is made in Chapter 5.

The standard metric unit of both weight

Fig. 5. A scientist is comparing standard weights with known standards of mass on an extremely sensitive balance.

Courtesy National Bureau of Standards

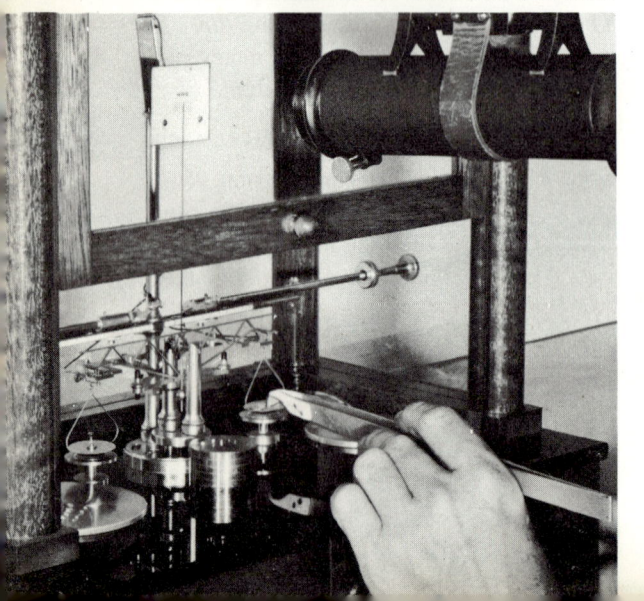

and mass is the *kilogram*. Kilo, you will recall, means 1000, so kilogram means 1000 grams.

The standard kilogram is the mass of a certain metal cylinder (see Fig. 6) made equal to the mass of a liter of water at four degrees centigrade. Since a liter is 1000 cc., what is the mass of one cc. of water? Of 430 cc. of water in grams? In kilograms?

In conclusion, you should remember the following:

METRIC UNITS OF WEIGHT AND MASS
1000 grams (g.)   = 1 kilogram (kg.)
1000 kilograms (kg.) = 1 metric ton
.001 gram (g.)   = 1 milligram (mg.)
1 cc. of water weighs 1 gram

Does the metric system meet the requirements of a scientific system of measurement as listed on page 16? How many grams are there in a metric ton? In two kilograms? How many milligrams are there in one gram? What is the symbol for gram? For kilogram?

The relationships between the metric and English systems of measurement. Until the United States adopts the metric system for everyday use, it will be necessary for science students in our country to learn both the English and the metric systems, know the relations between them, and be able to change measurements from one system to the other. The following table will aid in the latter.

CONVERSION TABLE FOR METRIC AND ENGLISH WEIGHTS AND MEASURES

Length

1 millimeter	=	.03937 inch
1 centimeter	=	.3937 inch
1 meter	=	39.37 inches
1 meter	=	3.28 feet
1 meter	=	1.09 yards
1 kilometer	=	.62 mile

1 inch	=	2.54 centimeters
1 foot	=	30.48 centimeters
1 yard	=	91.44 centimeters
1 yard	=	.914 meter
1 mile	=	1.6094 kilometers

Weight and Mass

1 gram	=	.035 ounce
1 gram	=	.0022 pound
1 kilogram	=	2.2 pounds
1 metric (long) ton	=	2200 pounds

1 ounce	=	28.35 grams
1 pound	=	454 grams
1 English (short) ton	=	908 kilograms

Volume

1 liter	=	1.06 quarts
1 quart	=	.946 liter

Attempts to set up an international system of measurement. In 1875 the International Conference on Weights and Measures was called in order to bring an end to some of the chaos in international trade caused by the many different systems in use. Representatives of thirty different countries, including the United States, attended. As a result, the International Bureau of Weights and Measures was established near Paris, France, and the metric system was made the standard international system. In the Bureau are kept the original standard units. Why do you suppose the metric was chosen in preference to the English system?

The United States received Meter Number 27 (copy 27) and Kilogram Number 20, which is the twentieth copy of the original kilogram of mass. About 1893 the United States Congress passed a law making these units the legal standard, but this did not bring about common usage. In most other countries, including the so-called backward countries, the metric system was adopted in both science and everyday affairs.

Units of time. The basic unit of time is the *second*, which is $\frac{1}{24 \times 60 \times 60}$ or $\frac{1}{86,400}$ part of a *mean solar day*. The solar day is the time between two successive passages of the sun across any given me-

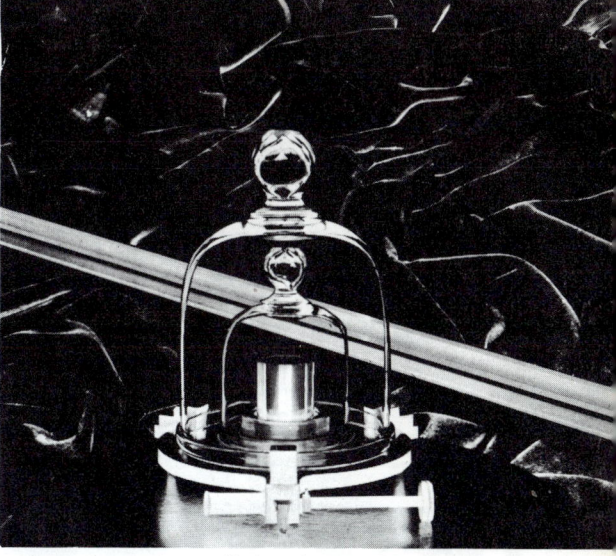

Courtesy National Bureau of Standards

Fig. 6. These exact duplicates of the international standards of mass and length serve as a basis for weights and measures in this country.

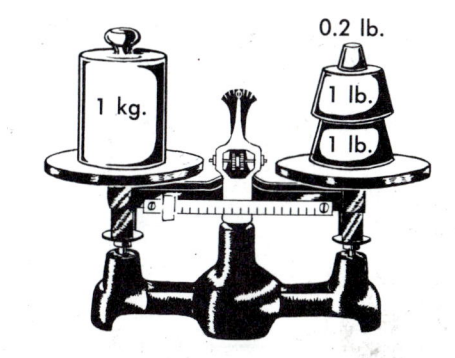

Fig. 7. Comparison of metric and English units of mass.

ridian. It varies in length at different times of the year. The mean solar day is the average of all the solar days in a year. It is divided into 24 hours of 60 minutes each. The minute is divided into 60 seconds.

The earth's surface is also divided into twenty-four time zones. Each zone is 360 degrees ÷ 24, or about 15 degrees wide, and the time in each zone, known as *standard time,* differs from that of the zone next to it by one hour. There are four standard time zones in the United States as indicated in Fig. 9. A football game broadcast in Los Angeles at four o'clock in the afternoon is heard at what time in Denver? In Kansas City? In Pittsburgh? In Detroit? In Miami? In Nova Scotia? What are the shortcomings of this system?

The Army and Navy use a different time system. Each new day begins at midnight, which is designated as 2400 hours. One minute past midnight is 0001 hours; 40 minutes past is 0040 hours; 60 minutes past is 0100 hours. One hour past noon is 1300 hours. What would 6:30 in the evening be by this system? See Fig. 10.

Courtesy Columbia University

Fig. 8. This atomic clock uses the energy given off by ammonia molecules to provide a more accurate standard of measuring time than the currently accepted standard of the earth's rate of rotation.

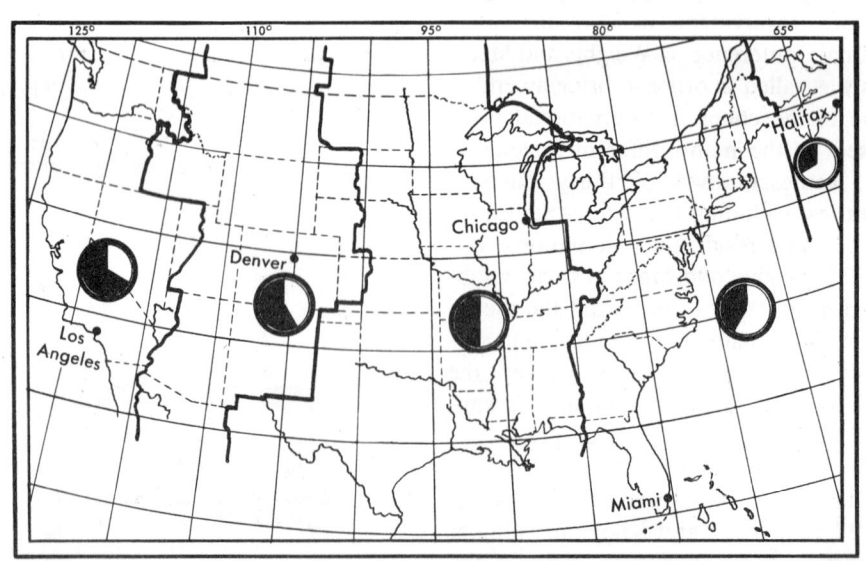

Fig. 9. In which standard time zone do you live? Neglecting the time for travel, do you gain or lose time in traveling from east to west? From west to east?

THE ROLE OF MEASUREMENT IN SCIENCE

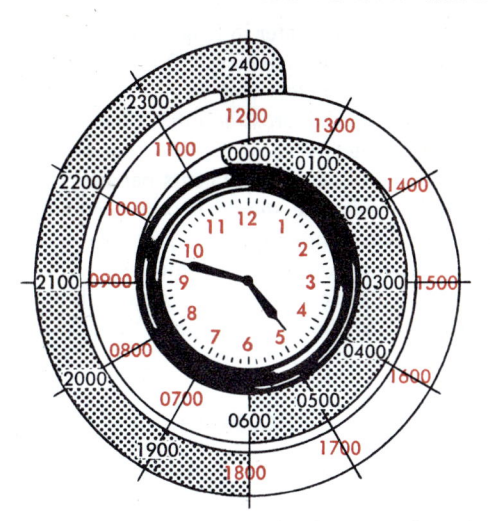

Fig. 10. Comparison of military and civilian methods of reckoning time.

SUMMARY AND CONCLUSIONS

From our studies, we have seen that there are two systems of measurement widely used, the metric and the English. Except for units of time, the metric system is based on, and is in agreement with, our decimal number system; the English system is not. With the metric system everything is measured in terms of three standards units: the meter, the kilogram, and the second, or in related terms derived from these.

The legal standards of measurement in the United States are those of the metric system, but the system itself is not commonly used here except in science. However, as the world grows smaller there will be greater and greater need for the United States to adopt it for general use, as practically all other countries have done. Two systems of measurement are a great burden to carry.

QUESTIONS FOR REVIEW

1. What is measurement?
2. What are the three basic quantities which we need to measure in our study of physics? What are the standard basic units for measuring these in the metric system? English system?
3. Why should any system of measurement provide several different units for measuring each different basic quantity, such as length? How should the different quantities be related if the system is to be most efficient?
4. Why should the units be accurately defined and be made as nearly as possible in accordance with the definition; that is, why should a foot be the same length in all parts of our country? Are such requirements a restriction of individual liberty?
5. Does the metric system meet with the requirements of scientific measurement? Does the English system? Give reasons for your answers, using examples.
6. What is the meaning of milli? Centi? Deci? Kilo?
7. What are the chief shortcomings of our present system of measuring time? What is the system used by the Army and Navy?
8. Give reasons for and against the adoption of the metric system for all measurement in the United States.

EXERCISES

1. How many inches in a foot? Yard?
2. How many feet in a mile? Yard?
3. How many square feet in a square yard?
4. How many square inches in a square foot?
5. How many cubic inches in a cubic foot?
6. A meter is equivalent to how many centimeters? Millimeters? Decimeters? Kilometers?
7. What is the abbreviation for centimeter? Millimeter? Kilometer? Gram? Kilogram? Square centimeter? Liter? Cubic centimeter? Meter?
8. A rectangle is 10 cm. long and 5 cm. wide. What is its area?
9. Explain what kind of quantity each of the following units measures: (a) meter, (b) square centimeter, (c) cubic centimeter, (d) kilogram, (e) liter, (f) millimeter, (g) centimeter, (h) milliliter.
10. Twenty meters are equivalent to how many millimeters? Centimeters? Kilometers?
11. Two thousand centimeters are equivalent to how many millimeters? Meters?

12. Two thousand millimeters are equivalent to how many centimeters? Meters?
13. Draw a line 5 centimeters long. How many millimeters long is it? How many inches?
14. Draw the diagram of a square whose edge is 1 centimeter long; a cube whose edge is 1 centimeter long.
15. Copy and complete the following:

    (a) 1 in. = ? cm.
    (b) 1 ft. = ? cm.
    (c) 1 m. = ? in.
    (d) 1 lb. = ? g.
    (e) 1 kg. = ? lb.
    (f) 1 ton = ? lb.
    (g) 1 metric ton = ? lb.
    (h) 1 liter = ? qt.
    (i) 1 min. = ? sec.
    (j) 1 m. = ? ft.
    (k) 1 km. = ? mi.
    (l) 1 mi. = ? km.
    (m) 1 qt. = ? liter
    (n) 1 qt. = ? cc.

16. Which of the following quantities is the largest? (a) 2.5 lb.; (b) 950 grams; (c) 800,000 milligrams; (d) the weight of 2 liters of water.
17. Which of the following quantities is the largest volume? (a) ½ quart (liquid); (b) 500 cc.; (c) 1 liter; (d) 400 grams of water.
18. Find your height (a) in centimeters; (b) in meters.
19. Find your weight (a) in kilograms; (b) in grams.
20. Estimate the weight of this book in kilograms; in grams.
21. A box is 20 cm. long, 10 cm. deep, and 10 cm. wide. What is its volume in cc.? In liters?
22. A box is 30 cm. long, 20 cm. wide, and 40 cm. deep. What is its volume in cc.? In liters?
23. The area of a rectangle is 2880 sq. in. What is its area in sq. ft.?
24. A 16-lb. shot weighs how many kilograms? How many grams?
25. A dictionary weighs 3 kilograms. How many pounds does it weigh?
26. Which is greater in length, the 220-yard dash or the 200-meter dash? Find the difference in both meters and yards.
27. The 5-mile cross-country race is how many kilometers?
28. If gasoline costs 10 cents per liter, how much at this rate should it cost per gallon?
29. A gun whose range is 5000 yards has what range in meters? Kilometers?
30. An athlete runs the 100-yard dash in 10 seconds. At the same rate how long would it take him to run 100 meters?

PROJECTS

1. Find out how the original standard kilogram and meter are checked so that when the copies of these are compared with the originals, it is known that the copies rather than the originals have or have not changed.
2. See if you can devise a decimal time system.
3. Make a report to your class concerning the cost of short measurement to the consumer. Find out the laws governing the testing of measuring devices in your state or city.
4. Work out a duodecimal number system (proceeding by twelves instead of tens). Determine whether or not a system of measurement based on this number system would be better than our present metric system. This would be a good problem for your science club to consider.
5. Compare the decimal system with the Roman system from the standpoint of adding, multiplying, dividing, and subtracting.

READING YOU WILL ENJOY

1. Bendick, Jeanne, *How Much and How Many.* Whittlesey House, McGraw-Hill Book Company, Inc., New York, 1947. The story of weights and measures, simply told and engagingly illustrated.
2. *Precision, a Measure of Progress.* Department of Public Relations, General Motors, Detroit 2, Michigan, 1952. An excellent pamphlet telling about the development of accuracy in measurement.

Chapter 4

The Role of Mathematics in Science

The Problem. During World War I, Albert Einstein, a German mathematical physicist who later became an American citizen, made an extraordinary and unexpected prediction which rocked the centers of learning in astronomy, physics, and mathematics in all parts of the world. By making an assumption which most scientists believed to be false, Einstein predicted by means of mathematical reasoning that, due to gravity, a beam of light which passed near a heavenly body would be attracted by the body and hence would be bent toward it. Also he predicted the amount that the beam would be bent by the sun.

Immediately, astronomers in all parts of the world had a burning desire to test Einstein's prediction. The British Astronomical Society, with the consent of its government, began preparations for making the test during the next total eclipse of the sun, which would take place two years later. Only during such a total eclipse could light from a star beyond the sun be observed as it passed near the sun. Since the closest suitable place from which the eclipse could be observed was in the wilds of South Africa, the test would require much equipment and the services of many men. When the test was made the results verified Einstein's prediction beyond a doubt.

Why the British government granted the astronomical society the privilege of testing a prediction made by a citizen of an enemy country, particularly when all the men and materials needed to make the test were also needed on the battlefield to break the critical deadlock between the British and German armies, may be difficult for many to understand. Certainly the granting of the privilege laid the British government wide open to criticism by the opposition political party. However, the fact that the grant was made was a great tribute to both Einstein and science.

Furthermore, the fact that Einstein's prediction proved to be true, although it was based on a supposedly false assumption, showed what the human intellect is capable of accomplishing when allowed to work unfettered, but guided and checked by a fruitful hypothesis. Also his work showed how mathematics can be used as a precise and exacting tool in reasoning. In this chapter our problem is to become reacquainted with the language and symbols of mathematics so that we, too, can use this tool in our reasoning.

The formula. The most-used device in mathematics is the *formula*. This is a shorthand statement for solving problems. For example, the formula $A = LW$ is the shorthand statement that the area of a

Fig. 1. The late atomic scientist Enrico Fermi using some mathematical tools.

Town and Country Photographers

rectangle equals its length times its width. In $A = LW$, what is represented by A? L? W? LW?

PROBLEM 1: What is the area of a rectangle whose width is 10 ft. and whose length is 20 ft.?

SOLUTION: $A = LW$
Substituting, $A = 20 \times 10$
$A = 200$ sq. ft.

PROBLEM 2: What is the width of a rectangle whose area is 300 sq. ft. and whose length is 20 ft.?

SOLUTION: $A = LW$
Substituting, $300 = 20W$
Dividing,* $W = 15$ ft.

Writing definitions as mathematical formulas. Very often it is necessary to write definitions as mathematical formulas. For example, the definition, rate (R) is the distance (D) traveled per unit of time (t), is written:

$$R = \frac{D}{t}$$

What symbol represents rate? Is? Distance? Per? Time?

*The student should recall that according to the rules of algebra, when both sides of a statement of equality (an equation) are divided by the same number, except zero, the equality is not destroyed.

EXERCISE: Write each of the following definitions as a formula, using the symbols given:
1. The rate of pay (R) is the total pay (P) per unit of time (t) in hours.
2. Pressure (P) is force (F) per unit area (A).
3. Power (P) is the work (W) done per unit time (t).

Ratios and how to write them as formulas. Formulas often involve *ratios*. A ratio compares numbers by division. We compare three with four by dividing 3 by 4, which gives $\frac{3}{4}$. This is called the ratio of 3 to 4. The ratio of 4 to 3 is written $\frac{4}{3}$.

What is the ratio of 1 to 2? 2 to 4? 3 to 6? x to y? y to x?

Many ratios are equal. For example,

$$\frac{1}{2} = \frac{2}{4} = \frac{3}{6} = \frac{4}{8}.$$ Explain.

Many mathematical statements can be written as ratios. For example, that *pi* is the ratio of the circumference of a circle to the diameter is written $\pi = \frac{C}{d}$. What word or phrase in the statement does each of the following symbols represent: π? C? d? $=$?

EXERCISE: Write each of the following statements as a formula.
1. K is the ratio of X to Y.
2. K is the ratio of Y to X.
3. The current (I) in an electric circuit is the ratio of the voltage (E) to the resistance (R).

Proportions and how to write them as formulas. Proportions are also involved in formulas. *An expression of equality between two ratios is called a* **proportion**. As an example, $\frac{4}{5} = \frac{8}{10}$ is a proportion. Note that the product of 4 and 10 equals

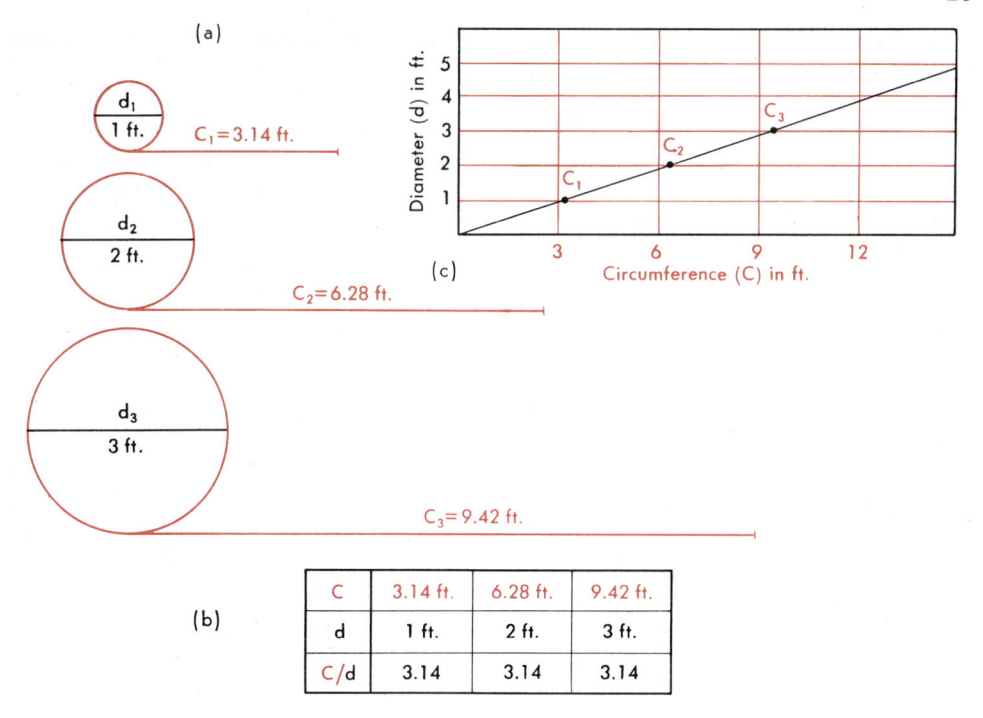

Fig. 2. The circumference of a circle is directly proportional to its diameter.

the product of 8 and 5 (4 × 10 = 8 × 5). How could you use this fact to find one missing number, x, in the proportion $\frac{3}{4}=\frac{6}{x}$? Show work.

Variation. Many quantities—time, area, distance, and so forth—may change in a physical event. If a quantity changes or varies, it is called a *variable*. If a quantity does not change, it is called a *constant*. For example, if you drive an automobile 30 miles per hour and no faster or slower, its rate is constant. The distance and the time both change and both are variables. Furthermore, the greater the time the greater the distance; the smaller the time, the smaller the distance. The distance is said to vary *directly* as the time.

Direct variation and how to write direct variations as formulas. In Fig. 2 you will find the diameters and circumferences of a number of circles. Study of these data shows that as the diameter is doubled, the circumference is doubled; as the diameter is tripled, the circumference is tripled; and so on. Furthermore, if you divide the first circumference (C_1) by the first diameter (d_1), the second circumference (C_2) by the second diameter (d_2), and so on, you will find the quotient (result of division) is the same in every case. That is, $\frac{C}{d}=3.14$. The quantities represented by C and d are called variables. 3.14 is the constant called pi (π).

This relationship between the circumference and diameter of a circle is called a **direct variation.** The earmarks of a direct variation are that as one variable *increases*, the other *increases*; and vice versa, as one quantity *decreases*, the other *decreases*. Also, if one variable is divided by the other, the quotient (answer) is a constant (an unchanging value) which is often represented by the letter k. The fact that the circumference (C) of a circle varies directly as the diameter (d) is written as follows in three different ways:

1. $C \propto d$
2. $k = \dfrac{C}{d}$
3. $C = kd$

In (1), what does the symbol $\propto$ represent? In (2) you will recognize that the direct variation is written as a ratio. In (3), what is the value of k? Often, when a direct variation is written as a formula, step 2 is omitted.

How to write a direct variation as a proportion. Above, in our study of circles we found that $\dfrac{C_1}{d_1} = 3.14$ and $\dfrac{C_2}{d_2} = 3.14$. Therefore, since things equal to the same thing are equal to each other, then $\dfrac{C_1}{d_1} = \dfrac{C_2}{d_2}$. This relationship, which is an equality of two ratios, is called a *proportion*. This is a fourth manner in which a direct variation may be written.

EXERCISE: The volume (V) of a gas varies directly as its absolute temperature (T). Write this direct variation in four different ways.

Using the symbols given here and referring to the example above, we have:

1. $V \propto T$
2. $k = \dfrac{V}{T}$
3. $V = kT$
4. $\dfrac{V_1}{T_1} = \dfrac{V_2}{T_2}$

Note that (2) is a ratio and that (4) is a proportion.

EXERCISES AND PROBLEMS: Using the letters indicated and k for the constant, unless otherwise stated, express each of the following direct variations in four different forms.

1. The cost (C) of oranges varies directly as the number (N) purchased.
2. (a) The elongation (E) of a rubber band varies directly as the force (F) causing it.
   (b) What is the value of k if a force of 8 oz. stretches the band 4 in.?
3. (a) The area of a circle varies directly as the square of the radius (r).
   (b) When the area of a circle is 154 sq. cm. and the radius is 7 cm., what is the value of k?
4. (a) When the width (W) of a rectangle is constant, its area (A) varies directly as its length (L).
   (b) What is the value of the constant (W) when A is 140 sq. in. and L is 10 in.?
5. Write two formulas which express the relationship between the variables in the following table. What is the value of k? Can there be more than one value of k? Explain.

Table 1

X	1	2	3	10	30	50	100
Y	2	4	6	20	60	100	200
k							

How to picture a direct variation by means of a graph. To make a graph, usually two lines are drawn at right angles to each other, one horizontal and the other vertical, as shown in (c) of Fig. 2. The point at which the lines cross is called the *origin*. You may recall from geometry that the horizontal line is called the *x-axis*, or *axis of abscissas*, and the vertical line the *y-axis*, or *axis of ordinates*.

Using the data in Fig. 2, we prepared the graph by laying off on the horizontal line equal intervals of circumference and by laying off on the vertical line equal intervals of diameter. Then for each diameter and corresponding circumference a point was located as shown in the graph.

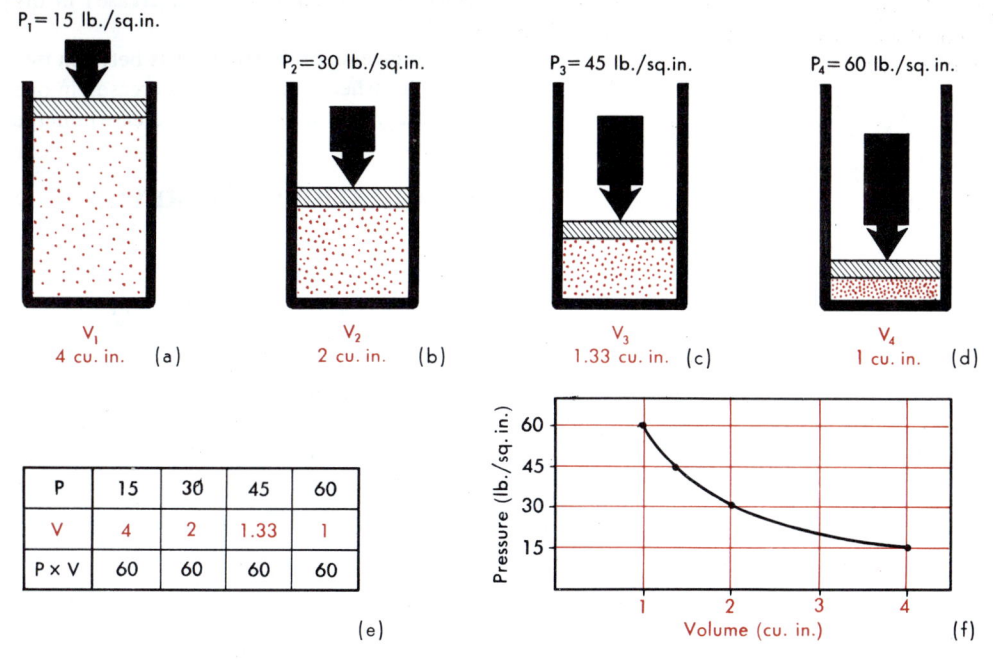

Fig. 3. The volume of a given mass of gas is inversely proportional to the pressure.

All these points were then connected by a line which is a graph showing that the circumference of a circle varies directly as its diameter.

PROBLEM: Make a graph of the data given above in Table 1.

Inverse variations and how to write them as formulas. In (a) of Fig. 3 is shown a cylinder full of gas whose volume (V_1) is 4 cubic inches. The pressure (P_1) on the gas is 15 pounds per square inch. In (b) the pressure on the gas has been increased to 30 pounds per square inch, and the volume has decreased to 2 cubic inches. As a result, when the pressure was doubled, the volume was halved. In (c) it shows that when the pressure was tripled, the volume was reduced to one-third the original volume. Thus, *as one variable increases, the other decreases. Such a relationship is known as* **inverse variation.** That the volume, V, varies inversely with the pressure, P, is written as follows:

$$V \propto \frac{1}{P}$$

Further study of the preceding data shows that if we multiply the first volume V_1 by its pressure P_1 and the second volume V_2 by its pressure P_2, and so on, the product in each case is 60, a constant. That is, $PV = 60$. See (e) of Fig. 3. The graph of this inverse variation is shown in 3(f).

In general, this inverse variation is written as follows: $PV = k$. This means that pressure varies inversely as volume. *Thus, when one variable multiplied by another equals a constant, the variation is called an inverse variation.*

How to write an inverse variation as a proportion. Study of the compressed gases above showed that

$$P_1V_1 = 60$$

and

$$P_2V_2 = 60$$

Therefore

$$P_1V_1 = P_2V_2. \text{ Why?}$$

Dividing by P_1V_2, we have

$$\frac{P_1V_1}{P_1V_2} = \frac{P_2V_2}{P_1V_2}$$

Hence,

$$\frac{V_1}{V_2} = \frac{P_2}{P_1}$$

This latter form is, as you probably recognize, a proportion.

EXERCISES AND PROBLEMS: Using the letters indicated, and k for the constant unless otherwise indicated, express each of the following in the forms (a) $x \propto \frac{1}{y}$, (b) $k = xy$, (c) $\frac{x_1}{x_2} = \frac{y_2}{y_1}$.

1. Electrical current (I) varies inversely with resistance (R).
2. The intensity (I) of light varies inversely with the square of the distance (D).
3. (a) When distance (D) is constant, the rate (R) varies inversely with the time (t).
   (b) If the rate is 25 mi./hr. and the time is 4 hr., what is the value of D?

SUMMARY AND CONCLUSIONS

1. A ratio compares numbers of the same units by division.
2. A proportion is an equation which states that two ratios are equal.
3. If a quantity changes, it is called a variable. If it does not change, it is called a constant.
4. A direct proportion exists between two variables when an increase (decrease) in one variable yields an increase (decrease) in the other.
5. An inverse proportion exists between two variables when an increase (decrease) in one variable yields a decrease (increase) in the other.

QUESTIONS FOR REVIEW

1. What is a formula?
2. What is a ratio?
3. What is a variable? A constant?
4. Is *pi* a variable or a constant?
5. When are two variables directly proportional to each other?
6. When are two variables inversely proportional to each other?
7. How are two variables related when their product is a constant?
8. What is a proportion?
9. Express as a definition:

$$pi = \frac{\text{circumference}}{\text{diameter}}$$

EXERCISES

1. Write the formulas which express the relationship between the variables in the table below.

Table 2

X	1	2	3	4	6	8	12	16	24	48
Y	48	24	16	12	8	6	4	3	2	1

2. Make a graph of the data in the table above.
3. Write each of the following either as a proportion or as an ordinary formula.
   (a) The cost (C) of shoes varies directly as the cost of leather (L).
   (b) The densities (D_1 and D_2) of two equal volumes of two different substances are directly proportional to their weights (W_1 and W_2).
   (c) The forces F_1 and F_2 exerted on two pistons are directly proportional to the areas A_1 and A_2 of the pistons.
   (d) The volume of gas varies inversely as the pressure.
   (e) The area (A) of a circle varies directly as the square of its radius (r).

(f) Velocity (V) is the distance (D) traveled per unit of time (t).

(g) Acceleration (a) is the change in velocity ($V_2 - V_1$) per unit of time (t).

4. Write the formula which expresses the relationship between the variables in the table below.

Table 3

X	1	2	3	20	30
Y	3	6	9	60	90

5. Make a graph of the data in Table 3, above.

PROJECTS

1. *How to chain a right angle.* Take a length of clothesline and divide it into twelve equal lengths by tying knots in it. Then tie the ends together and peg the rope at the point at which the right angle is to be set out. Finally, figure out two other points at which the rope can be pegged so as to form a right triangle. What is the length of each of the three sides? What other number of equal lengths of rope is convenient for chaining a right angle?

2. Make a study of an abacus and explain how it is used to add and to multiply. See the Hogben reference below for instructions on its use.

READING YOU WILL ENJOY

1. Hogben, Lancelot, *Mathematics for the Million*, Chapters 1 and 4. W. W. Norton and Company, Inc., New York, 1937. A very challenging book that gives meaning to mathematics. Shows that it is a mental tool that can be used to further learning.

2. Hooper, A., *A Mathematics Refresher*, pp. 1-74. Henry Holt and Company, New York, 1946. Gives a good review of elementary arithmetic, geometry, and algebra. Chapter 10 includes graphs.

Chapter 5

Force, Gravity, Weight, Mass, Density, and Friction

The problem. In our study of matter and motion, we have used the terms *force, gravity, weight,* and *mass,* but have made no clear distinction among them. In this chapter we hope to discover what is meant by gravity, whether mass is the same as weight, whether you weigh the same at sea level as on a high mountain top, what causes things to fall "down" instead of "up," and the meanings of a few terms.

What is force? If you found a pocketbook and it suddenly moved as you stooped to pick it up, you would suspect that someone was playing a trick on you— that by some hidden means the pocketbook was being pushed or pulled. This you would suspect because you know from experience that a body *at rest* cannot move unless a *force* (push or pull) is exercised on it.

Or again, if you were exercising your dog and he made a dash for his archenemy, the cat, you know that you would have to hold tightly to the leash and pull on it in order to stop him. Here we see that a force (push or pull) is required to *stop* a moving body. Also, if you rolled a ball across a level floor and wanted then to *change its direction,* you would have to give it a sidewise push or pull, or hit it head on.

Furthermore, if you want to compress or stretch a spring, bend a metal rod, break a stick, flatten a meat ball, or *change the shape* of a body in any other way, a force is required.

In conclusion, we may say that *a force is a push or a pull.* But to be more exact, a **force** *is that which tends to produce or destroy motion, change the direction of motion, or change the shape of a body.* When you slide on ice what force stops your motion?

How are forces measured? The definition of force itself gives us four clues to ways in which it might be measured. We might measure it by the amount of motion it can cause; the amount of motion it can destroy; the amount of change of direction it can produce; or the amount of distortion or change of shape it can cause.

Obviously, the first three effects would be difficult to measure. The last is not. As shown in Fig. 1, the distance which a steel coil spring, piece of rubber, or other elastic body is stretched, up to what is known as the *elastic limit,* varies directly as the force applied. That is, if the force is doubled, the distortion is doubled; if the force is tripled, the distortion is tripled, and so on. As stated in **Hooke's Law,** which was discovered by Robert Hooke (1635-1703), an Englishman,

FORCE, GRAVITY, WEIGHT, MASS, DENSITY, AND FRICTION

the amount of change in the shape of an elastic body is proportional to the force applied, provided the elastic limit is not exceeded.

The spring balance is based on Hooke's Law and is used widely to measure force. Forces are measured in pounds, ounces, tons, grams, kilograms, and other units commonly called units of weight.

Gravitation and weight. When it was first proposed that the earth is round like a ball, few would accept the idea. One reason for rejecting it was that most people believed everything on the earth, except those things at the very "top," would fall off unless they were tied or held on by other means. Furthermore, they asked, how could a person live on the underside with his head down all the while? And how could a ship sail from the top to the bottom of a sphere and then up again?

The proponents of the round-earth theory argued that everything is held on the earth by an invisible force called *gravity*. The earth, they said, is like a great magnet which attracts everything on it, causing stones and other heavy bodies to fall toward the center of the earth unless they are held up by some means or other. *The gravitational force or pull exerted on a body by the earth is the* **weight** *of a body.* Since weight is a force, it can be measured by a spring balance.

Is gravity a local affair, confined solely to the earth? The theory of gravity was very upsetting to those who believed the earth to be flat. It turned their "world" upside down. Such nonsense, they said, was blasphemy.

Fortunately, there were a few thinking people who believed otherwise. One of these was a young Englishman by the name of Isaac Newton (1642-1727), who was perhaps one of the most brilliant men who have ever lived. Oddly, he was born the same year that Galileo died.

Newton was interested in astronomy and gravitation, and he knew, as we know, that a force is necessary to make a moving ball or other body change its direction, or move in a circle. So, as he observed the

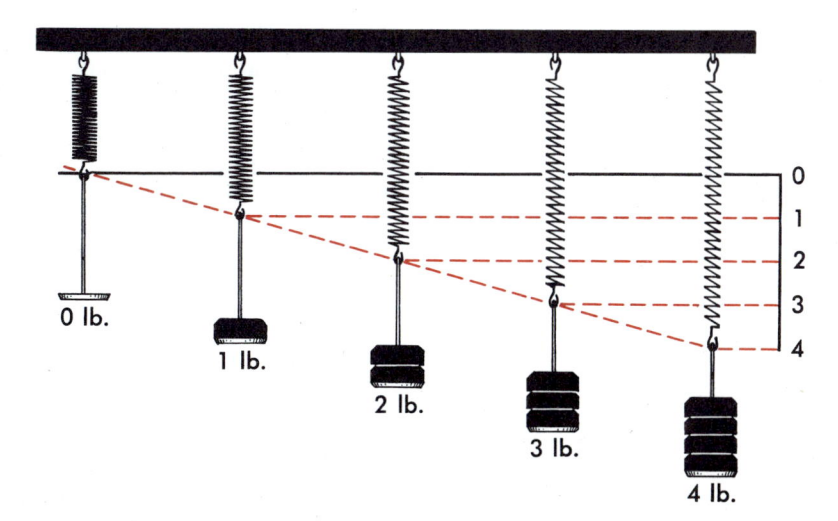

Fig. I. The distortion produced on a body varies directly as the applied force, provided that the elastic limit is not exceeded. A substance reaches its elastic limit when it does not return to its original shape after the applied force is removed.

moon moving in a circular orbit about the earth, he asked himself if gravitational attraction is confined solely to the earth and bodies on it, or whether it extends out even beyond the moon, and keeps the moon in its orbit by constantly pulling it toward the earth.

At the age of twenty-three, Newton began working to answer this question. Men knew that the earth behaves like a magnet and that the force of attraction between two magnetic poles increases with the strength of the poles and decreases as the distance between them increases. Also, it had been proposed that the other planets and the sun are magnets and that the planets are kept in their orbits by magnetic attraction.

Newton's law of universal gravitation. Newton rejected the magnetic theory because he said that the sun was very hot and that if a magnet is heated to a high temperature, its magnetism is destroyed. Nevertheless this theory seemed to have influenced his thinking, for he proposed:

Any two bodies attract each other with a force that is proportional to the product of their masses and inversely proportional to the square of the distance between them.

Written in the language of mathematics,

$$F \propto \frac{M_1 M_2}{d^2}$$

That is, $\quad F = K \dfrac{M_1 M_2}{d^2}$

Here F is the force of attraction, M_1 and M_2 are the two masses, and d is the distance between the two centers of mass. K is the constant of proportionality, which is found experimentally. See Project 1.

In case one of the bodies is the earth, whose mass is M_E, and another is a body such as a stone, with a mass M, then the weight W of the stone can be found from the formula:

$$F = W = K \frac{M M_E}{d^2}$$

Some consequences of Newton's law of universal gravitation. Since the mass of the earth, M_E, is constant, then according to the formula, $W = K \dfrac{M M_E}{d^2}$, the weight of any other body should vary directly as its mass, M, and inversely with the square of its distance from the earth's center. Therefore, two spherical solid lead balls having identical diameters, and at equal distances from the center of the earth, should weigh the same. Do they?

On the other hand, if one of these two balls with identical diameters had been hollow, or had been made of wood, its **mass,** *the quantity of matter in it,* would have been less than the mass of the solid lead ball. Which ball would weigh more?

Also, since the weight of a body varies inversely with the square of its distance from the center of the earth, then as this distance increases the weight of a body decreases. Consequently, a body should weigh more at sea level than on top of a mountain. Does it? Experiment shows that a bag of sugar which weighs 1000 grams at sea level weighs only 999 grams at an elevation of 4 miles.

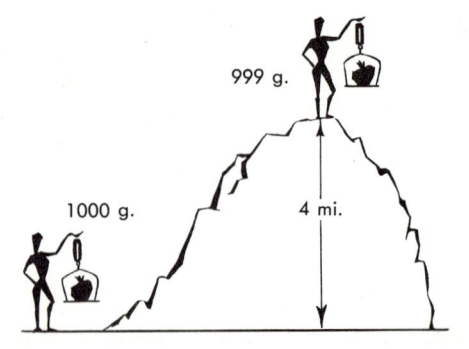

Fig. 2. Account for the difference in weight of the bag of sugar.

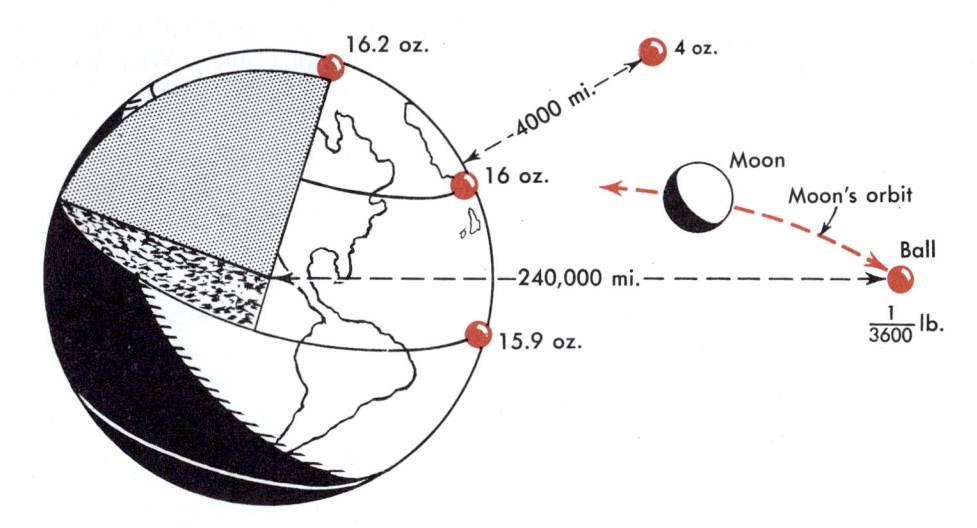

FORCE, GRAVITY, WEIGHT, MASS, DENSITY, AND FRICTION

Fig. 3. As the distance of an object from the center of the earth increases, the weight of the object decreases. What kind of variation is represented by this relationship?

Furthermore, because the earth bulges a little at the equator and is flattened slightly at the poles, then a body should weigh more at the poles than at the equator or at some latitude in between. Does it? Experiment shows that a ball or some other body that weighs 16 ounces at sea level 45° north latitude weighs 16.2 ounces at the pole and 15.9 ounces at the equator. All these facts agree with what can be predicted with Newton's formula.

Also, as shown in Fig. 3, the ball that weighs 16 ounces, or 1 pound, at sea level 45° north latitude should weigh only 4 ounces, or ¼ pound, at 4000 miles above sea level, 8000 miles (2 radii of the earth) from the earth's center. At the distance of the moon, 240,000 miles from the center of the earth, which is equivalent to 60 radii of the earth, the same ball should weigh $\frac{1}{3600}$ pound. How these consequences can be verified will be discussed later.

More about mass and how it is measured. We know from experience that the weight of a body varies directly as the quantity of matter in it. Obviously *quantity of matter* is an awkward expression and for this reason it is called *mass*. How, though, is mass measured?

We have already seen that volume is not a measure of mass, because the mass of a solid lead ball is greater than the mass of a wooden ball of the same volume or size. What about weight? Is it a measure of mass? We have seen that the weight of a ball having a mass of 1 pound varies from 1 pound at the earth's surface to $\frac{1}{3600}$ pound at 240,000 miles from the center of the earth. *Hence, weight is not a measure of mass.*

No easy way of measuring mass is apparent until we stop to think that at any place in the universe the earth's gravitational pull on any two equal masses is the same for both. Consequently, on a beam balance like the one shown in Fig. 4, the standard weights and the goose, having equal masses, will balance each other. Therefore, if the mass of the weights is 10

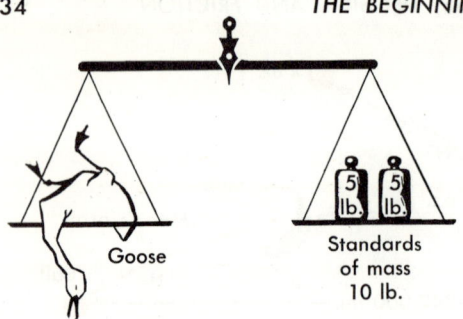

Fig. 4. To determine the mass of the goose, we are comparing its unknown mass with known masses of standard weights on a beam balance.

pounds, the mass of the goose is also 10 pounds. Unfortunately, finding mass by means of a beam balance is called weighing, which incorrectly implies that weight is determined.

Units of mass and weight. Unfortunately both mass and weight are measured in the same units: in pounds, ounces, tons, grams, and kilograms. This fact adds to the difficulty of distinguishing between mass, weight, and force. In this book, in order to avoid confusion between units of mass, of weight, and of force, terms such as *grams, pounds, tons,* and others will be used to designate mass. In cases where the meaning would not otherwise be clear, the terms *pounds of weight, grams of weight,* and *kilograms of weight* will be used to designate weight, and *pounds of force, grams of force,* and *kilograms of force* to designate force.

It would be well to remember that the international standard of mass is a kilogram platinum-iridium cylinder and that the mass of each weight used in weighing on a beam balance is equivalent to it in mass or is a fractional or a multiple part of this kilogram.

Density. All of us have heard it said that lead is heavier than wood, that iron is heavier than aluminum, and that water is heavier than oil. Also you may have heard it argued that a pound of lead weighs more than a pound of feathers. What do such statements mean and why do people make them?

Confusion of thought and lack of the necessary vocabulary to express clearly the crucial point involved are no doubt the reasons. In such instances it is wise to analyze the situation so as to gain an understanding of the factors involved.

Evidently, the statement that lead is heavier than wood is an endeavor to say that a given volume of lead, for example, a cubic inch, weighs more than a cubic inch of wood. In other words, the mass of a cubic inch of lead is greater than the mass of a cubic inch of wood. The word used to express this idea clearly is *density*. *Density is mass (quantity of matter) per unit volume*. Mathematically, then:

$$D = \frac{M}{V}$$

Thus, the density of water is *1 kilogram (1000 grams) per liter at 4 degrees centigrade*, the temperature at which water is most dense. See page 243. Ordinarily, and for most purposes in this book, we say that the *density of water is 62.4 pounds per cubic foot, 1 kilogram per liter, 1 gram per cubic centimeter, or 0.036 pound per cubic inch*. See Fig. 5.

Units. It is of the highest importance to realize that the physical quantities with which we deal have units associated with them. Distances are measured in centimeters, feet, or miles; time is measured in hours, minutes, or seconds; speed is measured in mi./hr. or ft./sec., etc. In problems involving physical quantities the units must be treated as if they were numbers, and the operations indicated in the problems must be performed not only on the numbers, but on the units accompanying the numbers as well. For example, if we divide 4 feet by 3 seconds the answer is

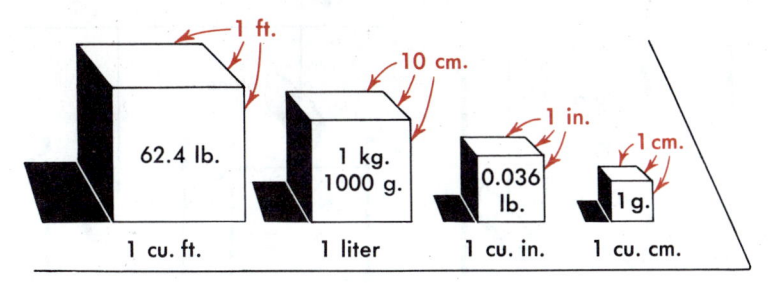

FORCE, GRAVITY, WEIGHT, MASS, DENSITY, AND FRICTION

Fig. 5. Comparison of the density of water in the metric and English systems of measurement. The density of water per cu. in. is found by dividing 62.4 lb. per cu. ft. by the number of cubic inches in a cubic foot, or 1728.

$$\frac{4 \text{ ft.}}{3 \text{ sec.}} = \frac{4}{3} \frac{\text{ft.}}{\text{sec.}}, \text{ not just } \frac{4}{3} \text{ or } \frac{4}{3} \text{ ft.}$$

We must perform on the units (feet and seconds) the operation indicated (in this case, division). To find the distance a car, going at the rate of 30 mi./hr., covers in 4 hours, we multiply 30 mi./hr. by 4 hr. The result is 30 mi./hr. × 4 hr. = 120 mi. It is not just 120 or 120 mi./hr., since the hours in the numerator and the denominator cancel each other out, and the units, miles, were left in the numerator. If we wish to find the density of a substance, 20 grams of which occupy 4 cubic centimeters, we divide 20 grams by 4 cubic centimeters and obtain for the answer 20 g./4 cc. = 5 g./cc. We have performed on the units the same operation—namely, division—as on the numbers.

For a further explanation of unit analysis, see pages 639–643.

PROBLEM 1: What is the density of a stone whose mass is 500 lb. and whose volume is 3 cu. ft.?

SOLUTION: $D = \frac{M}{V}$

Substituting, $D = \frac{500 \text{ lb.}}{3 \text{ cu. ft.}}$

Solving, $D = \frac{167 \text{ lb.}}{\text{cu. ft.}}$

PROBLEM 2: What is the mass of 10 liters of water? 10 cu. ft. of water? 10 cc. of water?

PROBLEM 3: What is the approximate volume of 250 lb. of water?

DENSITIES OF COMMON SUBSTANCES
(GRAMS PER CC.)

Aluminum	2.7	Lead	11.3
Beeswax	0.96	Mercury	13.6
Brass	8.4	Nickel	8.6
Copper	8.9	Paraffin	0.87 to 0.91
Glass	2.5 to 3.6	Platinum	21.5
Gold	19.3	Silver	10.5
Ice	0.92	Water	1.00
Iron	7.1 to 7.8	Zinc	7.1

Finding the volume of an irregularly shaped body. The density of a body can be found providing its mass and volume are known. We can usually determine mass by "weighing" the body on a beam balance. The volume of a cylindrical, rectangular, or cubical body can be computed mathematically. This method is very impractical, however, if the body is irregular in shape like an ordinary stone.

To find the volume of an impenetrable solid body which sinks in water, a graduated cylinder partly filled with water may be used, as shown in Fig. 6. The water level is read before and after the stone is submerged and the difference in readings gives the volume of the body.

With larger bodies, an overflow can is

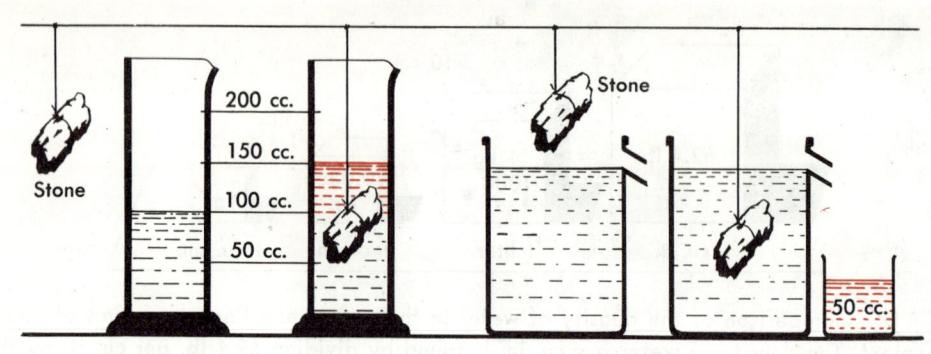

Fig. 6. Since two substances cannot occupy the same place at the same time, it is possible to calculate the volume of an irregular solid by the displacement of water.

used. After it is filled brimming full of water an empty catch bucket is placed under the spout and then the body is sunk. The volume of displaced liquid equals the volume of the body. How would you find the volume of an irregularly shaped body which floats?

Balanced and unbalanced forces. We already know that if a man weighs 160 pounds and sits in a chair, the chair must exert an upward force of 160 pounds. If the chair exerts less force than 160 pounds, then the man will crash to the floor along with the chair.

Also we know that if the 160-pound man sits so that his weight is equally distributed among the four legs, then each leg must exert an upward force of 40 pounds; the sum of the four upward forces must equal 160 pounds. Hence,

if a body is at rest, then the sum of the forces acting in one direction on it must balance the force, or the sum of the forces, acting in the opposite direction. When such forces balance, a body is said to be in equilibrium.

Other conditions necessary for equilibrium will be treated in Chapter 13.

What is force of friction? Often in the teaching of the meaning of force of friction, the story is told of the hopeful, would-be inventor who asked the opinion of a famous scientist concerning an engine which the inventor had designed to run without fuel or any other source of power. Rather than tell the inventor that his design was worthless, the scientist asked the inventor what he was going to do about friction. In reply the inventor said, "To heck with friction! I'll use plenty of grease."

To the disappointment of many, friction cannot be disposed of so easily. Regardless of how much grease is applied when the surface of one body is rubbed on the surface of another body, a force known as *friction* is always present to resist the motion.

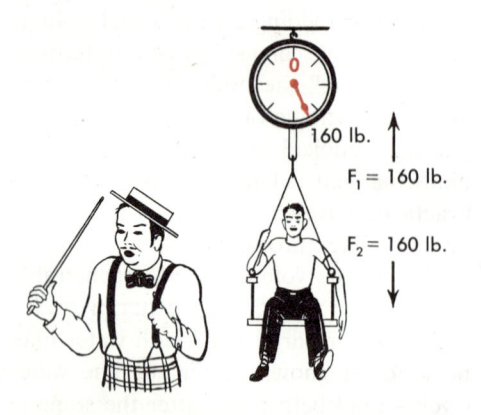

Fig. 7. The weight of the man is determined by measuring the gravitational attraction between the earth and the man.

$F_1 = 160$ lb.

$F_2 = 160$ lb.

FORCE, GRAVITY, WEIGHT, MASS, DENSITY, AND FRICTION

It should not be thought, however, that friction is always a liability. If it were not for friction, how could automobiles, trains, airplanes, and hundreds of other bodies be started and stopped? The problem of force of friction is to eliminate it as nearly as possible where it is not wanted and to increase it as much as possible where it is needed most.

What factors affect force of friction? Most of us already know that it is easier to pull a sled on ice, on snow, or on wet grass than on a concrete sidewalk or on the bare ground. We know, too, that rubber-soled shoes will not slide on a wooden floor the way leather-soled shoes do. Seemingly, then, the force of friction is affected by the nature of the substances that are rubbed together.

We know also that as the load on a sled increases the force of friction increases. That is, as the force which pushes the bodies together increases, the force of friction increases. We know the rougher the bodies the greater the friction and the smoother the bodies the less the friction.

As shown in Fig. 8, the area of the surfaces, other factors being equal, does not affect the force of sliding friction. Likewise, speed does not affect the force of friction. Experiment will show, however, that the *starting* force of friction is far greater than *sliding* force of friction.

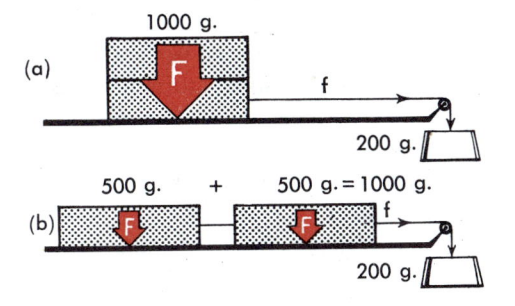

Fig. 8. Friction does not depend on the area of contact between the surfaces.

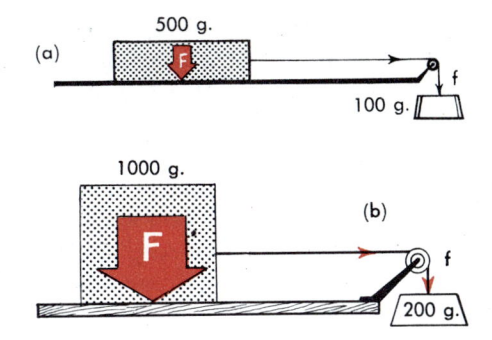

Fig. 9. Friction (f) varies directly as the force (F) pressing the surfaces together.

Coefficient of friction. We know from experience that if all other factors are equal, as the load on a sled or other sliding body increases, the force of friction increases. This is shown in Fig. 9. That is, as the force (F) which presses the sliding surfaces together increases, the force of friction (f) increases. Mathematically:

or
$$f \propto F$$
$$f = kF$$
and
$$k = \frac{f}{F}$$

where k is a constant called the *coefficient of sliding friction*.

PROBLEM 1: What horizontal force is required to pull a 10-lb. loaded wooden box on a level glass plate when the coefficient of sliding friction between glass and wood is 0.15?

SOLUTION: $f = kF$
Substituting, $f = 0.15 \times 10$ lb.
$f = 1.5$ lb.

PROBLEM 2: Two football players push a 500-lb. loaded charging sled with a horizontal force of 150 lb. What is the coefficient of friction?

PROBLEM 3: If the coefficient of friction between a 5-lb. dictionary and your desk top is 0.18, what horizontal force is necessary to slide the dictionary at constant speed?

Uses to which a knowledge of force of friction can be put. It is common knowledge that a well-lubricated bearing turns more easily than a dry one, that soap on the sliding surfaces of a desk drawer, or on a window that sticks, makes either slide easier, that sand or ashes on ice or snow prevent slippage, and that soap and water help in removing a tight-fitting ring from one's finger.

A most important application of the "laws" of friction, and one that every automobile driver should know, is that in stopping in the shortest distance possible, skidding of the car wheels should be avoided because *sliding friction is only about half as great as the possible maximum friction when the wheels are turning.* If the wheels skid, *release the brakes for an instant and then apply them again* but

Fig. 10. More friction, not less, is a basic requirement of this tractor. Notice the special construction of the tractor chain and the heavy tread of the tire.

Courtesy Caterpillar Tractor Co.

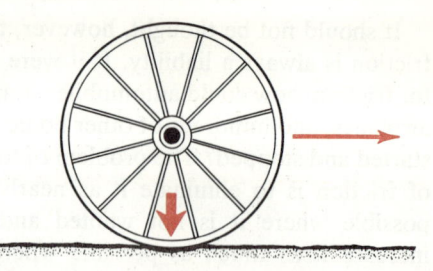

Fig. 11. Rolling friction is due to the depression of the surface of the roadbed caused by the weight of the object acting downward. Thus, the wheel must roll up a slight hill.

not hard enough to cause skidding. On icy roads "pump" your brakes in stopping. Application of this knowledge may save a life; perhaps yours.

Rolling friction. Most of us know from experience that on a sidewalk or on bare ground it is far easier to pull a boy in a wagon than on a sled. The rolling friction of the wheels is far less than the sliding friction of the runners. The ancients discovered this fact when they observed that round stones or small logs which rolled under sled runners reduced the force necessary to pull a sled.

Like sliding friction, rolling friction is affected by several factors. For example, when a wheel rolls on a level concrete highway, a slight depression is caused under the wheel so that it has to roll up a minute hill as shown in Fig. 11. Of course this depression, as well as the rolling friction, can be reduced if the road surface is hardened and made more substantial. Also rolling friction can be decreased if the wheel tread is made harder. Bicycle tires with high pressure cause less friction than low-pressure tires.

Rolling friction caused by the depression in the roadbed can be decreased greatly if the tread on the tires is widened and the diameter of the wheels is increased. Explain.

FORCE, GRAVITY, WEIGHT, MASS, DENSITY, AND FRICTION

SUMMARY AND CONCLUSIONS

1. A force is that which tends to produce or destroy motion, change the direction of motion, or change the shape of a body.
2. A force may be measured by the distortion which it can produce on a body.
3. Weight of a body is the gravitational force of attraction between the earth and the body. Weight, like other forces, may be measured by a spring balance.
4. The law of universal gravitation is that all bodies attract each other; the attraction is mutual. Mathematically:

$$\text{Force} = K \frac{M_1 M_2}{d^2}$$

$$\text{Weight} = K \frac{M M_E}{d^2}$$

5. Mass is the quantity of matter in a body. It can be measured by means of a beam balance.
6. Density is mass per unit volume.

$$\text{Density} = \frac{\text{Mass}}{\text{Volume}} = \frac{M}{V}$$

7. The density of water is 62.4 pounds per cubic foot, 1 gram per cubic centimeter, 1 kilogram per liter, or 0.036 pound per cubic inch.
8. A body at rest is said to be in equilibrium. For this to be true, the sum of the forces acting on the body in one direction must equal the sum of the forces acting in the opposite direction.
9. Force of sliding friction increases with the roughness of the rubbing surfaces, is dependent on the nature of the rubbing surfaces, and varies directly as the forces which press the surfaces together.
10. Coefficient of friction $(k) =$
$$\frac{\text{force of friction }(f)}{\text{force }(F)\text{ pressing the surfaces together}}$$

QUESTIONS FOR REVIEW

1. Write the definition of force as we have defined it in physics. Give five examples of force.
2. Name four possible ways of measuring force implied by the definition of force. Which one of these is most commonly used?
3. What is Hooke's Law? What does it have to do with measuring force?
4. What is weight? How is weight measured?
5. Name five units by which force is measured.
6. It is said that a body in Australia falls in the opposite direction from a body in America. Do you agree with this? If so, how do you account for it?
7. It is sometimes said that the Mississippi River in flowing from the north to the south flows uphill. Explain.
8. Why does a bag of sugar weigh more at sea level than on top of a high mountain? More at the earth's poles than at the equator?
9. In terms of the formula $W = K \frac{MM_E}{d^2}$, explain why a solid lead ball weighs more than a hollow one of the same diameter. More than a wooden ball of the same diameter.
10. What is mass? How is mass measured? Does the mass of a body necessarily change as the weight of a body changes? Explain.
11. What is the law of universal gravitation?
12. What observation caused Newton to suspect that gravitational attraction was not confined solely to the earth?
13. Explain at least three distinct consequences of the law of universal gravitation and explain how each might be tested experimentally.
14. Write the definition of density in words and then as a mathematical formula.
15. Give at least three different units in which the density of water may be stated.
16. Why is it more exact to say that lead is denser than feathers than to say that lead is heavier than feathers? Explain.
17. How is the force of sliding friction affected by the area of the rubbing surfaces? By the speed? What is meant by the coefficient of friction?

THE BEGINNING OF PHYSICS

EXERCISES AND PROBLEMS

1. What is the mass of each of the following quantities of water: (a) 10 cc.? (b) 10 cu. ft.? (c) 10 liters?
2. The mass of a cubic foot of water is 62.4 lb. What is the density of water in lb. per cu. in.? (There are 12 in. × 12 in. × 12 in., or 1728 cu. in., in a cubic foot.)
3. What is the mass of 2 cc. of lead? 10 cc. of beeswax? (See table of densities.)
4. A tank is 6 ft. long, 4 ft. wide, and 5 ft. deep. How many pounds of water can it hold?
5. The mass of a stone is 450 lb. Its volume is 3 cu. ft. What is its density?
6. The mass of a block of wood 7 cm. by 7 cm. by 3 cm. is 98 g. What is its density?
7. A rectangular tank is 20 cm. long, 5 cm. wide, and 10 cm. deep. (a) What is its volume? (b) What mass of water will the tank hold?
8. The mass of a piece of metal is 144 lb. Its volume is 720 cu. in. What is its density?
9. A manufacturer wants to make a 500-g. brass weight. How many cubic centimeters will be required if the density of brass is 8.4 g. per cc.?
10. An icebox is 18 in. long, 15 in. wide, and 12 in. deep. The density of ice is 0.92 that of water. What mass of ice will the icebox hold?
11. What is the mass of a gold brick which is 8 in. long, 4 in. wide, and 2 in. thick? Gold is 19.3 times as dense as water.
12. If the mass of the water in a container is doubled, how is the weight of water affected?
13. At the earth's surface, approximately 4000 mi. from the center of the earth, a lead shot weighs 16 lb. How much would it weigh if it were above the earth's surface 4000 mi.? 12,000 mi.? 16,000 mi.? 240,000 mi.?
14. At the earth's surface the mass of a man is 160 lb. What would be his mass if his distance from the earth's center of mass were 8000 mi.? 12,000 mi.? 16,000 mi.? 240,000 mi.?
15. How is the force of attraction between two bodies affected when the distance between them is doubled? Tripled? Halved?
16. How is the force of attraction between two bodies affected when the mass of one is doubled? Mass of both is doubled? Mass of both is tripled?
17. A horizontal 200-lb. force is required to pull a 1000-lb. crate at uniform velocity on a level floor. What is the coefficient of friction? The force which acts perpendicular to the floor is how many pounds?
18. In sliding a 400-lb. box on a level floor the minimum force is 100 lb. What is the coefficient of friction? The force that pushes the box and floor together?
19. The coefficient of friction between ice and the runners on a sled is 0.10. What horizontal force is necessary to pull a sled whose weight is 300 lb.?
20. The coefficient of friction between wood and ice is found to be 0.09. What horizontal force is required to push a 240-lb. cake of ice on a wooden floor for a distance of 10 ft.?

PROJECTS

1. In a more advanced book, find how the constant K in the law of universal gravitation was determined. Knowing the value of this constant and knowing your own weight and mass, find the mass of the earth. Explain your findings to the class. See reading reference below.
2. Compute the volume of the earth in cubic feet. Then using the mass of the earth just found in (1), compute the average density of the earth in pounds per cubic foot. Use 8000 miles as the diameter of the earth.

READING YOU WILL ENJOY

Taylor, L. W., *Physics, the Pioneer Science*, pp. 167-170. Houghton Mifflin Company, Boston, 1941. Explains how K was determined in the formula $F = K \dfrac{M_1 M_2}{d^2}$.

Unit 2

Forces in Water and Other Liquids

One thousand gallons of water a minute swirl over the large flow table in the unit photograph as engineers attempt to solve a practical problem in hydraulics, the study of liquids in motion. The water flows past the straightening waves in the foreground and around the oversize wooden turbine blades. By studying the flow patterns on this testing device, the engineers can determine the best shapes for turbine blade designs in automatic transmissions for automobiles, trucks, and buses.

In this unit, you will discover some of the dynamic aspects of fluids—both at rest and in motion. Do you realize that even the placid waters of a dammed-up lake are exerting powerful forces? After you have mastered some of the basic principles underlying liquid forces, you will be able to apply your knowledge to innumerable practical problems. Why are dams built thicker at the bottom than at the top? Why is it easier to lift a stone under water than in air? Why does a floating object seem to be weightless? These and many other problems await your solution.

6. LIQUID FORCES IN OPEN VESSELS
7. SPECIFIC GRAVITY AND ARCHIMEDES' PRINCIPLE
8. MACHINES WHICH TRANSMIT FORCES THROUGH LIQUIDS—HYDRAULIC MACHINES

Unit Photograph Courtesy General Motors Corp.

Chapter 6

Liquid Forces in Open Vessels

The problem. Unknowingly man has often been his own worst enemy, and modern man seems to be no exception. Nothing illustrates this better than a victim of flood water eagerly reading an account of his own plight in a newspaper made from trees whose roots were adapted to hold back the waters that cause floods.

Forces in liquids can be one of man's greatest sources of wealth or one of his greatest curses, depending upon whether they are controlled and directed for useful ends or are allowed to unleash their fury against the works of man and nature.

In a few parts of our nation rampaging flood waters and rivers have been tamed and used to develop hydroelectric power, irrigation, recreational facilities for hunting, boating, and fishing, and to develop other forms of wealth. In other areas the very opposite is true. Every year torrential rains gut thousands of acres of farm land, carrying away hundreds of tons of rich topsoil, flood and destroy millions of dollars' worth of homes, crops, factories, machinery, and livestock, and leave in their wake homeless people, filth, disease, poverty, and death. Such unnecessary waste is one of the greatest threats to our nation's future welfare.

However, control of flood waters and the development of water power are only two of the many problems involving forces in liquids. Another is the design of steel ships which every year carry billions of tons of food, clothing, machinery, lumber, fuel, and other products to all parts of the world. Since a piece of steel does not float, how can a ship made of steel do so?

Then, too, there is the design of machines which transmit forces through liquids. Such machines are called *hydraulic machines*. Examples are the hydraulic press, hydraulic elevator, hydraulic lift, and hydraulic brakes. Last, but not least, are the problems of supplying our great industrial cities and rural homes with plenty of pure water and of disposing of the waste water and sewage in a sanitary way.

To learn how to solve these problems we must first make a study of forces in liquids.

Total force on the bottom of an open container. One of the simplest situations involving forces in liquids is the downward force F on the bottom of a tank filled with water, as shown in Fig. 1. This force F obviously equals the weight W of the water in the vessel. But, since weight W equals

FORCES IN WATER AND OTHER LIQUIDS

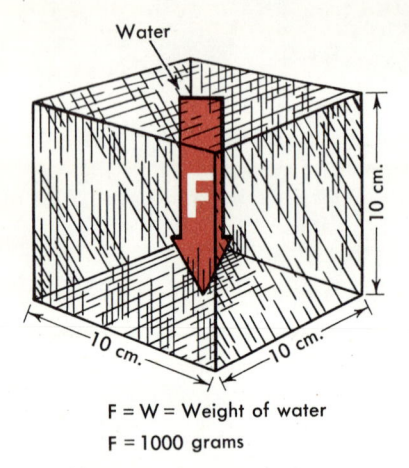

F = W = Weight of water
F = 1000 grams

Fig. 1. How is the total force on the bottom of the container computed?

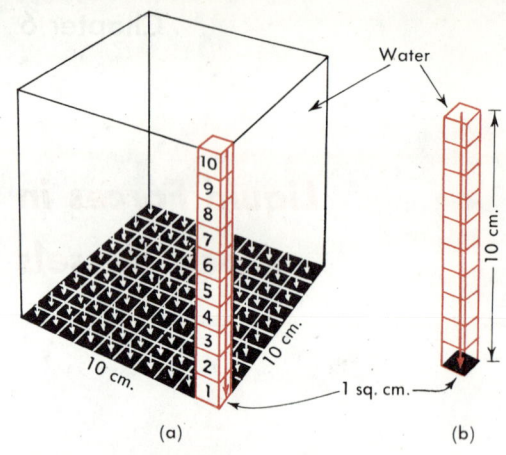

Fig. 2. By dividing the total force by area, we can find the pressure.

the volume V of the liquid times its density d, then $F = Vd$. That is,

since $\qquad W = V \times d$
and $\qquad F = W$
then $\qquad F = V \times d$

Furthermore, since the volume V equals the area A of the bottom times the height h, then the total force,

$$F = Ahd$$

In Fig. 1, what is the area A of the bottom of the tank? Using the dimensions shown, we can compute the force on the bottom in the following manner:

$F = A \times h \times d$
$F = 100 \times 10 \times 1$
▶ $F = 1000$ grams force

The red arrow indicates that you should refer to the section on unit analysis, pages 639-643.

PROBLEM: A rectangular tank is filled with water. Its length is 10 cm., width 4 cm., and height 4 cm. What is the total force on the bottom? Force on 1 sq. cm.?

What is pressure? In dealing with forces exerted by both liquids and gases it is often more useful to know, and easier to find, the force exerted on a single square inch, square centimeter, square foot, or other unit of area than to know the total force. For example, when we want to know if there is enough air in an automobile tire, we find out by determining the force exerted on one square inch instead of measuring the total force inside the tire. *Force per unit area is called* **pressure**.

This definition, pressure P is force F per unit area A, is written mathematically as follows:

$$P = \frac{F}{A} \quad \text{(See page 24.)}$$

How is pressure computed? To compute the water pressure P on the bottom of the container in Fig. 2, we must know the total force F on the bottom, which is 1000 grams force, and the area A, which is 100 sq. cm. Substituting in

$$P = \frac{F}{A},$$

we have: $\qquad P = \dfrac{1000 \text{ g.}}{100 \text{ sq. cm.}}$

Dividing, $\qquad P = \dfrac{10 \text{ g.}}{\text{sq. cm.}}$

Usually this answer would be written as 10 g. per sq. cm. or as 10 g./cm.[2]

LIQUID FORCES IN OPEN VESSELS

PROBLEM: A rectangular tank is filled with water. The bottom is 10 cm. by 5 cm. The height is 5 cm. What is the pressure on the bottom?

The chief difficulties with this method of finding pressure are that it is indirect and that, for irregularly shaped vessels, volume (V), and hence force (F), are difficult to compute. Fortunately, this difficulty can be surmounted.

Since
$$P = \frac{F}{A}$$
and
$$F = Ahd,$$
then
$$P = \frac{Ahd}{A} = hd$$

Using this formula, find the pressure on the bottom of the container in Fig. 2. Does your answer check with the one above?

In order to grasp better the meaning of the formula $P = hd$, let us study Fig. 3. Here it is seen that a liquid column 4 cm. tall rests on each square centimeter of bottom area. Each column really consists of 4 cc. of water, stacked one upon the other. Substituting the number of cubes for h and 1 g./cm.³ for the density of fresh water in the formula

$$P = hd,$$

we have: $P = 4$ cm. $\times$ 1 g./cm.³
and: $P = 4$ g./cm.²

PROBLEM: What is the downward pressure in water when the depth is 8 cm.? 20 cm.? 1 meter?

Suppose the dimensions of the vessel are in feet instead of centimeters. As shown in Fig. 4, the unit area of the bottom surface becomes 1 sq. ft. instead of 1 sq. cm., and 4 cu. ft. of water, each weighing 62.4 lb., rest on top of this unit area. Substituting 4 ft. for the height h and 62.4 lb./ft.³ for d in the formula

$$P = hd,$$

we have: $P = 4$ ft. $\times$ 62.4 lb./ft.³
and: $P = 249.6$ lb./ft.²

Knowing the pressure in pounds per square foot, we can find the pressure in pounds per square inch by dividing 249.6 lbs./ft.² by 144 in.²/ft.², since 144 is the number of square inches in a square foot. Thus:

$$P = \frac{249.6}{144} = 1.73 \text{ lb./in.}^2$$

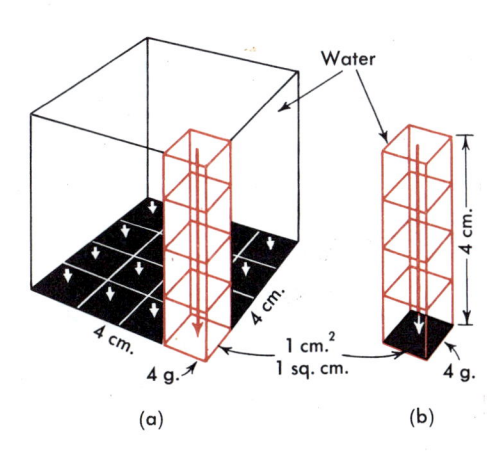

Fig. 3. The pressure on the bottom of this container is 4 g./sq. cm.

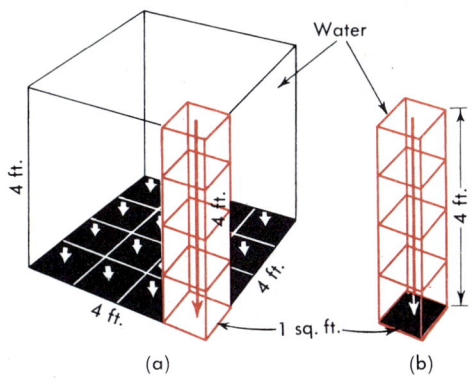

Fig. 4. Since the height is expressed in feet, the density must be in lb./cu. ft.

Is there, however, a more direct way of finding the pressure in lb./in.²? One possibility is to change the depth (4 ft.) to 48 in. and consider the unit of surface area on the bottom to be 1 sq. in. As a result the pressure is the weight of 48 cu. in. of water, which weighs 0.036 lb./in.³ It is found as follows:

$$P = hd$$
$$P = 48 \text{ in.} \times 0.036 \text{ lb./in.}^3$$
$$P = 1.73 \text{ lb./in.}^2$$

Does this pressure agree with that found above? What is the pressure in lb. per sq. in. caused by a column of water 12 in. deep? *This answer should be memorized for future use.*

In conclusion, we see that the pressure on the bottom of a container can be computed by either of the following formulas

$$P = \frac{F}{A} \quad \text{or} \quad P = hd$$

But when the formula $P = hd$ is used, to keep the units straight the density must be in:

(a) g./cc. when the depth is in centimeters,
(b) lb./cu. ft. when the depth is in feet, or
(c) lb./cu. in. when the depth is in inches.

The density of water is 1 g./cc., 62.4 lb./cu. ft., or 0.036 lb. per cu. in. A column of water 1 ft. high exerts a pressure of 12 in. × 0.036 lb./in.³, or 0.43 lb./in.² See Fig. 5.

PROBLEM 1: Find the pressure exerted by a column of water (a) 20 cm. high; (b) 20 in. high; (c) 20 ft. high, in lb./ft.²; (d) 20 ft. high, in lb./in.²

PROBLEM 2: Find the area when the total force is 500 lb. and the pressure is 100 lb. per ft.²

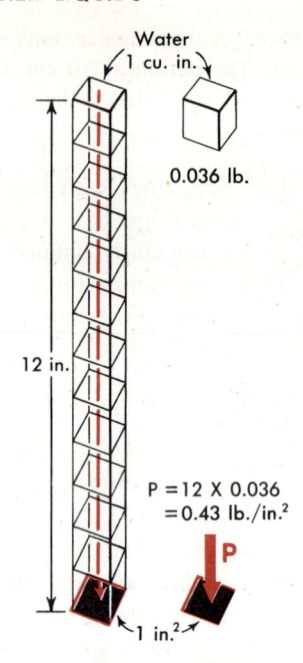

Fig. 5. Computing the pressure in lb./in.² Since the depth is expressed in inches, the density must be in lb. per cu. in.

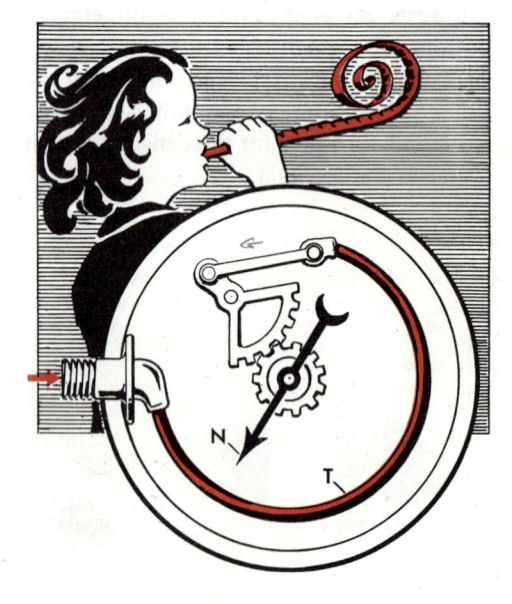

Fig. 6. The principle of the Bourdon gauge. In which direction does the pointer move when the pressure of the fluid increases? Decreases?

LIQUID FORCES IN OPEN VESSELS

How is fluid pressure measured? One ingenious device for measuring pressure is the *Bourdon gauge*. It consists chiefly of a curved metal tube, *T*, as shown in Fig. 6. When fluid (gas or liquid) pressure is applied inside the tube, it straightens out similarly to the way that the blow-out toy in Fig. 6 does when air pressure in it is increased.

As the tube, *T*, straightens out it sets in motion a system of cogs and levers which turn the needle, *N*; and the greater the pressure the farther the needle is turned. Usually the gauge is calibrated to read in pounds per square inch. Such gauges are used to measure air, steam, and gas pressures as well as liquid pressures. Many automobile tire gauges are of the Bourdon gauge type.

Another type of pressure gauge is the *open-tube manometer*. It consists of a U-tube partially filled with mercury or some other liquid, as shown in Fig. 7, and is based upon the principle that when a group of open connecting vessels, such as those shown in Fig. 8, are filled with liquid, the liquid "seeks" the same levels in all vessels.

When, however, the pressure is increased on the liquid in one vessel, the liquid is forced up in the other vessels. And in the case of the manometer it is pushed upward in the opposite side of the tube until the pressure being measured exactly equals the pressure caused by the difference in levels of the two liquid columns. Knowing this height (h) (see Fig. 7), and knowing that the density of mercury is 0.49 lb. per cu. in., we can compute the pressure with the formula $P = hd$.

PROBLEM: When an open-tube manometer is attached to a water faucet, the difference in heights of the mercury columns is 70 in. What is the pressure?

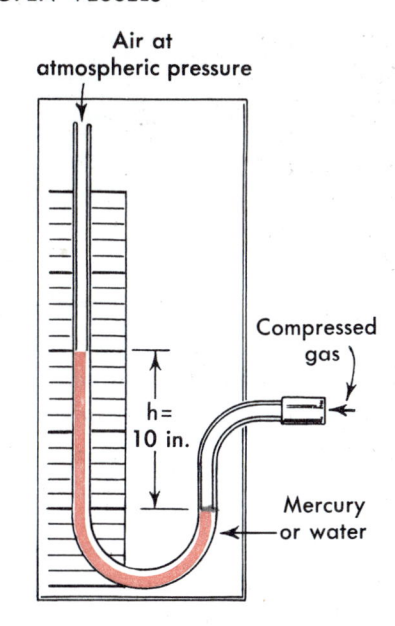

Fig. 7. The open-tube manometer. Multiplying the difference in liquid levels by the density of the liquid gives the pressure of the gas.

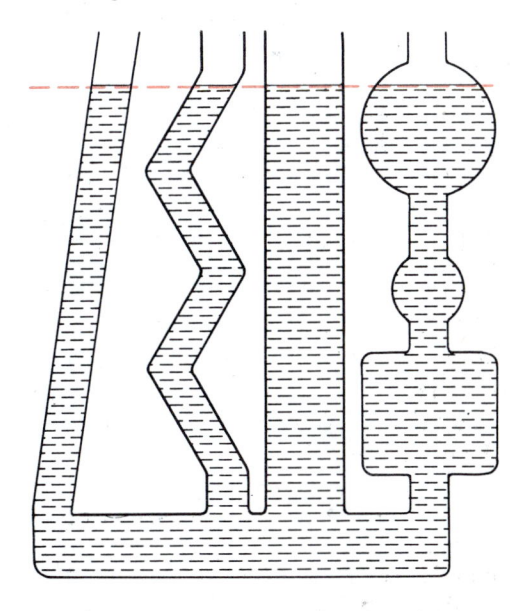

Fig. 8. To equalize the pressure, the liquid rises to the same level in each container. The shape and size of the container have no effect on the pressure.

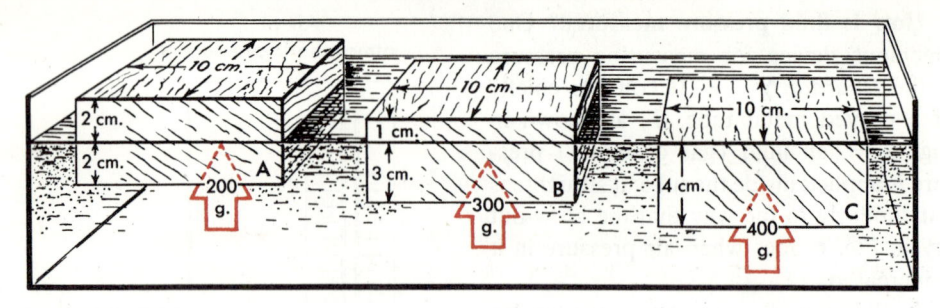

Fig. 9. A floating object displaces its own weight of the liquid in which it is immersed. To compute the upward pressure on each block, divide the weight of the block (the weight of water displaced) by the area of the bottom of the block.

SOLUTION:
$$P = hd$$
Substituting,
$$P = 70 \times 0.49$$
whence
$$P = 34.3 \text{ lb. per sq. in.}$$

Does the cross-sectional area of the manometer tube affect the pressure reading? Explain.

Fig. 10. More power for Chile! This penstock rising 1200 meters high will feed water from a reservoir to large turbines that will be used to turn electric generators.

Courtesy United Nations

"Head of water" and other units for measuring pressure. Rather than change all pressures to pounds per square inch or pounds per square foot, engineers often express the pressure in *head of water* or *water head*. For example, the pressure caused by a column of water 100 feet high is called a water head or head of water of 100 feet, which is equivalent to a mercury head of 88.2 inches.

PROBLEM: Water which furnishes the power to drive a turbine wheel drops 200 ft. in a pipe straight down the side of a mountain. At the turbine, what is the water head? Mercury head? Pressure in lb./sq. in.? Remember that a water head of 1 foot is equivalent to a pressure of 0.43 lb./sq. in.

Upward forces exerted by liquids. Most of us know that in a swimming pool we can support our entire weight on our finger tips merely by taking hold of the edge of the pool. Furthermore, we know that it is easier to lift a stone under water than in air. Apparently when a body is submerged in a liquid, it is lifted or *buoyed up* by the liquid. This buoyant force assists in supporting a body against the downward pull of gravity. The body is therefore said to "lose weight"—that is, to undergo *apparent loss of weight*.

LIQUID FORCES IN OPEN VESSELS

How can we compute the upward forces and pressures exerted by a liquid? To answer this question let us resort to experiment by placing in water a rectangular block of wood, A, weighing 200 g. and having the dimensions shown in Fig. 9.

Since the block floats and hence is in equilibrium, the liquid must exert an upward force of 200 g. on the bottom of the block. And since the area of the bottom is 100 cm.^{2}, the upward pressure must be 200 g. $\div$ 100 cm.^{2}, or 2 g./cm.^{2} Compare the upward pressure in water 2 cm. deep with the downward pressure, $P = hd$, at this same depth.

To further test our findings let us place in water another wooden block, B, weighing 300 g. and having the same dimensions as A. As shown in the same figure, it sinks 3 cm. Obviously, to support the block the water must exert 300 g. of force upward on its bottom. And using the formula $P = F/A$ we find the upward pressure is 300 g. $\div$ 100 cm.^{2}, or 3 g./cm.^{2} Does this upward pressure equal the downward pressure at a depth of 3 cm. in water?

In conclusion, it seems that the upward and downward pressures at any point in a liquid are equal and that therefore both can be found by the formula $P = hd$. What is the upward pressure 10 cm. deep in gasoline whose density is 0.77 g./cc.? What is the downward pressure?

Compute the weight of water displaced by block A in Fig. 9 and compare it with the weight of A. Do the same for blocks B and C.

How does sidewise pressure compare with downward and upward pressures? Bricks stacked straight up and down, one on top of the other, exert downward and upward pressure but exert none sidewise. If they did, what would happen? Unlike bricks, water cannot be "stacked up" unless it is placed in a retaining vessel. And if we bore holes in the side of a vessel containing water, we see that the water spurts out sidewise perpendicular to the containing sides, and that the deeper the water the faster and farther it is ejected. This seems to indicate that the water exerts sidewise pressure which is proportional to the depth and *acts at right angles or perpendicular to the walls of the container.* See Fig. 11.

A method of comparing downward, upward, and sidewise pressure is shown in Fig. 12. Mercury is poured into the three different open-tube manometers until it stands at the same height in all three.

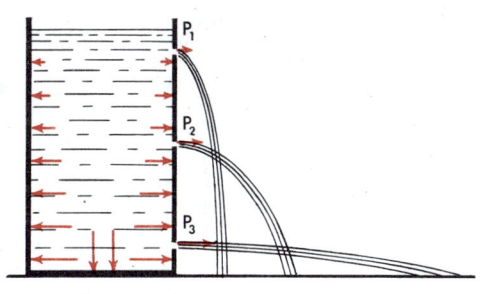

Fig. 11. Since sidewise pressure also depends on the depth, the liquid spurts out of the container with the greatest force from P_3.

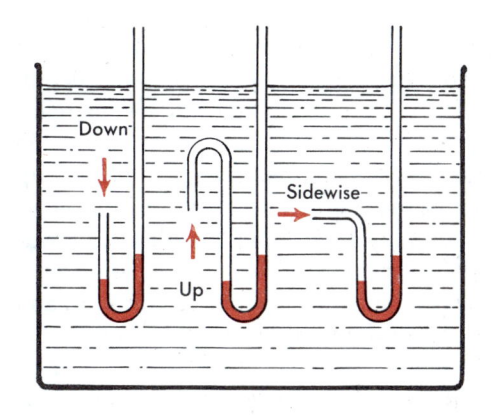

Fig. 12. The pressure at a given depth in a liquid is the same in all directions. If this were not true, the water would move in a particular direction.

50   FORCES IN WATER AND OTHER LIQUIDS

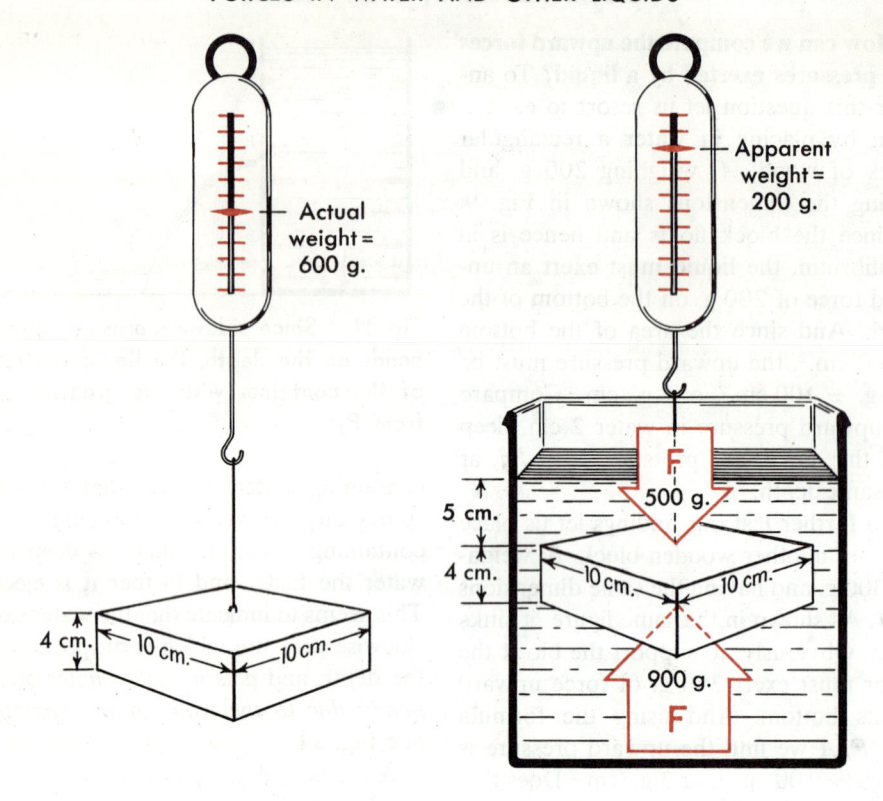

Fig. 13. An object submerged in water loses weight, or is buoyed up by a force, equal to the weight of water displaced. The buoyant force is due to the difference in total force on the top and bottom surfaces of the object.

These are lowered into the water until all three open ends are at the same depth. The water pressure pushes the mercury down in one side of each tube and up in the other. Since the mercury is pushed up to the same level in all three tubes, it shows that at any given depth the sidewise, downward, and upward pressures are equal. Hence, sidewise pressure, like upward and downward, can be calculated by use of the formula $P = hd$.

Calculation of sidewise force. In calculating the total force against a dike or dam we must remember that the sidewise pressure increases gradually from zero at the surface to a maximum value at the bottom. The bottom sidewise pressure we can find by the formula $P = hd$.

Obviously neither the sidewise pressure at the surface nor that at the bottom can be used to compute total sidewise force. The logical pressure to use is the average pressure, which obviously equals that halfway down the side. That is, average pressure $P = \dfrac{h}{2} \times d$, where h is the total depth of the liquid. Since sidewise force equals average pressure $\times$ area, then

$$F = \dfrac{hd}{2} \times A$$

LIQUID FORCES IN OPEN VESSELS

PROBLEM 1: What is the total force against the face of a dam which is 100 ft. long and 20 ft. high?

SOLUTION:
$$F = \frac{hd}{2} \times A$$
$$F = \frac{20 \times 62.4}{2} \times 100 \times 20$$
$$F = 1{,}248{,}000 \text{ lb.}$$

PROBLEM 2: What is the total force against the face of a dam which is 150 ft. long and 10 ft. high?

Why does a body which sinks "lose" weight when it is submerged in a liquid? We have already seen that a body which floats in a liquid apparently "loses" all its weight, and one which does not float apparently "loses" part of its weight. For a floating body the apparent loss of weight is due to the upward pressure on the bottom. What causes the apparent loss of weight in a body that sinks?

One possibility is that the loss is due to the difference between the upward force on the bottom of the body and the downward force on top. If this hypothesis is true, the difference should equal the loss of weight of the body, which can be determined experimentally. What then should be the difference between the downward force and the upward force on the body in Fig. 13, which loses 400 g. of weight when weighed in air and then in water?

To test our hypothesis we must find the upward and downward forces on the body.

Since the top surface is 5 cm. deep, then the downward pressure $P = hd$

$$P\downarrow = 5 \times 1$$
or $$P\downarrow = 5 \text{ g./cm.}^2$$

The total downward force,
$$F\downarrow = P \times A$$
$$F\downarrow = 5 \times 100$$
$$F\downarrow = 500 \text{ g.}$$

On the bottom side, 4 cm. deeper, the upward pressure,
$$P\uparrow = 9 \times 1$$
or $$P\uparrow = 9 \text{ g./cm.}^2$$

The upward force,
$$F\uparrow = P \times A$$
$$F\uparrow = 9 \times 100$$
$$F\uparrow = 900 \text{ g.}$$

Subtracting the downward from the upward force $(F\uparrow - F\downarrow)$, we have $900 - 500 = 400$ g. Hence the loss of weight equals 400 g. Since the object originally weighed 600 g. in air, and since it has appeared to lose 400 g., it now weighs 200 g. Does this loss agree with that obtained by experiment? Seemingly, what caused the loss? What is the volume of the body in Fig. 13? What weight of water does it displace?

Another very interesting relationship, which you doubtless observed in the above experiment, was that the volume of the body was 4 cm. × 10 cm. × 10 cm., or 400 cc. This means that the weight of water displaced is 400 g., which also equals the weight lost by the body.

In conclusion, it seems that

when a rectangular solid is immersed in a liquid, its apparent loss of weight equals the weight of liquid displaced.

Whether or not this same principle holds for an irregularly shaped body can be determined as shown in Fig. 14. Here a 100-g. stone is being weighed in air and then in a full overflow can. The loss of weight in water is found as follows:

Weight of stone in air	100g.
Weight of stone in water	60g.
Loss of weight in water	40g.

Weight of water displaced by stone 40g.

FORCES IN WATER AND OTHER LIQUIDS

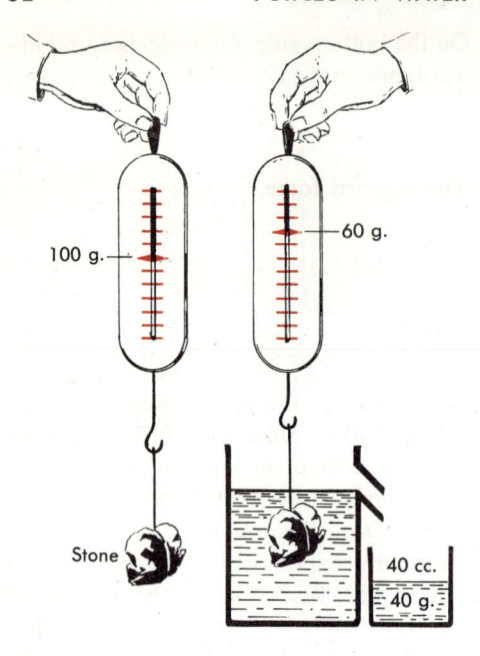

Fig. 14. The apparent loss of weight of the stone equals the weight of water displaced.

Hence we see that when an irregularly shaped body is immersed in water, its loss of weight equals the weight of water displaced. Does this same principle hold for a floating body? See Fig. 15, and explain the results.

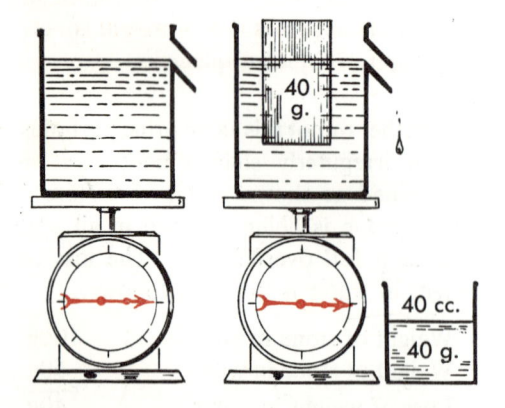

Fig. 15. The weight of water displaced by a floating body is equal to the weight of the object.

SUMMARY AND CONCLUSIONS

1. Pressure is force per unit area. That is,
$$P = \frac{F}{A}, \text{ and } F = P \times A$$
2. Pressure = Depth (h) × Density (d). That is, $P = hd$.
3. At any depth in a liquid which is at rest, the pressure is equal in all directions.
4. Liquid pressure is always perpendicular to the surface of the container.
5. Average sidewise pressure on a container equals the pressure halfway down the side. The total sidewise force equals the product of the average pressure and the area. That is,
$$P = \frac{h}{2} d, \text{ and } F = \frac{hd}{2} \times A$$
6. In using the formulas $P = hd$ and $P = \frac{h}{2} d$, the units of density must be substituted in the following manner:
   (a) as g./cc. when the depth is in centimeters;
   (b) as lb./cu. ft. when the depth is in feet;
   (c) as lb./cu. in. when the depth is in inches.

Remember that the density of water, unless otherwise stated, is considered to be 1 g./cc., 0.036 lb./cu. in., or 62.4 lb./cu. ft. Also, the pressure of a column of water 1 ft. deep is 0.43 lb./in.²

7. When a body is submerged in a liquid, the apparent loss of weight equals the total upward force on the bottom minus the total downward force on top.
8. When a body is placed in a liquid, the apparent loss of weight equals the weight of the liquid displaced. A floating body sinks to a depth such that it displaces its own weight of liquid.

QUESTIONS FOR REVIEW

1. What is pressure?
2. What formula is used to find pressure in an open vessel when only depth and density of the liquid are known? When total force and area are known?

LIQUID FORCES IN OPEN VESSELS

3. From your past experience, do you believe that a liquid is compressible to any degree?

4. In using the formula $P = hd$, in what units must the density be expressed when the depth, h, is given in centimeters? Feet? Inches?

5. Compare the downward, sidewise, and upward pressure at any point in a liquid.

6. When sidewise force is to be determined, how is the pressure determined?

7. Explain why a body submerged in a liquid apparently weighs less than it does in air.

PROBLEMS

1. What is the density of water in grams per cubic centimeter? Pounds per cubic foot? Pounds per cubic inch? Grams per liter?

2. What is the mass of the water which fills a rectangular container 20 cm. long, 10 cm. wide, and 10 cm. tall? What is the total force on the bottom? What is the force per square centimeter on the bottom? Check your last answer by using two different methods.

3. What is the weight of water in a swimming pool which is 20 ft. long, 10 ft. wide, and 5 ft. deep? What is the pressure on the bottom in pounds per square foot? In pounds per square inch?

4. What is the weight of water in a container which is 20 in. long, 5 in. wide, and 10 in. deep? What is the pressure on the bottom in pounds per square inch? Pounds per square foot?

5. What is the pressure in water in an open container at a depth of 20 cm.? 20 ft.? 20 in.? 100 ft.? State the last answer in pounds per square inch.

6. A 100-pound girl wears a spike heel. What is the pressure in pounds per square inch on the floor when all her weight is on one heel which has an area of 1 sq. in.? ½ sq. in.? ¼ sq. in.?

7. A pin point has an area of $\frac{1}{1,000,000}$ sq. in. If a force of 10 lb. is exerted on the pin, what is the pressure exerted by the pin point in pounds per square inch? Explain in terms of the formula, $P = \frac{F}{A}$, why a sharp knife cuts better than a dull one.

8. Mercury stands 76 cm. deep in a glass tube. Find the pressure on the bottom of the tube. (The density of mercury is 13.6 g./cc.)

9. If the density of mercury is 0.49 lb./cu. in., what is the pressure on the bottom of a vertical tube in which mercury stands 30 in. high?

10. What is the pressure in pounds per square inch caused by a column of water 34 ft. high? Compare answers 9 and 10.

11. What would be the pressure in pounds per square foot on a diving bell, such as a benthoscope, when it is 4500 ft. below the surface? (The density of sea water is 64 lb./cu. ft.)

12. A man dives into sea water to a depth of 20 ft. What is the force on each square foot of his body? Square inch?

13. Boulder Dam is about 550 ft. above the surface of the water of the river below. What is the sidewise pressure at the base of the dam? Why must the base of a dam be thicker than the top of the dam?

14. If a pressure of 86 lb./sq. in. is needed to run fire-fighting apparatus, what height of water is needed? What water head is needed?

15. What is the weight of a flat boat which sinks 2 ft. into water and is 20 ft. long and 10 ft. wide?

16. If coal is loaded onto the boat in Problem 15 until the boat sinks another foot deeper into the water, what would be the weight of the coal?

17. A metal cube, 5 cm. on each edge, is suspended in water so that the top surface is 6 cm. under water. What is the downward force on top of the cube? What is the upward force on the bottom? What is the loss of weight?

PROJECTS

1. Weigh yourself and use this weight to compute the approximate volume of your body. Assume your density equals that of fresh water.

2. Make a study of an atomic-powered sub-

marine and explain how it surfaces and how it submerges. See modern science magazines and modern encyclopedias. Report your findings to your class.

READING YOU WILL ENJOY

1. Beebe, William, *Half Mile Down*. Harcourt, Brace and Company, New York, 1934. Deals with the exploration of deep sea life.
2. Blair, Clay, Jr., *The Atomic Submarine and Admiral Rickover*. Henry Holt and Company, New York, 1954. Tells about the first nuclear-powered submarine, *Nautilus*, known as "the first true submersible" because it can remain under water for weeks without surfacing.

Chapter 7

Specific Gravity and Archimedes' Principle

The problem. During every age, the fraudulent substitution of cheap and sometimes nearly worthless materials for the real and more costly has been an aggravating problem, particularly for the consumer.

One of the oldest recorded and most spectacular instances of this kind dates back as far as 250 B.C. to the time of King Hiero, who suspected that one of his supposedly solid gold crowns had been made of a mixture of copper, lead, and other cheap metals with gold. The problem of determining the purity of the crown the king allotted to Archimedes. Fortunately for his own future welfare, Archimedes was ingenious enough to solve the problem by making use of his understanding of forces in liquids.

Today in industry, tests of purity, which likewise involve forces in liquids, are made of hundreds of mixtures of solids as well as mixtures of liquids. In this chapter one of our problems is to discover the principles on which these tests are based.

Another problem involving forces in liquids is how to know before launching that a steel ship will not plunge to the bottom as a piece of steel would, but will sink into the water only a certain distance and no farther. Other questions are why some swimmers cannot float and what other swimmers can do in order to learn quickly how to float.

How Archimedes determined the purity of King Hiero's "solid gold" crown. Archimedes' exact procedure is not known, but it is believed that he first found that a piece of pure gold is 19.3 times as heavy as an equal volume of water. That is, a cubic inch, a cubic centimeter, or any other volume of gold weighs 19.3 times as much as an equal volume of water. Archimedes also found similar ratios for copper, lead, silver, and other metals which he suspected might have been used in the crown.

The ratio of the weight of a substance to the weight of an equal volume of water is called the **specific gravity** *(abbreviated* **sp. gr.**) *of the substance.* Another term sometimes used for this ratio is **relative density.** That is:

Specific gravity (sp. gr.) =

$$\frac{\text{weight of a substance}}{\text{weight of an equal volume of water}}$$

Once Archimedes had determined this relationship for gold and other metals, his next step was to weigh the crown, find the weight of an equal volume of water, and then divide the weight of the crown by the weight of water. If the ratio did not equal

FORCES IN WATER AND OTHER LIQUIDS

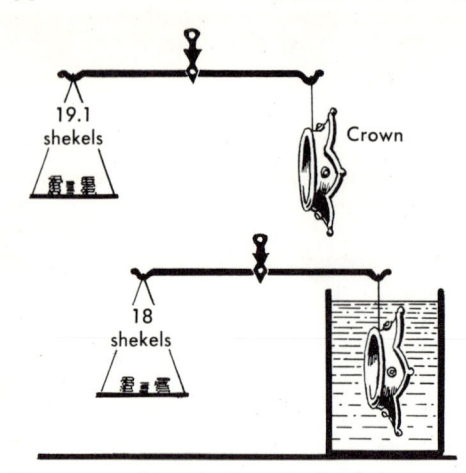

Fig. 1. Archimedes' method of determining the specific gravity of Hiero's crown.

19.3, he would then know that the crown was not pure gold.

Weighing the crown was easy, but how to find the weight of an equal volume of water stumped Archimedes. He thought of many possible ways. He even considered melting the crown, molding it into a cube, cylinder, or some other regularly shaped body, and then computing the weight of an equal volume of water as we did on page 44. But this method he ruled out because it would ruin the crown and probably bring the king's wrath upon his head. For weeks the problem haunted him.

Finally one day, as he was submerging himself in a full tub of water in a public bathhouse, the solution to his problem flashed through his mind. Excited and elated by his discovery, he jumped from the tub and ran naked through the streets for home, shouting "Eureka! Eureka!" meaning "I have found it! I have found it!"

Although history does not make clear what Archimedes thought he had found, he must have believed that the volume of the overflow from the full tub was equal to the volume of the parts of his body which were submerged. Does this agree with what we discovered in our study of density? (See pages 35 and 36.)

Archimedes' Principle. Archimedes must also have sensed that there must be some relationship between the buoyancy on his own body and the weight of the overflow, for in his tests he discovered that

when a body is totally or partially submerged in a liquid, its apparent loss of weight equals the weight of liquid displaced. That is, the body is buoyed up with a force which equals the weight of the displaced liquid.

This is known as **Archimedes' Principle.** Does it agree with what we discovered on page 51?

Since the apparent loss of weight of a body submerged in water equals the weight of an equal volume of water, the specific gravity formula can be rewritten:

$$\text{Sp. gr.} = \frac{\text{Weight of a body}}{\text{Loss of weight in water}}$$

Although the legend does not tell whether the tests showed that the king's crown was made of pure gold, we can illustrate Archimedes' method by assuming that he discovered the following:

Weight of the crown in air = 19.1 shekels*
Weight of crown in water = 18   shekels
Loss of weight in water   = 1.1 shekels

Then, specific gravity $= \dfrac{19.1 \text{ s}}{1.1 \text{ s}} = 17.3$

Knowing that the specific gravity of gold is 19.3, of silver 10.5, of copper 8.9, and of lead 11.34, what would you say about the purity of the king's crown?

PROBLEM: A stone weighs 10 lb. in air and 6 lb. when submerged in water. What is its specific gravity?

*The shekel, in ancient times, was a unit of weight as well as a coin.

SPECIFIC GRAVITY AND ARCHIMEDES' PRINCIPLE

How can we find the specific gravity of a body that floats? Since a floating body is only partly submerged, the volume of liquid it displaces must equal the volume of only that part of the body that is submerged. Therefore, to find the weight of a volume of water equal to the volume of the *whole* body, we can use neither the overflow-can method nor the loss-of-weight method unless we can devise some way of sinking the body so as to cause it to displace a volume of water equal to the *whole* volume of the body.

As any good fisherman knows, we can sink an ordinary floating body by tying a lead or other dense sinker to it. But this complicates the problem because then two bodies must be dealt with instead of one. In using the overflow-can method we can surmount this difficulty by filling the can after the sinker only has been submerged, as is shown in Fig. 2. Then when the body, the piece of paraffin illustrated, is caused to sink, the weight of water displaced equals that displaced by the paraffin. Therefore, since:

$$\text{sp. gr.} = \frac{\text{weight in air}}{\text{weight of water displaced}}$$

then, sp. gr. of paraffin $= \frac{20}{22} = 0.9$

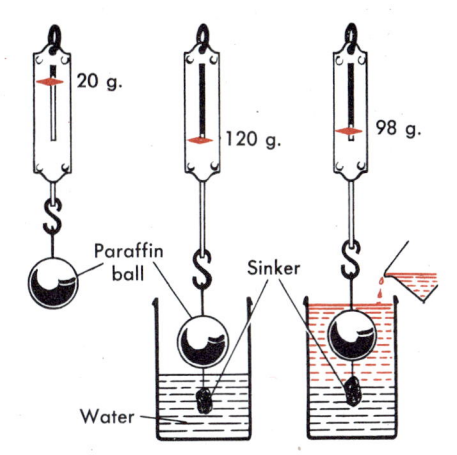

Fig. 3. In this method, the difference between the two losses in weight is equal to the weight of water displaced.

Using the same apparatus, we may modify the loss-of-weight method in the manner shown in Fig. 3. As a project, demonstrate this method to the class.

How can we find the specific gravity of a liquid? Finding the specific gravity of a liquid is very much like finding it for any other substance. We do it by measuring a certain volume of the liquid, weighing it, measuring an equal volume of water, weighing it, and computing the answer.

For precise measurement, a *specific gravity bottle,* or *pycnometer,* is often used (see Fig. 4). First the empty bottle is weighed and then, after it is filled with the liquid whose specific gravity is to be found, the bottle is weighed again. Finally, the bottle is filled with pure water and weighed again. After the weight of the empty bottle is subtracted from each of the two weighings, the resulting figures represent the

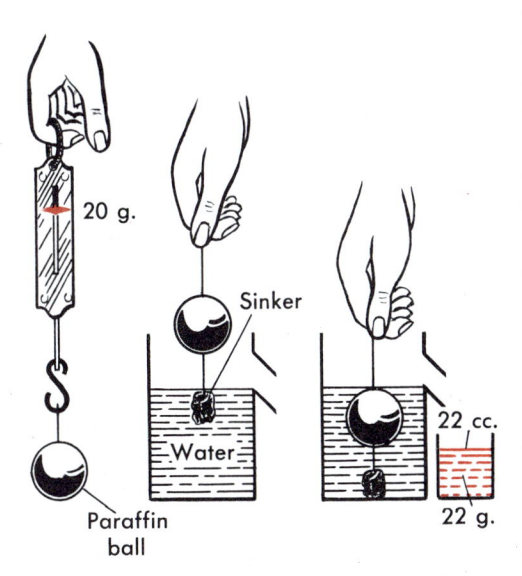

Fig. 2. Finding the specific gravity of a floating body by means of a sinker and the overflow-can method.

FORCES IN WATER AND OTHER LIQUIDS

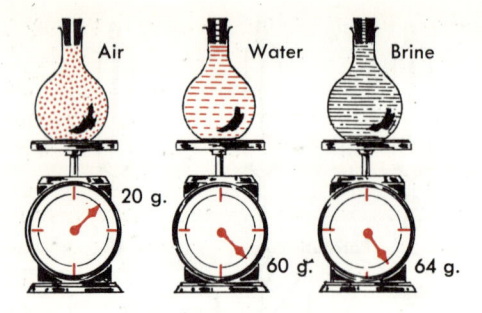

Fig. 4. In the bottle method of determining the specific gravity of a liquid, three separate weighings are required. Why? How is the specific gravity calculated?

weights of equal volumes of the liquid and pure water. The ratio of the weight of the liquid to that of the equal volume of water is the specific gravity of the liquid in question. The formula for finding the specific gravity of a liquid by the bottle method is as follows:

$$\text{Sp. gr.} = \frac{\text{Weight of liquid}}{\text{Weight of equal volume of water}}$$

PROBLEM: Find the specific gravity of the brine, using the data given in Fig. 4.

The sinker method of finding specific gravities of liquids. Another ingenious way of finding the specific gravity of liquids is the so-called *sinker* method. The method is interesting because the proof of the formula used is based entirely upon Archimedes' Principle. The method is illustrated by the following:

PROBLEM: A stone weighs 160 g. in air, 100 g. in brine, and 105 g. in water. What is the specific gravity of the brine?

SOLUTION: Apparently the stone loses 60 g. in brine and 55 g. in water. And it is obvious that the stone displaces the same volume in each of the liquids. Therefore, the losses of weight, 60 g. and 55 g. respectively, represent weights of equal volumes of the brine and the water.

In other words, 60 g. is the weight of brine whose volume is exactly equal to that of the stone, and 55 g. is the weight of the same volume of water. The ratio of the two losses of weight is similar to the comparison we make when finding the specific gravity of the brine by the bottle method. That is, the specific gravity of brine may be computed by substituting in the following formula:

$$\text{Sp. gr.} = \frac{\text{Loss of weight in brine}}{\text{Loss of weight in water}}$$

$$\text{Sp. gr.} \atop \text{(brine)} = \frac{60 \text{ g.}}{55 \text{ g.}} = 1.09$$

The hydrometer method for finding the specific gravities of liquids. Possibly you know that ships and other floating bodies "ride" higher in sea water than in fresh water. They sink until they displace their own weight of liquid. The greater the specific gravity of a liquid the higher a body floats in it; the less the specific gravity of the liquid, the deeper the body sinks.

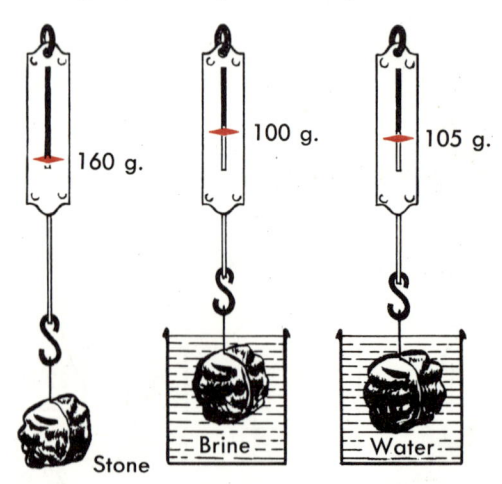

Fig. 5. Finding the specific gravity of a liquid by the sinker method. Why does the stone lose more weight when submerged in brine than in water?

SPECIFIC GRAVITY AND ARCHIMEDES' PRINCIPLE

ators, the percentages of sugar in sugar solutions, and the purities of hundreds of other solutions used in industry. The instrument used in checking storage batteries is called a battery tester. See Chapter 35, Fig. 12. It looks like a large medicine dropper inside of which there is a small hydrometer. The tip of the instrument is inserted into the opening at the top of the battery and liquid is drawn from the battery cells.

The small hydrometer then floats in the liquid. If the battery is fully charged the hydrometer should read about 1300, which means the specific gravity is 1.3. If it reads 1150, the specific gravity is 1.15, and the battery is completely discharged. A battery testing below 1200 is

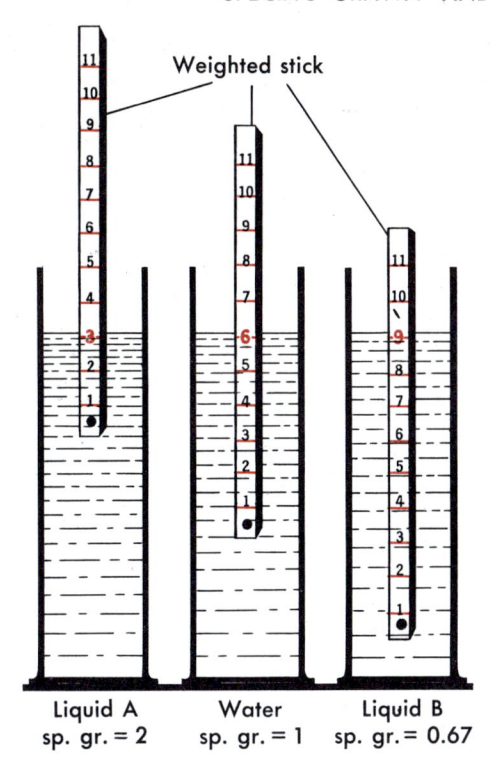

Liquid A	Water	Liquid B
sp. gr. = 2	sp. gr. = 1	sp. gr. = 0.67

Fig. 6. A wooden stick, if properly calibrated, can be used to determine the specific gravity of liquid.

Consequently, as shown in Fig. 6, the weighted stick sinks twice as far in pure water, whose specific gravity is 1, as it does in liquid A, whose specific gravity is 2. And it sinks 1.5 times as far in liquid B, whose specific gravity is 0.67, as it does in water. Hence, we see that if a weighted stick were properly marked or calibrated it could be used to determine specific gravity. Such an instrument is called a *hydrometer*. In order to make the hydrometer more sensitive and to obtain more accurate results it is made as shown in Fig. 7.

The hydrometer, when properly calibrated, is used for checking the charges in storage batteries, the freezing temperatures of the solutions in automobile radi-

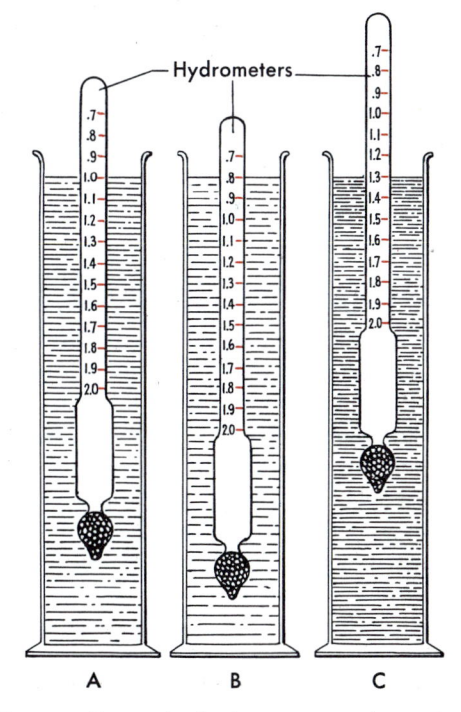

Fig. 7. From the hydrometer readings, determine the specific gravity of each liquid. Which liquid might be water? Why is the largest number placed at the bottom of the hydrometer?

too low for use in an automobile and consequently should be charged. Why the specific gravity of the solution in a storage battery changes with the amount of charge is discussed on page 408.

What is the relationship between specific gravity and density? To find the relationship between density and specific gravity, let us compare the two for several different substances as given in the following table:

Table 1

SPECIFIC GRAVITIES AND DENSITIES
OF WATER, MERCURY, AND ALUMINUM

	Sp. gr.	Density (g./cc.)	(lb./ft.³)	(lb./in.³)
Water	1	1	62.4	.036
Mercury	13.6	13.6	848.64	.49
Aluminum	2.67	2.67	166.6	.096

Thus we see that the specific gravity of water is 1 and the density of water is 1 g./cc. The specific gravity of mercury is 13.6 and its density is 13.6 g./cc. Apparently specific gravity and density in grams per cubic centimeter are *numerically* equal, but this does not mean that they are *actually* equal, any more than two dogs equal two cats. Density is mass per unit volume, whereas specific gravity is a ratio which is expressed by a number only.

The data above also show that the density of water in pounds per cubic foot is numerically 62.4 times as great as its specific gravity. Since the same relationship holds for other substances, the density of mercury in pounds per cubic foot equals its specific gravity, 13.6, times 62.4.

Thus we see that *to find the density of a substance in pounds per cubic foot,* we must multiply its specific gravity by 62.4 lb./cu. ft. Or to find the specific gravity when density is given in pounds per cubic foot, divide the density of the substance by the density of water—62.4 lb./cu. ft. That is:

$$\text{Sp. gr.} = \frac{\text{Density of a substance}}{\text{Density of water}}$$

PROBLEM: The specific gravity of a substance is 3. what is its density in lb./cu. ft.? In lb./cu. in.? In g./cc.?

Table 2

SPECIFIC GRAVITIES
OF SOME COMMON SOLIDS AND LIQUIDS

Alcohol	0.79	Lead	11.3
Brass	8.4	Maple wood	0.75
Copper	8.9	Mercury	13.6
Cork	0.2	Osmium	22.5
Gasoline	0.66-0.69	Paraffin	0.87-0.91
Glass	2.5-3.6	Platinum	21.5
Ice	0.92	Silver	10.5
Iron, wrought	7.8	Turpentine	0.87

Why do some bodies sink and others float? To answer this question, let us suppose that the volume of your body, the space which you occupy, is exactly 2 cubic feet. See Fig. 8. Will you sink or float? This will depend upon your weight. If you are the athletic, muscular type, you may weigh as much as 126 lb. In fresh water, with your body completely submerged, the buoyancy would be 2 × 62.4, or 124.8 lb. This is 1.2 lb. less than your weight; therefore, you would sink. If your weight were 126 lb. and your volume were 2 cu. ft., what would be your density? Specific gravity?

If you are a different type, you may occupy 2 cu. ft. of space and weigh as little as 123 lb. If so, you would displace 123 lb. of fresh water, whose volume is less than 2 cu. ft. This means that part of your body would be out of the water and hence you would float. In this case, would the density of your body be less or more than the density of water?

Again, suppose that your volume is 2 cu. ft. and your weight is 126 lb. Would you sink or float in sea water whose density is 64 lb./cu.ft.? If your body were completely submerged, it would be buoyed up by 2 × 64, or 128 lb. of force, which

SPECIFIC GRAVITY AND ARCHIMEDES' PRINCIPLE

Fresh water
Density = 62.4 lb./cu. ft.

Sea water
Density = 64 lb./cu. ft.

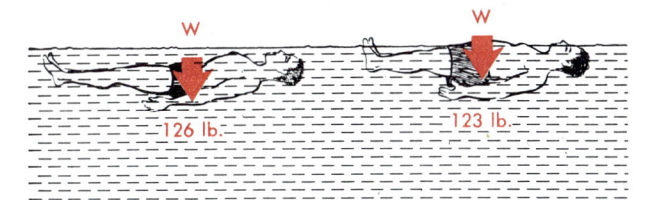

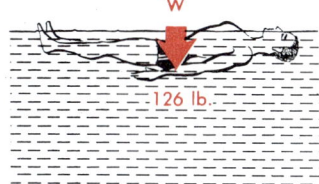

Fig. 8. The volume of each boy is 2 cu. ft. Calculate the density of each boy. Use your results to explain why the 126-lb. boy floats in sea water, but not in fresh water. Why does the 123-lb. boy float in fresh water? How would he float in sea water?

is 2 lb. more than your weight; consequently you would float.

In case your density were the same as that of sea water, you would neither sink deeper nor rise when totally submerged. What would happen if you expanded your chest? Contracted it? Explain.

In conclusion, we may say that:
1. A body sinks completely in a liquid if its weight is more than the weight of liquid which it displaces.
2. A body completely submerged in a liquid will neither sink farther nor rise in a liquid if its weight equals that of the liquid which it displaces.
3. A body submerged in a liquid will rise and float if its weight is less than that of the liquid which it displaces.
4. When a body is placed in a liquid, it sinks if its density is greater than the density of the liquid, and it floats if its density is less than the density of the liquid.

According to Archimedes' Principle, how can a body be caused to sink or float? When a body sinks, its weight is greater than the buoyant force or weight of liquid which it displaces. Hence, we can increase the tendency to float (a) by decreasing only the weight of the body, or (b) by increasing only its volume and hence the buoyancy. A submarine employs the former principle when it surfaces. Water is pumped from inside the ballast tanks until the weight of the submarine is less than the upward buoyant forces exerted by the water on the outside. When this condition exists, the submarine rises to the surface. To sink, the submarine takes on water until its weight is greater than the buoyant forces.

Fig. 9. Archimedes' Principle still applies in the Atomic Age. The atomic-powered submarine *USS Nautilus* on her maiden voyage off the Connecticut coast.

Courtesy General Dynamics Corp.

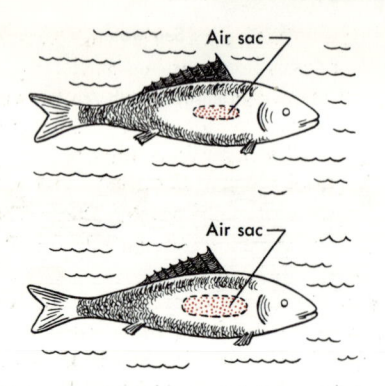

Fig. 10. What is the effect of an increase or a decrease in the size of the air sac?

When a fish wants to surface, it increases the buoyancy on its body. To do this it allows an air sac inside its body to expand. This increases its volume with no increase in weight. Increase in volume increases the volume of water displaced and the upward buoyancy exerted by the water. When the upward force becomes greater than the weight, the fish is forced upward. To sink, the fish decreases its volume until the upward buoyancy is less than its weight.

Water wings and life-saving jackets greatly increase one's volume as well as buoyancy without any appreciable increase in weight. Some modern bathing suits are made so that they can be inflated with air, making it possible even for non-swimmers to bathe in safety. Ships carry life-saving suits which can be inflated and used for the dual purpose of keeping the wearer afloat and warm at the same time. Rubber rafts that can be inflated after landing on water are standard equipment of airplanes that fly over water routes.

SUMMARY AND CONCLUSIONS

1. Archimedes' Principle: A body either partly or wholly immersed in a liquid is buoyed up by a force equal to the weight of the displaced liquid.

2. Specific gravity = $\dfrac{\text{Weight of body}}{\text{Weight of equal volume of water}}$

3. To find the weight of equal volume of water:
 (a) Compute volume. Weight of water = Volume × density of water.
 (b) Weigh a body in air and then in water. Apparent loss of weight equals weight of equal volume of water.
 (c) Weigh liquid and then weigh an equal volume of water.
 (d) Find loss of weight of a submerged solid in water.

4. In the metric system the density of a substance in g./cc. numerically equals the specific gravity.

5. In the English system the density of a substance in lb./cu. ft. numerically equals 62.4 times the specific gravity of the substance.

6. To increase the buoyancy on a body submerged in a liquid, increase the volume of the body or decrease the weight of the body.

QUESTIONS FOR REVIEW

1. What is the meaning of specific gravity?
2. Why are no units required in order to express specific gravity?
3. Explain how adding water to milk changes the specific gravity of the milk.
4. What is Archimedes' Principle?
5. According to Archimedes' Principle, what is the buoyant force on a liter of iron submerged in water? On a liter of stone? On a 1-ounce cork that floats in water?
6. What is a hydrometer?
7. Explain the relationship between specific gravity and density in (a) the English system; (b) the metric system.
8. If the specific gravity of a substance is 2, what is its density in g./cc.? In lb./cu. in.? In lb./cu. ft.?
9. Explain how a fish can surface and sink without propelling itself up or down.
10. Explain how a submarine submerges and surfaces.
11. Explain the purpose of water wings in learning to swim. Do water wings make one lighter? Explain.

SPECIFIC GRAVITY AND ARCHIMEDES' PRINCIPLE

12. When a fish is placed in a vessel of water, does the total weight increase? Do this experiment and explain.
13. A small balloon filled with air is weighted so that it barely floats in water. If it is submerged a short distance in the water, it sinks to the bottom. Explain. Check this by experiment.
14. Describe a method of measuring the specific gravity of (a) an irregularly shaped solid denser than water; (b) a solid less dense than water; and (c) a liquid (three different methods).
15. Do you think that you could float in gasoline? Explain.
16. When an anchor is lifted, why does it seem heavier as it is lifted above the surface of the water?
17. Is it easier to float in water 10 feet deep than in water 6 feet deep? Explain. Give mathematical proof.
18. What things can we do in order to learn quickly how to float?
19. Why is it that some people cannot float?
20. If a piece of iron is dropped into the ocean, will it sink all the way to the bottom? Explain.
21. In the making of a hydrometer to measure the specific gravities of liquids that are both denser and less dense than water, will the numbers indicating the specific gravities of liquids that are denser than water be placed above or below 1 on the hydrometer? Explain.

PROBLEMS

1. What is the mass of 50 cc. of water?
2. What is the volume of 50 g. of water?
3. What is the density of water in g./cc.? In lb./cu. ft.? In lb./cu. in.?
4. What is the specific gravity of water?
5. What is the apparent loss of weight when a cubic foot of lead is submerged in water? When a cubic centimeter of lead is submerged? When a liter of gold is submerged? When a 1-pound block of wood floats in water?
6. A stone weighs 100 g. in air. Its volume is 60 cc. What is its weight in water? Its apparent loss of weight in water?
7. A stone weighs 100 g. in air. It weighs 75 g. in water. What is the specific gravity of the stone? What is its volume?
8. The liquid in a bottle weighs 185 g. The same volume of water weighs 100 g. What is the specific gravity of the liquid? Density in g./cc.?
9. When a stone is submerged in water, what is its volume if its loss of weight is (a) 1000 g.? (b) 62.4 lb.? (c) 124.8 lb.? (d) 1 g.?
10. A boat displaces 20,000 cu. ft. of water when empty and 30,000 cu. ft. when loaded. What is the weight of its load? What is the weight of the empty boat?
11. Suppose that Archimedes had found that Hiero's crown weighed 20 shekels in air and 18 in water. Would it have been pure gold?
12. A stone weighs 100 g. when it is weighed in air and 40 g. when it is completely submerged in water.
    (a) What is the loss of weight in water?
    (b) What is the weight of water displaced?
    (c) What is the volume of the stone?
    (d) What is the specific gravity of the stone?
    (e) What is the density of the stone in g./cc.? In lb./cu. ft.?
13. A rectangular block of wood weighs 75 g. in air. Its dimensions are 5 cm. × 5 cm. × 4 cm. What is its specific gravity? Its density in g./cc.? Its density in lb./cu. ft.?
14. In Problem 13, what part of the wooden block would sink below the surface in water?
15. A glass sinker weighs 26 g. in air, 16 g. when submerged in water, and 18 g. when submerged in oil. Find the specific gravity of the oil.
16. A certain metal block weighs 120 g. in air, 100 g. when submerged in pure water, and 95 g. when submerged in salt water. What is the specific gravity of the salt water? Of the metal block?
17. A piece of paraffin weighing 60 g. in air weighs 86.5 g. when attached to a sinker and both are submerged in water. If the weight of the sinker in water is 95.7 g., what is the

FORCES IN WATER AND OTHER LIQUIDS

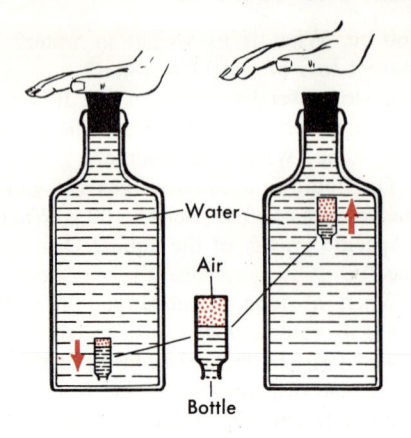

Fig. 11. Explain why the bouncing bottle sinks or rises.

mercury is hidden but the ball can be seen. If a glass container is used, the inside should be painted white up as far as the milk. This would make a good exhibit at your science fair, which you could begin planning now and hold later in the year.

4. Place some mercury, water, and gasoline in a tall, narrow beaker and then put into it an iron nut, a wooden block which sinks in the gasoline, and a cork. Explain what you observe.

5. *How to float an egg.* Place an egg in the bottom of a tall vessel such as a graduated cylinder, fill with water, then add salt slowly. Stir the solution and observe the egg. Explain.

specific gravity of the paraffin? What is its density? Its volume?

18. A ball of iron weighs 300 g. in air. Its specific gravity is 7.5. What is its volume?

19. The 300-gram ball in Problem 18 is floated in mercury. What volume of the ball is submerged in mercury?

20. If the specific gravity of a 500-gram cake of ice is 0.9 and it floats in water, what volume of the ice is under water?

21. If all the volume of an iceberg above water were dynamited off, would the rest of the iceberg sink? Explain.

PROJECTS

1. Make and explain the bouncing bottle (sometimes called Cartesian diver) in Fig. 11.
2. Using a gold or silver cup, or some other metal body, determine its purity.
3. *How to float an iron ball in milk.* Float an iron ball in mercury and then cover the mercury with just enough milk so that the

READING YOU WILL ENJOY

1. Lynde, C. J., *Science Experiences with Inexpensive Equipment,* pp. 57-67. International Textbook Company, Scranton, Pennsylvania, 1950. Interesting experiments which deal with specific gravity, buoyancy, and kindred phenomena.

2. Richardson, J. S., and G. P. Cahoon, *Methods and Materials for Teaching General and Physical Science,* pp. 268-269 and 271-274. McGraw-Hill Book Company, Inc., New York, 1951. Contains many interesting experiments concerning specific gravity.

3. Taylor, L. W., *Physics, the Pioneer Science,* pp. 91-94. Houghton Mifflin Company, Boston, 1941. Explains how Archimedes discovered the law of buoyancy.

4. U. S. Bureau of Naval Personnel, *Basic Hydraulics,* pp. 8-10. U. S. Government Printing Office, Washington 25, D. C., 1945. This book is simply written and profusely illustrated. Many diagrams are in color.

Chapter 8

Machines Which Transmit Forces through Liquids: Hydraulic Machines

The problem. A fascinating sight is that of a heavy truck or bus being lifted with very little effort by means of a hydraulic jack. How can so little effort, or force, overcome so much resistance?

Other but less spectacular hydraulic machines are the hydraulic presses used in baling cotton, rags, and paper; hydraulic brakes on automobiles, trucks, and buses; hydraulic lifts on tractors used to lift heavy loads on farms and in factories; hydraulic chairs used to lift customers in a barber shop; and many other devices, some of which are as simple as a toothpaste tube. All these machines make use of forces in liquids and for this reason are called *hydraulic machines*.

Just as fascinating as the feats that can be performed with a hydraulic jack is the situation pictured in Fig. 1. Here, in vessel A there are 300 g. of water, in B there are 200 g., and in C there are 100 g. Each vessel contains water 10 cm. deep and the area of each base is 20 sq. cm.

Applying the formula $P = hd$, we find that the pressure, P, equals 10×1, or 10 g./cm.² for each of the three bases. Using this pressure and applying the formula $F = P \times A$, we find that $F = 10 \times 20$, or 200 g. for all three containers. Nonsense, you say. How can only 100 grams of water in vessel C exert 200 grams of force on the bottom?

This apparently illogical situation is known as the *hydrostatic paradox*.

How Pascal solved the hydrostatic paradox. In his attempt to solve the hydrostatic paradox, Blaise Pascal (1623-1662) placed vessels similar to those shown in Fig. 2 on a special weighing machine which measured the force on the bottom of each one. Here we see that the total force on each bottom is 200 g. Dividing the force by the area of the base of each vessel, we find that the pressure equals $\frac{200}{20}$, or 10 g./cm.², just as we predicted using the formula, $P = hd$.

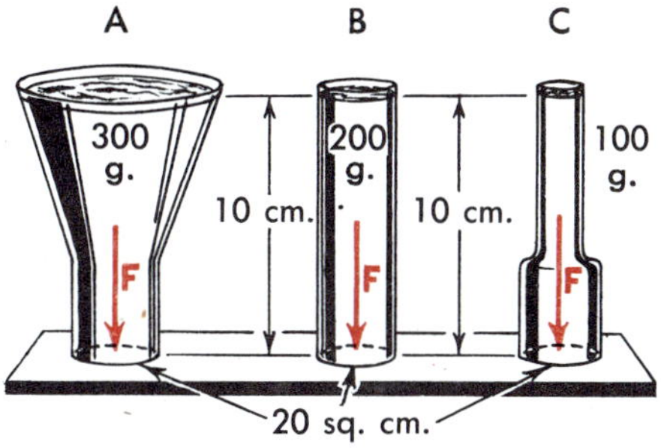

Fig. 1. The weight of water in each container differs, but the pressure and the total force on the bottom are the same.

FORCES IN WATER AND OTHER LIQUIDS

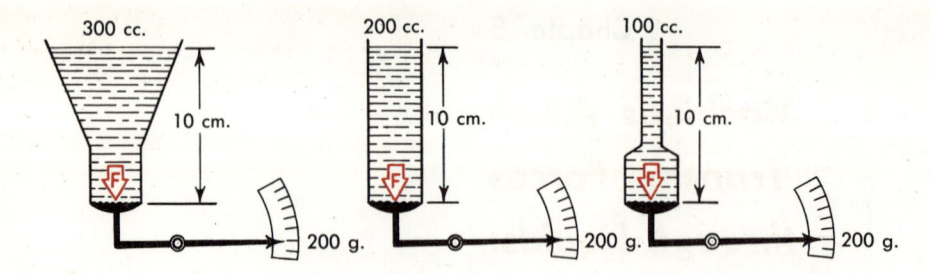

Fig. 2. Weighing shows that the liquid force, F, on each bottom is 200 g. The unreasonableness of this situation is known as the hydrostatic paradox. Upon what two factors does the pressure of a liquid at any point in a container depend?

Thus, contrary to common sense, the pressure at any point in a vessel is totally independent of the shape of the vessel and is dependent solely on the depth and density of the liquid. Still, it is almost unbelievable that 100 g. of water in vessel C can exert a force of 200 g. on the bottom of C.

How is the hydrostatic paradox explained? To explain the hydrostatic paradox, let us consider the vessel in Fig. 3, which is filled with water. Since the depth is 15 cm., the pressure at any point on the bottom is 15 g./cm.^{2}. This pressure is easy to explain at a point such as A because a column of water 15 cm. tall stands directly over this point. But at B the column is only 5 cm. tall and the weight of the column over 1 sq. cm. is only 5 g. This amount is 10 g. short of that needed to account for the 15 g./cm.^{2} at B. One way of accounting for this extra 10 g./cm.^{2} is to assume that the pressure at the bottom of the neck is transmitted undiminished to

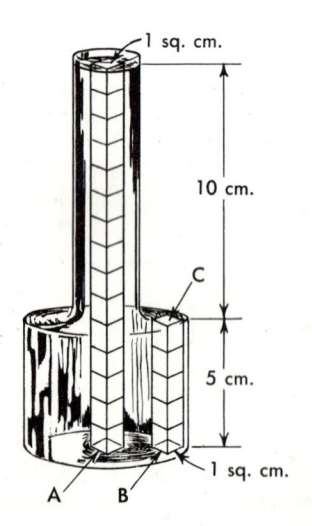

Fig. 3. The pressure due to the column of water above the 5-cm. mark is applied to the confined liquid below.

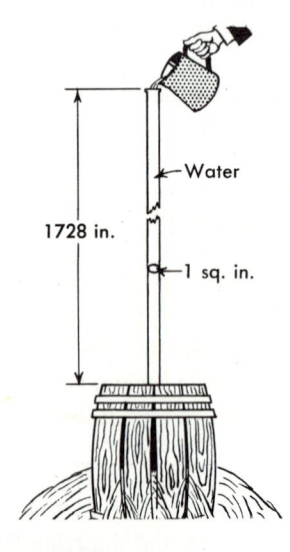

Fig. 4. Explain how the 62.4 pounds of water added to the filled barrel causes the barrel to break.

HYDRAULIC MACHINES

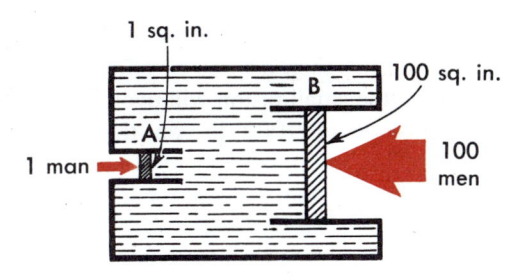

Fig. 5. One hundred men were required to hold B in place when one man pushed on A.

all parts of the vessel below. But is this assumption true?

If it is true, then we have a unique device for multiplying forces. And consequently, if we attach a rubber hose or an iron pipe to a barrel, as shown in Fig. 4, and fill the barrel and the pipe with water, simple calculations show that a tremendous force can be exerted inside the barrel with a small weight of water.

For example, when the cross section of the pipe is 1 sq. in. in area and the water head is 144 ft. (1728 in.), then, since

$$P = hd$$
$$P = 1728 \times 0.036$$
$$P = 62.4 \text{ lb./sq. in.}$$

Assuming that the area of the inside surface of the barrel is 4000 sq. in., then the total force on the inside of the barrel is 249,600 lb., which is a tremendous amount of force to exert by means of only 62.4 lb. of water in the pipe.

If the cross-sectional area of the pipe above were ½ sq. in., what would be the pressure inside the barrel? The total force inside the barrel? The weight of water in the pipe?

Pascal's Law. Pascal devised another apparatus to demonstrate the transmission of forces through liquids. As shown in Fig. 5, it contained two pistons, one of which was one hundred times as great in area as the other. Pascal calculated that if one man were to push on the small piston, it would take 100 men to hold the large piston in place.

In conclusion, Pascal stated the principle that is now known as **Pascal's Law,** as follows:

When any part of a confined liquid is subjected to pressure, the pressure is transmitted equally and undiminished to every portion of the inner surface of the containing vessel.

How do hydraulic machines work? Study of the hydraulic press shown in (a) of Fig. 6 shows that a hand lever operates a small piston, P, which pumps a liquid (oil) from a small cylinder into the bottom of a larger cylinder. This forces the large piston, P_1, upward. As Pascal stated, the pressure is the same on both pistons, but the forces are in proportion to the areas. For example, if in (b) of Fig. 6 the area a of the small piston is

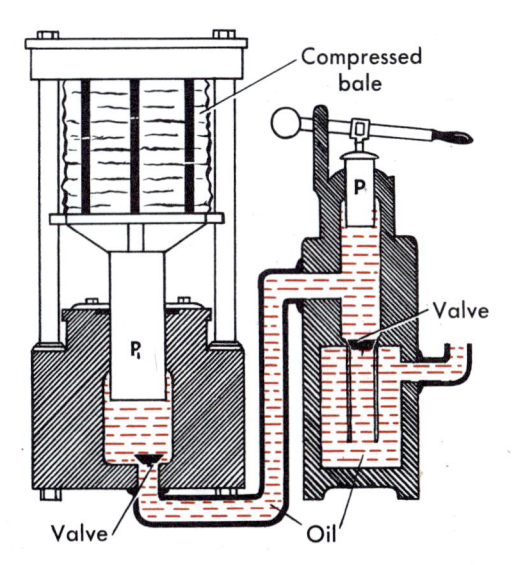

Fig. 6. (a) Cross section of a hydraulic press used to bale cotton.

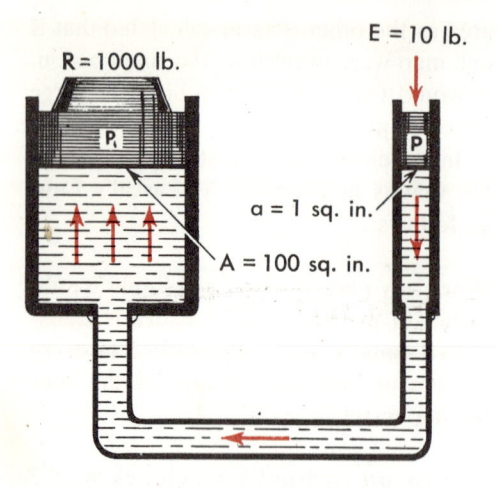

FORCES IN WATER AND OTHER LIQUIDS

1 sq. in. and the area A of the large one is 100 sq. in., then a force or effort E of 10 lb. on the small piston will overcome a resistance R of 1000 lb. on the large piston. This multiplication of force produced through the use of a machine is called the *mechanical advantage* of the machine. In this case it is $\frac{1000 \text{ lb.}}{10 \text{ lb.}}$, or 100.

Remember that the pressures are equal but the forces vary directly as the areas of the pistons. That is:

$$\frac{\text{Resistance }(R)\text{ overcome by large piston}}{\text{Effort }(E)\text{ on small piston}}$$

$$= \frac{\text{Area }(A)\text{ of large piston}}{\text{Area }(a)\text{ of small piston}}$$

or

$$\frac{R}{E} = \frac{A}{a} = \text{mechanical advantage (M.A.)}$$

But since the areas of two circles are proportional to the squares of the diameters, as you will recall from geometry, then:

$$\frac{R}{E} = \frac{D^2}{d^2} = \text{M.A.}$$

Fig. 6. (b) What is the pressure on the surface of P_1? If the effort moves downward one inch, how far does R move?

Fig. 7. Pascal's principle is applied on a gigantic scale in this 18,000-ton hydraulic press. Note the size of the large cylinders.

Courtesy United States Steel Corp.

PROBLEM: If a force of 20 lb. is exerted on piston A, whose diameter is 1 in., what force will be exerted on piston B, whose diameter is 20 in.?

SOLUTION: $\quad \frac{R}{E} = \frac{D^2}{d^2}$

Substituting, $\quad \frac{R}{20} = \frac{400}{1}$

$R = 8000$ lb.

Hydraulic brakes. For years the design of effective and reliable brakes was a major problem for automobile manufacturers. The chief difficulty was to find a method of exerting equal pressures on all

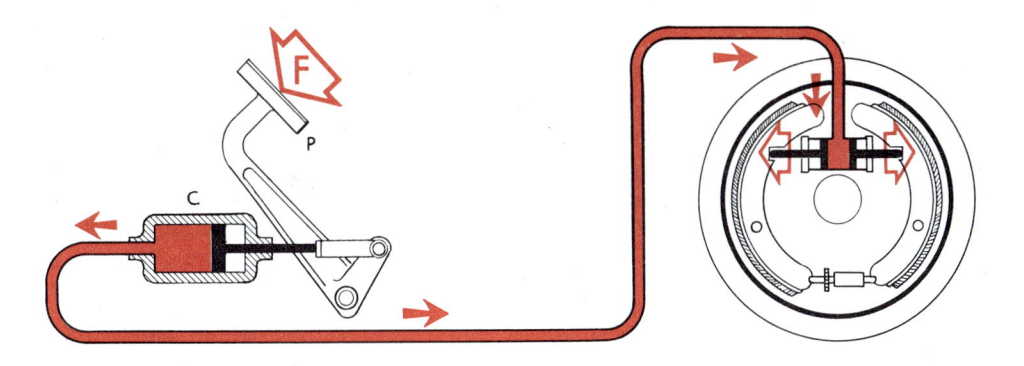

Fig. 8. Cross section of a hydraulic braking system. When force is applied on the brake pedal, pressure is exerted on the piston of the master cylinder C. In accordance with Pascal's Law, this pressure is transmitted undiminished through the brake fluid to each of the brake cylinders. There, the pistons in the brake cylinder are forced apart, causing the brake shoes to press against the brake drum. Thus the wheel is brought to a stop.

four wheels. And until this was perfected, four-wheel brakes were never satisfactory. The solution was found in the hydraulic brake.

The operation of the hydraulic brake is shown schematically in Fig. 8. When the driver wishes to apply the brakes, he pushes down on the brake pedal, P, with a force F. The pressure thus produced in the cylinder, C, is transmitted equally and undiminished to each of the brake cylinders located at the brake drums of the four wheels. The forces produced operate the brakes within the drums. If the four cylinders have the same diameters, the four forces are equal. What must be done if more force is desired on the front brakes?

Another problem of automobile design. The electric carriages and the puffing steam-powered automobiles which our grandfathers drove did not need either a clutch or a gear-shift type of transmission to put the car in motion or to climb steep hills. The gasoline engine, however, when in high gear and running at the slow speed needed for starting, has always had the inherent weakness of being unable to exert enough *torque* (twist) through the drive shaft connecting the engine and rear wheels to overcome the resistance to starting.

To eliminate this weakness a clutch and gear system combination was used with only fair satisfaction. In low gear the engine was able to run at a fairly high speed, while the rear wheels turned slowly because their speed was reduced by the gears. Thus in reducing the rear-wheel speed, the torque (twist) was multiplied enough to put the automobile in motion. Once in motion the car was shifted into intermediate gear, in which the rear wheels turned faster even though there was no change in the speed of the engine. Then when the automobile was well in motion it was shifted into high gear.

Fluid drive. As a step toward eliminating both the clutch and the gear shift, a fluid (oil) transmission was developed.

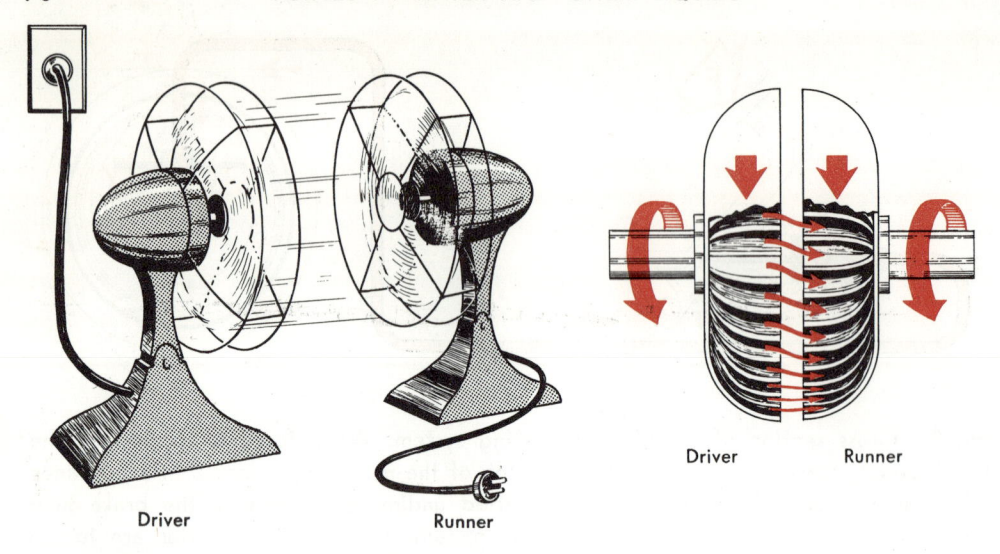

Fig. 9. The air currents from the driver fan strike the blades of the runner and cause them to turn. Similarly, the fluid whirling in the segments of the driver is transmitted directly to the runner, thereby setting it into motion.

The principle is simple and can be demonstrated with two electric fans, as shown in Fig. 9. The *driver* fan on the left is run by electricity. As it turns it forces air against the other fan, called the *runner,* causing it to turn. Air leaving the runner circles around and comes back to the driver, where the speed of the air is boosted again.

In the fluid drive transmission, two identical fanlike units are set facing each other in an oil-filled case or housing. The driver is connected with the engine and the runner connects with the rear wheels through the drive shaft.

When the engine is idling, the driver slushes the oil with insufficient force to set the runner moving. But as soon as the speed of the engine increases sufficiently, the oil is thrown against the runner blades with such force that the runner begins to turn. Gradually and smoothly the power is transmitted to the wheels. The runner never spins quite as fast as the driver, but at driving speeds the difference is small.

Further improvements. The problem of adequate torque was only partly solved by the fluid transmission described above. In this drive the runner had no more torque than the driver, and for this reason a clutch and a gear shift had to be used to pull the car up hills and through mud, sand, and snow. They were also needed for driving in reverse.

Obviously the next step was to find a fluid coupling which would multiply the torque of the runner. This was accomplished by putting between the driver and the runner a set of fixed blades, called the *stators,* which directed the fluid so that the runner turned slower than the driver but had greater torque than the driver. But as usual, with the solution of one problem another developed: at driving speeds the stators slowed up the runner too much.

To remedy this situation, the stators were fixed so that they automatically began rotating when a certain speed was reached. As a consequence it was possible for the speed of the runner to approach that of the driver. Thereby, need for a clutch was eliminated.

Blood pressure and circulation in the human body. Perhaps you have never stopped to think about it, but the circulatory system of your body is actually a hydraulic machine. As you know, the heart acts as a pump which forces blood through the blood vessels of the human body. During what is known as the *compression stroke,* or *systole,* the blood is squeezed out of the heart into the arteries past valves which prevent its direct return to the heart. Then the heart relaxes, during which time it is filled with blood from the veins and the lungs. The refilling is known as the *filling stroke* or *diastole.*

How is blood pressure measured? One of the greatest boons to modern medicine was the discovery of methods of determining blood pressure and the diagnosis of diseases of which abnormal blood pressure is a symptom. Blood pressure is usually measured at the same horizontal level on the body as the heart. Why? The instrument used consists of a flat, thin-walled, airtight rubber tube to which a U-tube manometer filled with mercury is attached. The rubber tube is wrapped around the arm, as shown in Fig. 10, and then air is pumped into the tube, causing it to expand and squeeze the arm until the flow of blood in the main artery is completely stopped.

Then with a stethoscope the doctor listens to the main artery as he slowly deflates the inflated tube. When the pressure in the tube gets down to that in the artery, the doctor hears blood beginning to pulse through the artery again. The flow of blood is also indicated by slight pulsating change in the height of the mercury column. The *systolic* pressure, the peak pressure in the artery just as the heart completes a compression stroke, is

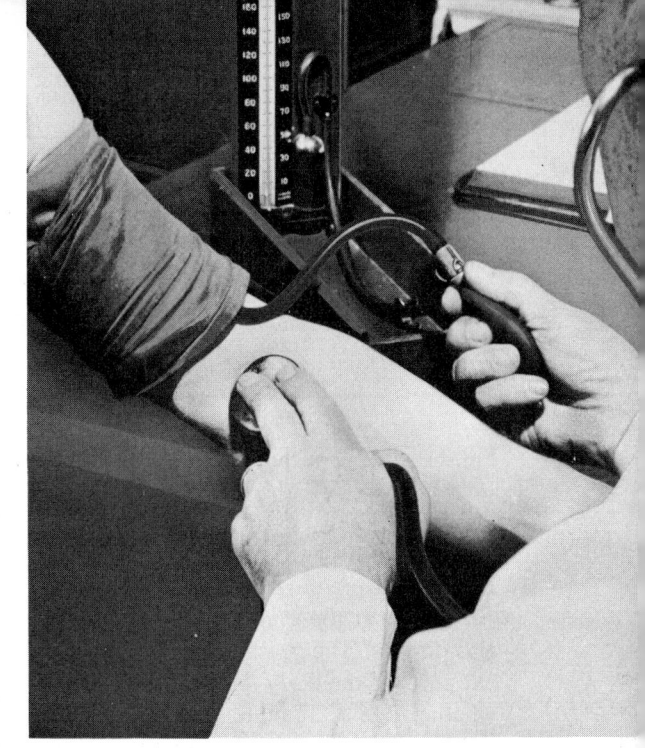

Fig. 10. The sphygmomanometer used in determining a person's blood pressure works on essentially the same principle as an open-tube manometer. By reading the height of the mercury column supported by the air in the inflated tube at various intervals, the systolic and diastolic blood pressures are measured.

given by the height in millimeters of the mercury column that the air in the inflated tube supports.

Next the doctor lets out more air. When the pulse sounds change again, indicating that the tube has stopped interfering with circulation, he again takes the pressure. This, the *diastolic* pressure, is that which keeps the blood moving between heartbeats when the heart is relaxing and being refilled with blood.

For a healthy high school student the systolic pressure should be equivalent to that caused by a column of mercury about 120 millimeters high; the diastolic, about 75 millimeters. Factors which cause the blood pressure to increase are exer-

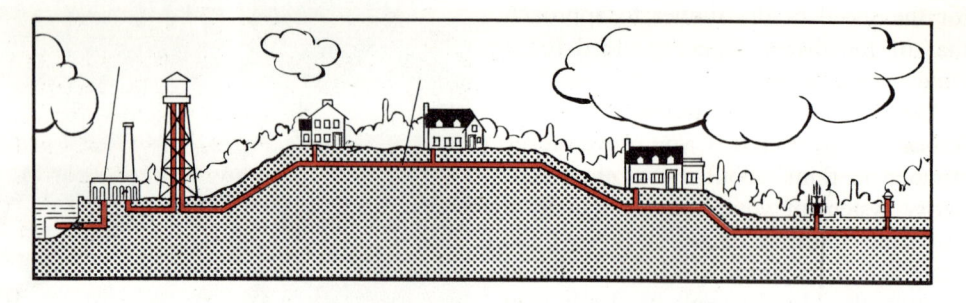

Fig. 11. How water is stored and distributed to homes and elsewhere by a city-water system. What type of water system is illustrated here?

cise, increase of age, drugs, and disease. Low blood pressure is natural with some people but it too can be caused by drugs and disease. The pressure varies in different parts of the body and it depends upon whether one is standing, sitting, or lying down. The change in pressure in veins with position of the hands can be seen through observation of the veins in the backs of the hands when they are held above one's head, on a level with the heart, and when allowed to hang straight down. Explain the cause of the difference.

How modern communities are supplied with water. A town or a group of houses located in a mountainous or hilly region often obtains water from a reservoir or lake which is at a much higher level than the houses. With such a system, called a *gravity* system, the water in the reservoir flows out through the system of communicating pipes and rises into the houses.

The least common system is the *direct pressure* system. Here the water is pumped directly into the mains. The engines or motors which drive the pumps are equipped with automatic controls which are regulated by the pressure in the mains. The chief shortcoming of this system is that the pressure may fluctuate widely if water is not pumped into the system as fast as or faster than it is used.

The most common system is a combination of gravity and pumping systems. Direct pumping furnishes the average demand and the reservoirs furnish a uniform pressure and a reserve supply when larger amounts are needed. This system furnishes adequate pressure at all times. Its shortcomings are that the reservoirs are costly and the water must be pumped against the back pressure of the reservoirs.

Water is usually sold by thousands of gallons or by cubic feet, with the cost per unit decreasing as the quantity of water used increases. Most water plants are publicly owned, efficiently run, and rates are low. There are few services rendered the citizen from which he derives as much good and satisfaction for the money spent as his water supply and the disposal of sewage. These two things are among the most important accomplishments of modern civilization, yet they are among the least heralded by those who sing the praises of modern life.

SUMMARY AND CONCLUSIONS

1. The shape of a vessel has nothing to do with liquid pressure. Liquid pressure in an open container is dependent solely upon two factors—the depth and the density of the liquid.

2. The pressure exerted anywhere on a confined liquid is transmitted through the liquid equally and undiminished to every portion

HYDRAULIC MACHINES

of the interior of the containing vessel. This fact is commonly known as Pascal's Law. In a hydraulic press the forces exerted on two pistons are in the same ratios as their areas. However, the pressure on the small piston equals that on the large piston.

3. $\dfrac{\text{Force }(R)\text{ on large piston}}{\text{Force }(E)\text{ on small piston}} = \dfrac{\text{Area of large piston}}{\text{Area of small piston}}$

$$\frac{R}{E} = \frac{A}{a}$$

4. $\dfrac{\text{Resistance }(R)}{\text{Force }(E)} = \dfrac{\text{Diameter squared of large piston}}{\text{Diameter squared of small piston}}$

$$\frac{R}{E} = \frac{D^2}{d^2}$$

5. $\dfrac{R}{E}$ = M. A. (mechanical advantage of machine).

QUESTIONS FOR REVIEW

1. What is a hydraulic machine?
2. What is pressure? Name three commonly used units of pressure.
3. If the area of a surface and the pressure on it are known, how is the total force on the surface computed?
4. In Fig. 2, explain why the total force is the same for all three vessels.
5. What is the hydrostatic paradox?
6. What is Pascal's Law? Mention several everyday applications of this law.
7. Why is the explosion of dynamite below the surface of water so destructive to animal life in the water?
8. Why is it a good idea not to fill a jug or vacuum bottle entirely full before applying the stopper?
9. In a hydraulic press, compare the pressures on the pistons. Do the same for the total force on the pistons.
10. What is meant by the mechanical advantage of a machine?
11. In taking blood pressure, what is meant by (a) the diastolic pressure; (b) systolic pressure?
12. In what units is blood pressure measured?

PROBLEMS

1. The area of the small piston of a hydraulic press is 1 sq. in. and the force exerted on it is 100 lb. The area of the large piston is 125 sq. in. What is the pressure on the small piston? On the large piston? What is the total force exerted on the large piston?
2. What is the mechanical advantage of the hydraulic machine in Problem 1?
3. What is the mechanical advantage of a hydraulic press if the area of the large piston is 500 times the area of the small piston?
4. The diameters of two pistons of a hydraulic press are 1 in. and 6 in. respectively. What is the mechanical advantage?
5. The diameter of the inlet pipe of a hydraulic lift is 1 in. The diameter of the large piston is 10 in. What force at the inlet must be applied to lift a 4000-lb. automobile which is on a rack that weighs 2000 lb.?
6. The area of the small piston of a hydraulic jack is ¼ sq. in. A force of 100 lb. is applied to it and it lifts a 10,000-lb. body which rests on the large piston. What is the minimum area of the large piston? What is the M. A.?
7. A 144-lb. man stands on the large piston of a hydraulic press, which is 12 in. by 12 in. If the small piston is 1 sq. in. in area, at what height must the water stand in the tube to balance the weight of the man?
8. The piston in a dentist's chair has an area of 10 sq. in. The chair and the patient in it weigh 300 lb. What force must be exerted on the plunger, whose area is ½ sq. in., in order to operate the chair?
9. How far must the plunger of Problem 8 move in order to lift the patient 1 ft.?
10. The systolic blood pressure of a person is shown to be equivalent to 150 mm. of mercury. This is equivalent to how many centimeters of water?

PROJECTS

1. Ask a doctor to come to your class and demonstrate how blood pressure is taken and explain the precautions which must be taken when blood and other liquids are injected into the blood stream by the gravity method. What height of water column meas-

ured in feet gives the same pressure as the normal blood pressure of a 20-year-old person?

2. Connect one end of a rubber tube with a funnel and the other end with a hot-water bottle. Place a board on the hot-water bottle, fill the tube and bottle partly full of water, then stand on the board and continue pouring water into the tube. Can you lift yourself? Demonstrate and explain to your class.

READING YOU WILL ENJOY

1. Magie, W. F., *A Source Book in Physics*, pp. 75-80. McGraw-Hill Book Company, Inc., New York, 1935. Explains the discovery of Pascal's Law and the earlier hydraulic machines.

2. Richardson, J. S., and G. P. Cahoon, *Methods and Materials for Teaching General and Physical Science*, pp. 269-271. McGraw-Hill Book Company, Inc., New York, 1951. Gives experiments dealing with Pascal's Law.

3. Taylor, L. W., *Physics, the Pioneer Science*, pp. 97-99. Houghton Mifflin Company, Boston, 1941. Tells how Pascal solved the hydrostatic paradox and discovered the law that bears his name.

4. U. S. Bureau of Naval Personnel, *Basic Hydraulics*, pp. 1-66. U. S. Government Printing Office, Washington 25, D.C., 1945. Simply written and profusely illustrated.

Unit 3

Forces in Air and Other Gases

Conquering the sound barrier was a milestone in airplane flight. Now, new problems are arising to challenge the physicist and aeronautical engineer—problems in stability and control at speeds exceeding 1500 miles per hour, or approximately twice the speed of sound. At such high speeds, scientists are concerned with the friction between the airplane surfaces and rapidly moving streams of air. The friction may generate enough heat to melt an airfoil. This makes it necessary to consider a heat, or thermal, barrier. How do scientists study the power forces unleashed by currents of air?

One method is suggested in the unit photograph of a wind tunnel that duplicates conditions encountered in flight. Giant fans shoot gusts of air at the scale model of a research plane and then impart a curving or rotary motion to the air stream to simulate the conditions in rolling flight. By analyzing the motions of the model during such rigorous tests, scientists can collect enough data to design improvements in the control surfaces of the airplane. Research of this kind is but one important application of the principles governing fluids in motion.

9. FORCES CAUSED BY THE EARTH'S ATMOSPHERE
10. COMPRESSION AND EXPANSION IN GASES
11. FORCES IN HIGH-SPEED LIQUIDS AND GASES

Unit Photograph Courtesy NACA

Chapter 9

Forces Caused by the Earth's Atmosphere

The problem. Most of us, like fish that live at the bottom of the ocean totally unaware of water pressure, fail to recognize the part played in our daily activities by forces in air and other gases. Nevertheless, such forces play an active part in practically everything that happens on the earth, ranging from cream-whipping and cake-baking to the explosion of hydrogen bombs.

Forces in gases turn windmills, sustain airplanes, propel rocket ships, inflate automobile tires, facilitate breathing, drive air hammers, power gas engines, carry away topsoil, blow down our homes, and bring rain which supplies water for man and other living things.

But how can air and other gases exert forces? Is air matter? Does air have weight? Does it occupy space? Does it exert pressure, and if so, how is its pressure measured? And how are the forces in gases controlled and put to work to man's advantage? These are a few of the questions which we must answer to solve the problem of forces in gases.

Is air matter; that is, does air occupy space and have weight? We have all heard people speak of an "empty" bottle, jug, or glass tumbler, suggesting that air in a container does not occupy space and therefore, by definition, is not matter. On the other hand, we have all pushed a glass tumbler mouth downward into water and have seen that the water did not rise appreciably in the tumbler. And if we turned the tumbler right side up under the water, we saw a large bubble escape, after which the tumbler filled with water. Only as the air bubbled out did the water fill the container. Therefore we may conclude that air occupies space. See Fig. 1.

We can determine whether or not air has weight by weighing a liter flask fitted with a stopcock, pumping the air from it with a vacuum pump, closing the stopcock, and again weighing the flask. The results show that the empty flask weighs about 1.29 g. less than the full one. Although the density of air varies with temperature, moisture content, and pressure, under standard conditions, which are explained on page 82, the density is *1.29 grams per liter, 1.25 ounces per cubic foot,* or about *2 pounds per cubic yard.* What is the approximate mass of the air in your classroom? See Fig. 2.

How are forces in gases measured? From experience we know that the Bourdon-type gauge, which we discussed on page 47, is used to measure air pressure in automobile tires. In the laboratory the

FORCES IN AIR AND OTHER GASES

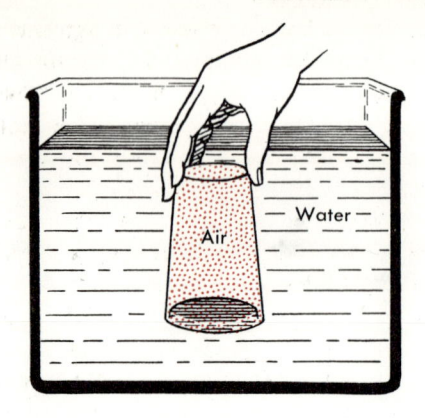

Fig. 1. Why does not the tumbler fill with water? What must you do in order to fill the tumbler with water? What does this show?

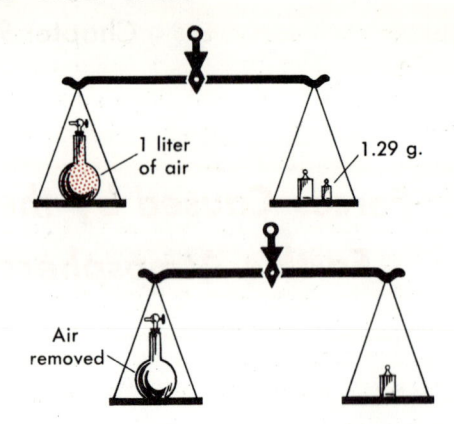

Fig. 2. Air has weight. After the air has been removed from the 1-liter flask, the flask weighs 1.29 grams less. The density of air is 1.29 grams per liter.

open U-tube (manometer) is often used (see Fig. 7 in Chapter 6). For low gas pressures it is filled with water, and for higher pressures with mercury. Usually the gas pressures are then calculated with the formula $P = hd$.

PROBLEM: When the difference in water levels of an open-tube manometer is 20 in., what is the gas pressure?

SOLUTION: $P = hd$
Substituting, $P = 20 \times .036$
or $P = 0.72$ lb./sq. in.

What would be the pressure if the difference in water levels were 20 cm.? Difference in mercury levels were 20 cm.? 20 in.?

Does the atmosphere exert pressure? We can perform an old but fascinating trick by completely immersing a tumbler bottom side down in water, turning it bottom side up, and then slowly drawing it upward. When this is done, to the surprise of the uninitiated, the water stays in the tumbler as long as the rim is totally under the surface of the water. Similarly (Fig. 3), if we put a piece of paper over the mouth of a tumbler of water, hold the

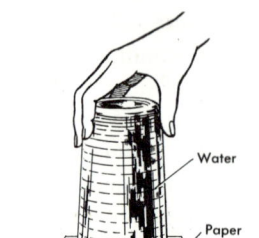

Fig. 3. What causes the water to remain in the glass tumbler?

Fig. 4. When air is exhausted from the tin can, the can "collapses."

paper on the tumbler, and turn the tumbler upside down in air, the water does not run out when the support is removed from the paper*. The paper remains apparently glued to the tumbler. And if we exhaust the air from an empty tin can, the sides collapse inwardly as shown in Fig. 4. These observations, along with the fact that air has weight, tend to prove that the atmosphere exerts pressure.

Furthermore, if we go up in an airplane or deep into a mine our eardrums "pop." This experience gives us cause to believe not only that atmospheric pressure exists, but also that it changes with the altitude or depth.

In spite of these observations, which seem to support the hypothesis that the atmosphere exerts pressure and that it varies with altitude, there are still the possibilities that the sides of the tin can were either pulled or pushed in because nature abhors a vacuum. "The universe," said Aristotle's followers, "would sooner fall to pieces than permit an abhorred *Nothing* in its place."

Does nature abhor a vacuum? It was known to miners, even before the time of Aristotle, that water cannot be pumped more than 34 feet high with a "suction" pump. Galileo discovered this fact when his cistern pump failed to work and he called in a repairman. Finding nothing wrong with the pump, the repairman measured the water in the cistern and found the water level to be too low. And he told Galileo that it was not possible, whether the pump was large or small, to lift water a hairbreadth more than 18 cubits, or about 34 feet, above the level of its surface.

What the workman told Galileo puzzled him, for he knew it was not in agreement with Aristotle's doctrine that nature abhors a vacuum. "Why," he asked, "does nature's abhorrence of a vacuum suddenly stop at about 34 feet above the water level?"

What causes water to rise in a "suction" pump and soda pop to rise in a straw? Only by performing a crucial experiment in which the effect of atmospheric pressure, if it exists, is entirely eliminated can we determine whether air pressure, suction, or the abhorrence of a vacuum causes water to rise in a tube as it does in a so-called suction pump.

To make this test, fit a bottle with a one-hole stopper in which a glass tube has been inserted, as shown in A, Fig. 5. Then remove the stopper and fill the bottle completely with water. Next replace the stopper, making certain that no air is under it and that the stopper is airtight. Then suck on the tube. If the water rises, what will this prove?

Next, repeat the experiment, using the two-hole stopper which allows air to reach the surface of the water. See B, Fig. 5.

---

*An ordinary piece of screen wire in the mouth of a milk bottle will serve the same purpose as the paper and dramatize the experiment still more.

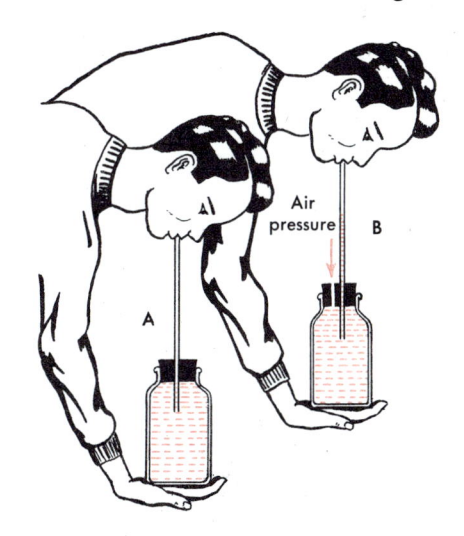

Fig. 5. Why does the water rise in tube B, but not in tube A?

FORCES IN AIR AND OTHER GASES

Since the water does not rise in the tube when suction is applied in the absence of air, but does rise in the presence of air, then evidently the air does exert pressure which causes the water to rise.

How Torricelli measured atmospheric pressure. Galileo, like all great teachers, was not content with merely cramming the minds of his students with the accepted beliefs of his day. Instead, he aimed to open new worlds for them to conquer by pointing out the contradictions among accepted beliefs. It was Evangelista Torricelli (1608-1647) whom he inspired to challenge the old belief that nature abhors a vacuum.

Knowing that with a suction pump air pressure pushes water only 34 feet high, Torricelli reasoned that it would push mercury, which is 13.6 times as dense as water, only $\frac{1}{13.6}$ part of 34 feet, which is a little less than 30 inches. But instead of using a suction pump, Torricelli used a long glass tube closed at one end. Torricelli filled the tube with mercury, put his thumb over one end, inverted the tube, and then submerged the open end in a cup of mercury before taking his thumb away. This instrument is known as a *Torricellian* or *mercurial barometer*. See Fig. 6.

When the tube was over 30 inches long, the mercury in it fell, leaving a space above, and there were no signs of air bubbles passing up through the mercury. Torricelli found, too, that the vertical height of the column of mercury was not affected when the tube was tilted sidewise or when tubes of different diameters were used, as shown in Fig. 7. At sea level the vertical height was about 30 inches.

When Torricelli reported his results, another bitter controversy was set off. Torricelli claimed there was a partial vacuum above the mercury in the barometer, but

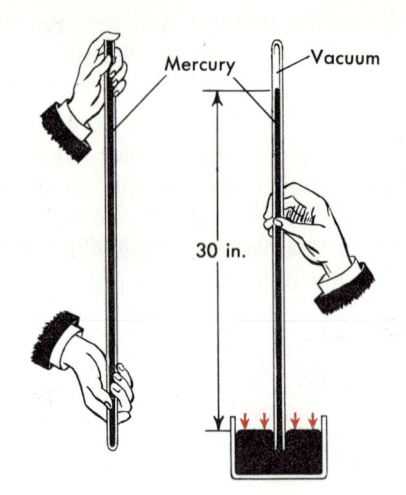

Fig. 6. The Torricellian, or mercurial, barometer. What causes the mercury to rise to a height of approximately 30 inches?

the followers of Aristotle claimed that this was preposterous because Aristotle had said that nature abhors a vacuum.

Pascal tests Torricelli's method of measuring atmospheric pressure. When Blaise Pascal, who had also been a student of Galileo, heard of Torricelli's experiment,

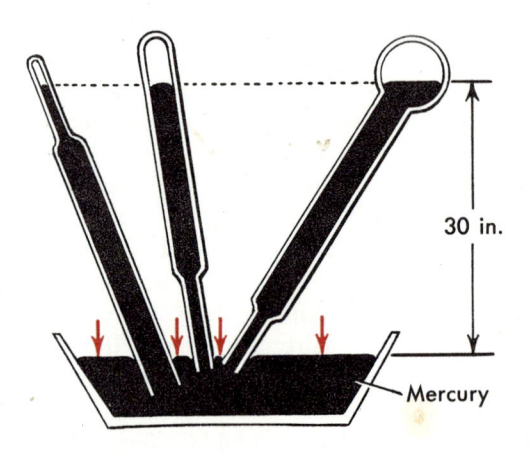

Fig. 7. What factors do not affect the height of a column of mercury in a barometer?

he was skeptical of the results. But unlike Aristotle's followers, who resorted to name-calling and argument, Pascal began planning a group of crucial experiments designed to prove or disprove Torricelli's conclusions.

In 1647 he gave some public demonstrations at Rouen, France, using Torricellian tubes. His opponents, known as "Plenists," argued with him that the apparent void (vacuum) at the top of the tube was full of rarefied air. Pascal confounded them with demonstrations employing tubes of various shapes and sizes, including two that were 46 feet long, and a siphon with one arm 50 feet high and the other 45 feet.

In another test, Pascal carried a Torricellian barometer to the top of the tower of Saint-Jacques-de-la-Boucherie in Rouen, and found a decrease in the height of the column. Later, near the tower, a statue of Pascal was erected in honor of the event. Look for it if you ever visit this spot in France.

Still not satisfied, Pascal enlisted his brother-in-law to carry a barometer up nearby Mt. Puy de Dôme and observe any fluctuations in the height of the mercury column.

In the climb of about 2700 feet, the barometer fell approximately 3 inches. On the return trip the observations were repeated, and the mercury rose in proportion to the loss in altitude. *For every 900 feet of change in altitude the barometer reading changed about 1 inch.* When the party again reached the foot of the mountain, they found that the barometer read the same as when they started up the mountain and that a second barometer left in the care of an observer had not varied during their absence. Explain the reason for their using the second barometer.

In conclusion, Pascal said:

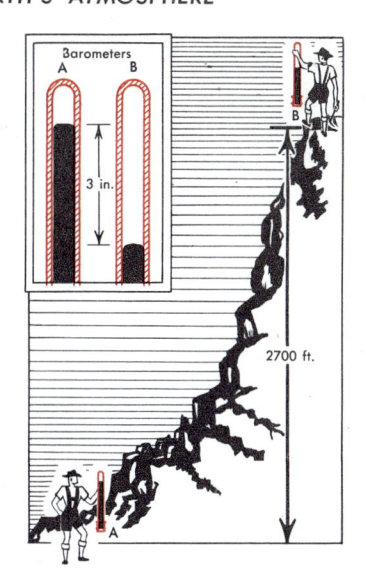

Fig. 8. The barometer reading decreases (falls) about 1 inch for every increase of 900 feet above sea level.

Nature has no repugnance for the Void; she makes no effort to avoid it. All the effects that have been attributed to this horror proceed from the weight and pressure of the air, and that is the sole and veritable cause; it is from ignorance of it that imaginary horror of the void was invented, to make an explanation. This is not the only circumstance wherein, man's weakness having failed to find the true causes, he has expressed (the cause) by specious names which fill the ears and not the minds.

Did this practice die along with the idea that nature abhors a vacuum?

How standard atmospheric pressure was established. Torricelli and Pascal both showed that atmospheric pressure varies not only with the altitude but also with weather conditions. To establish a standard pressure the altitude chosen was sea level and the average of a great number of pressures taken over a considerable period of time was found. The average pressure

FORCES IN AIR AND OTHER GASES

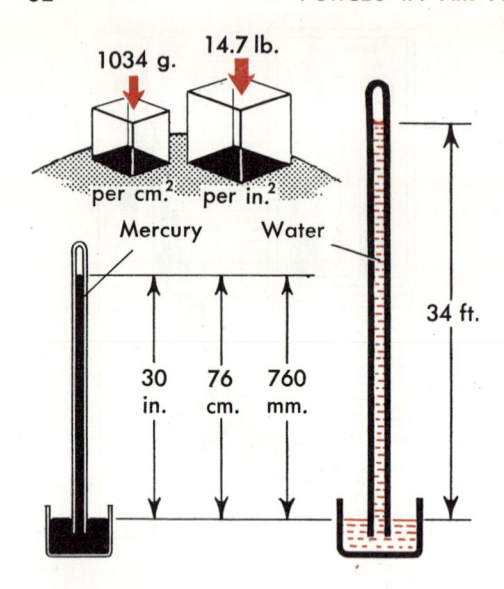

Fig. 9. Equivalents of standard atmospheric pressure. These values should be memorized. Note carefully the units used in each case.

proved to be equivalent to that of 76 centimeters or 30 inches of mercury when at zero degrees centigrade. The pressure in grams per square centimeter can be computed as follows:

$$P = hd$$
$$P = 76 \times 13.6$$
$$P = 1033.6 \text{ g./cm.}^2$$

and in pounds per square inch:
$$P = hd$$
$$P = 30 \times .49$$
$$P = 14.7 \text{ lb./in.}^2$$

In conclusion, *standard atmospheric pressure is equivalent to 1033.6 g./cm.²; 14.7 lb./in.²; 30 in. of mercury; 76 cm. or 750 mm. of mercury; or 34 ft. of water.* It is also expressed in *millibars* and *atmospheres.* Standard temperature is 0°C.

For practical use, 1033.6 is often changed to 1034 or 1000 and 14.7 is changed to 15. Also, up to 18,000 feet, a change of altitude of 900 feet causes a change of about 1 inch in the height of mercury in a barometer tube.

The modern mercury barometer. The modern mercury barometer consists essentially of a Torricellian tube, and reading it consists simply in measuring accurately the height of the mercury column above the mercury level in the cup or bowl.

The tube is enclosed in a cylindrical metal case on which a scale in inches or centimeters, or both, is etched. A slot in the metal case makes it possible for the mercury level in the tube to be seen. See Fig. 10.

When the air pressure decreases, some of the mercury flows out of the tube into the bowl. When the pressure increases, some of the mercury in the bowl flows into the tube. Therefore, to provide a fixed point above which the height of the column may be measured, a small ivory peg is mounted on the case so that it sticks

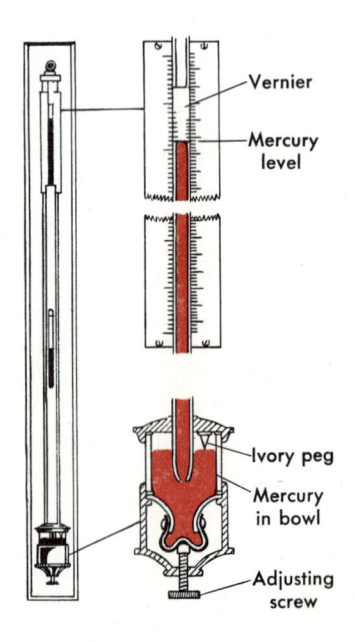

Fig. 10. A mercury barometer. How is the mercury level in the bowl adjusted?

FORCES CAUSED BY THE EARTH'S ATMOSPHERE

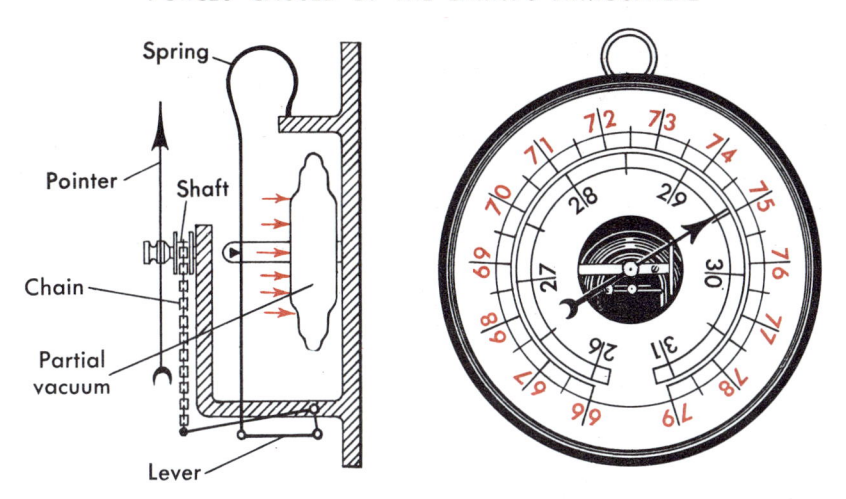

Fig. 11. An aneroid barometer. As the atmospheric pressure changes, the sides of the chamber collapse or move farther apart. The up-and-down motion of the chamber is multiplied by a system of levers and transmitted to the pointer. In what units is the dial graduated?

down into the bowl. The bowl is made so that it can be raised or lowered as a screw is turned, thus permitting the mercury level in the bowl to be adjusted. *Before a reading is taken, the bowl should be raised or lowered so that the mercury level in the bowl coincides with the tip of the peg.*

For really accurate work, the reading must be corrected if the temperature is not zero degrees centigrade, because the height of the column varies with changes in temperature as well as with changes in atmospheric pressure.

The aneroid barometer. Since the mercurial barometer is about three feet long and should stand or hang vertically, it is awkward and inconvenient to carry about. Consequently, its use is very impractical on airplanes, ships, and many other places where barometers are needed. In such places the *aneroid* (without liquid) barometer, which is quite small, is used. The aneroid barometer consists of a partially evacuated, airtight, circular chamber made of thin metal with corrugated sides.

Increase in atmospheric pressure pushes in the sides, and as the atmospheric pressure decreases the sides spring back into position. As shown in Fig. 11 this motion, which is very slight, is multiplied several times by the multiplying levers and by the small chain connected to the shaft that moves the pointer, or hand. The instrument is usually calibrated to read in both inches and centimeters of mercury.

The altimeter. We have discovered that near sea level the barometer falls about 1 inch for every 900 feet of ascent. This is equivalent to a fall of 1 millimeter for every 11 meters. Knowing the relationship between ascent and the decrease in pressure, it is possible to calibrate an aneroid barometer so that it records ascent or distance above the starting elevation. Such an instrument is called an *altimeter*. It is used by airplane and balloon pilots, mountain climbers, and explorers.

Another very useful application of the aneroid barometer is found in the *barograph*. The system of levers noted in the description of the aneroid barometer is attached to a long hand which holds a pen

FORCES IN AIR AND OTHER GASES

Fig. 12. The barograph is a recording barometer that gives a written record of the barometer readings for a whole week. Instead of a pointer, a pen is attached to the system of levers that multiplies the movement of the top of the evacuated can. The barometer readings are then recorded on the cylinder scale sheet, which makes one complete revolution each week.

Courtesy Taylor Instrument Co.

at its outer end. The pen rests against a sheet of specially prepared graph paper which is wrapped about a cylinder that is rotated by clockwork. Thereby the pen makes a continuous trace which gives a permanent and continuous record of the atmospheric pressure. Fig. 12 shows a portion of a one-week record.

The Magdeburg hemispheres. Otto von Guericke (1602-1687), mayor of Magdeburg, Germany, and evidently a colorful showman, working independently of Torricelli and Pascal, performed experiments that helped to verify their work.

Guericke not only invented the first vacuum pump, but he also did some very spectacular experiments with vacuums. He made two hollow hemispheres about 22 inches in diameter whose edges were so smooth that when they were covered with a thick grease and fitted together, they made an airtight sphere. He then pumped the air out of the sphere and closed the stopcock. In one demonstration before the Emperor of Germany, as many as two eight-horse teams were required to pull the hemispheres apart.

In most physics laboratories today, two smaller hemispheres of this kind, 3 to 4 inches in diameter, are found. If you have such hemispheres, fit them together, evacuate them, and try to pull them apart. Then compute the force with which you would have to pull if they were perfectly evacuated.

How high is the atmosphere? If the density of the atmosphere were the same at every altitude as it is at sea level, we could find the height of the atmosphere by using the formula $P = h\,d$. This would make it about five miles high, a height above which some of our mountain peaks extend. But if no atmosphere existed there, these peaks could not be snowcapped, because there would be no water vapor from which snow could form. Furthermore, propeller-driven airplanes could not fly at these heights.

We know, however, that such peaks are snow-capped and that moisture and air are found at still greater altitudes. Aviators, rockets, balloons carrying self-recording instruments, and pilot balloons have reached the altitudes shown in Fig. 13.

By different methods the height of the atmosphere has been estimated to vary from 50 to 500 miles. For example, the reflection of light from the sky at sundown shows there must be atmosphere at least 50 miles high and, during an eclipse of the moon by the earth, the shadow cast shows that it must extend much farther. Also, the height at which meteors become visible, made so by air friction, indicates that the atmosphere extends out many miles.

FORCES CAUSED BY THE EARTH'S ATMOSPHERE 85

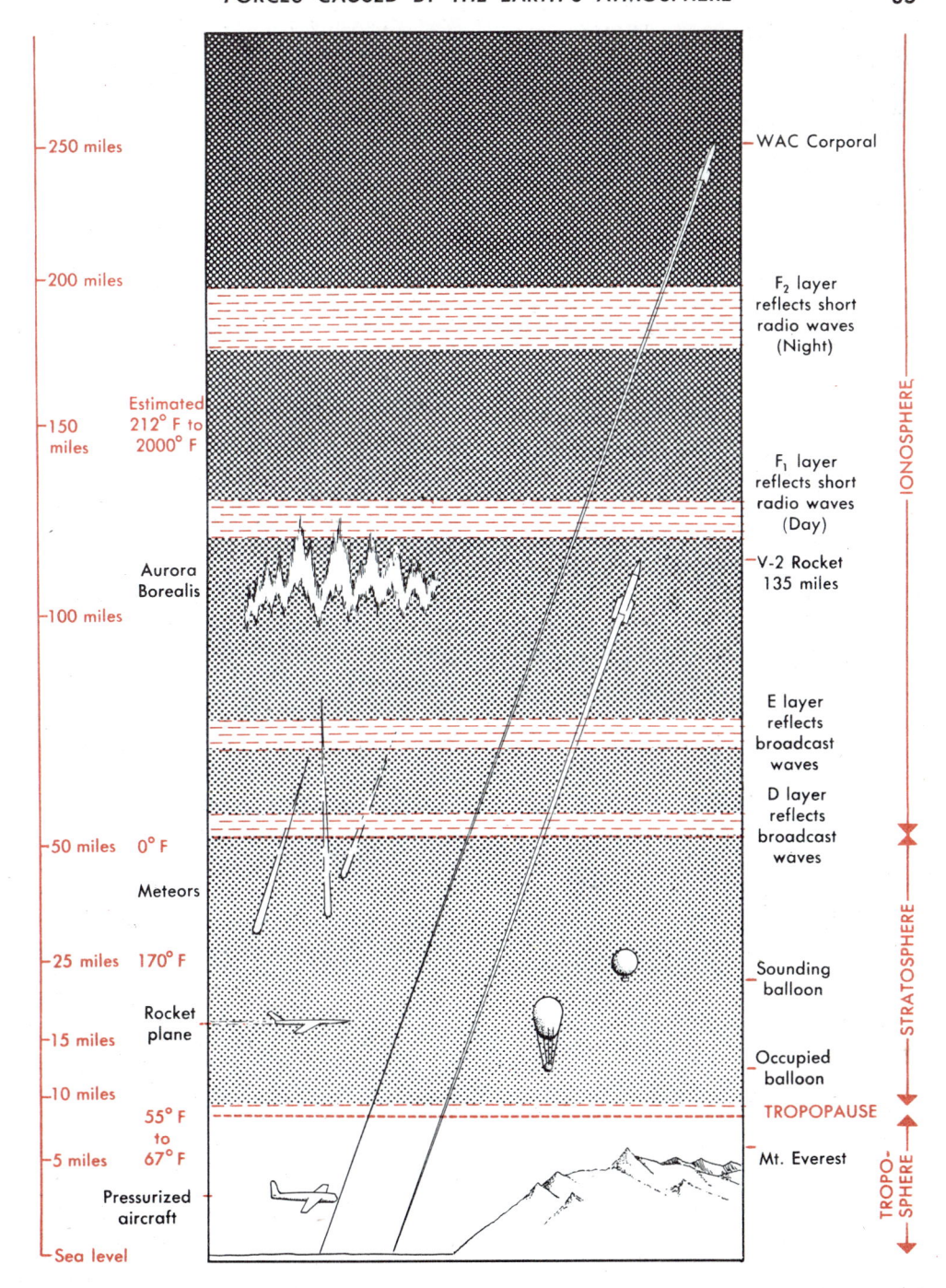

Fig. 13. A cross section of the earth's atmosphere, showing the various layers of the atmosphere and the extent of man's efforts to probe them. Note the role of the ionosphere in radio communication.

At about 18,000 feet the barometer reads approximately 15 inches, which means that about half of the atmosphere is below and the other half above this altitude. Above about 35,000 feet no clouds are formed and the temperature is fairly constant, reaching temperatures as low as 67 degrees below zero Fahrenheit. The upper cloudless portion of the atmosphere is called the *stratosphere*. The portion below the stratosphere is called the *troposphere*.

Machines that depend upon atmospheric pressure. The lift pump. The common lift pump has been in use since before the time of Aristotle—since before the fourth century B. C. At best, with 1 atmosphere of pressure it will not lift water over 34 feet, and, because of mechanical imperfections, the limit is usually about 28 feet.

As shown in Fig. 14 (a), a lift pump has two valves, one of which is in the piston P. When the piston is pulled up, valve A is closed and B is open. As a result the pressure under the piston is lowered and the atmospheric pressure which acts downward on the surface of the water in the well forces water up the pipe past valve B.

When the piston is lowered, valve B closes and traps the water above it, which flows through the piston valve above the piston. Then the next time the piston is raised the water is lifted high enough so that it flows through the spout.

The force pump. To pump water, oil, or other liquids from a deep well, a force pump is often used. It operates much like a lift pump, but the piston and the cylinder in which the piston is fitted must be deep in the well within 28 feet of the surface of the liquid. Make an enlarged copy of the diagram of the force pump shown in (b) of Fig. 14 and use it to explain how a force pump works. Or better still, if your teacher has a glass model of a force pump use it in your explanation instead.

A force pump is used to pump water into tanks in homes which have their own water supply system. Usually such tanks are located in the basement. The water is forced into the tank and the air in the tank is compressed. Then the air will force the water to all parts of the house.

The siphon. Place a glass or rubber tube filled with water or some other liquid in the position shown in Fig. 15 and the liquid will flow from vessel A to vessel B. If B is then raised until the liquid level in it is higher than that in A, the direction of flow will be reversed.

This instrument, called the *siphon,* is used to transfer liquids from vessels which cannot easily be overturned, or is used to draw off layers of liquids without disturbing other layers. For example, cream can be removed from the top of a milk bottle

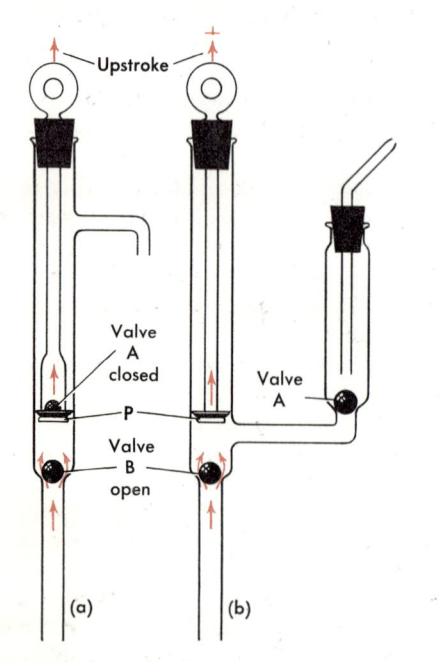

Fig. 14. (a) The lift pump. (b) The force pump. Note that the piston of the force pump has no valve.

FORCES CAUSED BY THE EARTH'S ATMOSPHERE

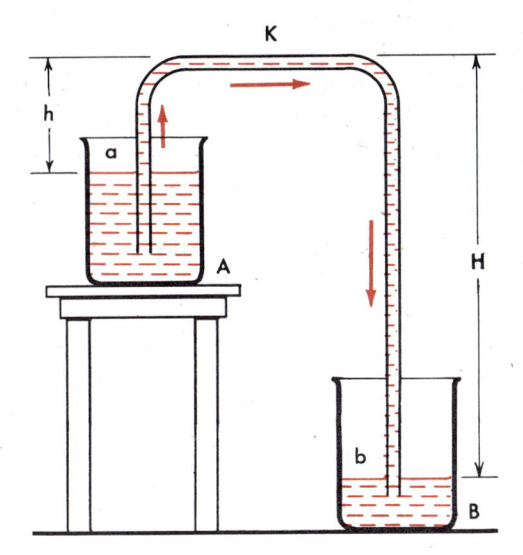

Fig. 15. The operation of a siphon is due to the difference in the effective, or net, pressures, of the two columns of water.

or the milk can be removed from under the cream.

To observe how the siphon works, see Fig. 15. If water flows from A to B, then the force in the tube must be greater in that direction than in the other. Let us analyze the situation. At a inside the tube, the upward pressure is equal to the atmospheric pressure minus the downward pressure due to the column of water of height h. At b, the upward pressure is the atmospheric pressure minus the pressure due to the column of water of height H. Hence the upward pressure at a exceeds the upward pressure at b by the pressure of a column of water of height $(H - h)$. Hence when $H - h = 0$, the water will cease to flow because the upward pressure at a will equal that at b. The water in both vessels will then be at the same level.

The water will also cease to flow when the bend K is more than 34 feet above a, for then, as in the top of a long Torricellian tube, a vacuum will form because the atmospheric pressure is insufficient to push water that high. Would a siphon work in a vacuum? What happens when the water level in B becomes higher than in A? When the water level in B is lowered still more?

SUMMARY AND CONCLUSIONS

1. Air is matter; it occupies space and has weight. At 0° centigrade, under 76 cm. of mercury pressure, the density of air is 1.29 g./l., 1.25 oz./cu. ft., or 2 lb./cu. yd.
2. Atmospheric pressure is equivalent to:
    (a) 30 in. of mercury
    (b) 76 cm. (760 mm.) of mercury
    (c) 34 ft. (1034 cm.) of water
    (d) 1034 g. (about 1 kg.) per sq. cm.
    (e) 14.7 lb. (about 15 lb.) per sq. in.
3. Atmospheric pressure decreases with elevation, about 1 in. of mercury per 900 ft. when near sea level. Half of the atmosphere is below 18,000 feet altitude.

QUESTIONS FOR REVIEW

1. A 1-gram piece of lead will fall faster in air than a 1-gram feather. Explain.
2. Give proof that (a) air occupies space; (b) air has weight.
3. Under standard conditions, what is the mass of air per liter? Per cubic foot? Per cubic yard?
4. Does an inflated football weigh more than a deflated one? How could you prove your answer?
5. What is a manometer and for what is it used?
6. Give three possible hypotheses, along with one logical consequence of each, as to why water rises in a suction pump.
7. Give three observable phenomena which seem to indicate that the atmosphere exerts pressure.
8. What idea of Aristotle's, as long as it was believed, blocked the way to discovery of why water rises in a suction pump?
9. Explain Torricelli's experiment.
10. If Pascal's party had carried an inflated bladder up the mountain, what do you sup-

88   FORCES IN AIR AND OTHER GASES

pose would have happened to its size? What would this tend to prove?

11. What did Torricelli believe was above the mercury in his barometer tube? What consequently should happen if the tube were tipped sidewise? What did Torricelli's opponents believe was above the mercury? What consequently should have happened when the tube was tipped sidewise? What actually happened? What did this tend to prove?

12. Why will milk run out of one hole of a tin can faster when two holes of equal size are punched in the top, rather than one?

13. Why did Torricelli use mercury rather than water in his barometer tube?

14. Explain how the atmospheric pressure is measured by a barometer.

15. Explain how the ink is caused to flow into a fountain pen when it is filled.

16. Since pressure supports the mercury in a barometer, what should happen to the height of the mercury when air is removed from the bell jar in Fig. 16? When air is blown into the bell jar?

PROBLEMS

1. A room is 26 ft. long, 15 ft. wide, and 10 ft. high. Find the approximate weight of air in it.

2. When the barometer reads 74 cm. of mercury, what is the atmospheric pressure in g./cm.^{2}?

3. If a water barometer reads 34 ft., what is the pressure in lb./sq. in.?

4. When 1 atmosphere of pressure is exerted on a boy's chest, what force is exerted per square foot? Why does this not crush the boy?

5. A barometer in an airplane reads 24 in. of mercury. What is the altitude of the plane above sea level?

6. A barometer in an airplane gives the atmospheric pressure as 13 lb./sq. in. What is the altitude of the plane above sea level?

7. An airplane is 3000 ft. above sea level. What is the approximate reading of the barometer in inches of mercury? Centimeters of mercury? Lb./sq. in.?

8. An airplane is 4000 ft. above sea level. What is the reading of the barometer in lb./in.^{2}? Inches of mercury?

9. At the bottom of a mountain the barometer reads 29 in. When carried to the top of the mountain it reads 27 in. What is the approximate difference in altitude?

10. Will this same variation in pressure with altitude (Problem 9) continue the higher one goes? Explain why.

11. An airplane pilot adjusts his altimeter so that it reads the correct altitude before he takes off. During the flight the atmospheric pressure on the ground increases 0.2 in. Approximately how many feet will the altimeter be in error, and which way, when the pilot lands?

12. If the atmospheric pressure were 14 lb./sq. in., over about what height could water be siphoned?

13. With 1 atmosphere of pressure, over about what height could alcohol, having a density 0.8 that of water, be siphoned?

14. How many atmospheres of pressure are exerted on an air bubble which is in water 68 feet below the surface?

EXERCISES

1. Below are a number of statements. Some are true and some are false, but all are logical consequences either of Aristotle's hypothesis

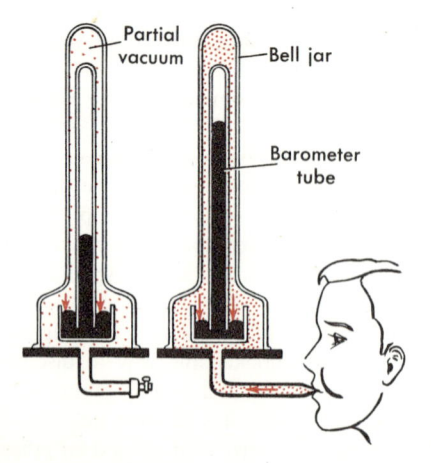

Fig. 16. Account for the mercury levels.

that nature abhors and fills all vacuums or of Torricelli's hypothesis that partial vacuums can exist and that atmospheric pressure supports the mercury in a barometer tube. The statements that support Aristotle's hypothesis are to be marked A. Those that support Torricelli's and Pascal's hypothesis are to be marked P. Do not write in this book.

(a) The space above the mercury in a barometer must be filled with either air or mercury vapor.

(b) If a barometer tube is tipped, the mercury should not fill up the space above.

(c) There should be no limit to the height to which water can be pumped by a suction pump.

(d) Water in a completely filled, closed, airtight bottle can be sucked up a hollow tube which sticks into the water.

(e) A liquid whose density is half that of water can be pumped to a maximum height of about twice that to which water can be pumped.

(f) There should be no limit to the height through which water can be siphoned.

(g) The space above the water in a water barometer is a partial vacuum containing some water vapor.

(h) If a mercury barometer is placed in a bell jar and air is pumped from the jar, the height of the mercury column should remain the same.

(i) If a barometer is carried up a mountainside, the barometer reading should decrease.

2. In (1), state by means of (yes) or (no) whether or not each logical deduction agrees with experiment and observation.

3. In one of his stories, Mark Twain tells of stopping to "boil" his thermometer as he went up a mountain. What was his purpose?

4. What is meant by priming a pump?

PROJECT

Make an aneroid barometer and calibrate it for use as an altimeter. What factors other than atmospheric pressure affect it and, as a consequence, what precautions must be taken when it is used? Carry it from the lower floor to the top floor of a tall building.

READING YOU WILL ENJOY

1. Conant, J. B. (Editor), *Harvard Case Histories in Experimental Science*. Case 1, *Robert Boyle's Experiments in Pneumatics*, pp. 11-38. Harvard University Press, Cambridge, 1950. Tells about Torricelli's invention of the barometer and the experimental tests of the logically deduced consequences based on the idea that air has weight and exerts pressure, and that the mercury in a barometer is supported by atmospheric pressure.

2. Richardson, J. S., and G. P. Cahoon, *Methods and Materials for the Teaching of General and Physical Sciences*, pp. 192-198. McGraw-Hill Book Company, Inc., New York, 1951. Deals with easily constructed apparatus that can be used to demonstrate the effects of air pressure. Also shows simple ways of measuring air pressure, density of a gas, and volume of a gas.

3. Taylor, L. W., *Physics, the Pioneer Science*, pp. 101-105. Houghton Mifflin Company, Boston, 1941. Explains how Torricelli invented the barometer.

Chapter 10

Compression and Expansion in Gases

The "spring" in gas. Almost anyone who has squeezed a tennis ball in his hand knows that as the pressure increases, the volume of the air inside the ball decreases. And when the pressure on the outside is released, the ball "springs" back to its original size. The same is true of a rubber balloon.

Pascal and his co-workers seem to have been the first to discover this important phenomenon and they did it in a rather peculiar but convincing manner. When Pascal's co-workers carried a barometer up the mountainside, they took along a partly inflated bladder. They observed that its volume gradually increased as they ascended the mountain. Then, as they descended, the volume decreased until they reached their starting elevation, where the bladder had returned to its original size.

You might perform a similar experiment by carrying a partly inflated rubber balloon up to a considerable height in an airplane, and returning to your original starting point. If you went too high, what might happen to the balloon?

Or simpler still, partly inflate a small rubber balloon, place it in a bell jar, and then exhaust the air from the jar. As you do so the pressure outside the balloon is reduced. As a result, the balloon expands until the forces inside and outside are in equilibrium. And when you let the air back into the bell jar, and thereby increase the pressure outside the balloon to its original amount, the balloon returns to its original size. See Fig. 1.

From these experiments, it seems that as the pressure on a given mass of gas increases, the volume decreases, and as the pressure decreases, the volume increases. Although Pascal was among the first to observe this phenomenon, Robert Boyle (1627-1691), an Englishman, first discovered in 1662 the exact mathematical relationship which is known as Boyle's Law.

How Boyle found the mathematical relationship between the pressure and the volume of a given mass of gas. In his investigations, Boyle trapped some air (see Fig. 2) in the short arm of a J-tube by pouring a little mercury into the tube so that the mercury stood at the same level in both arms. This assured him that the trapped air was under only 1 atmosphere of pressure, which he knew to be approximately 30 inches of mercury. Repetition of Boyle's original experiment gives the following data:

COMPRESSION AND EXPANSION IN GASES

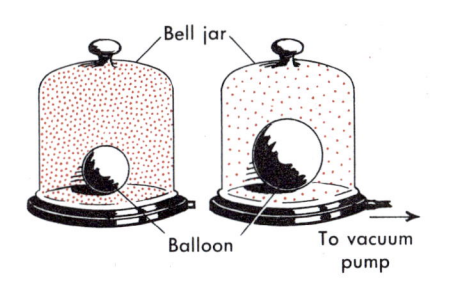

Fig. 1. Explain why the balloon increases in size as the air is pumped from the bell jar.

Volume of Air in cc.	Pressure in Atmospheres	Pressure times Volume
$V_1 = 100$	$P_1 = 1$	$P_1 \times V_1 = 100$
$V_2 = 66\frac{2}{3}$	$P_2 = 3/2$	$P_2 \times V_2 = 100$
$V_3 = 50$	$P_3 = 2$	$P_3 \times V_3 = 100$
$V_4 = 33\frac{1}{3}$	$P_4 = 3$	$P_4 \times V_4 = 100$
$V_5 = 25$	$P_5 = 4$	$P_5 \times V_5 = 100$

Study of the above data shows that in every case the pressure times the volume equaled 100 (a constant) and that when the original pressure, P_1, was doubled the original volume, V_1, was halved. And when the original pressure was tripled the volume became one-third of V_1. What happened when the pressure was multiplied by four?

Mariotte discovered one precaution which must be taken as the pressure is changed: *The temperature of the gas must remain constant, because heating the gas will cause it to expand.*

Boyle's Law, including Mariotte's contribution, is as follows:

The volume of a given mass of gas varies inversely with the pressure providing the temperature of the gas does not change.

In the language of algebra, then

$$\frac{P_1}{P_2} = \frac{V_2}{V_1}$$

Another way to state the same relationship is:

The product of the pressure and the volume of a given mass of gas is constant providing the temperature does not change.

Or, $P_1 \times V_1 = P_2 \times V_2$

Also, $PV = K$

Keeping the units straight. In using these formulas, it does not matter in what units the volume and pressure are measured, except that both volumes must be measured in the same units and both pressures must be measured in like units. For example, if one pressure is measured in pounds per square inch, the other one must be measured likewise, and if one volume is measured in cubic inches, the other one must be measured the same way. As a rule, the metric and English units are not mixed.

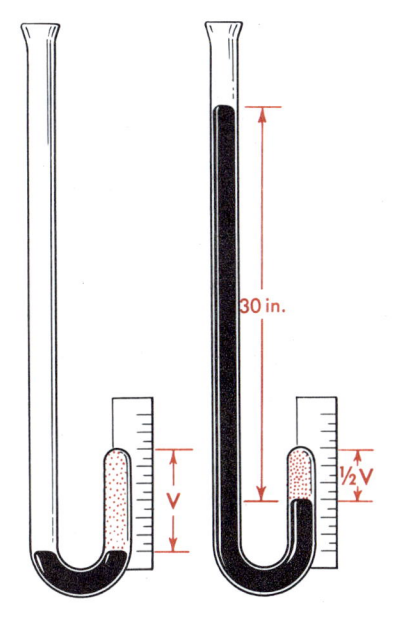

Fig. 2. Account for the height of the mercury column when V is halved.

PROBLEM 1: A certain mass of air in the atmosphere occupies 20 cu. ft. when the barometer reads 28 in. of mercury. What volume will it occupy when the atmospheric pressure equals 30 in. of mercury?

SOLUTION: $P_1V_1 = P_2V_2$
Substituting, $28 \times 20 = 30 \times V_2$
$30 \times V_2 = 560$
▶ $V_2 = 18.67$ cu. ft.

PROBLEM 2: A certain mass of gas occupies 10 cu. ft. when the total pressure on it is 75 lb./in.² How much volume will it occupy if the pressure is 100 lb./in.²?

Gauge pressure, absolute pressure, and Boyle's Law. When an automobile tire is deflated, the small amount of air remaining in the tire is at the same pressure as the air outside. This is approximately 15 lb./in.², or 1 atmosphere. If, however, we measured the pressure in the tire with an ordinary gauge, we would find the pressure to be zero. The *gauge pressure is the difference between the pressures inside and outside the tire.*

Therefore, when the tire is pumped to a gauge pressure of 25 lb./in.², the actual pressure, known as the *absolute pressure,* is 25 plus 15, or 40 lb./in.². In other words, to find absolute pressure, we must add the equivalent of 1 atmosphere to the gauge pressure. For example, if an open manometer shows that a gas pressure is equivalent to 20 inches of mercury, the absolute pressure is 20 plus 30, or 50 inches of mercury. And since Boyle's Law is true only for absolute pressures, all gauge pressures must be changed to absolute pressures when this law is used.

PROBLEM 1: A truck tire holds 5 cu. ft. of air. The gauge pressure is 75 lb./in.² Find the volume of the air when it is released at 1 atmosphere of pressure.

SOLUTION: $P_1V_1 = P_2V_2$
Substituting, $90 \times 5 = 15 \times V_2$
▶ $V_2 = 30$ cu. ft.

Explain how P_1 was found; how P_2 was found.

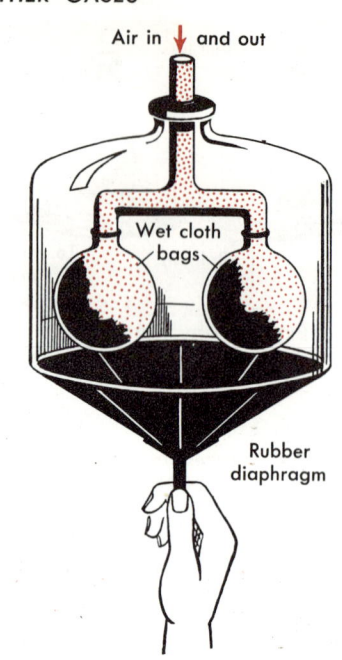

Fig. 3. (a) Account for the changes in pressure and volume when the diaphragm is pulled down and when the diaphragm is released.

PROBLEM 2: A truck tire holds 5 cu. ft. of air when its gauge pressure is 90 lb./in.² What volume of air at 1 atmosphere of pressure had to be pumped into the tire?

Atmospheric pressure and Boyle's Law. One of the most outstanding examples of the application of Boyle's Law is breathing. This can be demonstrated as shown in Fig. 3a. When muscular contraction pulls down the diaphragm, the space (volume) around the lungs is increased. This causes a decrease in pressure around the lungs, making it less than the atmospheric pressure outside. As a consequence, air flows from the area of higher pressure to that of lower pressure inside the lungs. Retraction of the diaphragm decreases the volume of the space around the lungs and causes the pressure to be greater inside the lungs than outside. As a consequence, air and waste gases given off by the lungs flow out. The respirator shown in Fig. 3b has a diaphragm which is run by a motor. As a result the air pressure in the cylinder is alternately increased and decreased so that air is forced in and out of the patient's lungs.

Another example of growing importance is the effect on the human body caused by air pocketed in the sinuses and other body cavities when one takes off in an airplane and climbs quickly to high altitudes. As the atmospheric pressure outside decreases, the volume of the air inside the cavities tends to increase. This often causes very severe pain, but can be avoided to some extent if altitude is gained more slowly. Explain. What happens when altitude is lost very rapidly? What is done in modern passenger planes to prevent these effects?

Vacuum and compression pumps. The vacuum pump, as we have said, was invented by Otto von Guericke in 1650. However, Robert Boyle, working independently of Guericke, also invented such a pump a few weeks later.

A simple mechanical pump is shown in Fig. 4. It consists of a metal cylinder, C,

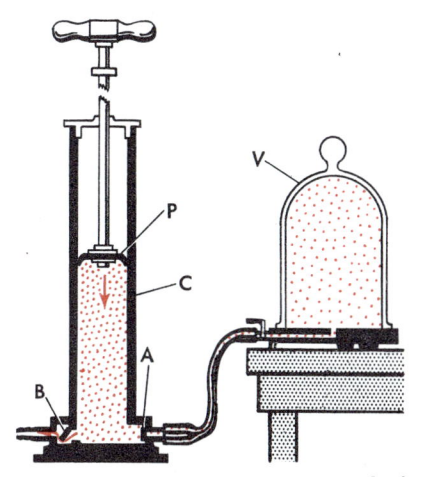

Fig. 4. Explain the valve action of the pump.

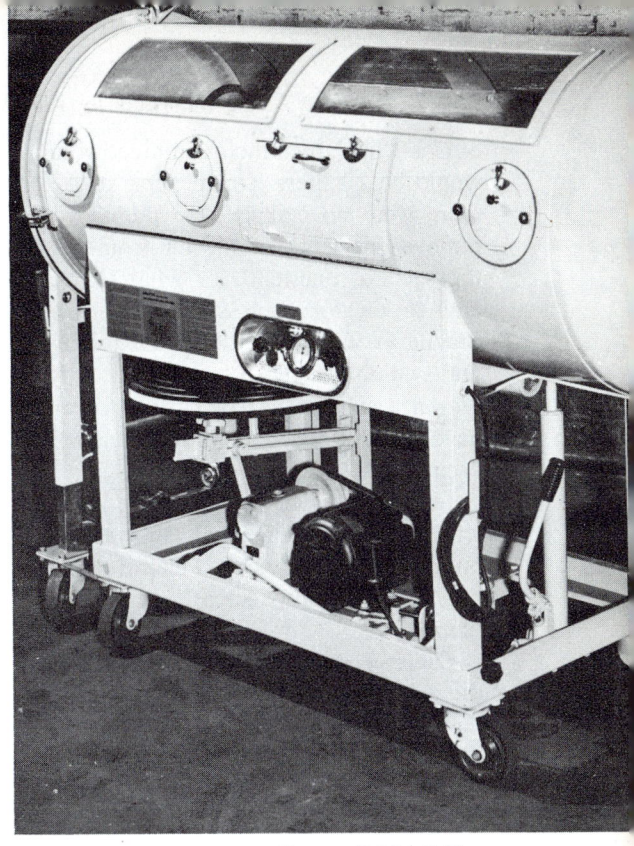

Courtesy Drinker-Collins

Fig. 3. (b) A motor-driven respirator causes alternate increases and decreases in the air pressure within the cylinder, thereby forcing air in and out of a patient's lungs.

fitted with a piston, P, and having at the lower end two short tubes fitted respectively with the valves A and B. When the piston is raised, the air pressure inside C is decreased. Valve B is forced shut by the greater pressure outside the pump and valve A is pushed open by the greater pressure in vessel V, and air flows from V to C until the pressures in the two vessels are equal.

When the piston is pushed down, it compresses the air in C, which causes valve A to close and valve B to open so that air flows out of C. Thus with each stroke a certain fraction of the air in the bell jar, V, is removed. For example, suppose the capacity of V is 9 liters and that of C is 1 liter; then their combined volume would be 10 liters. On the first stroke, if there were no leakage, the pump would remove one-tenth of the air from V; on the second, one-tenth of what was left; and so on for each succeeding stroke. But never would all the air be removed, and within V there would be only a *partial vacuum*. Nearly perfect vacuums have been produced, but never an absolute vacuum.

In case a vessel were connected to outlet B, it is evident that air would be pumped into it. Hence a vacuum pump of this kind may also act as a *compression pump*.

Other uses of the vacuum pump. Unless the air is first removed from a light bulb, the filament will burn up. In some types, the bulb is refilled with an inert gas that does not affect the filament. In making X-ray and radio tubes, vacuum bottles, and evacuated walls, a vacuum or exhaust pump is used. The milking machine is also dependent upon the vacuum pump.

Other uses of partial vacuums. Liquids boil at lower temperatures in a partial vacuum than in open air. This makes it possible to evaporate, or boil off, the water from solutions such as those of milk and sugar at temperatures low enough so that scorching does not take place. Water can be removed quickly from apples, potatoes, prunes, grapes, and milk in partial vacuums in the production of dried foods. Also, water can be removed from milk, orange juice, grape juice, and other juices in the production of concentrated juices, which are then canned and kept frozen until they are used. The advantage of this method over others is that the low boiling temperatures, made possible by reduced pressure, do not destroy the vitamins and the fresh taste, as is done when the liquids are prepared by ordinary boiling at atmospheric pressure. If the pressure of air is greater than 1 atmosphere the boiling temperature is greater than 212°F.

The vacuum cleaner. The vacuum cleaner consists chiefly of a fan driven by

Fig. 5. A high-vacuum pump. As the cylinder rotates eccentrically within the bottom chamber, gas or air from the system to be exhausted is forced out through the outlet pipe.

Courtesy Kinney Manufacturing Co.

Fig. 6. A vacuum cleaner consists essentially of an electric motor used to drive an exhaust fan. When the motor is running, the fan pushes air away from the blades, creating a partial vacuum.

Courtesy Hoover Vacuum Co.

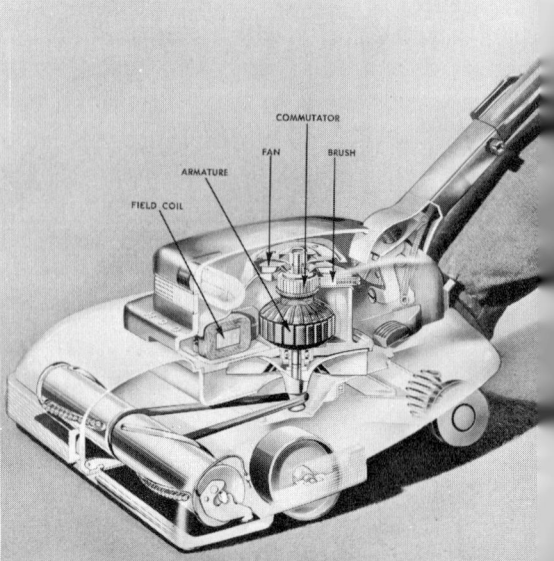

an electric motor. The fan pushes the air away in front of the blades and leaves a partial vacuum behind them. As the air is pushed by the greater outside pressure up through the carpet and into the mouth of the tube which leads to the fan chamber, the dirt is carried out of the carpet by the air. A rotary brush is sometimes used to sweep and beat the rug.

After the air passes the fan it is forced through a bag or some other container which filters out the dust and dirt. These can be removed by various means, depending upon the type of cleaner.

Uses of compressed air. Compressed air has hundreds of uses. This is mainly because when air is put under pressure it will exert greater expansive force and by means of pipes and tubes these forces can be piped through considerable distances.

(a) *Air brakes.* One example is the Westinghouse air brake used on trains. It is operated directly from a compressed air tank on the engine or underneath the car itself. Like the hydraulic brakes on an automobile, the brakes can be applied to all wheels at the same time. Furthermore, the brakes are constructed so that, if the car is disconnected from the engine, they automatically apply themselves. Air brakes are used also on many trucks and buses.

(b) *Diving bells and suits.* As we have already discovered, if we force a glass tumbler, mouth downward, into water, the water will not rise appreciably in the tumbler; the height will depend upon the depth. See Chapter 9, Fig. 1.

When a *diving bell* is lowered into water, the air in it is compressed in the same way, but a compressor above it forces more air into the bell; as a consequence, water does not enter the bell at all. Fresh air must be continuously pumped into the bell to give the men working in it an adequate supply. The surplus of course bubbles out.

Courtesy U. S. Navy

Fig. 7. Navy divers being readied for a deep-sea dive. Compressed air is pumped into the diver's helmet.

The important part of the *diving suit* is the helmet, which is screwed on the top of a waterproof canvas suit. Usually the helmet is supplied with air in the same manner as the diving bell. In other cases the diver carries his own supply of compressed air. Weighted shoes help to cause the diver to sink.

(c) *Pneumatic dispatch.* In dry goods stores and office buildings, compressed air is used to transmit packages, letters, receipts, and many small items. Various rooms are connected with pipes. A compression pump at the sending end and an exhaust pump at the receiving end produce a difference of pressure sufficient to drive a tight-fitting closed cylinder through the pipe. The article to be transmitted is placed in the cylinder.

(d) *Other uses of compressed air.* Compressed air is used in pneumatic lifts, such as those used in grease racks in filling stations; in compressed air tools such as riveting hammers, rock drills, and sandblasts for cutting and polishing; and in

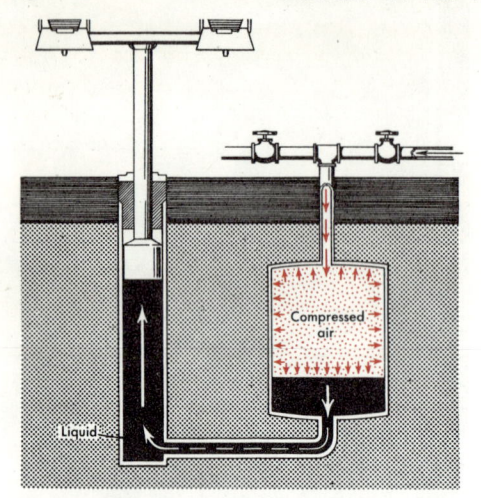

Fig. 8. Compressed air is used in the pneumatic lift. How is a car raised or lowered?

many other similar tools. In submarines it is used to force water from various chambers when the submarine is making ready to surface. It is also used to ventilate mines and tunnels.

"Lighter than air" machines. According to Archimedes' principle, a body immersed in a fluid (liquid or gas) is buoyed up by a force equal to the weight of the displaced fluid.

Since air has weight, it will buoy up a body with a force equal to the weight of air which the body displaces. For this reason a soap bubble or a balloon filled with hydrogen, whose density is about one-fourteenth that of air, will float in air.

The density of air is about 0.08 lb./cu. ft. That of illuminating gas is 0.05 lb./cu. ft.; helium, 0.011 lb./cu. ft.; and hydrogen, 0.006 lb./cu. ft. Hence, the lifting values of these gases in lb./cu. ft. are as follows:

Table 1
LIFTING VALUES OF GASES

Illuminating gas	$0.08 - 0.05$	$= 0.030$ lb./cu. ft.
Helium	$0.08 - 0.011$	$= 0.069$ lb./cu. ft.
Hydrogen	$0.08 - 0.006$	$= 0.074$ lb./cu. ft.

If a dirigible or balloon is to rise, its weight plus the weight of the gas needed to fill it must be less than the weight of the air it displaces. A balloon will rise to the height where its weight equals the weight of air that it displaces. Water is often carried as ballast which the balloonist releases if he wants to go higher. He may descend by releasing gas.

Dirigibles are filled with gas but are also powered by engines. Find the different ways which they have for gaining and losing altitude.

Although hydrogen is the lightest gas known, dirigibles in the United States are not filled with it because it is highly flammable. Nonflammable helium is used instead. The United States has a virtual monopoly on helium, which is found in Texas, Oklahoma, and Kansas.

SUMMARY AND CONCLUSIONS

1. *Boyle's Law:* At constant temperatures, the volume of a given mass of gas varies inversely with the absolute pressure.

$$\frac{P_1}{P_2} = \frac{V_2}{V_1}, \text{ or } P_1 V_1 = P_2 V_2$$

2. Absolute pressure = gauge pressure + atmospheric pressure.

3. Archimedes' Principle applies to fluids—i.e., liquids and gases. The lifting power of a gas unit volume is the difference between the density of air and the density of the gas in question.

4. The net lifting power of a balloon is weight of air displaced minus the combined weight of the balloon and the gas it contains.

5. Balloonists ascend by dropping ballast and descend by allowing gas to escape from the bag.

QUESTIONS FOR REVIEW

1. In measuring atmospheric pressure, state to what each of the following numbers refers and name the unit with which each is associ-

COMPRESSION AND EXPANSION IN GASES

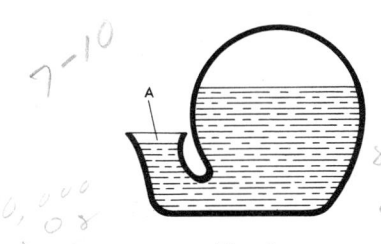

Fig. 9

ated: (a) 30; (b) 34; (c) 14.7; (d) 76; (e) 15; (f) 760.
2. (a) State Boyle's Law. (b) What was Mariotte's contribution to Boyle's Law?
3. Distinguish between absolute and gauge pressure.
4. What is the approximate absolute pressure, measured in atmospheres, on a bubble of air that escapes from a diver's suit 34 feet below the surface of a lake?
5. Explain, in terms of Boyle's Law, how humans breathe.
6. Explain in terms of Boyle's Law how air is exhausted from the bell jar in Fig. 4. Describe the changes in the pressure and volume of the confined gas during the piston strokes.
7. Explain in terms of Boyle's Law why the ink does not run out of the inkwell in Fig. 9. Also explain why ink runs into A only as it is used.
8. Why does not a balloon rise to the top of the atmosphere as a cork rises to the upper surface of water? Explain the conditions when a balloon ceases to rise.

4. Under standard conditions a gram of air occupies about 800 cc. Approximately what volume would it occupy at about 18,000 feet altitude? Assume no change in temperature.
5. At 18,000 feet, how many inhalations would an aviator have to make in order to obtain the same amount of air in his lungs as he would obtain in one inhalation at sea level? Assume temperatures are equal.
6. The relative humidity of air varies directly as the quantity of water vapor per cubic foot of air. Assuming no change in temperature, if at sea level the relative humidity of a given mass of air is 80 per cent, what would be the relative humidity of the same air at 18,000 feet above sea level?
7. Water is forced into a 50-gallon tank until it is two-thirds full of water. If no air escapes from the tank, what is the pressure within the tank? Assume the original pressure to be 1 atmosphere.
8. Under the pressure produced in Problem 7, to how great a height could the water be forced in a pipe?
9. A balloon filled with helium gas weighs 200 lb. The balloon occupies 10,000 cu. ft. of space. At sea level, what load would it lift?
10. A diving bell having vertical sides is lowered into water 34 ft. deep. (a) What part of the bell will the water fill? (b) What will be the absolute pressure on the confined air? (c) What will be the absolute pressure in the bell when enough air is pumped into the bell to force out all the water?

PROBLEMS

1. If 100 cu. ft. of gas at an absolute pressure of 500 lb./sq. in. is allowed to expand until it occupies 1000 cu. ft., find the pressure after expansion.
2. A cylinder contains 10 cu. in. of air at 1 atmosphere of pressure. What is the volume of this gas when it is compressed so that the pressure is 8 atmospheres? Assume no change in the temperature.
3. A truck tire has a capacity of 1500 cu. in. and is inflated so that its absolute pressure is 105 lb./sq. in. Find the volume the air would occupy if the tire were to blow out.

PROJECTS

1. Make and demonstrate to your class the apparatus shown in Fig. 3a. Also compare your apparatus with the respirator shown in Fig. 3 (b).
2. Make a report on the disease commonly known as the "bends" which is contracted by divers and airplane pilots. Also explain how the patient can avoid attacks.
3. *How to find the weight of an automobile without weighing it.* First find the absolute pressure in each tire, then find the area of the surface on which each tire rests, and

finally find the force that each tire exerts on the ground by using the formula, $F = PA$. Then add the four forces. Their sum should equal the weight of the automobile. If possible, check your computed weight by weighing.

READING YOU WILL ENJOY

1. Conant, J. B. (Editor), *Harvard Case Histories in Experimental Science.* Case 1, *Robert Boyle's Experiments in Pneumatics,* pp. 57-70. Harvard University Press, Cambridge, 1950. Explains the discovery of Boyle's Law.

2. Fraser, Charles G., *Half Hours with Great Scientists,* pp. 105-117. Reinhold Publishing Corporation, New York, 1948. Gives brief but interesting accounts of Torricelli, Pascal, and Guericke.

3. Lynde, C. J., *Science Experiences with Home Equipment,* pp. 2-30 and 50-52. International Textbook Company, Scranton, Pennsylvania, Second Edition, 1949. Lists many simple, but interesting, experiments using expansion and compression of air.

4. Magie, W. F., *A Source Book in Physics,* pp. 85-88. McGraw-Hill Book Company, Inc., New York, 1935. Explains Boyle's discoveries.

Chapter 11

Forces in High-Speed Liquids and Gases

The problem. During the horse-and-buggy days, when transportation by land and water moved at a snail-like pace, the problem of forces in high-speed fluids (liquids and gases) was of little concern. But in the modern age, particularly in transportation, there are continually greater and greater demands for faster airplanes, trains, boats, motor buses, automobiles, jet planes, and rocket ships, even though fantastic speeds have already been reached. Likewise, in sports, there are demands for "faster" baseball pitchers, for better curve-ball artists, for longer home-run hitters, for longer-driving golf players, and for fewer "hooks" and "slices" in golf. As a consequence the problem of forces in high-speed gases is constantly in the forefront.

Simple problems involving forces in moving fluids. Forces in high-speed gases are often studied in wind tunnels. We can make a simple tunnel by placing two books on a table, as shown in Fig. 1, and laying a sheet of paper over the space between the books. Through the tunnel air is blown. Naturally, when this is done we might expect the air pressure in the tunnel to be increased and the paper to be lifted off the books.

Contrary to "common sense" and to what we have just anticipated, the paper is forced *down* between the books, and the faster the air is blown through the tunnel the greater the downward force. What causes this to happen?

As we have learned, in order for the paper to be forced down, an unbalanced force must act on it. The pressure on top of the paper must be increased or the pressure below the paper must be decreased; or both could happen. But since the air on top of the paper is undisturbed, it is very improbable that the pressure on top is increased. Seemingly, then, the pressure inside the tunnel is decreased, and the faster the air is blown through the tunnel, the greater the decrease in pressure.

Daniel Bernoulli (1700-1782), a Swiss mathematician, discovered this principle and it was named in his honor. He stated it somewhat as follows:

As the speed of a fluid increases there is a decrease in pressure, and conversely, as the speed of a fluid decreases, the pressure increases.

Predicting and testing the consequences of Bernoulli's Principle. As should be the case, many of you are not fully convinced

100 FORCES IN AIR AND OTHER GASES

Fig. 1. What happens to the sheet of paper when air is passed under it?

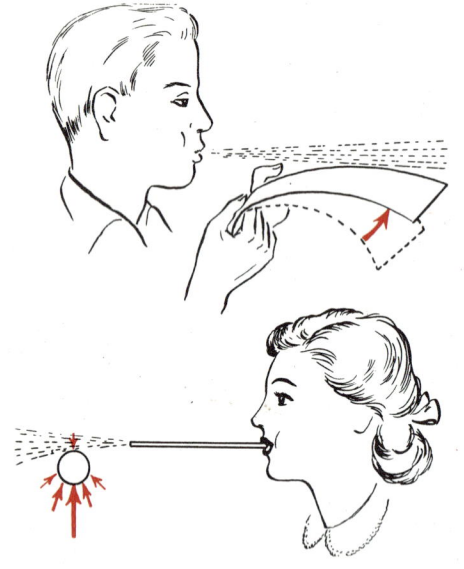

Fig. 2. Explain why the paper rises and what supports the ping-pong ball.

that Bernoulli's Principle is true. Regardless of whether or not you are convinced, it is our responsibility as scientists to consider the logical consequences of the principle and to test them by experiment.

If the pressure decreases with the speed of air, then if we blow air fast enough over the top of a sheet of paper, as shown in Fig. 2, so as to decrease the pressure on top of the paper, the greater pressure on the bottom should lift the paper. This is exactly what happens. Or if we direct a stream of air over the top of a ping-pong ball by blowing air through a soda straw, then, if the pressure on top of the ball is reduced enough, the greater pressure on the bottom should support the ball. This prediction you will also find to be true. It is easier to do this experiment with compressed air. Without it a little practice is necessary to keep the ball in the air.

The atomizer and the paint gun. Two practical applications of Bernoulli's Principle are found in the atomizer and the paint gun. The essentials of both are shown in (a) of Fig. 3. In operation, air is blown through tube A across the top of tube B, where the air pressure is reduced by the rapidly moving air. This causes the air

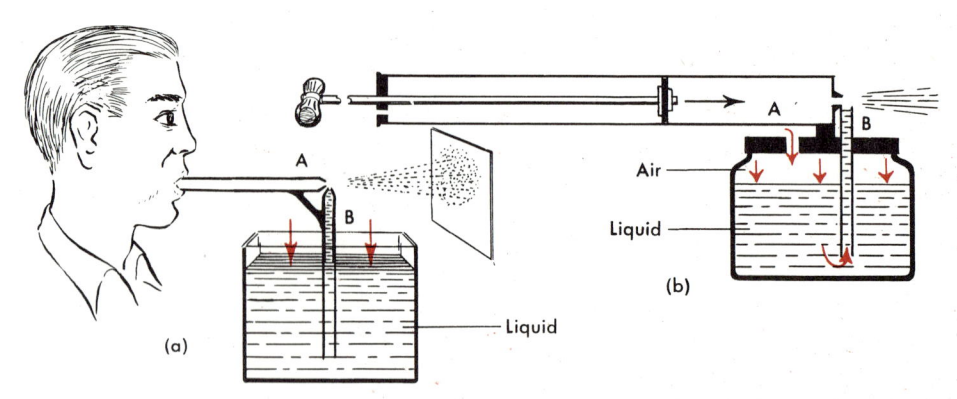

Fig. 3. The operation of the atomizer in (a) and the spray gun in (b) depends on Bernoulli's Principle. In each case, the increased speed of the air above the top of tube causes the liquid to rise in the tube, producing a fine spray of the liquid.

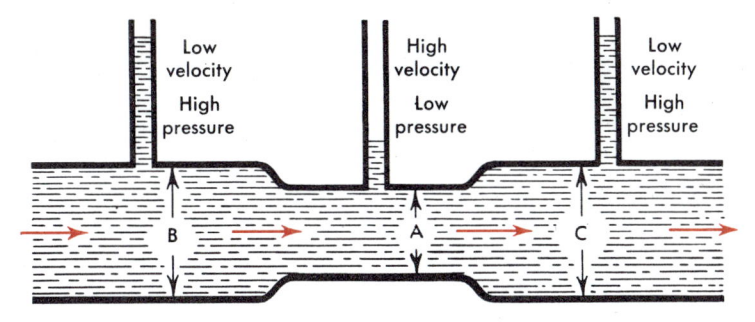

Fig. 4. As the velocity of the fluid increases in pipe A, what happens to the pressure at A? Compare the pressure at A with the pressures at B and C.

pressure inside B and on the liquid in tube B to be less than the atmospheric pressure on the liquid surface outside the tube. Because of this difference in pressure, the liquid is forced up tube B. If the liquid is forced to the top of the tube, it is caught in the stream of air and broken into a fine spray. If the stream of air is produced mechanically (Fig. 3b), and tube B is fitted into a glass container with screw top, we have an atomizer.

If a compressed air source furnishes the stream of air, we have the essentials of a paint or spray gun which is used extensively in painting automobiles, furniture, and many other things.

PROBLEM: Suppose that a 12-inch water pipe must be spliced with an 8-inch pipe. The walls of which pipe must withstand the greater pressure? Which pipe should be stronger? Explain. See Fig. 4.

What causes a baseball to "curve" and a golf ball to "hook" or "slice"? To be able to throw a "curve" ball is the ambition of every young boy, while the tendency to "hook" or "slice" is a mental hazard for practically all golf players. What causes baseballs and golf balls to curve?

Most of us know that the "curve" is somehow connected with the spin of the ball. And from our definition of force, we know that more force must be applied on one side of the ball than on the other side in order to make a ball curve from straight-line motion. How is this force produced?

To study this problem, let each of us picture himself as a baseball pitcher pitching the ball so that it spins counterclockwise when viewed from the top. As a result of the spin, the side A shown in Fig. 5 is spinning in the same direction as the air current due to the forward

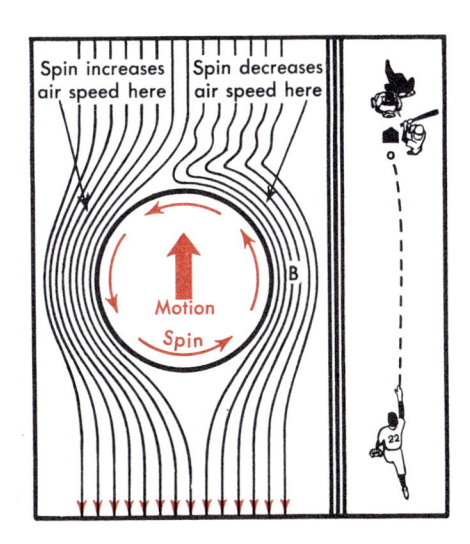

Fig. 5. A spinning baseball travels along a curved path. Explain why the baseball curves away from the batter.

102 FORCES IN AIR AND OTHER GASES

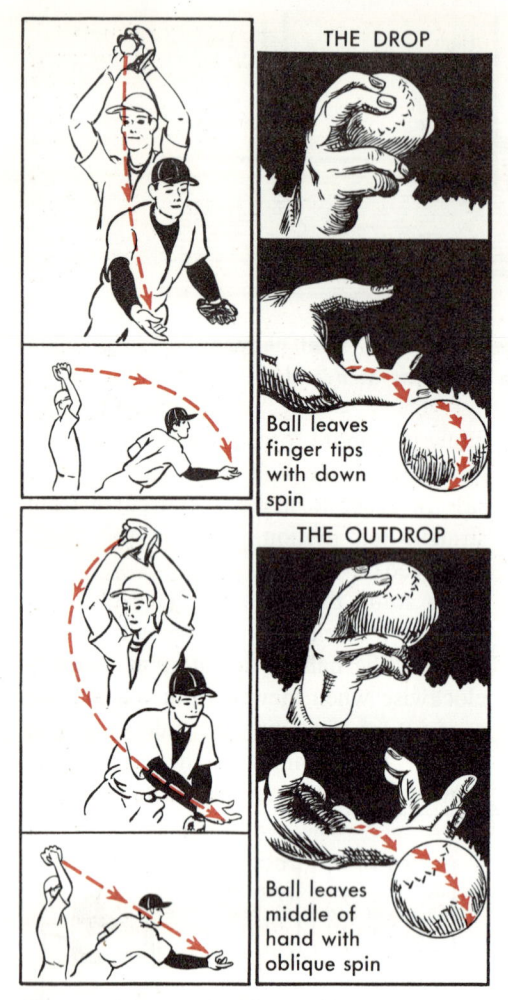

THE DROP

Ball leaves finger tips with down spin

THE OUTDROP

Ball leaves middle of hand with oblique spin

Fig. 6. How to hold a ball and throw it so as to pitch a drop and an outdrop.

Fig. 7. How will each ball travel?

Courtesy A. C. Spalding & Bros.

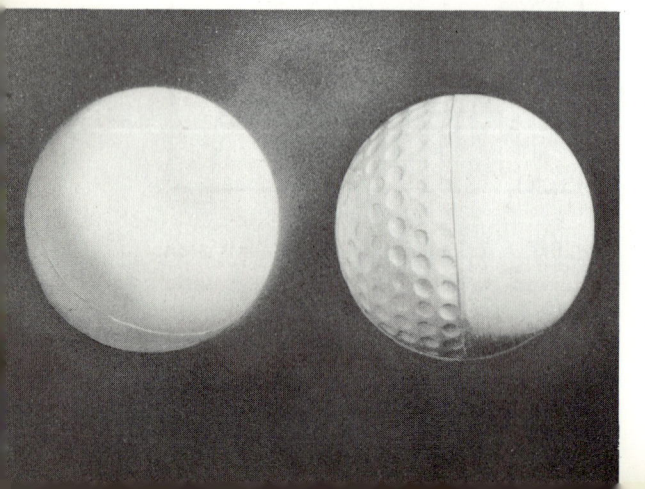

motion of the ball, thus causing an increase in the air speed and a decrease in the pressure on this side of the ball. The opposite side B of the ball, due to the spin, is moving against the air current and dragging air around with it, causing a decrease in the air speed and more pressure on this side than on side A. Since the pressure on the right side B, when viewed by the pitcher, is greater than on the left side, the ball curves to the pitcher's left, away from a right-handed batter.

The same counterclockwise spin of a golf ball causes it to hook. The reverse spin causes the ball to slice. What must be the direction of spin to cause a ball to curve upward? Downward? What causes a "knuckle" ball, which does not spin, to curve?

How to pitch a curve. To pitch a curve, grip the ball with the fingers along the seam with the pressure applied by the second finger. The forefinger merely acts as a guide. The thumb also should grip a seam. The curve is thrown with a simple turn of the wrist (without snap) which gives all the spin needed provided you "follow through" properly. See Fig. 6. Do not crouch or bend your elbow in making the delivery. Intelligent practice is the answer to mastering the pitching and controlling of curves. More will be said about the follow-through in a later chapter.

Why the dimples on a golf ball? Ask a group of golf enthusiasts why there are dimples on a golf ball and you may find that you have started an argument about dimpled versus smooth golf balls.

The most convincing argument for the dimpled ball is that it will not glance sidewise from the face of the club as badly as a smooth ball does when it is hit. To offset this argument, the smooth-ball enthusiasts claim that once the smooth ball is in flight it will travel straighter and

FORCES IN HIGH-SPEED LIQUIDS AND GASES

much farther than the dimpled ball. What is your opinion?

To settle the debate, golf ball manufacturers resorted to experiments rather than arguments. They made a number of identical golf ball centers and covered some of them with dimpled covers and the others with smooth covers. Then they designed a machine for hitting the balls. Six regulation balls were hit first. Each of them went straight out in an ascending flight and landed about 230 yards down the fairway. Then the smooth balls were hit.

For the first ten yards, the smooth balls followed the same path as the dimpled ones. Then they leveled off for another ten yards, and suddenly took a nose dive, hitting the ground about thirty yards away, rolling for a total distance of about fifty yards.

This astonishing behavior of the smooth balls is due to the formation of a partial vacuum behind the ball so that the air pressure in front of the ball is much greater than the pressure behind it. This difference becomes so great that the ball is virtually stopped, and it drops to the ground. With the dimpled ball, the little air pockets in the cover take air around behind the ball and dump it there into what would otherwise be a fairly good vacuum. As a result, the air pressure on the rear of the ball is almost as great as on the front of the ball.

What lifts an airplane? An airplane is driven forward by either a rotating propeller or a jet blast which causes the wings and other parts of the plane to strike air, producing a *relative* wind. This has the same effect as wind blowing across the plane. Air streaming across a section of a wing or foil is shown in Fig. 8. What produces the upward force which lifts the plane?

As you see, the front of the wing is

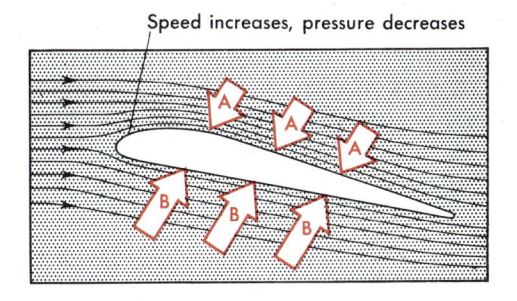

Fig. 8. The lifting effect on an airplane wing is due to the greater pressure on the bottom of the wing than on the top.

tipped upward as it is for the take-off. Air striking the underside of the wing flows past it smoothly and its speed relative to the wing is about the same as the relative speed of the still air below the plane.

But on top of the wing the situation is different. Here the top of the wing and the air a few feet above it form a narrowed tube effect similar to that shown in Fig. 4. The air that strikes the front of the wing is funneled above the wing, as shown in Fig. 8, so that the wind speed on the top of the wing is much greater than the wind speed on the bottom of the wing. And in accordance with Bernoulli's Principle the air pressure on top of the wing is less than it is on the bottom. As a result, when the unbalanced upward force becomes greater than the weight of the airplane, the plane is lifted. The wind speed necessary to lift a small plane is about 40 miles per hour.

Fluid friction. Friction in a gas or a liquid is caused when either is made to flow around a stationary object, or when an automobile, airplane, bullet, submarine, ship, or some other object is caused to move through a fluid.

Experiment shows that at low speeds the flow of fluid around a body, as shown in (a) of Fig. 9, is smooth and regular,

FORCES IN AIR AND OTHER GASES

and that the *friction is proportional to the velocity of the body.*

As the velocity increases, a point is reached where turbulence, as shown in

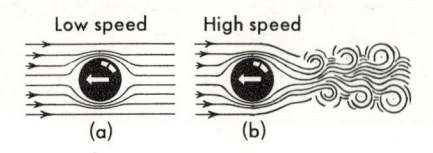

Fig. 9. At low speed, the streams of air around the body show no turbulence; at high speed, there is much turbulence.

(b) of Fig. 9, sets in and friction increases rapidly and becomes approximately proportional to the square of the velocity.

Turbulent flow is characterized by small symmetrical pairs of eddy currents, or whirls, that form behind the object. This causes the friction to be much greater than it is when the fluid moves smoothly around the body.

When the velocity increases still further, the eddies, instead of forming symmetrical pairs, form first on one side and then on the other, as shown in Fig. 9 (b).

The waving of a flag in the wind, or the waving of a rag tied behind a fast-moving truck, is direct evidence of the whirlwinds that follow each other alternately along the sides of the body. Past 30 miles per hour the turbulent flow increases very rapidly.

As the velocity of a body approaches the velocity of sound, friction again increases rapidly. This fact is treated further below.

Streamlining. When a body is shaped so that the fluid flows over it smoothly, as shown at the top of Fig. 10, the body is said to be *streamlined*. Streamlining reduces turbulence, and hence friction, to a minimum. If the streamlined body consists of three sections, *A*, *B*, and *C*, as illustrated, we can see that section *B*, by itself, will offer maximum resistance to the fluid. If the round nose section, *A*, is added to *B*, the resistance will be considerably reduced. It will be reduced even more, however, if the pointed tail section, *C*, is combined with *B*. And resistance will practically disappear, as we have noted, if all three sections are combined as shown.

Why is the force of friction so great as the speed of a body approaches the speed of sound? When a bullet, airplane, or other body moves through air, it compresses the air ahead. At speeds below the speed of sound this compressed air is of little consequence because it moves away with the speed of sound, which is approximately 750 miles per hour. The ratio of the speed of a body in air to the speed of sound in air is called the *Mach number*. Hence by definition the Mach number for the speed of sound is 1. What is the Mach number of a guided missile whose velocity is 1500 mi./hr.? 375 mi./hr.?

When the speed of a bullet or plane is

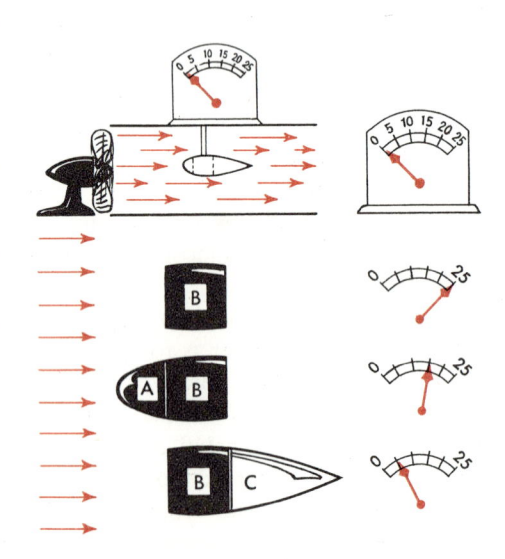

Fig. 10. Approximate relative air resistances of different shaped objects having the same cross-sectional area.

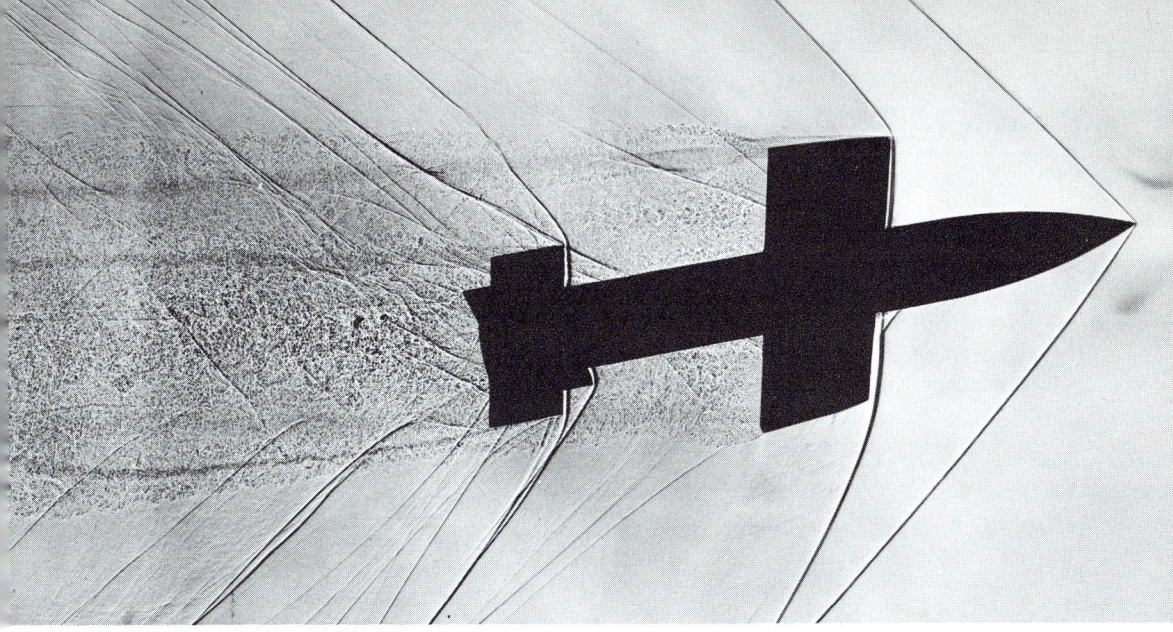

Courtesy Exterior Ballistics Laboratory, Aberdeen Proving Grounds

Fig. 11. Shock waves produced by a cone-cylinder in flight at Mach number 2.67.

greater than the velocity of sound the condensed air at the nose of the body can be transmitted sidewise, *but not forward*. Why? Photographs taken of missiles traveling faster than sound show this clearly. They show two waves, somewhat similar to water waves, one at the front and the other at the tail of the missile. These waves form what are said to be *shock waves,* and when they come from a bullet or from the tip ends of an airplane propeller they sound like the crack of an explosion. See Fig. 11.

As the speed of a plane approaches the speed of sound, since the compressed wave in front cannot escape, the nose of the plane virtually has to carry along a wall of compressed air. And as a result the drag is increased, the lift is increased, and sometimes instability of the pilot's control is produced.

Beyond the speed of sound, at supersonic speeds, the compressed air waves are more predictable. Nevertheless, as shown in Fig. 12, as the speed of a plane increases past Mach number 1, the horsepower must be increased very sharply.

This graph also shows why it will be difficult to fly at speeds approaching the apparent speed of the sun, which at the equator is approximately 1000 miles per hour. One way to reduce the terrific drag is to fly in the upper rarefied atmosphere, which can be done best by rocket ships. This topic is discussed more fully on page 186.

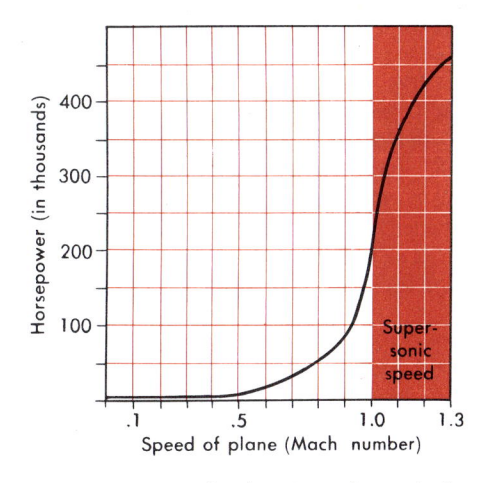

Fig. 12. A graph showing the relation between Mach numbers and the horsepower requirements.

SUMMARY AND CONCLUSIONS

1. Bernoulli's Principle: Whenever there is an increase in the speed of a fluid, either gas or liquid, there is a decrease in pressure, and, conversely, as the speed of a fluid decreases, the pressure increases.
2. Bernoulli's Principle applies to the paint gun and atomizer, lift of an airplane, a ball that curves, and the determination of wind speed.

QUESTIONS FOR REVIEW

1. If two ping-pong balls are hung as shown in Fig. 13 and a stream of air is directed between them, what will happen? Explain.

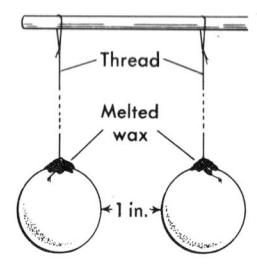

Fig. 13

2. Explain how a pitcher throws an "outdrop."
3. The "knuckle" ball when thrown by a pitcher is not supposed to spin. Explain why it curves and why a knuckle-ball pitch is said to be "hard to catch."
4. In driving a golf ball or hitting a baseball, what kind of spin should you give the ball so that the maximum distance will be attained? Explain how you should hit a ball to obtain this kind of spin.
5. Explain what supports an airplane.
6. Could a propeller-type airplane be used to fly to the moon? Explain your answer.
7. If the liquid container of an atomizer were filled completely and the hole in the top of it became closed, would the atomizer work? Explain.

PROJECTS

1. Using either a ping-pong ball or a ball made by sandpapering a large cork into the shape of a sphere, demonstrate to the class how to pitch curves such as the drop, in, out, outdrop, upshoot, and knuckle ball.
2. Make a further study of such topics as shock waves, Mach number, supersonic speeds, sonic barrier, and other topics concerned with high-speed travel.
3. Do the demonstrations that deal with Bernoulli's Principle and are pictured in this book. Most of the apparatus needed can be found in your home.
4. Most jet planes are, of necessity, highly streamlined. Make a drawing of a well-streamlined automobile and compare it with one of modern design.
5. Put a ping-pong ball in a funnel, hold the funnel upright, and then endeavor to blow the ball out of the funnel by blowing up through the spout. Explain the result. Invert the funnel with the ball in it and try again. Explain the result.

READING YOU WILL ENJOY

1. Ley, Willy, *Rockets, Missiles, and Space Travel*, pp. 361-368. The Viking Press, New York, 1951. Tells in detail the origin of Mach number. Contains much interesting information concerning space travel.
2. Lynde, C. J., *Science Experiences with Home Equipment*, pp. 41-51. International Textbook Company, Scranton, Pennsylvania, 1949. Suggests and pictures several demonstrations of Bernoulli's Principle.
3. Richardson, J. S., and G. P. Cahoon, *Methods and Materials for Teaching General and Physical Science*, pp. 412-413. McGraw-Hill Book Company, Inc., New York, 1951. Contains several experiments that illustrate Bernoulli's Principle and streamlining. Explains how to build a wind tunnel which can be used for testing wing sections of airplanes.

Unit 4

Forces and the Equilibrium of Bodies

Without a knowledge of how to achieve a balance of forces, the construction of the bridge in the preceding photograph would be impossible. The weight of the bridge span pulls downward along the vertical supporting rods. Why does the bridge not collapse? Apparently, there are other forces which must be considered. These are the forces acting on the slanting cables which support the bridge.

As you study forces and the motions they produce, you will discover how it is possible to overcome large resistances with little effort. Perhaps you will save yourself some effort in mowing the lawn or opening a classroom window with a window pole. This unit may also help you to understand why bridge cables on a suspension bridge sag so much, as well as how to analyze the forces lifting an airplane.

12. HOW TO COMBINE AND CONTROL FORCES
13. LEVERS, MOMENT OF FORCE, CENTER OF GRAVITY, AND STABILITY OF BODIES

Unit Photograph Courtesy Standard Oil Co. (N. J.)

Chapter 12

How to Combine and Control Forces

The problem. We have all heard the old saying, "For want of a nail the shoe was lost, for want of a shoe the horse was lost, for want of a horse the rider was lost, and for want of a rider the battle was lost."

Similarly, we might say that for want of a knowledge of forces many football games have been lost, many foolish swimmers have been lost, and many reckless automobile drivers have been lost. Also, for such want, many golfers, swimmers, baseball players, shot putters, and discus throwers have failed to reach the heights of which they were capable; and many persons, when lifting heavy objects, have unnecessarily injured themselves. Every physical act involves forces. So if we are to live intelligently in a world where the misapplication of force may mean life or death, success or failure, then we must have a knowledge of forces and how to combine them to accomplish our purposes.

What do we already know about forces? We have already defined force as push or pull; or that which causes motion, destroys motion, changes the direction of motion, or changes the shape of a body. We know, too, that every body is at all times acted upon by forces. Gravity pulls all earthly bodies downward toward the center of the earth. And any body above the earth will fall unless it is supported by an upward force equal to its weight. Furthermore, gases and liquids exert pressure at right angles to the surfaces of all bodies which they contact.

Combining forces which act in the same direction. In Fig. 1, Rover pulls to the right with a force of 20 pounds and Fido pulls in the same direction with a force of 30 pounds. The total force is 20 pounds plus 30 pounds, or 50 pounds. Consequently, a single force of 50 pounds acting in the same direction would have the same effect as the two, and could be substituted for them.

A single force which produces the same effect as two or more other forces is called the **resultant** *of the several forces.*

To balance, or hold in equilibrium, the 30-pound and 20-pound forces, another force of 50 pounds must act in the opposite direction. *One force which balances or holds in equilibrium one or more other forces is called the* **equilibrant** *(balancer) of these forces.* Note that the equilibrant and the resultant are equal in magnitude (size) but opposite in direction.

Combining forces by graph. As we have seen, all forces have two characteristics:

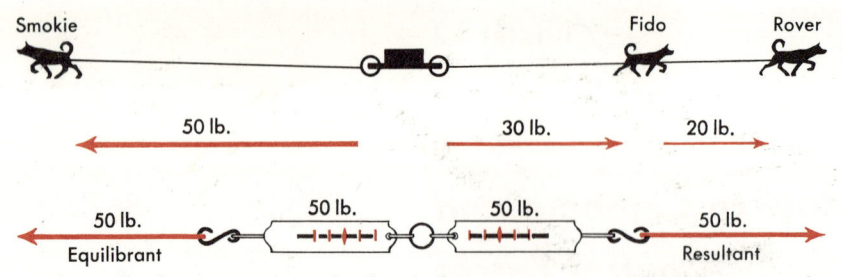

Fig. 1. When two forces act on a body at the same point and in the same direction, the resultant is equal to the sum of the two forces.

direction and size (magnitude). Any quantity having these two characteristics can be represented by an arrow and is called a *vector* quantity. The length of the arrow represents the magnitude (size) of the force and the arrowhead shows its direction. In this book the tail of the arrow will show the point of application of the force. Many forces can be combined by graphical methods that cannot be combined by simple arithmetic or algebra.

To represent a force by means of an arrow, a convenient scale is chosen. For example, in Fig. 2 a line that is 1 centimeter long represents 10 pounds of force. Hence, a line 2 centimeters long represents Rover's 20-pound force. Fido's force of 30 pounds is represented by a line 3 centimeters long. The lines representing these forces are combined in the manner shown. The resultant is an arrow 5 centimeters long, which represents a force of 5 times 10, or 50 pounds. What shows the direction of the resultant? What represents its magnitude?

Using a scale in which 1 centimeter represents 10 pounds, what length of arrow represents a force of 100 pounds? Of 60 pounds? What force would be represented by an arrow whose length is 15 centimeters? 8 centimeters?

The composition of forces which act in opposite directions. Next let us suppose that Fido pulls east on one end of a rope with a force of 30 pounds and that Rover pulls on the other end in the opposite direction with a force of 20 pounds. Here the resultant is 30 minus 20, or 10 pounds east, which is the difference of the two forces.

To solve this problem graphically we can again use the scale of 1 centimeter to 10 pounds. The solution is shown in Fig. 3. Since the resultant arrow is 1 centi-

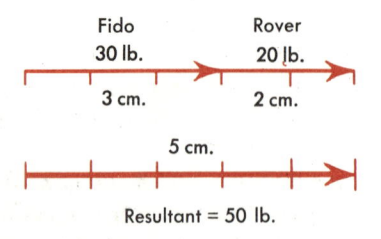

Fig. 2. Combining forces by means of vectors. According to the scale, 1 centimeter represents 10 pounds of force.

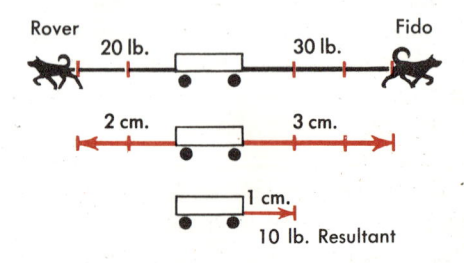

Fig. 3. When two forces act in opposite directions, the resultant is equal to their difference.

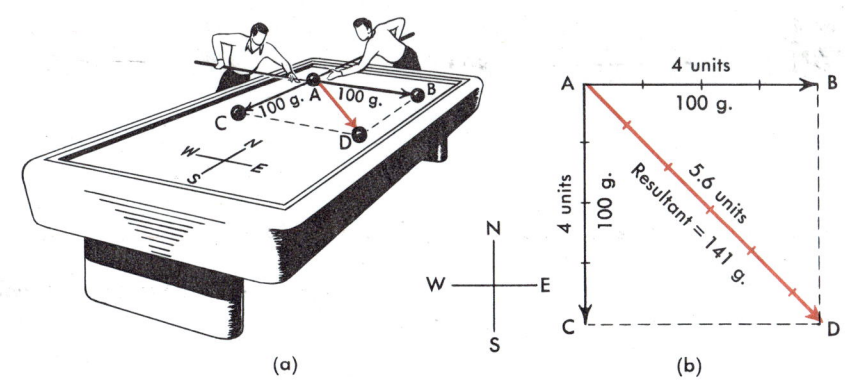

Fig. 4. Graphically combining two equal forces which act at right angles at a point by the parallelogram method. The resultant is the diagonal of the parallelogram.

meter long it represents a force of 10 pounds. What did we say represents the magnitude (size) of a force? What shows its direction?

The composition of two forces which act at a point at right angles. So far in this chapter we have considered only parallel forces. Now let us turn our attention to how to combine two forces which act at right angles at a point. To illustrate the problem let us assume that two players simultaneously strike a billiard ball with equal forces at right angles, as shown in Fig. 4. Each strikes it with a force of 100 grams. One hits it due east and the other due south. What is the direction and magnitude of the resultant?

Apparently, since the forces are equal, the resultant would be southeast; its direction would divide the angle between AB and AC in (a) of Fig. 4 into two equal parts. Beyond this, past experience tells us little about the resultant, so let us try the graphical method for solving the problem.

If we use the scale of 1 centimeter to 25 grams, as shown in (b) of Fig. 4, then an arrow 4 centimeters long drawn east from A to B will represent the 100-gram force which acts eastward. And an arrow 4 centimeters long drawn due south from A to C will represent the other force. The resultant force we know will have to be drawn southeast from A, but how far shall we draw it?

Since the resultant force should produce the same effect as the two acting independently, then the resultant arrow should extend as far south as C and as far east as B. We can locate this point, which we shall call D, by extending a dotted line due east from C, parallel and equal to AB, and by extending another dotted line from B due south parallel and equal to AC. Where the two lines intersect is the point D. And the length of the solid line drawn from A to D represents the magnitude of the resultant force. The figure is a parallelogram and the resultant is the diagonal of the parallelogram. Hence, the method is called the *parallelogram method*.

When measured, the resultant is found to be 5.6 centimeters long, which represents 25 times 5.6, or 140 grams. Do you see a shorter method?

Composition of forces by computation. Students of geometry will see that ACD is a right triangle and AD is the hypotenuse whose square equals the sum of the squares of the other two sides. Hence, using forces instead of dimensions:

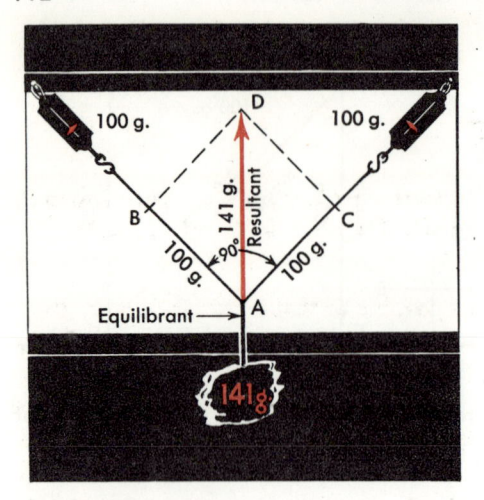

Fig. 5. The experiment shows the correctness of the solution for Fig. 4 both by the graphical method and by calculation.

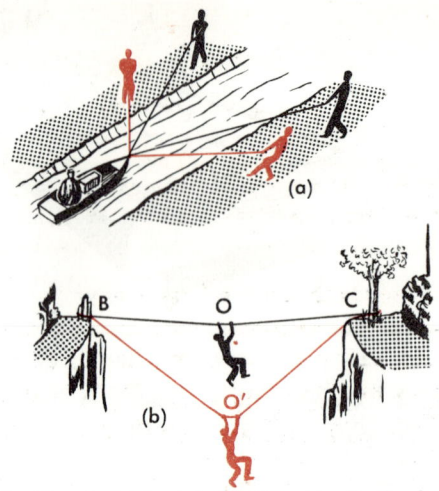

Fig. 7. (a) The smaller the angle the less force required. (b) In which case is the rope likely to break?

$$100^2 + 100^2 = AD^2$$
That is, $\quad 10{,}000 + 10{,}000 = AD^2$
And $\quad\quad\quad\quad\quad\quad 20{,}000 = AD^2$
Or $\quad\quad AD = \sqrt{20{,}000} = 100\sqrt{2}$
That is, $\quad\quad\quad\quad\quad\quad AD = 141$ grams

PROBLEM: A force of 5 lb. acts due east and a force of 5 lb. acts due north at the same point. What is the magnitude and direction of the resultant? Find the magnitude by two different methods.

Will experiment verify our conclusions? If the resultant of the above two 100-gram forces is 141 grams, then two such forces when acting at right angles, as shown in Fig. 5, should lift 141 grams. This, we find, is true.

Finding the resultant of two unequal forces which act at a point at right angles to each other. To demonstrate such a solution, we shall refer to Fig. 6, where a 40-gram force acts east at a point A and a 30-gram force acts north. The scale is 1 cm. = 10 g. The arrow AB is drawn 4 units long to represent the 40-gram force, and the arrow AC is drawn 3 units long to represent the 30-gram force. On these two lines we complete the parallelogram $ACDB$ by drawing BD parallel and equal to AC, and CD parallel and equal to AB. Dotted lines are used to complete the parallelogram so as to distinguish these from the arrows. Finally, from A the arrow AD is drawn to represent the resultant force. Since it is 5 centimeters long, it represents 5 times 10 grams, or 50 grams.

The diagonal must be drawn from the point A of application and not from B to C or vice versa. Explain the consequences in case you were to make this error.

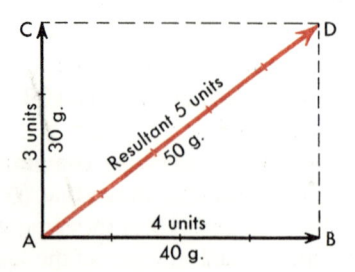

Fig. 6. Combining two unequal forces which act at right angles.

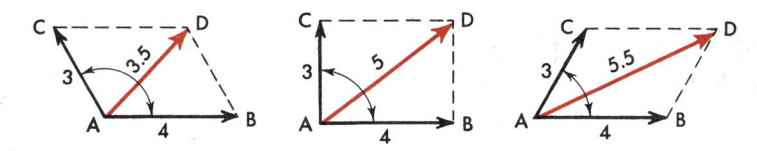

Fig. 8. As the angle between the forces decreases, what happens to the magnitude of the resultant? At what angle would the resultant be the smallest? Largest?

What is the most effective angle for obtaining the maximum resultant? Usually when we apply forces, we like to obtain the maximum effect with the minimum effort. How to do this is often a problem. For example, if John and Tom pull a canoe upstream, as shown in Fig. 7(a), would it be easier if they made the ropes long and the angle between the forces small, or if they made the ropes short and the angle large? Or, if a group of soldiers went across a deep canyon, hand over hand on a none-too-stout rope, would it be wiser if they made the rope long and angle BO'C small, or if they stretched the rope tightly and made angle BOC large? See (b) of Fig. 7.

We can answer the first question by referring to Fig. 8, in which the same two forces act at different angles. Here it is seen that the resultant gradually increases as the angle between the forces decreases. Hence, in order to obtain the maximum resultant with the minimum effort, the forces should be made as nearly parallel as possible so that the angle between them approaches zero. Now answer the questions above concerning Fig. 7.

The resolution of forces. When a sprinter starts from a crouching position, the force which pushes his body forward is not in the same direction as the runner moves. It pushes him upward and forward. Likewise, when you push a lawn mower, pull a sled, push an automobile forward when standing at its side, and exert hundreds of other forces, the force is not applied in the same direction as the body moves.

Any force, such as that required to push a lawn mower, can be regarded as the resultant force of two component forces which are equivalent to the applied force. As shown in Fig. 9, the applied force may be *resolved* into two forces: one which pushes the mower forward (the *effective component*) and one which pushes it into the ground (the *ineffective component*).

To find these two forces, to which the

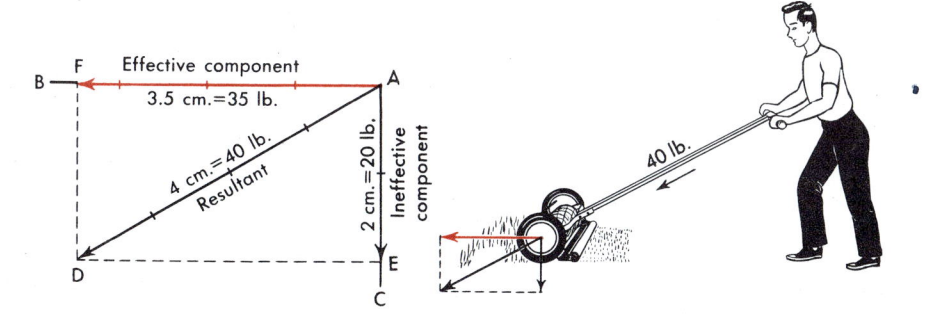

Fig. 9. Resolving a force into its effective and ineffective components.

114 FORCES AND THE EQUILIBRIUM OF BODIES

40-pound force is equivalent, a scale of 1 centimeter to 10 pounds was chosen. To represent the applied 40-pound force an arrow *AD*, 4 centimeters long, was drawn from *A*. Then from point *A* the solid horizontal line *AB* and the vertical line *AC* were drawn. Next from *D* the line *DF* was drawn parallel to *CA*. The intersection of *AB* and *DF* marks the length of the horizontal side. Then from *D* the line *DE* was drawn parallel with *BA*. The line *AE* represents the vertical component of *AD*. As shown, *AE* is 2 centimeters long and represents 2 times 10, or 20 pounds. *AF* is 3.5 centimeters long and represents 3.5 times 10, or 35 pounds.

The process of resolving a force into two components is known as the *resolution of forces*.

Hence, in conclusion, we see that the applied force of 40 pounds in Fig. 9 can be resolved into a horizontal component of 35 pounds and a vertical component of 20 pounds. The 35-pound horizontal force, the effective component, pushes the lawn mower; the 20-pound vertical force, the ineffective component, is waste. Without increasing the applied force, explain what could be done to increase the horizontal (effective) component; the vertical (ineffective) component. In starting, a runner should make the angle between the ground and the line of force as small as possible without falling down. Why?

PROBLEM: John pulls on a sled rope with a force of 100 lb. Find the horizontal component of the force when the angle between the rope and the level ground is (a) 0°; (b) 30°; (c) 60°; (d) 90°.

How to get a truck out of a mud hole. A rather far-reaching application of the resolution of forces is shown in Fig. 10. Here a truck is stuck in a mud hole. To pull it out a 40-foot steel cable is stretched tightly from the truck to a tree. When a man exerts a 200-pound force at the center *C* of the cable in the direction of *CA*, how much force is exerted on the truck?

For convenience (though any other scale would do) let us represent the tension in *AB* and *AD* by the length of the cable and construct the parallelogram *ABED*, making *AE* the resultant. Since the cable is 40 feet long, each component, *AB* and *AD*, is represented by a line 20 feet long. When the displacement *CA* is 6 inches, then ½ foot represents 200 pounds and 1 foot represents 400 pounds. This means that the tension in the cable is 400 × 20, or 8000 pounds, and this amount is exerted on the automobile.

In case the displacement *CA* were 1 foot, then *AE* would be 2 feet but would

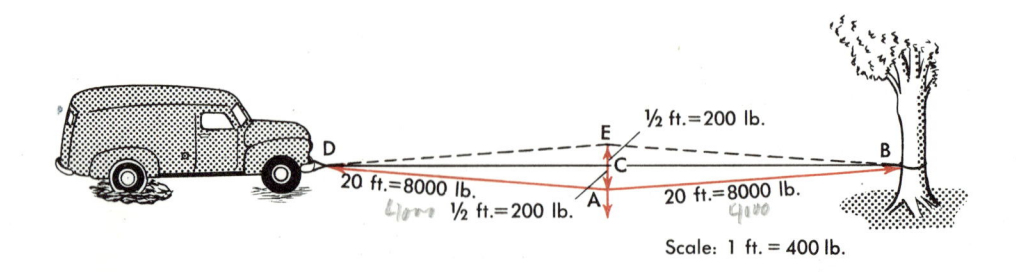

Fig. 10. How to get a truck out of a mud hole with a long steel cable. Note that components of the force are much greater than the force itself.

HOW TO COMBINE AND CONTROL FORCES

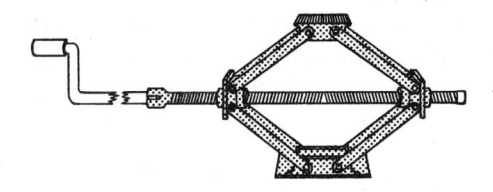

Fig. 11. The automobile jack.

still represent only 400 pounds. As a result, the tension in the cable would be only 4000 pounds instead of 8000. That is, as the length of CA increases the tension in the cable decreases. However, when the tension on the cable ceases to move the truck, the slack in the cable can be taken up and the car can be moved a little farther. In other words, when the displacing force is constant, the tighter the cable and the smaller the displacement CA, the greater the tension in the cable.

The principle just stated explains why in winter a very few pounds of ice on a telephone wire can break it; why a perfectly good clothesline when stretched tightly may break and drop the clothes on the ground; why a child can break a tightly stretched clothesline by swinging on it; why hammock ropes will carry the load when the sag is large but will break when stretched tightly; and why there must be so much sag in the long steel cables that support a suspension bridge. It also explains in more detail why the soldiers in Fig. 7 (b) should not stretch the rope tight.

Another application of the same principle is in the design of certain kinds of automobile jacks, as shown in Fig. 11. If possible, borrow a wrench or cutting tool making use of this principle and explain it to the class.

The truss. Experience shows that it is much easier to break a stick or wire in two by bending it than it is by pulling it in two. And we know, too, that a board 1 inch thick and 12 feet long, if laid across a stream, say 10 feet wide, would hardly support a person's weight if he walked across it. Of course, we could make the bridge safer by using a thicker board. Is there, however, a cheaper way by which the strength of the board can be increased?

If we nail a block of wood on the bottom of the board and then nail a length of wire (wood strips may be used instead) to the block and board, as shown in Fig. 12, the board is made very rigid and bends very little under many times as heavy a load as before. The board we say has been *trussed,* and when it is reinforced in this manner we call the combination a *truss*.

To understand the cause of the increased strength we must recall that it is harder to pull a wire apart than it is to break it in two by bending. If we examine (b) of Fig. 12 we see that, if the board

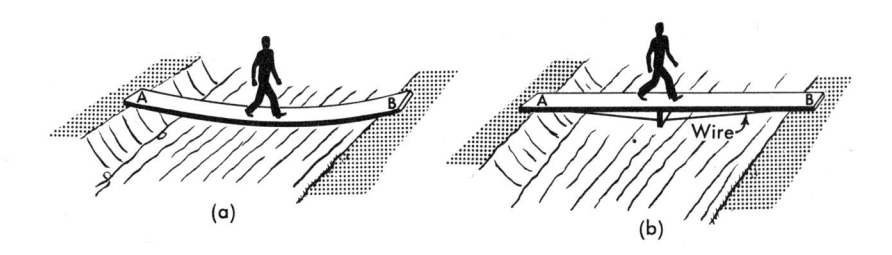

Fig. 12. If a board sags badly, its strength and rigidity may be increased many times by the addition of very little material. The combination is called a truss.

AB is to bend very much, the supporting wire will have to be pulled in two, which is difficult to do. As a result the truss has many times the strength of the board alone with very little increase in the quantity of material used.

The truss has wide application in building. Every boy who has built model airplanes knows that trusses are used inside airplane wings. They are used in the frameworks of buildings, in non-sag gates, in many types of bridges, and in other building where the greatest strength combined with the minimum quantity of materials is required.

How a boat sails into the wind. That a boat can sail into the wind sounds like a contradiction. And why the wind does not push the boat backward is difficult to see. Yet every skipper of a sailboat knows that a boat will sail into the wind.

To understand this, you should recall that the wind blowing against a slanting sail, such as SS' in Fig. 13, exerts a force perpendicular to the sail. This force is represented by the arrow CP. The force CP can be resolved into two components; one, effective component CF, which points forward parallel with the keel; the other, CL, which is ineffective in propelling the boat forward and tends to tip it over and move it leeward. Tipping and sidewise movements are prevented to a great extent by the keel. The result is that the boat is driven forward. Explain the course which a boat must take if it sails from A to B when the wind is blowing from B toward A. See if you can explain why a boat can sail faster across the wind than with the wind.

What supports an airplane? As we learned on page 103, an airplane is pulled forward by a propeller or is pushed forward by a reaction force when a jet of hot gases is expelled to the rear. This force is called the *thrust*. As a result, air strikes the bottom side of the wing, exerting a force perpendicular to the wing. This force OX can be resolved into two components: one, OL, straight up, which is called the *lift;* the other, OD, the *drag*. (See Fig. 14.)

Also on the top of the wing there is a decrease in pressure, which increases the effectiveness of OX. (See page 103.) As the speed of the airplane increases, all the four forces increase. And when the lift is greater than the weight of the plane, the airplane rises.

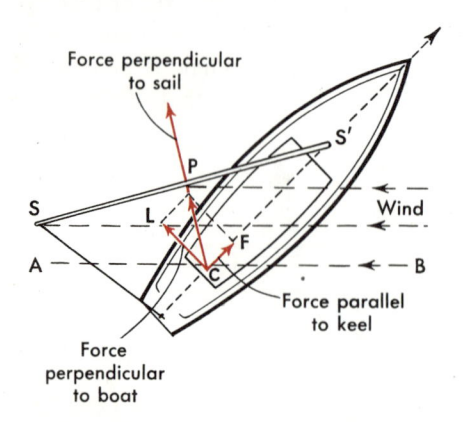

Fig. 13. Forces which act to cause a boat to sail into the wind. How is force CL overcome?

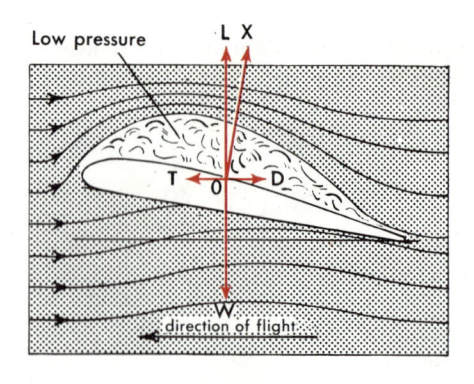

Fig. 14. The force OX is resolved into its two components: OL, the lift, and OD, the drag. Explain what causes the lift.

SUMMARY AND CONCLUSIONS

1. A force is a vector quantity, having both magnitude and direction.
2. The resultant of two or more component forces is one force which has the same effect as the several forces and may be substituted for them.
3. Finding the resultant of several forces is called composition of forces.
4. The resultant of two parallel forces which act in the same direction is their sum.
5. The resultant of two parallel forces acting at the same point and in opposite directions is their difference.
6. Forces can be represented graphically by arrows drawn to scale. Direction is indicated by the arrowhead; magnitude, by the length of the arrow; point of application, by the tail of the arrow.
7. The resultant of two nonparallel forces which act at a point can be found by the principle of the parallelogram of forces. The resultant is represented by the diagonal of the parallelogram drawn from the point where the forces act.
8. The equilibrant is equal in magnitude and opposite in direction to the resultant.

QUESTIONS FOR REVIEW

1. What two characteristics are common to all forces?
2. If two boys pull east on a rope with forces of 40 lb. and 30 lb. respectively, what is the combined force? What are the magnitude and direction of the resultant? Of the equilibrant?
3. Compare the magnitudes and directions of two single forces acting at the same point when one of the forces holds the other in equilibrium.
4. If a force of 20 lb. is represented by an arrow 1 cm. long, what length of arrow would represent a 100-lb. force? A 10-lb. force?
5. When a force is represented by an arrow, what part of the arrow indicates the direction of the force? Magnitude of the force? Point where the force is applied?
6. When two nonparallel forces act at a point, what happens to the resultant as the angle between the forces increases? What angle between the forces gives the maximum resultant?
7. Which requires stronger ropes to support a given weight, a hammock or a swing? Give reasons. Assume that both are at rest.
8. Why will a tightly stretched clothesline often break when loaded with clothes, whereas a loosely stretched line with the same load will not break?
9. When lifting a heavy weight, should one keep his legs far apart or fairly close together? Explain.
10. In chinning oneself, should one keep his arms roughly parallel or spread far apart? Explain.
11. Explain how a football guard and tackle working together should charge an opposing lineman to push him out of the play most effectively.
12. Show by means of a diagram the proper starting position of a runner who expects to make the quickest possible getaway.

PROBLEMS

Each solution should be accompanied by a diagram.

1. Find the direction and magnitude of the resultant of the following combinations of forces when they act in the same direction and when they act in opposite directions in the same straight line: (a) 5 lb. and 10 lb.; (b) 20 lb. and 30 lb.; (c) 34 lb. and 16 lb.
2. Using a scale of 1 cm. to 10 lb., draw arrows representing a force of 20 lb. acting north; 25 lb. east; 28 lb. west; 22 lb. northwest.
3. Using the graphical method, find the resultant of a 30-lb. force which acts north at a point and a 40-lb. force which acts east at the same point. Check your answer by computation.
4. Find the resultant of a 30-lb. force and a 40-lb. force acting at the same point when the angle between them is (a) 45°; (b) 135°.
5. A soccer ball is kicked by two boys at the same time. One kicks toward the east with a force of 60 lb. and the other kicks

118 FORCES AND THE EQUILIBRIUM OF BODIES

toward the southwest with a force of 30 lb. In what direction will the ball move and what will be the effective force which moves the ball?

6. A force of 30 lb. acts toward the east and one of 50 lb. acts toward the south at the same point. Find the resultant and the equilibrant, using the graphical method.

7. Two forces of 24 lb. and 30 lb. act at the point *C*. Find the resultant when the angle between them is (a) 180°; (b) 135°; (c) 90°; (d) 60°; (e) 0°.

8. Find the equilibrant of two forces of 100 lb. each when the angle between them is 60°.

9. A boy pushes a lawn mower with a force of 36 lb. The handle makes an angle of 40° with the ground. Find the effective and noneffective components of the force.

10. A sled is pulled by a rope that makes an angle of 30° with the ground. The tension in the rope is 20 lb. Find the horizontal and vertical components. Which force is effective; which noneffective?

11. A boy opens the upper sash of a window by exerting a 20-lb. pull on a slanting pole. The pole makes an angle of 30° with the wall. Find (a) the vertical pull on the window; (b) the horizontal pull on the window.

12. A 60-lb. boy sits at the middle of a hammock which is 10 ft. long. The hammock sags 3 ft. What is the pull or tension in the hammock ropes?

PROJECTS

1. Mount a sail on a roller skate, set it in front of an electric fan, and turn on the current. Then set the sail so that the apparatus will move parallel to the wind, at right angles to the wind, and into the wind.

2. Bring to class a wrench or an automobile jack that makes use of the principle shown in Fig. 11, and demonstrate the principle.

READING YOU WILL ENJOY

Swezey, K. M., *After-Dinner Science*. Whittlesey House, McGraw-Hill Book Company, Inc., New York, 1948. "How Does an Airplane Fly?" pp. 14-15, and "Why Ropes Break under Light Loads," pp. 74-75.

Chapter 13

Levers, Moment of Force, Center of Gravity, and Stability of Bodies

The problem. In Chapter 5 (page 36), we discovered that, when a body is in equilibrium (balance), the sum of the forces acting on it in any one direction must equal the sum of the forces acting in the opposite direction.

Look at Fig. 1, in which both levers are in equilibrium. If any one of the weights is moved either toward or away from the axis of rotation, or *fulcrum*, F, the lever will be thrown out of balance even though the sum of the forces acting downward is still equal to the sum of the forces acting upward. What conditions are necessary to hold a body in balance, or equilibrium?

What are the conditions necessary for a uniform lever, balanced at its center, to be in equilibrium? The lever A in Fig. 1 is in equilibrium. Study of this lever shows that $W_1 = W_2$, $d_1 = d_2$, $d_3 = d_4$, $W_1 \times d_1 = W_2 \times d_2$, $W_1 \times d_3 = W_2 \times d_4$, and
$$\frac{W_1}{d_2} = \frac{W_2}{d_1}.$$
See how many more relationships you can discover.

But lever A is a special case. Using a lever like B to test the above relationships, we find that only one of them, $W_1 d_1 = W_2 d_2$, is true. This is shown as follows:

$$W_1 d_1 = W_2 d_2$$
200 g. × 20 cm. = 100 g. × 40 cm.
4000 cm.-g. = 4000 cm.-g.

Repeated tests of the relationship, $W_1 d_1 = W_2 d_2$, show that the product of the force W_1 and its distance d_1 from the fulcrum equals the product of the force W_2 and its distance d_2 from the fulcrum. The product of the force and its distance from the fulcrum (the force arm) is called the *moment of the force*.

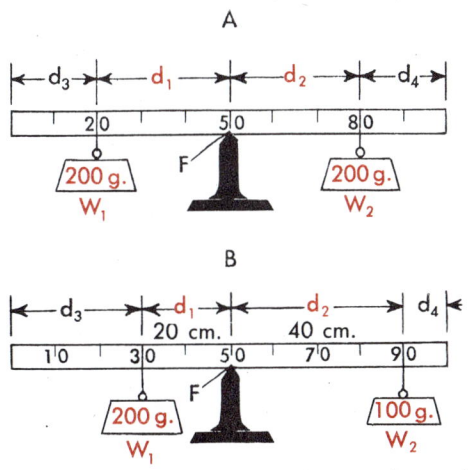

Fig. I. In both levers, the product of force W_1 and lever arm d_1 is equal to the product of force W_2 and lever arm d_2.

120   FORCES AND THE EQUILIBRIUM OF BODIES

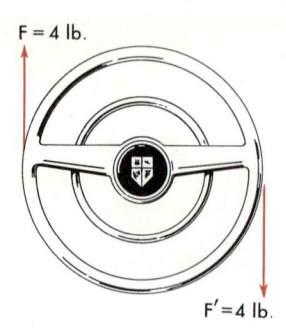

Fig. 2. Explain why the steering wheel is not in equilibrium.

Now consider the steering wheel in Fig. 2. Notice that it is being acted on by a downward force of 4 pounds and by an upward force of 4 pounds. Although the force upward equals the force downward, the wheel is not in equilibrium. Instead, it is rotating clockwise about its axle. What conditions are necessary to hold the wheel in equilibrium?

The lever principle. The moment of the force tending to turn the lever in Fig. 3 clockwise is $W_2 \times d_2$, which equals 100 × 40, or 4000 cm.-g. The moment of the force tending to turn the lever counterclockwise equals 200 × 20, or again 4000 cm.-g. That is, when a lever is in equilibrium or balance, the

counterclockwise moment
 = clockwise moment

Or,

$$W_1 \times d_1 = W_2 \times d_2$$
200 × 20 = 100 × 40
4000 cm.-g. = 4000 cm.-g.

This is known as the *lever principle*, or *principle of moments*.

Does the principle of moments apply to Fig. 4? In Fig. 4, two forces tend to rotate the lever clockwise, whereas only one force tends to rotate it counterclockwise.

As in Fig. 3, the counterclockwise moment equals 200 × 20, or 4000 cm.-g.

Inasmuch as the principle of moments applies to Fig. 4, then the clockwise moments must also equal 4000 cm.-g. The moment of W_2 equals 100 times 20, or 2000 cm.-g. The moment of W_3 equals 50 times d_3, or 50 times 40, or 2000 cm.-g. The latter added to the moment of W_2 gives 4000 cm.-g., making the total clockwise moments equal the counterclockwise moments of force. Thus, it appears that in Fig. 4,

$$W_1 d_1 = W_2 d_2 + W_3 d_3$$

That is,

200 × 20 = 100 × 20 + 50 × 40
4000 cm.-g. = 4000 cm.-g.

Verify these conditions by further experiment. Change the positions of the weights.

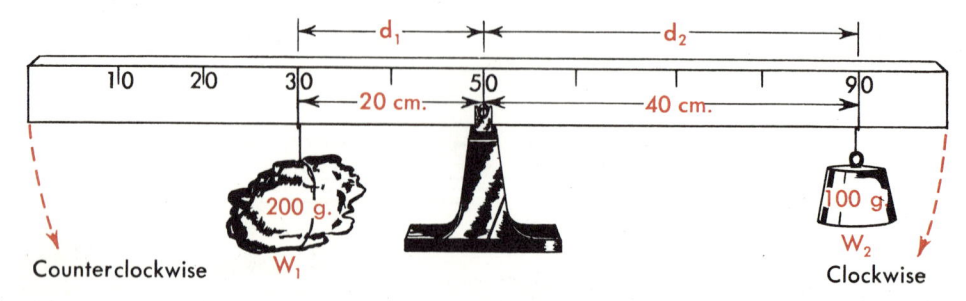

Fig. 3. Since the counterclockwise moment $W_1 \times d_1$ equals the clockwise moment $W_2 \times d_2$, the lever is in equilibrium and does not rotate.

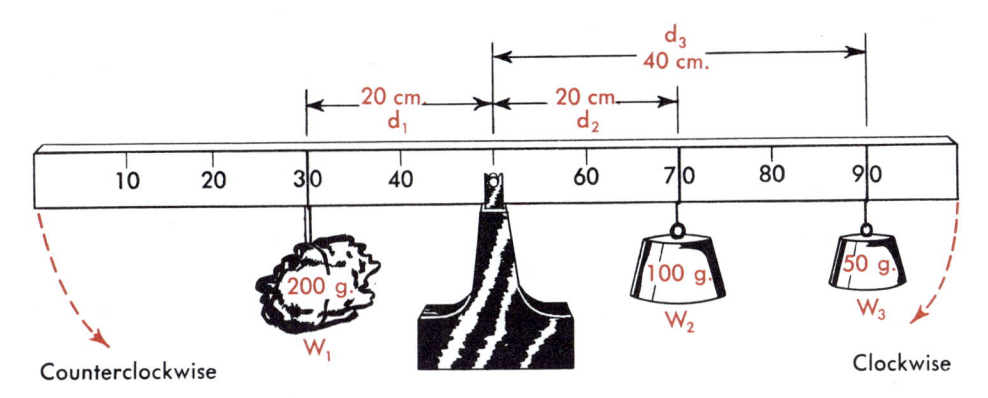

LEVERS, MOVEMENT OF FORCE, AND CENTER OF GRAVITY 121

Fig. 4. Explain why the lever does not rotate.

Hence, when a lever is in equilibrium the sum of the moments of force tending to turn the lever clockwise about the fulcrum or axis of rotation equals the sum of the moments of force tending to turn the lever counterclockwise.

PROBLEM: In Fig. 5 a 50-lb. weight 2 ft. from the fulcrum is lifted by a force E applied 6 ft. from the fulcrum. What is the value of E?

If   Clockwise moments =
            Counterclockwise moments
Then $400 \times 80 = 300 \times 80$
And $32{,}000 = 24{,}000$

This we know is absurd. Is the principle of the lever untrue, or have we failed to apply it correctly?

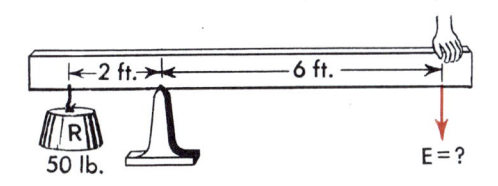

Fig. 5

SOLUTION: Clockwise moments =
          Counterclockwise moments

$$50 \times 2 = 6E$$
$$100 = 6E$$
$$E = 16.6 \text{ lb.}$$

Further test of the lever principle. Fig. 6 shows a lever in equilibrium with the fulcrum, F, at the lower end. Hence,

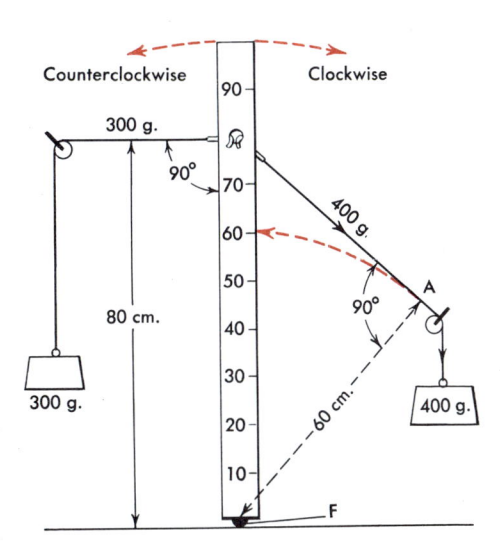

Fig. 6. Why must the perpendicular distance be used in calculating the moment produced by the 400-g. force?

You will note that the 300-g. force, like all other forces on levers studied up to this point, acts at right angles to the lever, and the distance from its line of action to the fulcrum is the *perpendicular* distance. The direction of the 400-g. force, however, is not perpendicular to the lever. Using the perpendicular distance *FA*, we now find that the clockwise moment is 400 × 60, or 24,000 cm.-g., instead of 32,000 cm.-g. as calculated above.

Hence, in the light of this new evidence we must revise our definition of the moment of a force as follows: *The* **moment of a force** *is the product of the force and the perpendicular distance from its line of action to the axis of rotation.* Compare this with the definition given on page 119.

Laws of equilibrium. In conclusion, it appears that

when forces act on a body so that it is in equilibrium, then:

1. The sum of the forces acting in one direction equals the sum of the forces acting in the opposite direction. This is sometimes called *the first condition for equilibrium.**

2. The sum of the moments of force tending to rotate the body clockwise about any axis of rotation equals the sum of the moments of force tending to rotate it counterclockwise about the same point. This is known as *the second condition for equilibrium.*

What is the couple? We found that the wheel of Fig. 2 is not in equilibrium, even though the forces acting on it are equal and opposite. Would it be in equilibrium if the forces were acting oppositely in the same straight line?

Further study of the figure shows that both forces have clockwise moments around any point between them that we

*See Chapter 5, page 36.

might consider the axis of rotation. This, then, is a special case, in which the only effect of the force is to produce rotation. Two equal and opposite forces acting in different straight lines on a body are called a *couple,* the moment of force of which is equal to the product of one of the forces and the perpendicular distance between them. To balance a couple an equal and opposite couple must be applied.

One high school student rather appropriately defined a couple as "two forces that go around together." Can you think of other applications of the couple besides the steering wheel of an automobile?

Classes of levers. Levers are divided into three classes, depending upon where the fulcrum is placed with respect to the forces. As shown in Fig. 7, the fulcrum is not always between the resistance and the effort.

First class levers have the fulcrum between the forces; that is, between the effort *E* and the resistance or load *R*. Examples are the teeter-totter and a pair of scissors, as the figure shows. *Second class* levers have the load, or resistance to be overcome, between the effort and the fulcrum. Examples are a nutcracker and a wheelbarrow. *Third class* levers have the effort between the fulcrum and the resistance. Examples are the forearm and a pair of tweezers.

The solution of any lever problem is not affected by the class of lever. The lengths of the effort arms and the resistance arms are always the respective perpendicular distances from the lines of action of the forces to the fulcrum. When three values are known, the fourth can always be computed.

PROBLEM: Find the effort, *E,* for each of the levers in Fig. 8 and state the class of each lever. In each case neglect the weight of the lever.

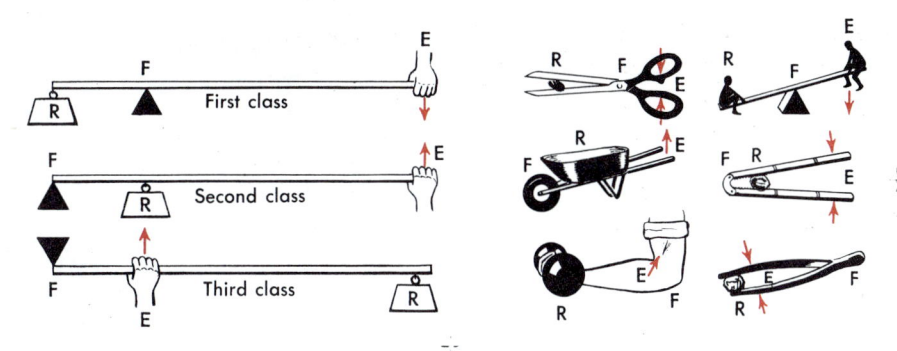

LEVERS, MOVEMENT OF FORCE, AND CENTER OF GRAVITY 123

Fig. 7. The three classes of levers and several common applications.

Center of gravity. In deriving the principle of levers, we did not consider the weights of the levers because, before we applied the forces, we balanced each lever (meter stick) so that one half of the lever balanced the other half. Now let us consider a more general case of setting up a uniform 100-g. lever with its axis of rotation at the 30-cm. mark, as shown in Fig. 9. Assuming that the principle of moments applies to this situation, our problem is to find the simplest means of dealing with the weight of the lever. What

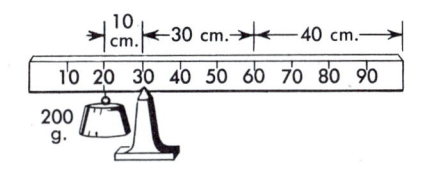

Fig. 9. The weight of the lever produces a moment.

is the weight of a 1-cm. length of the lever if the whole lever weighs 100 g.?

Taking moments about the fulcrum, we see that the counterclockwise moment due to the 200-g. weight equals 200 × 10, or 2000 cm.-g. The 30 cm. of lever on the left can be considered as balancing 30 cm. on the right, next to the fulcrum. This leaves 40 cm. or 40 g. of lever on the extreme right unaccounted for. The question is how to deal with these 40 g. of mass which are distributed over 40 cm. of lever. Can they be considered to act at one point? If so, where? At the 100-cm. mark, 60-cm. mark, halfway between these two points, or at some other point? The most logical choice is the 80-cm. or halfway mark. That is, we are assuming that the entire 40 g. of mass, and hence its weight,

Fig. 8

124   FORCES AND THE EQUILIBRIUM OF BODIES

are concentrated at the 80-cm. mark, 50 cm. from the fulcrum. But does this satisfy the formula:

$$W_1 d_1 = W_2 d_2 ?$$
Substituting, $200 \times 10 = 50 \times 40$
$$2000 \text{ cm.-g.} = 2000 \text{ cm.-g.}$$

Hence, if we assume that the entire mass of the 40 cm. of lever is concentrated at its midpoint, the law of moments is satisfied. Does this tend to prove that our assumption is true?

If the mass of 40 cm. of meter stick is concentrated at its geometric center, then logically the entire 100-g. mass of the lever should act at the 50-cm. mark, which is 20 cm. from the fulcrum. Therefore, according to the lever principle:

$$W_1 d_1 = W_2 d_2$$
$$200 \times 10 = 100 \times 20$$
$$2000 \text{ cm.-g.} = 2000 \text{ cm.-g.}$$

Hence, we see that the lever principle can be satisfied by our assuming that the entire mass as well as the entire gravitational attraction is concentrated at a certain point. *The point at which the mass and gravitational attraction of a body seem to be concentrated is called its* **center of gravity (c.g.).**

How a fisherman makes use of the center of gravity of a fishing pole to find

Fig. 10. Finding the weight of the fish.

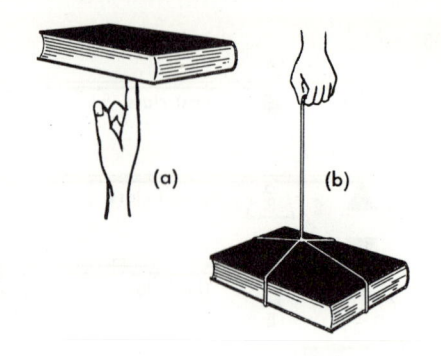

Fig. 11. Finding the center of gravity.

the weight of a fish. A fisherman has a 10-foot pole which he knows weighs 2 pounds. He balances it on his finger and finds that its center of gravity is 3 feet from the large end. Then he ties the fish to this end, as shown in Fig. 10. As a result, the pole now balances 1 foot from the large end.

Using the formula $W_1 d_1 = W_2 d_2$
And substituting, $W_1 \times 1 = 2 \times 2$
He finds
$$W_1 = 4 \text{ lb., the weight of the fish.}$$

Note that d_1 is the distance from the fish to the fulcrum, d_2 the distance from the center of gravity of the pole to the fulcrum, and W_2 the weight of the fishing pole.

How to find the center of gravity of a body. For a circular, rectangular, or square plate of uniform thickness and density, the center of gravity is at the geometrical center. If such a body is supported directly below this point, as the book is supported in (a) of Fig. 11, the body will balance on the point and will not rotate.

The center of gravity of the book in (a) of Fig. 11 will be located near the center page, directly above the point of support. In (b) of Fig. 11 the center of gravity of the book will be located directly under the point of support on the center page. If, however, the center of gravity is not under the point of support, the book will tip

LEVERS, MOVEMENT OF FORCE, AND CENTER OF GRAVITY

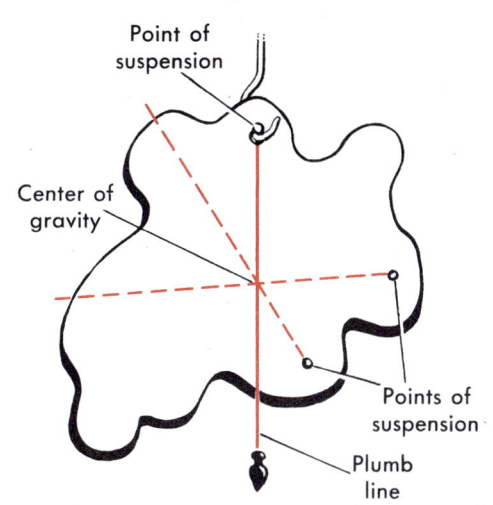

Fig. 12. Finding the center of gravity of an irregularly shaped object.

until the center of gravity is directly under the support and is in the lowest possible position that it can attain. The tilting, or rotation, is caused by the fact that the clockwise and counterclockwise moments about the support are not equal.

Similarly if any other body, such as an irregular object, is supported as shown in Fig. 12, the center of gravity will be under the point of support. It can be found if the body is suspended from two points, first one and then the other, and a plumb line is dropped from each point of suspension in turn. Experiment will verify that the center of gravity will be at the point where these two lines intersect. An irregularly shaped solid is generally suspended from three points. For many bodies such as hoops, automobile tires, cups, and horseshoes, the centers of gravity are actually located in space outside of the bodies. Find the approximate center of gravity of your own body. Will it be different for different positions?

Center of gravity and stability. From the time we are born until we die we are continually trying to maintain our physical equilibrium, trying to keep gravity from giving us a sudden spill. The designers of automobiles, boats, dishes, floor lamps, tables, and hundreds of other things are confronted with the problem of making such things stable and attractive at the same time. Our problem is to find what determines the stability of a body.

To answer this question let us consider Fig. 13, in which the cones A to F are arranged in order of decreasing stability. Stability depends upon how difficult it is to knock a body over or how well it maintains its position when pushed. Cone A is most stable. B, which is less stable than A, differs from A in mass only. The mass of C is the same as the mass of B, but the center of gravity of C is higher than that of B. The base of D is smaller than the base of C, but the mass and center of gravity of D are the same as for C. The center of gravity of E is directly over the edge of the base instead of over the center of the base, where it should be if the cone is to be most stable. Cone F is the least

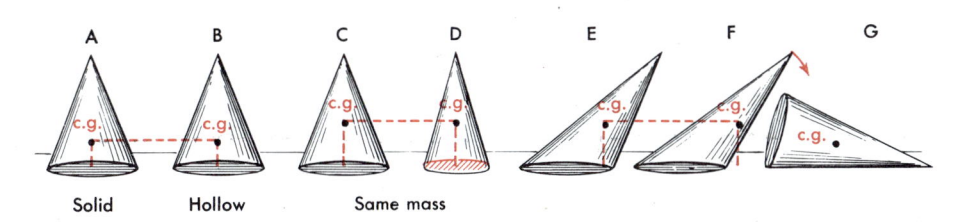

Fig. 13. Cones arranged according to their stability. Explain why each cone from B to F is less stable than the one immediately preceding it.

Fig. 14. Explain how the roly-poly doll assumes an erect position.

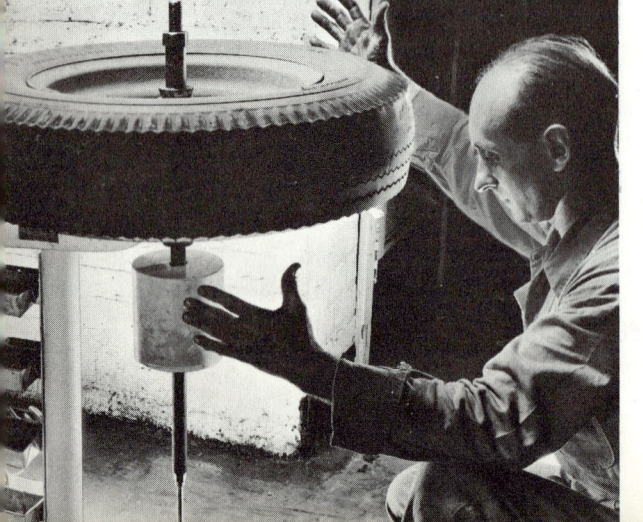

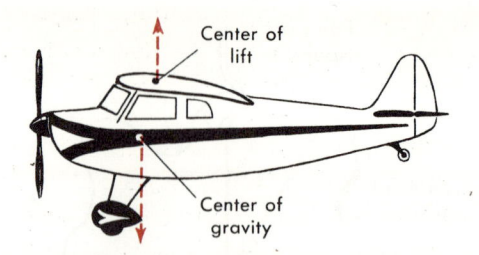

Fig. 15. What would this plane have a tendency to do?

stable of all. In fact, it is tipping over. Its center of gravity is not over its base. Cone *G* will be considered later.

Hence, in conclusion,

we can increase the stability of a body by:
(a) increasing the mass of the body;
(b) increasing the area of the base;
(c) lowering the center of gravity of the body;
(d) keeping the center of gravity directly over the base and as near the geometric center of the base as possible.

In case the center of gravity is not above the base, that is, if a plumb line dropped from it falls outside the base, the object

Fig. 16. Balancing a wheel to determine whether the axis of rotation is at the center of gravity.

Courtesy General Motors Corp.

will tip over. From this standpoint, cone *G* in the position shown is of special interest. Its center of gravity is always above its base—the part on which it rests. If cone *G* is displaced it has no tendency to seek another position. Its equilibrium is said to be *neutral*.

If *A, B, C,* and *D* are tipped slightly, so their centers of gravity are raised but are still above their bases, they will again erect themselves. If, however, they are tipped so that a plumb line from the center of gravity of each cone falls outside its base, then they will all be in unstable equilibrium and will tip over on their sides in the position of cone *G*.

Roly-poly and humpty-dumpty dolls. The equilibrium of a marble when resting on a flat surface is always neutral if its center of gravity is at the geometric center of the sphere. If, however, the center of gravity is off center, the marble will tend to take a position where its center of gravity is above the point of support and as low as possible.

A roly-poly doll is designed to take advantage of this principle. It is designed with a curved base. Its center of gravity is below the center of curvature of the curved bottom, as shown in Fig. 14. As a result, when the doll is tipped, its center of gravity is raised and the point of support shifts. Now the center of gravity is no longer above the point of support, but is in such a position that the force of gravity tends to rotate the doll, until the doll resumes its erect position. Note that the c. g. is then at the lowest possible point.

This same principle applies to the design of airplanes and of ships and other floating bodies. A floating body always turns so that its center of gravity is in the lowest possible position. Hence, in the design and the loading of a ship it is important to keep the center of gravity low as well as directly over the keel. In storms, cargoes may shift so that the center of gravity of the ship is not directly over the keel, and as a result the ship will list or turn over completely. Explain why an airplane is designed and loaded so that its center of gravity is as nearly as possible in a vertical line with, and over, the center of lift. In Fig. 15, what will the airplane have a tendency to do? Why?

Rotating bodies and their centers of gravity. If you toss a baton or even a pencil into the air so that it rotates end over end, it rotates about its center of gravity. Design an experiment to test this statement. Also, if you throw a baseball so that it spins, it likewise rotates about its center of gravity. What is the result if the center of gravity is not at the geometric center of the ball?

If a wheel is designed so that its center of gravity is at its axis of rotation, the wheel will turn smoothly without wobbling. However, if the center of gravity is off the axis of rotation the wheel will wobble and, if rotated rapidly, may cause severe vibration. Consequently, for smooth performance, a whirling skater, toe dancer, aerialist, toy top, airplane propeller, or automobile wheel must rotate about an axis which passes through the center of gravity and is perpendicular to the plane of rotation.

Often flywheels, crankshafts, drive wheels, automobile wheels, and many others must be counterbalanced so that the axis of rotation is at the center of gravity. For years crankshafts for engines were balanced by trial and error, with results that were frequently poor. Finally, an engineer figured by mathematics how to design and build a balanced crankshaft. Since then, higher and higher engine speeds have been attained with a minimum of vibration.

How to figure in the weight of a lever. In much practical work—for example, in the construction of a bridge—the weight of the lever cannot be neglected when we determine the forces necessary to hold it in equilibrium. We have already found that the law of moments can be satisfied if we assume that the entire weight of a body is concentrated at its center of gravity.

PROBLEM: John and Tom (Fig. 17) are carrying a 200-lb. lion on a 20-lb. pole. The pole is 15 ft. long and its center of gravity is 5 ft. from John, who is carrying end *A*. The 200-lb. lion is tied 8 ft. from John. How much is lifted by Tom? By John?

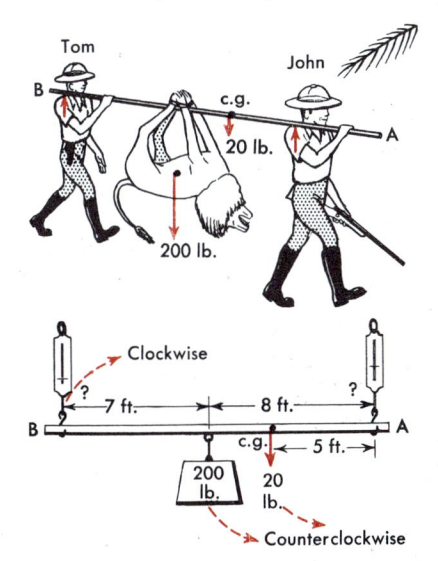

Fig. 17. Do the laws of equilibrium apply in this case?

SOLUTION: Assuming that there is a fulcrum at A, we have:

Clockwise moment (due to the force Tom is exerting upward) = $15x$.

Counterclockwise moment (due to weight of pole) = $20 \times 5 = 100$ lb.-ft.

Counterclockwise moment (due to weight of lion) = $200 \times 8 = 1600$ lb.-ft.

Equating the clockwise and counterclockwise moments, we have:

$$15x = (100 + 1600) \text{ lb.-ft.}$$
$$15x = 1700 \text{ lb.-ft.}$$
$$x = 113.3 \text{ lb.}$$

Hence, we see that Tom is lifting 113.3 lb. How much does John lift? Solve, using two different methods.

SUMMARY AND CONCLUSIONS

1. When forces act on a body so that it is in equilibrium, then:

(a) The sum of the forces acting in one direction equals the sum of the forces acting in the opposite direction.

(b) The sum of the moments of force tending to rotate the body clockwise about its axis of rotation equals the sum of the moments of force tending to rotate it counterclockwise; that is,

$$W_1 d_1 = W_2 d_2 + W_3 d_3$$

2. The moment of a force is the product of the force and the perpendicular distance from its line of action to the fulcrum.

3. The center of gravity of a body is a point at which the entire mass and weight of the body can be considered to be concentrated.

4. We can increase the stability of a body by (a) increasing its mass, (b) increasing the area of its base, (c) lowering its center of gravity, (d) keeping the center of gravity as nearly as possible over the center of the base.

QUESTIONS FOR REVIEW

1. Show by means of a diagram the relative positions of the fulcrum, effort, and resistance for the following levers: oar on boat, can opener, pump handle, and sugar tongs.

2. What name is given to the product of force and the length of the lever arm?

3. Explain how you would find the approximate center of gravity of this book.

4. Why is a boy harder to knock over when standing on both feet than on one foot? When standing on his hands and knees than when standing straight up on both feet? For the latter give two reasons.

5. Give two ways in which a football player can increase his stability.

6. Which is harder to knock over, a chalk box full of chalk or one full of lead? Explain.

7. State three ways in which the stability of a body can be increased.

8. Explain two relationships between the center of gravity and the base which must be satisfied when an egg is at rest on a flat table.

9. Why do you generally lean forward in climbing a hill and lean backward when walking down a steep hill?

10. Explain in terms of center of gravity, base, and moment of force, why a ball will roll down a smooth inclined plane. Make a diagram showing the center of gravity of the ball and the surface of the ball which is in contact with the inclined plane.

11. Which is more stable, a man standing in a canoe or one sitting in a canoe? Explain.

12. Why is it easier to balance an inverted bowl on the end of your finger than to balance it when it is upright?

13. Explain the various ways in which the stability of modern automobiles has been increased.

14. In loading a transport airplane, or a boat that carries freight, in what place should the load be placed if the greatest stability is desired? What may be the result if this is not done?

15. What would happen if the center of gravity of the truck in Fig. 18 were at B? At A?

PROBLEMS

1. A 100-lb. boy sits 4 ft. from the fulcrum of a teeter-totter. How far from the fulcrum

LEVERS, MOVEMENT OF FORCE, AND CENTER OF GRAVITY 129

Fig. 18

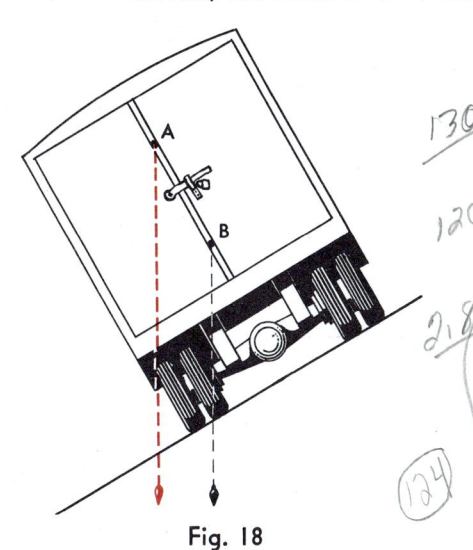

must a 75-lb. boy sit in order to balance the board?

2. An 80-lb. boy sits at one end of a 12-ft. teeter-totter. How far from the other end must a 100-lb. boy sit in order to produce equilibrium?

3. A uniform meter stick is balanced at its midpoint. Then a 500-g. weight is placed at the 20-cm. mark. What effort should be applied at the 90-cm. mark in order to balance the meter stick?

4. What is the mechanical advantage of the lever used in Problem 3? See page 68.

5. The effort arm of a lever is 10 ft. long and the resistance arm is 2 ft. long. What effort is required to balance a load or resistance of 1000 lb.? What is the mechanical advantage of the lever?

6. A 3-ton load of coal is passing over a bridge 60 ft. long. If the load is 25 ft. from one end of the bridge, how much of the weight is supported by each pier? First make a diagram to show the location of the forces.

7. A boy and a man carry a weight of 160 lb. on a uniform bar which is 12 ft. long. How far from the man must the weight be placed in order that the man may carry 100 lb.? Neglect the weight of the bar.

8. Two upward vertical parallel forces of 60 g. and 140 g. are applied at opposite ends of a meter stick. Find the maximum weight that will be supported and its location on the stick. Neglect the weight of the meter stick.

9. What force is needed to lift one end of a uniform steel bar which is 20 ft. long and weighs 260 lb.?

10. A telephone pole is 30 ft. long and weighs 300 lb. The center of gravity is 12 ft. from the larger end. What force is required to lift the smaller end?

11. A fisherman has a 2-lb. fishing pole 12 ft. long. Its center of gravity is 4 ft. from the larger end. The fisherman hangs a fish at the larger end and the pole then balances 20 in. from the larger end. What is the weight of the fish?

12. A 15-ft. plank, whose center of gravity is at the 7.5-ft. mark, balances at a point 5.5 ft. from one end when a 14-lb. weight is hung at that end. Find the weight of the plank.

13. A uniform steel girder is 30 ft. long and weighs 4 tons. A load of 1500 lb. is hung 8 ft. from one end. What force is necessary at each end of the girder in order to support the girder and its load?

PROJECTS

1. The tin can in Fig. 19 can actually be made to roll uphill. Make this apparatus and explain it. This could be used in your science open house or science fair.

2. Stand with your heels and hips against a wall and then endeavor to pick up a pencil on the floor in front of you without bending

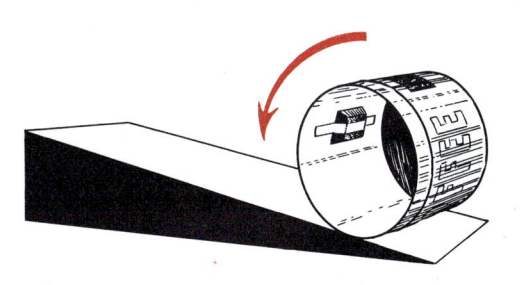

Fig. 19

your knees or moving your feet and hips out from the wall. Explain the results in terms of the laws of equilibrium just studied.

3. Study the effect of the position of the center of gravity on stability by the use of a weighted round-bottom flask. A quantity of lead shot is put in the flask and melted paraffin is poured over the shot and allowed to harden.

4. Find approximately your own center of gravity when your body is straight and stiff. Will its position change if you bring your knees up under your chin?

READING YOU WILL ENJOY

1. Aviation Education Research Group, *Science of Pre-flight Aeronautics,* Revised Edition. The Macmillan Company, New York, 1944. Produced for pre-induction training of military personnel, this book deals with many practical problems involving forces.

2. Bavier, R. N., *Faster Sailing.* Dodd, Mead and Company, New York, 1954. Deals with wind forces that act on sailboats and explains how to utilize these forces in order to win races and break records. Easy to read.

3. Richardson, J. S., and G. P. Cahoon, *Methods and Materials for Teaching General and Physical Science,* pp. 277-282. McGraw-Hill Book Company, Inc., New York, 1951. Contains several experiments that can be used to illustrate stability, equilibrium, and composition of forces.

4. Swezey, K. M., *After-Dinner Science,* pp. 56-57. Whittlesey House, McGraw-Hill Book Company, Inc., New York, 1948. Describes two stunts that dramatize the relationship between stability and a low center of gravity.

Unit 5

The Riddle of Motion

Defying gravity is getting to be a habit of scientists. The unique "flying platform" in the unit photograph is capable of a vertical takeoff without the conventional rotor blades, wings, tail, or propellers of the ordinary helicopter. The principle by which the disk-shaped flying machine operates is known as "the ducted fan." Through two holes in the platform, air is sucked in by two fans that rotate in opposite directions. The fans then thrust the air away with great force, propelling the device upward. At the same time, the sucking action of the fans helps to lift the plane by reducing the air pressure over the flaring lip and increasing the pressure under the lip. What principle is applied here?

Although the device looks as though it might be easily tipped over, it is actually very stable. The stability of the platform is due to the gyroscopic effect produced by the counter-rotating fans. You will understand this effect better after you have studied rotary motion. This spectacular flying platform demonstrates what can be accomplished by applying the basic principles of motion.

14. DISTANCE, VELOCITY, TIME, AND ACCELERATION
15. A FURTHER STUDY OF FALLING BODIES
16. NEWTON'S LAWS OF MOTION
17. CIRCULAR AND ROTARY MOTION
18. PROJECTILE MOTION

Unit Photograph Courtesy U. S. Navy

Chapter 14

I Essence of Chapter
II Key Terms
III Key Ideas
IV Development

Distance, Velocity, Time, and Acceleration

A problem of motion. One of the worst black marks to be recorded against our fast-moving "nation on wheels" is the slaughter of people on our highways by high-speed automobiles. During World War II and the wars which followed, the death toll caused by automobiles exceeded the number of Americans killed in battle. Furthermore, the chances of a person on the home front being killed by an automobile were greater than the chances of a soldier in the combat areas being killed in combat. If war is what Sherman called it, then what should be said about the traffic conditions which exist in almost every city, hamlet, and countryside in America?

No sane person would think of allowing small children, ignorant of the consequences involved and of the chances they would be taking, to play "cops and robbers" with sticks of dynamite and real revolvers loaded with real ammunition. However, we do allow people who are almost totally ignorant of the laws of motion and the chances they are taking, to drive high-powered automobiles at speeds which cause them to be just as dangerous and destructive as sticks of dynamite. Consequently, any sensible program designed to decrease this heavy death toll should aim to teach every automobile driver the basic laws and concepts of motion. In this chapter we will discuss the simplest of these.

Average velocity* and distance. You already know that if you drive an automobile 200 miles in 5 hours, the average speed or average velocity, $\overline{V}$, is $\dfrac{200 \text{ mi.}}{5 \text{ hr.}}$, or 40 miles per hour. At this average speed, how far could you drive in 8 hours?

In other words, the average velocity, $\overline{V}$, equals the distance, S, divided by the time, t:

$$\overline{V} = \frac{S}{t}$$

Or
$$S = \overline{V}t$$

Other ways of finding average velocity. Regardless of the kind of motion, distance can always be found with the formula, $S = \overline{V}t$. Time can usually be found by means of a clock or watch, but the average

---

*To the teacher: The difference between speed and velocity has not been emphasized in this text. Velocity is ordinarily defined so that it has two characteristics, magnitude and direction. Speed is said to have only magnitude. Many physics books, including college texts, go to great lengths to explain these differences and then use the two terms interchangeably.

velocity, $\overline{V}$, is not always determined so easily.

In case an automobile travels at a uniform, unchanging velocity, for example, 30 miles per hour, obviously the average is the same as the constant velocity, 30 miles per hour.

Or if a car starts from rest (zero velocity) and gains speed at a constant rate, as shown in Table 1, then the average velocity can be found by several different methods. One method is to find the sum of the velocities and to divide it by the number of velocities, thus obtaining the average.

Table 1
TIME AND VELOCITY

Time in seconds	Velocities mi./hr.	Velocities ft./sec.
0	0	0
1	4	6
2	8	12
3	12	18
4	16	24
5	20	30
6	24	36
		Sum = 126

Adding the recorded velocities in column 3 we find the sum is 126. Dividing this sum by 7, the number of recorded velocities, we get 18 ft./sec. That is,

$$\overline{V} = \frac{126}{7}, \text{ or } 18 \text{ ft./sec.}$$

The distance traveled during the 6 seconds is found as follows:

$$S = \overline{V}t$$
$$S = 18 \times 6$$
$$S = 108 \text{ ft.}$$

Study the speeds in column 3 of Table 1 to see if you can discover two shorter ways for finding the average.

PROBLEM: What was the average velocity during the first 4 seconds? How many feet did the automobile travel during the first 4 seconds? During the first second?

Units of velocity. Velocity is generally defined as the *distance traveled per unit of time*. Therefore, if the velocity of an automobile is 60 mi./hr., then at this rate it should travel 60 miles in 1 hour. In 1 minute, the automobile should travel 1 mile, or 5,280 feet. And in 1 second it should travel $\frac{5,280}{60}$, or 88 feet. In conclusion, the velocity, 60 mi./hr., can be expressed in several different ways, depending upon the units of time and distance. That is,

60 mi./hr. = 1 mi./min. = 88 ft./sec.

Therefore, since any given velocity may have several equivalents, care must be taken to keep the units straight in formulas like $S = \overline{V}t$. If the velocity is in mi./hr., then the time must be in hours, and if the velocity is in ft./sec., then the time must be in seconds. In what unit must the time be if the velocity is in ft./min.?

PROBLEM: What is the velocity in ft./sec. when the velocity in mi./hr. is 30? 15? 6? 3? 1?

In some books, 1 mile per hour is considered to be equal to 1.5 feet per second. Using this relationship, 60 miles per hour equals how many feet per second?

Accelerated motion. In Table 1 (see column 3) the velocity increases. During the first second the velocity increases from zero to 6 ft./sec. During the second second the velocity increases from 6 ft./sec. to 12 ft./sec., and during each succeeding second the velocity increases the same amount. In other words, the velocity changes at the rate of 6 ft./sec. every second. *The rate of change of velocity is called* **acceleration.**

What is the acceleration in column 3 in Table 1?

DISTANCE, VELOCITY, TIME, AND ACCELERATION

PROBLEM 1: An automobile is now traveling 50 mi./hr. Ten seconds ago it was traveling 20 mi./hr. What was the total change in velocity? Assuming that the velocity change took place at a uniform rate, same change each second, what was the change of velocity during 1 second? What was the acceleration?

PROBLEM 2: Four seconds ago a ball was traveling 80 ft./sec. Now its velocity is zero. What was the total change in velocity? How much did the velocity change during 1 second? What was the acceleration?

Uniform, positive, and negative acceleration. In case the rate of change of velocity (increase or decrease) is uniform, the acceleration is *uniform acceleration*. If the velocity is increasing, the acceleration is *positive;* and if the velocity is decreasing, the acceleration is *negative*.

Do the data in Table 1 show that the acceleration is uniform? Positive or negative?

Table 2
VELOCITIES OF AN AUTOMOBILE

Time (sec.)	Trial I (mi./hr.)	Trial II (ft./sec.)	Trial III (ft./sec.)	Trial IV (ft./sec.)
0	0	0	0	0
1	3	2	3	4
2	6	4	6	2
3	9	6	9	5
4	12	8	12	7

PROBLEM 1: Study Table 2 and answer the following questions:
(a) In which trial is the automobile not uniformly accelerated?
(b) In Trial II, what is the velocity at the end of the first second? Second second? Third second? What is the change of velocity each second? What is the acceleration?
(c) What is the acceleration for Trial I? Trial III?
(d) What is the average velocity during Trial II? Trial III?
(e) What distance does the automobile travel during the four seconds of Trial II? Trial III?   ANSWER FOR TRIAL II: 16 ft.
(f) For Trial I, what is the velocity in feet per second at the end of the first second? Second second? Fourth second?
(g) For Trial I, what is the change in velocity in mi./hr. each second? In ft./sec. each second? What is the average velocity in ft./sec. for the 4 seconds? How many feet does the automobile travel in 4 sec.?
ANS.: 36 ft. (approx.).

PROBLEM 2: An automobile is now traveling V ft./sec. and t seconds ago it was traveling V_0 ft./sec.
(a) What was the change in velocity during t sec.?
(b) What was the change in velocity during 1 sec.?
(c) What was the acceleration?

If you have solved Problem 2 correctly, you have found that:

$$\text{acceleration, } a = \frac{V - V_0}{t}$$

And if you make the first, or initial velocity, V_0, equal to zero, you have:

$$a = \frac{V}{t}$$

Or, $$V = at$$

PROBLEM 3: If an automobile starts from rest and its acceleration is 2 ft./sec./sec., what is its velocity at the end of 7 sec.? ½ sec.? 5½ sec.?

PROBLEM 4: The velocity of a sprinter is 30 ft./sec. After 3 seconds his velocity is zero. Find his negative acceleration (rate at which he loses velocity), assuming it to be uniform.

SOLUTION: $$a = \frac{V}{t}$$

Substituting, $$a = \frac{30 \text{ ft./sec.}}{3 \text{ sec.}}$$

Dividing, $$a = \frac{10 \text{ ft.}}{\text{sec.} \times \text{sec.}}$$

This answer may also be written as 10 ft./sec./sec., or as 10 ft./sec.^{2}, and it means that the sprinter decreases his velocity at the rate of 10 ft./sec. each second.

How is the average velocity found for uniformly accelerated motion? The data found in column 3 of Table 1 (see page 134) show that the motion was uniformly accelerated. The average velocity, 18 ft./sec., was found by finding the sum of the velocities and dividing it by the number of velocities. Perhaps, however, you discovered that 18 was halfway between zero and 36. That is, 18, the average velocity, $\overline{V}$, was half of the sum of the initial velocity, V_0, and the final velocity, V:

$$\overline{V} = \frac{V_0 + V}{2}$$

PROBLEM: If the initial velocity of a uniformly accelerated automobile is 40 mi./hr. and the final velocity is 60 mi./hr., what is the average velocity? How far would the automobile travel at this average velocity in 3 hours? ANS.: 150 mi.

Further consideration of the formula $\overline{V} = \frac{V_0 + V}{2}$ shows that if the initial velocity is zero, then the average velocity

$$\overline{V} = \frac{0 + V}{2}$$

That is,
$$\overline{V} = \frac{V}{2}$$

And since $V = at$

then
$$\overline{V} = \frac{at}{2}$$

PROBLEM 1: A uniformly accelerated body starts from rest and travels for 10 sec. Its acceleration is 4 ft./sec.² What is (a) the final velocity? (b) the average velocity? (c) the total distance traveled?

SOLUTION:

(a) $V = at$
$V = 4$ ft./sec.² × 10 sec.
$V = 40$ ft./sec.

(b) $\overline{V} = \frac{V}{2}$

$\overline{V} = \frac{40}{2}$, or 20 ft./sec.

(c) $S = \overline{V}t$
$S = 20$ ft./sec. × 10 sec.
$S = 200$ ft.

PROBLEM 2: A uniformly accelerated body starts from rest and travels for 8 sec. Its acceleration is 3 ft./sec.² What is (a) the final velocity? (b) the average velocity? (c) the total distance traveled?

The relationship among distance, acceleration, and time. So far, in finding distance we have used the formula $S = \overline{V}t$. This requires that we first find average velocity and then distance, making the solution an indirect, two-step procedure. Can one step be eliminated when acceleration and time are known?

In the case of a body that starts from rest, we already know that average velocity

$\overline{V} = \frac{\text{final velocity}}{2}$, or $\frac{V}{2}$, and that $V = at$.

Therefore, $\overline{V} = \frac{at}{2}$. Explain.

Substituting

$\frac{at}{2}$ for $\overline{V}$ in the formula $S = \overline{V}t$,

we have $\quad S = \frac{at}{2} \times t$

or $\quad S = \frac{at^2}{2} = \tfrac{1}{2}at^2$

PROBLEM 1: Starting from rest, how far will a sled slide in 5 sec. if its acceleration is 4 ft./sec.²?

SOLUTION: $\quad S = \tfrac{1}{2} at^2$

Substituting, $S = \tfrac{1}{2} \times \frac{4 \text{ ft.}}{\text{sec.}^2} \times (5 \text{ sec.})^2$

or $\quad S = \frac{2 \text{ ft.}}{\text{sec.}^2} \times 25 \text{ sec.}^2$

and $\quad S = 50$ ft.

DISTANCE, VELOCITY, TIME, AND ACCELERATION

PROBLEM 2: Starting from rest with an acceleration of 4 ft./sec.², what length of time is required for a sled to slide 72 ft.?

SOLUTION:
$$S = \tfrac{1}{2} at^2$$
Substituting,
$$72 = \tfrac{1}{2} \times 4 \times t^2$$
or
$$72 = 2t^2$$
Dividing,
$$t^2 = 36$$
Hence,
$$t = \sqrt{36}, \text{ or } 6 \text{ sec.}$$

PROBLEM 3: A uniformly accelerated body starts from rest and travels 400 ft. in 10 sec. What is its acceleration? What is its final velocity?

The relationship among velocity, acceleration, and distance. The formula $V = at$ gives the relationship among velocity, acceleration, and time, and the formula $S = \tfrac{1}{2} at^2$ gives the relationship among distance, acceleration, and time. So far, however, we have no relationship among distance, S, velocity, V, and acceleration, a.

One way to obtain this relationship is to substitute for t^2 in terms of V and a in the formula $S = \tfrac{1}{2} at^2$. Solving for t in the formula $V = at$, we get $t = \dfrac{V}{a}$. Squaring both sides, $t^2 = \dfrac{V^2}{a^2}$. Substituting $\dfrac{V^2}{a^2}$ for t^2 in $S = \tfrac{1}{2} at^2$, we have:

$$S = \tfrac{1}{2} a \times \frac{V^2}{a^2}$$

Dividing,
$$S = \frac{V^2}{2a}$$
or
$$V^2 = 2aS$$

PROBLEM 1: Starting from rest, how far must a car travel to attain a velocity of 30 mi./hr. if the acceleration is 10 ft./sec.²?

SOLUTION: The velocity and acceleration are given, but one involves miles and hours and the other feet and seconds. We can remedy this by changing 30 mi./hr. to its equivalent, 44 ft./sec.

$$V^2 = 2aS$$
Solving for S,
$$S = \frac{V^2}{2a}$$
Substituting,
$$S = \frac{44 \text{ ft./sec.} \times 44 \text{ ft./sec.}}{2 \times 10 \text{ ft./sec.}^2}$$
or
$$S = 96.8 \text{ ft.}$$

PROBLEM 2: The velocity of a uniformly accelerated rolling ball is 20 ft./sec. It started from rest and has traveled 40 ft. What has its acceleration been?

In conclusion, according to mathematical logic, distance S can always be determined if the average velocity $\overline{V}$ and time t are known.

$$S = \overline{V} t$$

If the velocity is constant, the average velocity
$$\overline{V} = \text{constant velocity}$$

If the motion is uniformly accelerated, average velocity
$$\overline{V} = \frac{V_0 + V}{2}$$

If the starting velocity $V_0 = $ zero,
$$\overline{V} = \frac{V}{2}$$

Also, if a body is uniformly accelerated from rest,
$$V = at$$
$$S = \tfrac{1}{2} at^2$$
$$V^2 = 2aS$$

Testing our theory and formulas of motion by experiment. The formulas developed above are all theoretical. Therefore, to be scientific we must test the formulas and their conclusions by experiment.

137

THE RIDDLE OF MOTION

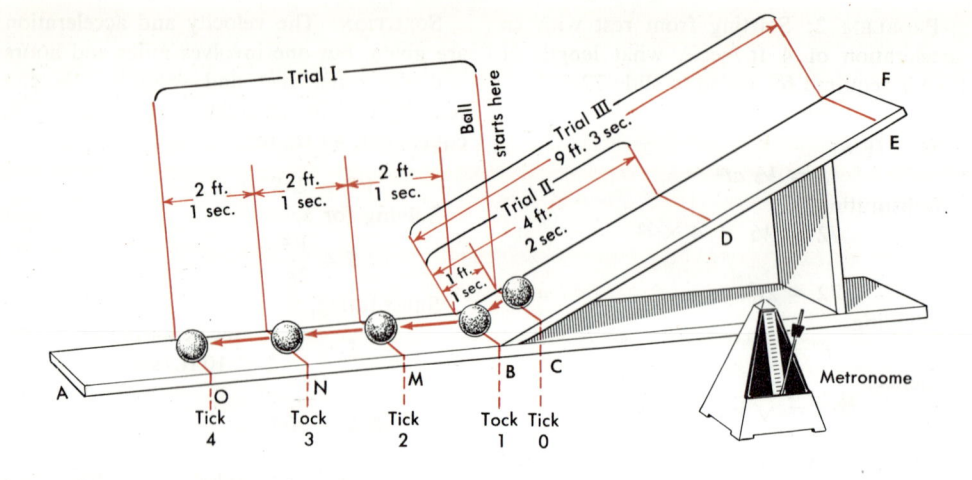

Fig. 1. An experiment on accelerated motion.

Motion on inclined planes. Galileo was the first to study accelerated motion by experiment. To do this he rolled balls down inclined planes. For a timing device he used water which dripped from a leaky bucket.

In our study, which students and teacher can easily duplicate, we, too, roll balls down an inclined plane. The timing device is a metronome set to click every second.

The inclined plane FB should be about 10 feet long and at the bottom of it there should be hinged another plane BA which should be at least 9 feet long. See Fig. 1. To keep the balls on the inclined planes, tack two chalk lines (cords) on the plane, one along each edge of each plane's surface.

The purpose of plane BA is to determine the velocity of the ball when it reaches the bottom of plane FB. The plane BA should be sloped just enough downward toward A to counteract friction so that the ball, when it rolls onto the plane, will neither gain nor lose velocity; that is, the ball will not be accelerated or decelerated. As a result, the distance which the ball rolls on BA in 1 second is the velocity of the ball at B. If this is not clear, the student should recall the definition of velocity (see page 134).

The plane FB (see Fig. 1), on which the motion is accelerated, is sloped just enough so that if the ball is released at C it will roll 1 foot, the distance CB, in 1 second. The ball should be released at C at the same time that the metronome clicks and it should arrive at B at the next click of the metronome. See column 2 of Table 3.

Table 3

Trial	1 Experimental distance (S) (ft.)	2 Time (t) (sec.)	3 Final velocity (V) (ft./sec.)	4 Acceleration (a) (ft./sec.^{2})	5 Average Velocity $\bar{V} = \frac{V}{2}$	6 Computed Distance $S = \bar{V}t$ or $S = \frac{1}{2}at^2$
	0	0	0	0	0	0
I	1	1	2	2−0=2	$\frac{2}{2}$=1	1×1
II	4	2	4	4−2=2	$\frac{4}{2}$=2	2×2
III	9	3	6	6−4=2	$\frac{6}{2}$=3	3×3
IV	—	—	—	——	——	——
V	—	—	—	——	——	——

DISTANCE, VELOCITY, TIME, AND ACCELERATION

If, during the second second, the ball is observed closely, it will be seen to roll 2 feet from B to M. During the third second it will again roll 2 feet from M to N. Thus, in Trial I on plane BA, the ball rolls 2 feet each second and therefore its velocity at B is 2 feet per second. The velocities are recorded in column 3 in the table.

In Trial II, the ball should be started at D. In 2 seconds it will roll 4 feet from rest at D to B. During the third second it will roll 4 feet from B to N. Hence at B the velocity of the ball is 4 feet per second.

In Trial III, in 3 seconds the ball will roll 9 feet from rest at E to B. During the fourth second it rolls 6 feet from B to O. Hence at B the velocity of the ball is 6 feet per second.

Copy the experimental data in Table 3, and see if you can complete the table without reading further. Use the formulas developed on page 137. Do not write in the book.

Checking the computed and experimental results. Referring to columns 1, 2, 3, 4, let us make a study of these data similar to the study made on page 135 of the data in Table 2. The purpose is to determine whether the computed and experimental values agree.

PROBLEM 1: (a) In column 3, what was the velocity at the end of the first second? Second second? Third second? What would be the velocity at the end of the fourth second? Fifth second? Does the formula $V = at$ apply to these data?

(b) What was the acceleration of the ball as it rolled down the inclined plane EB? Was the acceleration constant?

(c) What was the average velocity $\overline{V}$ during the first second? During the first two seconds? During the first three seconds? What would you predict it to be during the first four seconds? First five seconds?

(d) Using the respective average velocities in (c) above, compute the distance traveled on the inclined plane FB during the first second; during the first two seconds; during the first three seconds. What distance do you predict the ball would travel during the first four seconds? During the first five seconds?

(e) Using the formula $S = \frac{1}{2}at^2$ and the fact that on plane CB the ball is accelerated 2 ft./sec.², compute the distance which the ball travels during the first second, during the first two seconds, during the first three seconds, and so on. Do your computed answers agree with the experimental distances given in column 1?

PROBLEM 2: Using the experimental velocities and distances, and the acceleration given in Table 3, check to see whether the formula $V^2 = 2aS$ applies to the motion of the ball down the incline.

Combining velocities. If a brakeman on top of a freight train runs toward the engine with a velocity of 22 ft./sec. and the train is traveling 30 mi./hr. (44 ft./sec.), then with respect to the track the brakeman would be traveling 44 + 22, or 66 ft./sec., which is 45 mi./hr. We have combined the velocities by finding their sum. That is, $V = v_1 + v_2$, where V is the resultant velocity of the two components v_1 and v_2.

If, however, the brakeman had been running toward the caboose, his velocity with respect to the track would have been

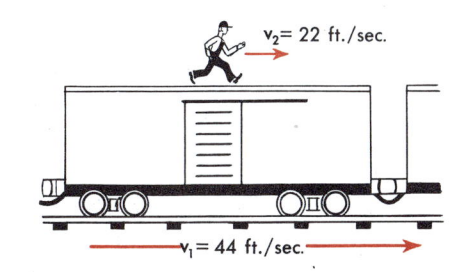

Fig. 2. How fast is the brakeman moving relative to the train? To the track?

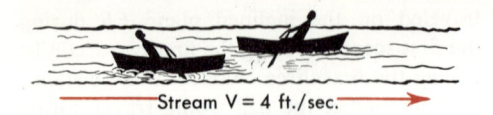

Fig. 3. If the boy rows 4 ft. per sec. in still water, what is the speed of the boat downstream? Upstream?

Stream V = 4 ft./sec.

44 − 22, or 22 ft./sec., which is 15 mi./hr. Similarly, if a boat travels 9 ft./sec. in still water, in a stream which flows 4 ft./sec., it would travel 13 ft./sec. downstream and 5 ft./sec. upstream. Explain.

Now let us suppose that a hunter wants to cross a flooded river which is 8 mi. wide in a rowboat that averages 4 mi./hr. in still water. He heads his boat straight across the stream, which is flowing 3 mi./hr. How far downstream will the boat land and what time will be required to cross the river?

If there were no current and the water were calm, the boat's path would be a straight line, AB, directly across the river, and the time required would be $8/4$ or 2 hr. When the stream is flowing 3 mi./hr. the boat has two velocities: one downstream 3 mi./hr., another straight across the stream 4 mi./hr. These are combined graphically as shown in Fig. 4(b).

As shown there, the resultant velocity is 5 mi./hr., but the component straight across the river is 4 mi./hr. Hence, the time required to cross the 8-mile river is 2 hr., and the distance which the boat floats downstream is 2 × 3 or 6 mi. below the place where the boat was launched.

Now let us suppose that the boat travels 5 instead of 4 mi./hr. in still water, and that the hunter wants to travel straight across the river. To do so he has to head his boat across and upstream. As shown in (b) of Fig. 5, the velocity component in this direction is 5 mi./hr.; the velocity along the actual course is 4 mi./hr.; and the drift is 3 mi./hr. The time required to cross the stream is $8/4$ or 2 hours. Using a protractor, find the angle BAC. What simple instrument could the hunter use to keep him on the proper course?

SUMMARY AND CONCLUSIONS

1. Velocity is the distance traveled per unit of time.
2. Distance = average velocity × time. That is, $S = \overline{V}t$.
3. Acceleration is change in velocity per unit of time.
4. For uniformly accelerated motion, when the body starts from rest, the average veloc-

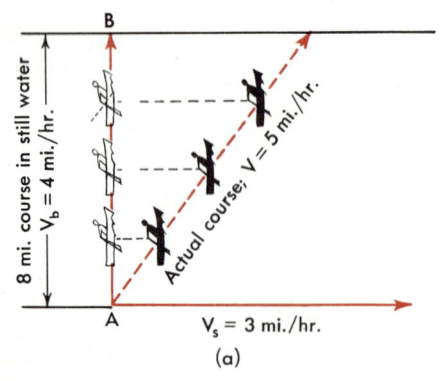

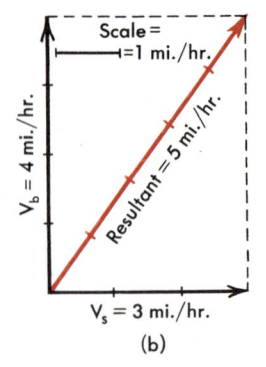

Fig. 4. Combining velocities. The hunter heads the boat straight across the stream and lands downstream as shown.

DISTANCE, VELOCITY, TIME, AND ACCELERATION

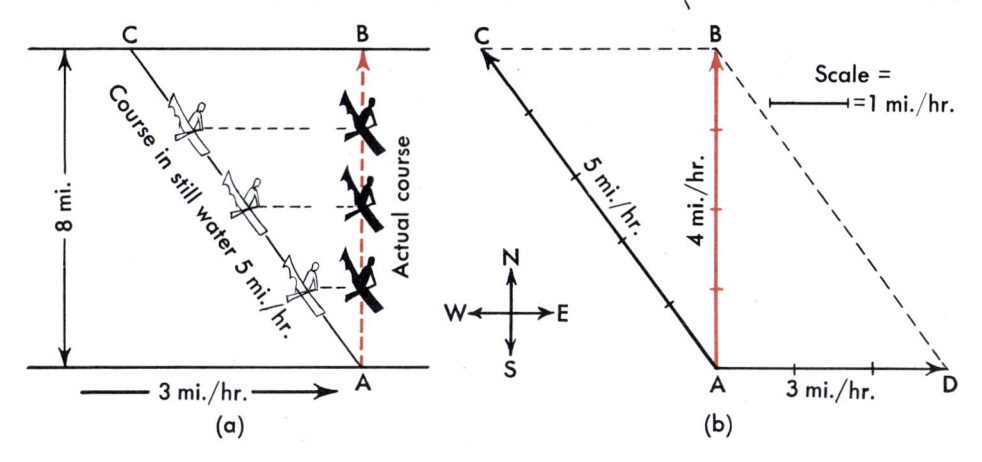

Fig. 5. Combining velocities. What is the resultant velocity of the boat relative to the land?

ity, $\overline{V}$, equals the final velocity V divided by two, $\overline{V} = \dfrac{V}{2}$. When the body does not start from rest, $\overline{V} = \dfrac{V_0 + V}{2}$, where V_0 = the initial velocity and V = the final velocity.

5. The equations for uniformly accelerated motion, <u>starting from rest</u>, are:
   (a) $V = at$
   (b) $S = \frac{1}{2} at^2$
   (c) $V^2 = 2aS$

6. We combine two parallel velocities by finding their algebraic sum. If the two are at some angle other than 180° or zero degrees, we combine them by graph, using vector diagrams.

QUESTIONS FOR REVIEW

1. What is velocity? How is average velocity found when distance and time are known?
2. What is acceleration?
3. Does the speedometer of an automobile measure velocity or acceleration?
4. A boy is paid 50 cents the first day he works; $1.00 the second; $1.50 the third day; and so on. His pay is said to be uniformly accelerated. What is the acceleration? What would his pay be for the tenth day? Write the formula which would give his pay for any day in question.
5. Find the average speed in ft./sec. of (a) total amount of money that the boy of Question 4 would earn at the end of any given day, starting with the first day.
6. When an airplane is to be landed on the deck of an aircraft carrier, the carrier usually is steaming at top speed into the wind and the plane approaches from the rear. Explain the reasons for making landings in this manner.

PROBLEMS

1. 120 mi./hr. is equivalent to how many mi./min.? How many ft./min.? How many ft./sec.?
2. Assuming that 1 mi./hr. is equivalent to a velocity of 1.5 ft./sec., find the velocity in ft./sec. of (a) 20 mi./hr.; (b) 80 mi./hr.; (c) 50 mi./hr.
3. The following velocities are equivalent to how many miles per hour: (a) 15 ft./sec.? (b) 60 ft./sec.? (c) 100 ft./sec.? (d) 150 ft./sec.?
4. An automobile was driven 180 mi. in 6 hr. What was its average velocity? At this rate how far would it travel in 10 hr.? 15 hr.?
5. Write the formula which would give the a track man who runs the 100-yard dash in 10 sec.; (b) a swimmer who does the 440-yard swim in 5 min.

6. An automobile started from rest and its velocity was read then and each second thereafter for 6 sec. The readings, in mi./hr. converted to ft./sec., were as follows: 0, 3, 6, 9, 12, 15, 18. What was the average velocity in ft./sec.? What distance did the automobile travel in 6 sec.?

7. What was the average velocity for the automobile in Problem 6 during the first 5 sec. of travel? How far did it travel in the first 5 sec.? What was the average velocity during the last 5 sec.? How far did the automobile travel during the last 5 sec.?

8. A runner moving 30 ft./sec. stops in 5 sec. Find (a) his negative acceleration; (b) his average speed while he is stopping; (c) the distance traveled while stopping.

9. If the acceleration of a ball, which starts from rest, is 8 ft./sec.^{2}, what will its velocity be after 1 sec.? 2 sec.? 8 sec.?

10. A subway train attained a speed of 33 mi./hr. (50 ft./sec.) in 40 sec., after leaving a station. What was its acceleration? Assume the acceleration was uniform.

11. A ball starts from rest and has an acceleration of 6 ft./sec.^{2}. What will its velocity be at the end of 1 sec.? 2 sec.? 3 sec.? 10 sec.?

12. In Problem 11, what is the average velocity during the first 10 sec.? What is the distance traveled during the first 10 sec.? Solve the latter two different ways.

13. If the acceleration of a rolling ball, starting from rest, is 8 ft./sec.^{2}, what distance will it travel in 5 sec.? If the ball travels for 10 sec., what will be its average velocity during the last 6 seconds? What distance will it travel during these 6 seconds?

14. If the negative acceleration of a train is 2 ft./sec.^{2}, what distance will it travel while stopping in 1 min.?

15. A ball with an acceleration of 8 ft./sec.^{2} has traveled 64 ft. from rest. What is its velocity? How many seconds has it been in motion?

16. If an automobile traveling 30 ft./sec. can stop in 20 ft., what is the negative acceleration?

17. An airplane was launched from a ship by means of a catapult. The distance the airplane was pushed was 60 ft. and its velocity was 70 mi./hr. Find the acceleration given the plane.

18. In trying to find out how rapidly a man can be stopped without bodily injury, a rocket sled containing a human volunteer was slowed from 150 mi./hr. to 75 mi./hr. in 1/5 sec. What was the negative acceleration in mi./hr./sec.? ft./sec.^{2}? What was the average velocity in ft./sec.? What distance did the sled travel?

19. If an automobile traveling 60 ft./sec. can be stopped in 80 ft., what is the negative acceleration?

20. What distance is required to stop an automobile going 30 mi./hr. if the negative acceleration is 4.5 ft./sec.^{2}?

21. Assuming that the negative acceleration is 4 ft./sec.^{2}, what distance is required to stop an automobile which is traveling 60 mi./hr.? 80 mi./hr.?

22. Bob Feller, one of the "fastest" pitchers of all time, could throw a ball about 145 ft./sec. Suppose that the time required for him to move his hand from the back to the front part of a pitch is 2/15 sec. (a) Find the average acceleration. (b) Find the distance from the rearmost position to the foremost position of the pitch.

23. A man rows a boat in still water at the rate of 4 mi./hr. He heads it straight across a river which is 2 mi. wide. The boat is carried downstream by the current at the rate of 3 mi./hr. How far downstream will the man be when he lands? How far will he be from where he started? What will be his resultant speed?

PROJECTS

1. Consult an insurance agency concerning the number of automobile accidents that occur in the United States and in your community each year. Then make a report to the class. Also think of as many ways as possible to remedy this situation in your community, especially near your school building. Consult the safety officers and others concerning the problems. Above all things be careful when driving. It may save your life.

2. Make a chart showing the distances required to stop an automobile which is traveling at various speeds. Assume the negative acceleration to be 4.5 ft./sec.^{2}.

3. Under the supervision of your instructor and police officers, check the reliability of your chart, using automobiles with brakes in good working order. Then make other charts showing your findings.

READING YOU WILL ENJOY

1. Hogben, Lancelot, *Science for the Citizen,* pp. 270-283. Alfred A. Knopf, Inc., New York, 1938. Contains an interesting and penetrating discussion of the problem of motion.

2. Richardson, J. S., and G. P. Cahoon, *Methods and Materials for Teaching General and Physical Science,* pp. 282-283. McGraw-Hill Book Company, Inc., New York, 1951. Explains how to measure the speeds of bodies.

3. Sutton, R. M., *Demonstration Experiments in Physics,* pp. 37-43. McGraw-Hill Book Company, Inc., New York, 1938. Contains a number of interesting experiments involving motion.

Chapter 15

A Further Study of Falling Bodies

The problem. As you may recall from Chapter 1, experimental physics is supposed to have begun when Galileo climbed to the top of the Leaning Tower of Pisa and dropped together a cannon ball and a musket ball.

According to tradition, the event was a dramatic one. We can imagine how Galileo must have felt as he climbed the stairs before the unfriendly crowd, and how, when the signal was given for the simultaneous release of the balls, a hush and a feeling of expectancy must have spread over the audience. We can imagine, too, the disappointment Galileo's associates must have felt as they saw the balls fall together and hit the ground together. Although some of them must have felt deep in their hearts that they were fighting a losing battle, still none of them would admit it. Instead, they hurried back to Aristotle's books to make sure that they had not misread his writings by chance. And much to their delight they found they had made no mistake. For there it was, that the speed of a falling body is proportional to its weight.

The net result was that Galileo's opponents multiplied. A less determined young man and one not thoroughly honest with himself would have given up the fight. But the antagonism only caused him to work even harder in his study of motion, particularly the study of falling bodies. With the exception of the social antagonism, Galileo's problem was much the same as ours; namely, that of finding the nature of the motion of a freely falling body.

What is the nature of the motion of a freely falling body? Since the velocity of a body in free fall increases with both the time and the distance fallen, then probably the motion is uniformly accelerated. Assuming this is true, our problem would almost be solved provided that we could find the acceleration, because we already know the laws governing uniformly accelerated motion.

Unfortunately, there is no instrument that can be attached to a falling body to determine its acceleration directly as a speedometer determines the speed of an automobile. Moreover, with the apparatus found in most high school laboratories the rapidly changing velocities needed to compute the acceleration of a falling body cannot be determined with either enough exactness or enough consistency for us to know whether the acceleration is uniform and constant.

A FURTHER STUDY OF FALLING BODIES

For days this problem haunted Galileo. Finally, he got the "hunch" that perhaps free fall is the same kind of motion as that on an inclined plane. Free fall, Galileo assumed, is a special case of motion down an inclined plane—a case in which the plane stands straight up and down instead of slanting.

Galileo believed that he could use an inclined plane to slow up or "dilute" the motion of free fall sufficiently so that he could measure both velocity and distance with a high degree of accuracy. With the data thus obtained, he could formulate the general laws of motion on inclined planes.

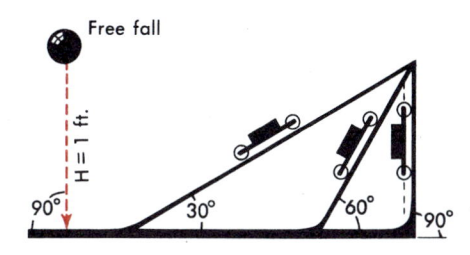

Fig. 1. Free fall and motion down an incline.

He could then modify these to fit the special case of falling bodies. Even though Galileo was on the right track, he never did find the actual acceleration of a freely falling body.

Galileo did make a discovery that may help us. He discovered that if a ball rolls down several different nearly frictionless inclined planes, each having a different length and a different angle of incline but all having the same height, the velocity that the ball acquires is the same at the foot of each plane. This meant, Galileo believed, that the velocity acquired by a body in descent depends solely on the vertical height fallen through and is independent of the angle of inclination and length of plane. That is, if the height, H, of several different inclined planes is 1 foot, as shown in Fig. 1, the velocity of the car when it rolls down each is the same at the bottom for all the planes.

Using a car with nearly frictionless wheels, as shown in Fig. 2, for a plane 1 foot high the velocity of the car at the bottom is 8 ft./sec. The velocity is this amount for planes having different inclinations but all having the same vertical height of 1 foot.

Therefore, it is logical that when a freely falling body drops 1 foot from rest, it should have the same velocity (8 ft./sec.) as that of a car that drops 1 foot in rolling down an inclined plane. Knowing the distance $S = H = 1$ ft., and the velocity $V = 8$ ft./sec., we can compute the acceleration of a freely falling body by using the following formula:

$$V^2 = 2aH$$

Substituting, $8 \times 8 = 2 \times a \times 1$
Multiplying, $2a = 64$
Dividing, $a = 32$ ft./sec.^{2}

Hence we see, theoretically at least, that the acceleration of a freely falling body is *32 ft./sec.*^{2}. A new symbol, g, is used for the acceleration in free fall.

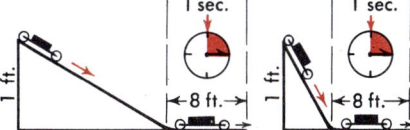

Fig. 2. The heights of the inclined planes are equal. The distance that the cart rolls in one second on each horizontal plane is 8 ft. What is the velocity of the cart?

THE RIDDLE OF MOTION

Testing our computed value of g by experiment. There is no simple, direct way of testing the acceleration just computed. However, if g is 32 ft./sec.², then we should be able to compute the distance a body will fall in ¼, ½, 1, 2, and any other number of seconds, and the results should agree with those found by experiment. For example, in ½ second the distance a ball should fall from rest is found as follows:

$$S = \tfrac{1}{2}gt^2$$
$$S = \tfrac{1}{2} \times 32 \times \tfrac{1}{2} \times \tfrac{1}{2}$$
$$S = 4 \text{ ft.}$$

We can check this distance, as shown in Fig. 3, by suspending a pendulum 39.1 inches long so that it will swing just clear of the floor. Four feet above the lowest point of the swing and about an inch to one side drive a nail as shown. Tie a long silk thread to a steel ball and pull the ball to the upper nail by the thread. Then pull back the pendulum with a short piece of twine and hold the thread and the twine in one hand, as shown. Finally, sever the thread and the twine simultaneously so that the ball falls and the pendulum swings and note when the ball and pendulum strike each other. Experiment will show that the time for the pendulum to swing the distance that it does is ½ second. How far does the ball fall?

This experiment shows that g, the acceleration of a freely falling body, is approximately 32 ft./sec.². The correct value is 32.16 at sea level at 45° north latitude. It varies slightly with the location, depending upon the distance from the center of mass of the earth. In this book, unless otherwise stated, g in the English system of units will be 32 ft./sec.². In the metric system g is 980 cm./sec.², or 9.8 m./sec.².

Other predictions as to how far a freely falling body travels in various times are given in Table 1. During World War II the United States Army Air Forces made some very exacting checks on these data and found that for streamlined bodies they agree very closely with the experimental values up to a distance of about 600 feet. Thus Galileo's case was proven beyond a shadow of a doubt.

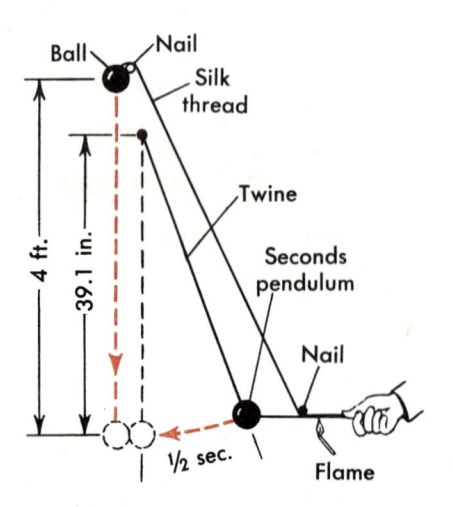

Fig. 3. The seconds pendulum bob and the falling ball collide at the end of ½ second. How far has the ball fallen?

Table 1
DISTANCES THAT A BODY FALLS DURING VARIOUS TIMES, IN SECONDS

Time (sec.)	Distance (ft.) $S=\tfrac{1}{2}gt^2$	Velocity (ft./sec.) $V=gt$	Distance traveled in last sec. (ft.)
0	$D_0=0$	$V_0=0$	
1	$D_1=16$	$V_1=32$	$D_1-D_0=16$
2	$D_2=64$	$V_2=64$	$D_2-D_1=48$
3	$D_3=144$	$V_3=$?	$D_3-D_2=$?
4	$D_4=$?	$V_4=$?	?
5	$D_5=$?	$V_5=$?	?
6	$D_6=$?	$V_6=$?	?

Copy and complete this table.

If a body is accelerated twice 32, or 64 ft./sec.², its acceleration is said to be 2 g's. If its acceleration is 96 ft./sec.², its acceleration is 3 g's. What is the acceleration in ft./sec.² of a body whose acceleration is 4 g's? Experiment shows that a human body can be accelerated as much as 30 g's for a very small fraction of a second without injury.

In conclusion, we see that the acceleration g of a falling body is uniform and is 32 ft./sec.² In the metric system, g is 980 cm./sec.², or 9.8 m./sec.².

Hence, the formulas which apply to uniformly accelerated motion in general also apply to the motion of falling bodies. However, in order to distinguish the general formulas from those for falling bodies, the a in each case is changed to g, as shown below:

General formulas for accelerated motion	Formulas for free fall
$V = at$	$V = gt$
$S = \frac{1}{2}at^2$	$S = \frac{1}{2}gt^2$
$V^2 = 2aS$	$V^2 = 2gS$

The nature of the motion of a body that is thrown straight upward. In (a) of Fig. 4, it is shown that if a frictionless ball is released at the top of an inclined plane so that it rolls down the plane and up another, the ball will go up the second plane until its vertical height is the same as the starting height. Then when the ball rolls back down the second plane it will roll back up the first plane until it reaches its original height. This indicates that the velocity of the ball, at the point where it starts up either plane, is exactly the same as when it rolls past that point on the way down the plane.

On the way up the plane, the rate of loss of velocity (negative acceleration) seems to equal the rate of gain of velocity (positive acceleration) on the way down. That is, the motion up the incline seems to be the very opposite, or reverse, of the motion down the incline. What is the velocity of the ball at the highest point that it reaches?

These facts, plus what we know about falling bodies, indicate that if a cannon ball is fired straight up (Fig. 4b), it will lose velocity at the rate of 32 ft./sec.², just as it gains velocity on the way down at the rate of 32 ft./sec.² At the top of the flight the upward velocity should equal zero, and when the ball returns to the point from which it was fired its velocity should equal the velocity with which it was fired upward. The time in flight up should equal the time down. What else would be true of the up-and-down motion? The experiments that prove all these reasoned consequences are left to the students.

In dealing with bodies that are thrown straight up, the V in the formulas $V = gt$ and $V^2 = 2gH$ becomes the initial velocity or starting velocity and not the final velocity.

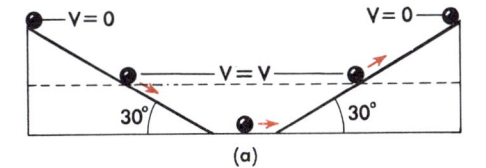

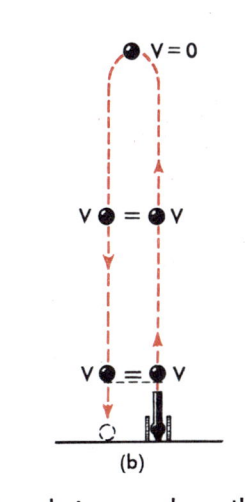

Fig. 4. In what way does the up-and-down motion of a ball thrown straight up resemble that of the ball in (a)?

PROBLEM 1: If a ball is thrown straight up with a velocity of 96 ft./sec., what time is required for it to reach the uppermost point of its flight?

SOLUTION:
$$V = gt$$
Substituting,
$$96 = 32t$$
Solving for t,
$$t = 3 \text{ sec.}$$

If we wish to know how high the ball goes, we make use of the following formula:
$$S = \tfrac{1}{2} gt^2$$
Substituting,
$$S = \tfrac{1}{2} \times 32 \times 3 \times 3$$
$$S = 144 \text{ ft.}$$

PROBLEM 2: Assuming no air resistance, if a ball is thrown straight up with a velocity of 144 ft./sec., what time is required for it to reach the uppermost point of its flight? How high will it go? How long will it be in flight? What will be its velocity when it returns to the same height from which it was thrown?

Fig. 5. When the parachute opens, the jumper reaches a terminal velocity of 18 to 22 feet per second.
Courtesy Department of Defense

Air friction and terminal velocity. During the first several feet through which a body such as a stone falls, there is little air resistance in proportion to its weight. One reason for this is that the velocity is low. But since the air resistance varies approximately as the square of the velocity, at higher speeds the air resistance may be considerable. When a stone falls so fast that the *drag*, or air resistance, equals the gravitational pull, it has reached its *terminal velocity*, which is constant.

Very small objects like dust particles and water droplets, and objects such as feathers which have low densities and relatively large surface areas for their weights, have very low terminal velocities and hence fall only short distances before their velocities are constant. A raindrop falls about 18 feet before reaching its terminal velocity. A man jumping from a plane reaches a terminal velocity of about 120 mi./hr. (176 ft./sec.) if he delays opening his parachute. When the parachute is opened, the terminal velocity is decreased to about 12 or 15 miles per hour, or to about 18 to 22 feet per second. Twelve miles per hour is equal to the velocity gained in a jump from a height of 5 feet.

It has been calculated that a hollow iron sphere 5 inches in diameter weighing 2.6 pounds, if released at 20,000 feet, would fall 6,300 feet before reaching a terminal velocity of 240 miles per hour (352 feet per second). The ball would accelerate rapidly at first and decelerate later because of the greater air resistance at lower altitudes.

The pendulum. Why the pendulum should be studied along with falling bodies and motion on inclined planes may not be apparent. Perhaps a short study of the history of the pendulum will give us the reason.

Tradition has it that in 1583, when Galileo was a medical student at the University of Pisa, he became fascinated one Sunday, when attending church, by the motion of a huge hanging lamp which had been lighted and left swinging. Using the beats of his pulse as a timing device, he timed the to-and-fro motion. The discovery that he made started Galileo upon a new quest.

Disregarding the small effects of friction and air resistance, Galileo found that a pendulum swings as far beyond the center position of the arc as it was from this position when it started. Also he pointed out that the height of the pendulum before the swing and its height after completion were equal. This was also true, you will recall, for a car or ball that rolled down one inclined plane and up another. Could a ball and two inclined planes, properly arranged, be used as a pendulum?

It should be noted that for a simple pendulum, the distance from A (Fig. 6) to the center of the mass of the ball is called the *length* of the pendulum; also, that the mass of the cord is negligible in comparison with the mass of the ball or pendulum *bob*. The time required for a pendulum to swing in one direction through its complete arc and back again to the starting position is called the *period* of the pendulum.

The laws governing a simple pendulum. Most of us know that the shorter the pendulum, the faster it swings back and forth; that is, the period seems to decrease as the length of the pendulum decreases. But such knowledge is of little importance unless we know how much faster it swings for any given shortening of the length. Another factor that might affect the period is the mass of the pendulum. You will recall, however, that when a car or ball rolls down an inclined plane, the mass of the body does not affect the time. Is this true of the pendulum?

In order to answer these questions, four

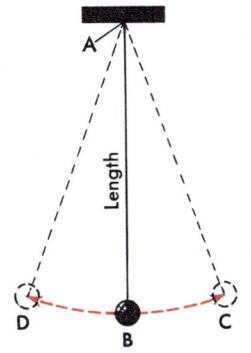

Fig. 6. The time required for this pendulum to travel from D to C and back to D again is the period of the pendulum.

simple pendulums are suspended as shown in Fig. 7. M, N, and O are made of metal and P is made of wood, making its mass much less than the mass of O. The lengths of M, N, and O are in the ratio of 1 : 4 : 9; for example, 20, 80, and 180 cm. The length of P is the same as the length of O.

When O and P are set in vibration and timed with a stop watch, the periods are found to be equal. The mass of the pendu-

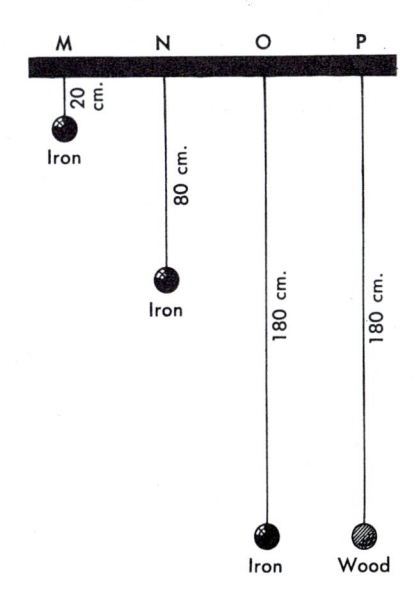

Fig. 7. How are the periods of M, N, and O related?

lum seems to have nothing to do with the time. If the arc is less than about 16°, this equality of time is true regardless of whether the arc is 1 degree or 16 degrees.

When the periods of all the pendulums are determined, it is found that the period for M is 0.35 second; for N the period is 0.70 second, and for O and P it is 1.05 seconds. That is, the ratio of the periods is 1 : 2 : 3, which equals the ratio of the square roots of the respective lengths:

$$1 : 2 : 3 = \sqrt{1} : \sqrt{4} : \sqrt{9}.$$

Hence, in conclusion:

1. **The period (time of a complete vibration) is independent of the material and mass of the pendulum.**
2. **The period is independent of the length of the arc (up to about 16°) through which the pendulum swings.**
3. **The period is proportional to the square root of the length of the pendulum.**

A little thought will show that the period of vibration must depend upon the force of gravity. For as shown in Fig. 6, when the pendulum falls from C to B it is gravity which accelerates it. Hence, the greater the acceleration due to gravity, the more quickly it falls to D and hence the smaller the period. Experiment verifies this and shows that there is a fourth principle governing the motion of a pendulum. It is:

4. **The period of vibration of a pendulum is inversely proportional to the square root of the acceleration, g, due to gravity.**

Combining these into a single formula, we have:

$$t = K\sqrt{\frac{l}{g}}$$

in which t is the time in seconds, l is the length of the pendulum in feet or centimeters, and g is in ft./sec.^{2} or in cm./sec.^{2}. By experiment, the constant K is found to be 2π. Hence the formula for finding the period, t, is as follows:

$$t = 2\pi\sqrt{\frac{l}{g}}$$

PROBLEM: What is the length of a pendulum whose period for one complete vibration is 1 second?

SOLUTION:

$$t = 2\pi\sqrt{\frac{l}{g}}$$

Solving for l,

$$l = \frac{t^2 g}{4\pi^2}$$

Substituting,

$$l = \frac{1^2 \times 980}{4(3.14)^2}$$

$$l = \frac{980}{9.87 \times 4}$$

$$l = 24.8 \text{ cm.}$$

What would be the length of a pendulum which requires 1 second to traverse the arc one way? Such a pendulum is called a *seconds* pendulum.

Center of percussion and center of oscillation. It is well known that if a batter wants to hit a baseball the maximum distance, he must hit it at a certain place on the bat. This place at which the most effective blow can be produced is called the *center of percussion*. A blow struck near either the large end or the handle end of the bat gives a painful sting to the hands. Little or no sting is felt when the ball is hit at the center of percussion. Although it is not apparent, there is a relation between the center of percussion and the center of oscillation of a pendulum.

If we suspend both a baseball bat, as shown in Fig. 8, and a pendulum of the same length, the period of the bat is

A FURTHER STUDY OF FALLING BODIES

General formulas for accelerated motion
(a) $V = at$
(b) $S = \frac{1}{2}at^2$
(c) $V^2 = 2aS$

Formulas for free fall
$V = gt$
$S = \frac{1}{2}gt^2$
$V^2 = 2gS$

5. For a pendulum, the period of a complete vibration is directly proportional to the square root of the length of the pendulum and inversely proportional to the square root of the acceleration due to gravity, g. That is:

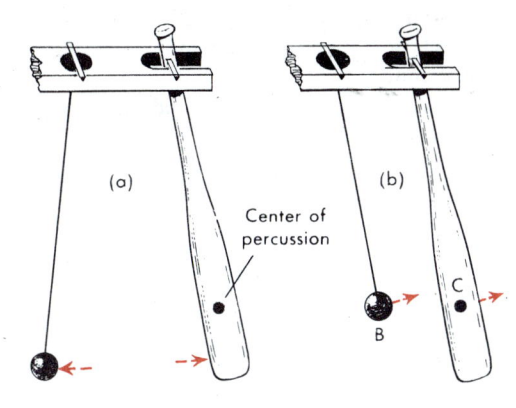

$$t = 2\pi \sqrt{\frac{l}{g}}$$

Fig. 8. How do the periods of the ball and bat compare in (a) and (b)?

shorter than the period of the pendulum. In case, however, the pendulum is shortened until its period is the same as that of the ball bat, the center of percussion of the bat is located directly opposite the center of the ball B at the point C. And if a hole is bored through the bat at C and the bat is suspended so that it can swing about this point, the periods of the bat and pendulum will again be equal.

SUMMARY AND CONCLUSIONS

1. We see that the acceleration of a body moving down a nearly frictionless inclined plane is constant and hence the formulas $S = \frac{1}{2}at^2$, $V = at$, and $V^2 = 2aS$ all apply to such motion.
2. Free fall is a special case of the motion on an inclined plane.
3. The acceleration, g, of a freely falling body expressed in various units is:

(a) $g = 32$ ft./sec.^{2}
(b) $g = 980$ cm./sec.^{2}
(c) $g = 9.8$ m./sec.^{2}

4. For free-fall motion the general formulas for accelerated motion are changed as follows:

QUESTIONS FOR REVIEW

1. Why did Galileo endeavor to solve the problem of falling bodies by studying the motion of bodies on inclined planes?
2. What assumption did Galileo make concerning the motion of a body rolling down an inclined plane and the motion of a freely falling body?
3. Define velocity and then write your definition as an algebraic formula.
4. When several different inclined planes have different lengths but equal heights, compare the velocities at the bottom of each when a frictionless car rolls from the top to the bottom.
5. What is the acceleration of a freely falling body? What causes it to vary at different points on the earth's surface?
6. What is meant by the period of a pendulum?
7. What effect does the doubling of the mass have on the period of a pendulum?
8. If the length of the arc of a pendulum is increased, how is the period affected?
9. If the length of a pendulum is increased four times, how is the period affected?
10. If g, the acceleration of a falling body, is increased, how is the period of a pendulum affected?
11. Could a pendulum be used to find g, the acceleration of a falling body?
12. Assuming you have a pendulum clock, what adjustment of the pendulum bob should be made if the clock gains time? If it loses time? How are the adjustments made?

PROBLEMS

1. What is the velocity of a body, falling from rest, at the end of ¼ second? ½ second? 1 second? 2 seconds? What is the acceleration in each case?
2. What is the average velocity of a freely falling body during the first second of fall? During the first 2 seconds? First ¼ second? First ½ second?
3. How far does a freely falling body travel during the first ¼ second? ½ second? 1 second? 2 seconds?
4. What is the gain in velocity of a falling body during the third second of fall; that is, between the end of the second second and the end of the third second? What distance does the body fall during the third second?
5. How far does a freely falling body travel during the eighth second that it falls?
6. A falling body has traveled 256 feet from rest. What is its velocity? What length of time has it fallen?
7. A falling body has fallen 512 feet from rest. What is its velocity? What length of time has it fallen?
8. A ball is thrown upward from the ground with a velocity of 128 ft./sec. How long is required for it to reach the ground again? How high does it travel? What is its velocity when it again reaches the starting elevation?
9. What time is required for a freely falling ball to acquire a velocity of 80 ft./sec.? How far will it travel during this time? What will be its velocity in miles per hour?
10. How far would a body have to fall in order to acquire the speed of an automobile that is traveling 60 miles per hour? What would probably happen if you were to fall this far?
11. A boy standing on a bridge dropped a stone into the water below. If it took 3 seconds for the stone to reach the water, how high was the bridge above the water?
12. A ball is shot straight up with a velocity of 160 ft./sec. What is its upward velocity after 2 seconds? 3 seconds? 5 seconds?
13. In Problem 12, what would be the velocity of the ball after 6 seconds? At the end of 10 seconds?
14. What would be the length of a pendulum whose period for one complete vibration is 4 seconds?
15. What is the period of a pendulum whose length is 400 cm.?
16. What is the length of a pendulum whose period is π seconds?

PROJECTS

1. Find g, the acceleration of a falling body, by using a pendulum.
2. Make the apparatus shown in Fig. 9 and determine the reaction time for both hands and both feet for each student in your class. Make the height, H, of the apparatus about 1.5 feet. The height is adjusted so that the ball barely misses the hand. The observer being tested is supposed to jerk his hand or foot away when the operator drops the ball. Find the distance the ball falls. Then, using the formula $S = \frac{1}{2}gt^2$, determine the time. Of what importance is the reaction time when a person is driving an automobile? Make a graph showing the reaction time for each student tested.
3. Hold a meter stick suspended by one end between the thumb and forefinger and ask a

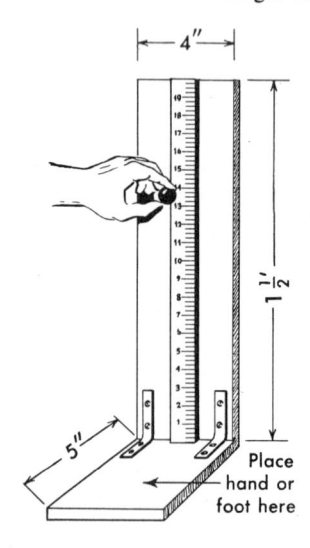

Fig. 9. Apparatus for determining reaction time.

friend to strike its edge with a mild blow at several different points, say at 50 cm., then at 90 cm., and finally at 66⅔ cm. Do it enough times so the results are evident to you. Try to discover the significance and some applications of your discovery. Then demonstrate and explain to your class.

4. Drill a small hole as near to the end of a meter stick as can safely be done. Drill another hole at the 66⅔ cm. mark. Support the meter stick on a nail, first at the end and then at the other hole, and in each case, using the stick as a pendulum, determine its period of vibration. A stop watch would help. Report and discuss your findings.

READING YOU WILL ENJOY

1. Hogben, Lancelot, *Science for the Citizen*, pp. 283-290. Alfred A. Knopf, Inc., New York, 1938. Galileo's attempt to determine the acceleration of a falling body.
2. Russell, Bertrand, *The Scientific Outlook*, pp. 13-40. W. W. Norton & Company, Inc., New York, 1931. The contributions of Galileo and Newton.
3. Swezey, K. M., *After-Dinner Science*. Whittlesey House, McGraw-Hill Book Company, Inc., New York, 1948. "The Pendulum Keeps Time," p. 62, and "Why a Baseball Bat Stings," p. 63.

Chapter 16

Newton's Laws of Motion

The problem. To many, the fact that a 1-pound ball falls as fast as a 2-pound ball is contrary to common sense. They know from experience that when a cart is pushed, a baseball is thrown, or a hockey puck is hit, the greater the force, the greater the velocity. Consequently they conclude, as Aristotle did, that the velocity varies directly with the force and that, therefore, the heavier a body is, the faster it falls.

Although experiment shows that freely falling bodies behave otherwise, it is not easy to explain why they do. Nor is it easy to explain why unequal forces cause a pushed cart to have unequal velocities but cause falling bodies to have equal velocities.

In this chapter, our aim is to resolve this paradox of motion. Originally it was Newton who resolved it and, in doing so, he not only discovered the basic principle for a new physics but also laid the cornerstone for a new civilization. You may recall that Newton was born the same year that Galileo died.

In free fall, why do a 1-pound ball and a 2-pound ball have equal velocities when gravitational forces act on them? One explanation of this seemingly unorthodox motion is that a resisting force retards the motion of all falling bodies and this force is twice as great for a 2-pound ball as for a 1-pound ball. Logically this explanation may be correct; but before many would accept it, the source and cause of the force would have to be found.

One possible cause of an "antigravity force" is the gravitational attraction that nearby heavenly bodies, such as the sun and moon, have for all earthly bodies. But if these forces are the cause, what should be the effect on a falling body when these heavenly bodies are not directly overhead—for example, when they are on the opposite side of the earth, or are rising or setting? Are these effects noticeable? Do you accept or reject this hypothesis?

Another possible cause is the centrifugal force that results from the rotation of the earth and that tends to throw bodies off the earth much as a spinning automobile wheel throws water and mud off the tire. But if this were the cause, then at the earth's poles, where the earth's centrifugal force is zero, a 2-pound ball should fall faster than a 1-pound ball. Explorers at the poles find this is untrue.

Another hypothesis is that the retardation is a natural characteristic of matter. Have you ever accidentally stubbed your toe on a solid table leg or a heavy stone or brick? If so, then you know that these bodies tend to "stay put"; they resist being

NEWTON'S LAWS OF MOTION

What should happen and what does happen when the elevator is accelerated straight up? See (b) of Fig. 1.

If you do not have access to an elevator, you can perform these experiments by modifying the apparatus as shown in Fig. 2.

Since in these instances the logical consequences of the inertia hypothesis agree with experiment, we may tentatively conclude that in free fall, inertia causes a heavy body to fall with the same speed as a light body. Hence, Aristotle's belief that a 2-pound ball falls twice as fast as a 1-pound ball was wrong because he failed to consider the effects of inertia. But what

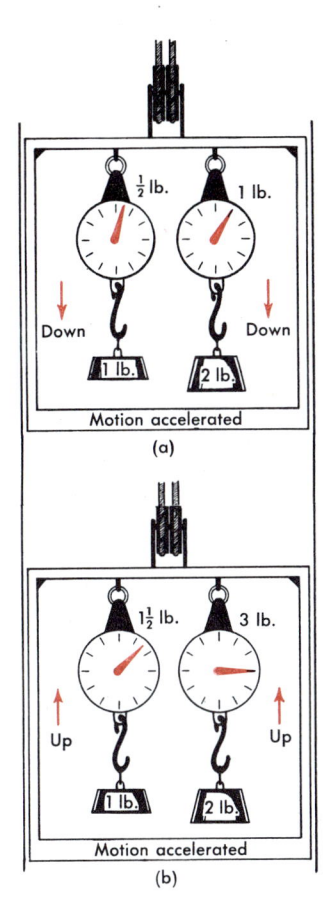

Fig. 1. Account for the scale readings.

set in motion; when at rest they tend to stay at rest. The tendency of a body at rest to stay at rest is called *inertia*. Other phases of inertia are discussed later.

Does inertia explain why, in free fall, a light and heavy ball fall together? In Fig. 1 a 1-pound mass and a 2-pound mass are each on a different spring balance in an elevator, and the elevator is accelerated downward. If the inertia hypothesis is correct, the inertia, the tendency of a body at rest to remain at rest, should tend to uphold each weight so that its apparent weight is reduced. And the reduction for the 2-pound weight should be twice that for the 1-pound weight. See Fig. 1 (a).

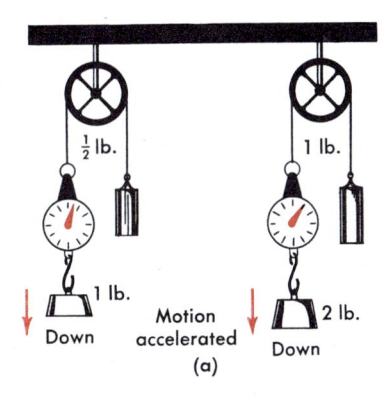

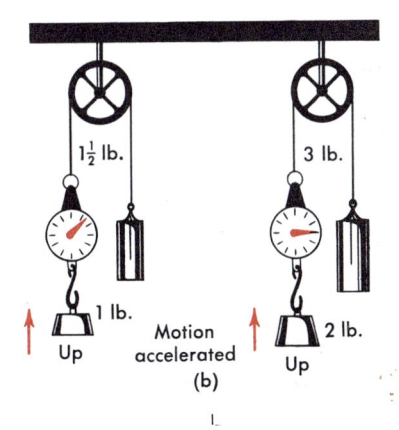

Fig. 2. What is the unbalanced force, the difference between the force up and the force of gravity, acting on each weight?

THE RIDDLE OF MOTION

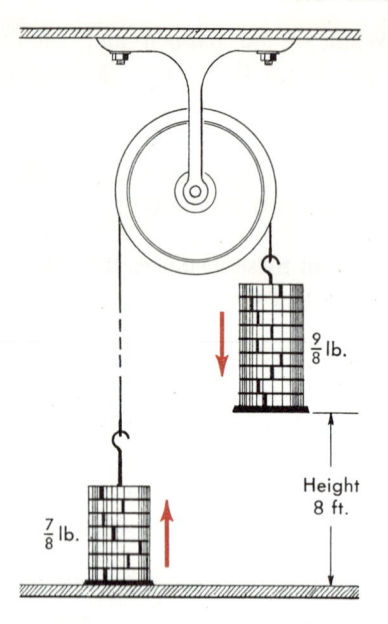

Fig. 3. Apparatus for finding the relation between the acceleration and the unbalanced force. The wheel is as nearly frictionless as possible.

about his assumption that velocity varies with force? Is it also false? Also, what about acceleration? Does it vary with force?

Is acceleration, velocity, or a combination of both, the real measure of force? To answer this question we will first resort to an experiment in which force is affected by only one of these possible factors at a time. Fig. 3 shows the equipment used, Table 1 gives the experimental results, and Fig. 4 shows the relationships discovered. Note that in every trial the total mass used was two pounds.

In trial 1 the relationship between force and velocity only was obtained. The acceleration was eliminated. This was done by making the velocity constant. The countermasses in Fig. 3 were adjusted so that *once the ball was set in motion* it did not gain or lose velocity. The results were obtained by making the countermasses each equal to one pound. Hence, the downward and upward forces were equal regardless of which way the system was started. As long as the velocity was constant, acceleration zero, the forces did not change with velocity. Therefore, the velocity of a body is not a measure of the force which acts on it. What about acceleration, then? Does it vary with force?

To answer these questions we will study the forces that act on the combined masses when the acceleration is varied by shifting parts of the masses from one side to the other, one-eighth of a pound at a time. See Fig. 3. The experimenter, however, should just release the mass and not set it in motion as he did when acceleration was zero. And if the data in the table are to be duplicated, then the masses should be adjusted so that the respective experimental times are the same as those in the table. The acceleration can then be computed with the formula $S = \frac{1}{2}at^2$. As you read further, refer to both Table 1 and Fig. 4.

In trial 2, the acceleration of the combined 2-pound mass was 4 ft./sec.^{2} and the unbalanced force was ¼ pound. In trial 3, the acceleration was 8 ft./sec.^{2} and the unbalanced force was ½ pound. In trial 4, the acceleration was 16 ft./sec.^{2}; the unbalanced force was one pound. In trial 5, the situation was the same as in free fall: the unbalanced force was 2 pounds, the same as the weight of the 2-lb. mass. Hence, the acceleration was 32 ft./sec.^{2} or 980 cm./sec.^{2}. The relationship between acceleration and the unbalanced force is shown graphically in Fig. 4b.

Hence, in conclusion,

the acceleration of a body varies directly as the unbalanced force acting upon it and is always in the direction of the unbalanced force.

NEWTON'S LAWS OF MOTION

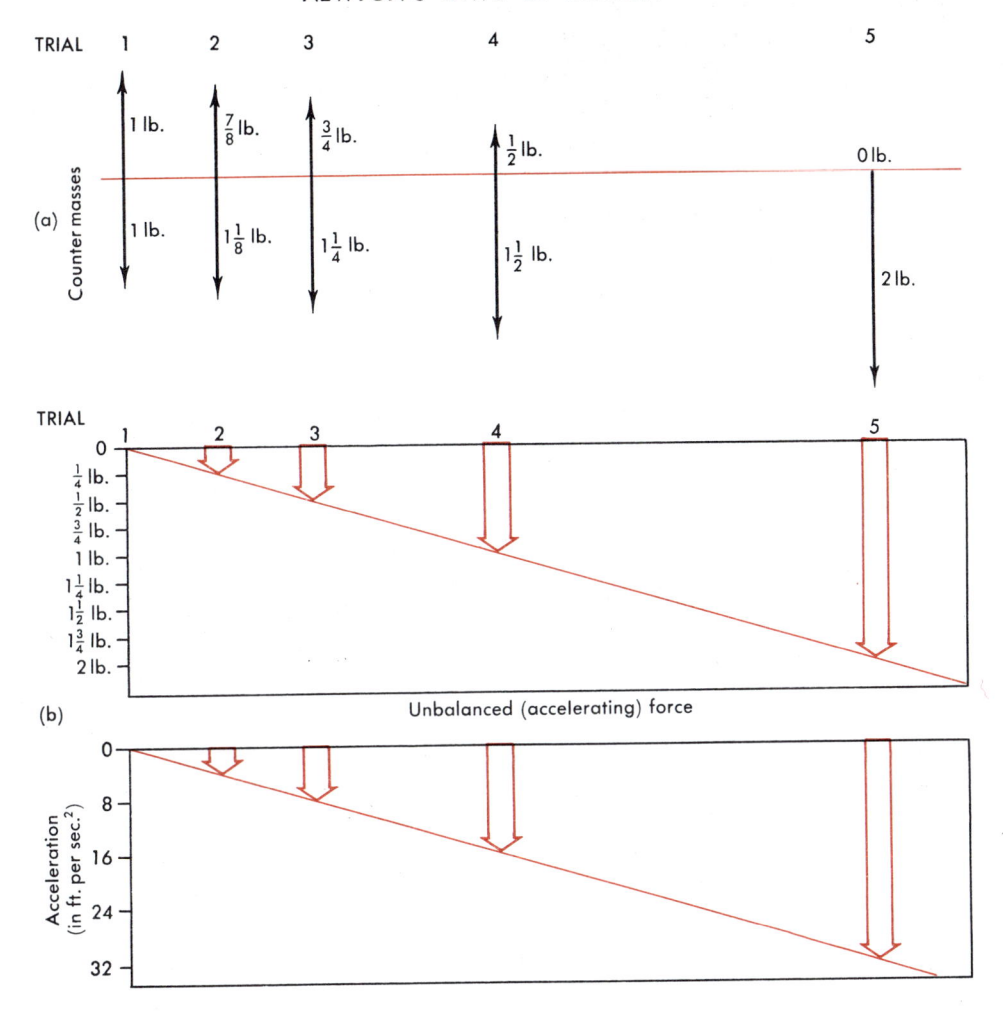

Fig. 4. The acceleration varies directly as the unbalanced force.

Table 1

Trial	Accelerated mass (lb.)	Unbalanced force (lb.)	Distance (ft.)	Time (sec.)	Acceleration (ft./sec.^{2})
1	{2 {2	Zero Zero	8 8	varied varied	Zero Zero
2	2	¼	8	2.0	4
3	2	½	8	1.41	8
4	2	1	8	1.0	16
5	2	2	8	0.71	32

Experimental data obtained through use of apparatus in Fig. 3. Distance traveled by mass was 8 feet. In trial 1, the velocity was constant. The mass was set in motion by the experimenter. In the other trials, the velocity was not constant; acceleration was not zero. The acceleration was computed with the formula $S = \frac{1}{2}at^2$. Note the relationship between the accelerations and the unbalanced forces.

Courtesy Northrop Aircraft Inc.

Fig. 5. One chicken dinner coming down! This chicken dinner is momentarily suspended in mid-air as the table was pulled out from under by a quick-starting sled. The sled is used to test the effect of acceleration on aircraft electronics equipment.

Furthermore, when the unbalanced force numerically equaled the total mass, the acceleration was 32 ft./sec.² or 980 cm./sec.².

PROBLEM: The mass of a cart is 100 lb. It is pulled on a level road by a horizontal force of 125 lb. The force necessary to overcome friction is 25 lb. What is the unbalanced force acting on the cart? What is the acceleration of the cart?

That the acceleration of a body is proportional to the unbalanced force is written mathematically as follows:

$$\frac{a}{a'} = \frac{f}{f'}$$

Here, f and f' represent the two unbalanced forces and a and a' represent the respective accelerations.

PROBLEM 1: Neglecting friction, if a 30-lb. force gives a cart an acceleration of 8 ft./sec.², what force is required to accelerate the cart 24 ft./sec.²?

SOLUTION:

$$\frac{f}{f'} = \frac{a}{a'}$$

Substituting,

$$\frac{30}{f'} = \frac{8}{24}$$

Solving,

$$f' = 90 \text{ lb.}$$

PROBLEM 2: What horizontal unbalanced force is necessary to accelerate a 160-lb. halfback 16 ft./sec.² if an unbalanced force of 160 lb. accelerates him 32 ft./sec.²?

PROBLEM 3: How much acceleration will be given a 16-lb. mass by an unbalanced force of 16 lb.? 8 lb.? 4 lb.? 1 lb.?

In free fall, why is not the acceleration of a 2-pound body twice that of a 1-pound body? If the acceleration varies directly with the unbalanced force, then logically in free fall the acceleration of a 2-pound body should be twice that of a 1-pound body. But experiment shows (Fig. 6a) this is untrue. We accounted for the experimental results by saying that the inertia of the 2-pound ball is twice that of the 1-pound ball.

Seemingly, the acceleration varies inversely with the inertia, which varies directly with the mass. Hence, as shown in Fig. 6 (b) we can see that, when the accelerating force is constant and the mass is doubled, the acceleration is halved, and so on. The acceleration varies inversely with the mass of a body.

Newton's second law of motion. The *law of acceleration* or *momentum,* which states that

the acceleration of a body varies directly as the unbalanced force acting upon it and inversely as the mass of the body,

was first formulated by Newton and is known as Newton's *second law of motion.*

NEWTON'S LAWS OF MOTION

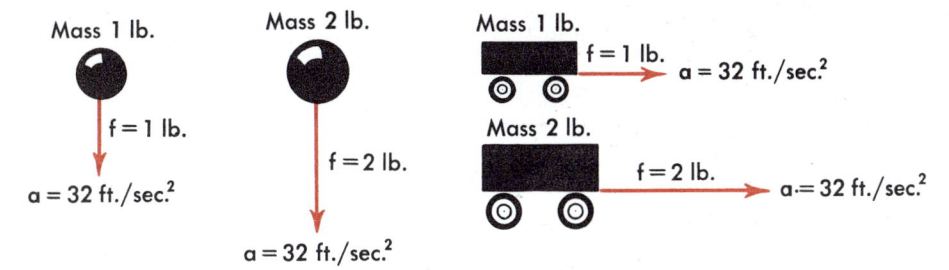

Fig. 6. (a) The acceleration of a body varies directly with the unbalanced force f acting upon it, when the mass is constant.

Mathematically, then

$$a \propto \frac{f}{m}$$

or,

$$ka = \frac{f}{m}$$

and

$$f = kma$$

In the equation $f = kma$, what is the value of k? We have already seen—in free fall, for example—that when the unbalanced force in pounds numerically equals the mass in pounds of the body, the acceleration is 32 ft./sec.² For example, an unbalanced force, f, of 1 pound gives a 1-pound mass, m, an acceleration of 32 ft./sec.² Substituting for the force and mass in

$$f = kma$$

we have $1 \text{ lb.} = k \times 1 \text{ lb.} \times 32 \text{ ft./sec.}^2$

Solving, $k = \dfrac{1 \text{ lb.}}{1 \text{ lb.} \times 32 \text{ ft./sec.}^2}$

or $k = \dfrac{1}{32 \text{ ft./sec.}^2} = \dfrac{1}{g}$

Make a similar development using metric units. Make the mass 1 gram and the force 1 gram. You should find k to equal $\dfrac{1}{980 \text{ cm./sec.}^2}$. That is, numerically, $k = \dfrac{1}{g} = \dfrac{1}{32}$ or $\dfrac{1}{980}$, depending on the units used.

PROBLEM 1: How much acceleration is given a 1-lb. mass by an unbalanced force of 2 lb.?

SOLUTION: $f = kma$

Substituting, $2 = \dfrac{1}{32} \times 1 \times a$

Solving, $a = 64 \text{ ft./sec.}^2$

Fig. 6. (b) The acceleration of a body varies inversely with the mass of a body, when the unbalanced force acting upon it is constant.

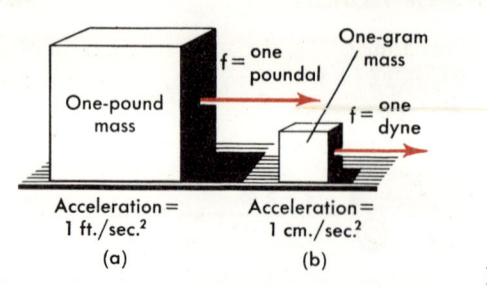

Fig. 7. (a) A poundal is that force which accelerates a 1-pound mass 1 ft. per sec.² (b) A dyne is that force which accelerates a 1-gram mass 1 cm. per sec.²

PROBLEM 2: How much acceleration is given a 1-lb. mass by an unbalanced force of 1 lb.? ½ lb.? ⅛ lb.? ¹⁄₃₂ lb.?

PROBLEM 3: How much acceleration is given a 1-gram mass by an unbalanced force of 1 gram? ½ gram? ¹⁄₁₀ gram? ¹⁄₉₈₀ gram?

The poundal—a new unit of force. We already know that an unbalanced force of 1 pound gives a 1-pound mass an acceleration of 32 ft./sec.². Consequently, in accordance with Newton's second law, an unbalanced ½-pound force gives a 1-pound mass an acceleration of 16 ft./sec.², a ⅛-pound force gives a 1-pound mass an acceleration of 4 ft./sec.², and an unbalanced force of 1/32 pound gives a 1-pound mass an acceleration of 1 ft./sec.².

The force that gives a 1-pound mass an acceleration of 1 ft./sec.² is called a *poundal*. See Fig. 7 (a).

Obviously, a poundal is 1/32 pound, and therefore 32 poundals equal 1 pound. Three pounds equal how many poundals? How many pounds equal 64 poundals?

PROBLEM: Using the formula $f = kma$, find the unbalanced force necessary to give a 10-lb. cart an acceleration of 16 ft./sec.². Find the answer in (a) pounds; (b) poundals.

SOLUTION:
(a) $f = kma$

$$f = \frac{10 \times 16}{32}$$

$f = 5$ lb.

(b) Since 1 lb. equals 32 poundals and $f = 5$ lb., then:

$f = 5 \times 32$, or 160 poundals

Do you see a shorter method for finding the force in poundals? If so, and it were used, what would be the value of k in the formula $f = kma$?

In the formula $f = kma$, what is the advantage of making $k = 1$ instead of 1/32? In finding the force in poundals in the problem above, we first found the force in pounds by dividing by 32 and then multiplied this answer by 32 to convert it to poundals. Obviously, dividing by 32 and then multiplying by 32 could be avoided entirely if k were made to equal 1 instead of 1/32. In other words, if you want to find the accelerating force, f, in poundals, then use the formula $f = ma$, in which the mass, m, is in pounds and the acceleration, a, is in ft./sec.².

PROBLEM: What unbalanced force in poundals is required to give a 10-lb. mass an acceleration of 16 ft./sec.²? This force is equivalent to how many pounds?

The dyne—a new unit of force in the metric system. We already know that in free fall an unbalanced force of 1 gram accelerates a 1-gram mass 980 cm./sec.². Consequently, in accordance with Newton's second law, an unbalanced force of ½ gram accelerates a 1-gram mass 490 cm./sec.², a 1/10 gram force accelerates a 1-gram mass 98 cm./sec.², and an unbalanced force of 1/980 gram accelerates a 1-gram mass 1 cm./sec.². The force that accelerates a 1-gram mass 1 cm./sec.² is called a *dyne*. See (b) of Fig. 7.

NEWTON'S LAWS OF MOTION

A dyne is 1/980 gram, and 980 dynes equal 1 gram. How many dynes equal 2 grams? How many grams equal 490 dynes?

Explain the advantage of solving for dynes of force rather than for grams of force in the formula $f = kma$.

PROBLEM 1: How much force is required to give a 100-gram mass an acceleration of 98 cm./sec.^{2}? Express the answer in (a) dynes; (b) grams.

SOLUTION:

(a) $f = kma$
$f = 1 \times 100 \times 98$
$f = 9800$ dynes

(b) $f = kma$
$f = \dfrac{1}{980} \times 100 \times 98$
▶ $f = 10$ grams

When k is made 1 in the formula $f = kma$, m is in grams, and a is in cm./sec.^{2}, in what units is f?

PROBLEM 2: An unbalanced force of 2 grams acts on a mass of 98 grams. What is the acceleration? When working this problem, use the formula $f = kma$.

Why are the poundal and the dyne called absolute units of force? The fact that the acceleration of a body varies directly as the unbalanced force gave scientists a new method to measure force and to establish units of force. And it was believed that the poundal of force, and similarly the dyne of force, were unchanging absolute units. For example, it was believed that regardless of whether a 1-pound mass was on a high mountain top, at the bottom of the deepest mine, at the equator, or at the North Pole, the unbalanced force required to give it an acceleration of 1 ft./sec.^{2}, the poundal, was the same everywhere. Unlike the weight of a body, which varies with its distance from the center of the earth (see page 32), the mass and inertia of a body were believed not to change; hence the poundal and dyne as defined could be considered absolute units of force at any place in the universe. Later it was discovered, however, that inertia does change with the velocity of a body. Nevertheless, the dyne and the poundal are still called absolute units.

How can the hitting force of a moving body be computed? We began this book (see page 1) by asking why heavy bodies fall harder than light ones. And now we have just finished a study of the forces needed to accelerate and decelerate bodies, so it appears that we can now answer this long-standing question.

We already know that $f = kma$, and that when a uniformly accelerated body starts from rest or comes to rest, $a = \dfrac{v}{t}$. See page 135. Substituting this value of a in $f = kma$, we have:

$$f = \dfrac{kmv}{t}$$

where v is the acquired velocity due to the force. If k is made $\dfrac{1}{32}$ or $\dfrac{1}{980}$, then both m and f will be in either pounds or grams. If, however, k is made 1, so that $f = ma$, then f must be in either poundals or dynes; that is, in absolute units.

Study of the formula $f = \dfrac{mv}{t}$ shows that the force with which, say, a moving baseball strikes an obstacle will vary directly as the product of the mass and the velocity of the ball but will decrease as the time taken to stop the body increases. See if you can now explain why a heavy body "falls harder" than a light one, assuming that the time for stoppage is the same for both objects.

The formula $f = \dfrac{mv}{t}$ should be of interest to all athletes. Most beginners in sports, and even professionals when under severe nervous tension, violate the principle that reduces the force in stopping a ball. They stiffen, and make their hands, arms, and whole body rigid. By so doing they decrease the time factor and increase the force, thus increasing the chances of dropping the ball or being injured.

The experienced athlete usually relaxes his hands, arms, and whole body as he catches a ball, allowing them to "give" with the ball. These actions tend to increase the time and therefore decrease the force, thus decreasing the chances for a fumble. Explain why, in falling, one should relax rather than stiffen his body and limbs, and explain why a boxer should "roll" with the punches.

The same formula $f = \dfrac{mv}{t}$, written as $v = \dfrac{ft}{m}$, should also be of interest to athletes and others who want to give their own bodies, or other bodies, the greatest velocity that is physically possible. Study of $v = \dfrac{ft}{m}$ shows that the velocity* varies directly as the product of the force and the time that the force acts on the body. That is, the greater the unbalanced force and the length of time it is applied, the greater the velocity. Increase in the mass of the body decreases the velocity. Hence, an overweight athlete is handicapped if he wants to attain top speed quickly. But in many athletic events, such as baseball, the mass of the body thrown is constant, so the athlete need not be concerned with its mass. His greatest concern should be how to make the product of the force and time a maximum.

*It should be kept in mind that the force mentioned here is the unbalanced force, and that the velocity varies with the force only because the body is being accelerated.

Fig. 8. In catching the football, the player's body "gives" with the ball. How is the force with which the ball strikes the player reduced?

Ewing Galloway

Fig. 9. A long wind-up gives the ball greater momentum by increasing the force and the time during which the ball is being acted upon.

Wide World

Courtesy A. C. Spalding & Bros.

Fig. 10. What differences in the swing and follow-through of an amateur (left) and a professional (right) are revealed in these multiple-exposure photographs?

With guns, every experienced hunter knows that the force that acts on the bullet can be increased by an increase in the quantity of powder in the shell. He also knows that a long-barreled gun, up to a certain length, has a higher muzzle velocity and shoots straighter than a short-barreled gun. The length of barrel of course does not increase the force on the bullet, but it does control the time factor. Explain.

An athlete can increase the force exerted, say, on a pitched baseball, by strengthening his body physically through proper training. The time of application of the force can be increased by proper "wind-up" and "follow-through." In Fig. 9, what is happening to the velocity of the baseball as the time factor increases?

In Fig. 10, the swing and follow-through of an amateur and a professional golf player are compared. Note that the horizontal distance the club head travels is considerably greater for the professional than for the amateur. This increases the time of action of the force. The professional thereby gives the ball greater velocity and gets longer drives than does the amateur, even though physically the amateur may be the stronger of the two. Also, because of the long follow-through the chances of the ball's being hit in the desired direction are increased.

In the shot-put, javelin throw, and many other athletic events, the time factor and hence the velocity can be increased by the proper follow-through. Explain why a tall pitcher can usually throw a ball faster than a short pitcher when both exert the same amount of force on the ball. Also explain why most short professional baseball pitchers are "curve-ball" rather than "speed-ball" pitchers.

Courtesy Department of Defense

Fig. 11. An artillery shell fired from this howitzer gets its momentum from the propelling force and the time it takes to travel through the barrel.

Momentum and impulse. If we clear the formula $f = \dfrac{mv}{t}$ of fractions, we have $ft = mv$. Both of these quantities are given special names and are quite important. The product of the force and time, *ft,* is called *impulse.* And the product of the mass and velocity is called *momentum.* Both of these will be discussed further in the next few pages.

Newton's first law of motion—the law of inertia. According to Newton's second law of motion, the acceleration of a body varies directly as the unbalanced force that acts on the body. This means that an unbalanced force is necessary to accelerate a body—to change its velocity. In other words, if a body is at rest it cannot move unless it is acted on by an outside force, and if it is in motion it cannot stop, increase or decrease its velocity, or change its direction unless an outside force acts on it. To stop, a moving body must be decelerated. This requires force. Accordingly,

if a body is at rest it will remain at rest, and if it is in motion it will remain in motion at an unchanging (constant) velocity in a straight line, unless it is acted upon by an unbalanced outside force.

This statement is known as Newton's *first law of motion,* or the *law of inertia.*

The tendency of a body in motion to stay in motion in a straight line, like the tendency of a body at rest to stay at rest, is called *inertia.* See page 155.

Many everyday experiences exemplify the law of inertia. We are aware that a rider may be thrown from his bicycle if it is stopped suddenly. Also the straphangers in a streetcar or subway train are thrown forward when the car stops suddenly and are thrown backward when it starts up suddenly. Also we know that we can shake ketchup out of a bottle by suddenly stopping the bottle when it has been set in rapid motion.

Newton's third law of motion. When the automobile began to take the place of the horse and buggy, it was not uncommon to see a driver futilely try to stop his automobile by pulling backward on the steering wheel and hollering "Whoa!" Somewhat similarly, when you were a child, perhaps you tried to make your toy wagon move forward by sitting in it and pushing on the front end with both feet. Or maybe you tried to lift yourself by your own bootstraps. If so, like the motorist just mentioned, you found the results disappointing.

The reason was that when you pulled upward on your bootstraps, an equal and opposite force pushed the boots down. The upward force is called the *action* and the downward push is called the *reaction.* These forces are always equal in magnitude and opposite in direction. Consequently their resultant is zero. That is,

NEWTON'S LAWS OF MOTION

Fig. 12. The boat is pushed backward as the boy pushes forward. Why?

To every action there is always an equal and opposite reaction.

The principle thus stated is known as Newton's *third law of motion,* or the *law of action and reaction.* Another application of it is shown in Fig. 12. Here a boy steps from a boat. As a result the boat is pushed backward and the boy is pushed forward. Two bodies and two forces are involved. One body, the boy, exerts the force, and the boat receives the force. The boy pushes the boat backward and the boat pushes the boy forward; the forces are equal in magnitude but opposite in direction.

Among the most spectacular applications of the law of action and reaction are the rocket bomb, rocket ship, and jet airplane. In each of these, hot burning gases shoot from the rear of the body. As the fuel burns (explodes), the hot gases are kicked rearward and the body is kicked forward. Explain, according to Newton's third law, why a trip to the moon could be made with a rocket ship but would be impossible with the ordinary propeller-type plane.

Similarly, a sprinter in starting pushes his body forward and the earth backward; when a gun is fired, equal and opposite forces push the bullet forward and the gun backward; when a body falls, the earth attracts the body and the body attracts the earth. Both are accelerated, but the mass of the earth is so large and the force so small that the earth's acceleration is not noticeable.

The law of action and reaction, impulse, and momentum. When a gun is fired, the force, f, that pushes the bullet forward equals the reacting force that pushes the gun backward, and the time, t, that the forces act is the same. Therefore, the im-

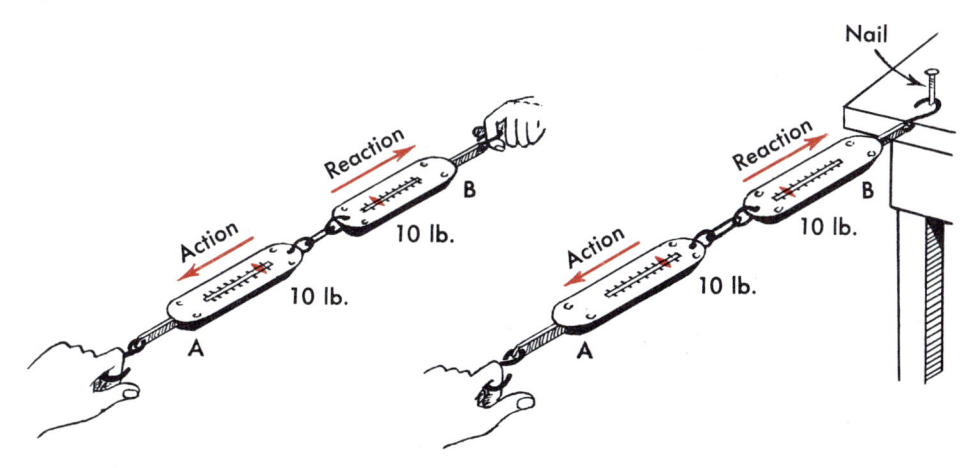

Fig. 13. This experiment demonstrates Newton's third law of motion. The force with which the spring balance is pulled at *A* is equal and opposite to the force with which the nail pulls on the spring balance at *B*.

THE RIDDLE OF MOTION

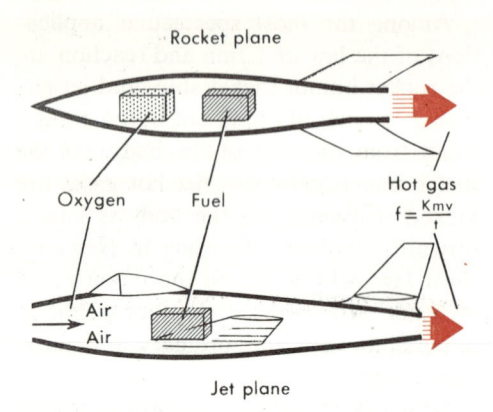

Fig. 14. How does Newton's third law of motion explain the thrust of rockets and jet planes?

pulse, ft, furnished the bullet is the same as that for the gun. (See page 164.) As a result of the impulse, the bullet acquires a momentum of mV. Here, m is the mass of the bullet and V is the velocity. Similarly, the gun acquires a momentum of Mv. Here, M is the mass of the gun and v is its velocity. But since momentum equals impulse, and the two impulses are equal, then the two momentums are equal. That is:

$$ft = mV$$
and
$$ft = Mv$$
Hence
$$Mv = mV$$

This relationship means that the velocities of the gun and the bullet vary inversely as their masses, and the larger the mass the less its velocity.

PROBLEM: An 8-lb. gun fires a 1-oz. bullet with a muzzle velocity of 1000 ft./sec. What is the velocity of the gun in recoil?

SOLUTION:
$$Mv = mV$$
Substituting,
$$8v = \tfrac{1}{16} \times 1000$$
$$v = 7.8 \text{ ft./sec.}$$

Fig. 15. (l.) The Air Force's long-range strategic missile, the *Snark*, which can travel 5,000 miles at 600 m.p.h. and can navigate itself by automatic celestial means. (r.) The *Matador* is a tactical missile that flies at supersonic speeds.

Courtesy Department of Defense *Courtesy Martin*

NEWTON'S LAWS OF MOTION

SUMMARY AND CONCLUSIONS

1. The reason that a 2-pound ball falls with the same acceleration as a 1-pound ball is that inertia of a body causes it to resist being set in motion. The inertia of a 2-pound ball is twice that of a 1-pound ball and is enough more for the 2-pound ball so that it offsets the difference in the gravitational forces that act on the two bodies.

2. Newton's first law, the law of inertia, is that a body at rest remains at rest, and one in motion continues at uniform speed in a straight line, unless acted upon by some unbalanced outside force.

3. The velocity of a body is not a measure of the force pushing it. The acceleration is the measure of the unbalanced force that acts on a body.

4. Newton's second law, the law of acceleration, is that the acceleration of a body varies directly as the unbalanced force acting upon it and inversely as the mass of the body. This relationship is expressed by either of the formulas:

$$f = ma$$
$$f = kma$$

In the formula $f = ma$, f will be in poundals when the mass is in pounds and the acceleration is in ft./sec.^{2}; and f will be in dynes when the mass is in grams and the acceleration is in cm./sec.^{2}. In the formula $f = kma$, where $k = \frac{1}{32}$, or $\frac{1}{980}$, f will be in pounds or grams respectively.

5. The poundal is the force required to accelerate a 1-pound mass 1 ft./sec.^{2}. The dyne is the force required to accelerate 1 gram of mass 1 cm./sec.^{2}.

6. The force that a moving body exerts when it strikes another body is given by the formula:

$$f = k\frac{mv}{t}$$

When the force is to be in poundals or dynes, $f = \frac{mv}{t}$. Also, ft is called impulse and mv is called momentum; $ft = mv$.

7. Newton's third law, the law of action and reaction, is that to every action there is always an equal and opposite reaction. This means that when a force is exerted, there must always be two bodies, one to exert and one to receive the force. Thus, two equal and opposite forces are always involved.

QUESTIONS FOR REVIEW

1. If you stand on a spring balance in an elevator and the elevator suddenly starts up, why does the balance read more? Why does it read less when the elevator starts down suddenly?

2. (a) What is inertia? (b) Explain why we can remove snow or mud from our shoes by stamping our feet. (c) When a person is riding in an elevator, what causes the dizzy sensation that he has when the elevator is stopped or started suddenly?

3. Explain why a person can be accelerated only about 6 or 7 times g without injury when his body is parallel with the direction of acceleration but can be accelerated 25 to 30 times g when his body is at right angles to the direction of acceleration.

4. Explain why a 2-pound ball does not fall twice as fast as a 1-pound ball.

5. Explain the chief purpose of heavy flywheels on engines.

6. What is the law of inertia? Give examples from your experience.

7. What is Newton's second law of motion? Describe an application of this law.

8. What is a poundal? Dyne?

9. Why are the poundal and dyne called absolute units?

10. (a) In the formula $f = ma$, if the mass is in grams and the acceleration is in cm./sec.^{2}, in what units is the force measured? (b) In what units is the force measured if the mass is in pounds and the acceleration is in ft./sec.^{2}?

11. A toy balloon is inflated and tossed into the air with its nozzle open so that the air escapes freely. What is the origin of the force that causes the balloon to dart about?

12. Could a rocket propel itself in a vacuum? Explain.

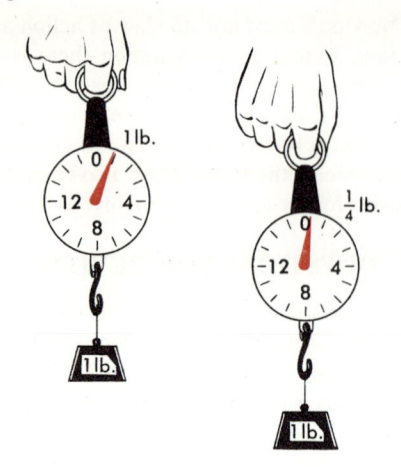

Fig. 16

13. In Fig. 16, which of the following conditions could be true?
(a) The apparatus is at rest.
(b) The apparatus is being moved up at a constant rate.
(c) The apparatus is being moved down at a constant rate.
(d) The apparatus is being accelerated upward.
(e) The apparatus is being accelerated downward.

14. Could one set up a powerful blower in a sailboat and propel the boat by blowing air against the sails? Explain your answer.

15. According to an article in one of our leading magazines, three chunks of coal flew out of a coal bucket into a schoolroom. Is the story in keeping with Newton's laws of motion? Later, a mischievous boy confessed that he had caused the coal to jump from the bucket. However, very often such stories appear in print. Do you know of any instance in which scientific observers have actually seen Newton's laws of motion violated in this manner? If you should observe and prove such a case, do you imagine that you would become famous?

16. Explain in terms of the formula $f = \dfrac{mv}{t}$ why one should relax one's body in a plane or automobile crash. What does a net do in breaking the fall of an aerialist? Why is a baseball player's hand not crushed by hard-hit balls?

PROBLEMS

1. A ball has a mass of 1 lb. Gravity pulls it toward the earth with a force of 1 lb. If the ball falls freely, find its acceleration.

2. A ball has a mass of 1 gram. Gravity pulls it toward the earth with a force of 1 gram. If the ball falls freely, what will be its acceleration in cm./sec.^{2}?

3. An unbalanced force of 1 lb. accelerates a 1-lb. mass 32 ft./sec.^{2}. What will be the acceleration of a 1-lb. mass when it is acted on by an unbalanced force of ½ lb.? ¼ lb.? ⅛ lb.? ¹⁄₁₆ lb.? ¹⁄₃₂ lb.? 1 poundal?

4. An unbalanced force of 1 gram gives a 1-gram mass an acceleration of 980 cm./sec.^{2}. What will be the acceleration of a 1-gram mass when it is acted on by an unbalanced force of ½ gram? ¼ gram? ¹⁄₁₀ gram? ¹⁄₉₈₀ gram? 1 dyne?

5. A 200-lb. cart is pushed on a smooth level highway. Neglecting friction, what horizontal force is required to accelerate it 4 ft./sec.^{2}?

6. If, in Problem 5, the friction were 10 lb., what force would be required?

7. (a) What unbalanced force is required to accelerate a 1-lb. ball 32 ft./sec.^{2}? (b) If a 1-lb. ball were accelerated straight up 32 ft./sec.^{2}, what would be the total force required?

8. What force is required to lift a 10-lb. ball straight up if the acceleration is 0 ft./sec.^{2}?

9. An unbalanced horizontal force of 10 lb. acts on a 50-lb. cart. What is the acceleration of the cart? If it starts from rest, what is its velocity at the end of 5 sec.?

10. A 200-lb. fullback starting from rest pushes backward on the ground with a force of 20 lb. What is his forward acceleration? His velocity at the end of 4 sec.? Distance that he has traveled at the end of 4 sec.?

11. What unbalanced force is needed to give a bus weighing 8 tons an acceleration of 2 ft./sec.^{2}? Starting from rest, how fast would the bus be going in 5 sec.?

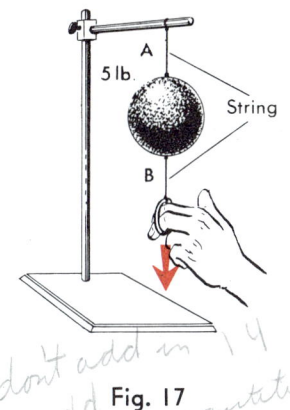

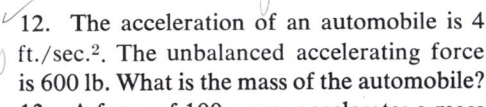

NEWTON'S LAWS OF MOTION

Fig. 17

Fig. 18

12. The acceleration of an automobile is 4 ft./sec.². The unbalanced accelerating force is 600 lb. What is the mass of the automobile?
13. A force of 100 grams accelerates a mass of 1000 grams. What is the acceleration of the body?
14. A man weighing 160 lb. stands on a spring balance in an elevator. How much does the balance read when the elevator is accelerated upward at 4 ft./sec.²?
15. A 5-oz. baseball that is traveling 80 ft./sec. is caught by a baseball catcher. The time required to stop the ball is $\frac{1}{50}$ sec. With what average force in poundals does the ball strike the catcher's glove? What is the average force in pounds?
16. An 8-lb. rifle fires a ½-oz. bullet with a velocity of 2,000 ft./sec. What is the velocity of the rifle? Use the formula $Mv = mV$.
17. What force is required to accelerate a 2000-gram mass 245 cm./sec.²? Express your answer in grams, kilograms, and dynes.
18. A 160-lb. man is strapped into a special type of wagon, or car, which is decelerated at the rate of 224 ft./sec.². What force is exerted on the man's body?
19. If a rocket ship burns 4 lb. of fuel per second and the gas formed escapes from the rear end of the rocket with a velocity of 6400 ft./sec., what force in pounds is exerted on the rocket? Use the formula $f = k\frac{mv}{t}$.
20. If at the distance of the moon a 1-lb. ball weighs $\frac{1}{3600}$ lb., what will be its acceleration as it falls toward the earth? See page 159.
21. In Problem 20, if the ball starts from rest, how far would it fall in 1 sec.? In 1 min.? How far would a 2-lb. ball fall in 1 min.? How far would the moon fall toward the earth in 1 min.? In 1 hr.? Use the formula $S = \frac{1}{2} at^2$. See page 136.

PROJECTS

1. Using the distance the moon falls toward the earth in 1 hr. (see Problem 21 above), find the period of the moon—the time it takes to make one complete revolution around the earth. The observed time is 27.3 days. If your computed time and the observed time agree, will this tend to prove Newton's laws of motion as well as his law of universal gravitation? Explain.
2. In Fig. 17, apply a gradually increasing downward force until either string A or B breaks. Repeat the experiment by applying the force very quickly. Explain the results.
3. Using the apparatus shown in Fig. 18, see if you can put the piece of chalk in the bottle without touching it.

READING YOU WILL ENJOY

Sutton, R. M., *Demonstration Experiments in Physics,* pp. 46-49, 50-55. McGraw-Hill Book Company, Inc., New York, 1938. Contains interesting experiments on each of the three principal laws of motion.

Chapter 17

Circular and Rotary Motion

The problem. To those unacquainted with Newton's laws of motion, it is almost unbelievable that a person can swing an open bucket of water over his head without spilling any of the water. It seems just as miraculous that an aviator who is not strapped into his seat can loop the loop without falling out of the plane. And it is almost as amazing that a spinning top and a rolling hoop, neither of which can stand by itself unless it is in motion, can stand without falling as long as it is rotating. The first two instances are examples of circular, or curved-line, motion, and the last two are examples of rotary motion. Our problem is to discover the laws governing these types of motion. Our first case for study will be the simplest possible, that of a ball that is whirled at uniform speed on the end of a string.

What conditions are necessary for a body to travel in a circle at constant velocity? According to the law of inertia, a body in motion tends to move in a straight line at a constant velocity unless acted on by an unbalanced force. Hence, in order to discover the conditions that exist when a ball is whirled in a circle at constant speed, we need to discover the force or forces that change its direction. Remember that the circular speed of the ball is constant.

Since the ball shown in Fig. 1 neither gains nor loses speed, then there can be no unbalanced force or component of an unbalanced force acting on it parallel with its direction of motion. What would happen if such a force existed? Therefore, the force causing change of direction can act only perpendicular to the direction in which the ball moves. This would be along the string toward the center of the circle. What did you say would happen if the force causing the change of direction were not perpendicular to the direction of motion?

The pull, F_4, which acts toward the center of the circle and deflects the ball from straight-line motion, is called *centripetal force*.

But centripetal force is not the only force acting when a body moves in a circle, because, according to Newton's third law, forces always act in pairs. If there is a centripetal force, there must be another force, F_3, equal in magnitude but opposite in direction. This force is called *centrifugal force*. Hence, in conclusion, when a body is moving in a circle at constant speed, the centripetal force equals the centrifugal force; and any forces or components of forces parallel with the direction of motion balance each other so that their resultant is zero.

CIRCULAR AND ROTARY MOTION

Applications of centrifugal force. Centrifugal force is felt by persons riding in an automobile or bus when the vehicle turns a sharp corner. It tends to throw them sidewise, away from the center of the curve. Centrifugal force causes mud to be thrown from a spinning automobile wheel, as shown in Fig. 2, and sparks to be thrown from a rotating grindstone in a similar manner. It causes water to be thrown out of clothes or off vegetables when they are rotated at high speed in a centrifugal drier. When the centrifugal force becomes greater than that of the adhesion of the water to the substances, the water is thrown out through perforations in the container. Sugar crystals and many other chemical crystals are separated from liquids in this manner.

Because airplanes travel at high speeds, centripetal and centrifugal forces are of much more concern in aviation than in other forms of transportation. This is especially true when an aviator loops the loop or goes into a power dive.

At the height of the loop, the centrifugal force on the plane must be greater than the weight of the plane and the pilot; otherwise both would fall.

The centrifuge. Many mixed liquids having different densities, such as cream and milk, will separate if allowed to stand for some time. This is due to the force of gravity. The denser liquid, milk in this case, settles to the bottom and the cream is buoyed to the top. Similarly, finely divided particles suspended in a liquid will, under the influence of gravity, settle to the bottom, as in the clearing of muddy water.

By means of a *centrifuge,* a rapidly rotating cylinder, such materials can be separated far more quickly by centrifugal force, which can be made to greatly exceed the gravitational force. At high velocities of rotation, the denser particles "fall outward" and the less dense particles are forced to the inside. Blood corpuscles are separated from blood fluids, and germs and viruses are also separated from fluids, in this manner.

If the centrifugal force on a body is, say, four times the gravitational force, then the acceleration in the direction of this force is 4 g's, 4×32 ft./sec.^{2} or 4×980 cm./sec.^{2} Experiments conducted by Air Force personnel with devices of the centrifuge type show that if a man lies crosswise with the direction in which he is accelerated he can stand about 20 to 30 g's for a fraction of a second. If he lies parallel with the direction of acceleration

F_1 = propelling force
F_2 = retarding force
F_3 = centrifugal force
F_4 = centripetal force

Fig. 1. F_3 is equal in magnitude, but opposite in direction, to F_4.

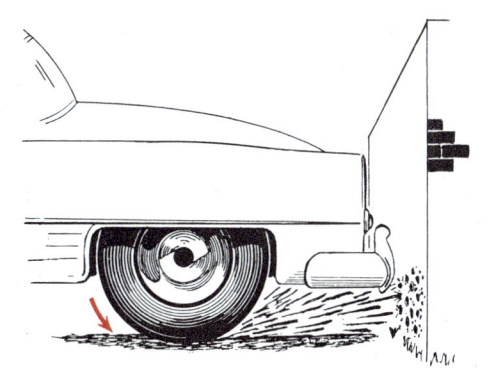

Fig. 2. The mud flies off at a tangent from the rapidly spinning wheel.

Courtesy Dr. Jesse W. Beams, University of Virginia

Fig. 3. The magnetically suspended rotor of this ultracentrifuge is driven by blasts of air or gas, causing it to make over 20,000 revolutions per second.

he will "black out" at about 6 g's of acceleration. Explain.

The small, very-high-speed *ultracentrifuge,* turning thousands of revolutions per second, can produce centrifugal forces hundreds of thousands of times greater than gravity. Even the heavier molecules (oxygen) in air can be separated from the lighter ones such as nitrogen.

Factors that affect centrifugal force. Centrifugal force can be measured by means of the apparatus shown in Fig. 5. When the mass of the ball is doubled, the centrifugal force is doubled; when the velocity is doubled, the centrifugal force is multiplied by four; and when the radius is halved, the centrifugal force is doubled. Hence, centrifugal force varies directly as the mass; directly as the square of the velocity; and inversely as the radius of the circle. That is,

Centrifugal force F (in poundals or dynes) $= \dfrac{mv^2}{r}$

Centrifugal force F (in pounds or grams) $= \dfrac{kmv^2}{r}$

PROBLEM 1: Knowing that $f = kma$ and centrifugal force $= \dfrac{kmv^2}{r}$, find the value of a in terms of v^2 and r.

PROBLEM 2: A 10-lb. ball is swung around on the end of a 5-ft. nylon cord. If the velocity of the ball is 20 ft./sec., what is the centrifugal force in pounds?

Fig. 4. (*l.*) Turntable used to study the effects of tumbling is spinning at 100 revolutions per minute. (*r.*) After being subjected to an acceleration of 6 g's on an electronically controlled centrifuge, the subject is at the "black-out" point.

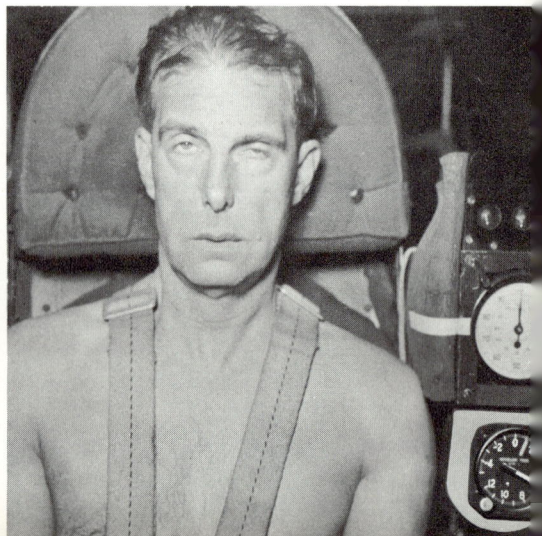

Courtesy Wright Air Development Center

CIRCULAR AND ROTARY MOTION 173

Diagram	Centrifugal force	Velocity	Mass	Radius
200 g.	200 g.	v	m	r
800 g.	800 g.	2v	m	r
400 g.	400 g.	v	2m	r
100 g.	100 g.	v	m	2r

Fig. 5. Determining centrifugal force.

SOLUTION:
$$F = \frac{kmv^2}{r}$$
Substituting,
$$F = \frac{10 \times 20 \times 20}{32 \times 5}$$
▶ $F = 25$ lb.

What would be the centrifugal force if the mass of the ball were doubled? If the velocity were doubled? If the radius were doubled? If the radius were halved?

PROBLEM 3: A 1-lb. ball is swung in a circle whose radius is 10 ft. The ball travels around the circle twice every second. Approximately what is the centrifugal force in (a) pounds? (b) poundals?

The banking of roadways. When an automobile, train, truck, or even a runner in track, goes around a curve, the centrifugal force tends to cause the body to skid or to tip toward the outside of the curve. For example, as a truck rounds a curve, two forces act on it, as shown in Fig. 6. One of these forces is its weight, W; and the other is the centrifugal force, $\frac{kmv^2}{r}$. To offset the effect of the centrifugal force and the tendencies of the vehicle to skid or tip over, the roadbed is banked so that the resultant of the centrifugal force and the weight of the truck is perpendicular to the surface of the road. If the resultant passes within the points of support A and B, the vehicle will not upset. But if the resultant passes outside these, the vehicle, if it does not skid, tips over.

In some states, signs indicate the speed at which the resultant force is perpendicular to the surface of the roadbed. Thus, a 40-mile curve is one on which an automobile going 40 miles per hour will just miss a tendency to skid or upset. What would be the tendency if the vehicle were driven faster than 40 miles per hour? Less than 40 miles per hour?

Why does not a rolling hoop or wheel tip over? If you stand a bicycle wheel, or a hoop with similar tread, on a horizontal surface and then let it loose, it will fall over. If, however, you give the body a push so that it rolls, it will remain erect. The difference in behavior seems uncanny.

Seemingly, either the rotation or the forward motion, or perhaps both motions, keep the wheel from falling over. In case rotation alone keeps the wheel erect, then, if we set a bicycle wheel or one similar to

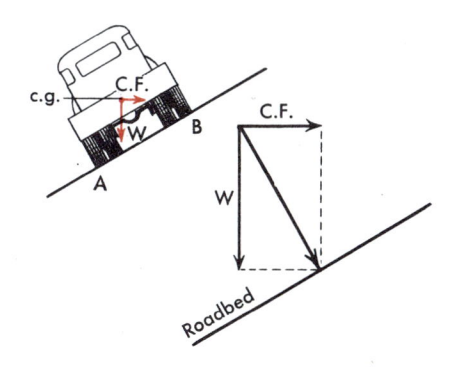

Fig. 6. The roadbed is banked to overcome the effects of centrifugal force.

it in rotation and support it, as shown in Fig. 8, it too should tend to stay in the plane in which the wheel rotates. Does it? Such a wheel is called a *gyroscope*.

Furthermore, if we attempt to change the plane of rotation by tilting the axle, we find this difficult to do. Experiments prove that both of these consequences are correct; hence we can conclude that when a body is rotating in a plane it resists any force that tends to change its plane of rotation. This tendency of a rotating wheel (gyroscope) to remain in one plane explains, at least in part, why a rolling hoop does not fall over and why the gyroscope in Fig. 8 is not pulled down by gravity.

But what about the forward motion of a non-rotating wheel? Does it tend to keep a wheel erect? We can answer this question by skidding a wheel along a slippery table top. As a result, we find that the motion alone without rotation does not tend to keep the wheel erect.

The gyrocompass. Since a rotating wheel tends to stay in the plane in which it is rotating, there are possibilities that it might be used as a direction indicator (compass) in much the same way that a magnetic compass is used.

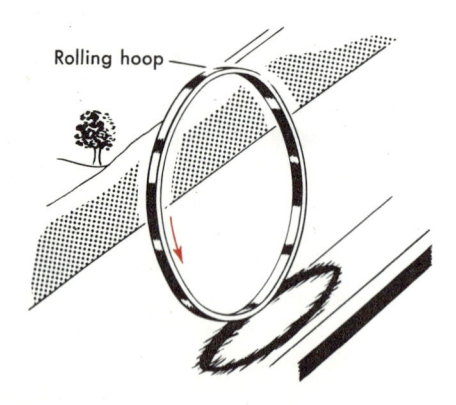

Fig. 7. What factors might be responsible for keeping the rolling hoop erect?

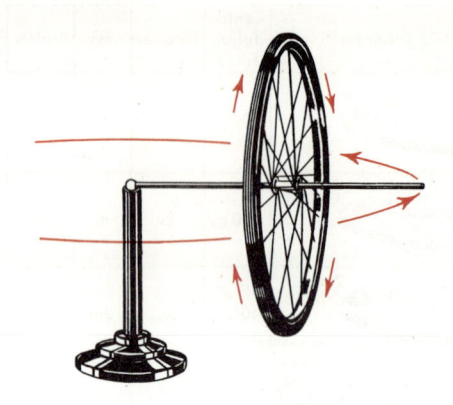

Fig. 8. The rotating hoop resists any tendency to change the plane in which it rotates.

For example, suppose that the axis of a spinning wheel were mounted horizontally in, say, an east-west direction, and that the wheel could turn in a horizontal plane on a vertical axis, as shown in Fig. 8. Then, if it were placed on an ocean liner, the rotating axis should maintain its east-west direction regardless of how many times its carrier changed direction, turned around, or pitched and rolled.

But, as we have found in many previous instances, logic and experiment do not always agree. If, for example, the gyroscope is set in an east-west direction in an ocean liner that sails west and is caused to undergo much pitching and rolling, the gyroscope will turn (*precess*) until it points north and south.

We can explain what happens by placing the axis of a rapidly rotating gyroscope in an east-west direction on a small table, as shown in Fig. 9, and by tipping the table so that the legs *A* and *B* stay on the floor. The faster the gyroscope is spinning and the greater its mass, the more difficult it is to tip the table. Regardless of this, as the table is tipped, the gyroscope begins turning on its vertical axis and will continue doing so until the axis of the rotating wheel is parallel with the axis *AB* about which the table is rotated.

A much better way of showing the same thing is to use a gyroscope such as is shown in Fig. 10. Set the wheel spinning with its axis in a horizontal direction. Stand erect and hold the gyroscope in your outstretched hand with arm held horizontally, then start turning your body round and round a vertical axis. Immediately the axis of the spinning wheel begins changing direction, and will continue doing so until its axis is parallel with the vertical axis about which you turn your body.

Complete explanation of these motions is beyond the scope of this course. It is enough for our purpose to note the fact that the spinning wheel will try to set its axis of spin parallel with the axis of any new spin that is forced upon it. Logically, then, if we are to use a gyroscope as a direction indicator, all we must do is to avoid causing the gyroscope to move about any axis not parallel with its own axis of spin. But here again logic fails to come through. For if we set the gyroscope on a table so that its axis of spin is in, say, an east-west direction, or a vertical direction, and watch it carefully, using a microscope

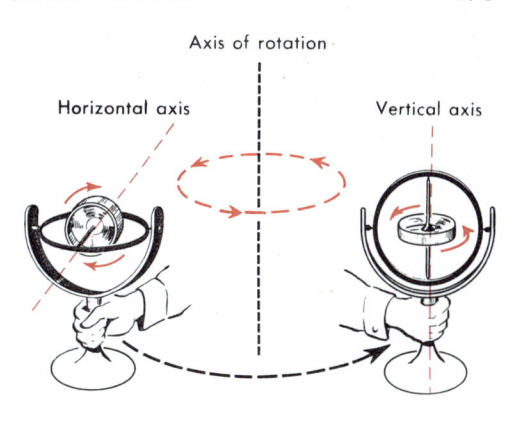

Fig. 10. Demonstrating precession.

to keep under observation a very fine mark on the gyroscope frame, we shall find that it is slowly changing direction. This indicates that some unseen slow spin is causing the gyroscope to precess.

One possible cause of this is the rotation of the earth on its axis. But if this is true, then when a gyroscope's axis of rotation precesses until it is parallel with the axis of the earth, which you perhaps know always points toward the North Star, precession should stop. Modern gyroscopes driven by electric motors, regardless of the direction in which they are pointed, will usually point true north in a very few hours, exactly as we predicted above.

This means, as Perry, the discoverer of the North Pole, pointed out, that spinning tops, flywheels, electric motors, airplane propellers, automobile wheels, and other spinning bodies are all tugging gently at their mountings, trying to tip so that their axes of rotation all point toward the North Star; that is, so that their axes of rotation are parallel with the earth's axis.

But will a gyroscope compass point in a direction parallel with the earth's axis when it is mounted in an ocean liner that is very likely, on its voyage, to be rolling

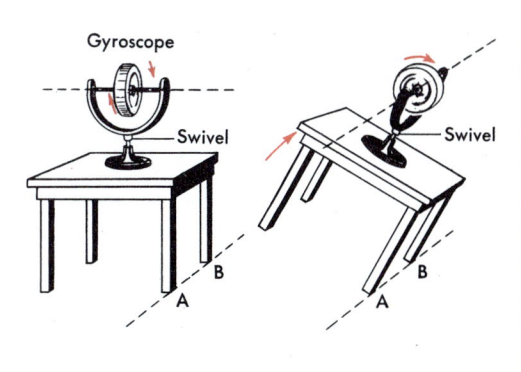

Fig. 9. The axis of the rotating wheel becomes parallel to the axis of rotation of the table.

Courtesy Sperry Gyroscope Co.

Fig. 11. The principles of the Gyro-Compass may be demonstrated by improvising the pull of gravity and turning the body to simulate the rotation of the earth on its axis.

and pitching, changing course, and so on? Yes, it will. By mounting the wheels so that it possesses three kinds of rotation simultaneously, by eliminating practically all friction in the bearings, and by making certain corrections such as those for latitude, engineers have built gyroscope compasses that retain a true north direction once they have been set in that direction.

Other uses of a gyroscope. A gyroscope called a *gyrostabilizer* is used to suppress the roll in a ship. Usually such gyroscopes are large rotating flywheels that may weigh several tons and turn as many as 1000 revolutions per minute. The axis is normally vertical. If the ship starts to roll, the spinning gyroscope resists the force which would change the direction of its axis of rotation and thereby greatly reduces the rolling motion. The gyroscope is also used to operate what is known as the *artificial horizon*. For details and uses, see a modern encyclopedia. Gyroscopes are also used as automatic pilots in airplanes and in rockets. If the proper mechanism is attached to the gyroscope, it and the plane can be controlled by radar or short-wave radio in another airplane several miles away.

Courtesy Sperry Gyroscope Co.

Fig. 12. The heart of the Gyro-Compass is a gyro rotor 10 inches in diameter that weighs 55 pounds. It spins at 600 r.p.m. A Gyro-Compass is nonmagnetic and therefore free from variation.

CIRCULAR AND ROTARY MOTION

Fig. 13. How is the speed of rotation increased by pulling the weights inward?

Another aspect of rotating bodies important for skaters, dancers, divers, and tumblers. An interesting experiment illustrating another important characteristic of rotating bodies is shown in Fig. 13. A boy stands on a turntable or sits on a swivel stool with weights in each hand. With arms fully extended horizontally he is set rotating slowly. Then, upon drawing his hands and the weights in toward his chest, as shown, he automatically rotates much faster. You will best appreciate the experiment by doing it yourself.

The principle is used by the expert roller skater or ice skater. The skater starts into a whirl on one foot, with hands and one leg outstretched. Then, drawing arms and outstretched leg in, he whirls faster and faster. For the greatest rapidity of whirl, the greatest possible amount of the mass must be located as near as possible to the axis of spin. Explain how a spinning quarterback, fullback, or toe dancer can make use of this principle.

The diver, acrobat, trapeze artist, and others make use of this principle, particularly in turning somersaults and flips. In order to rotate their bodies as easily and quickly as possible, they duck their heads in between their knees so as to roll themselves into a ball. Explain why this is done. When they want to come out of a turn, they extend their legs and body. This decreases the speed of rotation. See Fig. 14.

Fig. 14. This trapeze artist may be unaware of the principles of rotation, but he applies them nonetheless in executing this somersault in mid-air.

Courtesy Ringling Brothers, Barnum and Bailey Circus

SUMMARY AND CONCLUSIONS

1. Centripetal force is the force that causes a body moving in a circular path to change direction continuously. If the speed of the body is uniform, the direction of the centripetal force is at right angles to the path of the body and toward the center of the curve.
2. Centrifugal force is the force that is equal in magnitude and opposite in direction to the centripetal force.
3. Centrifugal force, like centripetal force, varies directly as the mass; directly as the square of the velocity; and inversely as the radius of curvature. C. F. = $\frac{kmv^2}{r}$ or $\frac{mv^2}{r}$.
4. A rapidly rotating wheel resists any force that tends to tip it from its plane of rotation.

QUESTIONS FOR REVIEW

1. Why is the earth flattened at the poles?
2. Why does mud flying from a rotating automobile tire tend to travel in straight lines?
3. What causes a body that is traveling in a circle to change direction? If the speed is uniform, what is the direction of this force with respect to the path of the body?
4. What is the importance of centrifugal force when a plane is looping the loop?
5. What is a centrifuge? List at least four uses of a centrifuge.
6. On a curve, why is the outer rail of a railroad track higher than the inner rail?
7. What is meant by a 30-mile road curve?
8. Why does not a rolling hoop or spinning top fall over?
9. What is a gyroscope?
10. For what are gyroscopes used?
11. What is precession and what is its cause?
12. Why does the axis of a spinning gyroscope tend to turn in a north-south direction? What advantage does a gyroscope compass have over a magnetic compass?
13. If a wheel of chance is placed slightly off center, will the position at which it will tend to stop be affected?
14. Explain why an acrobat, in doing flips and turns, rolls himself into a "ball."
15. A toe dancer, in making rapid turns, "spots" her eyes on a wall and holds her head in that position as long as she can. Explain why this is done.
16. A gyroscope could be mounted in an automobile and prevent it from turning over in going around a sharp curve. Explain the direction in which the axis should be pointed for this purpose.
17. The Mississippi River carries an enormous amount of soil from the north and deposits it in the region of its delta. What effect would this shift of mass have on the speed of rotation of the earth?
18. In Chapter 2, page 12, explain why the solid body rolled faster down the inclined plane than the lighter hollow body. Is your explanation now the same as it was in Chapter 2?
19. What is the purpose of giving a spin (spiral motion) to a kicked or thrown football, and to a rifle bullet when it is shot from a gun?
20. A regulation baseball weighs a little over 5 oz. If the density of the core were increased without affecting the diameter and weight of the ball, could the ball be made to curve more easily? Explain.

PROBLEMS

1. A boy whirls a ¼-lb. stone horizontally on a 4-ft. cord. If the speed of the stone along the curve is 32 ft./sec., what will be the tension on the string?
2. An athlete, in throwing a 16-lb. hammer, whirled with the hammer traveling in a circle of 4-ft. radius at the rate of 32 ft./sec. With what force did he have to hold onto the hammer to keep it from slipping out of his hands? (Hammer throwing is no longer allowed in scholastic competition. Why?)
3. An automobile weighing 3200 lb. starts around an unbanked curve of 200-ft. radius at a speed of 30 mi./hr. What force of friction must exist between the tires and the pavement in order to keep the car from

skidding off the road? Do you think this is a safe speed on such a curve?

4. A 2-ton truck carrying a 1-ton load rounded a curve of 100-ft. radius at the rate of 20 mi./hr. What was the centrifugal force of the truck and its load?

5. A car exerts a centrifugal force of 600 lb. when traveling in a circle of 600-ft. radius at a velocity of 50 ft./sec. How much does the car weigh?

6. In Problem 5, what would be the acceleration of the car toward the center of the circle?

7. What is the minimum speed at which a bicycle rider can loop the loop and stay on the overhead track of a loop that is 16 ft. in diameter? Remember that the centrifugal force must at least be equal to the combined weight, W, of the rider and bicycle.

8. A certain airplane pilot can stand an acceleration of 6 g's (192 ft./sec.^{2}). He makes a circular turn at 640 ft./sec. What is the smallest radius in which he can turn his plane?

9. A 3200-lb. car travels in a curve of a radius of 128 ft. Assuming that it does not tip over, how fast can it go without skidding, (a) if the coefficient of friction of rubber on dry concrete is 1; (b) if the coefficient of friction on wet concrete is ½? (Find the friction force and make it equal to the centrifugal force.)

PROJECTS

1. Design a golf ball that has less tendency to hook and slice than the ordinary ball.

2. Build, or demonstrate how you would design, the wheels of a soap-box-derby automobile.

3. Place a hard-boiled egg and an uncooked egg on a flat table top. Then spin each around a vertical axis. Explain the results.

4. Roll a can of tomato juice and a can of baked beans of exactly the same size down an inclined plane several times. Explain what happens.

READING YOU WILL ENJOY

Swezey, K. M., *After-Dinner Science*. Whittlesey House, McGraw-Hill Book Company, Inc., New York, 1948. "Which Egg Is Boiled?" p. 69; "Centrifugal Force May Fool You," pp. 72-73.

Chapter 18

Projectile Motion

The problem. When a baseball, javelin, bullet, cannon ball, rocket, or other body is thrown, shot from a gun, or launched in any similar manner, the body is called a *projectile*. The path of the projectile is called the *trajectory*.

The nature of projectile motion was never of much concern until the invention of long-range cannon which could shoot over hills and farther than the gunner could see. Even then very few people were concerned because there was little knowledge of how to aim long-range cannon so as to hit targets unseen by the gunner. The guns were therefore of little value except to scare the enemy and destroy his morale. But Galileo recognized the possibilities of long-range cannon and the advantage they would give a nation in the event of war, once the secret of aiming them accurately was discovered. For this reason he assigned to himself the task of discovering the nature of projectile motion.

Probably you, like most other high school students, are not greatly interested in aiming long-range cannon at targets you cannot see. But you may be interested in doing the broad jump, putting the shot, throwing the javelin, discus, or baseball, or hitting a "long" ball in baseball or in golf. Or you may be enthused about making a trip to the moon or engaging in other kinds of interplanetary travel. If you are, you should be interested in what is to follow in this chapter.

What do we already know about projectile motion? We already know (see page 147) that when a baseball or other projectile is thrown straight up, neglecting air resistance, the upward motion is the opposite of the downward motion. For example a ball, in going up, loses velocity at the rate of 32 feet per second each second. During the down flight, it gains velocity at the same rate. At any given height, the velocity of the ball going up numerically equals its velocity going down. Are the upward and downward motions of this special case true of projectile motion in general? Also, is the downward component velocity of a projectile that is fired horizontally the same as that of a freely falling body? Or does the projectile at first move in a straight line and then rather suddenly drop to the ground? Also, when its speed is small does a bullet or other projectile fall farther during the first second than it does when its speed is great? And is the horizontal motion of a horizontally fired projectile the same type of motion as the horizontal motion of a general case?

The nature of the path of a projectile that is fired horizontally. To study the path of a bullet that is fired horizontally, do the experiment pictured in Fig. 1(a). The blowgun is designed so that when the projectile leaves the end of the barrel an electrical circuit is broken. This releases a target from an electromagnet that holds it up. The result is that the target falls and the bullet hits the target. Both fall the same distance in the same length of time. Repeat this experiment several times, firing the projectile at various horizontal velocities. Also do the experiment pictured in Fig. 1(b).

In conclusion, it seems that *the downward motion of a projectile that is fired horizontally is the same as the motion of a freely falling body.*

This conclusion agrees with Newton's second law of motion. After the horizontally moving bullet leaves the gun, except for air resistance which we neglect for the present, there is no unbalanced force, other than gravity, acting on the bullet. Hence it is accelerated downward and in this direction only.

PROBLEM 1: If a bullet is fired horizontally 2000 ft./sec. from a height of 144 ft., in what time does it hit the ground? Assume no air resistance.

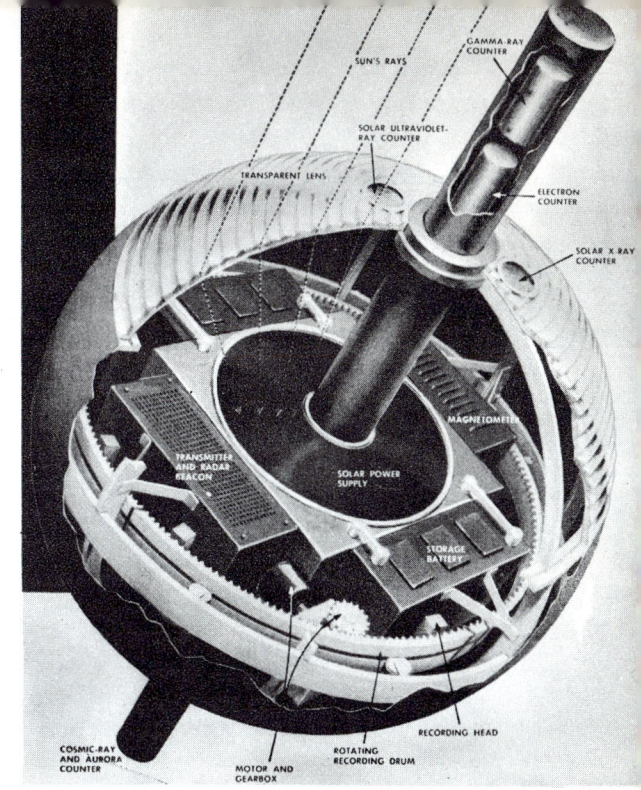

Courtesy Popular Science Monthly

Fig. 2. An artist's conception of a cutaway view of an earth satellite.

SOLUTION:
$$H = \tfrac{1}{2} gt^2$$
$$144 = \tfrac{1}{2} \times 32t^2$$
$$t^2 = 9$$
$$t = 3 \text{ sec.}$$

PROBLEM 2: If a bullet is fired horizontally 1000 ft./sec. from a height of 256 ft., in what time does it hit the ground? $t = 4$ sec.

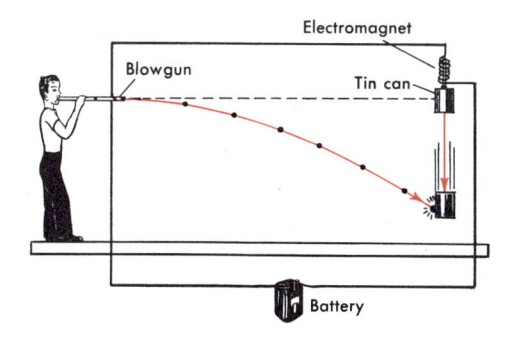

Fig. 1. (a) What does this experiment tend to prove?

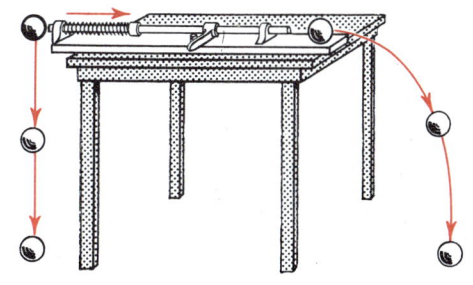

Fig. 1. (b) The freely falling body and the projectile reach the ground together.

$$S = v_1 \Delta t + \tfrac{1}{2} g \Delta t^2$$

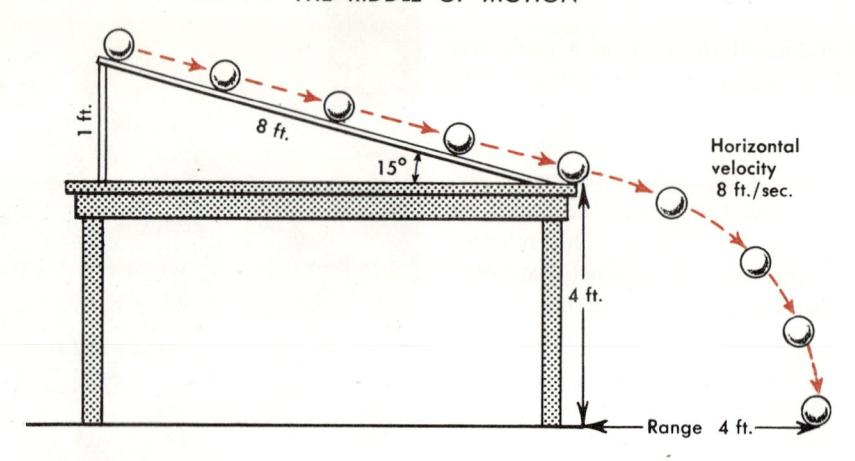

Fig. 3. Neglecting friction, the velocity of a projectile fired horizontally is constant. Can you explain why?

What is the nature of the horizontal motion of a projectile that is fired horizontally? Since, as explained above, no horizontal force acts on a projectile after it leaves the gun, logically then its horizontal velocity should be constant in accordance with Newton's second law.

To test this conclusion, set up an inclined plane 4 feet long, or more, on top of a table which is 4 feet high. See Fig. 3. Arrange the lower end of the plane so that the ball will roll smoothly onto the flat table top and will be directed in a horizontal direction off the edge of the table. Also, slope the inclined plane at such an angle that the horizontal velocity of the ball as it leaves the table top is 8 ft./sec. This velocity can be determined in the same manner as the velocity was determined at the bottom of the inclined plane in Fig. 1, page 138.

Since the projectile (ball) falls 4 feet, the time required for it to reach the floor is ½ second. Therefore, in case the horizontal velocity is constant, as we reasoned above, the horizontal distance, or range, R, is ½ × 8, or 4 feet. The results agree with this prediction and therefore tend to prove that when air resistance is negligible and a projectile is fired horizontally, *its horizontal velocity is constant*. That is,

$$R = Vt$$

PROBLEM 1: What is the range of the bullet in Problem 1 above?

SOLUTION:
$$R = Vt$$
$$R = 2000 \times 3 = 6000 \text{ ft.}$$

PROBLEM 2: What is the range of the projectile in Problem 2 above?

PROBLEM 3: A boy throws a stone horizontally from the top of a vertical cliff with a velocity of 100 ft./sec. It strikes the ground at the foot of the cliff in 2 sec. (a) What is the height of the cliff? (b) At what distance from the bottom of the cliff will the stone strike the ground?

The path of a projectile that is not fired horizontally. As you perhaps realize, the projectile paths studied thus far are special cases. Now let us study a general case by putting the target much higher than the gun, as shown in Fig. 4. Will the horizontal velocity of the projectile then be constant? And will the vertical velocity decrease at the rate of 32 ft./sec. every

PROJECTILE MOTION

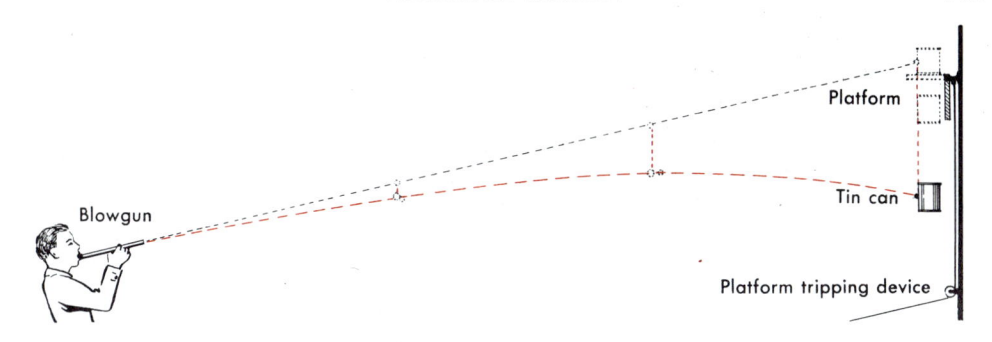

Fig. 4. The "fall" from straight-line flight for a projectile not fired horizontally is the same as that for a freely falling body.

second on the up flight and increase at the same rate on the down flight?

Logically, the answer in both cases is yes, because after the projectile leaves the gun, neglecting air resistance, there is no horizontal force acting on it. Its horizontal velocity should therefore be constant. And since the only force that acts on the projectile is gravity, the projectile should decelerate 32 ft./sec.² as it goes upward and accelerate at the same rate as it comes down.

But logic must always be tested by experiment. To do this (see Fig. 4), again fire the blowgun at the target. In case the bullet hits the falling target, then we will know that the bullet fell the same distance from a straight line course as the tin can fell. That this actually will happen is shown in Fig. 4. Therefore, neglecting friction, it appears that the up-and-down motion for all projectile motion is the same.

To determine the nature of the horizontal velocity of a projectile, fire a gun, as shown in Fig. 5, straight upward from a cart which is shoved across a table in a straight line at a constant velocity. The projectile thus has two component velocities, as the figure shows. The horizontal one is given it by the motion of the cart, the vertical one by the gun. In case the horizontal velocity is constant, the projec-

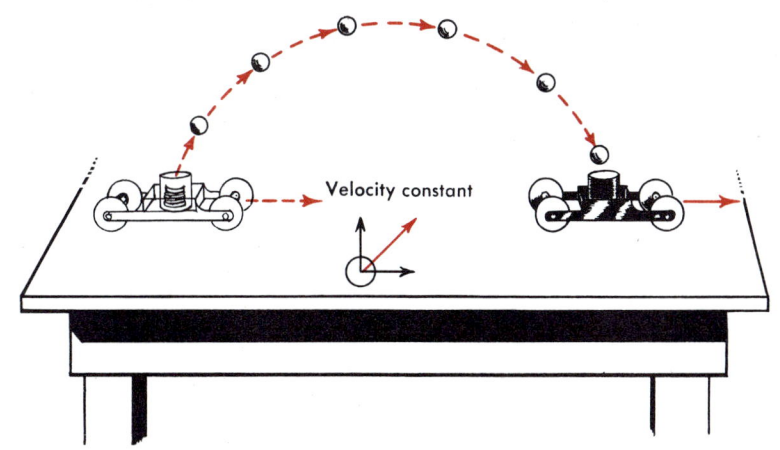

Fig. 5. The velocity of the wagon is constant. The projectile is fired straight up. What do the results tend to prove about the horizontal velocity of a projectile?

tile when it falls should land in the cart. This is exactly what happens. Hence it seems that for the general as well as the special case considered, the horizontal velocity of a projectile is constant. Remember that air resistance is not considered here.

Furthermore, the trajectory is a symmetrically curved line and the time, t, for the upward flight is the same as the time for the downward flight. The total time $T = 2t$.

At what angle with the horizontal should a body be projected so as to attain the maximum range? The answer to this question is of particular importance for the javelin and discus throw, shot-put, and running broad jump, and for driving a golf ball and batting a baseball. An easy way to find the best angle for the maximum range is by means of a toy gun that shoots a small projectile a few feet with a constant muzzle velocity. Also, a single solid stream of water shot from a glass tube or from a nozzle may be used.

As shown in Fig. 6, the maximum range for a given muzzle velocity is attained when the angle with the horizontal is 45°. If the angle is made either more or less than 45°, the range decreases. When the angle is 30° or 60°, 15° less or 15° more than 45°, the range is the same for both angles. At 75° and 15° the range is

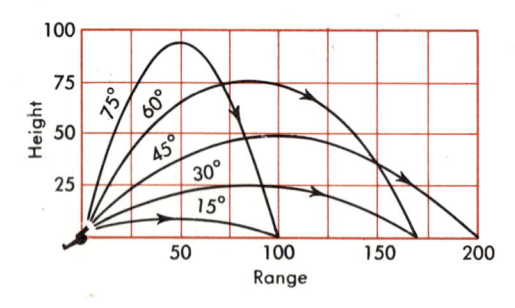

Fig. 6. The velocity is 80 ft./sec. in each case. At what angle is the greatest range?

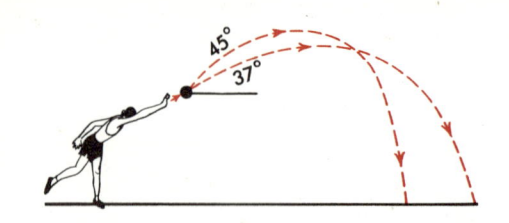

Fig. 7. Explain why the maximum range is attained at an angle of 37°.

the same for both angles but still less than in the previous cases cited. Hence, in conclusion, we see that the optimum angle is 45° and, if the angle is increased or decreased, the range is decreased.

There are several exceptions to the 45-degree rule. When, in comparison with the range, the projectile is launched from considerable height above the level at which it strikes the ground, then the rule does not hold. For example, in the shot-put, the shot may be launched from a height of 7 feet and have a range of about 42 feet. Then the height is about one-sixth of the range. In shooting a toy gun like the one shown in Fig. 6 from a height of about one-sixth of its range, you will find that the maximum range is obtained when the angle with the horizontal is about 37 or 38 degrees. See Fig. 7. Other exceptions are the discus, which sails in the air, and the golf ball or baseball with considerable spin. The best angle for the discus is about 35°.

How can we find the range when the angle is 45° and only the initial velocity is known? Already we can find the range by using the formula $R = \vec{V}T$, when $\vec{V}$ is the horizontal velocity and T is the total time, which is twice the time for the upward flight or twice the time for the downward flight, the two times being equal. But how can we find the maximum range when only the actual velocity V is known?

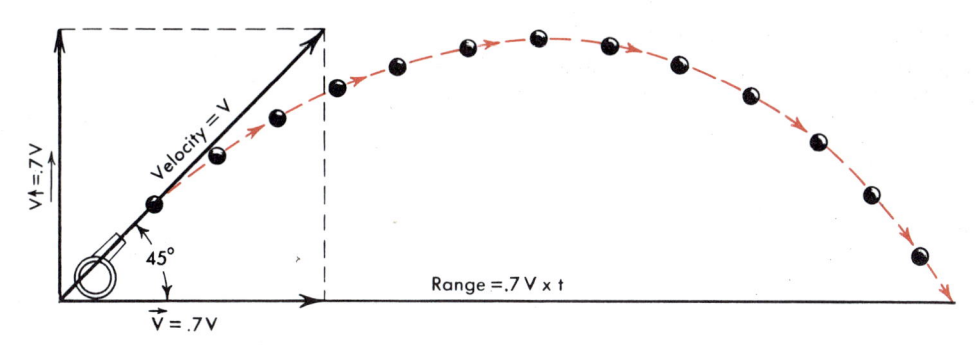

Fig. 8. The vertical velocity (V↑) equals .707 V. Also the horizontal velocity ($\vec{V}$) equals .707 V. These relationships are true only for the 45°-angle.

Study of Fig. 8 shows that when the angle is 45° the horizontal ($\vec{V}$) and the vertical (V↑) components of the velocity V are equal. That is, $\vec{V}$ = V↑.

Applying the Pythagorean theorem to Fig. 8 and solving for $\vec{V}$ in terms of V, we get:

$$\vec{V}^2 + V\uparrow^2 = V^2$$

Substituting $\vec{V}^2$ for $V\uparrow^2$,

$$\vec{V}^2 + \vec{V}^2 = V^2$$

or

$$2\vec{V}^2 = V^2$$

Dividing,

$$\vec{V}^2 = \frac{V^2}{2}$$

Extracting square root,

$$\vec{V} = \frac{V}{\sqrt{2}} = .707V$$

Likewise, $V\uparrow = .707V$

Substituting V↑ for $\vec{V}$ in the formula

$$R = \vec{V}T$$

we have $R = V\uparrow T = .707VT$. Why?

But the time depends upon the upward velocity .707V

and $.707V = gt$

Also, $t = \frac{T}{2}$

Hence, $.707V = g\frac{T}{2}$

and $T = \frac{1.41V}{g}$

Substituting for T in

$$R = .707VT$$

we have $R = .707V \times \frac{1.41V}{g}$

or $R = \frac{V^2}{g}$

In conclusion, when the target and the point from which the projectile is launched are about the same height, the maximum range is attained when: (a) the angle with the horizontal is 45°; (b) the velocity is maximum.

PROBLEM: A ballplayer throws a baseball at an angle of 45° with the horizontal and with a velocity of 100 ft./sec. Find (a) the range, (b) the vertical velocity, (c) the time the ball is in the air, (d) the horizontal velocity.

SOLUTION:

(a) $R = \frac{V^2}{g}$

Substituting,

$$R = \frac{100 \times 100}{32}$$

▶ $R = 312.5$ ft.

(b) $V\uparrow = .7V$
Substituting,
         $V\uparrow = .7 \times 100 = 70$ ft./sec.
                                 (approx.)

(c) $V\uparrow = 32t$
         $70 = 32t$
         $t = 2.18$ sec., or time up
         $T = 4.36$ sec.

(d)
Since $V\uparrow = \vec{V}$
and $V\uparrow = 70$ ft./sec.

Then $\vec{V} = 70$ ft./sec.   (approx.)

Note: You can check the range computed above by using the formula $R = \vec{V} \times T$.

The broad jump, discus throw, and javelin throw. In all events such as these, in which the maximum range is desired, the athlete should strive for greater and greater speed of the projectile at the take-off. This is because, as we have just seen, the range varies directly as the square of the velocity. A slow runner can never become a champion in the running broad jump. And a man with slow footwork may never become a champion in the javelin or discus throw or the shot-put unless he has superior strength. In baseball and golf, those who want long range must strive to swing the bat or club with maximum speed, although placing the ball is often more important than distance.

The high jump. The object in the high jump is to attain the maximum height, H. As shown in Fig. 9, for a given velocity, the height increases as the angle becomes larger. Accordingly, the best angle would be 90°. But there are other factors that must be considered. The height, H, varies also as V^2. It is impossible, however, for the jumper to have both velocity and a large angle. In fact, if a fast runner attains his maximum speed at the take-off and the angle is more than 70°, his horizontal

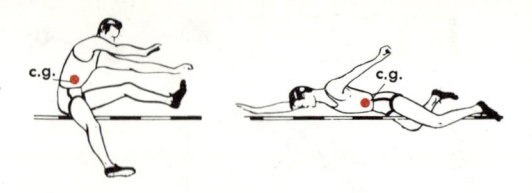

Fig. 9. With which style of jump must the jumper's center of gravity be raised the highest?

distance from the bar will be too small for him to get over the bar. Hence, the angle should be the largest possible one that enables the runner to get over the bar and still attain the greatest upward velocity of his body. Usually this angle is about 65°.

Another thing that a high jumper must give attention to is how to clear the bar while raising his center of gravity the least possible distance above it. When the scissors style is used, the center of gravity is at least 6 inches above the bar, depending upon the build of the athlete.

The popular style wherein the jumper goes over the bar face down brings the center of gravity closer to the bar than any other style. In all these events the mass of the projectile must be considered to be concentrated at its center of gravity.

Rockets. During and previous to World War II, the V-2 rocket projectiles were developed in Germany. After the war many of these were brought to the United States, where research has been going on ever since.

To obtain maximum range, a rocket is launched straight up. As the fuel is burned, hot gases are shot out of the rear of the rocket. The reacting force, in accordance with Newton's law of action and reaction, propels the rocket straight upward, causing accelerations as great as 12 to 15 g's. One g is 32 ft./sec.^{2}.

At a height of 30 to 40 miles a gyro-

Courtesy Steelways   *Courtesy Martin, Baltimore*

Fig. 10. (*l.*) V-2 single-stage rocket being readied for launching at White Sands, New Mexico. (*r.*) The Army's Redstone rocket is a ballistic missile capable of carrying an atomic warhead and striking targets within a 200-mile range.

Fig. 11. Powered by a rocket engine that develops 6000 pounds of thrust, the Bell X-1 research rocket plane has established a speed record of 1650 miles per hour in test flights. X-2 has achieved a speed of 1950 miles per hour.

Courtesy Bell Aircraft Co.

control turns the guiding fins so that the path is no longer vertical. At this level, just before the fuel is completely exhausted, the rocket reaches an angle of 45°. Here its velocity and acceleration are both at the maximum. Both the fuel load and the air resistance have reached a minimum.

From this level on, in the highly rarefied atmosphere, the path is the same as that of any other free projectile. After the rocket falls to the 30-to-40 mile level, atmospheric friction produces some deceleration, making it slightly less than 1 g, or that of a freely falling body. In 1954 a Navy Viking one-stage rocket reached a height of 158.4 miles. Previously, a two-stage rocket combining a German V-2 and an American Wac Corporal had reached a height of more than 250 miles.

SUMMARY AND CONCLUSIONS

1. The horizontal velocity for any projectile is constant. The range of a projectile equals the horizontal velocity times the time of flight.

2. The vertical motion of a projectile is the same as that for a body which is thrown straight up. When a projectile is moving upward, the upward component of its velocity decreases 32 ft./sec.^{2}, and when it is moving downward, the downward component of its velocity increases 32 ft./sec.^{2}.

3. The range of a projectile varies directly as V^2. The angle of projection for maximum range is 45° for a given initial velocity.

4. When the angle of projection is 45°, the range is given by the formula $R = \dfrac{V^2}{g}$.

5. $\qquad R = \vec{V}T$

QUESTIONS FOR REVIEW

1. When a projectile is thrown straight up, compare its upward and downward motion at the starting point and at two points other than the top point. What is the nature of the motion at the very highest point?

2. When a projectile is fired horizontally, what is the nature of the downward motion? Give evidence to support your answer.

3. When a projectile is fired horizontally, what is the nature of its horizontal motion? Do the horizontal and downward motions

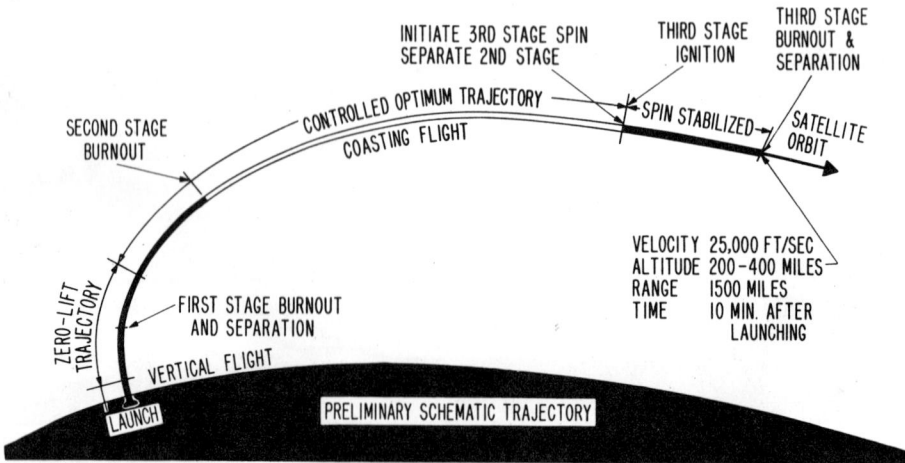

Courtesy Martin, Baltimore

Fig. 12. A drawing of the flight path, or trajectory, of the three-stage rocket that will be used to establish an earth satellite. The satellite, which will carry recording instruments, will travel in an elliptical orbit around the earth.

PROJECTILE MOTION

seem to affect one another or can they be thought of as two separate motions?

4. When a projectile is fired at, for example, an angle of 45° with a horizontal plane, what is the nature of its upward motion; downward motion; horizontal motion? Give evidence to support each answer.

5. What is meant by the range of a projectile?

6. Upon what two factors does the range of a javelin or similar projectile depend?

7. If two running broad jumpers have, at take-off, the same speed of 20 ft./sec. and the same angle of projection, but one weighs 200 lb. and the other 150 lb., which one, if either, will jump the farther? Give a mathematical proof.

8. In putting the shot, what is the best angle for obtaining the maximum range? Why does it differ from the best angle for throwing the javelin and baseball?

9. Will an increase in the velocity of a broad jumper from 10 to 11 ft./sec. give a greater increase in range than an increase from 20 to 21 ft./sec.?

10. What one factor has the greatest influence on the range of a projectile?

11. What happens to the range of a projectile if the acceleration due to gravity (g) increases? Decreases?

12. In landing a rocket plane on the moon, why would the rear end be headed toward the moon?

PROBLEMS

In all these problems air resistance is neglected.

1. A boy threw a ball horizontally from a point 16 ft. above the ground. The initial velocity of the ball was 80 ft./sec. What length of time was the ball in flight?

2. A bullet was fired horizontally from the muzzle of a rifle with a velocity of 1600 ft./sec. The bullet struck a coyote that was 800 ft. away. Find (a) the time of flight; (b) the distance the bullet fell.

3. From the top of a cliff, a boy threw a stone horizontally over the edge. The stone struck the ground 120 ft. from the foot of the cliff in 3 sec. (a) What was the height of the cliff? (b) With what horizontal velocity did the boy throw the stone?

4. Sketch the path of the stone in Problem 3 and show the position of the stone in (a) ½ sec.; (b) 1 sec.; (c) 2 sec.; (d) 3 sec.

5. An airplane flying horizontally at 240 mi./hr. dropped a bomb. The plane's altitude was 6400 ft. above the ground. (a) In what length of time did the bomb hit the target? (b) At what horizontal distance from the target was the bomb released? (c) What was the vertical velocity of the bomb when it hit the target?

6. An athlete threw a javelin at an angle of 45° and with a velocity of 80 ft./sec. (a) What was the range? (b) What length of time was the javelin in flight?

7. A baseball player threw a ball at an angle of 45° with the level ground surface. The initial velocity was 96 ft./sec. Find (a) the range; (b) the time of flight; (c) the initial horizontal velocity; (d) the initial vertical velocity; (e) the maximum height attained.

8. In Problem 7, the maximum height was what part of the range?

9. If in northern Canada, where g equals 32.25 ft./sec.², an athlete can throw a javelin 200 ft., how far should he be able to toss it in the Philippine Islands, where g equals approximately 32.00 ft./sec.²?

10. If the formula $R = \dfrac{V^2}{g}$ applies to the running broad jump when the angle of take-off is 45°, copy and complete the following table. The mass of the jumper is considered to be concentrated at his center of gravity.

Velocity (V) (ft./sec.)	V²	Range (R) (ft.)
15	—	—
16	—	—
17	—	—
18	—	—
19	—	—
20	—	—
21	—	—
22	—	—

PROJECTS

1. Using the data above, make a graph showing the relationship between the velocity at take-off and the range of the jumper. Study the data to find their significance in training for the running broad jump and then explain your conclusions to your track coach.

2. In order to determine the velocity with which you can throw a ball straight up, have a friend with a stop watch take the time required for the ball to leave your hand and return to the height at which it was projected upward. Use the formula $V = gt$, but remember that $t = \dfrac{T}{2}$.

3. Throw a baseball at an inclined angle of 45°. Determine the range and the time from which it leaves your hand until it hits the ground. Then use the formula $R = \dfrac{V^2}{g}$ and determine the velocity with which it was thrown. Also determine the horizontal velocity, $\vec{V}$, using the formula $R = \vec{V}T$. Then determine the horizontal velocity, $\vec{V}$, using the formula $\vec{V} = .707\,V$, where V is the value obtained from the formula $R = \dfrac{V^2}{g}$. Do your answers check? Also determine the vertical velocity in two different ways. Do they check? Repeat the experiment several times.

4. Determine the horizontal velocity with which you can throw a baseball. For best results you will need a stop watch and will need to be on top of a building or a cliff.

READING YOU WILL ENJOY

Swezey, K. M., *After-Dinner Science*. Whittlesey House, McGraw-Hill Book Company, Inc., New York, 1948. "Which Will Reach the Ground First?" p. 58.

Unit 6

Work and Machines

Underlying all the complex machines in use today are six simple machines that have been in use for over three thousand years—the lever, the wheel and axle, the pulley, the inclined plane, the wedge, and the screw. In the construction of the Egyptian pyramids, for example, the ramps on which huge blocks of stone were dragged to heights above the ground were inclined planes. In the ancient Greek world, Archimedes developed the principle of the lever and the Archimedean screw, a device for pumping water. Archimedes considered the lever such a powerful machine that he is said to have claimed that he could move the earth if he were given a lever long enough and a place to stand.

The unit photograph shows a pulley system being used today on a modern construction project to transport a load of steel beams. It does not take much imagination to realize the indispensable role played by these simple machines in our modern civilization. However, machines do have their limitations, because you cannot get something for nothing by using them.

19. WORK, POWER, AND ENERGY
20. SIMPLE MACHINES

Unit Photograph Courtesy M. J. Buerger, M.I.T.

Chapter 19

Work, Power, and Energy

The problem. Few, if any, words in the English language are used with greater confusion and variation of meaning than *work, power,* and *energy*. For example, some will say that playing baseball, sitting in class, and studying are all work; others will disagree. Most students, however, will agree that study is work, but many will have their doubts about baseball.

Likewise, many will agree that, in Fig. 1, John, Tom, and Charles are all doing work. John, we see, is pushing against a wall, while Tom is holding a 100-pound bar weight motionless above his head, and Charles is pushing a lawn mower. On the other hand, many will disagree. That the same kind of confusion exists concerning the meaning of power and energy will be shown later.

Neither in scientific nor in other kinds of thoughtful study should such confusion exist. Hence, our first problem in this chapter is to define work, power, and energy.

Defining terms. A definition, like a hypothesis, should be such that its logical consequences agree with experience and do not result in ridiculous situations. Can we formulate a definition of work that meets these standards?

In such an attempt let us study Fig. 1. Here we see that all three boys are doing one thing in common. Each is exerting a force for a period of time. Does work (W) therefore equal force (F) $\times$ time (t)?

Further study of Fig. 1 shows the possibility of another definition of work. Charles is doing something that neither Tom nor John is doing. Charles is mowing the lawn. *He is exerting a force through a distance.* And the thicker the grass, the greater the force required. Also, the greater the force and the distance the more grass is cut. Then does work (W) equal force (F) $\times$ distance (S)? Which definition of work, if either, meets the standards proposed above?

Only by considering the logical consequences of each definition can we answer this question. In case work equals $F \times t$, then what about the chair in which you may be sitting, the trunk of a tall tree, a boy leaning on the handle of a lawn mower, and a telephone wire on which a bird is sitting? Certainly we will have to agree that in these situations force is being exerted for a period of time and that, therefore, according to the definition $W = Ft$, work is being done.

Of course you might like to draw pay for leaning on the handle of a lawn mower, but you certainly would hate to pay anyone

WORK AND MACHINES

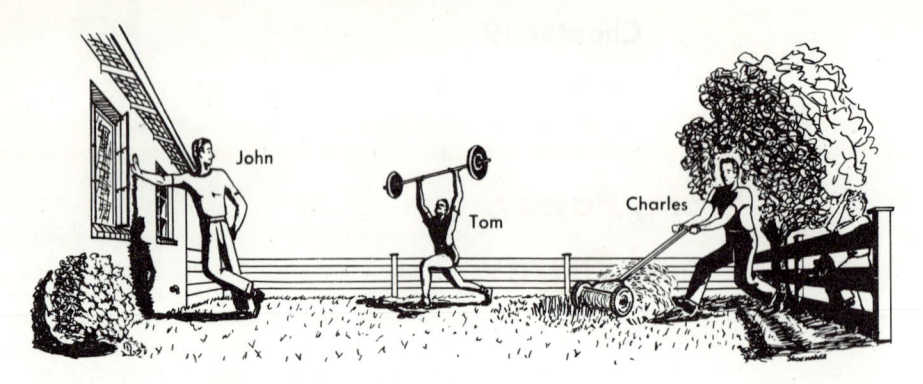

Fig. 1. Which boy, if any, is doing work? Explain your answer.

else for doing so, especially when he was supposed to be mowing your lawn. Hence, it appears that the mere exertion of force through a period of time, regardless of how tiring it may be, will not serve as the basis for a scientific definition of work.

On the other hand, if you hired Charles to mow your lawn, you would not mind paying him for pushing the lawn mower provided he pushed it through a distance, so as to thereby mow the lawn.

Assuming that **work** *equals force times distance,* or

$$W = FS,$$

explain which of the following are work: (a) holding a stack of books on your lap; (b) playing baseball; (c) chewing gum. Is time involved in this definition of work? Why would you reject the first definition?

What are the units of work in the English system? Assuming that work is defined in terms of force and distance, then the units of work must include units of the quantities force and distance. In the English system, the common unit of work is the *foot-pound* (ft.-lb.).

The **foot-pound** *is the amount of work done when a force of 1 pound acts through a distance of 1 foot.* See Fig. 2. The corresponding absolute unit of work is the **foot-poundal,** which is defined as *the work done when a force of 1 poundal acts through a distance of 1 foot.*

PROBLEM 1: How much work is done when a 100-lb. box is lifted through a vertical height of 5 ft.? (See Fig. 3a.)

SOLUTION:
$W = F \times S$
Substituting,
$W = 100 \times 5$
$W = 500$ ft.-lb.
or,
$W = 500 \times 32$ or 16,000 foot-poundals

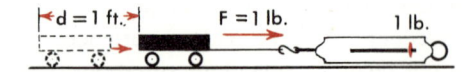

Fig. 2. One foot-pound of work is done when a force of one pound acts through a distance of one foot.

WORK, POWER, AND ENERGY

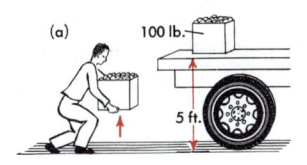

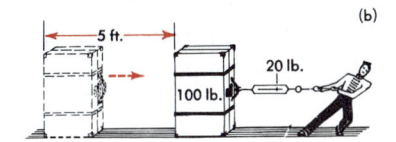

Fig. 3. Explain the difference in the amount of work done in (a) and (b).

PROBLEM 2: If a force of 20 lb. is required to slide the trunk in Fig. 3(b), how much work is done in sliding the 100-lb. trunk 5 ft.? ANS.: 100 ft.-lb.

What are the units of work in the metric system? In the metric system, the common units of work are the *gram-centimeter* and the *kilogram-meter*. The **gram-centimeter** *is the work done when a force of 1 gram acts through a distance of 1 centimeter.* See if you can write a definition of the kilogram-meter. See Fig. 4.

The absolute unit of work is the **erg** (*dyne-centimeter*), which is the work done when a force of 1 dyne acts through a distance of 1 centimeter. See Fig. 5.

The work done in lifting a 200-gram weight 5 centimeters is 200 × 5, or 1000

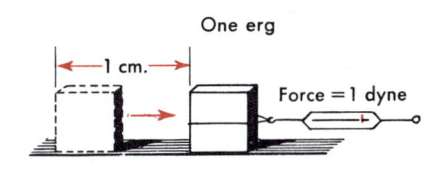

Fig. 5. An erg.

gram-centimeters. Also it equals 200 × 5 × 980, or 980,000 ergs. One gram-centimeter equals approximately 980 ergs. Because the erg is so small, the *joule*, 10,000,000 (10^7) ergs, is often used instead.

$$1 \text{ joule} = 10,000,000 \ (10^7) \text{ ergs}$$

PROBLEM: How much work is done when a 10-kilogram weight is lifted 10 meters? 20 centimeters? Express each answer in kilogram-meters, gram-centimeters, ergs, and joules.

What is power? Like work, the word *power* is used with great variety and confusion of meaning. The most powerful automobile is commonly believed to be the one that will climb the steepest hill in high gear, has the fastest pickup, will travel the fastest, or can pull the greatest load. Yet we know that a 30-horsepower tractor can pull much more than a 100-horsepower automobile, that a "souped-

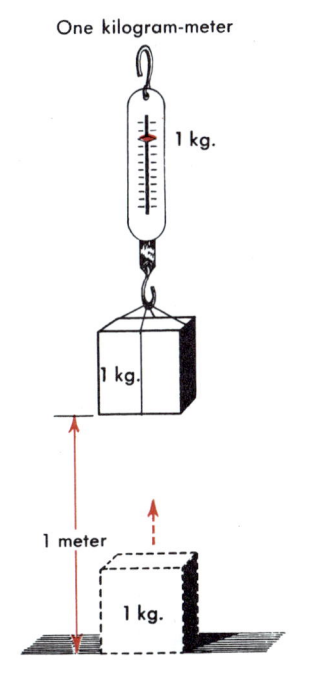

Fig. 4. How much work was done?

up" 90-horsepower "jalopy" can travel faster than an ordinary 150-horsepower automobile, and that a low-powered automobile, if properly geared, can climb in high gear hills that a much more powerful one cannot. Apparently, power is related to work; but the question is, how?

In the definition of work, only force and distance were considered as factors affecting the amount of work. Time was not included. Certainly the exclusion of time is in keeping with experience. For example, regardless of whether a boy takes two hours or four to mow a lawn, he does the same amount of work in either case.

Nevertheless, the time factor may be a very important one, especially if the work is being done by the hour. For example, if a big husky boy can mow a lawn in two hours, whereas a smaller boy takes four hours, then the larger boy should receive twice as much pay per hour as the smaller boy because the larger boy does twice as much work per hour.

The work done per hour, minute, second, or other unit of time is called *power*. Or, **power** *is the rate of doing work*. Mathematically:

$$\text{Power} = \frac{\text{Work}}{\text{Time}}$$

Or,

$$P = \frac{W}{t} = \frac{F \times S}{t}$$

What are the units of power? Not until the Scottish inventor, James Watt (1736-1819), improved the steam engine so that it became more than an expensive sensational toy was there much demand for a unit of power. One of the chief power needs of the day was to pump water and lift coal from the coal mines. At that time in England horses were the chief source of such power.

Since the purchaser of a steam engine was concerned with how many horses the

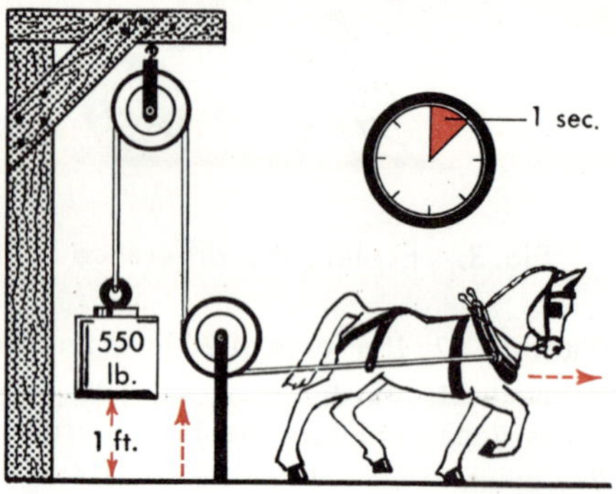

Fig. 6 A horsepower equals 550 foot-pounds of work done in one second, or 33,000 foot-pounds per minute.

engine would displace, it was only natural to rate the power of the engine in terms of the power of a horse; that is, in terms of how much work a horse could do in a day, hour, minute, or second.

James Watt found by experiment, as shown in Fig. 6, that a horse could pull or lift 550 pounds 1 foot high in 1 second. That is, in 1 second the horse could do 550 × 1, or 550 foot-pounds of work. In one minute the horse could lift the 550-pound weight 60 feet high. Consequently, Watt concluded that:

1 Horsepower (H.P.)
 = 550 ft.-lb. of work per sec.
 = 550 × 60 ft.-lb. of work per min.
 = 33,000 ft.-lb. of work per min.

That is:

$$\text{H. P.} = \frac{\text{Work } (F \times S)}{550 \times \text{ time in sec.}}$$

$$= \frac{\text{Work } (F \times S)}{33,000 \times \text{ time in min.}}$$

PROBLEM: An engine can lift 1100 tons of coal 100 ft. high in 1 hour. What is its horsepower?

SOLUTION:

$$H.P. = \frac{Work}{33,000 \times t}$$

$$H.P. = \frac{2000 \times 1100 \times 100}{33,000 \times 60}$$

▶ H. P. = 111.1

Solve the same problem, with the time in seconds.

Automobile engines develop from 60 to 300 horsepower; the modern locomotive develops from 1000 to 4000 H.P.; the motor in a household mechanical refrigerator develops about ¼ H.P. For a very short time, a good athlete can develop as much as 1 H.P. If he weighs 165 pounds and can climb 10 feet up a rope in 3 seconds, his:

$$H.P. = \frac{165 \times 10}{550 \times 3} = 1 \; H.P.$$

Over a period of time a man develops only about one-seventh (1/7) horsepower. Determine your maximum horsepower by the method suggested in Fig. 7 or as suggested above.

Fig. 7. Determining your horsepower.

Fig. 8. As a result of the work done in raising the block and tackle of this oil drilling rig, it acquires potential energy because of its position above the ground.

What is energy? From experience, you know that if a heavy stone fell some distance and landed on your toe, it would probably smash your toe. Or if the stone hit the top of a stake standing upright in a lawn it would drive the stake farther into the ground. In other words, the moving stone would possess the ability to exert a force through a distance and thereby, according to definition, possess the ability to do work. *The ability to do work is called* **energy.**

The ability of a body to do work because of its motion is called **kinetic energy.** Does falling water possess kinetic energy? Does wind?

You know, however, that many bodies are capable of doing work even though they are not in motion. Examples are water behind a dam, a bent bow used in shooting an arrow, a compressed or stretched spring, and a rubber balloon full of compressed air. None are in motion, yet potentially they are able to do work

WORK AND MACHINES

Fig. 9. Various examples of potential energy.

if they are "triggered" off or released so that they are set in motion. Such bodies are said to possess *potential energy*.

Potential energy *is defined as the ability of a body to do work because of its position or form—for example, its height; or because it is bent, stretched, or deformed in certain other ways*. See Fig. 9.

Which of the following possess kinetic energy and which possess potential energy: (a) a bent spring; (b) wind; (c) falling water; (d) compressed air; (e) a stone lying at the brink of a steep mountain wall?

The interrelationship between potential and kinetic energy. To study this relationship, let us refer to Fig. 10, which pictures a part of a miniature roller-coaster track. To operate, the 20-pound car is lifted from the bottom to the top of the inclined track at A, a height (H) of 4 feet. The work required is 20×4, or 80 foot-pounds.

At A, according to definition, the car possesses potential energy; energy is stored in the car because of its position. The question is, how much energy? Is all of the 80 foot-pounds of work done in lifting the car this high stored as potential energy, or is only part of it stored?

To answer this question it is necessary to discover how much work the car is capable of doing. If it can do 80 foot-pounds of work, then the potential energy of the car at A equals its weight W times its vertical height H.

Rolling down the track AC, the car

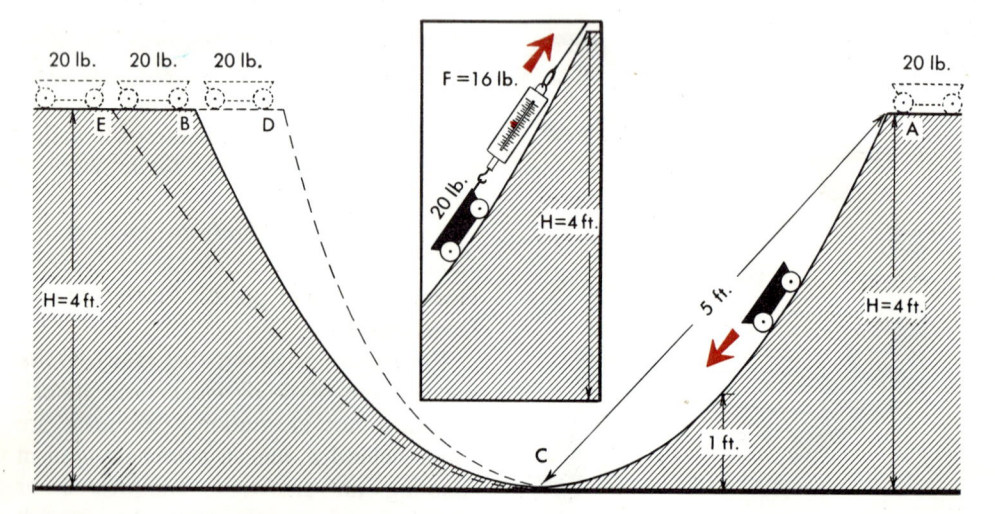

Fig. 10. Ideal frictionless roller-coaster for determining the relationship between potential and kinetic energy. If the cart coasted down AC, how far would it go up CE? CB? CD?

WORK, POWER, AND ENERGY

attains its greatest velocity at C, at the bottom. But instead of stopping here, as we might intuitively expect it to do, the car keeps right on going up the inclined plane BC. However, it never quite reaches a point as high as its starting point A.

Surprisingly, though, if the work done against friction is the same for all three tracks, BC, DC, and EC, the car will roll up to the same vertical height on each of the tracks, the steepness having nothing to do with the height that the car attains. This fact should be kept in mind.

Furthermore, the more the friction in the wheels of the car and the track is reduced, the higher the car goes. And presumably, if all friction were removed the car would again attain a height of 4 feet. Hence, in conclusion, it appears that when friction is absent the car at C possesses 80 foot-pounds of kinetic energy because it can lift itself 4 feet high, thus doing 80 foot-pounds of work. But where did this kinetic energy come from?

This question we have already answered. The original hypothesis was that if the potential energy at A were changed into kinetic energy and the car could do 80 foot-pounds of work, then the potential energy at A must have been 80 foot-pounds and therefore equal to the work done in lifting the car 4 feet high. At A:

P.E. = W × H

Also, since the kinetic energy of the car at C equals the potential energy of the car at A, then:

$$K.E._C = P.E._A = W \times H$$

PROBLEM: The hammer of a pile driver weighs 100 lb. It is 12 ft. above the top of a post that is being driven into the ground. What is the potential energy of the hammer? What will be its K.E. when it hits the post, assuming no friction?

SOLUTION:
(a) P.E. = W × H
Substituting,
P.E. = 100 × 12
P.E. = 1200 ft.-lb.
(b) K.E. = P.E. = 1200 ft.-lb.

How is kinetic energy computed directly by formula? Above, we found the K.E. by first finding the potential energy. But this method is indirect and applies only to special cases. Is there a more direct method?

To answer this question we will again refer to Fig. 10. You will note that the force of gravity which acts down the inclined plane is 16 pounds and the distance that it acts is 5 feet, so that 80 foot-pounds of work is done on the car by gravity. This also equals the K. E. of the car at C. That is, the gravitational force F times the distance S that it acts equals the kinetic energy of the car. That is,

$$K.E. = F \times S$$

But since the force F accelerates the car, then F = kma. Also, since at C the square of the velocity V² = 2aS, then

$$S = \frac{V^2}{2a}$$

Substituting, $K.E. = kma \times \dfrac{V^2}{2a}$

or, $$\mathbf{K.E. = \frac{kmV^2}{2}}$$

Remember that k = 1/32 or 1/980, depending on the units used. See page 159. In case the absolute units of work are wanted, then the formula is written,

$$\mathbf{K.E. = \frac{mV^2}{2}}$$

PROBLEM 1: A 32-lb. car has a velocity of 20 ft./sec. What is its K. E. in (a) foot-pounds? (b) Foot-poundals?

SOLUTION:

(a) $\text{K.E.} = \dfrac{kmV^2}{2}$

$\text{K.E.} = \dfrac{32 \times 20 \times 20}{32 \times 2}$

▶ K.E. = 200 ft.-lb.

(b) K.E. = ½ mV^2
K.E. = ½ × 32 × 20 × 20
K.E. = 6400 foot-poundals

PROBLEM 2: A 980-g. car has a velocity of 100 cm./sec. What is its K.E. in (a) gram-centimeters? (b) Ergs? (c) Joules?

SOLUTION:

(a) $\text{K.E.} = \dfrac{kmV^2}{2}$

$\text{K.E.} = \dfrac{980 \times 100 \times 100}{980 \times 2}$

▶ K.E. = 5000 gram-centimeters

(b) K.E. = ½ mV^2
K.E. = ½ × 980 × 100 × 100
K.E. = 4,900,000 ergs

(c) $\text{K.E.} = \dfrac{4{,}900{,}000}{10{,}000{,}000}$

K.E. = 0.49 joule

The transformation of energy. From our study so far it is quite apparent that a car on the roller coaster, as in Fig. 10, achieves its kinetic energy at the expense of potential energy. At the starting point, A, the energy possessed by the car is all potential, and at the lowest point, zero height, its energy is all kinetic. On the way down the incline the potential energy at the top is transformed into kinetic energy. At all intermediate points, since there is some velocity and some elevation, the car has both kinetic and potential energy.

If no work is done to overcome friction, all the 80 foot-pounds of potential energy possessed by the car at the top of the inclined plane in Fig. 10 is transformed without loss into 80 foot-pounds of kinetic energy at the bottom of the inclined plane at C. At any intermediate point the car, since it possesses both velocity and height, must possess both potential and kinetic energy whose sum is 80 foot-pounds and is constant. That is,

P.E. + K.E. = K, a constant.

PROBLEM 1: Referring to Fig. 10, find (a) the potential energy and (b) the kinetic energy of the car when its height is 1 ft. Assume no friction.

SOLUTION:
(a) P.E. = $W \times H$
Substituting,
P.E. = 20 × 1 = 20 ft.-lb.

(b) K.E. + P.E. = 80
K.E. + 20 = 80
K.E. = 60 ft.-lb.

PROBLEM 2: A man shoots a 1-lb. ball straight up from the earth's surface with an initial velocity of 80 ft./sec. (a) What is the initial kinetic energy of the ball? (b) What is the kinetic energy of the ball at the top of its flight? (c) What is its potential energy there? (d) What is the potential energy of the ball at a point 40 ft. above the ground? (e) What is its kinetic energy there? Assume no friction.

SOLUTION:

(a) $\text{K.E.} = \dfrac{kmV^2}{2}$

$\text{K.E.} = \dfrac{1 \times 80 \times 80}{2 \times 32}$

▶ K.E. = 100 ft.-lb.

(b) K.E. = zero, ball is at rest.

(c) P.E. = K.E.
100 ft.-lb. = 100 ft.-lb.

(d) P.E. = $W \times H$
P.E. = 1 × 40
P.E. = 40 ft.-lb.

(e) K.E. = 100 − 40
K.E. = 60 ft.-lb.

Friction and the transformation of energy. Referring again to Fig. 10, if friction

Fig. 11. Fontana Dam in the Great Smokies is an interesting study in the transformation of energy. What kind of energy is possessed by the water in the dam? By the water falling down the penstocks? What other energy transformations take place in the powerhouse inside the dam?

is involved, then at any point between A and C:

P.E. + K.E. + Work done against friction = K, a constant.

PROBLEM: Referring again to Fig. 10, assuming that force of friction caused by the wheels of the car and the track is 1 pound, how much kinetic energy will the car have when it reaches point C?

SOLUTION:
K.E. + P.E. + Work of friction = 80 ft.-lb.

Substituting,
K.E. + 0 + 1 × 5 = 80
K.E. = 80 − 5 = 75 ft.-lb.

Note that, since the length of the inclined plane is 5 ft. and the force of friction is 1 lb., then the work done by the car against friction equals 1 × 5, or 5 ft.-lb.

Obviously, the work done against friction by the car is lost by the car, but it is not destroyed. It is only changed in form. And if the car and the track are in an isolated system from which no energy can escape, the total energy in the system remains constant.

Law of conservation of energy. We have just seen that energy can be transformed from kinetic to potential and back again to kinetic. But in every transformation where friction is involved, energy escapes from the car. This does not mean that the energy is destroyed, but only that control over it has been lost. Not only is energy not destroyed, but it is not created. You can throw a ball and give it kinetic energy, but you do not create the energy. All you do is transfer it from your body to the ball. The fact that energy cannot be created or destroyed was one of the greatest

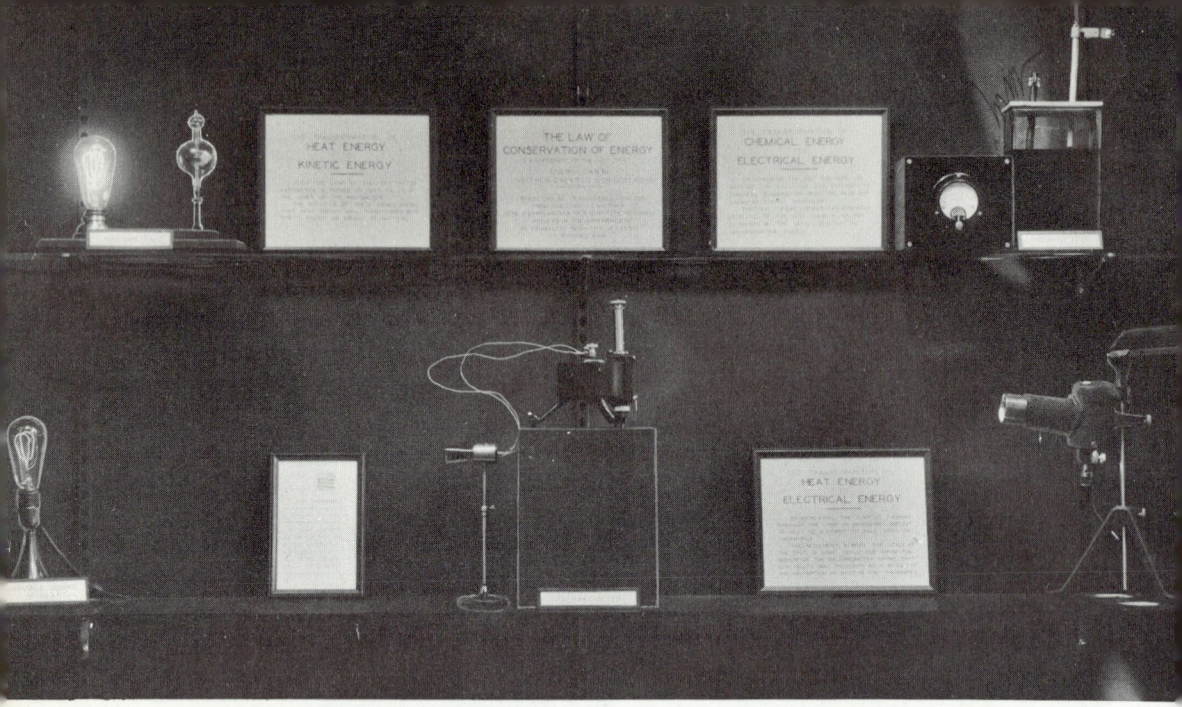

Fig. 12. Demonstration of the conservation of energy. (Top left) Heat energy from the lamp strikes the vanes of the radiometer and causes them to rotate. Heat energy is thereby transformed into kinetic energy. The voltaic cell (top right) transforms chemical energy into electrical energy. When light falls upon the thermocouple (bottom center), the unequal heating of the two conductors causes a flow of electricity.

discoveries in the history of mankind and is known as the *law of conservation of energy*. Later on we may have to modify the above statement of this law.

PROBLEM 1: A 4800-lb. automobile has a velocity of 80 mi./hr. (120 ft./sec.). (a) What is its kinetic energy? (b) In what distance can the automobile be stopped if the negative acceleration caused by the brakes is 4 ft./sec.²? (c) What force is required to stop the automobile in this distance?

SOLUTION:

(a) $\text{K.E.} = \dfrac{kmV^2}{2}$

$\text{K.E.} = \dfrac{4800 \times 120 \times 120}{32 \times 2}$

▶ K.E. = 1,080,000 ft.-lb.

(b) $V^2 = 2aS$

$120 \times 120 = 2 \times 4S$

▶ $S = 1800$ ft.

(c) $W = F \times S$

$1,080,000 = 1800\,F$

$F = 600$ lb.

PROBLEM 2: How far must the automobile in Problem 1 fall from rest in order to acquire the same amount of kinetic energy?

SOLUTION:

$\text{K.E.} = \text{P.E.} = W \times H$

$1,080,000 = 4800 \times H$

$H = 225$ ft.

Explain why it can be said that an automobile which is traveling at a high speed can be as destructive as a stick of dynamite.

· **Physics redefined.** In Chapter 1, we defined physics as a study of matter and motion. It now appears that physics is a study of matter and energy and the interchange of potential and kinetic energy among material things.

WORK, POWER, AND ENERGY

SUMMARY AND CONCLUSIONS

1. In doing work a force must act through a distance.

   Work = Force × Distance, or $W = FS$

2. The common units of work are the foot-pound, the gram-centimeter, dyne-centimeter or erg, foot-poundal, kilogram-meter, and joule. One joule = 10,000,000 ergs.
3. Power is the rate of doing work.

   Power = $\dfrac{\text{Work}}{\text{Time}}$, or $P = \dfrac{W}{t} = \dfrac{F \times S}{t}$

4. The common unit of power is the horsepower. One H.P. is 33,000 ft.-lb. of work done per minute, or 550 ft.-lb. per second.
5. Energy is the ability to do work.
6. Potential energy is energy possessed by a body because of its position or shape (distorted form).
7. Kinetic energy is the ability of a body to do work because of motion.
8. When one body does work upon another body, energy is transferred from the one to the other.
9. The potential energy of a body due to its height equals weight times height. That is,

   P.E. = $W \times H$

10. The potential energy of a falling body is transformed into kinetic energy.
11. When friction is not involved, the gain in kinetic energy of a falling body equals the loss in potential energy.
12. K.E. = $\dfrac{kmV^2}{2}$; k is $\tfrac{1}{32}$ or $\tfrac{1}{980}$, depending on the units used.
13. Also, K.E. = $\tfrac{1}{2}mV^2$. When the mass is in pounds and the velocity is in feet per second, the K.E. is in foot-poundals. When the mass is in grams and the velocity is in centimeters per second, the K.E. is in ergs.
14. Energy cannot be created or destroyed. It can be transferred from one body to another and can be transformed from one form to another. But in either case, some energy is always dissipated or lost. That energy cannot be created or destroyed is known as the law of conservation of energy.

QUESTIONS FOR REVIEW

1. What two conditions must be met if work is done?
2. According to your answer to Question 1, in which of the following is work being done: (a) girl playing a piano; (b) hungry boy eating; (c) man standing still with a bag of grain on his back; (d) a boy holding a door shut; (e) a boy climbing a tree; (f) water pressing against the side of a bucket?
3. What is a foot-pound? Gram-centimeter? Erg? Foot-poundal? Joule?
4. Why is more work done by a person in climbing a hill than in walking the same distance on the level?
5. What is power? What is the essential difference between work and power?
6. What is 1 horsepower?
7. Is the automobile with the greatest pickup necessarily the most powerful one? Explain.
8. Jack weighs twice as much as John. Jack can run up a staircase in 5 seconds, whereas John requires 10 seconds. Compare the powers of the boys.
9. What is energy? What is the test for the presence of energy?
10. If you raised a 12-lb. lead shot 1 ft., how much work would you do?
11. If you drop a 12-lb. shot 1 ft. onto the head of a nail and drive the nail into a board, how much work will have been done on the nail? Assume no loss in the transference of energy.
12. What becomes of your energy when you raise a book? Throw a ball? Drag a chair across a level floor?
13. What are the two basic forms of energy?
14. Trace the changes in energy in a roller coaster.
15. What is the law of conservation of energy?
16. What is the meaning of a perpetual motion machine?
17. A pendulum bob swings back and forth and it also rises and falls. Is there a transformation of energy from potential to kinetic and vice versa? Explain.

18. Why does a pendulum not continue to swing forever once it is set in motion?
19. Why does a tractor have less available power when it is pulling a load than when the power is taken off the flywheel?
20. Multiplying the velocity by 4 increases the kinetic energy of an automobile how many times?

PROBLEMS

1. How much work is done in lifting a 150-lb. trunk 4 ft. high?
2. How much work is done in lifting a 200-gram iron ball 10 cm. high? State your answer in gram-centimeters, ergs, and joules.
3. How much work would you do if you climbed 20 ft. high in a tree? (Use your own weight in solving this problem.)
4. A trunk weighs 100 lb., and 20 lb. of force are required to slide it on a level floor. How much work is done when the trunk is pulled 10 ft.? When lifted 10 ft. high?
5. A stairway is 20 ft. long and its vertical height is 8 ft. How much work would you do in walking up the stairway?
6. In 10 minutes, 1,000,000 lb. of water fall over a dam that is 66 ft. high. How much horsepower could be developed, assuming no loss of energy?
7. An escalator moves along an incline 30 ft./min. and carries 10 people per minute to the floor 20 ft. above. If each person weighs 150 lb., what horsepower is needed?
8. How long would it take a 1-H.P. motor to raise a ton of hay 30 ft. into a barn?
9. At 60 mi./hr. it is estimated that the air resistance on an automobile is 100 lb. and the rolling friction is 25 lb. What H.P. is required to keep the car moving at this rate?
10. The 96-lb. hammer of a pile driver is lifted 30 ft. What is its potential energy? What would be its kinetic energy after it had dropped 30 ft. onto the pile? What would be its potential energy as it hit the pile?
11. Which has more energy, a 1-lb. block of wood whose height is 1 ft., or a 1-lb. block of wood whose velocity is 8 ft./sec.?
12. What horsepower would an engine need to pump 33,000 lb. of water 100 ft. high in a minute?
13. A man who weighs 150 lb. carries 75 lb. of sugar 30 ft. high. How much work does he do? What per cent of the work done is useful?
14. A 4800-lb. automobile has a velocity of 60 mi./hr. (90 ft./sec.). (a) What is its kinetic energy? (b) How far would it have to fall in order to have this same amount of kinetic energy?
15. An unbalanced force of 200 lb. acts on a 3200-lb. automobile for a distance of 160 ft. (a) How much work is done on the automobile? (b) What is the kinetic energy of the automobile? (c) What is the acceleration of the automobile?
16. A 3200-lb. automobile started from rest and attained a velocity of 44 ft./sec. in 10 sec. (a) What was the change in kinetic energy of the automobile? (b) How much work in foot-pounds was done on the automobile? (c) At what horsepower was the automobile operating?
17. A 3200-lb. automobile is traveling 90 ft./sec. (a) Its kinetic energy is how many foot-pounds? (b) If the automobile is decelerated at the rate of 4.5 ft./sec.^{2}, what decelerating force is required?
18. A 1000-lb. pile driver is dropped on a steel post from the height of 16 ft. What is the kinetic energy of the pile driver when it hits the post? If the post is driven ⅓ ft., what is the average force exerted on the post?
19. A 3200-lb. automobile is traveling 15 mi./hr. (22 ft./sec.). What is its kinetic energy (a) in foot-poundals; (b) in foot-pounds?

READING YOU WILL ENJOY

1. Gaddum, L. W., and H. L. Knowles, *Our Physical Environment*. Houghton Mifflin Company, Boston, 1953. Chapters 37 and 38 contain an excellent discussion of work, power, and energy.
2. Richardson, J. S., and G. P. Cahoon, *Methods and Materials for Teaching General and Physical Science*, pp. 297-300. McGraw-Hill Book Company, Inc., New York, 1951.

Chapter 20

Simple Machines

The problem. If we step into the kitchen of a modern house, we may find many machines such as a food grinder, cake mixer, can opener, nutcracker, broom, and dust mop. In the basement we may find a washing machine and a coal stoker which fires the furnace. In the tool room there is usually a hammer, chisel, axe, hoe, rake, and spade. In other rooms we may find a vacuum cleaner and venetian blinds.

If we visit a factory, we may find automatic machines ranging in size from giant metal presses that bend, shear, twist, and stamp big sheets of steel, to smaller intricate automatic machines that seem almost intelligent as they select, count, sort, weigh, assemble, stamp, and wrap packages with greater precision and neatness, and in less time, than can be done by human hands.

In the modern office we find typewriters, adding machines, and calculating machines, some of which in a few seconds can compute answers for problems that would require weeks and even years for the best mathematicians to do.

If we study machines we shall find that many of them consist primarily of six simple machines: *levers, wheels and axles, inclined planes, wedges, screws,* and *pulleys*. By learning the scientific principles governing these, we should gain an understanding of more complicated machines.

The lever. We have already learned that a lever is usually a straight bar, such as a teeter-totter, that is free to rotate about a support F, called the fulcrum or pivot point. Also we know that one of the chief uses of the lever is to overcome a large resisting force R through a smaller applied force E.

And we already know, when a lever is in balance (equilibrium) the moment of force $W_1 d_1$, tending to rotate the lever in one direction about the fulcrum, equals the opposing moment of force $W_2 d_2$. That is, in Fig. 1:

$$W_1 d_1 = W_2 d_2$$

Substituting,
$$100 \times 6 = 300 \times 2$$
600 units of counterclockwise moment of force = 600 units of clockwise moment of force

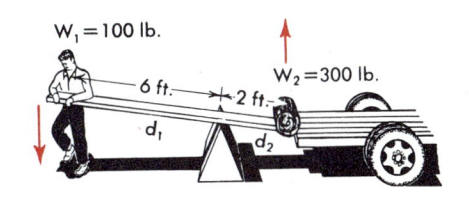

Fig. 1. When the lever is in balance, the counterclockwise moment $W_1 d_1$ equals the clockwise moment $W_2 d_2$.

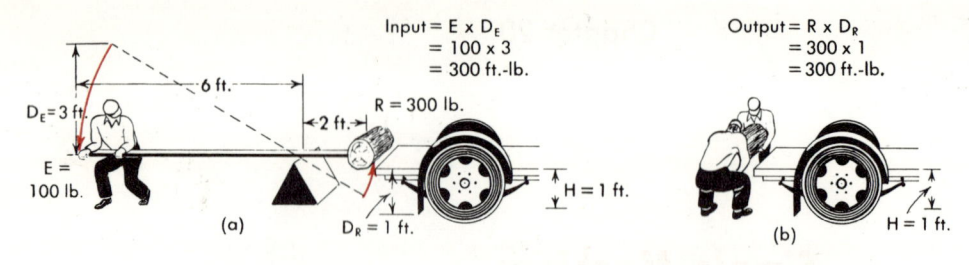

Fig. 2. The ratio of D_E to D_R is one method of expressing the I.M.A. of a lever.

Another thing you should recall about a machine (see page 68) is that the resistance R divided by the effort E equals the mechanical advantage (M.A.) of a machine. The M.A. of the lever in Fig. 1 is $\frac{R}{E} = \frac{300}{100}$, or 3. Remember that since the mechanical advantage is a ratio, no units are involved in expressing it.

You will observe in Fig. 2 that when the resistance is lifted 1 foot, the effort moves 3 feet. Dividing the *effort distance* (the distance through which the effort moves) by the *resistance distance* (the distance through which the resistance moves), we again get 3. The effort distance, D_E, divided by the resistance distance, D_R, gives the *ideal mechanical advantage* (I.M.A.)* of a machine. That is,

$$\frac{D_E}{D_R} = \text{I.M.A.}$$

Here the M.A. is called ideal because its value is the maximum and it is never affected by friction. Friction decreases $\frac{R}{E}$, which is called the *actual mechanical advantage* (A.M.A.). When friction is neglected, the I.M.A. equals the A.M.A.

Therefore, for a lever, $\frac{D_E}{D_R} = \frac{R}{E}$ when friction is not considered. Also, $E \times D_E = R \times D_R$. Why?

It should be observed in Fig. 1 that the ratio of the effort arm, d_1, to the resistance arm, d_2, is the same as the ratio of the effort distance, D_E, to the resistance distance, D_R, giving us another method for determining the I.M.A. That is,

$$\text{I.M.A.} = \frac{d_1}{d_2} = \frac{D_E}{D_R}$$

Hence, for the lever, $\frac{d_1}{d_2} = \frac{R}{E}$ when friction is not considered. Also, $E \times d_1 = R \times d_2$.

PROBLEM 1: A boy uses a 10-ft. pole to lift a large stone. The stone is at the 10-ft. mark, the fulcrum is at the 8-ft. mark, and the boy exerts an effort of 50 lb. downward at the other end of the pole. What is (a) the weight of the stone? (b) The I.M.A.? (c) The A.M.A.? Neglect the weight of the pole.

SOLUTION:
(a) $E \times d_1 = R \times d_2$
$50 \times 8 = 2R$
$2R = 400$
$R = 200$ lb.

(b) $\text{I.M.A.} = \frac{d_1}{d_2} = \frac{8}{2} = 4$

(c) $\text{A.M.A.} = \frac{R}{E} = \frac{200}{50} = 4$

PROBLEM 2: Two boys, John and Charles, sit on a 12-ft. teeter-totter. John weighs 150 lb. and Charles weighs 75 lb. Charles sits at the very end of the board. (a) How far from

*Sometimes called *theoretical mechanical advantage* (T.M.A.).

the fulcrum must John sit? (b) For Charles, what is the I.M.A.? (c) The A.M.A.? (d) What are these for John?

For John the mechanical advantage in Problem 2 is ½. Actually, John is at a mechanical disadvantage. He must exert 150 lb. of force to lift 75 lb. On the other hand, John can move Charles 2 ft. by moving only 1 ft. John is said to have a *speed advantage* of 2.

Does a lever or other machine do more work than is done on it? One man with a lever having an A.M.A. of 2 can easily lift a 300-lb. log. Without the lever, two men are required. Seemingly, then, the lever does the work of one man. Does it?

If the lever in Fig. 2 actually does perform the work of one man, then the work it does, $R \times D_R$, called the *output*, must be greater than the work done on it, $E \times D_E$, known as the *input*. Assuming no friction, $R \times D_R$ equals 300×1, or 300 ft.-lb. of work, and $E \times D_E$ equals 100×3, or 300 ft.-lb. That is, the output equals the input. Consequently, the lever appears to do no more work than is done on it. Does this agree with the law of conservation of energy?

The efficiency of a machine when friction is neglected. The ratio of the work output to the work input is called the *efficiency of a machine*. Usually it is expressed as a percentage.

The efficiency of the lever in Fig. 2a is obtained as follows:

$$\text{Efficiency} = \frac{\text{work output}}{\text{work input}}$$

Substituting,

$$\text{Efficiency} = \frac{300}{300} = 100\%$$

What is the efficiency of a machine when friction is not neglected? To find the effect of friction on output, input, and efficiency, let us consider the following:

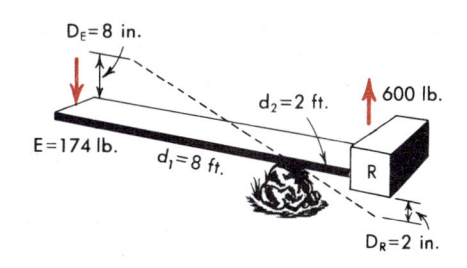

Fig. 3. Finding the efficiency of a lever.

PROBLEM: A lever 10 ft. long is used as shown in Fig. 3 to lift a 600-lb. block of concrete straight up 2 in., or ⅙ ft. The effort distance is 8 in., or ⅔ ft., and the effort is 174 lb. What is the (a) output? (b) Input? (c) Efficiency? (d) A.M.A.? (e) I.M.A.?

SOLUTION:

(a) Output $= R \times D_R$
$600 \times \frac{1}{6} = 100$ ft.-lb.

(b) Input $= E \times D_E$
$174 \times \frac{2}{3} = 116$ ft.-lb.

(c) Efficiency $= \dfrac{\text{work output}}{\text{work input}}$

$\dfrac{100}{116} = 86.2\%$

(d) A.M.A. $= \dfrac{R}{E}$

$\dfrac{600}{174} = 3.45$

(e) I.M.A. $= \dfrac{D_E}{D_R}$

$\dfrac{8}{2} = 4$

In conclusion, we see that because of friction, output is less than the input, and hence the machine does not do more work than is put into it. The output is less than the input by the amount of work done against friction.

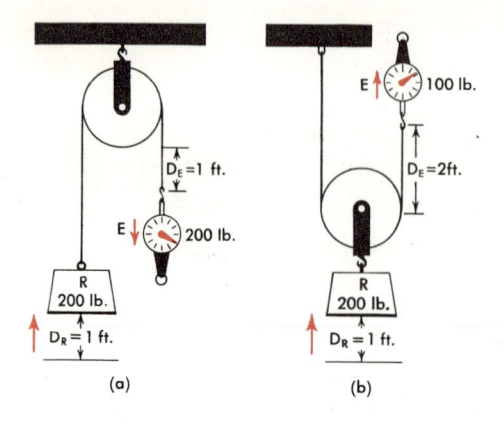

Fig. 4. (a) Single fixed pulley; (b) single movable pulley.

Input =
 output + work done against friction

Does this agree with the law of conservation of energy?

Since input is always greater than output, and efficiency = $\dfrac{\text{output}}{\text{input}}$, efficiency is always less than 100 per cent for any machine when friction is considered. Work done against friction is not destroyed; rather, control over it is lost. Friction is a "tax" that takes its toll when work is done. Explain why a *perpetual motion* machine has never been invented.

The efficiencies of common machines. The efficiencies of common machines range all the way from 5 per cent, which is that of a railway steam engine pulling a load, to about 95–99 per cent, which is that of an electrical transformer. The efficiencies of gasoline engines range from about 10 to 25 per cent, whereas a diesel engine may have an efficiency as high as 40 per cent.

Pulleys. A pulley may be used in one of two ways: either in a fixed position, as shown in Fig. 4a, or in a movable position, as in Fig. 4b.

The fixed pulley shown, neglecting friction, has a mechanical advantage of $\dfrac{R}{E} = \dfrac{200}{200}$, or 1. Its function is to change the direction of force. Often it is more convenient to lift a body by applying a downward rather than an upward force.

The single movable pulley in Fig. 4b has an actual mechanical advantage $\dfrac{R}{E} = \dfrac{200}{100}$, or 2. To move the load R upward, both supporting ropes must be shortened, and when the load moves up 1 foot the effort must move 2 feet. With the pulley, as with all other machines, the theoretical or ideal mechanical advantage equals the effort distance D_E divided by the load distance D_R. That is, the I.M.A. equals $\dfrac{2}{1}$, or 2. It is seen that the number of ropes supporting the resistance also equals the I.M.A. Was this true of the fixed pulley?

The input (see (b) of Fig. 4) equals the effort E times the effort distance D_E and is 100×2, or 200 ft.-lb. The output equals the load R times the height D_R and is 200×1, or 200 ft.-lb. What is the efficiency?

Hence, neglecting friction, for a pulley or system of pulleys the input equals the output, as for the lever. That is,

$$E \times D_E = R \times D_R$$

Block and tackle. The block and tackle (see Fig. 5) is a pulley system with a high mechanical advantage. Neglecting friction, for (a) of Fig. 5 the I.M.A. is 4, while that in (b) is 5. Also, four ropes support the load in (a) and five in (b). Does friction affect the I.M.A.? Explain.

PROBLEM 1: In (b) of Fig. 5, the 1000-lb. load R is lifted 4 ft. high. The effort is 250 lb. and it moves 20 ft. Find (a) the

SIMPLE MACHINES 209

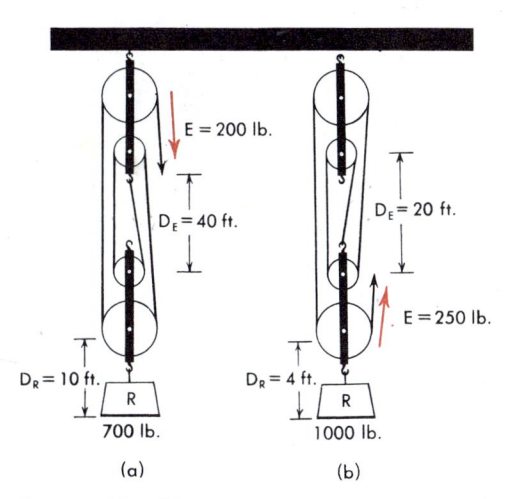

Fig. 5. The block and tackle. How many ropes support the load in (a) and (b)?

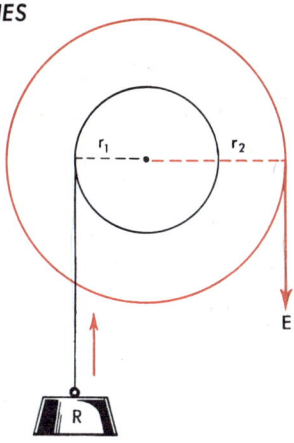

Fig. 6. In one revolution of the large wheel, the resistance R is raised a distance equal to the circumference of the axle.

I.M.A. by two different methods: (b) A.M.A.; (c) input; (d) output; (e) efficiency.

SOLUTION:
(a) I.M.A. = Number of ropes supporting the load = 5

$$\text{I.M.A.} = \frac{D_E}{D_R} = \frac{20}{4} = 5$$

(b) $\text{A.M.A.} = \frac{R}{E} = \frac{1000}{250} = 4$

(c) Input = $250 \times 20 = 5000$ ft.-lb.

(d) Output = $1000 \times 4 = 4000$ ft.-lb.

(e) Efficiency = $\dfrac{\text{output}}{\text{input}}$

$\dfrac{4000}{5000} = 80\%$

PROBLEM 2: See if you can discover another way for finding the efficiency, using the A.M.A. and I.M.A. found in Problem 1.

ANS.: Efficiency = $\dfrac{\text{A.M.A.}}{\text{I.M.A.}}$

PROBLEM 3: When a pulley system like the one in (a) of Fig. 5 is used, an effort of 200 lb. lifts a 700-lb. load 10 ft. high. (a) What is the effort distance? (b) I.M.A.? (c) A.M.A.? (d) Input? (e) Output? (f) Efficiency?

The wheel and axle. The most common wheel and axle is the doorknob. If you have tried to unlatch a door by turning the square bolt without the knob, you can appreciate the convenience of a knob. Another example is the rear wheel of a bicycle with attached sprocket wheel.

The wheel and axle really is another form of the lever. As shown in Fig. 6, a heavy load R is lifted by a rope wrapped around an axle of radius r_1 when we pull on a rope wrapped around a wheel of larger radius r_2. By exerting an effort E through the distance $2\pi r_2$, one revolution (circumference) of the wheel, we lift the load R a distance of $2\pi r_1$. As for all machines, the A.M.A. $= \dfrac{R}{E}$. The I.M.A. $= \dfrac{D_E}{D_R} = \dfrac{2\pi r_2}{2\pi r_1}$, or $\dfrac{r_2}{r_1}$. Explain.

For one revolution of the wheel:
Input = $E \times 2\pi r_2$
Output = $R \times 2\pi r_1$

The inclined plane. An iceman wishes to raise a block of ice weighing 200 lb. from the ground to the platform floor 4

Fig. 7. An inclined plane is a sloping surface used to raise an object from one level to another. Its mechanical advantage is the ratio of its length to its height.

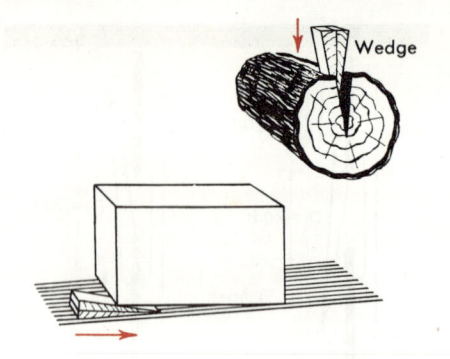

Fig. 8. A wedge is commonly two inclined planes placed base to base. In the wedge the incline rather than the resistance is moved.

ft. high, as shown in Fig. 7. To do this he pushes the ice up a 10-ft. inclined plane. What effort parallel to the inclined plane is required to push the ice at constant velocity up the plane?

If friction is neglected, the work input, $E \times D_E$, must be exactly the same as the work output, $R \times D_R$, required to lift the ice vertically from the ground. Therefore, since, for the inclined plane, $D_E = L$, the length of the plane, and $D_R = H$, the height of the plane, then

$$E \times L = R \times H$$
$$E \times 10 = 200 \times 4$$
$$10E = 800$$
$$E = 80 \text{ lb.}$$

What is its efficiency? I.M.A.? A.M.A.?

PROBLEM: An inclined plane is 10 ft. long and 2 ft. high. An effort of 200 lb. is required to pull an 800-lb. cart up the incline. What is the (a) I.M.A.? (b) A.M.A.? (c) Input? (d) Output? (e) Efficiency? (f) Work done against friction?

The wedge. The wedge, as shown in Fig. 8, is nothing more than an inclined plane that is moved under the load and lifts it. It is usually considered as two inclined planes put base to base. Examples are knives, razor blades, plows, and many other cutting tools.

The screw. A screw is really an inclined plane curved to form a spiral about a cylinder. As an example let us consider the jack screw, a device for lifting heavy bodies.

The distance between two successive threads is called the *pitch, p,* of the screw. When the screw is turned around once, the effort travels a distance $2\pi r$, as shown

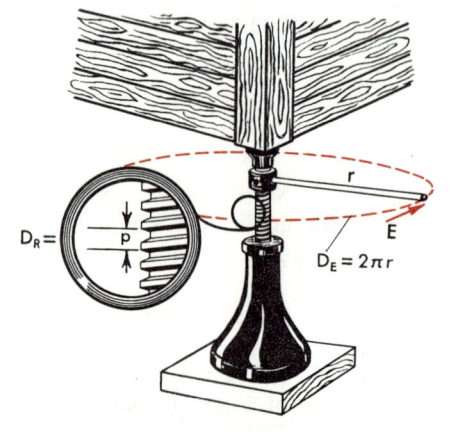

Fig. 9. A jack screw is a combination of an inclined plane and a wheel and axle.

SIMPLE MACHINES

in Fig. 9, and the load R is lifted the distance p.

Then, since for all machines the

$$\text{I.M.A.} = \frac{\text{Effort distance}}{\text{Resistance distance}}$$

for a jack screw the

$$\text{I.M.A.} = \frac{2\pi r}{p}$$

And as for all machines, the

$$\text{A.M.A.} = \frac{R}{E}$$

Neglecting friction, $\frac{R}{E} = \frac{2\pi r}{p}$. Why?

When the effort travels around the circle once, the

$$\text{Input} = E \times 2\pi r$$
$$\text{Output} = R \times p$$

But since

$$\text{Efficiency} = \frac{\text{Output}}{\text{Input}}$$

then

$$\text{Efficiency} = \frac{R \times p}{E \times 2\pi r}$$

PROBLEM 1: The handle of a jack screw is 21 in. long and the pitch of the screw is ¼ in. Neglecting friction, what force E must be applied to lift the rear end of a motor truck which weighs 4000 lb.?

SOLUTION:
$$E \times 2\pi r = R \times p$$
$$E \times 2 \times \frac{22}{7} \times 21 = 4000 \times \frac{1}{4}$$
$$132E = 1000$$
$$E = 7.6 \text{ lb.}$$

What effort would be needed if the jack screw is 25 per cent efficient?

PROBLEM 2: The handle of a jack screw is 28 in. long and the pitch of the screw is ¼ in. The effort required to lift a 4000-lb. weight is 25 lb. Find (a) the A.M.A.; (b) the I.M.A.; (c) the efficiency of the jack screw by two methods.

SOLUTION:

(a) $\text{A.M.A.} = \frac{R}{E} = \frac{4000}{25} = 160$

(b) $\text{I.M.A.} = \frac{2\pi r}{p}$

$$\frac{2 \times 22/7 \times 28}{\frac{1}{4}} = 176 \times 4 = 704$$

(c) $\text{Efficiency} = \frac{\text{output}}{\text{input}}$

$$\frac{4000 \times \frac{1}{4}}{25 \times 2 \times \frac{22}{7} \times 28} = \frac{1000}{4400} = .227 = 22.7\%$$

$$\text{Efficiency} = \frac{\text{A.M.A.}}{\text{I.M.A.}}$$

$$\frac{160}{704} = .227 = 22.7\%$$

Pulleys, belts, and gears. Wheels, belts, and gears are used chiefly to control speed or to change direction of force. High-speed, small-force power can be used to run a high-speed fan or centrifuge, for example, but not to operate a bulldozer or a metal-stamping machine. Each machine designed for a specific job must be run at certain speeds and be able to exert certain forces.

An example of change of speed and

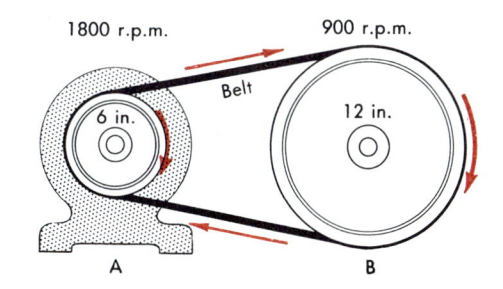

Fig. 10. The speed at which each wheel turns varies inversely with the circumference, or diameter, of the wheel. B makes half as many revolutions as A.

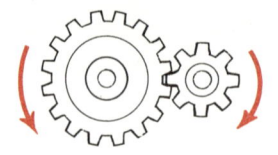

Fig. 11. For each revolution of the large cog wheel, the smaller wheel makes two revolutions.

force by pulleys and belt is shown in Fig. 10. Let us suppose here that pulley *A*, which is attached to an electric motor, is making 1800 revolutions per minute. How many revolutions will pulley *B* make?

Since in turning around once the small pulley moves the belt through the circumference of the small wheel, which is 6 × 3.14, or one-half the circumference of pulley *B*, then pulley *B* should make only one-half revolution. *The number of revolutions varies inversely with the diameters of the pulleys.* The number of revolutions has been reduced but the force has been increased. Can you explain what happens when the process is reversed—i.e., the number of revolutions is multiplied?

Gear wheels are used for the same purpose. In Fig. 11, a gear with 16 teeth or cogs meshes with one that has 8 teeth. If the big gear turns around once, the small one turns around twice; and conversely, if the small one turns twice, the big one turns once. The number of revolutions varies inversely with the number of cogs. On the other hand, the force, as well as the I.M.A., varies directly with the number of cogs. If in Fig. 11 the big wheel turns the small one, what is the speed advantage? The I.M.A.?

The automobile transmission. When an automobile driver shifts gears, he merely changes from one gear to another, both

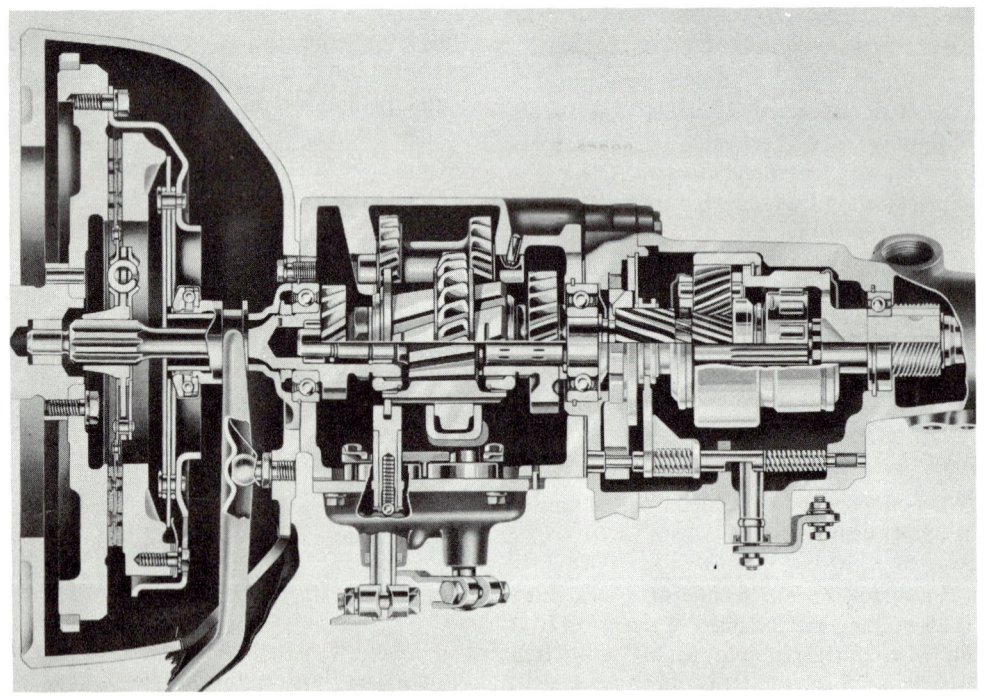

Courtesy General Motors Corp.

Fig. 12. A cutaway view of a standard automobile transmission, showing the clutch plates and the gears.

SIMPLE MACHINES

of a wheel and axle which are really cogwheels. At the bottom is a single movable pulley which is also a cogwheel. Connecting the wheel and axle and the movable pulley is a chain into whose links the cogs fit.

As the chain winds upon the large cogwheel it unwinds on the small cogwheel so that, when the effort travels the distance of the circumference $2\pi r_1$ of the large cogwheel, the chain unwinds $2\pi r_2$, the circumference of the small cogwheel. As a result the chain is shortened by the difference of the two circumferences, $2\pi r_1 - 2\pi r_2$. However, because of the movable pulley at the bottom, when the effort distance is $2\pi r_1$, the resistance or load is lifted a distance equal to $\frac{2\pi r_1 - 2\pi r_2}{2}$.

Hence, for the differential pulley, the

$$\text{I.M.A.} = \frac{2\pi r_1}{\frac{2\pi r_1 - 2\pi r_2}{2}}$$

or,

$$\text{I.M.A.} = \frac{2\pi r_1}{2\pi (r_1 - r_2)} \times \frac{2}{1}$$

That is,

$$\text{I.M.A.} = \frac{2 r_1}{r_1 - r_2}$$

where r_1 is the radius of the large upper wheel and r_2 is the radius of the axle.

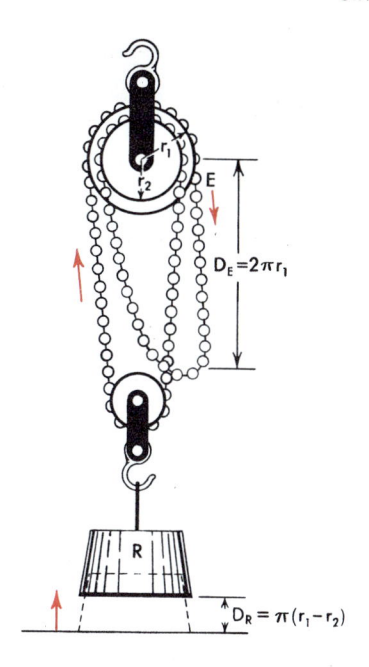

Fig. 13. A differential pulley, or chain hoist, is used to raise heavy weights.

of which are attached by a shaft to the rear wheels. Each of these gears has a different number of cogs, and meshes with a cogwheel that is connected with a countershaft. The countershaft is connected with the engine.

If the rear wheels need to exert more force to drive the car forward, a larger gear with more cogs is shifted so that it meshes with the gear on the countershaft. As a result, the force that the rear wheel can exert on the earth is increased. In case more speed is wanted, a cogwheel with fewer cogs is shifted so that it meshes with the gear on the countershaft.

The differential pulley or chain hoist. The differential pulley, which is also known as a chain hoist, is used in garages, machine shops, and factories to lift and lower heavy machine parts. This machine consists at the top, as shown in Fig. 13,

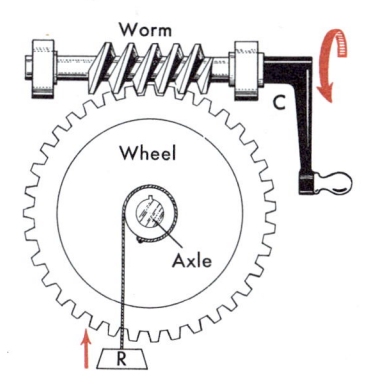

Fig. 14. A worm gear.

Cleveland Worm & Gear Co. *Courtesy Southern Pacific*

Fig. 15. (*l.*) Worm-gear drive in a speed reducer. (*r.*) This impact-speed indicator, which contains a worm gear similar to that found in speedometers, is used on a freight car to record the results of coupling with another car at varying speeds.

The worm gear. The worm gear consists of a screw-like worm on a shaft which meshes with a cogwheel, as shown in Fig. 14. One revolution of crank C rotates the worm so that it turns the cogwheel the distance between two successive cogs. Therefore, if the cogwheel has 25 teeth, the worm wheel shaft must turn through 25 revolutions in order to turn the cogwheel around once. As you can see, the worm gear affords a tremendous mechanical advantage. This device is commonly used to drive the rear axles of trucks and also to reduce the speed in speed counters. On steering wheels it reduces the force needed to turn the wheel.

SUMMARY AND CONCLUSIONS

1. Actual mechanical advantage = $\dfrac{\text{Resistance}}{\text{Effort}}$.

That is,
$$\text{A.M.A.} = \frac{R}{E}$$

2. Ideal mechanical advantage = $\dfrac{\text{Effort distance}}{\text{Resistance distance}}$.

That is,
$$\text{I.M.A.} = \frac{D_E}{D_R}$$

3. Work output = effort × effort distance
   $= E \times D_E$

4. Work input = resistance × resistance distance
   $= R \times D_R$

5. Efficiency = $\dfrac{\text{work output}}{\text{work input}}$
   $= \dfrac{E \times D_E}{R \times D_R}$
   $= \dfrac{\text{A.M.A.}}{\text{I.M.A.}}$

6. Work input = work output + work lost in overcoming friction

QUESTIONS FOR REVIEW

1. Explain why a tinsmith's shears have long handles and short blades and a tailor's shears have short handles and long blades.
2. Which one of the levers on page 123 has the greatest M. A.? Which one has the smallest M. A.?
3. What is the ideal mechanical advantage of a fixed pulley? Why use such a pulley?

SIMPLE MACHINES

4. What is the ideal mechanical advantage of a single movable pulley? When an effort moves 1 foot, how far does the resistance move?
5. Write in terms of the dimensions of the machine the ideal mechanical advantage of each of the following: (a) lever; (b) wheel and axle; (c) inclined plane; (d) differential pulley.
6. What would be the effect of increasing the number of cogs on the rear sprocket wheel of a bicycle? Of decreasing them? Of increasing the diameter of the rear wheel?
7. What does an overdrive do for an automobile?
8. What is *power steering* on an automobile?
9. How do you account for the low efficiency of the jack screw?

PROBLEMS

1. The resistance arm of a lever is 2 ft. long and the effort arm is 8 ft. long. What is the I.M.A. of the lever? What effort (neglecting friction) is needed to lift a 600-lb. stone?
2. What mechanical advantage is needed for a 100-lb. effort to support 600 lb.? Draw a first-class lever which will accomplish this. Show the effort, fulcrum, and load.
3. A man uses a pole 16 ft. long as a lever and lays it over a stump in order to pry up a load which is 4 ft. from the stump. The man weighs 150 lb. and applies all his weight to the other end of the pole. What load can the man support? Neglect the weight of the pole.
4. Draw a diagram of a single-fixed and a single-movable pulley combination so arranged that 50 lb. will support 150 lb.
5. In lifting a load 2 ft. with a system of pulleys, the effort moves 10 ft. If the load is 600 lb. and the effort is 125 lb., find (a) the I.M.A.; (b) the A.M.A.; (c) the input; (d) the output; (e) the efficiency.
6. Make a diagram of a system of pulleys which would give the I.M.A. given in Problem 5 and arranged so that a person could apply the effort by pulling down on the rope.
7. One end of a 20-ft. plank is 4 ft. higher than the other. It requires 160 lb. of effort to push a 600-lb. cart up the incline. What is the A.M.A.? I.M.A.? Input? Output? Efficiency of the inclined plane?
8. A cogwheel with 50 cogs meshes with one having 10 cogs. If the large cogwheel revolves once, how many times does the smaller one revolve?
9. The lever arm of a jack screw is 20 in. long. The pitch of the screw is ⅛ in. An effort of 200 lb. is applied to the handle of the jack screw and it lifts 12,560 lb. What is the I.M.A.? A.M.A.? Output? Input? Efficiency?
10. A motor scooter and its load of two boys weighs 500 lb. It climbs a hill, whose vertical height is 66 ft., in 1 min.
   (a) How much work was done against the force of gravity?
   (b) What horsepower was used in overcoming the force of gravity?
   (c) If the efficiency of the machine was 25 per cent, what was the horsepower of the motor?
11. The front sprocket wheel of a bicycle has 28 cogs and the rear sprocket has 7. The diameter of the rear wheel is 26 in. If a boy turns the pedals two revolutions per second, what is the speed of the bicycle in ft./sec.? Mi./hr.?
12. A winch, or wheel and axle, like that in Fig. 6, is used to raise 80 lb. of water. If the axle is 2.5 in. in radius, what length must the crank be if 20 lb. of effort lift the water? Neglect friction.
13. If in Problem 12 the water were lifted 20 ft., how far would the crank move?
14. The crank of a grindstone is 10 in. long and the diameter of the stone is 30 in. If 20 lb. of force are applied to the handle, what is the force of friction on the stone?
15. If in Problem 14 the coefficient of friction is 0.8, with what force is the implement that is being ground pushed against the grindstone?

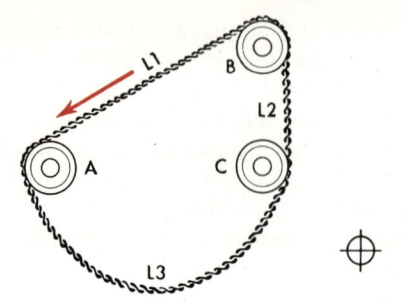

Fig. 16. A proposed perpetual motion machine.

PROJECT

Fig. 16 shows a proposed perpetual motion machine. The inventor argued that since L_1 is longer and heavier than L_2, and since the weight of L_3 is divided equally between L_2 and L_1, then the chain should keep moving counterclockwise. Make an apparatus similar to this and demonstrate it to the class. Find at least two fallacies in the inventor's argument.

READING YOU WILL ENJOY

1. Chase, Stuart, *Men and Machines*. The Macmillan Company, New York, 1935.
2. Richardson, J. S., and G. P. Cahoon, *Methods and Materials for Teaching General and Physical Science,* pp. 189-191. McGraw-Hill Book Company, Inc., New York, 1951.
3. Sutton, R. M., *Demonstration Experiments in Physics,* pp. 29-30. McGraw-Hill Book Company, Inc., New York, 1938.

Unit 7

Concerning the Nature of Matter

For years scientists have been attempting to photograph atoms in an effort to gain further knowledge about the structure of the atom. Through the use of a specially constructed microscope using two wave lengths of light, it is possible to photograph atoms of certain crystals, as shown in the unit photograph. The inset shows the image of atoms of marcasite, FeS_2, magnified 1.1 million times. The larger dark circular areas are iron (Fe) atoms with 26 electrons each, while the fainter darker areas are sulfur (S) atoms with 16 electrons each.

As you explore this unit, you will discover the fundamental building blocks of matter and some properties characteristic of all forms of matter.

21. MOLECULAR PHYSICS

Chapter 21

Molecular Physics

The problem. Thomas A. Edison spent years hunting the world over for a durable material suitable for the filament of his incandescent electric lamp. Today, hundreds of similar searches are going on. An example is the aircraft industry's search for strong, lightweight metals or alloys that will withstand extremely high temperatures and therefore be suitable for airplane bodies and engines in the jet age. Every tool, gadget, and machine used by man calls for matter of one or more different kinds, each having a different nature.

In order to make sharp knives, scissors, and razors, we need tough, hard materials. For making mattresses, pillows, and cushions, we need soft materials. For windows we need transparent materials; for window blinds, opaque materials. For the foundation of a house, we need materials that do not crush easily and will not weather away. For highways, we need materials that will not crumble or be ground away under the wheels of heavy traffic. Hence, we see that the nature of matter is of much concern to our well-being. Our problem is to examine the theories about its nature and to understand their consequences.

Theories concerning the nature of matter. "What is the nature of matter?" is a very old but fundamental question. Some 2000 years ago the philosopher Lucretius wrote his famous treatise, *Concerning the Nature of Things*. He argued that all matter—for example, stones, trees, animals, and water—was composed of innumerable small particles called *corpuscles* or atoms. An atom was a particle that could not be smashed, broken, cut, or further subdivided.

This theory implied that if water in a bowl were divided into drops and one of these were divided into smaller drops, each of which was divided again and again, eventually particles (atoms) would be reached which could no longer be divided.

There was a rival school of thought which contended that matter does not consist of particles. Its proponents argued that the matter in, say, a solid piece of gold is continuous. That is, it is all one solid, continuous mass. There are no vacant spaces in either gold or water, as there probably would be if they consisted of particles. See Fig. 1.

There was a vast difference between Lucretius' atomic theory and the continuous theory of matter. Lucretius' theory meant that possibly all matter could be reduced to a few different kinds of atoms, and therefore that relatively only a few kinds of atoms made up the thousands of

Continuous theory vs. Atomic theory

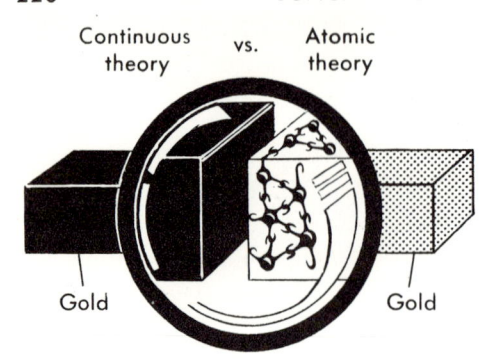

Gold — Gold

Fig. 1. Early theories of matter.

different kinds of matter, in much the same way that twenty-six letters of the alphabet make up the thousands of words in the English language. The atoms were believed to be Nature's fundamental building stones. Hence the problem of discovering the real nature of matter was to discover the nature of the atoms. The atomic point of view opened up a whole new world for study and experiment.

On the other hand, the theory that matter is continuous, not atomic or corpuscular in nature, closed the whole question and directed science down a dead-end street. For according to that theory, regardless of how extensively matter, such as a drop of water, might be divided, the smallest bit would be exactly like a bowl full. For this reason, the procedure of dividing matter in search of atoms was considered to be useless.

Testing the consequences of the opposing theories concerning the nature of matter. In case matter is made up of indivisible particles, there are several consequences that have to follow. First, there must be a limit to the diameter of each such particle, and therefore to the thinness to which a given volume of liquid can be spread and to the surface area that it can cover. Accordingly, a drop of oil, when actually placed on a smooth, apparently still water surface, should cover only a certain area and there should be a definite limit to the thinness of the film. According to your observations, is this true? According to the continuous theory, could this happen?

Another thing must be true if matter is corpuscular in nature. That is that "empty" space must exist between the atoms in a substance, such as a beaker of water, just as space exists between golf balls filling a bucket, potatoes in a basket, or bricks in a pile. And just as several quarts of sand can be poured into a bushel basket full of potatoes, so should it be possible for atoms of another substance to be poured between atoms of water.

To test this consequence, fill a glass tumbler brimming full of water so that if even one more drop is added, the water overflows. Then slowly add salt. As a result, if the salt dissolves, well over a teaspoonful can be added without causing a drop of water to overflow. Could this happen if no empty space existed in water? Which theory does this experiment tend to uphold? See Fig. 2.

A similar experiment is to mix a pint of alcohol with a pint of water. The result is that the total volume is less than two pints. Only by assuming that the salt and alcohol fill the empty spaces between the water particles can we account for the results of these two experiments. Both salt and alcohol are said to *dissolve* in water, and each is said to go into *solution*. Each disappears and becomes distributed throughout the solution. See Fig. 3.

In conclusion, it appears that *there is considerable empty space in a liquid and that this space results from the fact that a liquid is made up of particles.*

That empty space exists in even the denser solids is shown by the fact that water inside an iron ball can be squeezed through the walls by high pressure on the water. Similarly, but without high pressure,

Fig. 2. Does the water overflow?

poisonous carbon monoxide gas will go through the sides of a solid red-hot iron stove and has caused many deaths.

Proof of the existence or nonexistence of empty space in a gas is left to the student. With which theory does your conclusion agree?

Atoms and elements. Perhaps some of you are objecting to the statement that water cannot be subdivided because you know that water can be broken down to produce hydrogen and oxygen, and conversely, that hydrogen and oxygen can be united chemically to form water. In other words, a basic particle of water can be split in two. Does this mean that matter is not atomic in nature but is continuous?

Before discarding the atomic theory of matter, we should find out whether or not oxygen and hydrogen can be divided further. For many years after their discovery, no way was known by which they could be broken into simpler substances. For this reason hydrogen and oxygen, like several other substances, were called *chemical elements,* or just *elements.* All elements, however, were supposed to be made up of atoms, which in 1807, John Dalton, an English chemist, said were indivisible, eternal, and indestructible. Newton said that atoms were "so very hard as to never wear or break in pieces." Each element was supposed to be made up of like atoms, but the atoms of one element were unlike the atoms of another element. Up to the present time, 92 elements have been discovered in nature and several more (see page 628 which are very short-lived, and do not ordinarily exist in nature, have been manufactured by scientists.

The molecular theory of matter. If, as assumed by early scientists, an atom can not be subdivided, then the basic particles of water, which can be separated into hydrogen and oxygen, cannot be atoms. The smallest particles of water are called *molecules.* A molecule is often defined as the smallest particle of any substance that can exist and still be that substance. A molecule may consist of one, several, or many atoms.

In case two or more unlike atoms are united, usually a molecule of a *compound* is formed. If, however, the atoms are alike, usually a molecule of an element is formed. For example, if two hydrogen atoms and one oxygen atom are united chemically, they form *a molecule of the compound, water.* There are thousands of different compounds, and every year new discoveries add many to the already long list. Furthermore, like the number of possible words in the English language, the number of possible compounds is almost unlimited.

What holds the molecules together in solids and liquids? The attractive force that causes like substances (like molecules) to cling together is called *cohesion.* Therefore, it is cohesion which binds

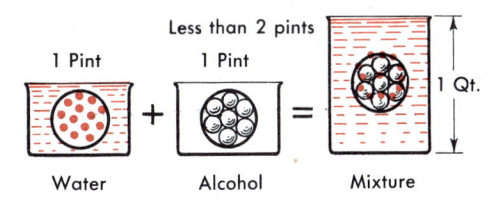

Fig. 3. Here is a case where one and one does not make two. Explain.

molecules of iron together to form a nail, molecules of carbon together to form a solid, hard diamond, and molecules of water together to form a lump of ice or drop of water.

From experience we know that cohesion is greatest in solids. It is what causes a solid to retain its shape and prevents it from crumbling when compressed and from being separated when forces tend to stretch it or to cut it in two. A slender steel cable of 1-inch diameter is strong enough to lift a locomotive. This shows the enormous cohesion between the molecules. Because of the great cohesive forces in solids, the molecules in a solid are not free to intermingle. With few exceptions they tend to be fixed within a limited space. However, there is evidence, which will be discussed in a later chapter, that they vibrate continuously.

Cohesion is much weaker in liquids than in solids but nevertheless is apparent. Galileo pointed this out when he observed large drops of water on cabbage leaves and wondered why they did not spread over the entire leaf. Similarly, when mercury is spilled on a table or water is spilled on a greasy surface, cohesion causes the small spheres of each liquid to form.

Among gases, cohesion is not ordinarily apparent. Think of evidence that supports this statement.

Adhesion. The force that causes the molecules of one substance to cling to the molecules of a different substance is called *adhesion*. The forces of adhesion are often very great, as in the case of glue and wood, water and glass, and oil and metal. It is the great adhesive force between the last two that keeps the oil in the bearings of machinery when tremendous pressures are applied to them. What are some of the things we could not do, were it not for adhesion? Would our hands get "dirty"?

How does the molecular theory explain capillarity? When one end of a long glass tube that is open at both ends is placed in water, as shown in (a) of Fig. 4, forces cause the water to rise in the tube to a certain height. The finer the bore of the tube, the higher the water rises. A tube with a hairlike bore is called a *capillary tube* and the liquid rise in it is called *capillarity*. How could you show that this rise is not due to atmospheric pressure?

Seemingly, water rises in capillary tubes because the adhesive forces between glass and water molecules are greater than the cohesive forces between water molecules. When a fine-bore tube is first placed in water, the glass walls immediately above the surface of the water attract molecules straight upward by adhesion. These molecules in turn attract other nearby molecules, pulling them up by cohesion. This process continues, filling up the space below as the water is pulled higher and higher. Cohesion prevents any of the water from dropping back. The water continues to rise until the upward pull is equalized by the weight of the liquid in the tube. Because of capillary action, liquids are soaked up by blotters, sponges, towels, soils, and many other substances. One of the best ways to observe this action is to hold one edge of a cube of sugar just beneath the surface of a cup of coffee.

If mercury instead of water is used, as in (b) of Fig. 4, you will find that the action is reversed. The mercury inside the tube will be depressed below the level of the mercury outside, and the depression will be greater in a tube of small bore than in one of larger bore. Also, when a clean glass rod is put in mercury, the mercury does not wet (cling to) the rod as water does to a glass rod. Thus, the cohesion of mercury molecules is greater than the adhesion between mercury and glass.

MOLECULAR PHYSICS 223

$F_c = \pi R^2 h d g$ $S = \frac{F}{\ell}$ $(2\pi R)$

(a) Water (b) Mercury

Fig. 4. In capillary tubes, water forms a concave surface, but mercury forms a convex surface. Explain.

Fig. 6. The oil forms a spherical ball when it is floated between the water and the alcohol.

How does the molecular theory explain surface tension? Galileo observed that a greasy needle will float on water and that a water bug can "skate" on water. As you realize, both behave contrary to Archimedes' law of flotation. However, once a needle breaks through the liquid surface, it sinks in accordance with Archimedes' law. How can we explain these phenomena?

When a needle "floats" on water, it can be observed that there is a slight depression of the water surface, which appears as though it might be stretched a little; but there seems to be enough cohesion between the surface molecules to keep the needle from breaking through. The surface molecules seem to act like an elastic membrane that stretches around the liquid and pulls the surface inward. This phenomenon is called *surface tension*.

It is because of surface tension that a falling drop of water becomes nearly spherical. Here the cohesive forces of surface tension draw the drop into an almost perfect sphere. For this reason we can make lead shot by letting molten lead fall from a sieve into a pool of water some distance below. The liquid drops tend to take the shape that has the smallest possible area for a given volume; namely, that of a sphere.

An experiment designed to illustrate the spherical state of a liquid drop is shown in Fig. 6. Here water was poured into the glass vessel and then alcohol was poured carefully on top of it. The alcohol, whose density is less than that of water, stayed on top, and a distinct boundary line was formed between the two liquids. Then olive oil, which is not soluble in either alcohol or water, and which sinks in alcohol but floats on water, was dropped into the container. The drop immediately became spherical in form and settled slowly to the boundary level, where it remained suspended as shown.

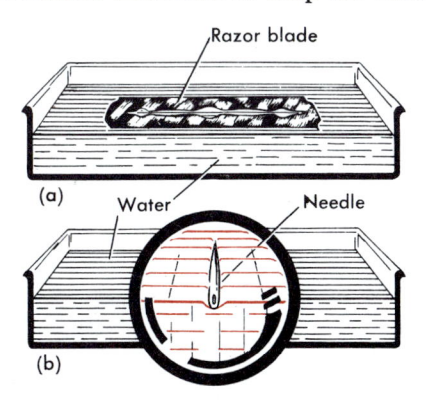

Fig. 5. Explain why these objects, both denser than water, can float on water.

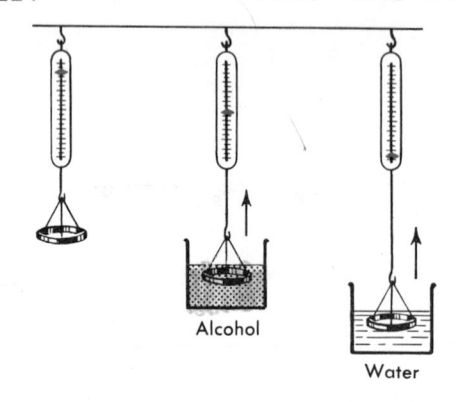

Fig. 7. Because of the greater surface tension, more force is required to lift the ring from the water than from the alcohol solution.

How can surface tension be reduced? Galileo also observed that it is almost impossible to float a needle on alcohol. And he showed that when alcohol (he used red wine) was added to a large drop of water on a cabbage leaf, the drop spread out and covered more area. These observations tend to prove that the cohesive forces among molecules of alcohol are less than those among molecules of water, and that when alcohol is mixed with water the cohesive forces are reduced and hence the surface tension is reduced. It is for this reason that when a few drops of alcohol are dropped on a water surface on which a needle is supported by surface tension, the needle sinks.

Soap, alcohol, soap substitutes, and many other substances reduce surface tension of water. As a result, a drop of soapy water, like Galileo's mixture of water and wine on the cabbage leaf, will wet a much larger surface than a drop of pure water would wet. Also, water with reduced surface tension will seep into cracks and crevices that water alone would not enter. It is for this reason that an alcohol solution may leak from a water-tight automobile radiator and that soapy water will

Fig. 8. The duck at the left is having difficulty keeping afloat. Its feathers were coated with a detergent.

Fig. 9. After some detergent is added to the water, the steel wool, which normally floats, sinks quickly to the bottom.

Courtesy Monsanto Chemical Co.

penetrate and clean fabrics and other materials much better than water alone. Raising the temperature of water also reduces its surface tension. This is one reason why hot soapsuds wash things "cleaner" than cold suds do.

When the surface tension of a liquid is decreased, its "wetting ability" is generally increased. Soapy water, if used to wash a greasy surface, will actually wet it and form a thin film over the surface, whereas water alone will form in spherical droplets on the greasy surface and do little wetting.

In recent years several complex new "wetting agents" have been invented. They are materials that decrease surface tension, thus making a liquid more penetrating than previously. The dyeing and cleaning industries are finding them especially useful. Wetting agents are also used in photography. They greatly shorten the time required for developing and fixing prints and films. They also reduce water spots and pinholes on negatives. Soap substitutes, or *detergents*, are good wetting agents.

How does the molecular theory explain the Brownian movement? In 1827, Robert Brown, an Englishman, observed that very fine undissolved particles dispersed in a liquid were in constant, zigzag motion in all directions. This motion is known as the *Brownian movement* (Fig. 10).

Brown accounted for the motion of the particles by assuming that the molecules of the liquid in which they were dispersed were moving, striking some of them head-on blows and others glancing blows. Of course particles with the least mass would be expected, as is the case, to be given the greatest velocity and to perform the fastest ceaseless dance. Minute drops of oil or particles of smoke suspended in air undergo the same kind of motion, which indicates that air molecules, like liquid molecules, are in constant motion.

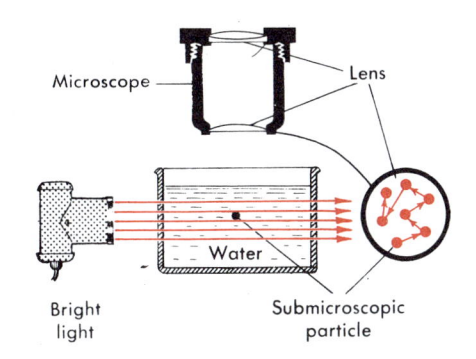

Fig. 10. An example of Brownian movement. What does it tend to prove?

To observe Brownian movement in a liquid, put a small amount of powdered pigment into some distilled water. Then put one drop of this solution on a microscope slide. By illuminating the slide with a strong light, you will see the microscopic pigment particles dancing about as they are continually being hit by water molecules. Since the pigment particles are thousands of times heavier than the water molecules, it is evident that the water particles must be moving with very high speeds. Brownian movement is one of our best supporters of the kinetic theory of matter (see page 227).

How does the molecular theory of matter explain the diffusion of liquids? If we fill a tall glass jar nearly full of water and then pour a concentrated solution of copper sulfate through a long thistle tube which reaches to the bottom of the glass jar, we will find, since this solution is denser than water, a fairly sharp line of separation between the water and the blue copper sulfate solution. After several days, however, we shall see that the blue solution has spread upward. In time the two liquids will become thoroughly mixed. This movement of a heavy liquid upward into the lighter one is called *diffusion* of a liquid. In accordance with the molecular theory, the heavy copper sulfate molecules

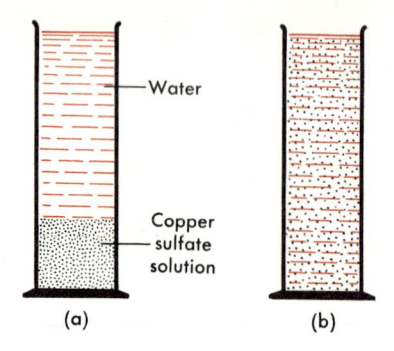

Fig. 11. The denser copper sulfate diffuses upward through the less dense water.

have independent motion of their own which results in their moving into the lighter liquid above. See Fig. 11.

How does the molecular theory explain osmosis? If tomatoes, cherries, raisins, grapes, and certain one-celled sea (salt-water) animals are placed in distilled or tap water for some time, they will burst open. Again, you may cut off the uppermost end of a medium-sized carrot and wrap some tape around the carrot near the top to prevent it from splitting. Bore a hole in it from the top—a hole about 3 inches deep and ½ inch in diameter. Fill the hole with molasses or concentrated sugar solution, then stop the hole tightly with a one-hole stopper in which a 3-foot glass tube has been inserted. Finally, place the carrot in distilled water, as shown in Fig. 12. After a few hours the liquid will rise several inches in the tube.

Since the liquid was lifted so high in the tube, it is quite evident that the distilled water passed through the carrot, even though the liquid level in the carrot was higher than the water level in the container. But what about the sugar solution? Did it pass through the walls of the carrot into the distilled water? If we taste the water, we find that some of it did.

But it is quite evident that the distilled water, or less concentrated solution, passed in through the walls of the carrot faster than the more concentrated sugar solution passed out through the walls of the carrot. This process is known as *osmosis*. The skin of an animal, a vegetable, or a fruit, or any similar membrane through which osmosis takes place, is called a *semipermeable membrane*.

Osmosis plays an important part in carrying liquids through plants and in the absorption of food and disposal of waste by cells in plants and animals. It also explains how food passes through the walls of the intestines, and it explains in part how sap solutions are forced to the tops of the trees. Explain why a dried prune swells up when put in water.

How does the molecular theory explain diffusion of gases? If we inflate a toy balloon and place it on top of a large glass jar which contains a few drops of gasoline or carbon disulfide solution, and then after about ten minutes release the air in the balloon, the odor of the gasoline, or carbon disulfide, will come from inside the balloon. How could either of these substances get into the balloon?

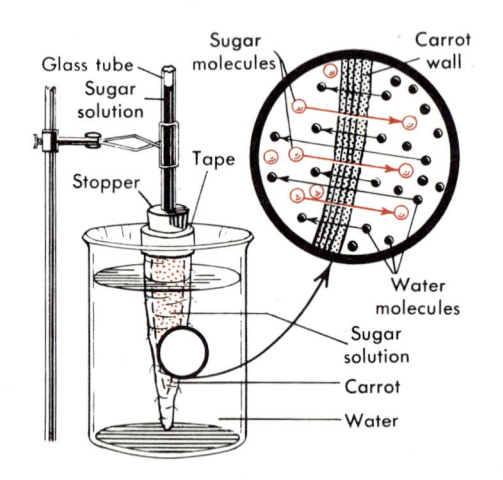

Fig. 12. The sugar solution rises in the tube because of osmosis. Osmosis may be regarded as diffusion through a membrane.

MOLECULAR PHYSICS

If we assume that the liquid in the jar vaporized, and that the vapor molecules spread in all directions, or *diffused,* and passed through the balloon, then the above phenomenon is explained. Experiments show that *the rate of diffusion varies inversely with the square root of the density of the gas.*

How does the molecular theory explain gas pressure? As we know, a liter of gas can be compressed into a very small fraction of its original volume. But as the volume decreases, the pressure increases. What is the cause of the pressure?

The fact that the gas can be compressed a great amount must mean that a very high percentage of the space in a given volume of gas is unoccupied. On the other hand, it has been well established that in 1 cubic centimeter of gas under standard conditions there are approximately 2.68×10^{19} (26,800,000,000,000,000,000) molecules.

To explain how a gas exerts pressure, it is assumed that these little particles travel at tremendous speeds. In the less dense gases, such as hydrogen, under standard conditions, molecules may travel at a rate as high as 7 miles per second, which is about fifteen times the speed of a fast rifle bullet.

These speedy little molecules travel in straight lines, hit one another, and strike the sides of the containing vessel. They are believed to be perfectly elastic. That is, they will bounce off the side of a vessel, or off each other, with the same speed as they had before impact. Otherwise they would gradually lose their velocity, and pressure would decrease, even though none of them leaked out of the container. Will a rubber ball that is thrown against a wall bounce off with the same speed with which it hits the wall? Would bouncing rubber balls continue indefinitely to bounce when placed in a box? Explain.

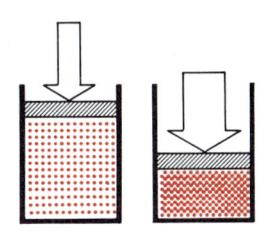

Fig. 13. Explain why halving the volume of a confined gas doubles its pressure.

When the volume of a given mass of gas is halved by an increase in pressure, the pressure of the gas is doubled. The density of the gas is also doubled, so that each molecule strikes the walls of the container twice as often as before. Heating a gas increases the velocity of the molecules and hence increases the pressure. Cooling it decreases the velocity. This explanation, in brief, is called the *kinetic theory* of gases. Since the molecules in all states of matter are believed to be in constant motion, the theory can be broadened to the *kinetic theory of matter.*

SUMMARY AND CONCLUSIONS

1. Matter can be subdivided into basic particles called atoms.
2. A molecule is the smallest particle of any substance that can exist and still be that substance. A molecule may consist of one, several, or many atoms.
3. There are 92 different natural elements.
4. The atoms in a molecule are held together by chemical bonds. The molecules in liquid and solid compounds and elements are held together by cohesion.
5. Cohesion is the attraction of like molecules. Adhesion is the attraction of unlike molecules.
6. Diffusion in gases and liquids is explained by the fact that the molecules in both are in motion. The smaller the mass of a molecule the greater its velocity.
7. Pressure in a gas is explained by the kinetic theory.

8. The surface of a liquid, because of cohesion, tends to contract and become as small as possible. This is surface tension.
9. Liquids are raised in small-bore open tubes which they wet or to which they adhere. Liquids are depressed in tubes which they do not wet or to which they do not adhere.

QUESTIONS FOR REVIEW

1. What is the difference between an atom and a molecule? An element and a compound?
2. What is cohesion? Adhesion? Capillarity? Surface tension?
3. How are the atoms held together in a molecule?
4. Explain why your hair clings together and to your head when it is wet but does not do so when it is dry.
5. Explain why a soap film stretched across the mouth of a funnel, held with the mouth down, will climb against gravity up the sides of the funnel.
6. What causes water to rise in a fine-bore tube, whereas the reverse action is true of mercury?
7. Give reasons why fairly hot soapy water washes dishes and clothes better than cold water with or without soap.
8. If dry corn or dried peas in the hold of a ship were to become wet, what might happen to the ship? Explain.
9. Explain two principles that influence the passage of water solutions several hundred feet upward from the roots to the top of a California redwood tree.
10. Explain whether or not the facts observed in the study of the Brownian movement agree with the kinetic theory of gases and with our explanation of osmosis.
11. Explain why one duck in Fig. 8 is having difficulty keeping afloat.
12. Would a tooth paste with a low surface tension be better, other factors being equal, than one with high surface tension? Explain.
13. Give evidence that the cohesive forces in a solid act but for very short distances.
14. Explain why some automobile radiators will hold water but will leak a solution of alcohol and water.
15. Most people like the taste of hot soup better than cold soup. In the light of our study, give one possible explanation as to why this is true.

PROJECTS

1. Devise an experiment which proves or disproves that the height of the liquid shown in Fig. 12 is not due to atmospheric pressure and is affected very little by capillarity.
2. Devise an experimental means for determining the relative surface tensions of liquids. Use one liquid as a standard and call its surface tension 1.
3. In the mouth of a quart-size glass milk bottle, fit a cap made of ordinary wire screening. Then fill the bottle with water, place your hand tightly over the mouth of the bottle, and turn the bottle upside down. Remove your hand and explain the results.

READING YOU WILL ENJOY

Swezey, K. M., *After - Dinner Science*. Whittlesey House, McGraw-Hill Book Company, Inc., New York, 1948. See pp. 28-37 in the section entitled "Water Is Wonderful."

Unit 8

The Universe of Heat

Practically all the important sources of heat energy are derived from the sun. Coal, oil, and gas simply represent the stored sunshine of past ages. Even the winds, which were once used on a wide scale as a source of power, are due to the radiations from the sun. As our fossil fuels—coal, oil, and gas—are being depleted, scientists are turning to other sources of heat energy to do work for us. The unit photograph shows one of the world's largest applications of the energy of the sun—the 40-foot solar oven on Mont Louis in the Pyrenees.

As rays from the sun strike the mirror, they are concentrated into a smaller area in a solar furnace where molecules capture the sun's energy and give it off in the form of heat. Many scientists believe that by tapping the vast energy of the sun directly, it will be possible to produce infinitely greater amounts of power than by utilizing atomic energy or any other known energy source.

22. WHAT ARE HEAT AND TEMPERATURE?
23. EXPANSION
24. MEASUREMENT OF HEAT
25. THE TRANSFERENCE OF HEAT
26. WORK AND HEAT

Unit Photograph Courtesy Stanford Research Institute

Chapter 22

What Are Heat and Temperature?

The problem. In our study of physics thus far, considerable emphasis has been placed on matter and energy. In fact, we have redefined physics (see page 202) as a study of matter and energy and their interrelationships.

Consequently, at the beginning of the study of heat we are curious to know whether or not this definition of physics will apply to heat. Thus we ask: What is the nature of heat? Is it matter? Is it a form of energy? What is temperature? How is heat measured? What occurs when a body gains or loses heat?

These and many other questions will be considered in this unit, but our immediate problem is to discover what heat and temperature are and how temperature is measured.

Is heat matter? Many early scientists believed that heat is matter. They thought it to be a fluid which could flow from one body to another. This fluid they called *caloric*. When a body became warm or hot, caloric was supposed to have flowed into it; when it cooled, caloric supposedly flowed out of the body.

The fact that most substances expand when heated and contract when cooled seems to uphold the matter theory, because matter occupies space. The trouble is that some substances expand when cooled and contract when heated. Also, if heat is matter, then a body should weigh more when it is hot than when it is cold. Experiment shows that this is not true. So, since the logical consequences of the theory that heat is matter fail to agree with experiment, we should discard the theory and turn our attention to finding a better one.

Is heat a form of energy? It was Benjamin Thompson, Count Rumford (1753-1814), an American military man, engineer, and soldier of fortune, who first seriously questioned the caloric theory.

While boring cannon he noticed the development of large quantities of heat, especially when a dull boring instrument was used. This perplexed Rumford. Also, the source of the caloric (heat) puzzled him. According to the caloric theory, the heat had to come either from the metal or from the surroundings. Both of these, in Rumford's opinion, were unlikely sources.

To check the theory, however, Count Rumford weighed the cannon barrel before boring and then weighed the borings and barrel together after boring. Both weights were found to be the same. Also he cooled the barrel in cold water, but still the barrel became hot. What did this prove? The results convinced him that the caloric, if it existed, could not have come from either the metal or the surroundings.

Since there was no other possible source of caloric, Rumford concluded that the heat produced must have come from the work done in boring the cannon. In other words, he concluded that *heat is energy*. Does this agree with Rumford's observation that a dull tool produced more heat than a sharp one?

To further test Rumford's theory that heat is energy, Sir Humphry Davy (1778-1829), a contemporary of Rumford's, devised a very simple but most crucial experiment. It consisted in rubbing two pieces of ice together in an atmosphere whose temperature was below the temperature of the ice. Even under these conditions the ice melted, and the conclusion was inescapable that the heat which melted the ice had been produced by the work done in overcoming the friction between the two pieces of ice.

You can perform a similar experiment by briskly rubbing a coin on a piece of wood for a few seconds. As a result, in accordance with the energy theory, the coin will become so hot that you cannot hold it in your hand.

Heat is what kind of energy? Assuming that heat is energy, it is only natural to ask, "What kind of energy is it?" We have already learned that potential energy is energy due to position or form, and that kinetic energy is due to motion. Could heat be one of these, or possibly both of them?

We know, too, that all matter is composed of tiny particles called molecules, and that when a liquid or a gas is being heated the Brownian movement can be observed to increase, which indicates increased molecular motion. Evidence of this kind is obtainable only for liquids and gases—not for solids. However, it is conceivable that the heating of a solid may cause increased vibration of its molecules.

Thus, experimental evidence, combined with logical deduction, leads us to the tentative conclusion that **heat** *is the kinetic energy of molecular motion.* Consequently, if m represents the mass of a molecule and V the average velocity of the molecules of a body, we know from previous study that each molecule will possess kinetic energy equal to $\frac{1}{2}mV^2$, and the body as a whole will have within it as many times this energy as there are molecules.

Is temperature the same as heat? In order to find the answer to this question we can perform a simple experiment. On a cold winter's night let us set out-of-doors a pan full of boiling water, a pan full of sand at the same temperature, and a tub full of water at 10°C and see which one reaches 0°C first. We shall find that they do so in this order: first, the sand; second, the pan of boiling water; and third, the tub of water.

These data indicate that temperature alone is not the sole measure of the heat content of a body, and that, therefore, temperature and heat are not the same. Seemingly the heat content of a body is dependent upon three factors: *temperature, mass,* and *kind of substance.*

What is temperature? Addition of heat to a body does not always change its temperature; but whenever the temperature is changed, there is always a change in its molecular energy. This indicates that temperature is a condition, or quality, of a body which depends upon its molecular energy at the time the temperature is taken. This leads us to the conclusion that **temperature** *is a measure of the average kinetic energy of the molecules of a body.* A simpler definition is that temperature is a measure of the *degree of heat* of a body.

Can heat exist as potential energy? If heat energy were potential, a body on being heated or cooled would have to change in shape or form, or its molecules would have to be shifted to a higher or lower potential, which is difficult to imagine. However, experiment proves that heat must be added to ice to melt it, and that *the temperature of the ice does not change* during the melting process. Similarly, heat is required to change water into steam, and the temperature of the water does not change during the boiling process. What happens to the heat energy that is absorbed during the process?

Since this absorbed heat does not stimulate any increased temperature, and thus any increased molecular motion, it cannot be in the form of kinetic energy. Since heat is energy and energy cannot be destroyed, then evidently, for a solid, the added energy is utilized in destroying the cohesive forces of the molecules as the state of matter is changed from a solid to a liquid. In the case of a liquid, added energy is required for the separation of the molecules when a liquid is changed to a vapor.

It can thus be said that the energy supplied to fuse (melt) a solid, or to vaporize a liquid, becomes potential energy (often called *latent* heat) of the disarranged or separated molecules of the liquid or gas. It thus appears that the heat energy of a solid would be all kinetic; that of a liquid would be both kinetic and potential with respect to a solid; and that of a gas, both potential and kinetic with respect to a liquid. Change of state will be more completely discussed in Chapter 24.

Do our senses measure temperature reliably? Have you ever entered your living room from out-of-doors in winter and exclaimed, "It's warm in here!" only to find later that it was actually chilly? Or have you entered your basement on a hot summer's day and thought it to be cool, only to discover that the basement temperature was actually in the eighties? These and other similar experiences lead us to believe that our senses are unreliable for determining temperatures.

Place on a table three drinking glasses, one filled with hot water, one with ice water, and one with tepid water. Now simultaneously place a finger of your right hand in the hot water and a finger of your left hand in the ice water. Keep them there until they become accustomed to the water temperatures, then place both fingers simultaneously in the tumbler of tepid water. What are the results?

You probably discover that to the right-hand finger the tepid water feels cold, whereas to the left-hand finger it feels hot. The invention of the thermometer provided us with a more objective method of temperature measurements.

The first thermometers. The operation of every temperature-measuring device depends upon some property of matter which causes the matter to change in some way as heat is given off or absorbed. Common thermometers are based upon the quite familiar tendency of matter in general to expand when heated and to contract when cooled.

The first thermometer was based upon this property of air. The inventor was that great scientist of old, Galileo. His air thermometer, or "thermoscope," as he called it, is shown in Fig. 1. It consists of an

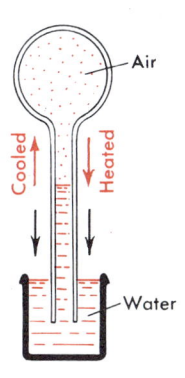

Fig. I. Galileo's thermoscope. What happens when the bulb is cooled? Warmed? Why is such a thermometer unreliable?

234 THE UNIVERSE OF HEAT

air-filled glass bulb on the upper end of a glass tube. When put into use, the bulb is first heated slightly, thus driving out some of the air by expansion, and the lower end of the tube is then placed in some colored water. As the air in the bulb cools, atmospheric pressure forces the water up the tube. The rising or falling of the liquid in the tube is easily understood as the air in the bulb is cooled or warmed. This action is the reverse of the kind with which we are familiar in most thermometers.

Since the height of the liquid in the tube is also affected by atmospheric pressure, temperature readings might be inaccurate. Why? In spite of these inaccuracies, Galileo was able to detect the higher temperatures of human bodies afflicted with fever. Apparently Galileo had no fixed thermometer scale, so all he could do was to compare one temperature with another.

A few years after Galileo's invention a French physician, Rey, constructed a thermometer using water instead of air. It consisted of a tube of small bore with a bulb at the bottom, similar to modern ones. But Rey failed to seal the top end of the tube, with the result that his readings varied from day to day as water evaporated from the tube.

Some of Galileo's students at Florence, Italy, constructed the first thermometer in which a liquid was allowed to expand in a sealed, partially evacuated tube.

How are thermometer scales made? Any thermometer scale, if it is to be accurate and comparable with other scales, must be based upon *two fixed points,* or temperatures, which are constant and which can be duplicated at any time. The fixed points used by Galileo's students were the temperature of snow on a cold

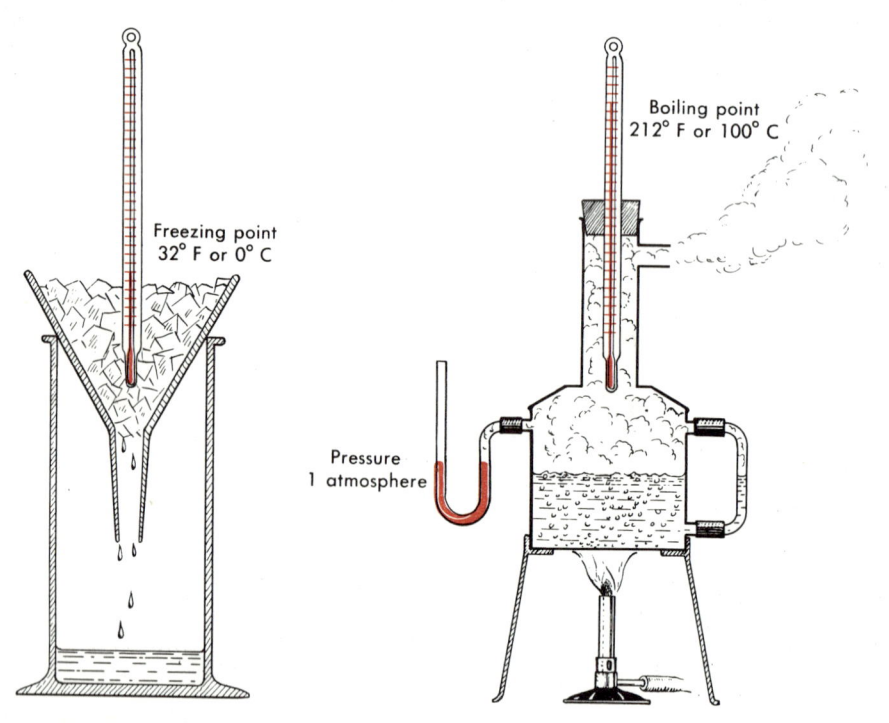

Fig. 2. The freezing and boiling points of water are used as the two fixed points on most thermometer scales.

WHAT ARE HEAT AND TEMPERATURE?

winter's day and the body temperatures of animals. They later used the temperature of melting butter as their upper fixed point. Just how "fixed" are these temperatures?

A thermometer with which we are familiar is the one introduced by Fahrenheit in about the year 1714. His lower fixed point was the temperature of a mixture of ice, common salt, and sal ammoniac. Believing this to be the lowest temperature attainable by artificial means, he called it zero on his scale. The upper fixed point was the temperature of the human body, which Fahrenheit called 12. The intervening space was divided into 12 equal parts, or *degrees,* and divisions of the same size extended above and below this range. Later this figure was multiplied by 8 to make the degrees a more practical size. On this basis the freezing point of water became 32° and the boiling point 212°. On our modern and more accurate Fahrenheit thermometers the normal oral (mouth) temperature of the human body is 98.6°.

Mercury is used in many of our modern thermometers. The method now used in placing a scale on a thermometer consists in using, as the fixed points, the freezing and boiling points of water at standard pressure. The bulb of the thermometer is packed in snow or ice, and the height reached by the mercury column is marked on the stem of the thermometer. Then the bulb and part of the stem is immersed in boiling water or steam at one atmosphere of pressure and the height of the mercury column is again marked. After this the intervening space on the stem is marked off in degrees in accordance with the scale desired.

What thermometer is used for scientific work? The thermometer used in all scientific work was first constructed by Celsius of Upsala, Sweden, in about the year 1742. The two fixed points he used were the freezing and boiling points of water, which are designated, respectively, as 0° and 100°. Because of the 100 divisions between these points this scale is called the *centigrade* scale. It may also be called the Celsius scale. On all thermometer scales, degrees above the zero mark are considered as positive and those below as negative.

How can readings on one scale be converted into their equivalents on another? Since both the Fahrenheit and centigrade scales are widely used in the United States, we should know both scales and be able to convert readings from one scale to the other. A study of Fig. 3 will help. Since there are 180 Fahrenheit degrees between

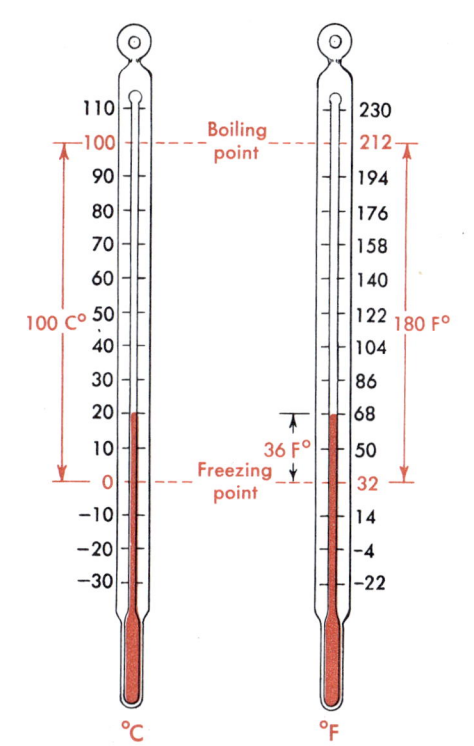

Fig. 3. A comparison of the Fahrenheit and centigrade scales. How are the formulas for converting from one scale to another derived?

the freezing and boiling points and only 100 centigrade degrees, the Fahrenheit degree must be 100/180, or 5/9, of a centigrade degree. Conversely, the centigrade degree must be 9/5 Fahrenheit degrees.

As a sample problem, let us convert 68°F to its centigrade equivalent. First, we note that the zero marks on the two scales do not coincide. Next in importance is the fact that the *actual reading* on the centigrade scale is the number of degrees above the freezing point (above 0°). Therefore, the centigrade reading must be the equivalent of the number of Fahrenheit degrees* (written F°) above the 32° mark. Thus, our first step in solving the problem must be to subtract 32 from our Fahrenheit reading.

$$68 - 32 = 36F°$$

Next, we find the centigrade equivalent of 36F°. This is

$$5/9 \text{ of } 36, \text{ or } 20C°$$

Since this is the number of centigrade degrees above the zero mark, our actual centigrade reading is 20°C. Try to reason out these steps in the reverse order and show that 20°C is equivalent to 68°F.

Analyzing the steps we followed in solving our problem, we find that: first, we subtracted 32 from our Fahrenheit reading (F); second, we multiplied this difference by 5/9 to obtain our centigrade reading. Putting this in the form of an equation, we have

$$C = 5/9 \ (F - 32)$$

Solve this equation for F.

It should be remembered that readings below zero on either scale must be considered as negative numbers and treated algebraically in your equations.

What are some special types of thermometers? The temperature ranges of thermometers depend upon the purposes for which they are used. Most of our household thermometers contain alcohol as the *thermometric* substance; some contain mercury. The temperature ranges of these thermometers depend upon the boiling and freezing points of the liquids used. Since alcohol freezes at −112°C and boils at 78°C, it can be used for both outdoor and indoor air temperatures anywhere on the earth's surface. Mercury, on the other hand, freezes at −39°C and boils at 357°C, so it cannot be used out-of-doors in winter in high latitudes. Candy and oven thermometers must be mercury-filled, since they must measure rather high temperatures.

Mercury is employed in a *clinical* or fever thermometer, since it is more accurate than alcohol. A clinical thermometer is shown in Fig. 4. Since it must be taken

---

*Thirty-six *Fahrenheit degrees* (36F°) means a *range* of that many degrees along the scale. Thirty-six *degrees Fahrenheit* (36°F) means a definite temperature, a fixed point on the scale.

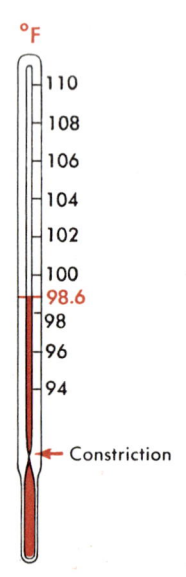

Fig. 4. A clinical thermometer. Normal body temperature is 98.6°F.

from the patient's mouth to be read, it must be so constructed that once the mercury has risen to the oral temperature it will not fall back again upon being removed from the mouth. This is accomplished by a constricted place in the bore of the tube, at which point the mercury divides when it contracts. To be forced past this constriction the mercury must be shaken down. The range of such a thermometer is usually from 94°F to 110°F.

The thermometers we use today are *calibrated* by use of a standard gas thermometer. The gas employed is usually hydrogen, although helium may be used. The range of temperatures that can be covered by these gases extends from less than a degree above *absolute zero* (see Chapter 23) to almost 1500°C, which is white heat. These thermometers are valuable as standards because hydrogen and helium obey the gas laws over a great range of temperatures.

SUMMARY AND CONCLUSIONS

1. Heat is a form of energy. It is defined as the kinetic energy of molecular motion.
2. The temperature of a body is a measure of the average kinetic energy of its molecules. It may also be defined as the degree of heat of a body.
3. Heat used to melt a solid or to vaporize a liquid becomes potential energy of the disarranged or separated molecules of the liquid or gas.
4. The construction of common thermometers is based upon the general tendency of matter to expand when heated and to contract when cooled.
5. Thermometer scales are based upon two fixed points, usually the freezing and boiling points of water.
6. The equations for converting Fahrenheit to centigrade readings and vice versa, may be expressed as follows:

$$C = \tfrac{5}{9}(F - 32);$$
$$F = \tfrac{9}{5}C + 32.$$

Courtesy Weston Electrical Instrument Co.

Fig. 5. Cutaway view of an electric resistance thermometer. Since the resistance of a conductor varies directly with its temperature, the temperature can be determined by measuring the amount of resistance to an electric current.

QUESTIONS FOR REVIEW

1. How would the range of a mercurial thermometer of a given length be affected by reduction of the size of the bulb? By enlargment of the bore of the tube? How would each of these changes affect the distance representing a degree on the scale?
2. How would you experimentally determine the accuracy of a mercurial thermometer?
3. Should a clinical thermometer be rinsed in hot or cold water? Why?
4. If glass expanded more than mercury, what would happen if a mercury thermometer were placed in hot water?
5. Define heat and temperature.
6. What points of evidence definitely refute the caloric theory of heat?

7. Describe Count Rumford's heat experiments and tell why Rumford concluded that heat is a form of energy.
8. Upon what factors does the heat content of a body depend?
9. When does heat exist as potential energy? As kinetic energy?
10. What are the advantages and disadvantages of the use of alcohol and mercury in thermometers?
11. Why is the centigrade scale superior to the Fahrenheit scale for scientific work?

PROBLEMS

1. The boiling point of water changes by 0.1C° for a change of 2.7 mm. in the barometric pressure. What will its boiling point be when the barometer reads 706 mm.? 787 mm.?
2. What are the freezing and boiling points of alcohol and mercury expressed in degrees Fahrenheit? See page 236.
3. Express the following Fahrenheit readings in their equivalents on the centigrade scale: 113°, 98.6°, 0°, −40°.
4. Express the following centigrade readings in their equivalents on the Fahrenheit scale: 25°, 4°, 37°, −40°.
5. The temperature of the sun's interior may be as high as 25,000,000°C. What would this be on the Fahrenheit scale? How important is the use of the constant, 32, in our conversion equation when we are dealing with such high temperatures?
6. Convert the following centigrade readings to Fahrenheit: 50°, 30°, −273°, −112°, 1500°, 6000°, 430°, 10,000°, −17.8°, 212°.
7. Convert the following Fahrenheit readings to centigrade: 104°, −10°, 50°, 100°, 1200°, 6000°, 430°, 10,000°.

PROJECTS

1. Design an experiment to show that mechanical energy can be transformed into heat. Try out the experiment and, if successful, demonstrate it to the class.
2. Design an experiment, other than any suggested in this chapter, to show whether our senses are reliable in measuring temperatures. Demonstrate it to the class.
3. If in your laboratory there are any thermometers which are not calibrated (have no scales attached), study up on the procedure and calibrate one of them.
4. Look up material about and give a report on a *maximum-minimum* thermometer.

READING YOU WILL ENJOY

1. Born, Max, *The Restless Universe*, pp. 14-28. Harper & Brothers, New York, 1936. A fascinating discussion of molecular motion, the laws of chance, and temperature in relation to molecular velocity.
2. Longstreth, T. Morris, *Understanding the Weather*. The Macmillan Company, New York, 1953. Chapter 9, pp. 38-41, gives some interesting and amusing details about temperatures, thermometers, and thermometric scales.
3. Parker, Bertha M., *Thermometers and Thermometry*. Row, Peterson and Company, Evanston, Illinois, 1942. A nontechnical presentation of methods of temperature measurement.

Chapter 23

Expansion

The problem. It is common knowledge that matter generally expands when heated and contracts when cooled. When a body of matter expands, its volume increases, and it is said to have *cubical,* or *volumetric,* expansion. However, we are often interested in the lengthwise expansion of a body, such as that of a railroad rail or a metal bar. This is called *linear* expansion. Automobile manufacturers are interested in the expansion of the area of a body, such as one made of sheet metal. This is called *superficial* expansion.

In this chapter we shall be mainly concerned with the linear expansion of solids and the cubical expansion of liquids and gases, how they affect us, and how we use them.

A problem in linear expansion. Let us take a walk down by the railroad track, either actually or in our imaginations, and examine the rails. If the weather is cold, we shall find the ends of the rails to be separated by as much as a quarter inch to a half inch; if the weather is hot, we may find the ends of the rails fitting snugly together. We therefore conclude that the linear expansion or contraction of the rails has been brought about by a change in temperature.

Consequently, if a railroad track is to be laid during cold weather, we can see that some provision should be made for the expansion that is certain to occur in warm weather. But how much space should be left between the ends of the rails to allow for this expansion?

Perhaps the results of an experiment will give us the clue for determining the space that must be allowed. Probably, in your own laboratory, there is an apparatus similar to the one shown in Fig. 2, which can be used to heat metal rods and measure their temperature changes and expansions. For our experiment let us use a 100-cm. steel rod and assume that for a temperature increase of 90C° its total expansion is 0.108 cm. From these data we can determine how much each unit length of the steel rod expands for each degree rise in temperature. Dividing the total expansion by the length of the rod and by the temperature change, we have

$$\frac{0.108 \text{ cm.}}{100 \text{ cm.} \times 90\text{C}°} = .000012 \text{ cm./cm./C}°$$

The result, .000012 cm./cm./C°, is the *change in length per unit length per centigrade degree change in temperature* of the steel rod, and is called the **coefficient of linear expansion** of steel. If we use k for the coefficient of linear expansion, e for the change in length of the rod, l for its original length, and t for its change in

Fig. 1. (l.) Laying expansion rollers during the construction of the George Washington Bridge between New York and New Jersey. (r.) Interlocking roadway expansion joints. As the bridge increases in length, the rollers supporting the free end of each section of the bridge move and the interlocking joints come closer together. In cold weather, the rollers move in the opposite direction and the interlocking joints move farther apart.

centigrade temperature, we can write a formula for determining the coefficient of linear expansion of any substance. Thus,

$$k = \frac{e}{lt} \quad (1)$$

or

$$e = klt \quad (2)$$

We can now determine how much space must be left between the rails of a given length when a railroad track is laid, providing we know the extremes of temperature to which it will be subjected. Let us assume that in our locality the yearly temperature range is from $-13°F$ to $104°F$, or a total of $117F°$, and that the rails are made of steel and are 40 feet long. $117F°$ are equivalent to $65C°$. Why? The coefficient of linear expansion of steel has been found to be .000012.* Substituting these data in equation (2), we have

$$\begin{aligned} e &= klt \\ &= .000012 \times 40 \times 65 \\ &= .0312 \text{ ft.} \\ &= .37 \text{ in.} \end{aligned}$$

Thus, we shall have to allow a space of about 0.4 in. between the rails if we lay them during the coldest weather, or we

*See Table 1 for other coefficients of linear expansion. Note that, in general, the coefficients differ from one another.

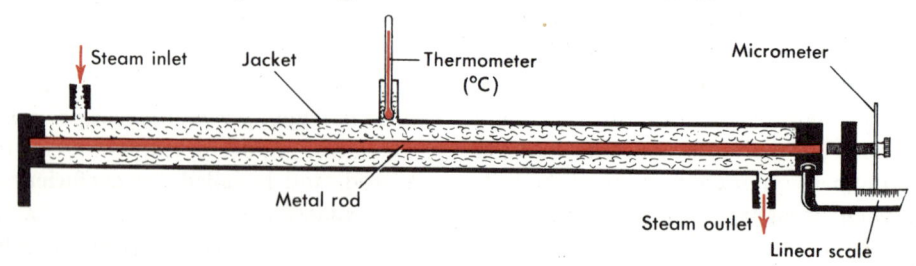

Fig. 2. Apparatus for determining the coefficient of linear expansion. The change in length is determined by means of the micrometer.

EXPANSION 241

can fit them snugly together if they are laid during the hottest weather.

PROBLEM: How much space should we allow if we lay the rails when the air temperature is 20°F?

SOLUTION: The temperature range is 84F° (104-20), or 46.7C°. Thus,

$$e = klt$$
$$= .000012 \times 40 \times 46.7$$
$$= .0259 \text{ ft.}$$
$$= .27 \text{ in.}$$

Equation (1) is sometimes written

$$k = \frac{l_2 - l_1}{l_1 (t_2 - t_1)} \quad (3)$$

in which l_1 represents original length, l_2 final length, t_1 original temperature, and t_2 final temperature. Thus, in equation (1), $e = l_2 - l_1$ and $t = t_2 - t_1$.

PROBLEM: A 60-cm. metal rod, after being heated from 8°C to 100°C, was found to be 60.127 cm. long. Find the coefficient of linear expansion of this metal and identify it by use of Table 1.

SOLUTION:

$$k = \frac{l_2 - l_1}{l_1(t_2 - t_1)}$$
$$= \frac{60.127 - 60}{60(100 - 8)}$$
$$= .000023 \text{ (aluminum)}$$

Table 1
COEFFICIENTS OF LINEAR EXPANSION
(Fractional Changes in Length per Centigrade Degree)

Aluminum	.000023
Brass	.000018
Bakelite	.000022
Cement and concrete	.000010 to .000014
Copper	.000017
Glass (ordinary)	.000009
Glass ("pyrex")	.000003
Ice	.000051
Iron (pure) and steel	.000012
Iron (cast)	.000011
Nickel steel (invar)	.0000009
Platinum	.000009

How would you attack the problem of determining the total seasonal change in length of the steel cables supporting the Ambassador Bridge which spans the Detroit River between Detroit, Michigan, and Windsor, Ontario?

PROBLEM: Solve equation (3) for l_2.

What is differential expansion? Fig. 3 shows a bar composed of strips of copper and iron riveted together so one can not slide over the other. This is called a *compound bar,* or *bimetallic bar.* Heating this bar will cause it to warp toward the iron, since the coefficient of linear expansion of copper is greater than that of iron. In other words, the warping of the bar is caused by what is called *differential expansion.* A metal whose coefficient of linear expansion is high not only will expand more than one whose coefficient is low but will contract more through a given lowering of temperature. What would happen if the above bar were cooled to a very low temperature?

What are some uses of differential expansion? Fig. 4 shows a kind of *thermostat,* a device for regulating temperature in a building or room. The heart of the thermostat is a bimetallic strip. Assuming the strip to be composed of brass on the

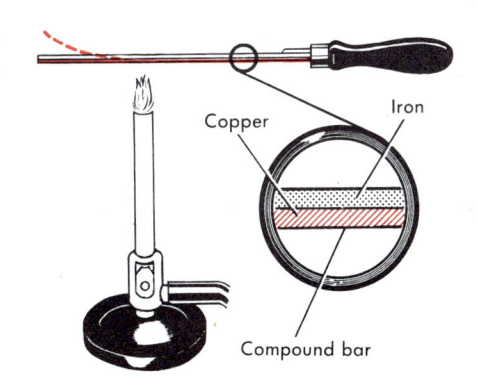

Fig. 3. Differential expansion. Why does the bar warp upward?

THE UNIVERSE OF HEAT

In our study of the gravitational pendulum (Chapter 4), we learned that an increase in its length increases its period of vibration. Thus, if the rod supporting the bob of a pendulum clock were to expand, the clock would lose time. Why? Fig. 5 shows a *compensation pendulum,* in which the upward cubical expansion of mercury offsets the linear expansion of the rod downward. If properly adjusted, a clock with such a pendulum should neither gain nor lose time as a result of temperature changes. Why? Think of other possible applications of the use of linear expansion, cubical expansion, and expansion like that of a bimetallic bar.

How does water expand? An experiment may help you to answer this question. Fill a wide-mouthed bottle with water and insert a two-hole stopper holding a centigrade thermometer and a drawn-out glass tube about 2 feet long (see Fig. 6). The water should completely fill the bottle and extend about three-fourths of the way up the glass tube. Extend the thermometer

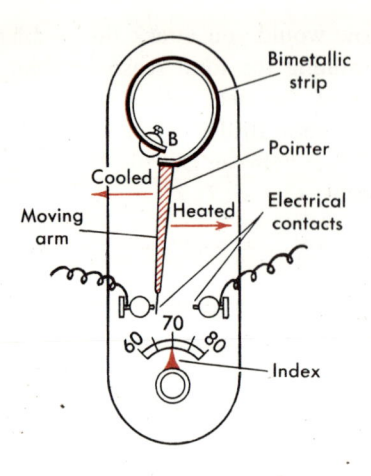

Fig. 4. Explain the operation of this thermostat. Account for the direction in which the arm moves upon heating and cooling.

outside and iron on the inside, and that moving the index will rotate the end *B* of the strip, try to explain how this device can regulate temperature.

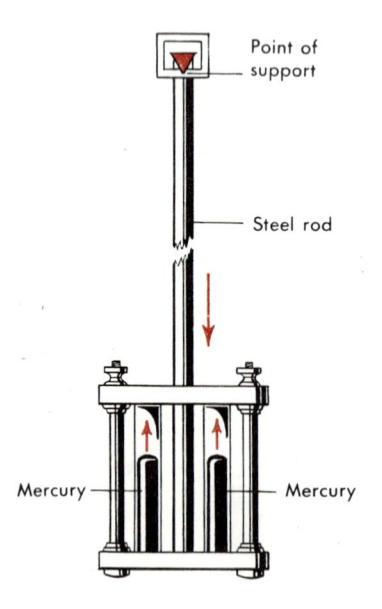

Fig. 5. A compensation pendulum.

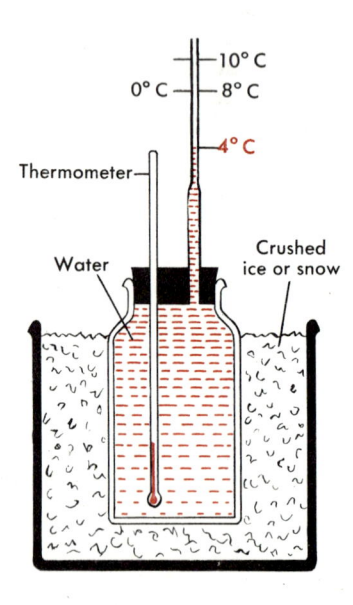

Fig. 6. Abnormal expansion of water.

EXPANSION

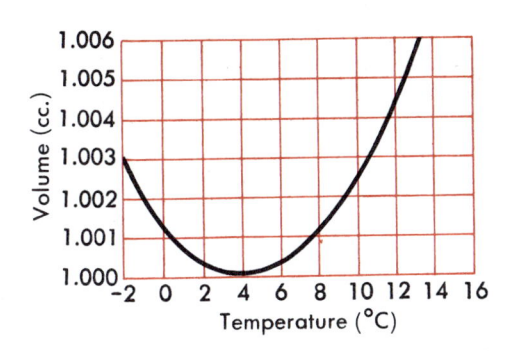

Fig. 7. The relationship between the volume and temperature of a gram of water.

almost to the bottom of the bottle. Now pack the bottle in snow or crushed ice and watch the level of the water in the tube closely as the water in the bottle is cooled.* You will find that the volume of water contracts as it is cooled. Mark the water level in the tube when the thermometer reads 10°C. Make another mark on the tube when the temperature is at 8°C and still another at 4°C.

It is at this point in your observations that you may be rather astonished. Instead of continuing to contract, the water now actually expands as it is cooled further. At 0°C the water level has risen to practically where it was at 8°C. If salt is used, the temperature may drop several degrees below zero with the water still remaining in the liquid state. It is then said to be *supercooled*. Supercooled water continues to expand as the temperature decreases.

Fig. 7 is a graph which shows the relationship between the volume and temperature of a gram of water. Although only a portion of the curve is shown, it seems to be rising more and more abruptly toward the boiling point. This means that water has its maximum volume, or minimum

*Cooling can be hastened by the addition of a small amount of salt to the snow or ice. Avoid too rapid cooling.

density, at the boiling point. Note that the graph bears out your experimental observations. Note also that a gram of water has a volume of exactly 1 cubic centimeter only at 4°C. This is the basis for our definition of the gram and kilogram (Chapter 3), for at this point it has maximum density. We refer to this peculiar behavior of water by saying that it has *abnormal* expansion.

What are some consequences of the abnormal expansion of water? Let us imagine what happens to a pond or lake as summer passes and cold weather comes. As the air cools, the surface water cools, and, as a result, its density increases. Thus it sinks through the warmer layers beneath. This continues until all the water has reached 4°C, at which time its density is a maximum. Further cooling of the surface water causes it to expand and its density to decrease. Thus, it floats on the water beneath until it reaches 0°C. Then it begins to freeze. Upon freezing it expands still further. Hence, the ice floats on the surface of the pond or lake. See Fig. 8.

The bottom waters of our largest lakes remain at 4°C the year around. For ex-

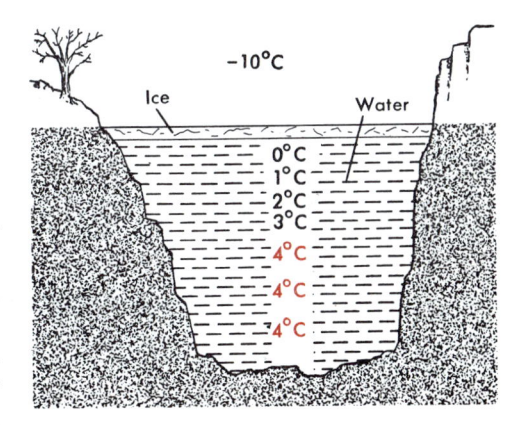

Fig. 8. Explain why the lake does not freeze solid.

ample, at a depth of 240 feet and below, Lake Superior always stays at 4°C.

If water continued to contract until it reached 0°C, all the water of a pond or lake would be cooled to that temperature, and, if the winter were long and severe, the water might freeze solid all the way to the bottom. Then, in summer, it might not have time to thaw out, let alone get warm enough for swimming. We can be certain that, were it not for the abnormal expansion of water, most or all of our aquatic life would never have developed.

What is the relation between the pressure and temperature of a gas? We have already learned how the volume of a gas is related to its pressure (Boyle's Law). You know that, if the temperature of a given mass of gas remains constant, the product of the pressure and volume is constant. But what happens if the volume is kept constant while the temperature is changed?

To answer this, refer to Table 2 and Fig. 9. As shown in the figure, the volume of gas used is 100 cc. at 0°C and 1 atmosphere of pressure, which we shall call P. The table shows that, when the temperature is raised to 136.5°C, the pressure increases to $3/2\,P$. At 273°C the pressure becomes $2P$, and at -136.5°C the pressure is reduced to $\tfrac{1}{2}P$. What would the pressure be at -273°C?

Table 2
RELATION OF TEMPERATURE TO PRESSURE
(Volume constant)

Pressure	Temp. °C	Temp. °A
2P	273	546
3/2P	136.5	409.5
P	0	273
1/2P	−136.5	136.5

Since the pressure changes from P to zero as the temperature changes from 0°C to -273°C, then the pressure must change 1/273 for every centigrade degree of

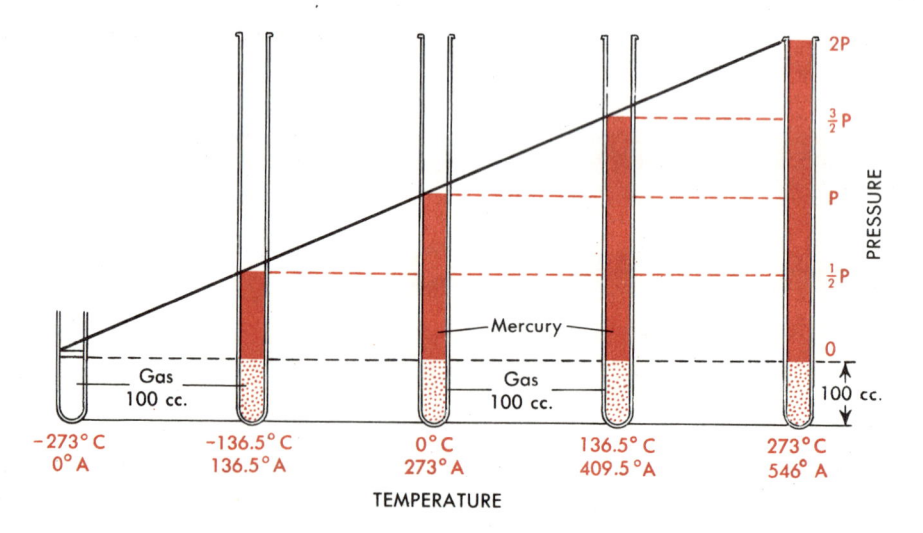

Fig. 9. When the volume of a given mass of gas is held constant, the pressure varies directly as the absolute temperature. What is the pressure at 136.5°A? At 273°A? At 341°A? Note that the graph of a direct variation is a straight line. At absolute zero, the gas exerts no pressure. Explain why in terms of the kinetic theory of heat.

EXPANSION

change in temperature. That is, if we start at 0°C and reduce the temperature one centigrade degree, the pressure will be reduced by 1/273, or 0.00366. This is called the *pressure coefficient* of gases.

What is the meaning of absolute zero? Fig. 9 shows that, if we were able to cool the air down to −273°C, its pressure would be theoretically reduced by 273/273 of its original pressure at 0°C. In other words, it would exert no pressure at all. Since, by the kinetic theory of gases, pressure is caused by the impacts of moving molecules, this must mean that at −273°C molecular motion would cease entirely. Furthermore, since heat is the kinetic energy of molecular motion, bodies must contain no heat whatever at this temperature. The degree of heat, or temperature, must therefore be the lowest that can be imagined. Because of this it is known as *absolute zero*. A scale of temperature which starts at this zero point is called the *absolute temperature scale* (°A in Table 2). It is also called the Kelvin (K) scale.

Since the divisions on the absolute scale are the same size as those on the centigrade scale, it is simple to convert centigrade readings into their equivalent absolute readings. We need only to add 273 to the centigrade reading (see Table 2). Thus, 10°C = 283°A; −10°C = 263°A; 100°C = 373°A; and −273°C = 0°A. How would you convert absolute readings into centigrade readings?

What is the relation between the absolute temperature and pressure of a gas? Another important fact shown in Fig. 9 is that the line connecting the various pressures is a straight line. This shows that

at constant volume the pressure of a given mass of gas is directly proportional to its absolute temperature.

Thus, if P_1 is the pressure of a gas when its absolute temperature is T_1, and if P_2 is its pressure when its temperature is T_2, then

$$\frac{P_1}{P_2} = \frac{T_1}{T_2}$$

PROBLEM 1: If the pressure of the air in a tire is 30 lb./in.² when its temperature is 20°C, what will its pressure be when its temperature is 50°C?

SOLUTION:
20°C = 293°A; 50°C = 323°A.
$$\frac{P_1}{P_2} = \frac{T_1}{T_2}$$
Substituting,
$$\frac{30}{P_2} = \frac{293}{323}$$
$$P_2 = 30 \times \frac{323}{293}$$
▶ = 33.1 lb./in.²

PROBLEM 2: A certain gas volume is under standard temperature and pressure. If its temperature is raised to 100°C, what will its pressure be, volume remaining constant?

SOLUTION: Standard temperature is 273°A. Why? 100°C = 373°A. Standard pressure is 760 mm. of mercury. Hence,

$$\frac{P_1}{P_2} = \frac{T_1}{T_2}$$
Substituting,
$$\frac{760}{P_2} = \frac{273}{373}$$
$$P_2 = 760 \times \frac{373}{273}$$
= 1038.4 mm.

What is the relation between the volume of a gas and its temperature? To answer this question, let us refer to the data of Table 3 and to Fig. 10. Note that the pressure remains constant, that the volume is changed by changes in temperature, and that the volume of air used is V when its temperature is 0°C. Also note that centi-

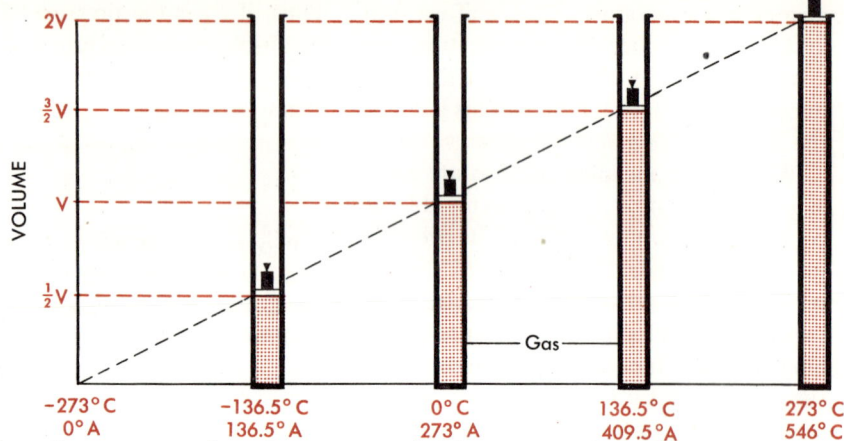

Fig. 10. When the pressure of a given mass is held constant, the volume is directly proportional to its absolute temperature. The change in volume of any gas at constant temperature may be found by converting the given temperatures to absolute temperatures and substituting in the formula: $\dfrac{V_1}{V_2} = \dfrac{T_1}{T_2}$.

grade temperatures are designated as t and absolute temperatures as T.

In conclusion, it appears that

under constant pressure the volume of a given mass of gas is directly proportional to its absolute temperature.

This statement is known as **Charles' Law**, in honor of Jacques A. C. Charles (1746-1823). Also the law is sometimes called **Gay-Lussac's Law**, in honor of Joseph L. Gay-Lussac (1778-1850).

Table 3
RELATION OF TEMPERATURE TO VOLUME
(Pressure constant)

Temp. (°C) (t)	Volume	Temp. (°A) (T)
273	$2V$	546
136.5	$3/2 V$	409.5
0	V	273
−136.5	$½ V$	136.5

If we let V_1 represent the volume of a given mass of gas when its absolute temperature is T_1, and let its volume be V_2 when its temperature is T_2, then

$$\frac{V_1}{V_2} = \frac{T_1}{T_2}$$

Problem 1: 500 cc. of oxygen is collected in the laboratory at a temperature of 23°C. What would its volume in liters be at standard temperature, pressure remaining constant?

Solution:

$$23°C = 296°A$$
$$\frac{V_1}{V_2} = \frac{T_1}{T_2}$$

Substituting,

$$\frac{500}{V_2} = \frac{296}{273}$$

$$V_2 = 500 \times \frac{273}{296}$$

$$= 461.1 \text{ cc.} = .461 \text{ liter}$$

Problem 2: 400 cc. of hydrogen is collected at 27°C. At what centigrade temperature would its volume become 424 cc., pressure remaining constant?

SOLUTION:
$$27°C = 300°A$$
$$\frac{V_1}{V_2} = \frac{T_1}{T_2}$$
Substituting,
$$\frac{400}{424} = \frac{300}{T_2}$$
$$T_2 = 300 \times \frac{424}{400}$$
▶ $= 318°A = 45°C$

How can we combine the laws of Boyle and Charles? In our previous study of gases we learned Boyle's Law and stated it in the form of a proportion, thus:

$$\frac{V_1}{V_2} = \frac{P_2}{P_1} \qquad (1)$$

Stating Charles' Law in the same form (see above),

$$\frac{V_1}{V_2} = \frac{T_1}{T_2} \qquad (2)$$

Proportion (1) assumes that temperature remains constant, and proportion (2) assumes that pressure remains constant. Let us suppose, however, that in an experiment we collect a certain volume of some gas, and then want to correct the volume for both a change in pressure and a change in temperature. A statement which combines the laws of Boyle and Charles into one general law would be very convenient in this case.

Since Charles' Law states that the volume of a gas varies directly with its absolute temperature, or

$$V \propto T$$

and, since Boyle's Law states that the volume varies inversely with its pressure, or

$$V \propto \frac{1}{P}$$

then the two can be combined into one law as follows:

$$V \propto \frac{T}{P}$$

Or by introducing the constant k this may be expressed as follows:

$$V = k\frac{T}{P} \qquad (3)$$

This relationship is known as the **general gas law** and means that

the volume of a given mass of gas varies directly with its absolute temperature and inversely with its pressure.

It can, however, be written in a more convenient form.

Letting the original volume, temperature, and pressure be represented by V_1, T_1, and P_1, respectively, it is true that

$$V_1 \propto \frac{T_1}{P_1}$$

or

$$V_1 = k\frac{T_1}{P_1} \qquad (4)$$

In a similar manner, letting the final volume, temperature, and pressure be represented by V_2, T_2, and P_2 respectively, then

$$V_2 = k\frac{T_2}{P_2} \qquad (5)$$

Solving equations (4) and (5) for k, we get, respectively,

$$k = \frac{V_1 P_1}{T_1}$$

and

$$k = \frac{V_2 P_2}{T_2}$$

Hence,

$$\frac{V_1 P_1}{T_1} = \frac{V_2 P_2}{T_2}. \quad \text{Why?} \quad (6)$$

Equation (6) is our formula for the general gas law. From this we can now state the law as follows:

The product of the volume and pressure of a given mass of gas is proportional to its absolute temperature.

PROBLEM 1: 40 cc. of hydrogen is collected in the laboratory under a pressure of 750 mm. of mercury and a temperature of 27°C. What will its volume be at a pressure of 720 mm. and a temperature of 17°C?

SOLUTION:
$$\frac{V_1 P_1}{T_1} = \frac{V_2 P_2}{T_2}$$
Substituting,
$$\frac{40 \times 750}{300} = \frac{V_2 \times 720}{290}$$
$$V_2 = 40 \times \frac{290}{300} \times \frac{750}{720}$$
▶ = 40.3 cc.

PROBLEM 2: In a laboratory 250 cc. of nitrogen is collected at 30°C and 740 mm. pressure. What would be the volume of this gas at standard conditions?

SOLUTION:
$$\frac{V_1 P_1}{T_1} = \frac{V_2 P_2}{T_2}$$
Substituting,
$$\frac{250 \times 740}{303} = \frac{V_2 \times 760}{273}$$
$$V_2 = 250 \times \frac{273}{303} \times \frac{740}{760}$$
▶ = 219.3 cc. at S. T. P.

SUMMARY AND CONCLUSIONS

1. Linear expansion applies particularly to solids. It is expansion lengthwise due to temperature increase.
2. The coefficient of linear expansion (k) of a substance is its change in length per unit length per centigrade degree change in temperature.
$$k = \frac{e}{lt}$$
3. The coefficient of volumetric expansion of a liquid is its increase in volume per unit volume per centigrade degree rise in temperature.
4. Water has abnormal expansion, its maximum density occurring at 4°C.
5. All gases have the same pressure coefficient; namely, 1/273 or 0.00366.
6. Absolute zero (−273°C) is the temperature at which all molecular motion ceases; in other words, the temperature at which substances would contain no heat whatever.
7. Under constant pressure the volume of a gas varies directly with its absolute temperature. This is Charles' Law.
$$\frac{V_1}{V_2} = \frac{T_1}{T_2}$$
8. The product of the volume and pressure of a given mass of gas varies directly with its absolute temperature. This is the general gas law.
$$\frac{V_1 P_1}{T_1} = \frac{V_2 P_2}{T_2}$$

QUESTIONS FOR REVIEW

1. Why is a thin glass tumbler less apt to crack than a thick one when hot water is poured into it?
2. Why can "pyrex" glass stand the shock of a sudden change in temperature?
3. When the bulb of a mercury thermometer is dipped into hot water, the mercury in the tube suddenly drops a bit before beginning to rise. Explain.
4. Why are steel structures riveted together with hot rivets?
5. If a steel bolt in a bronze bushing is stuck, what might be done to loosen the bolt?
6. The wires that are sealed in the glass of electric lamps should have the same coefficient of expansion as the glass. Explain.
7. Two thermometers are constructed in the same way, except that one has a spherical bulb and the other an elongated cylindrical bulb. Which one will respond more quickly to temperature changes? Explain.
8. A thermometer is to be made in such a way as to be able to respond to a wide range in temperatures. Should the bore of the tube be very fine or comparatively large? Why? Should the bulb be large or small? Why?
9. What does a nurse mean when she says her clinical thermometer is a two-minute thermometer?
10. Why might fountain pens that are nearly empty tend to leak while being used?
11. During the polishing of the 200-inch

mirror which is used in the Mount Palomar telescope, it was very important to keep the glass at constant temperature. Explain.
12. Why should the pistons of an engine be made of the same metal as the cylinder walls?
13. Why is it that the Great Lakes seldom freeze over from shore to shore, whereas inland lakes in the same latitudes almost always do?
14. Why might large rocks chip at their surfaces on hot summer days?
15. Explain how we can make balloons rise by simply filling them with hot air.
16. For flame tests in chemistry we use a platinum wire fused in a glass rod. Give two reasons why a brass wire could not be used.
17. To what temperature must all the water in a lake be cooled before the surface water begins to freeze? Explain.
18. Would you or the gas company gain financially by having the gas warmed before it passes through your gas meter? Why?
19. Why are concrete sidewalks made in sections with spaces between them?
20. Bread dough "rises" because carbon dioxide is formed in it. Is this an application of Charles' Law or Boyle's Law?
21. Some gasoline pumps have 10-gallon glass cylinders at the top for storage. Would it be more economical to buy gasoline at one of these pumps in the middle of a hot day or to wait until the cool of the evening? Why?
22. If the air above the ice in a lake is at a temperature of —17°C, what would you expect the temperature of the upper surface of the ice to be? The lower surface? The water in contact with the lower surface? The water at the bottom of the lake?
23. Why should surveyors' tape lines be made of invar instead of steel?

PROBLEMS

1. Some railroad rails are 90 ft. long and, of course, made of steel. How much change in length will they undergo if they are exposed to seasonal temperatures ranging from —25°C to 35°C?
2. Compute the coefficient of linear expansion of a 60-cm. metal rod which expands 1.02 mm. when the temperature rises 100C°.
3. An iron steam pipe extends 900 ft. through a tunnel from a boiler house to a school building. With no steam on, the pipe's temperature is 20°C. With steam under pressure passing through the pipe, its temperature reaches 120°C. What is the maximum change in length of the pipe, in inches?
4. A 200-ft. tape line is made of invar. How much will its length change in inches if its temperature is raised from —10°C to 30°C?
5. The steel cables of a certain bridge are 3 miles long. What will be their seasonal change in length if they are exposed to temperatures ranging from —10°F to 105°F?
6. A certain thermometer bulb holds 5.44 g. of mercury (density 13.6 g./cc.). The thermometer tube is 25 cm. long. If the coefficient of cubical expansion of mercury is .00018, what must be the diameter of the bore of the tube in order that it may be graduated from —10°C to 110°C?
       ANS.: .021 cm.
7. 25 cc. of a gas is collected under a temperature of 23°C. Pressure remaining constant, what will be its volume at 0°C?
8. If the air pressure in a tire is 500 g./cm.² at 10°C, what will it be at 40°C, volume remaining constant?
9. 500 cc. of hydrogen is collected when the barometer reads 730 mm. Temperature remaining constant, what would its volume be when the barometer reads 750 mm.?
10. During a chemical experiment 40 cc. of oxygen is collected at a temperature of 20°C and a pressure of 740 mm. Find its volume under standard conditions.
11. Under standard conditions a certain body of gas occupies a volume of 100 cc. Find its volume at 27°C and 800 mm. pressure.
12. If we have 500 cc. of gas at 0°C, at what centigrade temperature would its volume be 525 cc., pressure remaining constant?
13. If we have 250 cc. of a gas at 720 mm. pressure, at what pressure would its volume be 225 cc., temperature remaining constant?
14. Convert to standard conditions: 273 cc. of gas at 25°C and 735 mm. pressure.

PROJECTS

1. Devise and test a method, other than the one given in this chapter, for determining the coefficient of linear expansion of a metal.
2. Devise and build a fire alarm, using a compound bar.
3. Using a hydrometer jar and two thermometers, or similar equipment, determine the temperature at which water has its maximum density. Your biggest problem will be that of cooling the water to 0°C.

READING YOU WILL ENJOY

1. Dunning, J. R., and H. C. Paxton, *Matter, Energy, and Radiation,* Chapter 7. McGraw-Hill Book Company, Inc., New York, 1941. A textbook of physical science written in a straightforward manner.
2. Lemon, H. B., *From Galileo to Cosmic Rays.* The University of Chicago Press, Chicago, 1934. A simple but extremely readable presentation of the basic principles of physics. Chapter 14 discusses expansion.

Chapter 24

Measurement of Heat

The problem. In Chapter 22 it was shown that temperature is a measure of the degree of hotness or coldness and depends upon the average of the kinetic energies of the molecules in a body. The total heat in a body equals the sum of the kinetic energies of all its molecules.

Accordingly, it is reasonable to suppose that the heat in a body might be measured in units of kinetic energy—foot-pounds or ergs. This is not so far-fetched as some may suppose, but what a task it would be to measure the velocity and mass of each molecule and then total the kinetic energies! Hence, for practical reasons, we must reject this method.

Since, as we have already discovered, the quantity of heat in a body depends upon its mass, its temperature, and the kind of substance of which it is composed, perhaps we can measure it in terms of these factors.

What units are used to measure heat? Actually, the calorists of old measured heat by the method just proposed. The substance used as a standard was water. The unit quantity of heat was the amount of heat which must enter or leave a unit mass of water in order to change its temperature one degree. Similar units are still in use.

In the English system the heat unit is the **British thermal unit (btu)**, which is defined as *the amount of heat required to raise the temperature of 1 pound of water 1 Fahrenheit degree.*

In the metric system there are two units: (a) the **gram-calorie**, or **small calorie (cal.)**, which is defined as *the amount of heat required to raise the temperature of 1 gram of water 1 centigrade degree;* (b) the **kilogram-calorie**, or **large calorie (Cal.)**, which is defined as the *amount of heat required to raise the temperature of 1 kilogram of water 1 centigrade degree.* How many gram-calories make one kilogram-calorie? In our study the gram-calorie will usually be used.

How can we measure heat lost or gained by water? If we really understand the definitions of the heat units, it should be clear that 10 cal. will be required to raise the temperature of 10 g. of water 1C°. Also, to raise 10 g. of water 10C° will require 100 cal. Further, it will require 100 btu to raise the temperature of 10 lb. of water through 10F°. In general, then, for water,

Heat = mass × temperature change

or, $\qquad H = mt \qquad (1)$

If t_1 equals the initial temperature of the water and t_2 its final temperature, then

$$t = t_2 - t_1$$

Substituting in (1),

$$H = m(t_2 - t_1) \qquad (2)$$

252   THE UNIVERSE OF HEAT

PROBLEM 1: How much heat will be liberated if 90 g. of water at 100°C are cooled to 50°C?

SOLUTION:

$$H = m(t_1 - t_2)*$$

Substituting,
$$H = 90(100 - 50)$$
$$= 90 \times 50$$
$$= 4500 \text{ cal.}$$

PROBLEM 2: How much heat would be required to raise the temperature of 12 lb. of water from 32°F to the boiling point?

What is the law of heat exchange? Let us pour into a beaker 100 g. of water at 80°C and 100 g. of water at 20°C, stir the mixture well, and take its final temperature. We find it to be 50°C, halfway between the two initial temperatures. This indicates that the hot water lost 3000 cal. of heat, 100(80 − 50), and that the cold water gained an equal amount, 100(50 − 20). In other words,

$$\begin{pmatrix}\text{Heat lost by}\\\text{hot water}\end{pmatrix} = \begin{pmatrix}\text{Heat gained by}\\\text{cold water}\end{pmatrix}$$

or,

$$\begin{pmatrix}\text{Mass }(m_1)\text{ of}\\\text{hot water}\\\times\text{ temp. change}\end{pmatrix} = \begin{pmatrix}\text{Mass }(m_2)\text{ of}\\\text{cold water}\\\times\text{ temp. change}\end{pmatrix}$$

Whence,

$$m_1(t_1 - t_f) = m_2(t_f - t_2) \quad (3)$$

where t_1 is the initial temperature of the hot water; t_2, the initial temperature of the cold water; and t_f, the final temperature of the mixture.

The fact that

the heat lost by the hot body equals the heat gained by the cold body

*The lower temperature must be subtracted from the higher.

is called the *law of heat exchange*, which is based upon the law of conservation of energy. The use of this law in heat experiments is generally called the *method of mixtures*.

PROBLEM: 50 g. of water at 70°C are mixed with 70 g. of water at 10°C. What is the final temperature of the mixture? Use equation (3) above.

What is specific heat? Instead of mixing two equal masses of water, as we did above, let us now mix 100 g. of copper at 100°C with 100 g. of water at 0°C. Now, if we assume that each gram of copper, in cooling 1 centigrade degree, loses 1 calorie of heat, then we should expect the final temperature of the mixture to be halfway between 0°C and 100°C. Instead, however, we find it to be 8.5°C, not 50°C. Thus, the assumption that each gram of copper loses 1 calorie in cooling 1 centigrade degree must be false. How much, then, does each gram of it lose per degree change in temperature?

We know from equation (2) that the water gained a total of 850 cal., 100 × (8.5 − 0). According to the law of heat exchange the copper must have lost an equal amount. Letting x equal the number of calories it lost per gram per centigrade degree,

$$x = \frac{850 \text{ cal.}}{100 \text{g. }(100 - 8.5)\text{C}°}$$

$$= .093 \text{ cal./g./C}°$$

The above result is called the *specific heat* of copper. The **specific heat** of any substance is *the quantity of heat required to produce unit change in temperature in a unit mass of the substance.* Therefore, the specific heat of water is, by definition, 1 cal./g./C°.

The specific heats of some metals and a few other substances are given in Table 1. Note that water has the highest specific heat of all those given. This is true generally.

Table 1
SPECIFIC HEATS OF SUBSTANCES

Substance	Sp. Ht. (cal./g./C°)
Aluminum	.217
Brass	.090
Copper	.093
Iron	.113
Lead	.031
Mercury	.033
Zinc	.093
Air	.237
Ice	.5
Steam	.48
Water	1.000

How can we measure specific heat? Recalling equation (1), it should now be evident that we can use it for any substance, not just for water, provided we include a constant, s, which is the specific heat of the substance involved. Thus, the equation becomes

$$H = mts \qquad (4)$$

When water is the substance, s is unity. It should be remembered that t represents temperature change, not any specific temperature.

In our previous experiment with copper and water we disregarded the heat gained by the container of the mixture. For accurate results it must be included. To do this we use a special type of container, called a *calorimeter* (Fig. 1), which is designed to insulate the mixture from the air, thus preventing undue losses or gains of heat to or from the atmosphere. The inner *cup*, not the *jacket*, is the part that must be weighed, and its specific heat must be known.

Let us assume that we wish to determine

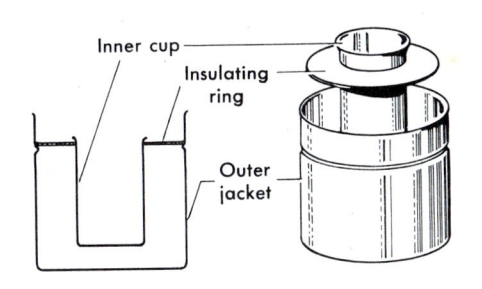

Fig. 1. Cross section of a calorimeter. Note the inner cup, jacket, and dead air space.

the specific heat of lead. The following are the steps we take: (a) Weigh the lead. (b) Heat it by submerging its container in boiling water or steam. (c) Weigh the calorimeter cup. (d) Add enough cool water to the cup to cover the lead. (e) Weigh the cup and cool water and compute the weight of the water (how?). (f) Take the temperatures of the boiling water and the cool water (the temperatures of the lead and the cup will be respectively the same). (g) *Quickly* transfer the lead from the hot water to the cool water. (h) Stir the "mixture" and take its final temperature.

Let us assume that the data thus obtained are as shown in the table. In accord-

Data Table

Wt. of cup	95g.
Sp. ht. of cup	.093
Wt. of cool water	210g.
Temp. of cool water and cup	20°C
Wt. of lead	200g.
Initial temp. of lead	100°C
Final temp. of mixture	22.2°C

ance with the law of heat exchange, we know that the heat lost by the lead will equal the heat gained by the cool water and the cup. Using equation (4), let the heat lost by the lead be mts; let the heat gained by the cool water be $m't's'$, and that gained by the calorimeter cup be

$m''t''s''$. Since s' is unity, s'' is .093, and t'' equals t' (why?), our equation can be written as follows:

$$\begin{pmatrix}\text{Heat lost}\\ \text{by lead}\end{pmatrix} = \begin{pmatrix}\text{Heat gained}\\ \text{by cool water}\end{pmatrix} + \begin{pmatrix}\text{Heat gained}\\ \text{by cup}\end{pmatrix}$$

or, $\quad mts = m't' + (m''t'' \times .093) \quad (5)$

Solving equation (5) for s, the unknown specific heat, and factoring out t', we have

$$s = \frac{t'(m' + .093m'')}{mt} \quad (6)$$

$.093m''$ is called the *water equivalent* of the calorimeter cup. Substituting our data from the table in equation (6), we get

$$s = \frac{(22.2 - 20)(210 + .093 \times 95)}{200(100 - 22.2)}$$

$$= \frac{2.2(210 + 8.84)}{200 \times 77.8}$$

$$s = \frac{481.4}{15560} = .031 \text{ cal./g./C}°, \text{ the sp. ht. of the lead}$$

Fig. 2. Fruit-growing regions are commonly located near large bodies of water. Since water is slow to warm up or to cool off, it retains its heat longer than the land.

Courtesy Wisconsin Conservation Department

What are some effects of the high specific heat of water? What boy hasn't waited impatiently in early summer for a lake to get warm enough for swimming? The land warms up so much more quickly. Why should it take so long for a lake to get warm? From the principles we have studied we should know at least two reasons. Surface water, warmed above 4°C, expands and floats on the colder water. Much agitation by the wind may be necessary to warm it to any great depth.

The land, however, is heated mainly at the surface. One need not dig very deeply to come to a place where the temperature is constant the year around. Then, too, the specific heat of water is considerably higher than that of land. It takes more heat, weight for weight, to heat water than it does to heat land. Naturally the Great Lakes and large inland lakes require more time to get warm than the small lakes; deep lakes more than shallow lakes. In fact, a shallow lake may be warmed from the bottom up. The sun's rays may penetrate to the bottom where they are *absorbed* by the dark sand, or muck, and converted into heat. Water thus warmed at the bottom will rise through the cool layers above. Why?

People who live near the shores of the Great Lakes feel the effects of the high specific heat of the water. The lakes warm up slowly in the spring and cool off slowly in the fall. The result is a climate which is ideal for fruit growing. Because of the cooling effect of water, fruit trees are kept from budding too early in the spring, thus tending to eliminate the dangers from late frosts. In the fall warm weather is prolonged, giving the fruit ample time to ripen and diminishing the possibility of damage from early frosts. A good example is the western coast of Michigan, which is a good fruit belt.

Many other places are so located as to have their climates tempered by large bodies of water. Some are the Hawaiian Islands, the British Isles, Norway, Florida, and Southern California.

Freezing and melting. We know that water freezes at 0°C. This is also the melting point of ice. In a mixture of water and ice, the ice will melt if heat is absorbed; the water will freeze if heat is removed from the mixture. Even if we heat the mixture, its temperature does not rise until all the ice is melted. The added heat merely changes the state from solid to liquid, and becomes the "latent" heat mentioned in Chapter 22, p. 233.

What is heat of fusion? To help answer this question we shall again use the method of mixtures. This time let us mix 10 g. of ice at 0°C with 10 g. of water at 90°C, and, as soon as all the ice is melted, take the final temperature of the mixture. Logically we might expect it to be 45°C, but instead it turns out to be 5°C.

Now, we know that after the ice is melted it will take 50 cal. of heat to raise the temperature of the resulting 10 g. of water from 0°C to 5°C. (Equation 1.) We also know that the hot water in cooling from 90°C to 5°C must have lost 850 cal. How can we account for the extra 800 cal.?

Our conclusion is that the 10 g. of ice, in melting, must have absorbed this much heat. Each gram, therefore, required 80 cal. of heat to melt it *without changing its temperature*. This is called the *heat of fusion* of ice. The **heat of fusion** of any substance is *the quantity of heat required to convert one gram of it from the solid state to the liquid state without changing its temperature.*

Each gram of liquid at its solidification (freezing) point will liberate just as much heat when it solidifies (freezes) as it will absorb when it fuses (melts). For ice, these facts can be shown by the simple equation:

1 g. of ice at 0°C + 80 cal. →
1 g. of water at 0°C

Subtracting 80 cal. from each side of this equation gives the converse of the above. Thus,

1 g. of water at 0°C − 80 cal. →
1 g. of ice at 0°C

It was once believed that a negligible quantity of heat was required to melt ice and snow. We now know that this is not true, and should be able to understand why it takes so long for ice and snow to melt. Can you explain why ice-covered lakes tend to prolong cool spring weather, and why late fall weather is made milder by the freezing of the lake water?

Table 2
FUSING POINT AND HEAT OF FUSION OF SUBSTANCES

Substance	Fusing Point °C	Heat of Fusion cal./g.
Aluminum	658	76.8
Ammonia	−75	108.0
Beeswax	61.8	42.3
Bromine	−7.3	16.2
Copper	1083	42.0
Ice	0	80.0
Lead	327	5.86
Mercury	−39	2.82
Sulfur	114.5	9.4
Tin	232	14.0
Zinc	419	28.1

All crystalline substances have a definite heat of fusion, but ice stands generally high by comparison.

The fact that ice has a high heat of fusion makes it valuable as a refrigerant. As the ice melts, each gram absorbs 80 calories from the air in the icebox, thus cooling it. Can you explain why wrapping the ice in paper or burlap tends to prevent refrigeration? Solid carbon dioxide, or "dry ice," is used in some types of refrig-

Fig. 3. Without regelation ice skating would not be possible. The ice beneath these skaters' blades melts under pressure, and then refreezes as they glide along.

Courtesy Rockefeller Center, Inc.

eration. Though more expensive than ice, it has certain advantages over ice as a refrigerant. Can you name them?

What is regelation? Most boys have had fun "packing" and throwing snowballs. Most skaters have discovered that, if they stand still on their skates for a while, the skates will freeze to the spot. The principle behind these phenomena is that the melting points of many substances are affected by pressure. The melting points of those that expand while freezing, such as ice, are slightly lowered by increasing pressure; the opposite is true for those that contract while freezing. A simple experiment will illustrate the principle.

Take two ice cubes and press them together firmly for a while. You will find them frozen together when the pressure is released. A more convincing experiment is one in which weights are attached to opposite ends of a wire and then hung over a cake of ice as in Fig. 4. In time the wire will melt its way through the ice, but *the ice will still be in one solid piece after the wire has passed completely through it.*

In each instance above, pressure is applied to the ice, thus lowering its melting point. At 1 atmosphere of pressure, ice melts at 0°C. Under 2 atmospheres it melts at $-.0075$°C. This change seems small, but under the wire with its attached weights, the pressure could easily be 32 atmospheres, thus lowering the melting point to $-.24$°C. Since the actual temperature of the ice is 0°C, it melts beneath the wire and oozes to the top side. Each gram in melting absorbs 80 calories of heat from the wire, which in turn absorbs it from the water directly above. The water, not being under pressure, refreezes as it gives up its heat. Other things being equal, a copper wire will win a race with an iron wire through a cake of ice, because copper is a better conductor of heat.

Now try to explain the phenomena of

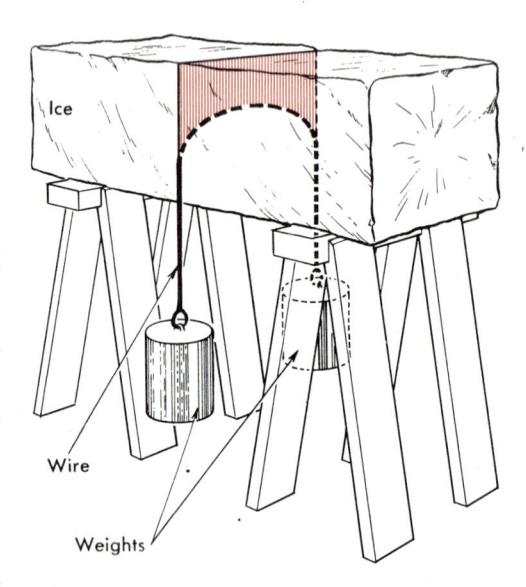

Fig. 4. Demonstration of regelation. Will the ice be cut in two? Explain your answer.

the snowballs, the ice skates, and the ice cubes, all of which are examples of **regelation,** which may be defined as the *melting of a substance under increased pressure and its subsequent freezing when the pressure is released.*

How can evaporation be explained? As we know, liquids left in open containers gradually disappear. The process involved is called *evaporation*. What we may not know is how evaporation occurs. Some things we do know, however, are the following. (a) Liquids evaporate more rapidly when hot than when cold. (b) Wet clothes dry more quickly on a windy day than on a calm day. (c) Liquids placed in open pans evaporate more quickly than when in containers with small openings. (d) Liquids in closed containers do not seem to evaporate. (e) Some liquids evaporate more rapidly than others. Those which evaporate the most rapidly are said to be the most *volatile*.

Furthermore, we know that standing on a windy beach in a wet bathing suit may make us chilly. This indicates that evaporation is a *cooling process,* and that heat must be involved in the process. Since heat is due to molecular motion, perhaps molecular motion is the basis of our explanation.

The liquid shown in the container of Fig. 5 is composed of rapidly moving

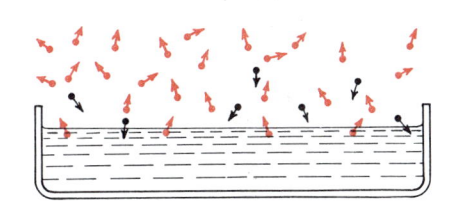

Fig. 5. A liquid cools by evaporation. Why is evaporation a cooling process?

molecules. If some of those near the surface are traveling in the right direction at the right moment, the fastest ones will escape from the liquid into the space above, thus removing heat from the remaining liquid and lowering its temperature. At higher temperatures molecular motion is more rapid; thus the rate of evaporation is greater. The wider the area of the exposed liquid the greater the opportunity for molecules to escape.

Some of the escaped molecules re-enter the liquid, but the rate of escape exceeds the rate of re-entering until the space above the liquid is *saturated*. We then have reached a state of *saturated vapor*. In a closed container this state is soon reached, hence the liquid does not appear to evaporate. In a vacuum the interference of air molecules is removed, and evaporation is more rapid.

Summarizing, the laws of evaporation may be expressed as follows:

The rate of evaporation of a liquid depends upon the nature of the liquid. The rate increases as

(a) the temperature of the liquid is increased;

(b) the exposed area of the liquid is increased;

(c) the vapor above the liquid is removed;

(d) the pressure on the liquid is decreased.

Some solids evaporate, as people who have stored clothes protected by moth crystals know. The process of changing from the solid state directly into the vapor state is called *sublimation*. The process is usually slow. Some solids which *sublime* are ice, moth crystals, sulfur, and "dry ice," which sublimes fairly rapidly.

What happens when water boils? When tap water is heated in a flask, the first small bubbles we see are composed of air (mostly oxygen) which has previously dissolved in the water. Later, steam bubbles appear at the bottom of the flask and condense as they rise through the cooler water above. But once the whole body of water has reached boiling temperature, the steam bubbles rise to the surface, expanding as they rise because of decreasing pressure (Boyle's Law).

What is heat of vaporization? If we place a thermometer in our flask of boiling water, we find that no matter how vigorously the water boils, its temperature will not rise above the boiling point. This shows that, once boiling has begun, any added heat serves only to change the water from the liquid to the gaseous state. In other words, it breaks down the cohesive forces between the liquid molecules and sets them free, thus becoming "potential energy of the separated molecules" (Chapter 22).

Each liquid, at its boiling point, requires a definite quantity of heat per gram to vaporize it without changing its temperature. This quantity is called the *heat of vaporization* of the liquid. Careful experimentation has proved the heat of vaporization of water at 100°C to be 539 cal./g. When steam, or any other vapor, recondenses into the liquid form, its heat of vaporization is liberated to its surroundings and may be called *heat of condensation*.

1 g. of water at 100°C + 539 cal.
$\rightarrow$ 1 g. of steam at 100°C

1 g. of steam at 100°C − 539 cal.
$\rightarrow$ 1 g. of water at 100°C

This principle has a tremendous effect upon weather conditions, especially in the case of hurricanes (Chapter 27).

PROBLEM: Steam at 100°C from a steam generator is passed into 200 g. of water at 10°C contained in a copper calorimeter weighing 100 g. The water is stirred constantly, and when the temperature reaches 38.7°C, no more steam is added. The weight of the added steam is computed to be 10 g. What is the heat of vaporization of the water (same as heat of condensation of the steam)?

SOLUTION: By the method of mixtures:
Heat lost by steam
+ heat lost by resulting hot water
= heat gained by cold water and calorimeter.
Letting H_V = heat of vaporization of water,

$10H_V + 10(100 - 38.7) =$
$200(38.7 - 10) + 100(38.7 - 10) \times .093$

or
$\qquad 10H_V + 613 = 5740 + 266.9$

and
$\qquad 10H_V = 5383.9$
$\qquad H_V = 538.4$ cal./g.

What are the laws of boiling? Let us boil some water in an open, round-bottomed flask and while it is boiling, remove the burner and quickly insert a solid rubber stopper. Now, if we invert the flask and run cold water over it, the water inside boils vigorously (Fig. 6) and will continue to do so for some time. Upon removing the stopper we hear air rush into the flask, and the temperature of the water may be found to be as low as 20°C. What is the explanation?

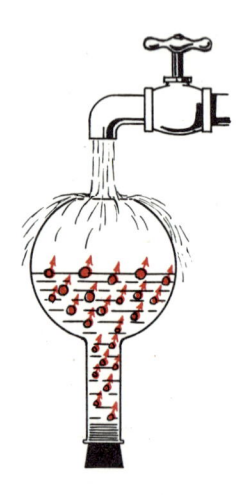

Fig. 6. The cold water causes a lowering in the external pressure on the surface of the liquid. Thus the water continues to boil at a temperature below its normal boiling point.

When the water boiled in the open flask, the steam must have forced the air out, which shows that the vapor pressure at the boiling point must at least equal atmospheric pressure. In fact, the **boiling point** of a liquid may be defined as *the temperature at which its vapor pressure equals the external pressure.* Running cold water over the flask caused the steam inside to condense, thus greatly decreasing the external pressure on the water and allowing it to boil at a lower temperature. Near atmospheric pressure, the boiling point of water changes 0.1C° for every pressure change of 2.7 mm. of mercury. What would its boiling point be at 733 mm.?

Had we boiled water under pressure greater than atmospheric, its boiling point would have been above 100°C. Had we dissolved some salt in the water, this too would have raised its boiling point. Had we mixed some alcohol with the water, the boiling point of the mixture would have been somewhere between the boiling points of water and alcohol. Water with gas dissolved in it would boil at a lower temperature than pure water.

Summarizing, the laws of boiling may be stated as follows:

The boiling point of a liquid
  (a) is constant under constant pressure;
  (b) rises as the external pressure is increased, and falls as it is decreased;
  (c) is raised when a solid is dissolved in the liquid;
  (d) is generally lowered when a gas is dissolved in the liquid;
  (e) when the liquid is a mixture, lies between the boiling points of the mixed liquids.

What is distillation? Let us assemble an apparatus like that shown in Fig. 7. In flask *A* let us put some sugar solution and boil it while passing cold water through

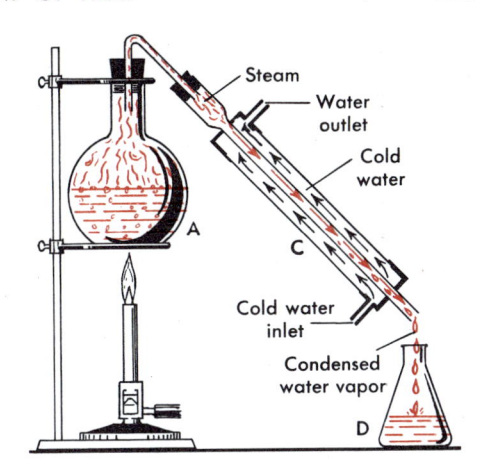

Fig. 7. Distillation using a Liebig condenser. Why is the cold water inlet at the bottom of the condenser? Can dissolved vapors be removed by distillation?

the *Liebig condenser, C.* Vapors from the boiling liquid will be condensed by the cold water and will collect in flask *D*. This is called the *distillate,* and the process is called *distillation.* Upon testing the distillate we find no sugar in it. In this manner solids can be separated from their solutions, since they do not distill off but are left in the distilling flask *A*.

Liquids, too, can be separated by distillation. If a mixture of water and alcohol is distilled, the first portion of the distillate will be almost pure alcohol. Since alcohol has the lower boiling point, it boils off first. From a mixture of several liquids, the one with the lowest boiling point distills off first; the one with the next higher boiling point comes next, etc. Separating liquids by this process is called *fractional distillation.* Many petroleum products are thus obtained. Try to formulate a definition of distillation.

How are gases liquefied? Any gas must first be cooled to a temperature called its *critical temperature* before it can be liquefied by any pressure, however great. The

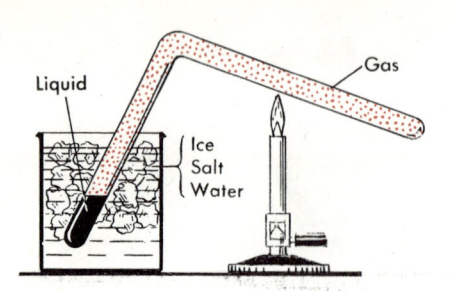

Fig. 8. Faraday's tube for liquefying gases. How is pressure produced in the cooled end?

pressure then needed to liquefy it at that temperature is called its *critical pressure*. Gases which, in the liquid form, have the highest boiling points are most easily liquefied.

Michael Faraday (1791-1867) was the first to successfully use this principle. He succeeded in liquefying such gases as chlorine, sulfur dioxide, and carbon dioxide by using a bent glass tube in which the gas was sealed (Fig. 8). Heating one end of the tube while cooling the other produced enough pressure in the cold end to liquefy the gas. The gases Faraday could not liquefy he called *fixed gases*. We can now liquefy all known gases by subjecting them to high pressure and cooling them by expansion. Water vapor is very easily liquefied. Why?

How does a refrigerator operate? The facts that a liquefying gas liberates its heat of condensation to its surroundings, and that a vaporizing liquid absorbs the same quantity from its surroundings, are fundamental in the operation of a refrigerator, whether of the mechanical or the gas type.

Figure 9 is a diagram of an electric refrigerator. Its important parts are the *compressor, condenser,* and *evaporator,* or freezing unit. The refrigerant must be a gas which can be liquefied at ordinary temperatures that is, its critical temperature must not be low. From the compressor the gas is pumped to the condenser, where it is cooled, usually by a fan. Here its heat of compression and heat of condensation are removed as it changes to a liquid. From the condenser the gas passes into the evaporator through an expansion valve.

In the evaporator the pressure is much lower, allowing the liquid to boil and change back to a gas. It is during this process that the box is cooled by the evaporating liquid as it absorbs its heat of vaporization from the surroundings. The gas now passes on into the compressor, and the operation is repeated. Thus, the same gas is used over and over, serving the purpose of conveying the heat from the inside of the box to the outside.

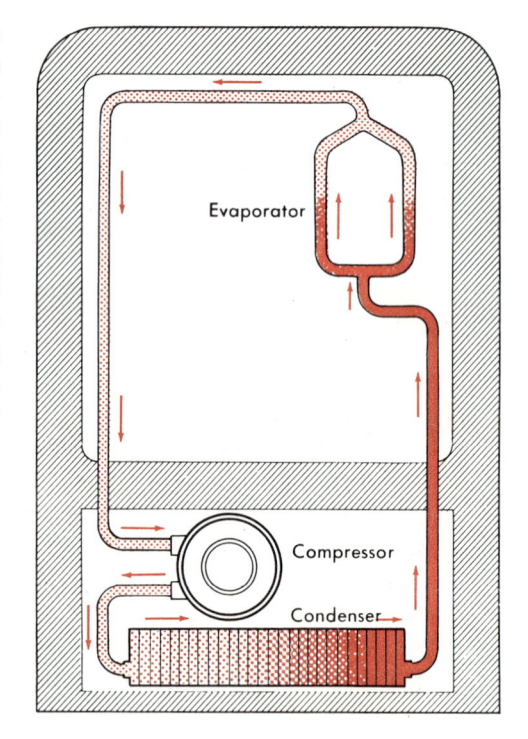

Fig. 9. The major parts of an electric refrigerator. In the evaporator, heat energy is absorbed in changing the liquid to a vapor.

SUMMARY AND CONCLUSIONS

1. The gram-calorie is that quantity of heat which will raise the temperature of 1 gram of water 1C°.
2. The kilogram-calorie is that quantity of heat which will raise the temperature of 1 kilogram of water 1C°. It equals 1000 g.-cal.
3. The British thermal unit is that quantity of heat which will raise the temperature of 1 pound of water 1F°.
4. The heat lost or gained by a given mass of any substance for a given temperature change may be measured by the equation $H = mts$.
5. When a hot and a cold body are mixed, heat lost by the hot body equals heat gained by the cold body, and each comes to the same final temperature. This is the law of heat exchange. Its use in heat experiments is known as the method of mixtures.
6. The specific heat of a substance is the quantity of heat required to produce unit change in temperature in a unit mass of the substance.
7. The number of calories of heat required to melt 1 gram of ice at its melting point is the heat of fusion of ice. It is 80 cal./g.
8. The melting of a substance under increased pressure and its subsequent freezing when the pressure is released is called regelation.
9. Evaporation is a cooling process.
10. The evaporation of solids is called sublimation.
11. The number of calories required to vaporize 1 gram of a liquid at its boiling point is called its heat of vaporization. For water it is 539 cal./g.
12. Near atmospheric pressure, the boiling point of water is changed by 0.1C° for every pressure change of 2.7 mm. of mercury.
13. The process of vaporizing a liquid by heat and condensing its vapor back into a liquid again in a separate container is called distillation.
14. The household refrigerator operates on the principle that an evaporating liquid absorbs heat from its surroundings, as well as from itself.

QUESTIONS FOR REVIEW

1. Which would be more effective as a foot warmer, a 2-lb. brick at 100°C, or 2 lb. of water at the same temperature in a hot water bottle? Explain.
2. Which contains the greater quantity of heat, a tub of water at 100°C or a small lake whose average temperature is 4°C?
3. Upon what factors does the heat lost or gained by a body depend?
4. Which probably contains the greatest quantity of heat: 10 lb. of copper, 10 lb. of mercury, or 10 lb. of water, assuming all to be at the same temperature? What would we have to know to be sure of the answer?
5. Explain the method of mixtures.
6. Which will liberate the greater quantity of heat in cooling from 100°C to 0°C: 100 g. of copper or 10 g. of water?
7. Which warms up or cools off more quickly, land or water? Why?
8. Is it the temperature or the melting of the ice in an icebox that is of greatest importance in keeping the icebox cold? Explain.
9. Why is it possible to pack snowballs?
10. If you were given a quantity of liquid and asked to evaporate it as quickly as possible, what things would you do, assuming you had the facilities with which to work?
11. Explain the things that occur when cold water is heated until it boils.
12. Why does the condensation of atmospheric water vapor into rain or snow tend to warm up the air?
13. Why would a tub of water placed in an old-fashioned cellar help to prevent canned food from freezing?
14. Why is a steam burn usually worse than a hot water burn?
15. Why does the reduction of the external pressure on a liquid lower its boiling point?
16. Why is it necessary to occasionally add extra alcohol to your automobile radiator during the cold winter months?
17. Explain why, when standing still on ice with your skates on, they will be more apt to be frozen fast to the ice on a reasonably mild winter day than on an extremely cold winter day.

PROBLEMS

1. How much heat is necessary to heat 23 g. of water from 20°C to 80°C? How much for 23 g. of iron?
2. How many btu are required to raise the temperature of 5 lb. of water from the freezing point to the boiling point?
3. How much heat is liberated when a mixture of 50 g. of water and 50 g. of lead at 100°C is cooled to 20°C?
4. If 500 cal. are absorbed by 400 g. of mercury at 20°C, what will be the final temperature of the mercury?
5. 200 g. of water at 40°C are mixed with 100 g. of water at 20°C. What is the final temperature of the mixture?
6. 200 g. of aluminum shot at 100°C are mixed with 200 g. of water at 10°C. What is the final temperature of the mixture?
7. Determine the heat of fusion of ice in terms of btu per pound.
8. The heat of vaporization of water, 539 cal./g., is equivalent to how many btu per pound?
9. What is the water equivalent of a 90-g. aluminum cup?
10. If 200 g. of lead shot at 100°C are mixed with 100 g. of water at 20°C in an aluminum container weighing 50 g., also at 20°C, what will be the final temperature of the mixture?
11. 400 g. of iron at 98°C are mixed with 100 g. of water at 14°C. The final temperature of the mixture is 40°C. Compute the specific heat of the iron. (Neglect the container.)
12. How much heat is required to convert 15 g. of ice at −10°C into steam at 110°C, atmospheric pressure being normal?
13. The heat of vaporization of liquid ammonia is 327 cal./g. If all the heat absorbed by 100 g. of liquid ammonia upon vaporizing were removed from a quantity of water at 0°C, how many grams of the water would be frozen?
14. A piece of metal weighing 400 g. has a specific heat of 0.2 cal./g./C°. If this metal, at 100°C, is placed in 200 g. of water at 40°C, what will be the final temperature? (Neglect the container.)
15. What is the boiling point of water when the barometer reads 720 mm.?
16. How many grams of ice at 0°C would be required to reduce the temperature of 2 kg. of water from 80°C to 10°C?
17. How many grams of ice at 0°C can be melted by the heat liberated by 20 g. of steam in condensing at 100°C and cooling down to 0°C?
18. Ten grams of steam at 100°C are mixed with 200 g. of water at 25°C in an aluminum container weighing 50 g. What is the final temperature of the mixture?
19. In an experiment, 20 g. of ice at 0°C were mixed with 250 g. of water at 40°C in an aluminum cup weighing 60 g. The final temperature was 31.6°C. Compute the heat of fusion of the ice.
20. Eight grams of steam at 99°C are passed into 225 g. of water at 15°C contained in a copper calorimeter weighing 85 g. The final temperature of the mixture is 35.6°C. Compute the heat of condensation of the steam in calories per gram.

PROJECTS

1. Devise a method of determining the heat of fusion of beeswax (melting point 61.8°C). Obtain some beeswax and demonstrate your method to the class.
2. Using some glass tubing about 1 cm. or more in diameter, make a Faraday tube, fill it with sulfur dioxide before sealing it, and see whether you can succeed in liquefying some of the gas. (Hint: draw out the ends of your tube until they are fine enough to be quickly sealed with a Bunsen burner as soon as you are sure the tube is filled with the gas from the chemical generator.)
3. Demonstrate regelation to the class. Use a piece of ice small enough so the weighted copper wire will not take too long to melt its way through.
4. Using your answer to Question 10 above, set up the proper equipment and demonstrate to the class how quickly you can cause a

MEASUREMENT OF HEAT

relatively small quantity of water, or a more volatile liquid, to be completely evaporated.

5. Devise a method of showing that water boils at higher than its normal boiling temperature under increased pressure. Demonstrate your method to the class.

6. Do some research on the gas type of refrigerator and explain its operation to the class.

READING YOU WILL ENJOY

1. *A to Zero of Refrigeration.* General Motors Corporation, Department of Public Relations, Detroit, 1950. A highly readable account of refrigeration from its earliest use to the present.

2. Dunning, J. R., and H. C. Paxton, *Matter, Energy, and Radiation,* Chapter 12. McGraw-Hill Book Company, Inc., New York, 1941.

3. Lemon, H. B., *From Galileo to Cosmic Rays,* Chapter 17. The University of Chicago Press, Chicago, 1934.

4. Swezey, K. M., *After-Dinner Science.* Whittlesey House, McGraw-Hill Book Company, Inc., New York, 1948. "A Calling-card Kettle," p. 42; "Water Does Not Heat until Ice Melts," pp. 48-49.

Chapter 25

The Transference of Heat

The problem. All of us know that heat energy "travels" from one place to another. By some process, heat from our furnaces is distributed to all parts of our homes. We can heat water in a tank by heating a coil of pipe properly connected to the tank. A stove poker, heated at one end, becomes warm or hot at the other end. Our fingers are burned if we touch a hot stove. Heat from the sun somehow reaches the earth through the vacuum of space. We may burn our faces and clothing simply by standing too close to a bonfire.

Knowing what we do about matter and heat, there seem to be several possibilities as to how heat might be transferred. The molecules of a liquid or gas might be heated at one place and then move to another. In a solid, where molecular motion is restricted, increased molecular vibration at one place might agitate greater vibration of the adjacent molecules, and these in turn might pass the energy on to still others, and so on throughout the body. In a vacuum, where there are no molecules, the story must be different. Without the presence of matter, heat transference must be accomplished in some other way, Since proper control of heat transference is essential to our ways of living, our problem is that of gaining a knowledge of the processes involved, and learning how to control and use them.

What is convection? We have seen smoke issuing from a chimney and drifting, sometimes skyward, sometimes toward the earth. We have warmed ourselves by standing in the draft of warm air from a hot-air register. We have seen the beautiful cumulus clouds that bring showers, as their thunderheads rise majestically into the blue sky above. We have seen the smoke from a cigarette or pipe as it curled upward toward the ceiling.

All of these are evidences of *convection currents,* which are caused by unequal heating of the air. When a portion of the air becomes heated more than the surrounding air, it expands and becomes less dense than the air around it. It is then forced to rise by the cooler, more dense air which flows under it and lifts it upward in accordance with Archimedes' Principle. Thus, we have a method by which *heat is transferred by a moving substance, brought about by unequal heating and a resulting inequality of pressure.* This is known as **convection.**

Convection occurs not only in gases, but also in liquids. The water in our hot water tanks and the air in our homes and schoolrooms are heated by convection. That portion of the fluid in actual contact with the hot pipe, furnace drum, or radiator is heated first. Then expansion results and convection currents are immediately started. Apparently a radiator might better be called a *convector*.

One can hardly overestimate the importance of convection. Winds are convection currents on a large scale. They bring us our changing weather conditions, without which life not only would be dull but would be practically impossible. The changing temperatures of the water in a lake or stream are brought about largely by convection.

Since the molecules of a solid are not free to flow or intermingle, solids cannot be heated by convection. Convection is confined to fluids and is the most important method by which they are heated. Figures 1 and 2 show respectively how convection currents in air and water can be demonstrated. Unequal heating of the air is accomplished by a lighted candle, and the direction of the currents is made visible by smoke from a smoldering piece of punk or tight roll of paper. Ink introduced into the water in the container just above the tubing makes the water currents visible. Devise other ways of showing convection currents.

What is conduction? Since heat cannot be transferred through a solid, such as an

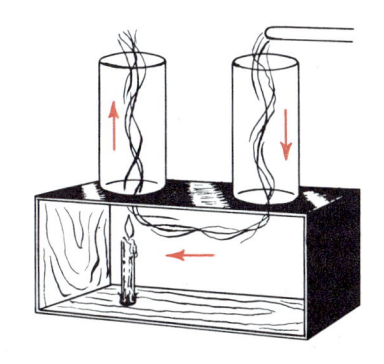

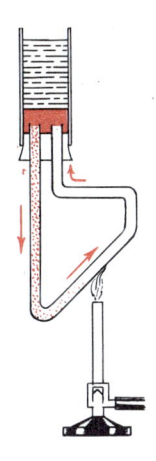

Fig. 2. Convection currents in liquids.

aluminum frying pan, by convection, then it must be passed on from one molecule to the next through the body. When the pan is set on a gas stove, the rapid vibration of the molecules in the flame agitates greater vibration of the aluminum molecules, which in turn pass the energy on through the pan. This method of heat transference is called **conduction.**

We know from experience that some solids conduct heat much better than others. The handle of a silver teaspoon, left in a cup of hot tea, soon becomes hot, whereas we can hold a burning match until the flame almost reaches our fingers. Thus, silver must be a good conductor and wood a very poor one.

Perhaps your chair is constructed of both wood and iron. If so, first feel the wood with your fingers, then feel the iron. Although they must both be at the same temperature, the iron feels cooler. This is because iron is a much better conductor than wood and conducts heat away from the fingers more rapidly, thus making them feel cool. Glass feels only slightly cooler than wood, because its conductivity is only slightly higher than that of wood.

An interesting experiment can be performed with a "crow's foot" composed of

Fig. 1. Convection currents in air.

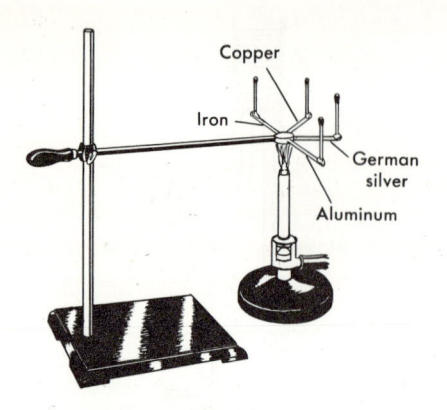

Fig. 3. Apparatus for comparing the heat conductivities of metals. Which match stick will fall off first?

rods of different kinds of metal (see Fig. 3). This device is known as a *conductometer*. With drops of melted paraffin, matchsticks are stuck to the metal rods equidistant from the junction. The junction is then heated with a gentle flame, and the order in which the sticks melt off indicates the relative conductivities of the metals. If the metals are iron, copper, German silver, and aluminum, in what order will they fall? (See Table 1.)

Table 1
CONDUCTIVITIES OF SUBSTANCES

Substance	Conductivity
Aluminum	0.480
Copper (pure)	0.918
German silver	0.07
Iron (pure)	0.161
(steel)	0.115
Mercury	0.0197
Silver (pure)	1.006
Brick (common red)	0.0015
Concrete	0.0022
Glass (window)	0.002
Ice	0.005
Paper	0.0003
Silk	0.000095
Ethyl alcohol	0.000423
Water	0.00131
Air	0.0000568
Nitrogen	0.0000524

In general, metals are the best solid conductors. The poorest conductor among the common metals is mercury, which is liquid at ordinary temperatures. The best heat conductor known is silver. Thermal conductivity is measured in terms of the number of calories transmitted per second through a plate 1 centimeter thick, across an area of 1 square centimeter, when the temperature difference is 1 centigrade degree. For example, Table 1 shows that approximately half a calorie of heat per second will be transmitted through a square centimeter of aluminum 1 centimeter thick when the temperature difference between the surfaces is 1 centigrade degree. The thermal conductivities of solids range from very good to extremely poor. Extremely poor conductors make good *insulators*.

Are liquids and gases good conductors? Let us put a piece of ice in a test tube, weight it down with a piece of metal, then almost fill the test tube with cold water (see Fig. 4a). We can now boil the water near the top with a Bunsen flame, but the ice at the bottom will not melt for some time. This shows that water is a very poor conductor.

This fact may be shown even more spectacularly by the experiment shown in Fig. 4b. Some ether is floated on top of the ice water and lighted with a match. The

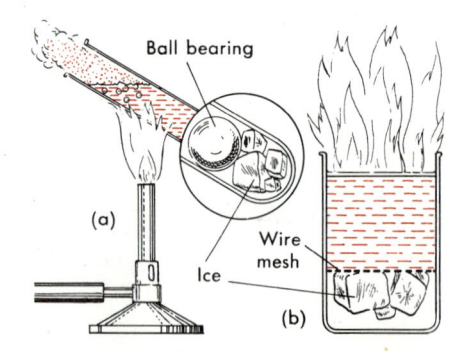

Fig. 4. What do these experiments show about the ability of water to conduct heat?

heat of the flame has little or no effect upon the ice at the bottom of the beaker, even when the water level is only a little above the ice. Liquids in general, except molten metals, are poor heat conductors; and their conductivities, with the exception of water, differ very little. The conductivity of water ranges from two to four times that of almost any other nonmetallic liquid.

Some of our experiences with air show it to be a poor conductor of heat. We can hold our hands close to the side of a hot stove or a burning match without getting burned. If air were a good conductor, this could not be done. Also, our bodies, when exposed to the air, would cool off much more rapidly than they do. Table 1 implies that gases are the poorest of all heat conductors. In other words, they are among the best insulators. Evidently a vacuum should be the best of all insulators, for since it contains no molecules, no kinetic energy of molecular motion can be transferred through it.

What is radiation? Since the transference of heat by both conduction and convection requires the presence of matter, the sun's heat cannot possibly reach us by either of these processes. This means that it must reach us by *radiation*. Warming our hands before a camp stove or a bonfire, even though the intervening air is cold, is evidence of radiation. How is such transference of heat energy accomplished?

The Dutch physicist Huyghens (see Chapter 41) in 1678 proposed the theory that all space is filled with a subtle fluid which is invisible and weightless. He called it *ether*, and considered it the medium through which radiant energy could be transmitted by wave motion. Heat waves are only one of several types of radiation which are studied in physics, all of which may be classified as *electromagnetic waves*. These waves vary greatly in length and in the amount of energy which they carry. All of them travel at the rate of 186,000 miles per second.

Thermal radiations vary in length from the longest *infrared* (0.005 cm.) to the shortest *ultraviolet* waves (0.000021 cm.). Such waves are readily absorbed by relatively dark surfaces and transformed into heat, by exciting the molecules of the absorbing body into more rapid motion. All bodies whose temperatures are above absolute zero are continually emitting and receiving heat energy by radiation. A body as hot as the sun, a lamp filament, or a glowing coal emits short waves which are detected by the sense of sight. Such radiation is called *light*. Cooler bodies, such as a hot stove, a steam radiator, or warm earth, emit the longer, invisible infrared waves, which are what we feel when we hold our hands beside a stove to warm them.

A body upon which radiant energy falls may absorb it, reflect it, or transmit it, depending upon the nature of the body's surface. If the energy is absorbed, it is transformed into heat; if it is reflected, its direction of travel is simply changed; if it is transmitted, it passes through the body without heating it. There are no perfect absorbers, reflectors, or transmitters of radiant energy. However, physicists make radiation measurements in terms of a perfectly black body, which would be not only a perfect radiator but also a perfect absorber. Light-colored bodies are generally both poor radiators and poor absorbers, but are generally good reflectors.

Some substances are transparent to heat radiation, others are opaque. Water is opaque to heat but transparent to light, whereas iodine solution is transparent to heat but opaque to light. Window glass is fairly transparent to the short heat waves from the sun, but it is fairly opaque to the longer waves from the radiators. Can you explain why a greenhouse acts as a "heat trap" and thus serves as a good place for plant culture?

How can we demonstrate reflection and absorption of radiant energy? Crookes' *radiometer* (Fig. 5) consists of a fairly well evacuated tube in which is mounted a pivoted wheel consisting of four vanes of aluminum, one side of each being polished and the other side coated with lampblack, the best known absorber and radiator of heat waves. When radiant energy from the sun or from some other source, such as a hot iron ball, falls upon the tube, the wheel revolves in the direction away from the blackened surfaces. This is because the polished surfaces reflect the radiations, whereas the black surfaces absorb them. This raises the temperature of the black surfaces above that of the shiny ones. Since the tube is only partially evacuated, molecules of air which bump into the vanes rebound with greater velocity from the black surfaces than from the shiny surfaces. Why? The reaction from these rebounding molecules is the

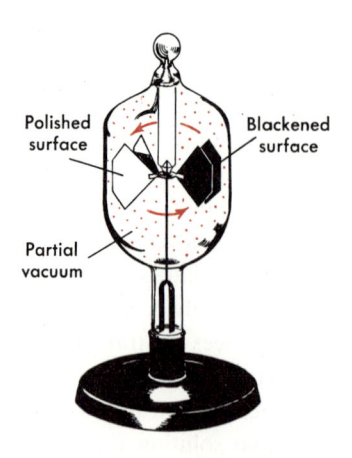

Fig. 5. Crookes' radiometer. Explain how it operates.

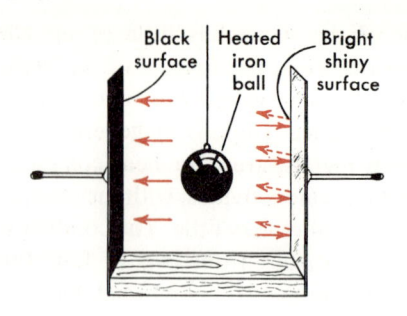

Fig. 6. Which match stick will fall first? Explain your answer.

cause of the wheel's rotation. Which of Newton's laws of motion is illustrated in this case?

Another experiment is illustrated in Fig. 6. Two sheets of galvanized iron are nailed to a block of wood. The inner surface of one is coated with lampblack, the other inner surface is polished. A match is attached to each outer surface with melted paraffin. Then a heated iron ball is suspended midway between the inner surfaces. In a short time the match on the black surface will melt off, whereas the other one may not fall at all. Can you explain this without any help from your instructor?

What are the laws of radiation? Since all bodies are sources of radiation, even a cake of ice radiates heat. Whether it receives heat faster than it radiates it depends upon the relative temperatures of the ice and its surroundings. If the surrounding temperature is lower than that of the ice, the ice will radiate heat faster than it receives it, and vice versa. Scientific experiments prove that

the rate at which a body cools by radiation is approximately proportional to the difference between its temperature and the temperature of the surrounding medium.

This is known as Newton's Law of Cooling.

Experience teaches us that the farther we are from a hot body the less intense is the radiation we receive. We also know that the hotter the body the more intense the radiation. Experiments prove that

the intensity of radiant energy is proportional to the fourth power of the absolute temperature of the source and inversely proportional to the square of the distance from the source.

Since the planet Mars is about 1.4 times as far from the sun as the earth is, it receives about half $\left(\frac{1}{1.4}\right)^2$ as much radiant energy as does the earth per unit area. The earth intercepts about 1/2,200,000,000 of the sun's total output.

How do we use convection? We have already referred to the heating of water and air by convection currents. Fig. 7 illustrates a common type of water heater. Can you explain its operation, giving reasons for the positions of the cold water inlet and the hot water outlet? Fig. 8 shows a cross section of a room being heated by a radiator. Explain the process

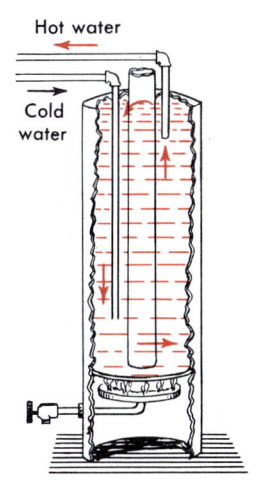

Fig. 7. A gas hot-water heater.

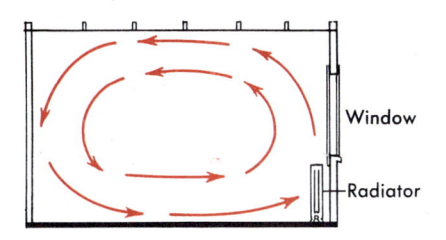

Fig. 8. Convection currents in a radiator-heated room. Why is the radiator placed next to the window?

fully. Why should the radiator be placed under the window rather than elsewhere?

Most of our homes are heated by one of three types of heating systems: *hot-air, steam,* or *hot-water*. In each of these convection plays the most important role. Each system has its advantages and disadvantages. We shall mention only a few.

The hot-air system is good for quick heat, but it is less efficient than steam or hot water in maintaining a steady temperature, unless *thermostatic control* and *forced circulation* by means of a fan are used. The humidity of the air is more easily controlled with the hot-air system. Steam heat is less quick in its action than hot air, but is more steady. The slowest of all but the most steady is the hot-water system. Why? A steam-heating system is more rapid in its action if special radiator valves are used—valves which do not permit air to flow back into the system once it has been forced out by the steam. This produces a partial vacuum in the system, and permits the water in the boiler to boil at a lower temperature. Most modern heating systems are now controlled by thermostats.

Figures 9 and 10 respectively show the principles of operation of hot-air and hot-water heating systems. Note the provisions for the return circulation of the hot air and hot water back to the heating plant.

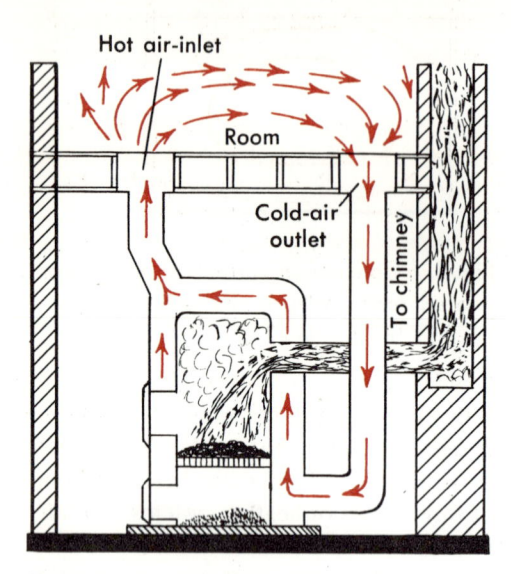

Fig. 9. A simple hot-air heating system.

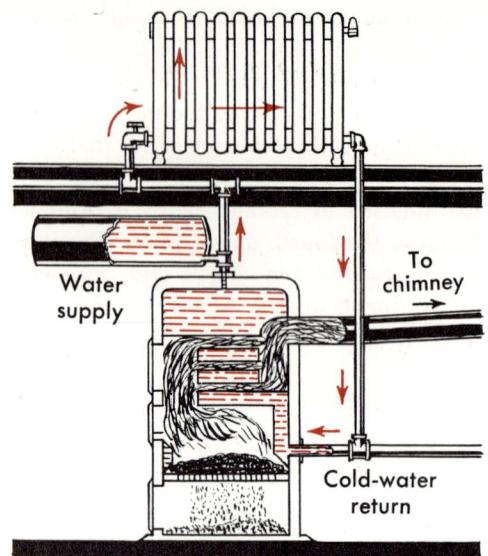

Fig. 10. A hot-water heating system.

Is this necessary in the steam-heating system?

How do we use conduction? One of our commonest uses of conduction is in the cooking process. Cooking utensils made of the best conductors are, in general, the most efficient. They readily conduct the heat from the source to the food within, not only through the bottom, but also along and through the sides. Aluminum is good for this purpose. Silver and copper are better conductors, but silver is expensive, and copper has the disadvantage of sometimes forming undesirable chemicals which taint the food. Do you think that black bottoms would increase the efficiency of the utensils? Why?

Conduction is important in the burning of fuel. When a stick of wood or piece of coal is heated to the kindling point, heat from the burning process is conducted to other parts of the fuel, which in turn begin to burn. Some engines are cooled by the use of conducting fins of copper or aluminum, which project outward from the engine blocks and rapidly conduct the heat away from the engines. From the fins the heat is radiated off or carried away by convection. Can you think of other ways in which we use conduction?

How do we use radiation? Since the heat of the sun reaches us by radiation, our very lives depend upon this method of heat transference. Although the air in our homes is heated largely by convection, radiation plays some part in the process. Steaks broiled in an oven and toast made in a toaster are browned by radiation. When we sit before an open fireplace, the little heat we receive is by radiation. Most of the heat is carried up the chimney by convection currents.

A type of heating system called *radiant heating* is rapidly gaining in popularity. Pipes heated by hot water, or electric coils heated by electricity, are embedded in the floors, walls, or ceilings, and the heating is accomplished largely by radiation. Many new school buildings and homes are being heated by this system.

How do we prevent heat transference? Since heat is transferred in only three ways, the most effective way to prevent its transference would be to guard against heat losses or gains by all three of these processes. Sometimes we are interested mainly in preventing heat conduction. The handles of some frying pans are made of poor conducting materials or of coiled metallic rods. In the latter case, although the metal may be a fairly good conductor, the heat has to travel so far along the coil that it is dissipated before reaching the place where the hand grasps it (Fig. 11). Stove-poker handles are sometimes made in this manner.

Fig. 11. Why doesn't the handle get hot?

We protect our hands and tables from hot dishes by using potholders and hot-pads made of insulating materials. Teacups are made of nonconducting material so the handles will not get hot. We like to wear cotton in the summer and woolen clothing in the winter. Light-colored cotton clothes are fairly good reflectors of the sun's radiation. Dark wool is a good absorber and an especially good insulator because its fibers have lengthwise air spaces within them. Since gases are extremely poor conductors, any *dead-air* space is an effective insulator. Dead air is air that cannot circulate and is therefore effective against loss or gain of heat by convection. Walls of houses usually have dead-air spaces within them.

Figure 12 shows the construction of the wall of a house designed to prevent losses or gains of heat. Can you explain its effectiveness? The effectiveness of most insulating material is based upon its nonconductivity and its ability to enclose many small dead-air spaces within it. Insulating batts to be tacked between the rafters, joists, and studding of a building are available. Sheets of aluminum foil between the studs reduce the amount of heat lost by radiation.

An efficiently insulated liquid container is the *vacuum bottle* (Fig. 13). It is a double-walled glass bottle mounted in a metal case. The space between the walls of the bottle is evacuated of air, and both

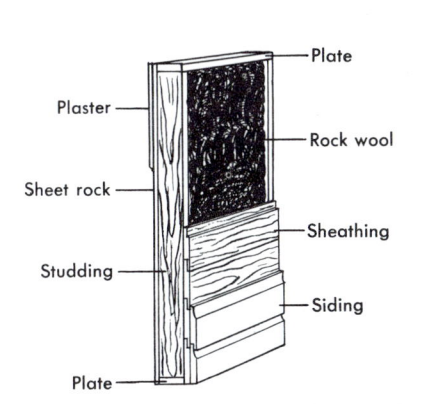

Fig. 12. A section of a wall designed to keep heat in or out. The dead-air spaces in the rock wool prevent heat losses.

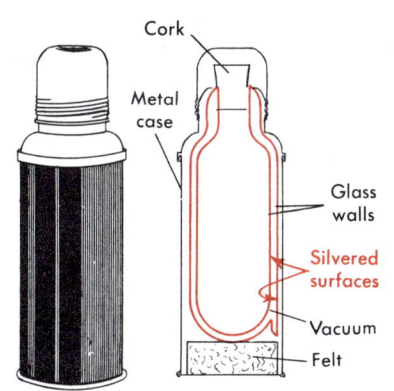

Fig. 13. A vacuum bottle. Why is it so efficient in preventing heat transference when well constructed?

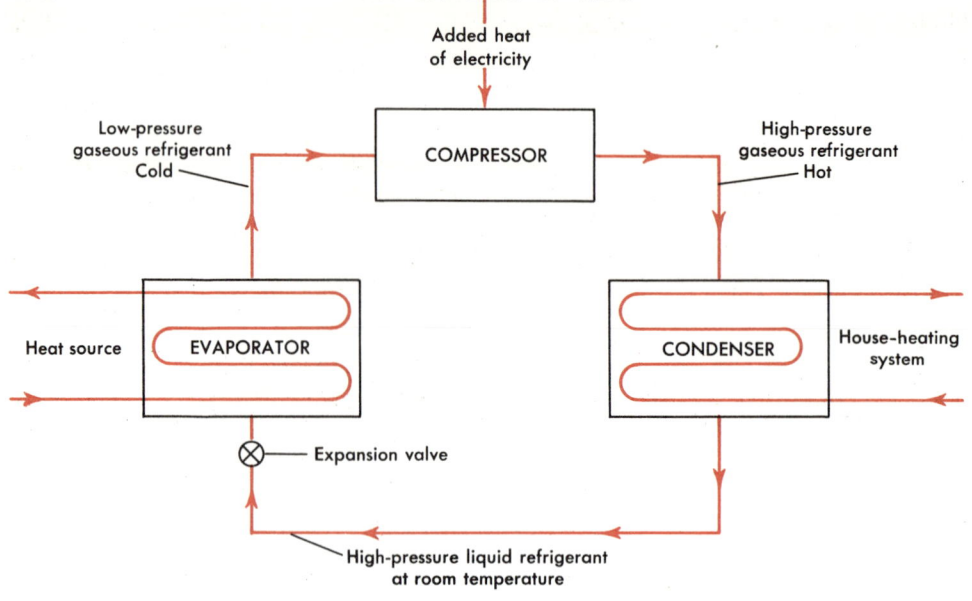

Fig. 14. A heat pump is essentially a refrigerator in reverse. During the change from the liquid to the vapor state, the refrigerant absorbs heat. Then compression raises its temperature. Upon changing back to the liquid state, the refrigerant gives off heat.

the inner and outer walls are silvered and highly polished. Can you explain how a vacuum bottle prevents heat transference by all three possible methods: convection, conduction, and radiation? Try to think of some other applications of the prevention of heat transference.

Reversed refrigeration, or the "fireless furnace." A comparatively new method of heating (Fig. 14) is based upon the principle of reversed refrigeration. It can be used to heat a house in winter and cool it in summer. In cooling a house it works on the same principle as a refrigerator. In heating a house it takes heat from the earth and puts it into the house.

In this heating system there is utilized the principle of the *heat pump,* as shown in the figure. Here a liquid refrigerant passes through the expansion valve, where its pressure is reduced; then through the evaporator, which is a coil of pipe embedded in the ground. Here, upon changing to a gas, it picks up its heat of vaporization directly from the ground. It then travels to the compressor, where work is done on it and its temperature is raised (hot gas). Then it passes through the unit coil, which is really the condenser, located in the air duct of the heating system. Here the hot gas condenses to a hot liquid and gives up its heat of vaporization (which it had picked up from the ground), heating the air to about 110°F. In the process the hot liquid refrigerant is also cooled and is then ready to pass again through the expansion valve and pick up another load of heat from the ground. The cycle is continuous.

Hence, we see that the refrigerant takes heat (H_2) from a low temperature source (the ground in this case); some work (W) is then done on it; and heat (H_1) is delivered at a higher temperature to the place where it is needed. The energy equation for this cycle is

$$H_1 = H_2 + W$$

In summer the direction of the refrigerant is reversed by means of a simple valve operation. The ground coil then becomes the condenser, and the unit coil becomes the evaporator. The energy equation is the same, but the heat is delivered to the ground instead of inside the house.

SUMMARY AND CONCLUSIONS

1. Heat is transferred by convection, conduction, or radiation.
2. The transference of heat energy from molecule to molecule through a body is called conduction.
3. The transference of heat by a moving fluid, caused by unequal heating, is called convection. Winds are huge convection currents.
4. The transmission of heat energy by electromagnetic waves is called radiation. Heat radiations travel with the speed of light.
5. Solids vary in heat conductivity from extremely good to extremely poor. Metals are the best conductors; liquids and gases the poorest.
6. Heat cannot be conducted through a vacuum.
7. Good absorbers of radiant heat energy are also good radiators.
8. The rate at which a body cools is approximately proportional to the difference between its temperature and the temperature of the surrounding medium.

QUESTIONS FOR REVIEW

1. Why aren't your fingers burned while holding the stick of a burning match?
2. Which would be the best insulator—brick, glass, or concrete?
3. Why is it possible for Eskimos to keep warm in ice huts?
4. If you were short of blankets, could you use newspapers in their stead by placing them between the sheets? Explain.
5. Can you explain why a chimney "draws"? Why do large factories have tall chimneys? (Give two reasons.)
6. What are the advantages of having your house insulated?
7. Why do storm windows help to keep a house warm in winter? Do they have any other advantages?
8. What keeps an automobile engine from getting too hot?
9. Why is it that in cold climates, fall crops are most apt to "winter kill" during those winters when not much snow falls?
10. Why should the damper of a fireplace be closed in the winter when there is no fire in the fireplace?
11. Why is the basement of a house usually the coolest place in the house during the summer?
12. If you wish to cool off a room quickly, how should the windows be opened?
13. Why is light-colored clothing more desirable in the summer and dark-colored clothing more desirable in the winter?
14. Why are thick-walled glass tumblers more apt to crack than thin ones when hot water is poured into them?

PROBLEMS

1. Make a diagram of the inside of an icebox and show by arrows how convection currents would travel inside the box. Where is the coldest place in an icebox?
2. The exposed portion of a concrete basement wall is 8 in. thick. If the temperature inside the basement is 72°F, and the outside temperature is 0°F, how much heat will be lost per hour per square foot of area of the wall? (See Table 1.)
3. How much heat per hour would be conducted through a windowpane 30 cm. wide, 50 cm. long, and ¼ cm. thick if the outside air temperature were 32°F and the inside temperature 68°F? (See Table 1 for conductivity of glass.)

ANS.: 864,000 cal.

PROJECTS

1. Bring from your homes several vacuum bottles of different makes and fill each with the same amount of hot water at the same temperature. Every four hours, take the temperature of the water in each bottle so as to determine which one is the best insulator of heat. Find out, if you can, the cost of each bottle and determine whether the cost is any indication of insulating efficiency.

2. Using a source of smoke so convection currents can be observed, make a study of the circulation of air in your living room at home. Use a thermometer to determine the distribution of heat; where one should sit to be away from cool drafts, the warmest spots and coolest spots in the room, etc. Make a drawing of the room and the convection currents, and make a report to the class.

3. Make a study of your home heating system and report to the class.

4. Using an electric reflector-type bathroom heater, a thermometer, water, and a tin can, one side of which is shiny and the other side coated with lampblack or soot, show the effects of the two different can surfaces upon the absorption, reflection, and emission of radiant energy.

READING YOU WILL ENJOY

1. Dunning, J. R., and H. C. Paxton, *Matter, Energy, and Radiation,* Chapter 4. McGraw-Hill Book Company, Inc., New York, 1941.

2. Swezey, K. M., *After-Dinner Science.* Whittlesey House, McGraw-Hill Book Company, Inc., New York, 1948. "Black Makes the Best Heat Radiator," pp. 38-39; "Heat Conductivity Varies," p. 41.

Chapter 26

Work and Heat (Thermodinamics)

The problem. Count Rumford showed that heat was produced by work done in the boring of cannon; Sir Humphrey Davy proved that enough heat could be developed through friction to melt pieces of ice; our own experiment with the silver coin proved that heat was produced by the energy expended in overcoming friction. In each case, *mechanical energy was transformed into heat energy by the process of doing work*.

Conversely, we know from observation that heat energy can be utilized in the accomplishment of work. All our heat engines furnish ample evidence of this fact. Hot steam, under pressure, can do work when allowed to expand; in gasoline engines, hot gases do work when they expand against movable pistons. In both instances the heated gases or vapors decrease in temperature; that is, they lose heat energy, and mechanical energy is the result. Our problem in this chapter is to discover how these relationships between work and heat are put to practical use.

How are work and heat related? From our definition of heat in Chapter 22, it follows that the heat in a body is proportional to the kinetic energy of its molecules, or

$$H \propto K.E.$$

Also, since work is the expenditure of energy and can be used to produce heat, it seems also to follow that work, W, is proportional to the molecular kinetic energy produced by it, or

$$W \propto K.E.$$

Then
$$H \propto W. \quad \text{(Why?)}$$

If we introduce a proportionality constant, J, we can set heat equal to work, thus:

$$W = JH \quad (1)$$

whence
$$J = \frac{W}{H} \quad (2)$$

J is known by several names, the most common of which is *the mechanical equivalent of heat*.

James Prescott Joule (1818-1889) was the first to determine this relationship between work and heat and show that it is a constant. Thus, it is sometimes called *Joule's equivalent*. His apparatus was like the one shown in Fig. 1. It consisted of an insulated copper container holding a churning device composed of both stationary and movable paddles. The movable paddles were made to rotate by weights falling at a constant speed. When the weights reached the base of their descent, they were lifted again, and the

275

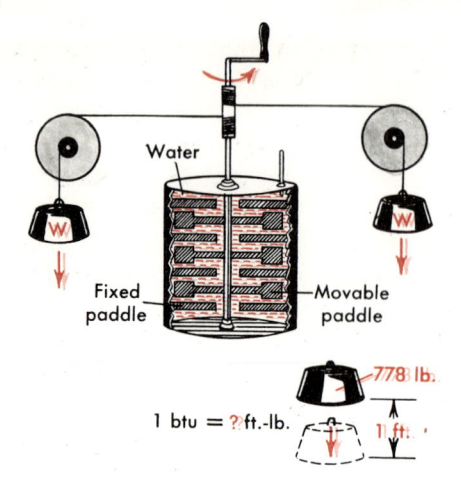

Fig. 1. Joule's apparatus for determining the relationship between work and heat.

operation was repeated over and over. The work done on the water raised its temperature.

From the values of the weights and the distances they fell, the work they did was measured and equated with the heat energy gained by the water. Thus the number of foot-pounds of energy required to produce a British thermal unit of heat was determined. Joule's results gave him 772 ft.-lb. per btu. Later experimentation established the constant as being 778 ft.-lb./btu.

As a result of Joule's work, both the fact that heat is a form of energy and the law of conservation of energy, first stated by him, were established. The assumption that heat is energy is the best way of explaining the production of heat when mechanical energy disappears and, conversely, the production of mechanical energy when heat disappears.

PROBLEM: If all the kinetic energy of a 3200-lb. car, traveling at 60 ft./sec., were transformed into heat, in how many btu's would it result?

SOLUTION:

$$\frac{\text{Energy in ft.-lb.}}{778 \text{ ft.-lb./btu}} = \text{btu}$$

and

$$\text{K.E.(ft.-lb.)} = \frac{kmV^2}{2}$$

Hence,

$$\text{btu} = \frac{mV^2}{2 \times 32 \times 778}$$

Substituting,

$$\text{btu} = \frac{3200 \times 60 \times 60}{2 \times 32 \times 778}$$

$$= 231.4 \text{ btu}$$

A unit of energy which is equivalent to 10^7 ergs was given the name of *joule* in honor of James Prescott Joule. The following are important constants:

1 btu = 778 foot-pounds
1 cal. = 427 gram-meters
1 cal. = 41,900,000 (4.19 × 10^7) ergs
1 joule = 10,000,000 (10^7) ergs
1 cal. = 4.19 joules
1 joule = 0.24 calorie

What is heat of combustion? One of Nature's storehouses of energy is plant life, both living and dead. Coal, petroleum, and natural gas are examples of substances in which heat is stored. Heat may be considered as available chemical potential energy. When these substances and substances derived from them are burned, their stored energy is released and used as a source of power for various purposes.

The amount of heat liberated when a unit mass or a unit volume (for gases) of a substance burns is called its *heat of combustion,* and is expressed in British thermal units per pound, calories per gram, or British thermal units per cubic foot, as in the case of gases. Obviously, those fuels having the highest heats of combustion should be able to furnish the most power, other things being equal. (See Table 1.)

Table 1
HEAT OF COMBUSTION OF FUELS

Fuel	btu/lb.	btu/ft.³
Coal (hard)	12,000	
Coal (soft)	13,000	
Gasoline	20,750	
Fuel oil	19,000	
Kerosene	19,800	
Methane		900
Propane		2,400
Natural gas		1,000- 2,100

How do we use the foods we eat? In our bodies the "fuel" that we eat furnishes us with energy required in the accomplishment of several things; namely, the maintenance of our bodily temperatures, the nutrition and repair of our body tissues, and the doing of physical work. Some energy is frequently stored in the form of fat and can be drawn upon when our bodies are ill. Experiments prove that only about 28 per cent of our food energy is converted into muscular energy. Thus, in the light of useful work done, we could claim an efficiency of only 28 per cent.

How is the energy content of foods expressed? We have heard fleshy people, as well as others, say, "I must watch my calories." What do they mean? We know that some foods furnish more energy than others. Most handbooks list the fuel values of foods in terms of kilogram-calories per hundred grams (see Table 2). We should remember, however, that we need, not only calories, but also proteins, vitamins, and minerals. A well-balanced diet for an average adult includes a daily requirement of 3000 kilogram-calories, 75 grams of protein, 0.69 gram of calcium, 1.32 grams of phosphorus, and 0.015 gram of iron.

What is the principle for heat engines? Most of us know something about heat engines and can probably call most of them by name. What we may not know are the principles by which they operate. We have shown how mechanical energy can be converted into heat energy. All heat engines make use of the reverse of this principle; namely, the conversion of heat energy into mechanical energy. This reverse process is based upon the fact that *whenever a gas does work upon expansion, it is cooled;* that is, *heat energy disappears and mechanical energy is developed.*

Probably most of us have discovered that air escaping from the valve of an inflated tire feels cool to one's hand. This is because the air is expanding and doing work on the hand and the surrounding atmosphere. The energy required to do this work is furnished from the heat possessed by the air before it expands. Thus, the average kinetic energy per molecule of air decreases, and the temperature of the air is reduced. *In all practical heat engines, mechanical energy is produced from the heat energy possessed by an expanding gas or vapor.*

Table 2
FUEL VALUES OF FOODS

Food	kg.-cal./100g.
Asparagus	23
Beef, lean roast	200
Bread (white)	262
Butter	769
Cake	386
Chicken	109
Eggs, whole	148
Fudge	356
Ham, medium fat	414
Ice cream	222
Lettuce	20
Milk, whole	69
Oleomargarine	752
Pie, apple	177
Pork chops	250-340
Potatoes (boiled)	92
Potatoes (fried)	160
Sugar (granulated)	400

How can we classify heat engines? The heat energy of the expanding gas or vapor used in a heat engine is furnished by the combustion of some fuel such as coal, gasoline, or fuel gas. When this combustion takes place *outside* the chamber (cylinder) in which the expansion takes place,

Fig. 2. Hero's steam engine. How is Newton's third law of motion applied in this device?

the engine is called an *external combustion engine*. Examples are the steam engine and steam turbine. When combustion takes place *inside* the expansion chamber, the engine is called an *internal combustion engine*. Examples are the gasoline, diesel, and jet engines.

What was the first steam engine? Probably the first steam engine ever made was a toy invented by Hero of Alexandria about two thousand years ago. Essentially it was a hollow ball with bent jets protruding from its sides (Fig. 2). When water was put in the ball and then heated, steam issued from the jets and produced rotation by its reaction on the jet tubes. The expanding steam did work in producing the rotation.

Not until early in the eighteenth century was steam used to do useful work, when Thomas Newcomen, an English blacksmith, invented the Newcomen engine for the purpose of pumping water from flooded mines in England. The essential features of his engine are shown in Fig. 3.

A piston, P, in the cylinder, C, was moved upward by a counterweight attached to a walking beam. This upward motion allowed steam to enter the cylinder below the piston through a hand-operated steam inlet valve, which was closed by hand when the piston reached its maximum height. A second valve, also hand-operated, admitted cold water. This condensed the steam and thus produced a vacuum inside the cylinder. Atmospheric pressure then forced the piston down, at the same time raising the pump's counterweight. The condensed water was drained off through a third hand-operated valve. The cycle was then repeated. Although Newcomen called his engine a steam engine, it was not one in the modern sense of the term. Can you explain why?

How does the modern steam engine operate? Many improvements on the steam engine have been made since the time of Newcomen. Some of these improvements were made by James Watt, who thus is considered the inventor of the modern steam engine. Perhaps his greatest improvements were the building of the *reciprocating* steam engine and the addition of the *centrifugal governor* to control its speed of operation (see Fig. 4).

With the axis of the governor attached to the shaft of the engine, the revolving metal balls, BB, speed up or slow down with the engine, causing the collar at A

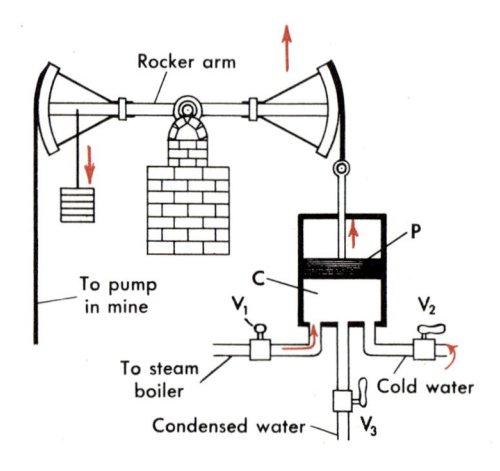

Fig. 3. The Newcomen engine. How must the valves be operated to move the piston up? Down?

WORK AND HEAT

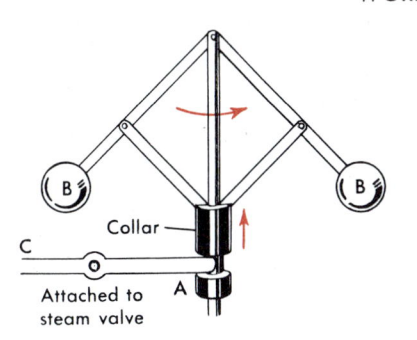

$HP = \dfrac{2N\,(PA \times L)}{33{,}000}$

Fig. 4. A centrifugal governor is used to control the engine speed.

to be respectively raised or lowered by changes in centrifugal force. A pivoted arm, AC, attached to the steam valve, thus regulates the flow of steam into the cylinder. Explain how this is done. Modern steam and gasoline engines use this device.

Figure 5 shows the essential parts of a reciprocating steam engine. Steam under high pressure flows from the boiler into the steam chest S, thence through the port N into the cylinder C on the right side of the piston P, driving the piston to the left and forcing any remaining steam in C' through port M and the exhaust E. The reciprocating motion of the piston is converted to rotational motion of the flywheel W through the connecting rod R and the crank D.

As the piston nears the left end of the cylinder, the eccentric F and eccentric rod R' cause the sliding valve V to move to the right far enough to close port N from the live steam and open it to the exhaust E. At the same time port M is opened, and the steam then rushes into the cylinder on the left side of the piston and forces it to the right. Just before the piston reaches the end of this stroke, port N is again opened, and the whole operation is repeated. The inertia of the heavy flywheel keeps the engine running smoothly.

Disadvantages of the reciprocating engine and some of their remedies. Since the piston must stop and start again twice for every revolution of the flywheel, much vibration may result, necessitating the use of heavy construction to guard against excessive wear on the machine. Also the exhaust steam may still possess enough energy to expand further. This means not only that some energy is wasted, but that additional energy must be used in operating the piston against the back pressure of the exhaust steam, which must be at least as great as atmospheric pressure.

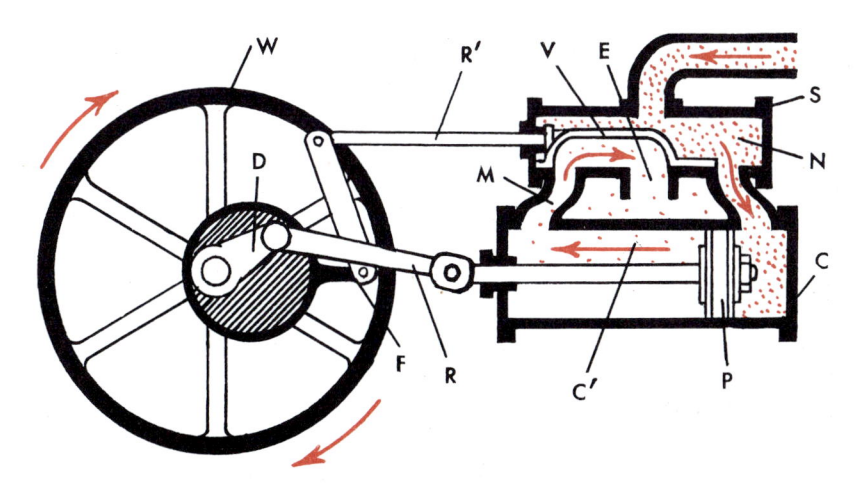

Fig. 5. Cross section of the reciprocating steam engine.

Some of these disadvantages have been overcome, in part, by the use of *condensing* engines and *multiple expansion* engines. Condensing engines are equipped with a condenser in which the exhaust steam is cooled with a spray of cold water. This creates a partial vacuum in the cylinder and reduces the backward pressure against the piston.

Multiple expansion engines are *compound* engines which have two, three, or four cylinders. Exhaust steam from the first cylinder enters a second cylinder in which it may further expand. From here it may enter a third and even a fourth cylinder. All the pistons of the cylinders are connected to the same main shaft. Since the total force of expansion is measured by the product of the area of the piston and the steam pressure (see page 44), and since the steam pressure in each cylinder is lower than in the preceding one, each succeeding cylinder and piston has a larger diameter than the preceding ones in order to equalize the total forces on the pistons.

In general, *stationary* engines may have higher efficiencies than moving engines, such as locomotives. This is due, in part, to the fact that locomotives must move *themselves*. Furthermore, they are also exposed to changing atmospheric conditions and are fanned by rapidly moving air.

How may the power of a steam engine be measured? We know that one horsepower is equivalent to doing work at the rate of 33,000 foot-pounds per minute (page 196). Thus, to measure the power of a steam engine, we can multiply the total force in pounds exerted on the piston by the distance in feet the piston moves per minute, and divide this product by 33,000. However, it is not this simple, because the pressure in the cylinder is continuously changing during the piston stroke.

An instrument called a *steam engine indicator* can be used. It automatically makes a continuous record of the pressure changes in the cylinder. By its use the average pressure during a single piston stroke and the average *difference* in pressure on the two sides of the piston can be obtained. The pressure difference is called the *mean effective pressure*. Using this value in the following formula, called the *PLAN* formula for obvious reasons, we can calculate the horsepower of an engine.

$$\text{H. P.} = 2 \frac{PLAN}{33,000} \qquad (3)$$

P is the mean effective pressure in pounds per square inch, L the length of the piston stroke in feet, A the area of the piston in square inches, and N the number of revolutions of the flywheel per minute. The constant, 2, appears because there are two power strokes of the piston per revolution.

PROBLEM: A steam engine operates at 120 rpm. The mean effective pressure in the cylinder is 50 lb./in.^{2} The area of the piston is 77 in.^{2} and the length of the stroke is 15 in. (5/4 ft.). What is the horsepower of the engine?

SOLUTION:

$$\text{H. P.} = 2 \frac{PLAN}{33,000}$$

Substituting,

$$\text{H. P.} = \frac{2 \times 50 \times 5 \times 77 \times 120}{33,000 \times 4}$$

$$= 35$$

How does the steam turbine operate? Some of the disadvantages of the reciprocating steam engine are overcome in the steam turbine. It is a rotary type of engine, thus eliminating the vibrations caused by the starting and stopping of pistons. Fig. 6 illustrates the basic principle of its operation.

High-pressure steam, so hot that it sometimes glows red, flows through sta-

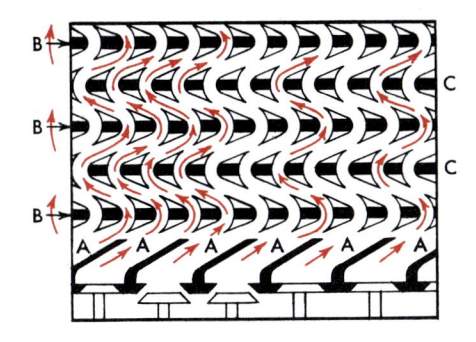

Fig. 6. Principle of the steam turbine.

tionary jets, *A,* which direct it obliquely against a series of blades, *B,* which are attached to a rotating drum called the *rotor.* The rotor is attached to the main shaft of the engine. The impact of the steam against these movable blades causes the rotor to rotate in the direction shown.

Between the sets of movable blades are sets of stationary blades, *C,* which are attached to the inner surface of the rotor casing. This part of the engine is called the *stator.* The expanding steam is directed from the first set of movable blades against the oppositely curved surfaces of the first set of fixed blades. These, in turn, direct it against the next set of movable blades, and so on. The fixed blades merely serve to redirect the steam against the movable sets of blades.

Since the pressure of the expanding steam decreases as it passes through the turbine, each successive set of blades must be larger in diameter than the preceding one to equalize the total force producing rotation. Fig. 7 shows the rotor and stator of a large steam turbine.

Steam turbines are used in the generation of electrical power and in many seagoing ships. At high speeds they operate

Fig. 7. Assembling a 125,000-kilowatt steam turbine. Incredible as it may seem, only the kinetic energy of steam molecules under pressure is harnessed to drive the giant rotor. Notice that the blades, or buckets, of the rotor gradually increase in size to allow for the expansion of the steam in passing through the drum.

Courtesy Westinghouse Electric Corp.

at higher efficiency than the reciprocating type of engine and produce less vibration. For a given horsepower they are also more compact. One disadvantage is that they cannot be reversed.

How does the gasoline engine operate? In the working of any gas engine a *cycle* of operations needs to be completed to keep the engine running. *First,* a proper mixture of the fuel vapor and air is introduced into the cylinder above the piston. *Second,* this explosive mixture is compressed so that when, *third,* the mixture is ignited at the spark plug, the piston will be driven downward. The *fourth* operation consists in expelling the burned gases from the cylinder.

If an engine completes the cycle by four successive piston strokes, it is a *four-stroke-cycle* engine. If only two strokes are necessary, it is a *two-stroke-cycle* engine. These terms are often contracted to four-cycle and two-cycle, but it is evident that they are inaccurate, since only *one* cycle is completed by either four or two strokes of the piston.

Figure 8 illustrates the operation of the four-stroke-cycle engine. Each drawing shows the same cylinder, with the piston, P, making one of the four strokes necessary to complete the cycle. Part (a) shows the *intake* stroke. Just before the piston reaches the bottom of this stroke, the intake valve, I, automatically opens and the fuel mixture, prepared in the carburetor, is injected by air pressure into the partial vacuum above the piston.

Part (b) shows the *compression* stroke, with valves I and E closed. Just before the piston reaches the top, a timing device causes an electric spark to jump the gap at the spark plug, igniting the fuel. The fuel burns explosively, producing high temperature and pressure. As a result the piston is forcibly pushed downward on the *power* stroke (part c). The final *exhaust* stroke is shown in part (d). Just before the piston reaches the top, the exhaust

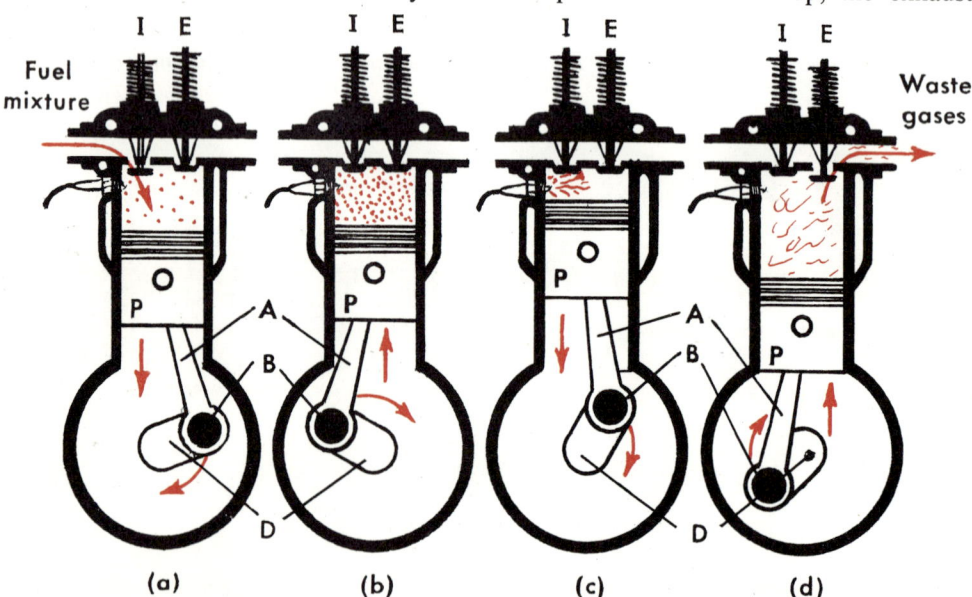

Fig. 8. The operation of the four-stroke-cycle engine. In the intake stroke, the fuel-air mixture is admitted. During the compression stroke, the mixture is ignited. The expanding gases then cause the wheel to turn. Finally, the exhaust gases escape.

valve *E* opens automatically, and the burned gases are ejected from the cylinder. Valve *E* is then closed and the cylinder is ready to start the whole cycle over again.

The piston is connected to the crankshaft *D* by means of the connecting rod *A* and the crank *B*. The valve action is controlled by means of a *cam* and *camshaft* which are operated directly from the crankshaft (Fig. 9). The *crankcase* houses the connecting rod, crank, and part of the crankshaft. Oil, placed in the crankcase, lubricates the moving parts. The smoothness of operation depends to a large extent upon a heavy flywheel attached to the crankshaft. Its momentum carries the engine through its cycle of operations from one power stroke to the next.

The modern automobile engine. Most of our gas engines are *multiple-cylindered*. Automobiles usually have four, six, or eight cylinders, though some having as many as twelve or sixteen have been made. Each cylinder is an engine in itself, each piston is connected to the same shaft, and each operates on its own cycle of four strokes. Teaming them together results in a smoothly running product. Other things being equal, the greater the number of cylinders, the more smoothly the engine should operate.

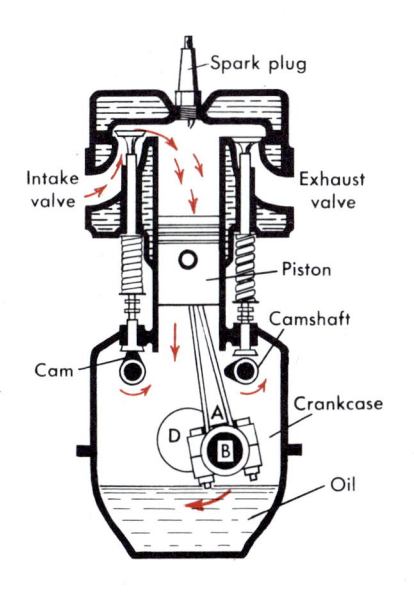

Any one-cylinder, four-stroke-cycle engine can have but one power stroke for every two revolutions of the crankshaft; a two-cylinder engine has one power stroke for every revolution; a four-cylinder, two for every revolution; a six-cylinder, three for every revolution, and so on. The more frequent the power strokes, the more smooth the running and the greater the power.

The following formula has been developed by the Society of Automotive Engineers (S.A.E.) for determining the horsepower of an automobile engine:

$$\text{H. P.} = \frac{D^2 N}{2.5} \qquad (4)$$

in which *D* is the diameter of the cylinders in inches and *N* is the number of cylinders. Try this formula on your car.

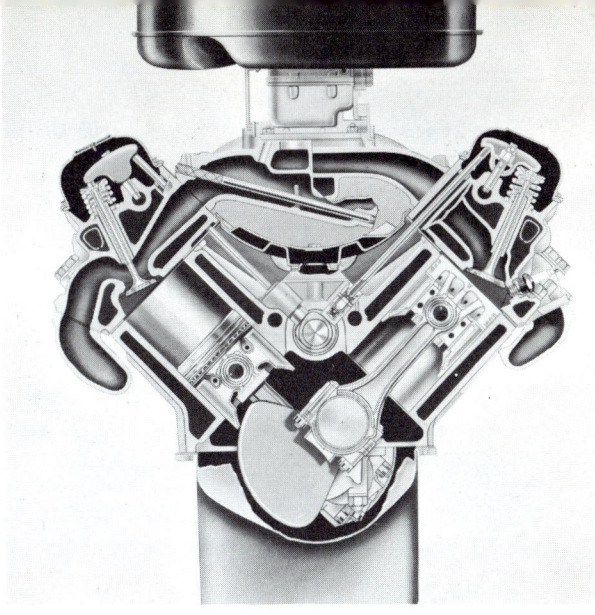

Courtesy Ford Motor Co.

Fig. 10. Cutaway view of an automobile engine showing V-type arrangement of the cylinders.

Fig. 9. How cams control the action of the intake and exhaust valves.

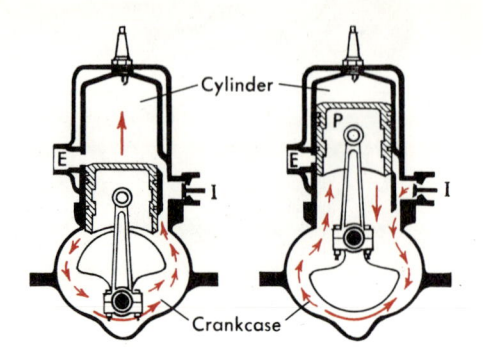

Fig. 11. The two-stroke cycle engine.

How does the two-stroke-cycle engine work? In this engine the cycle of operation is completed by two strokes of the piston *P* instead of four. Instead of intake and exhaust valves, there are openings on the sides of the cylinder called the *intake*

Fig. 12. Two-stroke-cycle diesel engine. After the entering air has been compressed, fuel under pressure is sprayed into the cylinder. The heat of compression ignites the fuel-air mixture.

Courtesy Detroit Diesel Engine Division

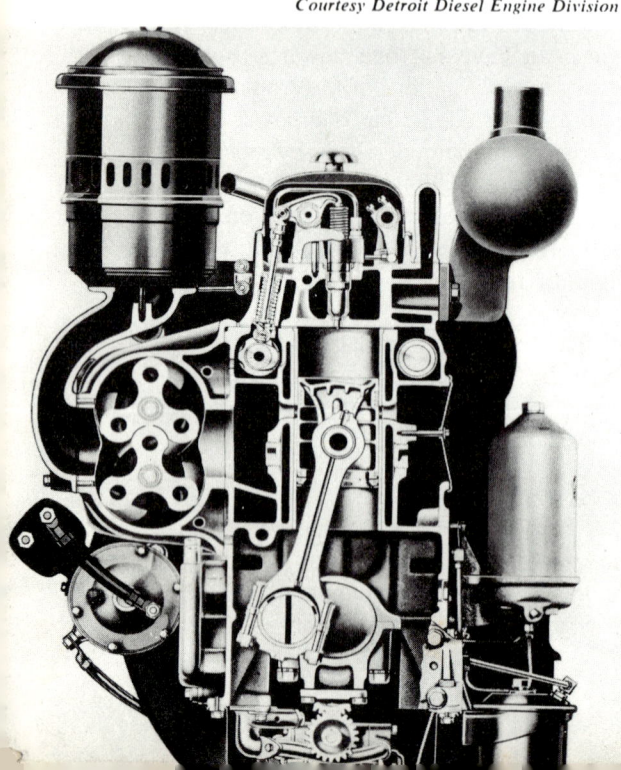

port, I, and *exhaust port, E,* which are opened and closed by the passage of the piston. The intake and power strokes are combined into one, as are also the exhaust and compression strokes. The fuel mixture is introduced into the crankcase (on the upward exhaust and compression stroke of the piston) before entering the cylinder on the downward power and intake stroke. Using Fig. 11, try to complete the explanation.

Since, in the two-stroke-cycle engine, there are twice as many power strokes per revolution of the crankshaft as there are in the four-stroke-cycle, such an engine, cylinder for cylinder, theoretically should be twice as powerful as the four-stroke-cycle type. Many of our outboard motors are of this type. Do you know other uses of them?

The diesel engine. This engine is of either the two-stroke-cycle or the four-stroke-cycle type (Fig. 12). It differs from the gasoline engine in the manner in which the fuel is ignited. Otherwise the operation is the same.

The diesel is a high-compression engine, the compression being so great that the fuel mixture is ignited by the heat of compression. No spark plugs are needed. On the intake stroke pure air is introduced into the cylinder. The compression stroke heats this air to a high temperature. Just before the beginning of the power stroke the fuel valve opens to admit oil vapors which are forced in by compressed air and ignited by the hot air in the cylinder. The exhaust occurs just as in the gasoline engine.

This engine is very compact, but because of the high peak pressure during the power stroke, it is very strongly and heavily built—too heavily, in fact, to be practical in the automobile. This is also true of the two-stroke-cycle gasoline engine. Many yachts, tractors, trucks, submarines,

Courtesy General Motors Corp.

Fig. 13. Experimental model of an automobile with a gas-turbine engine. Simpler in design than the conventional piston engine, the gas turbine consists of three basic parts: a compressor and two turbines. A stream of hot gases under pressure causes the turbine to rotate at tremendous speeds, thus transmitting power by a system of gears to the wheels of the car.

Fig. 14. A diesel engine is being used in this oil-drilling installation. Since drilling may be a continuous operation over a period of several months, diesel engines provide savings due to lower maintenance and fuel costs.

Courtesy Detroit Diesel Engine Division of the General Motors Corp.

COMBUSTION CHAMBER

COMPRESSOR

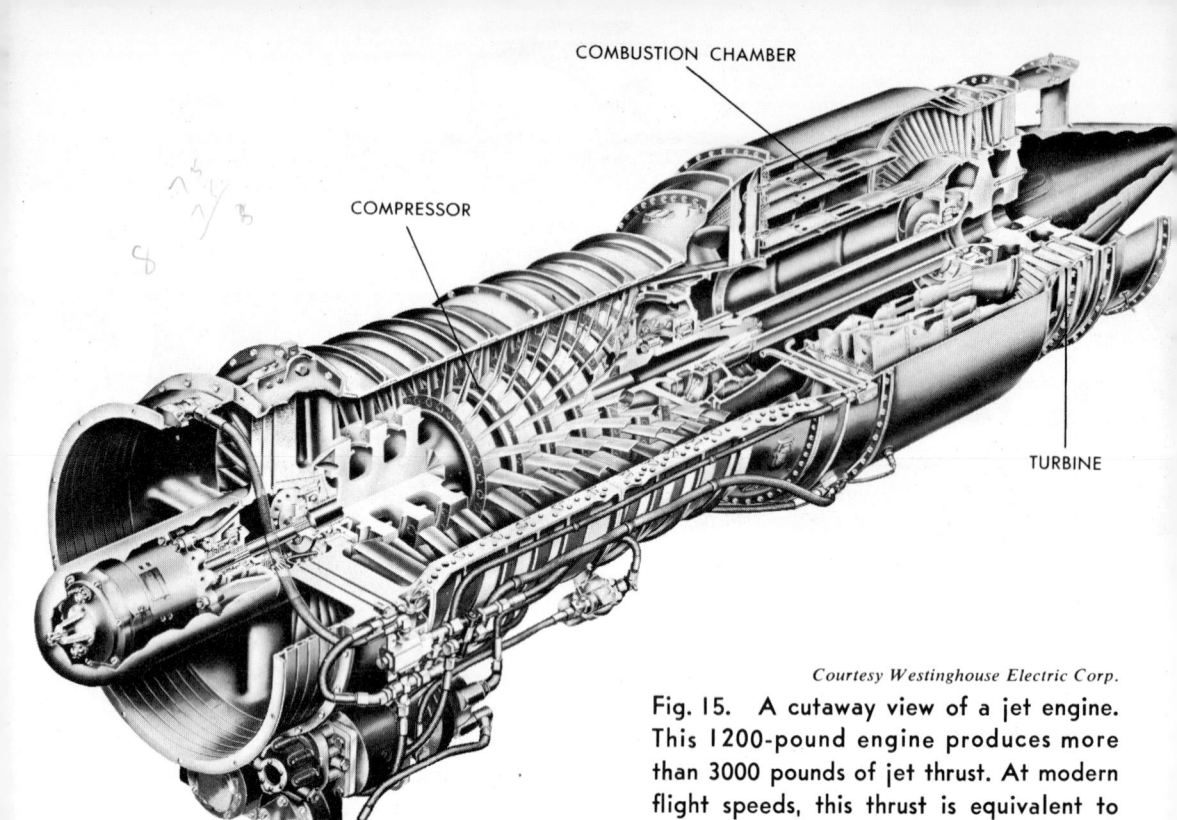

TURBINE

Courtesy Westinghouse Electric Corp.

Fig. 15. A cutaway view of a jet engine. This 1200-pound engine produces more than 3000 pounds of jet thrust. At modern flight speeds, this thrust is equivalent to more than 5000 horsepower.

ocean vessels, streamlined trains, and electric power plants are powered by diesel engines. They have the advantage of operating on inexpensive fuel oils.

The jet engine. Jet engines are capable of driving aircraft at very high speeds. Fig. 15 shows one type of jet engine, called the *turbojet*. It is used principally in high-speed aircraft. The air used in the combustion of the fuel enters the nose of the *shroud* through the air inlet duct and is compressed. After compression the fuel is mixed with the compressed air and is introduced into the combustion chamber. Here it burns very quickly, and the resulting hot and rapidly expanding gases escape at high speed through a small turbine and out the exhaust in the rear. In escaping they create a tremendous forward thrust on the aircraft. What law of motion is exemplified here? Could such a craft travel through space where there is no air?

The purpose of the turbine is to power small equipment, such as the generator, fuel pumps, and the compressor.

SUMMARY AND CONCLUSIONS

1. Heat is capable of doing work and work can produce heat. Each may be expressed in terms of the other.
2. The mechanical equivalent of heat, J, or Joule's equivalent, is equal to 778 ft.-lb./btu or 4.19×10^7 ergs/g.-cal.
3. The heat of combustion of a substance is the heat liberated when a unit mass (or a unit volume, for gases) of it is completely oxidized. It is expressed in btu/lb. or btu/ft.[3] For foods it is given in kg.-cal./100 g.
4. When a gas does work upon expansion, it is cooled; that is, heat energy disappears and mechanical energy is developed.
5. All practical heat engines operate on the principle of the production of mechanical energy from the heat energy possessed by an expanding gas or vapor.
6. Heat engines may be classified as external combustion or internal combustion engines.

WORK AND HEAT

7. A horsepower formula for a steam engine is H.P. $= 2\dfrac{PLAN}{33,000}$.

8. The principal parts of a steam turbine are the rotor and stator. Rotary engines are generally more efficient at high speeds than reciprocating engines.

9. Gasoline engines are either four-stroke-cycle or two-stroke-cycle engines. The former completes the cycle with four strokes of the piston; the latter, with two strokes. The cycle consists of intake, compression, power, and exhaust.

10. The diesel engine is either a four-stroke-cycle or a two-stroke-cycle engine. Its fuel is ignited by the heat of compression instead of by spark plugs.

QUESTIONS FOR REVIEW

1. What does the term *eccentric* mean as used in connection with the steam engine?
2. Define the term *cycle*.
3. How are automobile engines cooled?
4. How are airplane engines cooled?
5. What are some advantages of the gasoline engine over the steam engine?
6. What are some disadvantages of the gasoline engine?
7. Explain the shape of the upper end of the piston in the two-stroke-cycle engine.
8. Name some advantages and disadvantages of the two-stroke-cycle engine.
9. A steam turbine is inefficient at low speeds. Why?
10. Define heat of combustion.
11. A certain track coach used to give his long-distance runners a piece of loaf sugar before they entered a contest. Can you tell why?
12. Why is the modern steam engine called a reciprocating engine?
13. Construct a definition for the term *heat engine*.
14. How does an external combustion engine differ from an internal?
15. What are some advantages of a steam turbine over a reciprocating engine?
16. Why is the term *four-cycle engine* incorrect?
17. What are the essential differences between the four-stroke-cycle engine and the two-stroke-cycle?
18. Explain the operation of the steam turbine.
19. Why must the crankcase of a two-stroke-cycle gas engine be airtight?
20. How many power strokes are there for every revolution of the crankshaft in a 12-cylinder gas engine?
21. An overheated gasoline engine sometimes continues running after the ignition is turned off. Explain.
22. What causes a locomotive to puff?
23. What is the meaning of the term *counterbalance* as used in connection with the flywheels of engines?
24. What is the principle of a heat engine?

PROBLEMS

1. Prove that 427 gram-meters are equivalent to approximately 41,900,000 ergs.
2. Calculate the number of calories in a btu.
3. Calculate the number of foot-pounds equivalent to a calorie.
4. The area of the piston of a reciprocating steam engine is 125 in.^{2} and the mean effective pressure is 110 lb./in.^{2}. The piston stroke is 18 in. If the flywheel revolves at 200 rpm, what is the horsepower of the engine?
5. Find the S. A. E. specifications necessary to determine, and then determine, the horsepower of your automobile engine. How does it compare with its horsepower rating?
6. A toy steam engine has a piston whose diameter is ½ in. The piston stroke is 1½ in. and the steam pressure is 14 lb./in.^{2}. If the flywheel revolves 300 times per minute, what horsepower is developed by the engine? Use $\pi = \dfrac{22}{7}$. ANS.: $\dfrac{1}{160}$.
7. If all the kinetic energy of a 3000-lb. automobile, traveling at 75 mi./hr., could be suddenly transformed into heat, how many btu's would result?
8. If your body could transform all the energy in a 100-gram piece of apple pie into

muscular energy, it would enable you to climb a mountain how many feet high?

9. How efficient is an automobile engine if it works at the rate of 50 horsepower and uses 5 gallons of gasoline per hour? (See Table 1 for heat of combustion. Assume a gallon of gasoline to weigh 6 lb.)

ANS.: 20.4 per cent.

10. The mean effective pressure on the piston of a reciprocating steam engine is 100 lb./in.² The diameter of the piston is 14 in., and the length of its stroke is 21 in. The flywheel makes 150 revolutions per minute. Find: (a) the amount of work done on each stroke of the piston; (b) the equivalent of this work in terms of heat; (c) the horsepower output of the engine. Use $\pi = \frac{22}{7}$.

ANS.: (a) 26,950 ft.-lb.
(b) 34.6 btu.
(c) 245 H.P.

PROJECTS

1. Do a research study on the Newcomen engine, and, using Fig. 3, explain its operation to the class. If a nearby museum houses a Newcomen engine, examine it there.
2. Look up material on the life of James Watt, and make a report to the class.
3. In your home or school workshop build a toy steam engine.

READING YOU WILL ENJOY

1. Gaddum, L. W., and H. L. Knowles, *Our Physical Environment*. Houghton, Mifflin Company, Boston, 1953. Chapter 41 presents an excellent discussion of external- and internal-combustion engines.
2. Bush, George L., and Will S. Thompson, *New Senior Science*. American Book Co., New York, 1954. Chapters 1 and 2, Unit 7, present a very interesting discussion of steam, automobile, diesel and jet engines.

Unit 9

Weather and Climate

On the ground, the partially inflated balloon in the unit photograph looks quite harmless. Yet, flying aloft in the stratosphere, it has given rise to wild speculation about flying saucers from outer space; it has also been a source of controversy between the United States and Soviet Russia. Actually, of course, these stratospheric balloons are designed for a single purpose—to gather data about weather conditions. These high-altitude weather balloons record the temperature, the atmospheric pressure, and the relative humidity of air masses and transmit these readings to the ground by means of radio signals.

In this unit, you will discover how weather conditions are analyzed by applying some previously studied principles of fluid pressure and heat.

27. HUMIDITY AND WEATHER

Unit Photograph from Wide World

Chapter 27

Humidity and Weather

The problem. If there is one thing that is of common interest to all of us, it is probably the weather. It not only furnishes a subject for much idle conversation but it also governs many of our activities. It often decides for us whether we can go on a picnic or go skating, sailing, swimming, or skiing. It helps to determine what kind of clothes we wear, what we eat, and what kinds of houses we live in. It makes our vacations pleasant or miserable. And it affects the health, comfort, and prosperity of our entire population. Hence for many reasons we need to know more about weather than just enough to make pleasant conversation concerning it.

How are weather and climate defined? *Weather* is more or less arbitrarily defined as the atmospheric conditions which exist at a given place at a given time. *Climate* includes all the weather that occurs at a given place over a long period of time.

The climate of a given region remains fairly constant from year to year, but the weather may change drastically from one day to the next or even within a few hours. What is it that causes these changes? And what factors control weather and climate?

Atmospheric moisture. Moisture content of the atmosphere is one of the most important factors controlling weather. Even over a desert the air is never completely dry. Evaporation from oceans, lakes, and streams, as well as from land and its vegetation, results in moisture content as high as 4 per cent.

Table 1
MAXIMUM MOISTURE CAPACITY OF
1 CUBIC FOOT OF AIR

Temperature (degrees F)	Grains of Moisture
0	0.5
5	0.6
10	0.8
15	1.0
20	1.2
25	1.6
30	1.9
35	2.4
40	2.8
45	3.4
50	4.1
55	4.8
60	5.7
65	6.8
70	8.0
75	9.4
80	10.9
85	12.7
90	14.8
95	17.1
100	19.8

The actual amount of water which one cubic foot of air holds is called *absolute humidity*. It is usually measured in grains of moisture per cubic foot. A *grain* is about 1/7000 pound.

PROBLEM: What is the absolute humidity of air, ½ cubic foot of which contains 5 grains of moisture? 6 grains?

When air contains all the moisture it can hold, it is said to be *saturated*. As shown in Table 1, the moisture-holding capacity of air depends on its temperature. For example, at 1 atmosphere of pressure and at 15°F, 1 cubic foot of saturated air holds only 1 grain of moisture or water vapor. At 40° it holds 2.8 grains.

PROBLEM: How many grains will 1 cu. ft. of saturated air hold at 70°? 80°? 90°? See Table 1.

Usually, under natural conditions, air is not saturated. For example, at 70°F air may contain, or have an absolute humidity of, only 4 grains per cubic foot, whereas it would contain 8 grains if it were saturated. In other words, it contains 4/8 or 50 per cent of what it is capable of holding.

PROBLEM: A cubic foot of air at 90°F contains 7.4 grains of moisture. This amount is what fraction and what per cent of what this air would hold if it were saturated?

Relative humidity. *The ratio of the quantity of water vapor actually present (absolute humidity) in the air to the quantity necessary for saturation at the same temperature is called* **relative humidity (RH).**

$$RH = \frac{\text{absolute humidity}}{\text{quantity necessary for saturation}}$$

In the problem above, what is the absolute humidity? Quantity necessary for saturation? Relative humidity?

Relative humidity not only affects weather conditions but it also affects bodily health and comfort. For example, you may feel quite comfortable when the temperature is 85° or 90°F and the relative humidity is 25 per cent. On the other hand, at this same temperature you may feel hot, uncomfortable, and oppressed if the relative humidity is 80 or 90 per cent. Or, if the temperature is 68°F and the relative humidity is 25 per cent, you may feel chilly, whereas if the relative humidity is 60 per cent or above you may feel quite comfortable.

The difference in comfort caused by difference in relative humidity with no change in temperature is due to the fact that the human body is cooled in part by evaporation of perspiration, and that the rapidity of cooling increases with the rapidity of evaporation. That is, if the air is dry and hence the relative humidity is low, evaporation of perspiration, and hence cooling, is rapid. But in case the air is moist and hence the relative humidity is high, evaporation takes place very slowly, so that little cooling takes place. In other words, high relative humidity prevents cooling by evaporation, whereas low relative humidity is conducive to rapid evaporation which causes cooling. Note that dryness or wetness of air depends directly upon the relative humidity and only indirectly upon the actual amount of water vapor present.

Repeated experiment has shown that for bodily comfort and health the relative humidity should be between 40 and 60 per cent. In our homes and schools, however, during the winter months, the relative humidity often does not exceed 10 to 20 per cent. This condition causes rapid evaporation and drying of mucous membrane in the nose, throat, and lungs. Such a condition tends to induce colds and other respiratory diseases.

Furnaces have devices designed to increase the water vapor content of the air, but many of them either are not used or are inadequate. Some automatic humidifiers have been developed, but there is still room for improvement in this field.

To explain the low humidity in heated buildings in wintertime, let us suppose that the outside air is at 15 degrees Fahrenheit and that its absolute humidity is ½ grain per cubic foot, or 50 per cent of what it is capable of holding. See Table 1. Next, suppose that this outside air enters your home and its temperature is raised to 70 degrees. At this higher temperature, the moisture capacity is 4 grains per cubic foot. Thus, if no more water vapor is added, the relative humidity is lowered to ½/4, or to about 12 per cent.

In conclusion, if the absolute humidity remains constant, warming the air lowers its relative humidity, and conversely, cooling the air raises its relative humidity. The lower the humidity, other factors remaining the same, the faster the evaporation of perspiration. This cools the body and causes one to feel colder than he would if higher relative humidity were maintained. With high humidity little evaporation takes place. Hence, little cooling by evaporation takes place. This condition causes one to feel warmer than when the relative humidity is low. How should the relative humidity be kept in a home to keep it comfortable at the least cost, when heated? When cooled?

Relative humidity and the dew point. Study of Table 1 shows that at 70°F, 8 grains of moisture saturate 1 cubic foot of air. Now let us suppose that the temperature of the air in a room is 90 degrees and that its absolute humidity is 10.9 grains. Therefore, if we lower the temperature to 70 degrees, 2.9 grains of moisture will condense into water and the condensation will begin when the temperature of the air is lowered to 80°F, the temperature at which the sample of air becomes saturated.

The temperature at which a given sample of air is saturated, is called its *dew point*.

PROBLEM: Referring to Table 1, (a) What is the dew point of air whose absolute humidity is 4.1 grains per cubic foot and whose temperature is 80°F? (b) How much moisture would this cubic foot of air contain if it were saturated? (c) What would be the relative humidity of the air?

What causes dew and frost? On clear cool nights, loss of heat from blades of grass, leaves, etc., cools them enough so that the air in contact with them is cooled to the dew point. As a result, water vapor in the air condenses on these cool objects. The condensation is called *dew*. If the dew point is 32°F or below, the condensation appears as *frost*. If the dew point of the air were 28°, would frost occur on a night when the temperature dropped to 36°F? 30°F? 26°F?

How is the dew point determined? Knowledge of how dew is formed gives us one clue for finding the dew point. All we have to do is to find the temperature of the air in contact with a body when dew first begins to collect on it.

Usually the body used is a shiny metal container partially filled with water at room temperature (Fig. 1). Into it small pieces of ice are dropped slowly while the water is stirred. When the air in contact with the container is cooled sufficiently, a film of moisture will begin to collect on the outside of the container. Then the temperature of the water is taken. Next the

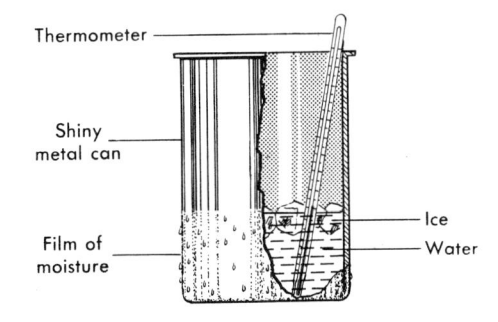

Fig. 1. Apparatus for determining the dew point of the air.

container is allowed to warm up to the temperature at which the film disappears. The average of the two temperatures is the dew point.

The dew point is of importance in finding relative humidity. If the dew point is known, the absolute humidity can be determined by use of Table 1. With this and the temperature of the air, its relative humidity can be computed.

PROBLEM: What is (a) the absolute humidity and (b) the relative humidity when the temperature of the air is 80°F and its dew point is 60°F? 50°F? 40°F? Remember that at the dew point, air is saturated.

A method that is often used in obtaining relative humidity is the *wet-and-dry-bulb thermometer,* or *hygrometer,* method. Two thermometers are mounted side by side, one, the wet-bulb, with a snugly fitting muslin wick attached to its bulb and dipping in water. The other thermometer is the dry-bulb thermometer. If the air is saturated, both thermometers will read the same, but the drier the air, the more rapidly the wet bulb will be cooled by evaporation and the lower its reading will be. Thus, the *difference* between the two thermometer readings is a good index of the relative humidity.

Another method, similar to the above, is the *sling psychrometer* method. This instrument (Fig. 2), which is another type of hygrometer, also has both a wet-bulb and a dry-bulb thermometer; but in this case the muslin wick is dipped in water and then the psychrometer is whirled through the air being tested. Again, the depression of the wet bulb is indicative of the relative humidity. Psychrometric tables have been prepared for such a device. See Table 2.

Table 2

PER CENT RELATIVE HUMIDITY AT 30 INCHES ATMOSPHERIC PRESSURE

$t-t'$ (degrees)	Degrees Fahrenheit					
	60	65	70	75	80	90	100
1	94	95	95	96	96	96	96
2	89	90	90	91	91	92	93
3	83	85	86	86	87	89	89
4	78	80	81	82	83	85	86
5	73	75	77	78	79	81	83
6	68	70	72	74	76	78	80
7	63	66	68	70	72	74	77
8	58	61	64	66	68	71	73
9	53	56	59	62	64	68	70
10	48	52	55	58	61	65	68
11	43	48	51	54	57	61	65
12	39	44	48	51	54	58	62
13	34	39	44	47	50	55	59
14	30	35	40	44	47	52	56
15	26	31	36	40	44	49	54
16	21	27	33	37	41	47	51
17	17	24	29	34	38	44	49
18	13	20	25	30	35	41	46
19	9	16	22	27	32	39	44
20	5	12	19	24	29	36	41

NOTE: $t - t'$ = depression of wet bulb.

Fig. 2. Sling psychrometer for determining the relative humidity.

Courtesy Taylor Instrument Co.

HUMIDITY AND WEATHER 295

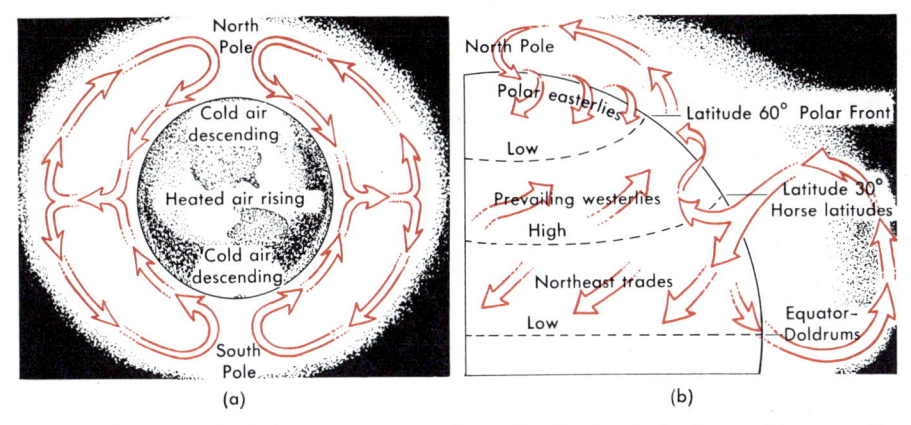

Fig. 3. If the earth did not rotate on its axis, the heated air would cause the air to circulate uniformly, as shown in (a). However, the rotation of the earth causes the winds to be deflected eastward, as shown in (b).

PROBLEM: If the dry bulb of the sling psychrometer reads 80°F and the wet bulb reads 65°F, what is the relative humidity of the air? Use Table 2.

What are the effects of sunshine (solar radiation) on weather and climate? It has been said that the weather is the greatest show on earth, with only three actors in the cast—solar radiation, moisture, and air. The sun (solar radiation) is the master of the other two because its unequal heating of the earth's surface causes unequal atmospheric pressures that cause winds which carry evaporated water vapor from oceans and lakes onto the land. How does this take place?

Were it not for the earth's rotation, the earth's atmospheric circulation (winds) would be much as shown in Fig. 3(a). Since the air is heated most near the equator, it would expand, become less dense, and be forced upward by the cooler air from the polar regions moving in to equalize the pressure. This rising air would "spill over" away from the equator and flow toward the poles, producing a continuous low-pressure region at the equator. At the poles the air would be cold and dense so that high atmospheric pressure would be produced.

However, as the spilled-over high-altitude air flows away from the equator toward the poles, the earth's eastward rotation causes the flow to be deflected eastward; and by the time it has reached about latitude 30°, its flow is almost entirely to the east. Thus, there is an accumulation of air in these latitudes, resulting in high-pressure belts which extend around the earth both north and south of the equator. These are called the *horse latitudes*. See Fig. 3(b).

From each high pressure (horse-latitude) belt, part of the air in the lower atmosphere flows poleward, causing winds known as *prevailing westerlies*. Another part flows south toward the equator, producing winds known as the easterly *trade winds*. The trade winds meet near the equator and more or less cancel each other out, producing a calm region called the *doldrums*.

Part of the air in the upper atmosphere of the horse latitudes is forced on toward the poles. It does not drop toward the earth's surface. As a result, by the time this air reaches the polar regions it is very cold and heavy (dense). There it settles, producing a large mass of air having a high pressure.

As this cold air piles up in the lower atmosphere, it is forced toward the equator. And at about latitude 60° (Fig. 3(b) the front of the polar mass, called a *polar front,* meets the much warmer and less dense westerlies and pushes under them, causing them to rise. The rising, relatively warm, light air produces low pressure belts, one on each side of the equator at about 60° latitude.

Spasmodically, however, a large polar mass of air, called a *polar high,* or *high,* breaks out toward the equator. The front edge, the edge toward the equator, is called a *cold front*. These highs and the cold fronts play a tremendous part in weather and climate. But before we can complete our discussion of them we must turn our attention to other aspects of weather.

Cloud formation and lapse rate. We have already seen that at the equator the lower air in the atmosphere is being heated because it is in contact with either very warm ocean water or warm land. Mostly it is in contact with warm water, which makes it very moist. As this very moist air is pushed up by the colder air to the north and the south, it expands.

But in expanding against pressure, however slight, work is done. Therefore, since the heat energy in the expanding air furnishes the work, the air is cooled. Consequently, if the rising air is cooled to its dew point, clouds form and precipitation in the form of rain may result. Does this explain the heavy rainfall in most parts of the equatorial belt?

If the rising air is unsaturated (has not reached its dew point) it will cool at the rate of approximately *5½ Fahrenheit degrees* for each *1000 feet* that it rises. *The temperature change of air in relation to elevation is known as* **lapse rate.** After rising air has reached its dew point, the lapse rate is approximately 3 Fahrenheit degrees per 1000 feet. As the water vapor condenses it releases heat. See page 258. This reduces the lapse rate.

It should be understood that these lapse rates apply only to rising or falling air, neither of which gains heat from, or loses heat to, the surrounding air. Usually in stationary air (neither rising nor falling), the temperature decreases with the altitude. Seldom, however, is the lapse rate of stationary air the same as that for rising or falling air.

PROBLEM 1: If the temperature of rising unsaturated air is 80°F at the ground level, what will be its temperature at 4000 ft.? 6000 ft.?

PROBLEM 2: If the air has a temperature of 20°F at the top of a mountain, what will be its temperature if it drops 8000 ft.? 2000 ft.?

Another point of importance is that since rising air expands, its absolute humidity (grains of moisture per cubic foot) decreases. Explain. For this reason the dew point of rising unsaturated air drops 1 Fahrenheit degree every thousand feet. That is, rising unsaturated air approaches its dew point at the rate of only 4½ degrees instead of 5½ degrees per thousand feet of elevation. Rising saturated air approaches its dew point at the rate of 2 Fahrenheit degrees per thousand feet.

PROBLEM: The temperature of ground air is 80°F. Its dew point is 53°F. How high will a sample of this air have to rise before clouds begin to form — i.e., dew point is reached?   ANS.: 6000 ft.

Other factors which affect cloud formation. We have explained that clouds are formed in unstable air when the dew

Cumulus   **Stratus**

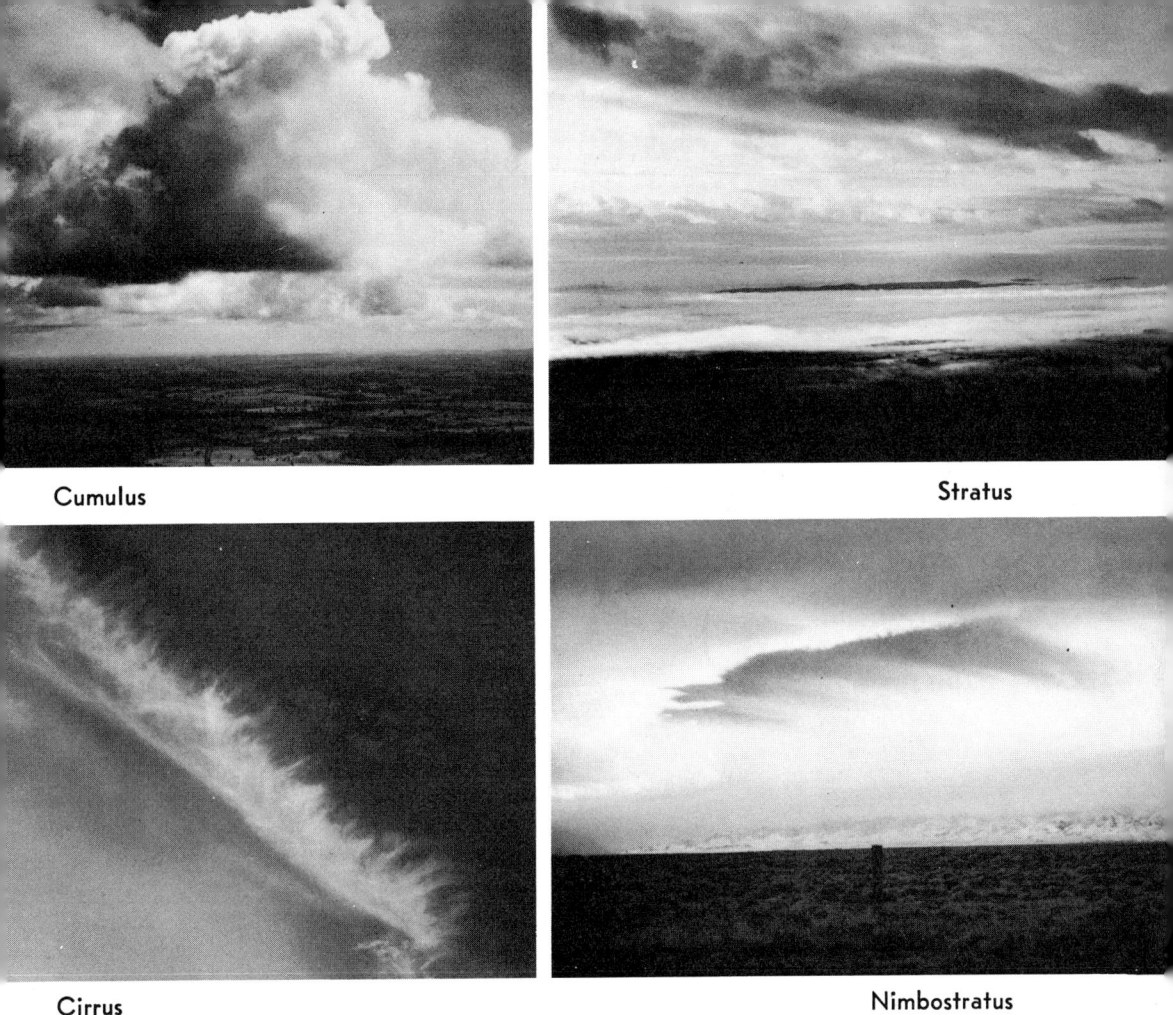

Cirrus   **Nimbostratus**

Courtesy U.S. Weather Bureau

Fig. 4. What kind of weather is associated with each of the above cloud types?

point is reached. But this is only part of what takes place in cloud formation. For water vapor to condense, dust or other particles are necessary as nuclei. Plant spores, bacteria, and salt crystals may also act as nuclei.

Icing and formation of snow. Oddly, clouds composed of water droplets are often found to be *supercooled;* that is, they exist in liquid form though below freezing temperature. Research workers at Eglin Air Force Base in Florida report unfrozen water droplets as low as $-60°F$. However, as soon as these clouds come in contact with a surface, such as the unheated surface of a passing airplane, the water drop-

lets instantly turn to ice and may rapidly coat the plane to the extent of overweighting it. This is called *icing.*

Usually, supercooled water droplets in a cloud form into tiny hexagonal ice crystals at about $-30°F$. Delicate, fibrous clouds called *cirrus* clouds are formed at high altitudes. These are composed of ice crystals which, under certain conditions, are the beginnings of snowflakes. The crystals drift downward through supercooled water droplets, and, since the vapor pressure over the water is greater than that over the ice, moisture evaporates from the water and condenses on the ice. Thus, the crystals grow and develop into hexagonal

Fig. 5. Photomicrograph of a snow crystal.
Courtesy Bausch and Lomb Optical Co.

snowflakes. Although all snowflakes are hexagonal, no two have ever been found exactly alike, in spite of the fact that thousands of them have been examined and photographed. See Fig. 5.

Partially melted snow, partially frozen rain, or a mixture of snow and rain is called *sleet. Ice storms* are caused by rain falling through a ground layer of air below freezing temperature. The rain, being supercooled while passing through this layer, freezes on contact with the cold surfaces of plants, the ground, buildings, and wires, coating them with ice. Such storms can be very damaging.

Local thunderstorms. One of the commonest storms in most highly populated regions of the world is the local thunderstorm. Unlike most storms, it takes place in one single mass of air. Also it takes place on hot, muggy, moist summer days, when the ground and the air above it are heated very hot by the sun and when the air in the upper atmosphere is unstable. The heating of the moist ground air produces rising columns of air atop of which *cumulus* (mushroom-shaped, billowy, and fluffy) clouds are formed. These develop into *cumulonimbus,* known also as thunderheads. *Nimbo* means *rain.* See Fig. 6.

The resulting liberated heat of condensation reduces the rate of cooling of the rising air and serves to prolong and intensify the upward convection currents before stability is reached. Thus, the peaks of the clouds are forced ever higher into the ice-crystal zone by cooler air pushing in from all sides. The ice crystals start a snowstorm in the upper cloud region, and action really begins in earnest.

In the center of the updraft there are downdrafts as violent as the updrafts (see Fig. 6). These carry the snowflakes down and they are melted into rain. Updrafts may hold the rain aloft for some time and then suddenly let go, resulting in a sudden downpour. Or the raindrops may be repeatedly carried aloft into freezing temperatures and be frozen into *hail*.

At the ground surface the descending cold air spreads out horizontally underneath the warm air which is flowing into the warm updraft. The spreading air causes

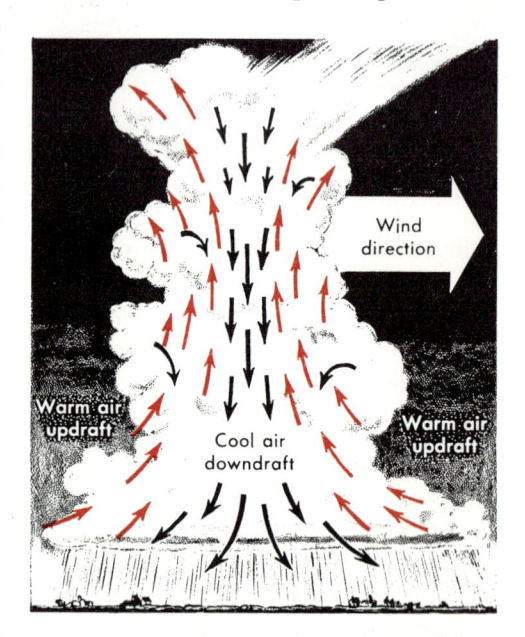

Fig. 6. Cross section of a thunderstorm. Convection currents cause the warm air to rise to the point where its vapor condenses.

HUMIDITY AND WEATHER 299

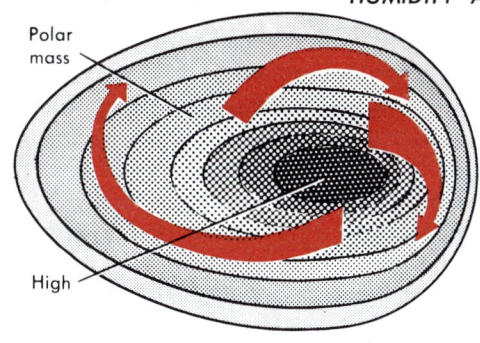

Fig. 7. (a) Circulation of winds about a high in a clockwise direction.

what is known as a *cold squall,* which often lowers the temperature of the ground air as much as 20 Fahrenheit degrees in a few minutes.

Conditions necessary for local thunderstorms are found in the doldrum belt throughout the entire year and are found in the middle latitude belts (30°-60°) during the summer. In winter the land seldom is heated enough to produce local thunderstorms.

Thunderstorms vary in duration from five minutes to about an hour, depending upon their location and magnitude. East of the Mississippi the average duration is about twenty-five minutes, and one storm may follow another. Their general direction of travel is that of the westerly winds.

Orographic precipitation. Most storms in which precipitation takes place have one thing in common—ground air is usually forced up until its dew point is reached. One of the simplest examples of this is a horizontally directed current of air which is blown over the top of a mountain. The increasing elevation of the land forces the air up. As a result, if the air is sufficiently moisture-laden and the mountain is high enough, the dew point of the air will be reached, clouds will be formed, and precipitation will result. Precipitation caused by forced ascent of air over mountains or other topographical barriers is known as *orographic precipitation.* In the United States, orographic precipitation is very common in the western parts of the states of Oregon and Washington. Explain the geographic situation which exists there.

Cold-front storms. We have seen that large, dry, cold, dense, high-pressure air masses form over the earth's poles. And we have learned that spasmodically a large polar mass of air, or high, breaks out of the polar region into the belt of the prevailing westerlies. The edge of the air mass toward the equator forms a cold front. See (b) of Fig. 7. At the center of any high the atmospheric pressure is greatest. Consequently the winds blow outward from the center. And due to the rotation of the earth, in the northern hemisphere the

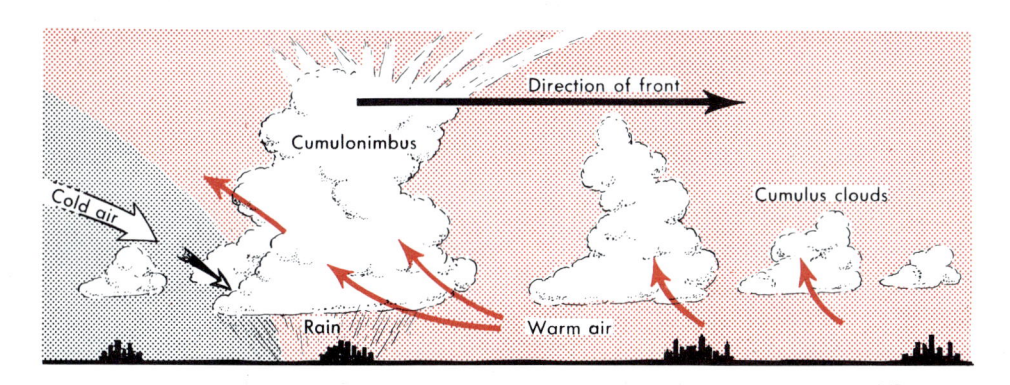

Fig. 7. (b) Cross section of a cold-front storm.

winds circulate clockwise about the center. See (a) of Fig. 7. In the southern hemisphere they circulate counterclockwise.

As an example, suppose that a cold air mass in northwest Canada pushes southward into the belt of the prevailing westerlies. As shown in (b) of Fig. 7, the cold air will push under the warmer air to the south. And if the warm air is moisture-laden and is pushed high enough so that its dew point is reached, precipitation will occur. In case the front moves over rough country, friction may slow down the lower layer, allowing the upper layers to surge ahead and spill over on top of the warmer air. Thus, convection currents of warm air are caused to spout upward through the cold air above, resulting in rapid condensation and a driving rain, often accompanied by thunderstorms, even in winter, along the cold front. The front passes in a few hours and the cold air mass has then taken over with quiet air and sunshine. In the summer this is welcome, but in winter new record low temperatures may result. When a cold front is approaching, what kind of clouds appear in the sky first? What kind of weather exists before the storm? After the storm?

Tornadoes. If the polar air mass which forms a cold front is not too cold, the upper cold air may surge ahead over the warmer air below as far as 50 to 100 miles. As a result, when the lower air breaks through the layer of heavy cold air above, the speed of the updraft may be terrific and it will acquire a twisting motion. The cloud formed is shaped like a funnel and the storm is known as a *tornado*. See Fig. 8.

Because of the high speed and the spiraling motion of the wind, a very low pressure is developed at the center of a tornado. Consequently, if the center passes over a house whose windows and doors are closed, the house may literally explode so that the walls are pushed outward. Although a tornado is very destructive, its duration is short, the area covered is usually small, and the probabilities of one occurring are slight in most regions.

Hurricanes. Probably no other storm receives as much publicity and attention as the *hurricane*. One reason is that it is the

Fig. 8. Stages in the development of a tornado with its characteristic funnel-shaped cloud that travels in a narrow path for distances as great as 100 miles.

Courtesy U.S. Weather Bureau

Courtesy U.S. Weather Bureau

Fig. 9. (a) Radarscope of a hurricane taken by Navy planes traveling into the "eye" of the hurricane.

Courtesy U.S. Weather Bureau

Fig. 9 (b) Typical damage caused by hurricane Carol in Rhode Island in September 1954.

"bully" of all the storms. As one weather man has said, "The atom bomb is to a hurricane about like a flea to an elephant."

Hurricanes originate over ocean water in the doldrum area where the solar radiation is intense, humidity is high, and the evaporation of ocean water is tremendous. In the Pacific area hurricanes are referred to as *typhoons*.

Apparently a portion of a large mass of tropical air is heated more strongly than the surrounding air, and it starts funneling upward in a natural updraft; it is cooled as it rises, and its moisture condenses into rain. Thousands of tons of rain are formed, liberating their enormous heat of condensation, which reinforces the updraft. This heat of condensation is one of the hurricane's main sources of energy.

As the air spirals upward the pressure at the ocean's surface beneath it is reduced, and more of the surrounding hot, moist air rushes in and keeps the updraft going. These incoming currents whirl counterclockwise north of the equator and clockwise south of the equator. Why? The whirling motion rapidly increases, causing considerable pressure difference between the rim of the hurricane and its center, where there exists a region of calm, called the *eye,* which varies in width from 4 to 40 miles. The width of the hurricane's winds may vary from 35 to over 100 miles. Its forward progress averages 10 miles per hour.

During August, September, and October, the Carribean Sea is a source region of hurricanes, but most of them never reach land. A few do strike the coast in the Gulf of Mexico and others hit the coast anywhere from Florida to New England. As soon as a hurricane hits land it begins to subside. Explain.

When a hurricane strikes, the winds start blowing, the pressure starts falling rapidly, and torrential rain slashes down. Suddenly the eye of the storm arrives, the winds may die completely, the sun may even shine; and the unwary may think the storm is over. Then suddenly the storm strikes from the opposite direction. Why? This time, however, the pressure rises rapidly, the winds slow down, the rain diminishes, and soon the storm is over.

A hurricane gives some advance warning of its approach in the form of a certain sequence of cloud formations, or in its effect upon sea waves which travel as far as 500 to 1000 miles ahead of the storm. But the surest warnings come from the Joint Hurricane Warning Center in Miami, Florida. How all the desired information is obtained is an exciting story, too long to be told here; but since the beginning of this weatherman's network, death and destruction due to hurricanes have been greatly reduced.

The cyclonic storm. In the belts of the prevailing westerlies, which includes most of the United States, *cyclonic storms* furnish much of the precipitation. The *cyclone*, however, is not a tornado, as many people believe.

The cyclone is formed when a polar mass of air moves into the westerlies, meets a warm moist mass of air and the warm air pushes into the cold mass of air, forming an *indentation* in the cold front. This is the beginning of a cyclonic storm.

Where the fronts first meet, the cold winds may be blowing from the northeast and the warm winds from the southwest. However, the indentation of the warm air in the cold air mass causes the westward moving winds to move northeastward. See (b) of Fig. 10.

But as the indentation in the cold mass increases in horizontal depth, and the warm air that has penetrated farthest to the north becomes more and more surrounded by cold air, the nearly surrounded warm air is forced to rise. This creates a low pressure area called a *low,* toward which the surrounding air flows in a general counter-

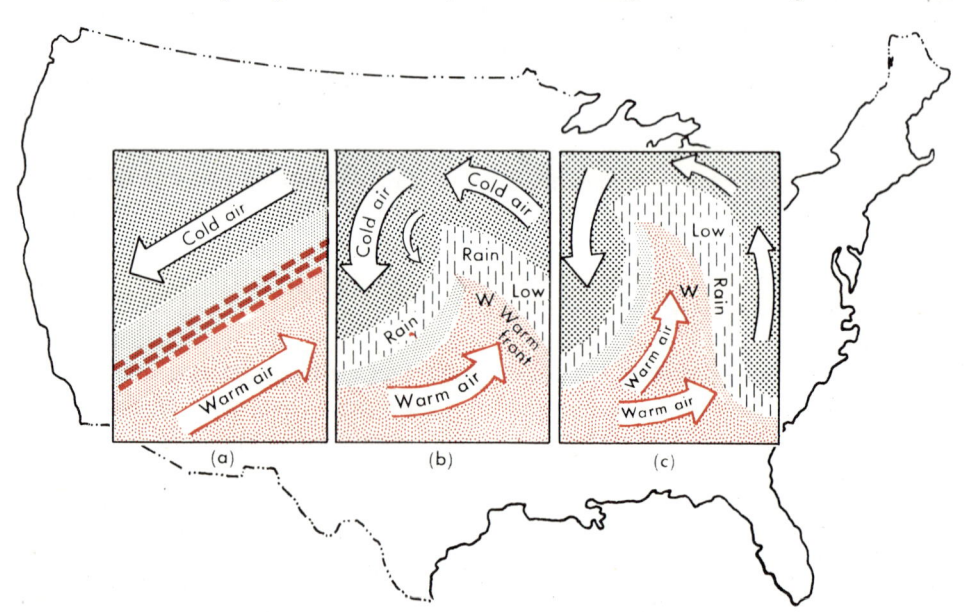

Fig. 10. Stages in the development of a cyclonic storm moving easterly. (a) The cold front meets warm air. (b) Warm air pushes into a cold-air mass, forming a cold front, warm front, and a low. (c) A more advanced stage of a cyclonic storm.

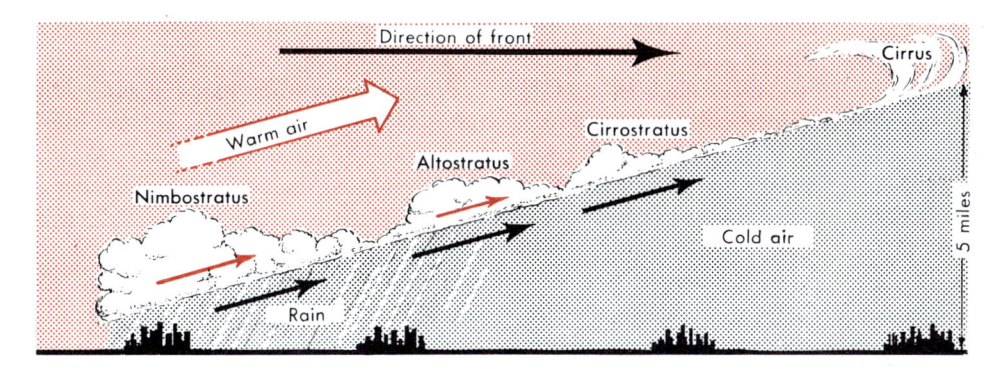

Fig. 11. Cross section of a warm front, showing the air masses and cloud systems associated with it.

clockwise direction. See (c) of Fig. 10. In the southern hemisphere the circulation is clockwise.

As the warm air at the center rises, its dew point may be reached, and clouds and precipitation may result. Hence, in the low region of a cyclonic storm rain or snow can be expected.

In general, the low, or center, of a cyclonic storm moves eastward. The western edge C of the indentation also moves eastward and southward. As the cold air behind C advances it pushes under the warm air in the indentation and forms a cold front, which we have already studied (Fig. 7b).

The front edge of the indentation, W, also moves east. Here, however, the lighter warm air in the indentation is pushed up over the colder, denser air to the east of it. Thereby a warm front is produced. See Fig. 11.

If the warm air is humid, as it ascends over the cold air it will reach its dew point, and clouds and precipitation will result. Since the ascent is gradual and relatively slow (compare with the ascent of air in a cold front), the rainfall or snowfall is usually not violent but gentle, steady, and drizzling in nature. And the precipitation may extend 200 to 300 miles ahead of the warm front.

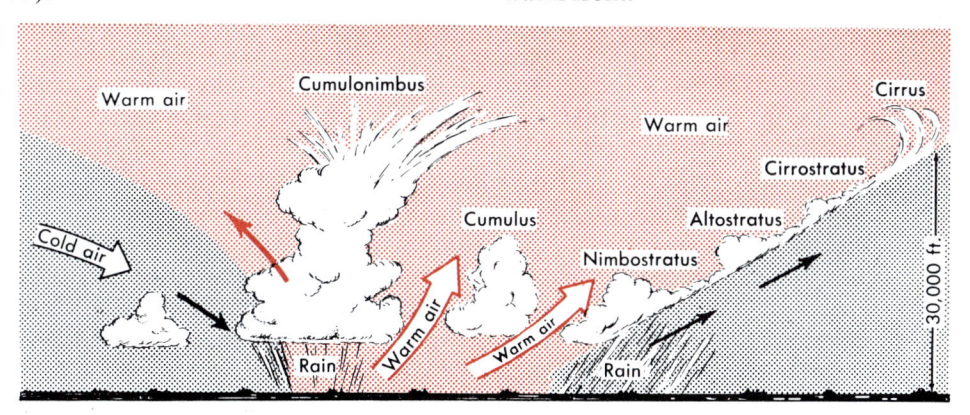

Fig. 12. A vertical section of a cyclonic storm, showing the fronts, the precipitation, and the cloud formations characteristic of each front.

Several hundred miles ahead of the ground-surface front the ascending air will have reached an altitude of 30,000 feet or more, at which moisture condenses to form ice crystals (see page 297), and then wisps of white cirrus clouds, often called *mare's-tails*, will be formed. As a warm front approaches, in what order will the clouds appear in the west?

In conclusion, the fully developed cyclonic storm consists of an indentation of a warm mass of air in a cold mass of air, which produces (a) a low-pressure center, (b) a warm front, and (c) a cold front. The warm air is between the cold front and the warm front. In the northern hemisphere the ground winds move toward and circulate around the low in a counterclockwise direction. See Fig. 12.

Generally following a polar-front cyclonic storm is a high-pressure area called an *anticyclone*. The air circulation is typical of all high-pressure centers. See Fig. 7a. Anticyclones are the results of the spasmodic projection of polar air masses into the belt of the prevailing westerlies, across which there is a procession of alternating cyclones and anticyclones, all moving in an easterly direction.

Forecasting weather. With our newly gained knowledge of weather, much of the mystery of forecasting weather should no longer be a mystery to us. For example, if we know the speed of the low in a cyclonic storm, then we should be able to predict fairly accurately the time for it to arrive at a place 400 miles east of its present location and the kind of weather that will prevail when it arrives.

Likewise, if we know the direction in which either a cold or a warm front is traveling, then we should be able to predict what kind of weather will prevail at a point in its path several hours before the front arrives, what kind of weather will prevail when it arrives, and the kind to be expected after it has passed.

How are weather maps made? Four times daily more than 750 weather observers in the United States, Canada, Mexico, the West Indies, and on ships at sea report the local temperature, barometric pressure, relative humidity, wind direction and velocity, precipitation, cloudiness, and other factors. From these data weather maps are drawn.

On the maps, points of *equal temperature* are connected by lines called *isotherms;* points of *equal pressure* are connected by lines called *isobars*. In general, isotherms extend in a west-east direction, whereas isobars are more or less circular, enclosing areas of high and low pressure. We have already learned (Chapter 9) that standard atmospheric pressure is equivalent to about 30 inches (29.92) of mercury. Pressures above and below this are considered high and low respectively.

However, in Fig. 13, you find the pressures given in *millibars* and, in some places, in inches. A milibar is a thousandth of a *bar,* which is an absolute unit of pressure equal to 1,000,000 dynes per square centimeter, which is the pressure of 29.53 inches of mercury at 0°C in latitude 45°, or the equivalent of normal atmospheric pressure at an altitude of 350 feet. Standard atmospheric pressure is equivalent to 1013 millibars. How many millibars equal 1 inch of mercury?

With all these data recorded and mapped, the professional weather man can make his forecast within a matter of minutes. And, contrary to what we may believe, he is accurate about 85 per cent of the time. Any would-be amateur forecaster would do well to make a thorough study of daily weather maps, as well as to observe weather conditions closely every day.

Can man control the weather? Until a

HUMIDITY AND WEATHER

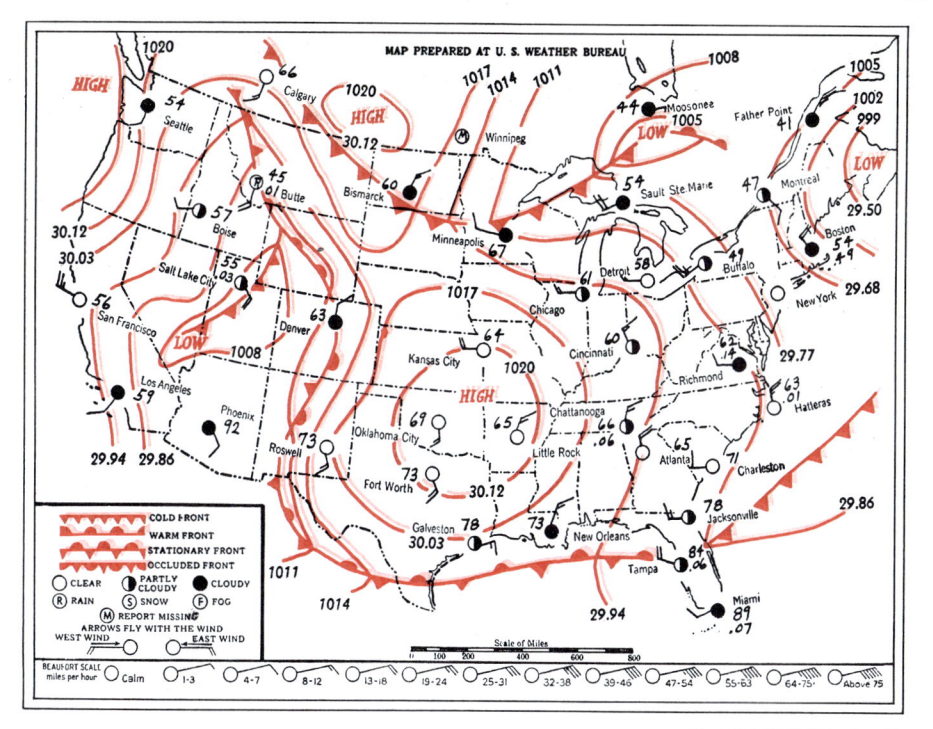

Courtesy U.S. Weather Bureau

Fig. 13. A weather map of the United States. Isobars and fronts are shown in red. A decimal fraction beneath a temperature reading shows the net precipitation in the six-hour period before the preparation of the map.

few years ago it was often truthfully said that "Everybody talks about the weather, but nobody does anything about it."

But this was all changed when, on November 13, 1946, Vincent J. Schaefer, of the General Electric Research Laboratory, succeeded in producing snow flurries in a cloud by dropping six pounds of dry ice into it from an airplane. Immediately rain makers raced to get cloud contracts. Cloud seedings were done in many areas. Arizona and Colorado complained of too much snow. In other places it was said to rain too hard or too little. States even complained against each other for vapor stealing. Finally, legislation on weather control was enacted. In some states one now has to have a license to make rain.

Soon, scientific investigations got under way to determine whether the excess rain was actually caused by the rain maker or was due to a naturally wet season. In various regions men made cloud seedings, both by dropping dry ice from airplanes and by producing silver iodide smoke from the ground. Their purpose in both cases was to furnish condensation nuclei, thus encouraging precipitation.

It was found that clouds had to be "ripe" for seeding in order to be productive; if not, they were dissipated instead. It appeared also that no more moisture than was available at the time could be made to fall, whereas in a natural storm more moisture-laden air is transported by wind to the storm area. There was no way to

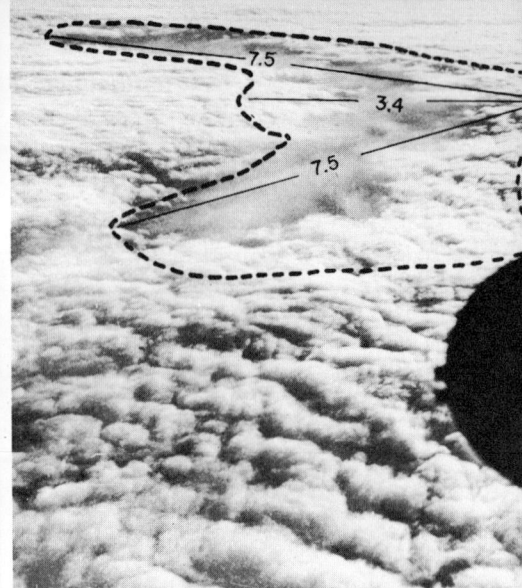

Courtesy General Electric Co.

Fig. 14. The three leading scientists in rainmaking research, Dr. Irving Langmuir, Dr. Bernard Vonnegut, and Dr. Vincent Schaefer, are watching a demonstration of snow-making in a home freezer. The cloud produced by breathing across the top of the freezer is seeded with dry ice. At the right is shown a gamma-shaped hole 15 miles long produced by seeding clouds with dry ice over Manhattan Island.

control this phase of it. "The results of 170 tests," says T. Morris Longstreth, "poured more cold water on rain makers' hopes than on the ground."

At the present time there seems to be no scientific basis for believing that we can control the weather and climate. However, we can produce small-scale local showers, prevent frosts in orchards and gardens, and dissipate fog over an area like an airport. But who knows what the future holds in store for us? New basic discoveries may be made and science may be able to control our weather and climate.

SUMMARY AND CONCLUSIONS

1. Weather is defined as the atmospheric conditions at a given place at any given time. The climate of a region is the sum of all its weather.
2. Weather is determined largely by solar radiation, winds, and moisture.
3. Absolute humidity is the weight of water vapor present per unit volume of air.
4. Relative humidity is the ratio of the quantity of water vapor present in the air to the quantity necessary for saturation at the same temperature. For bodily health and comfort it should be 40 to 60 per cent.
5. The dew point is the air temperature at which atmospheric water vapor begins to condense.
6. Clouds are formed by condensation of atmospheric water vapor upon nuclei, forming tiny particles of water or ice. Among the types of clouds are the cirrus and the cumulus. A nimbus cloud is a rain cloud.
7. Surface winds on the earth are deflected to the right by the earth's rotation.
8. The prevailing winds of the middle latitudes are the westerlies; those of the tropical and subtropical regions are easterly trade winds.
9. Lapse rate of air is the temperature change in relation to elevation.
10. Air masses are breeders of weather.
11. Cyclones cover large areas and are responsible for most of our precipitation in the middle latitudes. Cyclones are not to be confused with tornadoes.

QUESTIONS FOR REVIEW

1. Why is the moisture content of the air so important to our bodily comfort and health?
2. Why do films of moisture sometimes accumulate on the inside surfaces of our windows on cold winter days? Under what conditions does this film appear as frost?
3. Why do cold-water pipes drip with moisture on hot, humid days in summer?
4. If the relative humidity of the air is 50 per cent at 70°F, what is its absolute humidity? (See Table 1.)
5. What device, if any, is used in your home for increasing the water-vapor content of the air? Is it adequate?
6. Why does warming the air lower its relative humidity?
7. What is the relative humidity of air saturated with water vapor?
8. Where on the earth's surface is absolute humidity apt to be the highest?
9. Why does a person feel more comfortable on a hot dry day than on a hot humid day?
10. How low must the dew point be if frost is to appear? How do you account for the fact that frost often appears when the air temperature is in the neighborhood of 34°F?
11. Why is the average of *two* temperatures taken as the dew point in its experimental determination, as related on page 294.
12. How are rain, hail, and snow formed?
13. Describe the conditions necessary for the icing of an airplane.
14. What are the conditions necessary for an ice storm?
15. What is the lapse rate of dry, rising air? Of saturated rising air?
16. What part does heat of condensation play in the development of thunderstorms and hurricanes?
17. What is the purpose of cloud seeding?

PROBLEMS

1. What is the absolute humidity of air, ¼ cu. ft. of which contains 1.2 grains of moisture? 2.8 grains? (See Table 1.)
2. One cu. ft. of saturated air at 70°F contains how many grains of moisture?
3. One cu. ft. of air at 70°F contains 2.4 grains of moisture. What is its absolute humidity? Its relative humidity?
4. What is the dew point of the air of Problem 3? If 2 cu. ft. of this air were cooled to 25°F, about how much water vapor would be condensed into water?
5. A sample of air at 80°F has a relative humidity of 44.1 per cent. What is its absolute humidity? Its dew point?
6. An air sample has a relative humidity of 25 per cent at 90°F. What would its relative humidity be at 60°F? At what approximate temperature would it become saturated?
7. If the temperature of rising unsaturated air is 90°F at ground level, its relative humidity is 32.4 per cent, and its dew point is lowered 1 F° per 1000 feet of elevation, at what approximate altitude will the air reach its dew point? (Use lapse rates and Table 1.)
8. The wet bulb of a sling psychrometer reads 78°F and the dry bulb reads 90°F. What is the relative humidity of the air?
9. Assume that you use a sling psychrometer in your home and find the wet bulb to read 55°F when the dry bulb reads 75°F. What is the relative humidity of the air? Is it high enough for bodily health and comfort?
10. Unsaturated air is forced up a mountain 4000 ft. high. At the foot of the mountain the temperature of the air is 60°F. What is its temperature at the top of the mountain? Assume no loss of heat to surrounding air.
11. Unsaturated air at 20°F on top of a mountain drops 5000 ft. down the side of the mountain. What should the air temperature be after the descent?

PROJECTS

1. Measure the relative humidity of the air in your home and report your procedure and findings to the class.
2. Look up material on the sling psychrometer and its use, and make a report to the class.
3. Make a study of old-time weather "signs" and sayings, and try to determine whether

there is any truth in them. Report your findings to the class.

4. Check the weather predictions given in an almanac against the actual weather for a period of one month.

5. As a class, make a study of the weather in your locality for a period of two or three weeks, and try your skill at forecasting. Record twice daily such data as temperature, pressure, types of clouds and extent of cloudiness, wind direction and velocity, and any others that seem pertinent. Include a study of the Daily Weather Map, obtainable from the Superintendent of Documents, Government Printing Office, Washington 25, D. C.

READING YOU WILL ENJOY

1. Brooks, Charles F., *Why the Weather?* Harcourt, Brace and Company, New York, 1935.
2. Longstreth, T. Morris, *Understanding the Weather*. The Macmillan Company, New York, 1953. Chapter 21 contains excellent suggestions for the amateur forecaster.
3. Schneider, Herman, *Everyday Weather and How It Works*. McGraw-Hill Book Company, Inc., New York, 1951.
4. Tannehill, Ivan Ray, *Hurricanes: Their Nature and History*. Princeton University Press, Princeton, New Jersey, 1950.

Unit 10

Sound

Every day in your life you are constantly beset by a variety of sounds—the sound of people's voices in conversation, the roar of jets, the screeching of automobile brakes, the whirring noises of motors, the splashing of water, the hum of television receivers, as well as countless others. Some of these noises may not bother you; in fact, they may be pleasant to you. Physicists are definitely concerned with sound and are constantly seeking ways to control it or to use it for practical purposes.

In the unit photograph, a large power transformer is being sound-tested in the world's largest anechoic (without echoes) chamber. A technician is shown placing a microphone near the transformer so that the sound output may be analyzed. Engineers will then consider various methods of reducing the sound level by changes in the design of the transformer. This is but one example of how scientists attempt to control sound. In this unit, you will delve into the nature of sound and a number of practical problems. You will discover what causes echoes, why the pitch of an auto horn drops as the car speeds past you, and how high-frequency sound waves can work for you.

    28. THE NATURE OF SOUND
    29. MUSICAL SOUNDS

Unit Photograph Courtesy General Electric Co.

Chapter 28

The Nature of Sound

The problem. To start a heated argument, ask some friends whether or not sound would be produced if a tree fell to the ground with no one around to hear. Some will reply, "No. Sound is a *sensation* produced by a disturbance in the ear. Without a listener there can be no sound." Others will say, "Yes, because sound *is the disturbance* which excites the ear, and this disturbance is present regardless of the presence or absence of a listener."

This question, like many similar ones, causes needless controversy and can be answered only after a definition of sound has been accepted. Then the answer quickly becomes apparent to all.

The more modern point of view is that a listener cannot be separated from what he hears. A listener is as much a part of what he hears as that which starts the sound. The effect (sensation) is just as much a part of what he hears as is the cause. According to this point of view, would a sound be produced by the tree?

Another point of view is that sound is a phenomenon that *is capable of stimulating* the sensation of hearing. It is the disturbance; that is, the physical part, not the mental. In terms of this definition, would the falling tree produce a sound?

In this chapter it makes little difference which definition is chosen. The problem is to discover what starts a sound and how it gets to the ear.

What starts a sound? To answer this question we should study the various ways by which sound is produced. The strings of a guitar, violin, and other stringed instruments must be plucked or bowed. Flutes, clarinets, cornets, and other wind instruments must be blown. Drums, cymbals, bells, and other percussion instruments must be struck.

As scientists, however, we must be careful. The careless investigator might jump to the conclusion that *all* sounds are started by one of these methods. How, then, will he explain the "pop" which is produced when he pulls the stopper from a bottle? This sound is not started by any of these methods. It seems there must be other ways of producing sounds.

A similarity about the ways of starting *all* sounds is that a force must be applied and a resistance overcome; that is, work must be done. For example, a violinist does work when he draws a bow across a string and overcomes the resistance caused by friction. Likewise, when a string is plucked, a stopper is pulled from a bottle, or a paper is torn, a force is applied and resistance is overcome. Work appears to

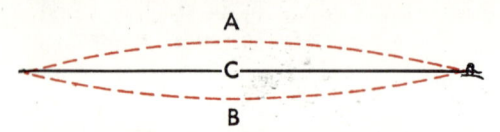

Fig. 1. Name the kind of energy the string has in each position.

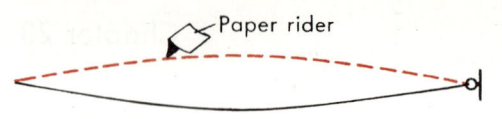

Fig. 2. Paper rider being thrown from a vibrating wire.

be done in every case. Now recall that energy is the ability to do work. Thus, *energy is always required to produce sound*.

What becomes of the energy required to produce sound? From previous study we know that when a violin is bowed, some work is done in overcoming friction and an equivalent amount of heat energy is produced. But is heat the only kind of energy produced? No, the string is set in motion. It vibrates back and forth, as shown in Fig. 1, and may continue to vibrate after the bow is removed. When it is in motion, it possesses kinetic energy; when it is at the position *A* or *B,* it must possess potential energy, because the string must be stretched to be in either of those positions. Where is the kinetic energy of the string the greatest? The least?

Does this mean that every source of sound is a vibrating body? From observation we know that some sounding bodies do vibrate. The strings of a bass viol can be seen to vibrate; pieces of chalk placed on a drumhead are seen to jump up and down after the head is struck and as long as a sound can be heard; the prongs of a tuning fork stuck into a glass of water cause a disturbance which shows they are vibrating. Fine cork dust in a glass whistle is seen to vibrate when the whistle is blown. One's finger placed on the diaphragm of a radio loud-speaker proves that it vibrates when producing a sound.

All the evidence seems to indicate that *a sound-producer is a vibrating body in which there is a constant interchange of kinetic and potential energy, and that the energy not converted to heat in producing the sound causes the body to vibrate.*

What becomes of the energy of the vibrating source? Apparently the energy which is not dissipated as heat is transformed into sound. This implies that sound is energy, which, if true, means that sound is able to do work.

To test this implication, open the top of a grand piano, depress the sustaining pedal (the one on the right), locate the wires for middle C, and astride one of these wires near its center place a paper rider (Fig. 2). Then blow this note on a trumpet or trombone, or simply hum the tone loudly, and watch the rider. Does it bounce about? Does the sound do work?

Since sound is capable of doing work, our conclusion that *sound is a form of energy* has been verified. Perhaps you can plan other experiments to test this conclusion.

What carries sound energy? While you were performing the experiment at the piano an important question may have come to your mind; namely, how did the energy from the trumpet get transferred to the piano string? In other words, what carries sound energy?

Many sounds that are produced must travel long distances before reaching our ears. It is not uncommon in war to hear the roar of heavy guns for a distance of twenty miles. Just how does a sound travel such distances? The medium separating most vibrating bodies from our ears is air. Is a material medium—gas, liquid, or solid —necessary for the transmission of sound? Does a vacuum transmit sound?

To find the answer to this question, Robert Boyle in 1660 used a vacuum pump invented by Guericke (page 84) and performed this experiment. He placed a watch in a glass container and pumped the air from the container. Boyle listened attentively for the ticking of the watch and was certain he heard nothing. This experiment has been repeated many times, and shows that a material medium is necessary for the transmission of sound.

Do liquids and solids transmit sound? Since air carries sound, whereas a vacuum does not, it is only natural to ask whether liquids do. If you have ever done any swimming near a running outboard motor, you know the answer to that question. Do solids transmit sound? Did you ever put your ear to the rail of a railroad track and hear an approaching train which you could not otherwise hear, or see? Perform the experiment shown in Fig. 3 and compare the loudness of the sounds produced by your striking the spoon when the end of the string is held in and then out of your ear. What do all these things show?

Evidence proves that sound can be transmitted through matter in all its states. In fact, it can be shown that liquids are better transmitters of sound than gases, and that solids, in general, are the best transmitters of all. Because sound travels through gases, liquids, and solids, but not through a vacuum, how does the study of sound agree with our definition that physics is a study of energy associated with matter?

What occurs in a medium when sound travels through it? There are only two imaginable ways by which sound energy can be transmitted through air. First, either the vibrating source knocks air molecules in all directions, much as an intermittent lawn sprinkler throws out its spray; or, second, the vibrating source sets up a disturbance in the air similar to that in water at a point where a stone strikes the surface of a quiet pool.

While we might explain the transmission of sound through air by saying that the vibration knocks air molecules in all directions, the picture fails completely when we extend it to solids, in which we know the molecules cannot move freely. Furthermore, it fails again when we try to explain why sound can be heard around a corner, because batted balls seldom curve around corners or through crooked tunnels or speaking tubes as sound does.

The alternative choice is that sound is a disturbance, or *wave*, which passes through a material medium. The particles of the medium transmit the disturbance but do not move along with it. This picture presents no difficulty as far as liquids and gases are concerned. And if our imaginations balk at picturing waves in solids, all we have to do is to recall that all solids are elastic and that their molecules are free to vibrate.

To show that solids can, and do, transmit waves of this sort, lay about six or eight marbles side by side between two

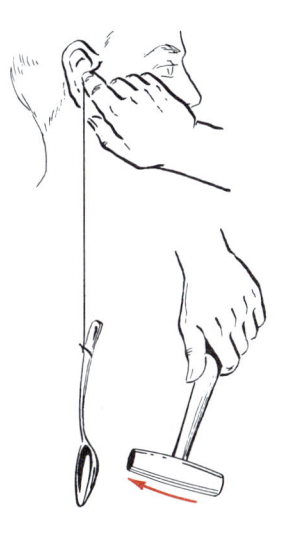

Fig. 3. Does the string (a solid) transmit sound?

Fig. 4. When marble *A* strikes marble *B*, what causes marble *C* to move? The marbles between *B* and *C* represent the transmitting medium.

meter sticks as shown in Fig. 4. Now roll another marble along the groove, causing it to strike one end of the row. The marbles in the middle of the row will not be perceptibly disturbed, but the one on the other end of the row will be kicked away some distance, showing that energy was transmitted by the marbles.

To picture the simplest imaginable case of sound transmission, let us suppose that we have an elastic ball (Fig. 5) for a source of sound and that, by some means, the ball is made to expand and contract regularly; that is, each point on the surface of the ball moves back and forth, outward and inward, along a radius of the ball. As the ball expands it pushes the air outward, crowding the air molecules closer together and thus producing a spherical region at its surface where the density and pressure are slightly greater than normal. This region is called a _condensation_.

A moment later the ball contracts, leaving at its surface a spherical region where density and pressure are slightly less than normal. This region is called a _rarefaction_. The molecules that formed the condensation crowd against the molecules beyond them and then swing back into the rarefaction next to the surface of the ball, where they are again in position to get pushed outward by the next expansion of the ball. Thus, the motion of molecules at the surface of the ball is passed on to molecules farther out, although the molecules themselves merely oscillate back and forth, toward and away from the source.

The combination of a condensation followed by a rarefaction, or vice versa, is called a *sound wave*. The vibrating ball thus sends out a succession of waves, or a *wave train,* as shown. Condensations are designated by *C;* rarefactions by *R*. Waves of this type are called _longitudinal_ waves, which means that, as the waves travel through the transmitting medium, the molecules of the medium oscillate back and forth _parallel_ to the direction in which the waves are traveling.

What are wave length, amplitude, and frequency? Also illustrated in Fig. 5 are a couple of other important points. The distances marked *l* represent the *wave length* of the sound. As is shown, the wave length is the distance from a point in a condensation to the corresponding point in the next condensation, or the distance from a point in a rarefaction to the corresponding point in the next rarefaction. In other words, _the wave length is the distance between two successive points in the same state of vibration_.

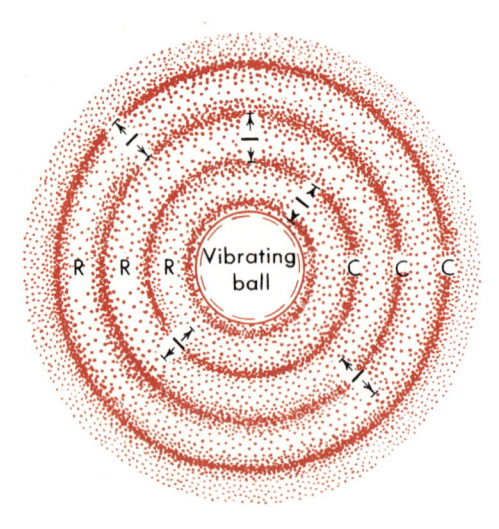

Fig. 5. Sound waves travel outward in all directions from a vibrating body.

Although it is not too evident in the figure, it is understandable that the air

Fig. 6. Focusing sound waves by means of an acoustic lens. By making a time exposure of a light source that varies directly in intensity with the sound produced, it is possible to show the pattern of rarefactions and condensations of a sound wave.

molecules, as the waves proceed, are displaced from their original positions in normal air. The maximum displacement is called the *amplitude* of vibration. It is seldom more than half a millimeter, and is usually less. The number of waves passing a given point each second is called the *frequency* of the sound. The frequency of the waves is usually, but not always, equal to the frequency of the vibration source.

What are the energy relations in the medium? Let us now analyze the energy relations in a medium carrying sound energy. A condensation is evidently a region where the air is momentarily compressed. What form of energy does it possess? At the moment of maximum condensation the air particles must come to rest; hence, in a condensation the energy of the air particles is potential in form. As the condensation moves outward, it acts on the surrounding air, thus imparting motion to neighboring particles. When the particles are moving most rapidly, they have maximum kinetic energy. Thus, there is developed the familiar exchange of kinetic and potential forms of energy which was observed before in other cases of vibrating bodies, as in the pendulum. In this case, however, the energy moves outward, away from the vibrating source. It is *energy in transition,* and may be called *sound energy.*

How do sound waves compare with water waves? You have sat in a rowboat and experienced the passage of surface water waves beneath you. As the waves advanced the boat did not advance with them but simply moved up and down approximately at *right angles** to the direction of the waves. Since a boat, chip, or other floating object behaves in this man-

---

*Actually the motion of the water particles in simple water waves is circular, but here we consider only the up-and-down, or vertical, component of the motion.

SOUND

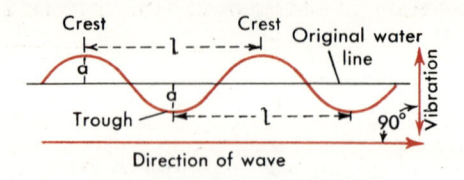

Fig. 7. Transverse waves. How are wave length and amplitude determined?

ner as a train of waves passes beneath it, the water particles themselves must be vibrating in the same manner. Waves of this sort, in which the particles of the transmitting medium vibrate at right angles to the direction in which the waves advance, are called *transverse* waves.

Figure 7 represents a couple of complete water waves which closely approximate transverse waves. As indicated, the parts of the curve above the original water line are called *crests;* those below are called *troughs.* The maximum displacement of the water particles is indicated by *a* and is called amplitude, just as in the case of longitudinal waves. Wave length is designated by *l* and, again, is the distance between two successive points in the same state of vibration. Also, as in longitudinal waves, frequency designates the number of waves passing a given point in one second.

How fast does sound travel? The fact that it takes time for sound to travel is verified by many of our common observations. All of us have seen the vapor escaping from a steam whistle on a distant locomotive or steamship and noted the time elapsing before the sound was heard. We have watched brilliant displays of lightning and noticed the time elapsing between the flashes and the sounds of the thunder.

Careful scientific measurements have established the velocity of sound through air at 0°C and 1 atmosphere of pressure to be very close to 1088 feet, or 332 meters, per second. At higher temperatures the velocity is greater, increasing at approximately the rate of 2 feet, or 0.6 meter, per second for each centigrade degree of increase in temperature. Thus, at 20°C the velocity would be 1128 feet per second (1088 + [2 × 20]). In general, the velocity (V_t) in feet per second at t°C is equal to the velocity at 0°C (V_0) plus $2t$; that is,

$$V_t = V_0 + 2t \tag{1}$$

How would Equation 1 be written if the

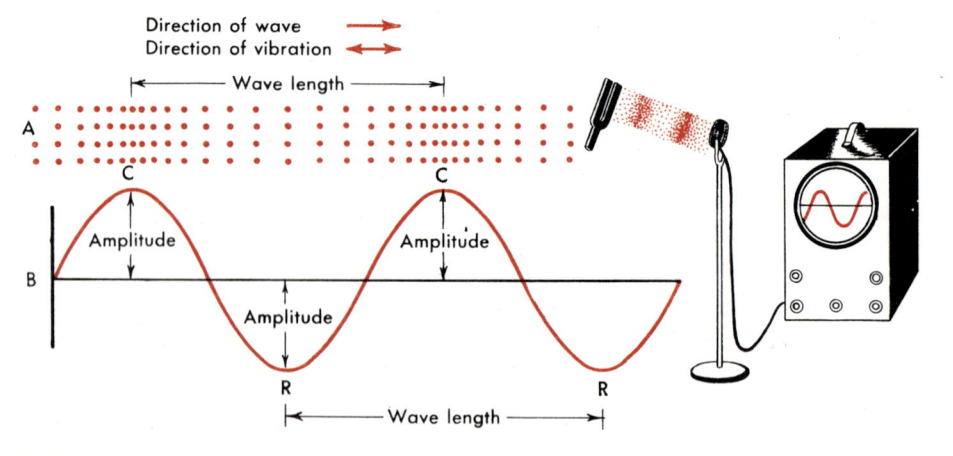

Fig. 8. Sound waves are longitudinal waves, but they are conveniently represented as transverse waves, as shown on the screen of an oscilloscope.

velocities were expressed in meters per second? What would be the effect if the air temperature were below zero centigrade?

PROBLEM: A flash of lightning was seen, and 5 seconds later the thunder was heard. How far away was the lightning if the air temperature was 21°C?

The velocities of sound through other substances vary greatly. Newton found that the velocity through any substance can be determined in terms of the elasticity and the density of the substance. The velocities of sound through several substances are given in Table 1. Those for the solids are at about 20°C.

Table 1
VELOCITIES OF SOUND
THROUGH VARIOUS SUBSTANCES

Substance	Velocity of Sound ft./sec.	m./sec.
Granite	19685	6000
Glass	18550	5500
Aluminum	16740	5140
Iron and Steel	16410	5000
Hardwood (lengthwise)	13120	4000
Copper	11670	3560
Water, 19°C	4794	1461
Air (1 atmosphere), 0°C	1088	332

What are loudness and intensity of sound? The loudness of a sound is determined by its effect upon one's sense of hearing, and is, therefore, very difficult to measure. Our observations tell us that the distance from the source is the most important factor, other things being equal. Since sound waves travel outward in all directions from the source of sound in concentric spherical patterns, one might expect the loudness to be inversely proportional to the square of the distance from the source. This should be true, since the areas of the surfaces of these waves are proportional to the squares of their radii. We find this same *inverse-square law* to apply in the cases of gravitation, light intensity, and electric and magnetic fields. However, in the case of sound, loudness and intensity decrease more rapidly than is provided for by this law. This is thought to be due to the effects of wind, temperature differences, absorption of sound energy by the air and other surrounding objects, and reflection by obstacles in the path of the sound.

Since loudness is so difficult to measure, physicists are prone to disregard it and to use another concept which they *can* measure. We have already discussed the idea that sound energy is energy in transition; that is, it flows outward from the source in all directions. It seems reasonable to assume that the rate at which this energy flows into a listener's ear should be an important factor in determination of the loudness of the sound.

Previously we learned that the rate of flow of energy is power. Thus, our unit of sound intensity should be a unit of power. But what unit of power should we use? Since the energy content of ordinary sounds is so small, the horsepower and the watt are much too large to be practicable. Therefore the physicist has chosen a unit equivalent to a millionth of a watt, called the *microwatt,* as the unit of sound intensity. We can define the intensity of a sound in a given region as *the power in microwatts transmitted through a square meter of surface* in that region.

What factors determine the intensity of a sound? If a tuning fork is struck lightly against a rubber stopper and its shank is then placed on a table top, a sound is heard. The table top is *forced* to vibrate by virtue of its contact with the tuning fork, and is said to have *forced vibration*. A sharper blow will cause the sound to be more intense or louder. Observations also tell us that lightly plucking the strings of a stringed instrument does not produce as intense a sound as does more vigorous

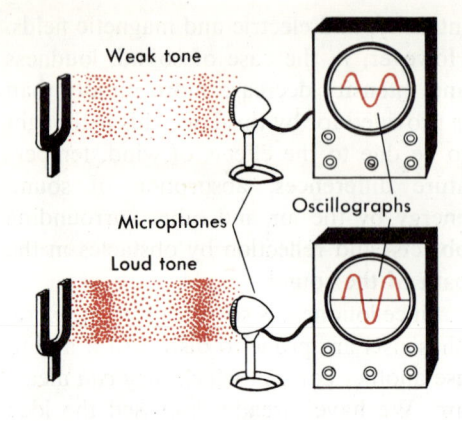

Fig. 9. How loud and weak tones are shown on an oscilloscope. Compare the heights of the crests above the horizontal in the top and bottom drawings. Upon what factors does loudness depend?

plucking. We are also familiar with the general fact that a large instrument usually produces a more intense sound than a small one. These experiences imply that *the intensity of a sound depends upon the amplitude of vibration* (Fig. 9) *and the area of the vibrating body.*

Although the amplitude of vibration of a sound source may be large, the amplitude of the particles of the transmitting medium, the air, is almost unbelievably small. (Except very near the source, where the amplitudes of the source and the air will be very nearly the same.) The ear is sensitive to an amplitude in air of around a thousand-millionth of a centimeter, and an amplitude in liquids and solids that is even smaller. An amplitude as large as a hundredth of a centimeter in air may result in a sound loud enough to damage the ear.

How intense are sounds? It has been indicated that the rate of flow of energy in connection with sound is very low. Just how intense are some of the sounds we hear? When you are carrying on an ordinary conversation with some of your friends, the rate of flow of energy is approximately 10 microwatts. Of course, any one ear receives much less than this. The rate of flow from a public speaker may be from about 200 to 2000 microwatts. The power of the loudest tones of a violin may be about 60 microwatts; the powers of the sounds from organ pipes may range from 140 to 3200.

The faintest sound that you can hear delivers approximately one-millionth of a microwatt per square meter; the loudest, about one million microwatts. It is evident that the ear is a very sensitive organ, capable of responding to sound intensities over a range of a million-million-fold, as well as detecting sounds whose frequencies range from about 20 to 20,000 or more vibrations per second. As might be expected, sensitivity to intensity and frequency varies with different individuals.

How are relative sound levels measured? It would be rather inconvenient as well as impracticable always to refer to sound intensities in terms of either microwatts per square meter or of ergs per second per square meter. We are much more apt to be interested in *comparing* one sound with another on a *relative* basis. To put it another way, we want to know how much louder or softer one sound is than one with which we are already familiar. This implies the use of *ratios* of sound intensities. When the intensity of a sound is ten times that of another, its *sound level* is said to be one unit higher than that of the other. This unit of sound level has been named the *bel* in honor of Alexander Graham Bell, whose name you have heard many times in connection with the telephone.

The lower limit of audible sound intensity (0.000001 microwatt/m^2), mentioned in the preceding section, is called the *threshold of hearing.* Its sound level is rated as 0 bels. Table 2 lists a number of sounds, together with their intensities in

THE NATURE OF SOUND

Table 2
INTENSITIES AND SOUND LEVELS OF VARIOUS SOUNDS

Sound	Intensity in mw./m.^{2}	Sound level in bels	Sound level in decibels
Threshold of hearing	0.000001	0	0
Ordinary breathing	0.00001	1	10
Quiet garden	0.0001	2	20
Turning page of newspaper	0.001	3	30
Average home	0.01	4	40
Vacuum cleaner	0.1	5	50
Ordinary conversation	1.0	6	60
Average radio	10.0	7	70
Heavy traffic	100.0	8	80
Elevated train	1000.0	9	90
Subway car (inside)	10000.0	10	100
Thunder	100000.0	11	110
Threshold of feeling	1000000.0	12	120

microwatts per square meter and their sound levels in bels. It should be noted that, whereas the intensities increase by ratios of 10, the sound levels in bels increase a unit at a time. This scale was chosen because observations show that the loudness of a sound perceived by the ear seems to vary as the logarithm of physical intensity. This is shown in the table. Because the bel is a rather large unit, a smaller unit, the *decibel* (0.1 bel), is often used. A change of one decibel in the volume of a sound is approximately the smallest change that a normal ear can detect.

The last item in the above table, *threshold of feeling,* indicates that sound can actually be felt. When the sound intensity reaches one million microwatts (1 watt) per square meter, the ear not only hears the sound but also experiences a tickling sensation. Even the skin can feel sound of this intensity. If the intensity becomes much greater than this, pain is felt in the ear.

What are the relationships among wave length, frequency, and velocity? Let us assume that the tuning fork in Fig. 10 has a frequency of 200 vibrations per second (v/s). This means it is emitting 200 complete sound waves each second. Let us further assume that d is the distance the sound travels in one second and that the air temperature is 20°C. Then d is 1128 feet (1088 + [2 × 20]). The 200 waves are thus spread out over this distance, and each wave must be 1128/200, or 5.64 feet in length. If the frequency were 400 vibrations per second, the wave length would be 2.82 feet—just half as much.

At a higher temperature, d would be greater and the wave length would be proportionately longer. Since the distance

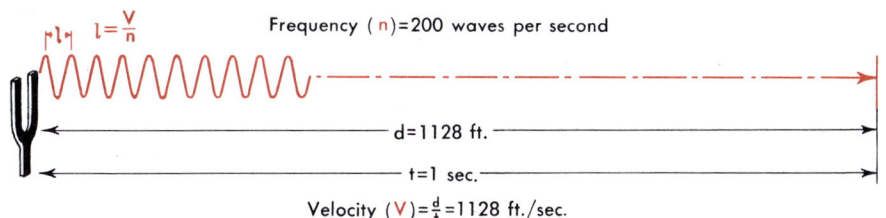

Frequency (n) = 200 waves per second
$l = \frac{V}{n}$
$d = 1128$ ft.
$t = 1$ sec.
Velocity (V) = $\frac{d}{t}$ = 1128 ft./sec.

Fig. 10. The velocity of a sound wave is equal to the product of the frequency and the wave length.

per second that sound travels is its velocity, and the number of waves per second is its frequency, it is evident that the wave length, *l*, of a sound is equal to its velocity, *V*, divided by its frequency, *n*. Thus,

$$l = \frac{V}{n} \qquad (2)$$

This relationship is an important one since it is true, not only for sound waves, but also for light waves, radio waves, and X-rays; in short, for all kinds of waves. If any two of the quantities in Equation 2 are known, the third can be easily computed.

PROBLEM: If a tuning fork vibrates 128 times per second, what will be the wave length of the sound produced if the air temperature is 25°C?

Interference—a crucial test of whether sound is transmitted as waves. We have pictured sound waves as trains of alternate regions of compressions and rarefactions, spreading out in all directions from the vibrating source, just like ripples spreading out from the spot where a stone strikes the surface of a pond. At any place in a sound-wave train the air is being alternately compressed and rarefied with the same frequency as the source, provided the source is stationary and there is no wind.

But have you ever observed the behavior of the ripples produced by *two* stones dropped into a pond some distance apart? Doubtless you have, and have noticed the peculiar patterns formed where the two wave trains meet. Where the crests of one train meet the crests of the other, higher waves result; that is, the amplitude of vibration is greater, and the waves are said to *reinforce* each other, or to experience *constructive interference*. Where the crests of one train meet the troughs of the other the amplitude is much less and, in fact, may be equal to zero. Here the waves

Constructive interference

Condensation

Rarefaction

Destructive interference

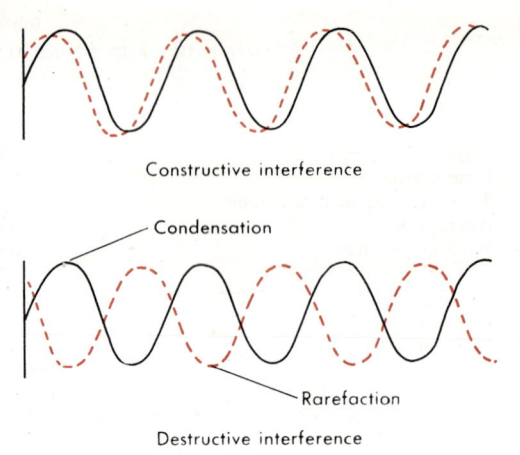

Fig. 11. **Constructive and destructive interference.**

tend to cancel each other, or, as the physicist puts it, *destructive interference* occurs. See Fig. 11.

Do these phenomena occur in the case of sound waves? If so, a sound should be more intense when the waves from two different wave trains meet in the same *phase*; that is, when condensation meets condensation and rarefaction meets rarefaction. If they meet in the opposite phase —that is, if condensation meets rarefaction—the sound should be less intense. In fact, if the waves exactly cancel each other, silence should result.

To test this hypothesis, let us experiment a bit. Strike a tuning fork and rotate it by the handle while holding it near your ear. You will note that in certain positions the sound is intensified, showing constructive interference, whereas in others little or no sound is heard. This is because the tuning fork has two vibrating prongs, each of the same frequency, and each sending out trains of waves. Thus, there must be regions in which the waves meet in opposite phase, and destructive interference occurs. Since the waves are of the same wave length and intensity, they exactly cancel each other and silence results. These regions of silence are approximately along the lines (which are really cross sections of surfaces) shown in Fig. 12.

The phenomenon of interference furnishes excellent evidence in support of the wave theory of sound. All kinds of waves are capable of suffering interference.

Can sound waves be reflected? Have you ever "hollered" down a rain barrel or a deep well, near a cliff or wooded hillside, or at some distance from the edge of a forest? If you have, you know that sound can be reflected. If the reflecting surface is 60 feet or more away from the source, the reflected sound can be easily distinguished from the original and is called an *echo*. In a narrow canyon with parallel walls an echo may be *multiple* or repeated; that is, it may be heard several times. It is evident that surfaces which reflect sound need not be smooth and polished, whereas they should be for the reflection of heat.

The reflection of sound can be readily demonstrated in your classroom by means of a watch, an ear trumpet, and two *parabolic* reflectors like the ones shown in Fig. 13. See if you can explain this experiment.

Uses of the reflection of sound. In buildings with properly arched ceilings, like the dome at the Capitol in Washington, D. C., or the "Whispering Gallery" at St. Paul's in London, it is possible to hear, in the rear of the auditorium, a whisper on the stage two hundred feet away. If we observe the ceiling of such an auditorium, it appears as though we were looking up on the inside of an empty eggshell. If a speaker stands at the center of the stage, sound waves traveling from him to a listener via any point on the ceiling will all travel the same distance. In other words, any distance from speaker to ceiling plus its corresponding distance from ceiling to listener will give a total sound path which is equal to any other similar path for a given listener. Can you see the reason for this type of construction? You can imagine the confusion that might result in a large auditorium if different portions of a given sound wave from a speaker were to require different intervals of time to reach a listener.

Can sound energy be absorbed? If the rear walls of an auditorium are of such a nature as to reflect a goodly portion of the sound from a speaker back to the stage, he will hear his own words a short time after he says them. To help prevent this the walls may be covered with certain kinds of materials, such as draperies, which partially *absorb,* instead of reflecting, the energy of the sound waves and transform it into heat. Proper treatment of walls and other surfaces **in a room will** aid in doing

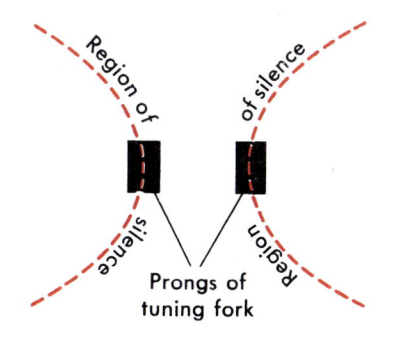

Fig. 12. Demonstration of destructive interference with a tuning fork.

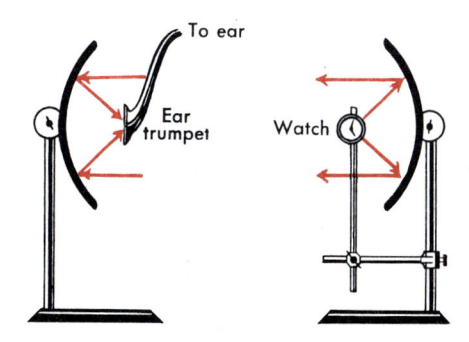

Fig. 13. Demonstration of the reflection of sound waves.

Courtesy Polytechnic Institute of Brooklyn

Fig. 14. Sound waves beyond the range of human hearing were used to produce this photograph of the bones of a hand.

away with *reverberations* which persist for a measurable time after the original sound has ceased. They are the principal disturbing factor affecting the sound properties of a room. The study of the sound properties of rooms and buildings has been very highly developed and comes under the heading of *architectural acoustics*.

Can sound energy be directed? Any high school boy or girl knows that a cheerleader can make himself heard better through the use of a *megaphone*. Such a device prevents the sound energy from spreading out in all directions and directs it toward the audience. The sound reflectors mentioned in a previous paragraph are used as sound directors, as are also the curved ceilings of auditoriums. Most of us have had occasion to use a *speaking tube* which directs and carries the sound energy to a given room that may be some distance from the building entrance. These examples show that the answer to our topic question is "yes." Perhaps you can think of other examples.

SUMMARY AND CONCLUSIONS

1. Sound is a disturbance in the air which produces the sensation of hearing. The sensation and the cause should be considered of equal importance.
2. Energy is required to produce sound. Sound originates in a vibrating body. Sound is a form of energy.
3. A material medium is necessary for the transmission of sound.
4. Sound travels in longitudinal waves, consisting of condensations and rarefactions. Another kind of wave is the transverse wave, consisting of crest and trough.
5. Wave length is the distance between two successive points in the same state of vibration.
6. The displacement of the particles of the transmitting medium is called amplitude. The term applies to the displacement of the particles in any vibrating body.
7. The amplitude of vibration for air waves is extremely small.
8. The number of vibrations per second is called frequency.
9. Sound energy is energy in transition.
10. Vibrations of air are the result of the passage of longitudinal waves through it.
11. The velocity of sound through air is 1088 ft./sec. at 0°C. It changes by 2 ft./sec. for every centigrade degree of change in temperature.

$$V_t = V_0 + 2t$$

12. Intensity of sound is measured in terms of the rate of flow of sound energy from its source. It may be expressed in microwatts per square meter or in ergs per second per square meter.
13. Intensity depends upon the amplitude of vibration and the area of the sounding body.

14. Relative sound levels are measured in bels, which are the logarithms of the relative sound intensities.

15. Wave length of sound is directly proportional to its velocity and inversely proportional to its frequency.

$$l = \frac{V}{n} \text{ or } V = nl$$

16. Destructive interference occurs if two wave trains meet in opposite phases of vibration; if they meet in the same phase, reinforcement occurs.

17. Sound waves can be reflected, absorbed, and directed. Sound which is reflected back to its original source is called an echo.

18. The study of the sound properties of rooms and buildings is called architectural acoustics.

QUESTIONS FOR REVIEW

1. What determines whether we should say that there is or is not sound in a forest when a tree falls without the presence of a listener?
2. Give some evidence, not stated in this chapter, to support the conclusion that energy is always required to produce sound.
3. Why is it more difficult to make yourself heard when speaking in the open air than when speaking in a room in your home?
4. Why would it be more difficult to make yourself heard up on a high mountain than at its base?
5. Why might one blast of a steamer whistle out on a lake be heard twice by a person standing on shore?
6. Define condensation; rarefaction.
7. Why is it difficult for marchers in a parade to keep in step with a band that is playing some distance from them?
8. Dogs are known to respond to whistles which people cannot hear. What is a plausible explanation of this?
9. Why is it easier to talk in an auditorium filled with people than in an empty one?
10. A timer in a foot race is standing at the finish line. Should he start his watch when he sees the flash of the starting gun or when he hears its report? Explain.

11. Explain the difference between longitudinal and transverse waves.
12. Of what advantage is it to a person who is hard of hearing to cup his hand around his ear when listening to a speaker?
13. Where on the decibel scale would you place the sound in your classroom?

PROBLEMS

1. Determine the speed of sound in miles per hour through air at a temperature of 20°C. At how many miles per hour does it travel through iron and steel? (See Table 1 on page 317.)
2. A man out in a duck boat fired his shotgun. Five seconds later the echo from the wooded shore reached him. If the air temperature was 10°C, how far was the boat from shore?
3. A gunner stationed 4500 feet from a cliff fired his gun and heard the echo from the cliff 8 seconds later. What was the velocity of the sound? What was the temperature of the air?
4. A timer at a track meet, standing at the finish line of a 200-meter race, started his watch at the sound of the starting gun. The air temperature was 20°C. Would his recorded time be too great or too small, and by how much?
5. A man saw a flash of lightning and 6 seconds later heard the thunder. The air temperature was 26°C. How far away did the flash occur?
6. While working in a field a farmer set his watch by the sound of a noon whistle which was 3 miles distant. How fast or slow would his watch be, air temperature being 16°C?
7. A boy dropped a stone into a deep well and heard it strike the water 4.5 seconds later. If the air temperature was 11°C, how deep was the well? (Hint: a quadratic equation is involved. Remember the laws of falling bodies.) ANS.: 288 ft.

PROJECTS

1. Devise a demonstration showing that sound is energy and can do work.

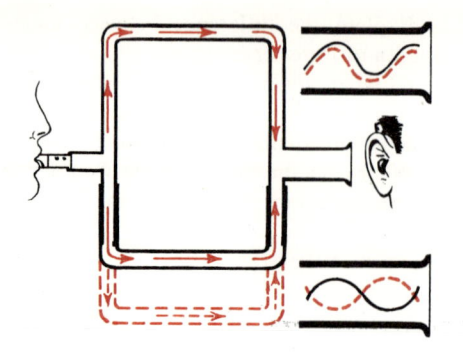

Fig. 15. An apparatus for producing sound interference.

2. Figure 15 shows an apparatus for producing sound interference. Obtain this apparatus, or improvise one like it, and explain how it works.

3. A "telephone," usable across a distance of 100 ft. or more, can be made with a piece of string stretched between the bottoms of two tin cans. Make and demonstrate such a telephone, and explain how it works.

4. *Class project.* Go out to the athletic field or to some other large open space and measure the speed of sound. Use a revolver with blank cartridges filled with gunpowder that is not smokeless. Using a stop watch, measure the time between the sight of the gun flash and the time when you hear the report coming to you over a carefully measured distance (a quarter of a mile, if possible). Average the results of several trials.

READING YOU WILL ENJOY

Swezey, K. M., *After-Dinner Science.* Whittlesey House, McGraw-Hill Book Company, Inc., New York, 1948. "How Sound Waves Travel," pp. 76-77; "Sound Cannot Travel through a Vacuum," p. 78; "A Gas Balloon Acts as a Sound Lens," p. 79; "Sound Waves Cancel Each Other," p. 80; "Hear through Your Teeth," p. 81.

Chapter 29

Musical Sounds

What is the difference between music and noise? It is difficult to distinguish between music and noise, for what may be music to one person may be just noise to another. Some people think that grand opera is most unmusical, whereas others love it. The neighing of a horse or the rumble of a lumber wagon may be noise to most people, but music in the ears of a lumberman. To a fond parent the crying of his newborn child may seem like music. To most of us, however, such sounds are just plain noise.

Most people will agree, though, that sounds originating with vibrating wires, reeds, tuning forks, air columns, and the vibrating vocal cords of a singer are musical. Just what, then, is essential in the production of a musical sound, or *tone?*

To help answer this question, use a *siren disk* like the one shown in Fig. 1. Rotate the disk rapidly at a constant speed, and blow a stream of air through a glass jet against each row of holes in turn. You will find that rows having equally spaced holes produce pleasant musical sounds, whereas the sound from the row of unequally spaced holes is just noise.

When the stream of air passes through a hole, a condensation is produced on the opposite side of the disk. Between holes the air cannot get through, and rarefactions are then produced. These *pulses* in the air are produced at regular intervals by the rows with equally spaced holes, but the other row produces pulses at irregular intervals.

Our demonstration thus shows that, <u>in producing a musical sound, it is essential that the vibrations occur in equal intervals of time</u>. Vibrations of wires, tuning forks, etc., are of this nature; those of trains, lumber wagons, etc., occur at irregular intervals, and their sounds are nothing but noises.

What is the meaning of pitch? <u>*Pitch* refers to the degree of highness or lowness of a tone</u>. To get the highest-pitched piano tones we strike the keys at the extreme right on the keyboard; the lowest tones are obtained at the extreme left. What causes this difference in pitch?

To help answer this question we can again use the siren disk. Most disks have rows of 24, 30, 36, and 48 holes, all equally spaced. As the disk rotates at a constant rate, blow a stream of air at each row of holes in turn, starting with the innermost row. Each row produces a musical tone that is pitched higher than the preceding one. Now change the speed of the disk while blowing at a single row.

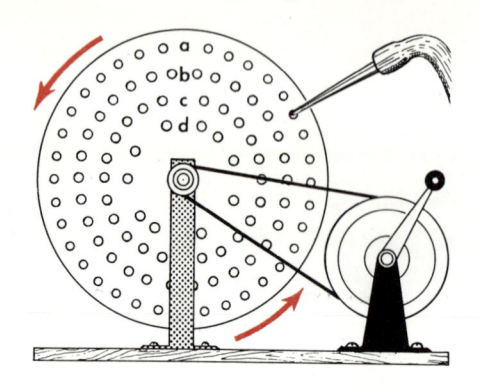

Fig. 1. Why does the row of equally spaced holes produce a musical sound?

You will find that an increase in speed raises the pitch; a decrease lowers the pitch. What do the results of this demonstration show?

By increasing the speed of the disk or by using a row containing a larger number of holes, you increase the number of pulses or waves per second sent out through the air. Hence, it appears that *the pitch of a sound depends upon the number of pulses or waves per second traveling from a sounding body to the ear.* Since pitch, as such, is so difficult to measure, physicists prefer to express it in terms of frequency, which is readily measured.

One might ask whether sounds of all frequencies travel at equal speeds. If high-pitched tones traveled faster or slower than low ones, how would a distant band sound if it contained a bass horn and a flute? Does a band sound this way? What is your conclusion?

What is the major diatonic scale? The tones produced by the siren disk in the last experiment were probably recognized by some of you as those of a *major chord*. The first three of these tones, from rows of 24, 30, and 36 holes, constitute a *major triad*. A disk having eight rows of holes; namely, 24, 27, 30, 32, 36, 40, 45, and 48, would produce all the tones of a *major diatonic scale*. Even if rotated at different constant speeds, the scale will be produced perfectly in each case. If it is rotated at 10⅔ revolutions per second, the frequencies will be as shown in the table below.

A tone having a frequency of 256 vibrations per second is called *middle C*. The scale in the table is known as the C scale, in which C is the *key tone*.

The numbers 24, 27, 30, etc., are the *relative vibration numbers;* the frequencies are the *absolute vibration numbers*. The ratios are obtained by division of each relative vibration number by the first one (24). *These ratios are the same for all major scales, regardless of what the key tone may be.*

Scales are always named according to their key tones; as the scale of C, the scale of D, etc. The entire scale of C and the syllables (applicable to any scale), together with their *vibration ratios* and frequencies, are shown in the table. The next tone above C' is D' (re'), whose frequency is 576 vibrations per second.

The tones C, E, and G make up the *tonic* triad of the C scale, since its lowest tone is the key tone of the scale. Note that 24:30:36 = 4:5:6. Any group of tones whose frequencies bear these ratios constitutes a major triad. Inspection of the C-scale shows two other major triads: F, A, and C', the *subdominant,* and G, B,

No. of holes	24	27	30	32	36	40	45	48
Frequencies (v/s)	256	288	320	341.3	384	426.6	480	512
Vibration ratios	1	9/8	5/4	4/3	3/2	5/3	15/8	2
Tones	C	D	E	F	G	A	B	C'
Syllables	do	re	mi	fa	sol	la	ti	do'

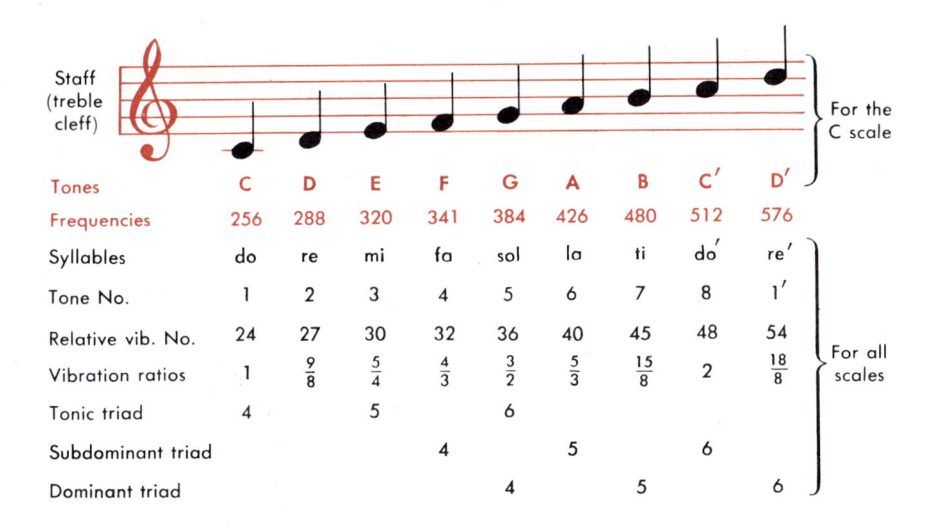

Staff (treble cleff)									
Tones	C	D	E	F	G	A	B	C′	D′
Frequencies	256	288	320	341	384	426	480	512	576
Syllables	do	re	mi	fa	sol	la	ti	do′	re′
Tone No.	1	2	3	4	5	6	7	8	1′
Relative vib. No.	24	27	30	32	36	40	45	48	54
Vibration ratios	1	$\frac{9}{8}$	$\frac{5}{4}$	$\frac{4}{3}$	$\frac{3}{2}$	$\frac{5}{3}$	$\frac{15}{8}$	2	$\frac{18}{8}$
Tonic triad	4		5		6				
Subdominant triad				4		5		6	
Dominant triad					4		5		6

Fig. 2. Relationships in the major diatonic scale.

and D′, the *dominant* triad. Since these three triads include all the tones of the major scale, it may be said that this scale is founded upon them. Fig. 2 brings all this information together, and may help to clarify the relationships.

What are musical intervals? We have learned that the production of the major scale with the siren disk is independent of the speed of rotation; that is, it is not the *actual* frequencies, but the *relative* frequencies that are important. So long as the vibration ratios remain constant, the proper relationships among the pitches of the tones will be maintained.

The term *musical interval* refers to the relative frequencies of two tones, and this depends upon the ratio, not the difference, between their frequencies. When this ratio is 2:1, as in the case of C′:C=512:256, or as 48:24, the interval is an *octave*. The ratio between the third and first tones of a major scale is 5:4 (30:24), as in the case of E:C. This is a *major third* interval. Try to find two other major third intervals in the scale of C.

Other important intervals are the *fourth*, 32/24, or 4/3; the *fifth*, 36/24, or 3/2; the *sixth*, 40/24, or 5/3; and the *minor third*, 36/30, or 6/5, as G:E in the C-scale. It is evident that an octave is an *eighth* interval. Locate as many of these various intervals as you can in the C-scale. A musician is able to recognize these intervals at once if they are sounded on a musical instrument, or sung.

Why are black keys used on pianos and organs? As we have stated, any tone of the C-scale can be used as the key tone for a major scale. If we use B_1 for our key tone its frequency is 240 v/s (480/2); the second tone is 9/8 of 240, or 270; the third is 5/4 of 240, or 300, etc. Fig. 3 compares the B_1-scale with the C-scale. Note that the frequencies for only three of the white keys correspond to those of the newly made scale; namely, B_1, E, and B. The others fall about midway between those of the C-scale.

Thus, if we wish to play the B_1 scale, five keys must be added between the white ones. These are the black keys

SOUND

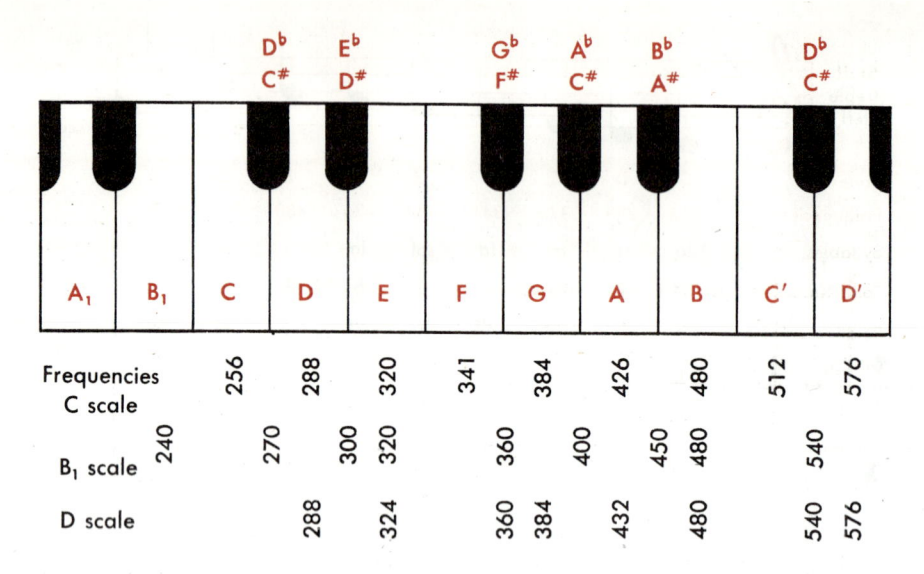

	D♭ C♯	E♭ D♯			G♭ F♯	A♭ C♯	B♭ A♯		D♭ C♯	
A₁	B₁	C	D	E	F	G	A	B	C′	D′

Frequencies C scale		256	288	320	341	384	426	480	512	576	
B₁ scale	240	270	300	320		360	400	450	480	540	
D scale			288	324		360	384	432	480	540	576

Fig. 3. Why are black keys used on a piano or organ? How are they named?

shown in the figure. The one between C and D is designated as either C♯ (C sharp) or D♭ (D flat); the one between F and G, as F♯ or G♭, etc. Without the use of black keys, piano playing, singing, and musical compositions would be confined to just one scale—the *natural* scale of C, so called because it contains no sharps or flats.

What is the even-tempered scale? Note that Fig. 3 shows the D scale as well as the C and B₁ scales. The given frequencies of the D scale present a problem not solved by the use of black keys. The frequencies of E and A for the D scale do not coincide with those of the C scale. Thus, two more keys must be added if we wish to play the D scale perfectly. Many other discrepancies are found if we calculate perfect scales for all the keys, including the black ones. In fact, about 70 keys per octave would be necessary to play all the scales perfectly. Obviously, such a complicated instrument would be very difficult to play.

This problem is solved through the use of the *even-tempered,* or simply the *tempered scale,* first suggested by Johann Sebastian Bach (1685-1750). The discrepancies noted above are so slight that the simple ratios of the perfect scale can be sacrificed and others, sufficiently near to them to satisfy a musical ear, can be substituted. The octave is thus divided into twelve equal intervals called *half steps* or *chromatic semitones.* Since the octave interval is still 2:1, each half-step interval has a ratio equal to the twelfth root of 2 ($\sqrt[12]{2}$), which is about 1.06. Thus, the frequency of any tone in the scale can be obtained by multiplication of the one below it by 1.06.

What is standard pitch? Standards of pitch have existed for less than three generations and have been commonly accepted for hardly twenty-five years. In general the standard pitch for physicists is C = 256 vibrations per second. Most of us know that musical instruments are

MUSICAL SOUNDS

tuned to a certain frequency of A above middle C. The physicist's A is 426.6 vibrations per second. In musical circles various standards have been used. *Concert pitch,* now little used, assigned 271 vibrations per second to middle C, making A equal about 450, which was too high. *International pitch* gave A as 435 vibrations per second; but the pitch now used the world over is one adopted by the American Federation of Musicians, which places A at 440. Although this is lower than concert pitch, some sopranos find it difficult to sing some of the arias composed by the old masters when pitched so high.

What is the Doppler Effect? Have you ever observed the sudden drop in the apparent pitch of an automobile horn, the gong of a fire truck, or the whistle or bell of a train as any of these sped past you? Even the whirring sound of an automobile seems to drop in pitch as it passes you on a highway. How are these phenomena explained?

Apparently the change of pitch is due to the relative motions of the sound source and the observer. Fig. 4 shows an engine with its whistle blowing while moving toward the observer O_1. As a result, the sound waves in front of the engine are crowded together and their wave lengths shortened, those at the sides are not affected, and those behind are drawn out and lengthened. With each new wave sent out, the train is closer to the observer than when the preceding wave started; hence, each new wave has less distance to travel than the preceding one. This results in more waves reaching observer O_1 per second than would reach him if the train were stationary. The effect is to increase the frequency, or raise the pitch, of the whistle. How are the frequency and pitch affected for observer O_2? O_3? O_4?

The apparent change in the pitch of a sound caused by the relative motions of the source and the observer is called the Doppler Effect. In general, the pitch of a sounding body is higher than its natural frequency when the source and the observer are approaching each other. When they are receding, the pitch is lowered. Give some illustrations of this effect from your own experiences.

What are sympathetic vibrations? In the previous chapter we used a demonstration to show that sound can do work. Why was the same tone as the one you hummed reproduced by the piano? The reason is that only bodies having the same frequencies can respond to each other in this manner. Two tuning forks of the same frequency can be used to illustrate the same thing (see Fig. 5).

Fig. 4. Does the relationship $V = nl$ apply to the Doppler Effect?

SOUND

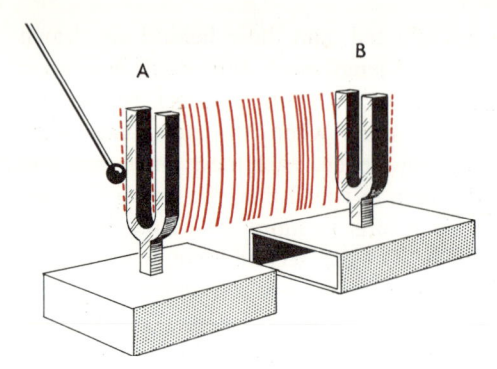

Fig. 5. Sympathetic vibrations.

When tuning fork *A* starts vibrating, it sends out condensations and rarefactions. The first condensation to reach *B* exerts a little pressure against its prongs, and displaces them slightly. The rarefaction which follows allows the prongs to fall back. Since *B* has the same natural frequency as *A*, each successive condensation and rarefaction from *A* serves to increase the amplitude of vibration of *B*. Thus, *B* soon emits an audible sound. Such vibrations are called *sympathetic vibrations*.

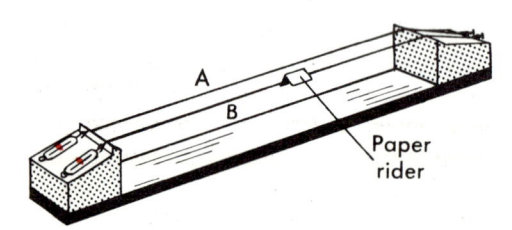

Fig. 6. Demonstrating sympathetic vibrations with a sonometer.

Sympathetic vibrations can also be demonstrated by use of a sonometer (Fig. 6) on which are mounted two wires under such tensions that their frequencies are the same. Plucking wire *A* causes the rider on *B* to be thrown off. Why? Why do your windows sometimes rattle during a thunderstorm?

Resonance—a special case of sympathetic vibrations. You may have noticed the hollow cylinders hung beneath the bars of a xylophone and wondered why they were there. The cylinders increase in length from the high-pitched tones to the low. An experiment will help us to understand the function of these *resonators*.

Hold a vibrating tuning fork over a tall hydrometer jar (Fig. 7). Now slowly pour water into the jar, and an intense sound will soon be heard. If more water is poured in, the effect is destroyed. Repeat the experiment, using a fork of higher frequency. It is now found necessary to pour in more water than before in order to produce *resonance*. That is, the air column above the water must be shortened so it will vibrate sympathetically with the tuning fork. What is the explanation?

Let *a* and *b* represent the extreme positions of a vibrating prong of the tuning fork. When the prong travels from *b* toward *a*, it sends a condensation down the tube. If the sound of the fork is to be reinforced, this condensation must be reflected by the water back to the prong just in time to unite with the condensation produced above the prong as it swings back toward *b*. Since the motion of the prong *b* to *a* is

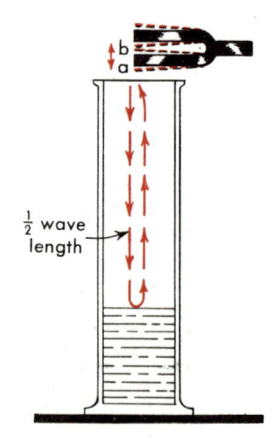

Fig. 7. Resonance in a closed tube.

MUSICAL SOUNDS 331

$L = \frac{\lambda}{4}$

(a)

Composite wave
(b)

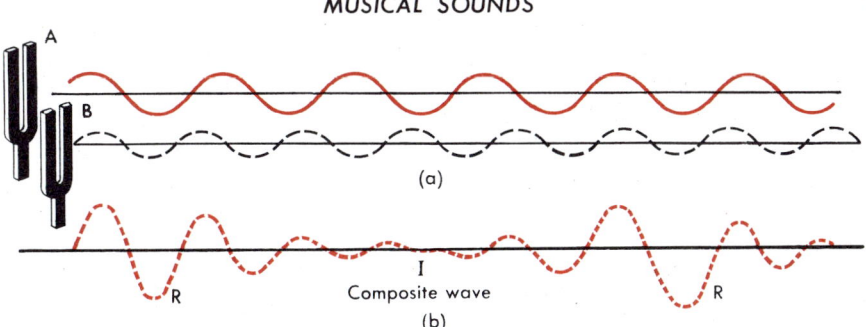

Fig. 8. The alternate reinforcement and interference of sound waves produce beats.

half a complete vibration, the distance down the tube and back again must be half a wave length of the sound produced. Thus, the length of the air column must be a quarter wave length. The diameter of the tube also affects the length of air column needed. Two-fifths of the diameter (d) of the tube should be added to the length (l') of the air column to obtain a quarter wave length (l) of the sound. Then

$$l = 4(0.4d + l'). \text{ (Why?)} \quad (1)$$

And, since

$$l = \frac{V}{n} \quad \text{(page 320)}$$

Therefore $\quad n = \dfrac{V}{l}$

$$n = \frac{V}{4(0.4d + l')} \quad (2)$$

PROBLEM: Resonance is produced when a vibrating tuning fork is held over an air column 1 ft. long. If the diameter of the tube is 1 in. and the temperature of the air in the tube is 20°C, what is the frequency of the fork?

SOLUTION:

$$n = \frac{V}{4(0.4d + l')}$$

Substituting,

$$n = \frac{1088 + 40}{4(0.4 \times \frac{1}{12} + 1)}$$

$$= \frac{1128}{4.13}$$

$$= 273.1 \text{ v/s}$$

What are beats and how are they produced? It has been stated (Chapter 28) that sound waves can suffer interference; and that they, if of the same wave length, may reinforce or cancel each other, depending upon whether they meet in the same or in opposite phases of vibration. What occurs, however, when two tuning forks of different frequencies are sounded side by side?

In Fig. 8(a) we see two such forks sending out trains of waves of different lengths. The waves from B are shorter than those from A. Fig. 8(b), a graph of the composite wave, shows the effect of these trains traveling together. They alternately suffer constructive and destructive interference, producing alternate regions of more intense sound (R) and silence (I), or near-silence. Thus, the sound appears to come in pulses, or *beats*. <u>*Beats are produced by alternate constructive and destructive interference of sound waves.*</u>

Two tuning forks of the same pitch can be used to demonstrate beats. A prong of one of the forks should be weighted slightly. This will make its frequency slightly less than that of the other. If they are then sounded together, beats will be heard.

What is the law of beats? Repeat the experiment described above, but add more weight to the already weighted fork. Now the beats come more rapidly than before. Apparently, the greater the difference in frequency between the forks, the more rapidly the beats are produced. *The number of beats that one hears per second is equal to the difference between the vibration frequencies of the sounding bodies.* This is the **law of beats.***

What is harmony? If we carry the previous experiment far enough, the beats can be produced so rapidly as to be indistinguishable by the ear. No more than four to six beats per second can be heard separately and counted. When the frequency of the beats reaches 16-20 per second, they are no longer heard as separate pulses. The ear interprets them as a new tone which, when heard with the original two tones, becomes very unpleasant and jarring. This is known as *dissonance.*

*There are also beats produced at a frequency equal to the *sum* of the two original frequencies.

Fig. 9. The wide range of frequency of sounds (30 to 4000 v/s) on a piano is made possible by striking strings that vary in length, tension, and mass.

Philip Gendreau

If, however, the number of beats per second is increased until the ratios of the frequencies of the sounding bodies approach the vibration ratios of the major scale, the resulting sound is pleasant or harmonious. This is called *consonance,* or *harmony.* You can imagine the complications, were we to attempt to figure out the beats and combinations of beats that result from all the various musical chords. Pythagoras, in the sixth century B. C., made the first attempt to classify harmonies and to show why they were consonant or dissonant. It can be readily understood that consonance for one person might be dissonance for another.

What are the laws of vibrating strings or wires? Some of us are familiar with the factors that determine the frequencies of strings used on stringed instruments. We know that a violinist places his finger far up on a string when he plays a high note; we know that tightening a string raises its pitch, and that long, thick, heavy strings produce low tones. These observations show that the *frequency of a wire* depends on its *length, tension,* and *diameter.* It also depends upon the kind of wire it is; that is, upon its *density,* or *mass per unit length.* Experiments prove that:

The vibration frequencies of strings or wires are

(a) inversely proportional to their lengths,

(b) directly proportional to the square roots of their tensions,

(c) inversely proportional to their diameters, and

(d) inversely proportional to the square roots of their densities.

PROBLEM: Express each of the above laws in general form as a proportion.

Examination of the strings of a piano will show the practical use of all these laws of strings.

MUSICAL SOUNDS

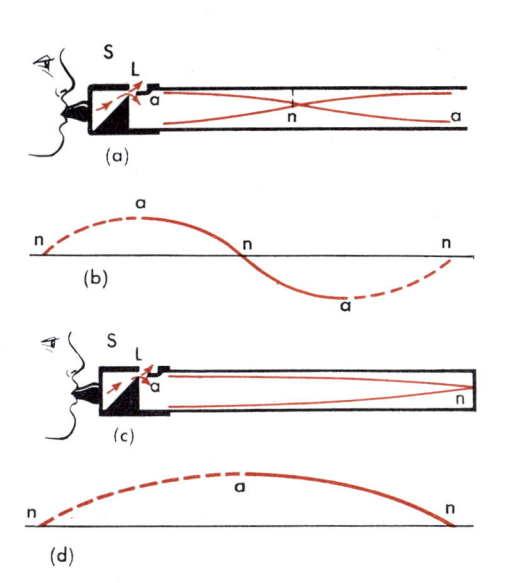

Fig. 10. (a) An open pipe. (b) Portion of a wave in an open pipe. (c) A closed pipe. (d) Portion of a wave in a closed pipe. Compare its length with that in (b).

How do air columns produce tones? If you have the opportunity, see the "insides" of a large pipe organ. The sight is both interesting and amazing. The pipes may vary in length from 2 inches to 20 feet or more. Some are made of wood, some of metal; some have square cross sections, others circular. Other instruments use vibrating air columns for tone production, but a study of organ pipes will help us understand the principles governing tone production in all wind instruments.

In Fig. 10(a) is shown a cross section of an *open* pipe; in (c), a *closed* pipe. In each case the air column is set in vibration by air blown through the slot, S, against the edge of a thin wood or metal lip, L. This causes the air to vibrate back and forth across the lip, causing condensations and rarefactions to travel rapidly to and fro through the tube, as in our experiment on resonance.

In the open pipe the air is free to vibrate at the opposite ends, marked a. These regions of maximum vibration are called *antinodes*, or *loops*, corresponding to the crests or the troughs of transverse waves. See Fig. 10(b). Condensations are reflected from the open ends of the pipe as rarefactions, and rarefactions are reflected as condensations. The reflected waves meet in the middle of the pipe in such a manner as to produce a point, on the opposite sides of which the vibratory motion of the air is in opposite directions. Thus, at this point (n), called a *node*, there is no vibration.

Study of Fig. 10(b) reveals the fact that a complete wave length consists of four times the distance from an antinode to a node. The solid portion, *ana*, of the wavy line shows the part of a wave that is produced in an open pipe. Thus, *the length of an open pipe is equal to one-half wave length of the sound produced.*

In the closed pipe the air is not free to vibrate at the closed end. Hence, a node is produced here, and an antinode at the open end. In the figure, parts (c) and (d) show that *the length of a closed pipe is equal to a quarter wave length of the sound produced.* Since frequency is inversely proportional to wave length, *the pitch of a closed pipe is one octave below that of an open pipe of the same length.* Note that the wave length for the closed pipe, Fig. 10(d), is twice that for the open pipe. By using pipes of different lengths we find that the shorter the pipe the higher the frequency, and vice versa. As with vibrating strings,

the frequencies of vibrating air columns are inversely proportional to their lengths.

What are overtones? In our discussion of strings and air columns we have assumed that they were vibrating *as wholes*. However, their vibrations are much more complicated than at first appears. That they

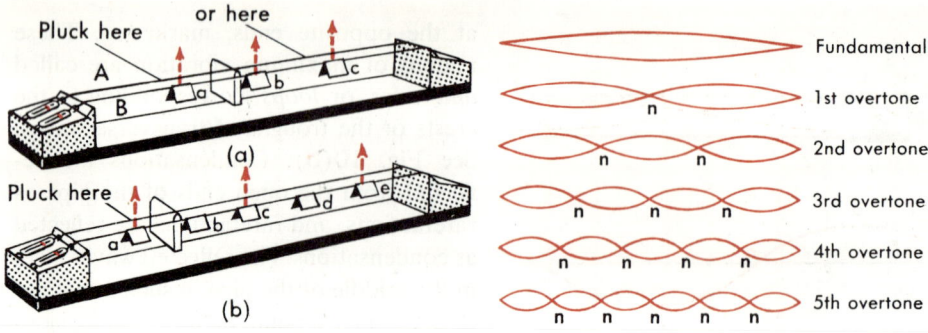

Fig. 11. Which riders are thrown off in (a)? in (b)? Why?

Fig. 12. How the overtone frequencies are related to that of the fundamental.

may vibrate *in parts,* or *segments,* can be easily demonstrated.

Using a sonometer of two wires of the same size, material, and length, and stretched to the same frequency (Fig. 11(a)), place a bridge under the middle of wire *A,* so that each of its segments produces a tone one octave above that of *B.* Now place three paper riders on *B* in the positions *a, b, c,* and pluck *A* at the middle of one of its segments. The fact that riders *a* and *c* are thrown off while *b* is undisturbed shows that *B* vibrates in two segments sympathetically with *A.* Each segment of *B* must, therefore, be emitting the same tone as the plucked segment of *A.*

Part (b) of the figure shows how wire *B* can be made to vibrate in three segments by our placing the bridge one-third of the distance between the ends of *A.* Riders *a, c,* and *e* will be thrown off, but *b* and *d* will be undisturbed. Here, again, points of no vibration are called nodes; those of maximum vibration are called antinodes, or loops. In this latter case, what will be the frequency of each segment of *B* compared to that of the wire when vibrating as a whole?

Vibrating as a whole, a wire produces its lowest possible tone, called its *fundamental.* The tones produced by vibration in parts are called *overtones.* It can be shown that *the frequencies of the overtones of a string are whole-number multiples of the frequency of its fundamental.* Such overtones are called *harmonics.*

Figure 12 shows how a string vibrates when producing its fundamental, and its first, second, third, fourth, and fifth overtones. The nodal points, *n*, are produced by the reflected waves meeting the oncoming waves in opposite phases of vibration, thus canceling each other at these points. The resulting waves thus produced are called *standing waves.* Waves in organ pipes are also standing waves.

The vibration of an air column in parts can be shown with an apparatus like the one in Fig. 13. Place a whistling device

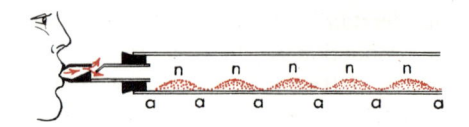

Fig. 13. Air column vibrating in segments.

in one end of a glass tube and sprinkle lycopodium powder (spores of lycopodium plants) evenly along the inside of the tube. Blowing the whistle will cause the powder to separate into heaps as shown. Blowing more or less forcefully changes the number

MUSICAL SOUNDS

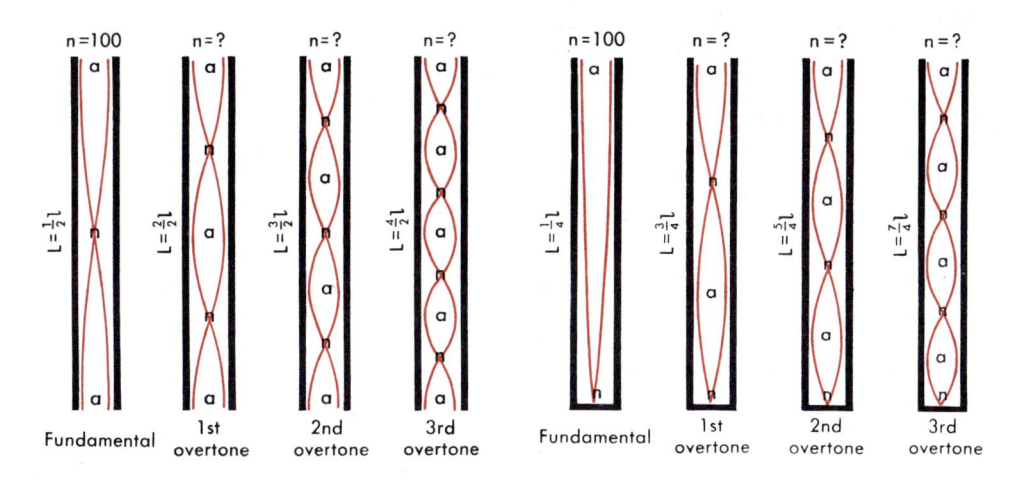

Fig. 14. Overtones in open pipes. What are the frequencies of the overtones if the fundamental frequency is 100 v/s?

Fig. 15. Overtones in closed pipes. What are the frequencies of the first three overtones?

and disposition of the heaps as well as the pitch of the tone heard. Nodes are formed at the peaks of the heaps, antinodes midway between the heaps. Note that antinodes are formed at the ends where the air is free to vibrate.

Figure 14 shows how the fundamental and the first three overtones are produced by an open pipe. For the fundamental the length of the pipe (L) equals one-half the wave length (l) of the sound produced; for the first overtone $L = \frac{2}{2}l$, for the second overtone $L = \frac{3}{2}l$, for the third, $\frac{4}{2}l$, etc. If the fundamental frequency is 100 vibrations per second, what are the frequencies of the overtones? How, in relation to the fundamental, do the overtones of open pipes compare with those of strings?

For closed pipes the case is different (Fig. 15). A node is formed at the closed end and an antinode at the open end. Thus, the only overtones possible are those whose frequencies are *odd multiples* of the fundamental frequency. Can you explain why?

What determines the quality of a sound? From our discussion it appears that a string or an air column may vibrate as a whole and in various segments at the same time (Fig. 16). Thus, the sounds they

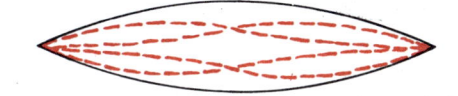

Fig. 16. Factors affecting the quality of a sound produced by a vibrating string.

produce may be combinations of their fundamentals and overtones. Up to now we have found sounds to differ in two respects—intensity or loudness, and frequency or pitch. However, experience tells us that they differ in another respect; namely, in *quality*. You can distinguish unseen friends by their voices, even if you are unable to see them. You can recognize various musical instruments by the qualities of their sounds.

Not until 1862 was the quality of sounds

understood, when the German physicist, Hermann von Helmholtz (1821-1894) stated that *the quality of a sound depends upon the number and relative intensities of the overtones produced by the sounding body*. We produce tones of entirely different quality by plucking a sonometer wire near the middle, then near one end. The latter produces a sound rich in overtones, whereas the former produces mainly the fundamental. Experience shows that *the quality of a sound depends upon the manner in which the sounding body is set in vibration*.

How can sound waves be pictured? A *cathode ray oscilloscope* can be used to demonstrate sound phenomena. This apparatus is being found in increasing numbers of high schools throughout the country. The basic function of the oscilloscope is to "draw" a "line graph" on its television-type screen depicting the way a voltage input is varying. (The theory of the oscilloscope is discussed in Chapter 49.) If a sound wave is intercepted by a crystal microphone, a small varying voltage is produced. The voltage varies with exactly the same frequency and magnitude as the sound wave. This changing voltage is led

Fig. 18. By means of ultrasonic agitation, two immiscible substances, water and mercury, form a fairly permanent suspension.

Courtesy Battelle Memorial Institute

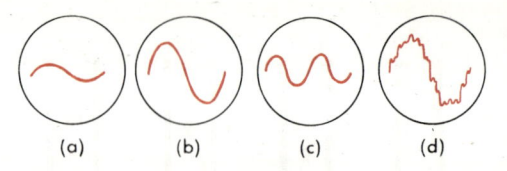

Fig. 17. (a) Low amplitude (256 v/s); (b) Higher amplitude (256 v/s); (c) Higher pitch (512 v/s); (d) Overtones with fundamental (256 v/s).

by wires to the oscilloscope, on whose screen are seen pictures like those shown in Fig. 17.

If a tuning fork with a frequency of 256 vibrations per second is struck lightly with a rubber mallet, the curve produced is like *a* of the figure. If it is struck harder, the curve is like *b*. The amplitude of vibration has increased. Striking a tuning fork of frequency 512 produces the graph of *c*. We see twice as many waves, indicating the ratio 1:2. Now if the 256 fork is struck with metal the picture is like *d*. Note that the fundamental is viewed along with overtones.

By playing different instruments and having different people speak to the microphone, we can view the graphs of their tones. It is surprising, however, to see the similarity in the graphs of different people saying the same vowel into the microphone.

What is ultrasonics? A study which has made much progress in the past few years is that of *ultrasonics*. As the name implies, this science consists in the production of vibrations whose frequencies are so high as to escape detection by the human ear. Some rather remarkable things have been done with these high-frequency waves, such as killing bacteria, setting objects afire, and sterilizing animals. It is difficult to say how far-reaching and practicable the results of this phase of the study of sound may be.

SUMMARY AND CONCLUSIONS

1. Musical sounds are the result of rapid regular vibrations of bodies.
2. The pitch of a sound is measured in terms of its frequency.
3. The major diatonic scale consists of a succession of tones whose vibration ratios are 1, 9/8, 5/4, 4/3, 3/2, 5/3, 15/8, and 2.
4. A major triad consists of three tones whose frequencies bear the relation 4:5:6. The major scale has three such triads.
5. A musical interval is determined by the ratio of the frequencies of two tones. An octave interval has the ratio 2:1.
6. Black keys make it possible to play a piano in any desired key.
7. The tempered scale consists of thirteen tones whose successive frequencies are each 1.06 times the frequency of the preceding tone.
8. The world's standard pitch places A at 440 v/s.
9. The apparent change in the pitch of a sounding body, due to the relative motion of the body and an observer, is called the Doppler Effect.
10. Sympathetic vibrations, or resonance, depends upon the fact that a body of a given frequency can impart vibrations to another of the same frequency.
11. Beats are caused by alternate constructive and destructive interference of sound waves.
12. The number of beats that one hears per second is equal to the difference between the frequencies of the sounding bodies. This is the law of beats.
13. The frequencies of strings or wires are inversely proportional to their lengths; directly proportional to the square roots of their tensions; inversely proportional to their diameters; and inversely proportional to the square roots of their masses per unit length, or densities.
14. The frequencies of vibrating air columns are inversely proportional to their lengths. The frequency of an open pipe is equal to twice that of a closed or stopped pipe of the same length.
15. Vibrating bodies may vibrate as wholes and in segments at the same time. When vibrating as wholes, they produce their fundamentals; when vibrating in segments, they produce overtones.
16. Frequencies of overtones of strings and open pipes are successive whole-number multiples (2, 3, 4, etc.) of their fundamental frequencies; for closed pipes, only the odd multiples (3, 5, 7, etc.) are possible.
17. The quality of a sound depends upon the number and relative intensities of the overtones produced by the sounding body.
18. Sound waves can be depicted by the cathode ray oscilloscope.

QUESTIONS FOR REVIEW

1. Is there any truth in the saying, "There is music in everything"? Explain.
2. How many major third intervals are there in the scale of C? How many fourth intervals? How many minor thirds?
3. On what instruments is a musician restricted to the use of the tempered scale? On what instruments is he not so restricted?
4. Why are soldiers ordered to "route step" (break step) when crossing a bridge?
5. Show how piano wires illustrate all the laws of strings.
6. Why is it possible to rotate phonograph records at different speeds without destroying the harmony of the music?
7. While singing in a shower stall a man discovered that a certain tone was greatly intensified. How could this be explained?
8. How can beats be illustrated by two ticking watches?
9. How does pushing a child in a swing illustrate the principles of resonance? What happens if the pushes occur at the wrong times?
10. The sixth overtone of a string is particularly dissonant. Why are piano mallets made to strike the strings about one-seventh of their lengths from one end?
11. Why are strings of stringed instruments plucked, struck, or bowed near one end rather than in the middle?
12. What are standing waves?

13. If the frequency of an open organ pipe 2.2 feet long is 256 vibrations per second, what is the frequency of a closed pipe 1.1 feet in length?

14. What methods are employed in setting into vibration the air columns of the piccolo, flute, clarinet, saxophone, cornet, trombone, and oboe? How are the lengths of their air columns regulated?

15. How many fundamental tones can be produced by the use of the three valves of a cornet? How, then, do you account for its wide range of possible tone production?

16. How are various tones produced by a person while speaking or singing?

17. Why is it important that all the pipes of a pipe organ be kept at the same constant temperature?

EXERCISES AND PROBLEMS

1. The middle tone of a major triad has a frequency of 300 v/s. Calculate the frequencies of the other tones.

2. Using E (320 v/s) as the key tone of a major scale, compute the frequencies of each of the other tones in an octave. How many black keys would have to be used in playing this scale on a piano?

3. Calculate the frequencies of the third, fourth, fifth, and octave intervals of G (384 v/s).

4. What is the interval between two tones whose frequencies are 180 and 150 v/s?

5. What is the wave length of the sound produced by G when the air temperature is 25°C?

6. What are the frequencies of the highest and lowest C's on a piano?

7. An air column 12 in. in length produces resonance with a certain tuning fork. If the air temperature in the column is 21°C, what is the frequency of the fork?

8. Set up four proportions, each illustrating a law of strings.

9. A string whose length is 90 cm. has a frequency of 192 v/s. All factors other than length being the same, what will be the frequency of a string whose length is 80 cm.? If these two strings are sounded together, how many beats per second will be produced? Will the resulting sound be consonant or dissonant?

10. The tension of a piano wire is 16 kg. What must its tension be to produce a tone an octave lower? An octave higher? A fifth interval higher? A minor third lower?

11. What must be the length of an open organ pipe if it is to produce the tone C', when the temperature of the air with which it is blown is 20°C?

12. If the frequency of A on a piano is 440 v/s, what is the frequency of middle C?

13. The cavity of a closed pipe whistle is 2 in. long. What will be its fundamental frequency if it is blown with air at 37°C?

14. Derive formulas with which the frequency of any overtone of a string, an open pipe, and a closed pipe can be calculated.

15. A closed organ pipe is 8¾ ft. long. What will be its fundamental frequency if blown with air at 16°C? To what key on a piano does this tone correspond? How long would an open pipe have to be to produce the same tone?

PROJECTS

1. Partially fill a series of eight equal-sized test tubes with water in such a way that, when lightly struck in succession, they will produce the major diatonic scale. Glass tumblers may also be used, or different lengths of wood as in xylophone.

2. Attach to a wall hook one end of a 15- or 20-ft. clothesline. Holding the other end in your hand, see if you can, with a rotary motion of your hand, cause the string to vibrate in standing waves with various numbers of segments. This is a good way to demonstrate the vibration of a string in parts. Tell what overtones are exemplified.

READING YOU WILL ENJOY

Swezey, K. M., *After-Dinner Science*. Whittlesey House, McGraw-Hill Book Company, Inc., New York, 1948. "Resonance Works Wonders," pp. 82-83, " 'Sound of the Sea' Is Due to Resonance," p. 84; "Sympathetic Milk Bottles," p. 85; "Pipe Organs and Aeolian Harps," pp. 86-87.

Unit 11

Static Electricity

You have undoubtedly seen gasoline trucks that have a chain dragging along the ground. Or perhaps you may have noticed a small vertical wire protruding from the roadway near tunnel or bridge toll collection booths. Or you may have received a slight shock on a winter day upon taking off your overcoat or upon touching a piece of metal after walking across a rug. These phenomena and others, such as lightning and the action of a condenser in a radio, are directly related to the study of static electricity. This unit will also introduce you to the amazing electron which does some useful, as well as some exceedingly harmful, things.

A striking demonstration of a phenomenon caused by static electricity is shown in the unit photograph. Man-made lightning is jumping the gap from the steel spheres of the Van de Graaf generator to the steel girders of the building. The lightning that you see is not electricity, but rather the result of electricity passing along that path through the air.

30. WHAT IS ELECTRICITY?
31. THE ELECTRON THEORY VERSUS THE ATOMIC THEORY OF MATTER
32. HOW DOES THE ELECTRON THEORY EXPLAIN LEYDEN JARS, CONDENSERS, AND LIGHTNING?

Unit Photograph Courtesy High-Voltage Engineering Corp.

Chapter 30

What Is Electricity?

The problem. Have you ever walked across a dry wool rug* and then held your finger near a metal doorknob or the end of someone's nose? What happened? Have you ever rubbed a cat's back and heard its hair crackle? Do this in the dark and see what happens.

What does your hair do when it is very clean and dry and you comb it with a hard rubber comb? What happens when the comb is then touched to bits of paper?

Most of these phenomena are not new. As long ago as 600 B.C. the Greeks observed that when yellow amber, a hard, dry resin which they found buried in the ground or lying on the shore of the Baltic Sea, was rubbed on wool or fur, it temporarily attracted lint and hair, and bits of straw and leaves. They called this amber *elektron,* and when it possessed the power of attracting other bodies it was said to be *charged*. From *elektron* we have coined the word *electricity,* and today charged bodies are said to be electrically charged.

When an electrical charge is produced by friction, it is often called *frictional electricity*. And since it remains fixed or stationary on bodies commonly electrified, or charged, it is also called *static electricity*.

But this static electricity is a far cry from many of the electrical phenomena that we now observe. Today we can almost unthinkingly flip a switch and flood a room with light; we can merely dial a number and talk across the continent; or we can turn a knob and hear as well as see a speaker from London, a ball game from Detroit, an orchestra from Paris, or a musical comedy from Hollywood. Yet in spite of our daily use of electricity, to most of us it is almost as mysterious as it was to the early Greeks. That items as unlike as sound, heat, light, pictures, and refrigeration can all be produced from the same source is almost unbelievable.

Our problem is to link all these seemingly unlike phenomena into a theory that not only explains what electricity is, but also enables us to control electricity and predict what it will do. To begin our study, let us start with the simplest electrical phenomena: the attraction and repulsion of charged bodies.

Why do some charged bodies attract and others repel? If we charge a rubber rod by rubbing it briskly with cat fur and then bring it near a pith ball suspended on a silk thread, as shown in Fig. 1, the ball is attracted to the charged rod. But on touching the rod, it is quickly repelled. Why?

---

*By this method as much as 30,000 volts of electricity can be generated on the body of a person having a very dry skin.

341

STATIC ELECTRICITY

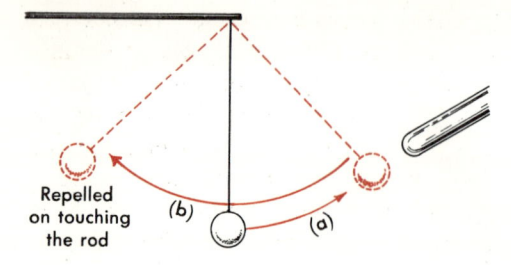

Fig. 1. How do you account for the attraction and the repulsion?

Possibly when the ball touches the charged rubber rod it too becomes charged. That the ball will now attract other pith balls and bits of paper shows that it is charged, as we anticipated. Apparently, then, charged bodies do repel each other.

To test this hypothesis further, charge one end of a rubber rod by rubbing it briskly with cat fur and support it as shown in Fig. 2. Then charge one end of another rubber rod and bring it toward the charged end of the supported rod. Do the results verify the conclusion that charged bodies repel?

Next, with two glass rods and a piece of silk repeat the experiment just explained. Again the two charged ends repel, again indicating that charged bodies repel.

But what happens when one of the charged rods is glass and the other is hard rubber? To the surprise of those who have not done these experiments before, the two charged ends attract each other. See Fig. 3. See if you can explain the results without reading further.

Study of these experiments shows that in each case of repulsion the two repelling bodies were alike in composition and were rubbed with the same kind of material. This indicates that possibly the repelling charges were alike and that therefore *like charges repel*.

On the other hand, the two attracting bodies were unlike in composition and were rubbed with unlike materials. This indicates that possibly the attracting charges were unlike and that therefore *unlike charges attract*. In conclusion:

Like charges repel.
Unlike charges attract.

Thus we have explained attraction and repulsion of charged bodies by assuming that there are only two kinds of electrical charges. The kind found on the glass in the above experiment is called *positive* ($+$); that found on the rubber is called *negative* ($-$). Two charged bodies repel each other because they have like charges, or they attract each other because they have unlike charges.

When your hair is charged by combing, are the hairs charged alike or differently?

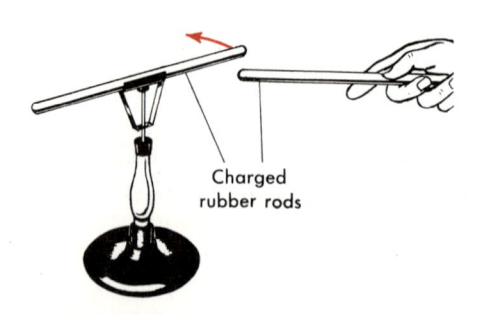

Fig. 2. The similarly charged rods repel each other.

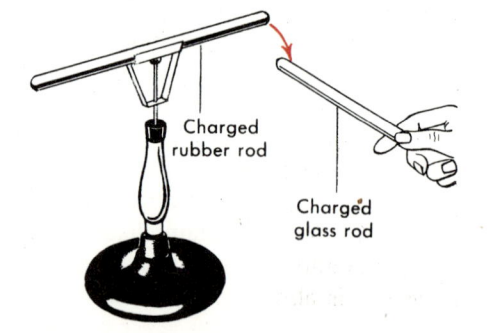

Fig. 3. The differently charged rods attract each other.

Fig. 4. Unlike charges attract; like charges repel.

Is the charge on the comb like that on your hair? Give evidence to support your answers and check them by experiment.

Neutral bodies. Bodies which are not electrified are called *neutral*. Neutral bodies—for example, neutral bits of paper and pith balls—are attracted by charged bodies. Why, we have yet to explain.

Coulomb's Law—the force between two charged bodies. It is common sense that the greater the charges on two bodies, the greater the force of attraction or repulsion between them. Also the greater the distance between the charges, the less the force of attraction or repulsion.

Charles Augustin de Coulomb (1736-1806) was the first to measure electrostatic forces. He found that

the force between two charged bodies is directly proportional to the quantity of charge on each body and inversely proportional to the square of the distance between them.

This statement is known as *Coulomb's Law*.

What is an electrical field of force? The fact that two charged bodies some distance apart exert forces on each other implies that the effect of one charge on the other is transmitted through space between them. Such a space or region is defined as a *field of force*.

The electrostatic field about two charged bodies some distance apart can be illustrated graphically if a glass plate is placed over them and lycopodium powder or fine bits of pith are sprinkled over the glass. As a result, the fine particles arrange themselves in lines similar to the lines shown in Fig. 5. For this reason, electric fields of force are said to be made up of *lines of force* and are represented by lines. The direction of a field of force at any point in the field is, according to general agreement, the direction in which a positive charge at the point is forced or urged. Hence the direction of the field about an isolated negative charge is toward the charge. See (a) of Fig. 5. The direction of the lines of force between a positive (+) and negative (−) charge is from the positive toward the negative. The field between two positive charges is shown in (b) of Fig. 5.

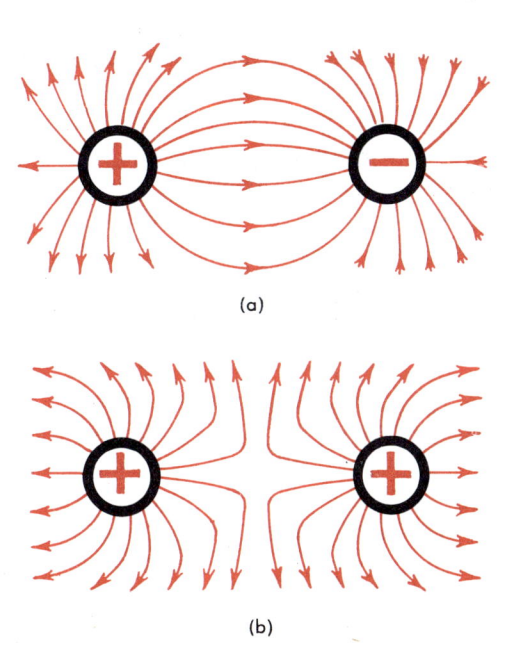

Fig. 5. (a) Lines of force about unlike charges. (b) About like charges.

How can we detect an electrical charge and determine its kind? The fact that a charged body attracts a neutral pith ball or bits of paper shows that it is charged, but this does not indicate the kind of charge. And since bodies with unlike charges attract, the same as a charged body and a neutral body attract, then attraction alone is not a reliable test of the kind of charge on a body. But since only like charges repel, repulsion of two charged bodies is reliable. Repulsion shows that the charges on both bodies are the same. Consequently, if the charge on one body is known the charge on the other is known.

Instruments for determining the kind of charge on a body. An instrument used to detect a charge on a body and to determine its kind is called an *electroscope*. The apparatus shown in Fig. 2 can be used as an electroscope. If the rod has a positive charge, then it is repelled by a body possessing a positive charge. If the rod has a negative charge, then it is repelled by a body having a negative charge. The trouble with this instrument is that it is not very sensitive and hence will not detect small charges.

(a) *Pith ball electroscope*. A very simple and sensitive electroscope can be made of a pith ball suspended on a silk thread, as shown in Fig. 1. In using this device, first charge the ball with the kind of charge that you suspect is on the body. If the ball is attracted by the body, repeat the test by putting a different kind of charge on the ball. When this is done, the charged body should repel the pith ball, which indicates that its charge is like that on the ball.

(b) *Gold-leaf electroscope*. A more sensitive form of electroscope is the so-called gold-leaf electroscope. It usually consists of two very thin leaves of aluminum, tinfoil, or gold, attached to one end of a brass rod which is mounted in sulfur

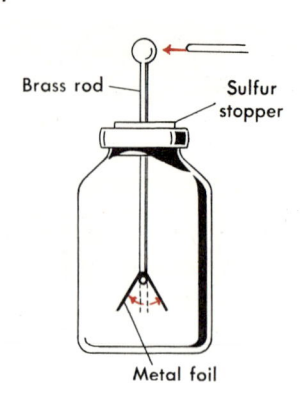

Fig. 6. A metal-leaf electroscope.

and placed in a glass jar, as shown in Fig. 6. The purpose of the jar is to support the rod and protect the leaves from air currents. A brass disk or knob is usually soldered to the top of the brass rod.

When either a positive or a negative charge is brought near the knob of the electroscope the leaves diverge, even when the charge is more than one or two feet away. Explain why this happens.

This makes it clear that a neutral body can be charged by the mere influence of a nearby charged body. This method of charging a body is called *induction*. The charge is said to be *induced*. As soon as the charged body is moved away from the electroscope the leaves collapse, showing the loss of their charge. Here we have another very simple test for the presence of a charge, but like the neutral pith ball, it does not determine the kind of charge. How, then, can a gold-leaf electroscope be used to reveal the kind of charge that is present on a charged body?

Fixing a charge on an electroscope by contact (conduction). When a negatively charged rod is touched to the electroscope knob and then separated from it, the leaves remain apart, indicating that they are charged alike. See Fig. 7. Evidently the charges, because of their mu-

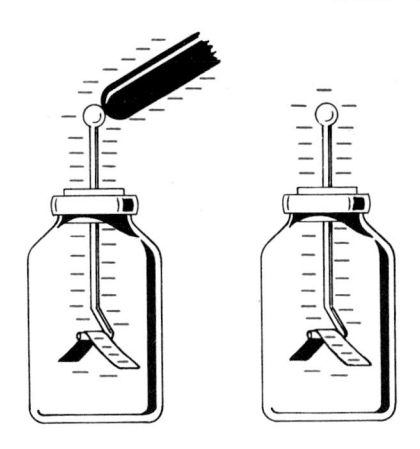

Fig. 7. Charging by contact.

tual repulsion, flow from the charged rod onto the knob of the electroscope and then repel similar charges already in the electroscope as far as possible onto the leaves. The charge is said to be *conducted* onto the electroscope, and for this reason the electroscope is said to be charged by *contact* or *conduction*. Here the charge is said to be *fixed* on the electroscope. Would you expect the charge on the electroscope to be like that on the charged rod? Test your answer, using a pith ball electroscope.

When a charge like that on the electroscope—say it is a negative charge—is brought toward the electroscope, the leaves spread farther apart, indicating that more charges are forced onto them. This we would expect to be the case because the negative charges on the upper part of the electroscope would be repelled by the negative charges on the rod and forced into the leaves.

What should happen to the leaves if a positively charged rod is brought near a negatively charged electroscope? Explain, and test your prediction.

Fixing a charge on an electroscope by induction. Bring a charged rod near an uncharged electroscope but do not allow the two to touch. At the same time, hold your finger on the opposite side of the electroscope knob. Then separate your finger from the knob, and finally remove the charged rod. You will find that a charge has been fixed on the electroscope and that it is unlike the one on the charged rod. Where did it come from?

Since the charge is unlike that on the charged rod, it could not have come from the rod. Did it come from your finger? If so, how? This is really the greatest mystery we have encountered so far in our study of electricity.

As a result of this experiment and others, several questions come to mind. Where does an induced charge come from? Why does a charged body attract a neutral body? What happens when a body is charged by friction? Is electricity matter? Is it energy? Or is it something else? These questions we must answer by whatever theory we propose.

Benjamin Franklin's theory of electricity. Benjamin Franklin believed that electricity is a single, fluid substance and that all matter normally contains this fluid. In the light of his experience as a bookkeeper, Franklin used the plus sign (+) to represent matter that possesses a *surplus*, or excess, of this fluid, just as modern balance sheets employ the same symbol. A substance that contains an excess of this fluid, he said, is *positively* charged. In a similar sense he used the minus sign (−) to designate a substance that is deficient, or lacking, in the amount of fluid it normally possesses. A substance that is deficient in fluid he described as being *negatively* charged. A substance that has neither an excess nor a deficiency of its normal quantity of the fluid he declared to be *neutral*.

Franklin further stated that if a substance possessing an excess of the fluid is connected to one that is deficient in it, the fluid will flow from where it is in excess to where it is lacking. Thus, he concluded that the electrical fluid whose existence he assumed, must flow from positively charged matter to matter which is negatively charged, or from (+) to (−). Do you see any weaknesses in Franklin's theory? Explain.

The electron theory. Instead of assuming that all matter contains "electrical fluid," let us make the following assumptions.

1. Matter is composed fundamentally of two types of particles called *electrons* and *protons*.

   (a) Each electron is exactly the same; it has negligible mass, is in constant motion in orbits around the nuclei of atoms, and is the unit negative charge.

   (b) Each proton is exactly the same; it has considerably more mass than the electron, is found in the nuclei of atoms, and is the unit positive charge.

2. Substances are unlike because they possess different numbers and different arrangements of these fundamental particles.

3. The electron, because of its negligible mass and because it exists outside the nuclei of atoms, is more readily moved than a proton.

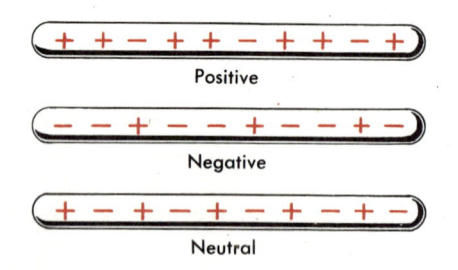

Fig. 8. Positive, negative, and neutral bodies.

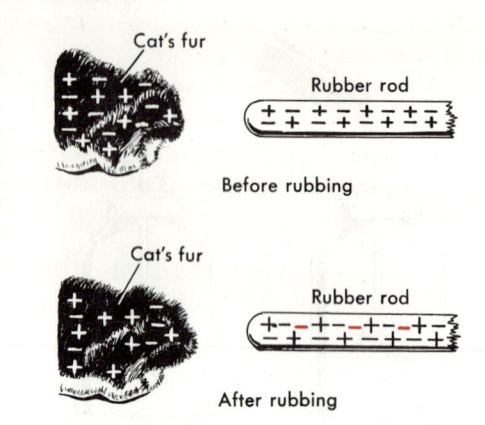

Fig. 9. Account for the charge on the rod.

4. A substance normally contains equal numbers of electrons and protons. Thus, the sum of the negative units equals the sum of the positive units, and the substance is electrically neutral. See Fig. 8.

5. When a neutral body *gains* electrons from some outside source, it acquires a negative charge. Thus, a body is *negatively charged* when it has electrons in *excess* of its normal number.

6. When a neutral body *loses* electrons, it acquires a positive charge. Thus, a body is *positively charged* when it has a *deficiency* of electrons.

7. It should be noted, therefore, that a body acquires an electric charge by gaining or losing electrons.

How does the electron theory explain what takes place when two bodies are charged by being rubbed together? When a rubber rod is rubbed with cat's fur, the rod, as you know, becomes charged negatively and the fur positively (Fig. 9). Again, when you comb your hair with a rubber comb, the comb becomes charged negatively and the hair positively. How does the electron theory explain these charges?

According to the electron theory, part of the energy used in rubbing the neutral bodies together transfers some of the electrons from the fur to the rod, making the fur positive and the rod negative. Authorities on the structure of matter tell us that a piece of fur holds its electrons less firmly than does a piece of rubber. It is for this reason that the electron transfer takes place from the fur to the rubber rather than in the opposite direction.

How does the electron theory explain attraction between a charged and a neutral body? Let us assume that a neutral pith ball consists of equal numbers of protons and electrons, Fig. 10(a). If a rod with a negative charge is brought near the ball, some of the electrons in the ball should be repelled toward the far side and the protons should be left unneutralized on the near side, as shown in Fig. 10(b). Since the positive side of the ball is nearer to the charged rod than is the negative side, then the force of attraction is greater than the repulsion. Hence, the ball is attracted toward the charged rod. But why, as soon as it touches the charged rod, is the ball repelled? See Fig. 10(c).

Evidently, when the ball touches the negative rod, some, though not all, of the surplus electrons on the rod are conducted onto the ball because of the attraction of the protons. The result is that the ball now possesses more electrons than protons and therefore has a negative charge. Consequently, since like charges repel, the rod and the ball now repel each other.

Do charges in a body shift when it is charged by induction? But what proof do we have that electrical charges move in the manner indicated above when a body is charged by induction? If the charges do shift, then, if the ball in Fig. 10(b) could be cut in two along an imaginary line between the positive and negative charges, one half of it should be positive and the other half negative.

Since it would be difficult to cut the ball without removing the charge from it, let us use, instead of one ball, two hollow metal balls, *A* and *B*, supported on glass or hard-rubber stands, and placed against each other as shown in Fig. 11. Then, when a rod with a negative charge is brought near *A*, a charge should be induced on the balls, as shown. And if the balls are then separated, the charge on *A* should be positive and that on *B* should be negative. Test this prediction, using an electroscope.

Another test of whether or not the

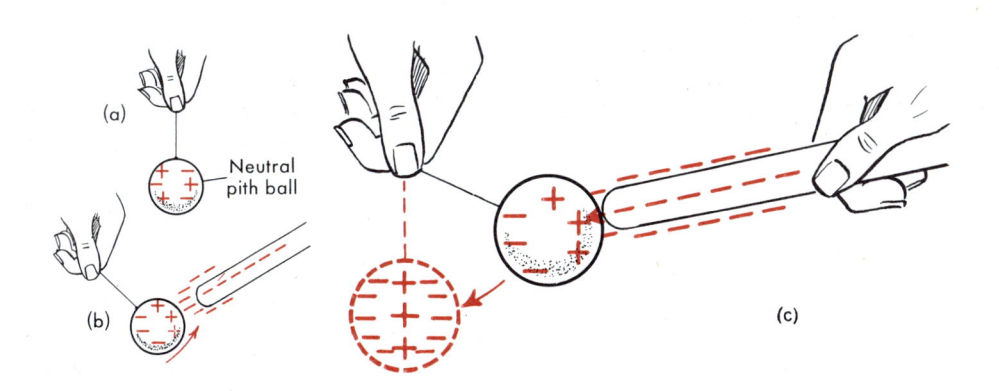

Fig. 10. The neutral pith ball is attracted by a charged rod, then repelled upon touching it.

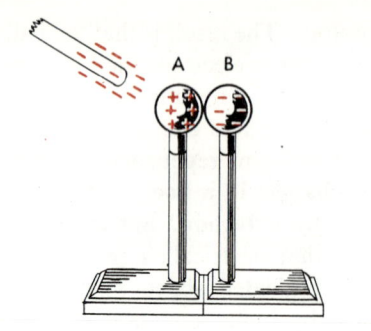

Fig. 11. Charging a body by induction.

charges shift when a body is charged by induction can be made if you touch ball *B* with your finger before you separate the balls (see Fig. 12). If the charges do move, then the negative electrons on the balls, since they are repelled, should move into your finger, leaving both balls with positive charges. Subsequently, when the balls are separated, both of them should have a positive charge. Test this prediction and also test your finger for a charge.

Repeat this experiment, using a rod with a positive charge. Explain the results, assuming that only the electrons are free to move in each body and from one body to another.

How does the electron theory explain the charging of an electroscope by induction? This is the question that we were unable to explain before we considered the electron theory. According to the electron theory, when a rod with a negative charge is brought near an electroscope, some electrons in the knob are repelled and flow into the leaves. Thus, the knob is charged positively and both leaves are charged negatively. As a result the leaves diverge. If the rod is removed, the electrons again distribute themselves over the knob and leaves, causing the electroscope to be neutral again.

But in case you touch the knob with your finger while the rod is still near the knob, as shown in Fig. 13, and then remove your finger before removing the rod, the electroscope is charged positively. This means that electrons have been removed from the electroscope, and evidently they were removed via your finger. The negative charges on the charged rod repelled those on the electroscope rod, forcing them to flow into your finger.

Thus, by the method just described, a charge was induced on the electroscope. The charged rod (inducing charge) never touched the electroscope in any way. The advantage of this method is that there is little danger of damaging the leaves because of their mutual repulsion.

Predict what would happen if you removed your finger from the knob on the electroscope after the charged rod was removed. Test this prediction.

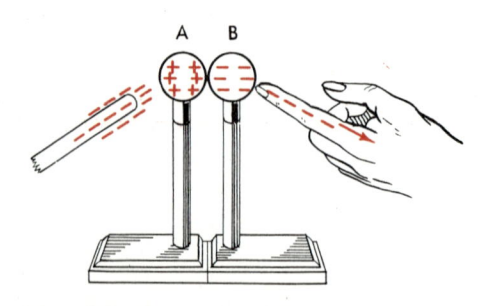

The mass of the proton and electron. Since we have assumed that electricity consists of two kinds of matter, electrons and protons, the consequences are that both must have mass and weight. How electrons and protons were actually weighed is a long story, most of which is beyond the scope of this book. Nevertheless, repeated experiments by many experimenters have confirmed again and again that the mass of an electron in round numbers is the unbelievably small amount, 9.11×10^{-28} gram, or 0.000,000,000,000,-000,000,000,000,911 gram.

Fig. 12. Charging positively by induction.

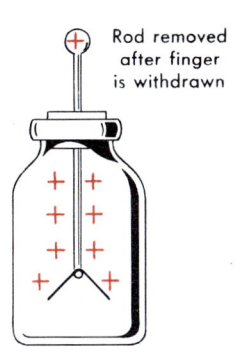

Fig. 13. Charging an electroscope positively by induction.

Also, it has been found that the mass of the proton is approximately 1840 times that of an electron. In comparison with the mass of the proton the mass of the electron is considered negligible or zero.

Thus, in the way of a preliminary conclusion we can say that so far the consequences of the assumptions of the electron theory of matter are agreeing with observation and experiment. Will they continue to do so?

SUMMARY AND CONCLUSIONS

1. When amber, glass, hard rubber, fountain pens, combs, and many other objects are rubbed with certain materials, they attract bits of hair, wool, lint, dry leaves, and pith balls. Such bodies are said to be electrically charged.
2. The charge produced on glass when it is rubbed with silk is called positive. The charge produced on hard rubber or vulcanite when it is rubbed with cat's fur is called negative.
3. Like charges repel and unlike charges attract.
4. Uncharged bodies are said to be neutral.
5. An electroscope is used to detect a charge and determine its kind.
6. When a body is charged by the bringing of a charged body near it, the resulting charge is said to be induced.
7. According to the electron theory, all substances consist of positive particles called protons and negative particles called electrons.
8. A body with a negative charge possesses more electrons than protons; a body with a positive charge possesses fewer electrons than protons; a neutral body possesses equal numbers of electrons and protons.

QUESTIONS FOR REVIEW

1. State the laws of attraction and repulsion.
2. What evidence do we have that there are two different kinds of electrical charges? Explain how to produce each.
3. Explain, in accordance first with Franklin's theory and then with the electron theory, the condition of a body when its charge is (a) positive; (b) negative; (c) neutral.
4. Upon what assumption is each theory in Question 3 based? What is a proton? An electron?
5. What is the simplest way to find out whether a body is charged?
6. Does an uncharged electroscope distinguish between the kinds of charges? Explain.
7. When two bodies are charged by friction, are the charges created? Explain what takes place, including the condition of each body before and after being charged.
8. Explain, using diagrams, why a neutral pith ball is attracted by a positively charged rod.

9. Explain how an electroscope is charged by (a) induction, and (b) conduction, when a body with a positive charge is used. Assume that only electrons are free to move.
10. When an electroscope has a positive charge, what happens when a like charge is brought near? An unlike charge?
11. Why do lint and dust cling to clothes which are being brushed?
12. Printing and mimeographing machines often become highly charged. Explain.
13. Calculate the number of protons required to make one gram.
14. If the distance between two charged bodies is doubled, how is the force of attraction or repulsion affected?
15. If the charge on one of two charged bodies is doubled, how is the force of attraction or repulsion affected?

PROJECTS

1. *The "jumping cats."* Cut pieces of paper in the shape of tiny cats and place them inside the lid of a coffee can. Cover the lid with a glass plate, rub the glass with a piece of silk, and explain what takes place.
2. With silk thread suspend two inflated balloons side by side but not quite touching each other. Then rub both of them with cat's fur and explain the results.
3. Make an electroscope. See page 344. Use an ink bottle that is larger than the ordinary size, a nail, a rubber stopper, and a small strip of very thin aluminum foil. Put the nail, point down, through the rubber stopper. Bend the sharp end of the nail at a right angle and hang the foil over the end of it. If a large nail is used, file the sharp end down to about $\frac{1}{12}$ inch in diameter before mounting the foil. Then put the stopper in the bottle.
4. Determine whether or not a charged rod will deflect a small stream of water as it runs from a faucet or other outlet.
5. Hold one end of a neon tube and scuff your feet on a rug. Then present the other end to an uncharged person, to a water faucet, or to a metal radiator.

READING YOU WILL ENJOY

1. Bragg, W. L., *Electricity,* pp. 1-43. The Macmillan Company, New York, 1936. This book is unique, simple, and interesting. Explains and pictures several interesting experiments involving static electricity.
2. Skilling, Hugh H., *Exploring Electricity,* pp. 1-14. The Ronald Press Company, New York, 1949. Tells very simply of the very earliest discoveries in electricity.
3. Suffern, M. G., *Basic Electrical Principles,* pp. 11-18. McGraw-Hill Book Company, Inc., New York, 1949. This book pictures in a simple manner several of the basic concepts studied in this chapter.
4. Sutton, R. M., *Demonstration Experiments in Physics,* pp. 249-270. McGraw-Hill Book Company, Inc., New York, 1938. In the pages cited this book contains about fifty experiments which pertain to static electricity.
5. Williard, Lester R., *Fundamentals of Electricity,* pp. 32-64. Ginn and Company, Boston, 1943. Explains static electricity very simply and contains a number of experiments.

Chapter 31

The Electron Theory versus the Atomic Theory of Matter

The problem. In Chapter 21, we learned that ninety-two elements have been discovered in nature. Recently scientists have produced several new elements. Also, we concluded that each element consists of particles called atoms, which for many years were believed to be indestructible and indivisible. All the atoms of a given element were believed to be identical, but unlike those of other elements.

Furthermore, our study included molecules. A molecule may consist of one or several atoms, depending on the substance. In most solids, it is said that the molecules are vibrating continually but are not free to move about as they are in gases and liquids.

Somewhat contrary to this molecular theory, in the past chapter we explained positive, negative, and neutral bodies by assuming that all matter consists of particles of electricity called electrons and protons and that these, not atoms, are the basic building stones of matter. This theory was called the electron theory of matter.

Does the electron theory mean that the atom, instead of being indivisible, can in fact be divided? If so, does this mean that the atomic theory is not true and that it must be scrapped entirely? Or is it possible that the two theories can be made to fit together harmoniously?

Conductors and insulators. Perhaps you have already observed that metals and pith balls cannot be charged, as rubber and glass can be charged, by your holding them in your bare hands and rubbing them. So far, we have supported the metals on glass and the pith balls by silk threads. Also, you may know that when a negative charge is brought near a metal rod which is supported as shown in Fig. 1(a), a like charge is induced at end B and an unlike charge is induced at end A. On the other hand, if a glass rod instead of a metal rod is used in this experiment, as shown in (b) of Fig. 1, little, if any, charge is induced on either end of the glass rod.

We have already explained the charge on the metal rod by saying that part of the electrons in the rod were repelled to the far end B, but the protons, being positive, remained at end A. Momentarily there was a movement of electrons in the rod. The movement of electrons is called *electric current*. Hence, there was an electric current in the metal rod.

But what happened in the glass rod? Seemingly, nothing took place. Little, if

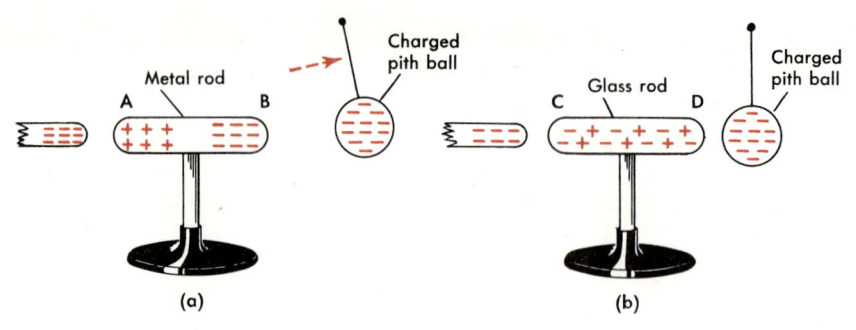

Fig. 1. What kind of charge is induced at end *B* of the brass rod? End *D* of the glass rod? Explain how these are determined.

any, charge was induced on the glass rod. It remained neutral from end to end, which indicated that the electrons and protons in the glass did not separate or move; they stayed "put." In other words, the glass seemed to resist the flow of electricity.

Any substance which offers *high resistance* to the flow of electricity is called a *nonconductor* or *insulator*. Rubber, glass, plastics, and silk are good insulators. Nonmetallic substances range from good to fair insulators. What kind of insulation material is used on telephone poles? For vacuum cleaner handles? For knobs for radios?

Substances which offer *little resistance* to the flow of electricity are called *conductors*. Platinum, silver, copper, and aluminum are among the best conductors. Other metals range from fair to good. What kinds of wires are generally used to conduct electricity? Explain why a metal body, when held in your hand, cannot be charged by rubbing as a nonconductor can be charged.

Of what do atoms consist and how are the parts arranged? According to the electron theory, every atom consists of electrons and protons which are arranged and behave much like the sun and planets in our solar system. The simplest possible of these miniature "solar systems" would be one whose central "sun," called the *nucleus,* consists of one proton about which revolves one electron, called a *planetary* electron. The positive nucleus attracts the negative electron, but centrifugal force keeps the speeding electron in its orbit. The charge on an atom is neutral (zero), which means that the atom must possess the same number of protons and electrons.

If all atoms are made up of electrons and protons, then logically the atom next in simplicity and in mass should consist of two protons and two electrons, the next of three protons and three electrons, the next of four protons and four electrons, and so on up to the largest atom. Is there any evidence to support this hypothesis?

Experiment shows that hydrogen is the least dense of all gases, and that *deuterium,* or *heavy hydrogen,* is twice as dense as

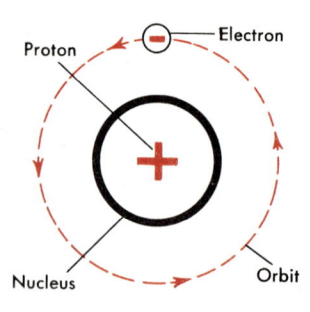

Fig. 2. A diagram of a hydrogen atom.

ordinary hydrogen. Then there is still another kind of hydrogen known as *tritium*, which is three times as dense as ordinary hydrogen. Furthermore, the mass of the helium atom is approximately four times that of the hydrogen atom. So far, fact and theory seem to be in agreement.

Nevertheless, we still must explain how the protons and electrons are arranged in the atom so that elements like hydrogen and helium have different chemical properties and so that the atoms of ordinary hydrogen, deuterium, and tritium can differ in mass and still have the same chemical properties.

How are the chemical properties of atoms explained by the electron theory? One possible explanation of this riddle is shown in Fig. 3. Here it is assumed that the chemical properties of an atom are determined by the number of electrons outside the nucleus of the atom. As shown, atoms of hydrogen, deuterium, and tritium, which all have the same chemical properties, have one electron apiece outside the nucleus of the atom. The helium atom has two electrons outside its nucleus, which accounts for the fact that its chemical properties differ from those of hydrogen. This explains the different chemical properties. What about the difference in mass?

Since there is one electron outside the nucleus of each of the first three atoms, then in the nucleus of the ordinary hydrogen atom there must be one proton, and in the nucleus of the deuterium (heavy hydrogen) atom there must be two protons and one electron. One electron and one proton when bound closely together, we shall assume, make a particle called a *neutron*. The neutron has a charge of zero —i.e., is neutral—and for practical purposes its mass is considered to be the same as that of a proton.

Name of particle	Electric charge	Mass
electron	−	Negligible
proton	+	Same as that of H atom
neutron	0	Same as that of H atom

In the nucleus of the tritium atom there are one proton and two neutrons. In the nucleus of the helium atom there are how many protons? How many neutrons?

The mass number of an atom. The total number of protons and neutrons in an atom is known as the *mass number*. The mass number of ordinary hydrogen is 1. Explain.

The mass number for deuterium, which contains one proton and one neutron, is 2. The mass number of tritium, which contains one proton and two neutrons, is 3. What is the mass number of helium? Explain.

**Mass number =
number of protons + number of neutrons**

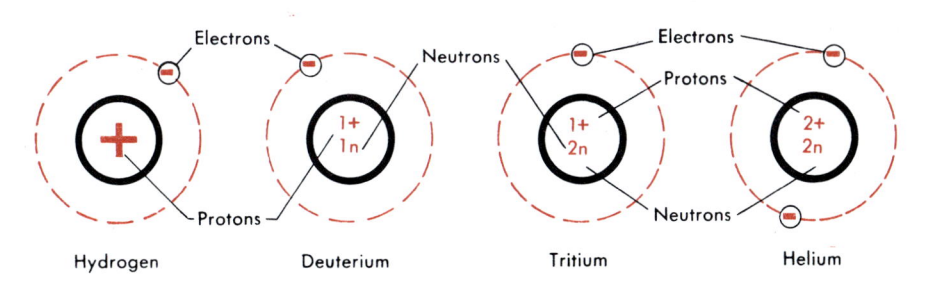

Fig. 3. Atoms of ordinary hydrogen, deuterium, tritium, and helium.

The mass number of an atom is indicated by a number written slightly above and to the right of the symbol used to represent the atom. The mass numbers of a few atoms are indicated as follows: hydrogen H¹, deuterium H², tritium H³, and helium He⁴.

The electrical charge on the nucleus and the atomic number. The total electrical charge on the nucleus of an atom equals the number of protons in the nucleus. The number of protons in the nucleus also equals the number of planetary electrons in the neutral atom (Why?) and is known as the *atomic number* of the atom.

**Atomic number =
number of protons = number of electrons**

The importance of the atomic number is shown by the fact that an element is defined as *a substance whose atoms all have the same atomic number*.

The atomic number of hydrogen is 1. Helium has two protons; its atomic number is 2. Lithium has three protons and atomic number 3, and so on up to the heaviest of the ninety-two atoms—uranium, which has ninety-two protons in its nucleus and atomic number 92. What is the atomic number of deuterium?

The atomic numbers of various elements are given in Table 1. In writing, the atomic number is usually put to the left and slightly below the symbol for the element. For example, ₁H, ₂He, and ₃Li mean that the atomic number of hydrogen is 1, of helium is 2, and of lithium is 3.

EXERCISE: For each of these elements ₁H¹, ₂He⁴, lithium, ₃Li⁷, and beryllium ₄Be⁹, what is the mass number? Atomic number? Number of electrons outside the nucleus? Number of neutrons in the nucleus?

The relative weights of the atoms. We have seen that the hydrogen atom is the smallest and has the least mass of all the atoms. Also, we have assumed that all other atoms consist of the equivalent of a whole number of hydrogen atoms. Logically, then, in a scale of relative atomic weights, the weight of the hydrogen atom could be 1, deuterium 2, tritium 3, helium 4, and so on, the same as the mass numbers.

For several reasons, however, the weight of the hydrogen atom was not chosen as the basis for comparison. Oxygen, whose mass number is 16, was chosen as the one to which the weights of all other atoms are compared. Oxygen was assigned atomic weight 16. For reasons which will be discussed later, the atomic weight of hydrogen, whose mass number is 1, was shown by experiment to be 1.008 instead of 1, as you might expect it to be. The atomic weights of several elements are given in Table 1. Most of the atomic weights are not whole numbers and differ slightly from the respective mass numbers.

Isotopes. We have seen that hydrogen, deuterium, and tritium all have the same chemical properties, and that each has the same atomic number, 1. Hence, all belong to the same element, hydrogen. All atoms having the same atomic number but different mass numbers are known as *isotopes*. Ordinary hydrogen, deuterium, and tritium are all isotopes of hydrogen. If deuterium is found mixed with ordinary hydrogen, give one logical reason why the atomic weight of hydrogen might be 1.008 instead of 1.

The arrangement of the electrons in the atom. We have compared the structure of an atom with the structure of our solar system, but there is one important difference between the two structures. In our solar system each orbit or path contains only one planet, whereas in the atom a

THE ELECTRON VERSUS THE ATOMIC THEORY OF MATTER

Table 1
ELECTRON DISTRIBUTION IN ELEMENTS

Atomic number	Mass number* or approx. atomic weight	Element name and symbol		K 2	L 8	M 18	N 32	O	P	Q
1	1	Hydrogen	H	1						
2	4	Helium	He	2						
3	7	Lithium	Li	2	1					
4	9	Beryllium	Be	2	2					
5	11	Boron	B	2	3					
6	12	Carbon	C	2	4					
7	14	Nitrogen	N	2	5					
8	16	Oxygen	O	2	6					
9	19	Fluorine	F	2	7					
10	20	Neon	Ne	2	8					
11	23	Sodium	Na	2	8	1				
12	24	Magnesium	Mg	2	8	2				
13	27	Aluminum	Al	2	8	3				
14	28	Silicon	Si	2	8	4				
15	31	Phosphorus	P	2	8	5				
16	32	Sulfur	S	2	8	6				
17	35	Chlorine	Cl	2	8	7				
18	39	Argon	A	2	8	8				
19	39	Potassium	K	2	8	8	1			
20	40	Calcium	Ca	2	8	8	2			
21	45	Scandium	Sc	2	8	9	2			
22	48	Titanium	Ti	2	8	10	2			
23	51	Vanadium	V	2	8	11	2			
24	52	Chromium	Cr	2	8	13	1			
25	54	Manganese	Mn	2	8	13	2			
26	55	Iron	Fe	2	8	14	2			
27	58	Cobalt	Co	2	8	15	2			
28	59	Nickel	Ni	2	8	16	2			
29	63	Copper	Cu	2	8	17	2			
30	65	Zinc	Zn	2	8	18	2			
31	69	Gallium	Ga	2	8	18	3			
32	72	Germanium	Ge	2	8	18	4			
33	74	Arsenic	As	2	8	18	5			
34	78	Selenium	Se	2	8	18	6			
35	79	Bromine	Br	2	8	18	7			
36	83	Krypton	Kr	2	8	18	8			
37	85	Rubidium	Rb	2	8	18	8	1		
38	87	Strontium	Sr	2	8	18	8	2		
39	88	Yttrium	Y	2	8	18	9	2		
40	91	Zirconium	Zr	2	8	18	10	2		

*If isotopes were included the mass numbers would appear in sequence, as the atomic numbers do.

single orbit may contain as many as thirty-two electrons or as few as one. The first seven orbits are designated by the letters K, L, M, N, O, P, and Q.

The maximum number of electrons, e, which each orbit is able to hold (out to orbit N) can be determined by means of the general equation $e = 2n^2$, where n is the orbit number. Thus:

Orbit number (n)	Orbit letter	Maximum number of electrons ($2n^2$)
1	K	$2(1)^2 = 2$
2	L	$2(2)^2 = 8$
3	M	$2(3)^2 = 18$
4	N	$2(4)^2 = 32$

The greatest number of electrons that can occupy any outermost orbit is eight. For the K orbit the maximum is two.

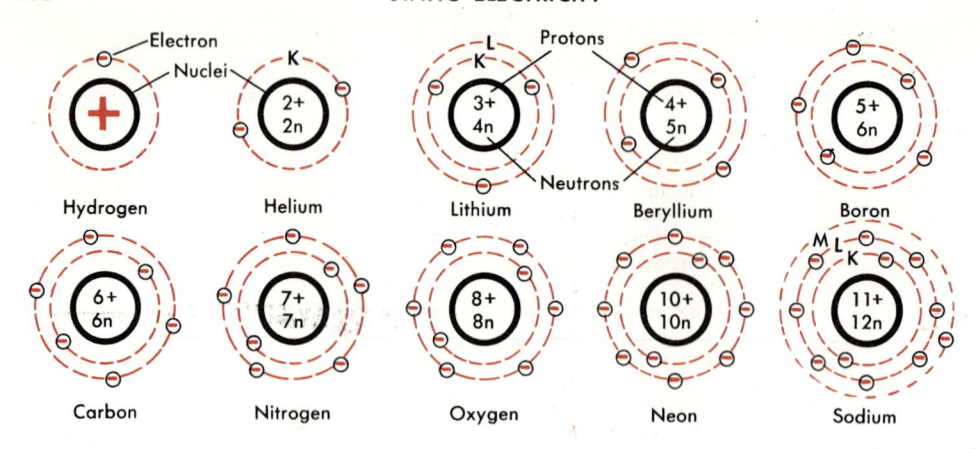

Fig. 4. Diagram of several atoms. What is the atomic number of each atom? Mass number?

As we have already pointed out, hydrogen consists of one proton and therefore has one electron outside its nucleus. Helium has two electrons outside its nucleus. These two fill the K orbit. Argon has atomic number 18. Two electrons are in the K orbit, 8 in the L orbit, and 8 are found in M orbit. Going on up to uranium, atomic number 92, and starting with the K orbit, we find the respective numbers of electrons, two, eight, eighteen, thirty-two, eighteen, twelve, and two. Make a diagram of uranium 238, whose mass number is 238 and atomic number is 92.

Why is a current believed to consist of moving electrons? Possibly you now see why an electric current is believed to be the movement of electrons. The protons, together with the neutrons, are all tightly imbedded in atomic nuclei, and a nucleus moves only when the whole atom moves. Such movement does not readily take place in solids.

Electrons, on the other hand, are outside atomic nuclei, and therefore are much less tightly bound to individual atoms than are protons. Especially among the metals do we find loosely held electrons. Metals are elements which have only a few, usually one, two, or three, electrons in their outer orbits, making these orbits relatively "empty." See sodium in Fig. 4. Electrons in these orbits are held loosely. Hence, metals are good conductors of electricity.

On the other hand, an atom whose outer orbit is essentially complete tends to gain instead of lose electrons. Only with difficulty does it lose electrons. The outer orbits of the inert elements, such as helium, neon, and argon, are completely filled (see argon in Fig. 5), and will ordinarily neither gain nor lose electrons. Such elements make poor conductors.

The nonmetallic elements, such as chlorine and nitrogen, have outer orbits which are nearly but not quite complete.

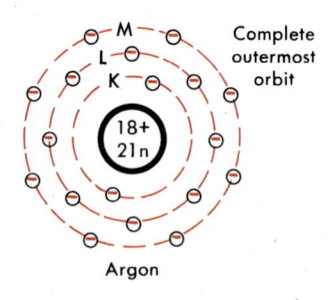

Fig. 5. Diagram of an argon atom.

These atoms gain electrons to fill the outer orbit completely, so that as a result each atom behaves as if it had a complete outer orbit.

Materials containing atoms of this type are poor conductors also. In resins, rubber, plastics, many other nonmetals, and the inert elements, the electrons are not free to move and therefore substances such as these are nonconductors, or insulators. Nonconductors are also known as *dielectrics*.

What takes place in the atoms of a conductor when a charge is brought near one end of the conductor? When an electrical charge, for example a negative one, is brought near a neutral atom of a good conductor, as in Fig. 6, the repulsion of like charges forces the one or two loosely held electrons out of the outer orbit, leaving the rest of the atom behind. This atom is now a charged particle and is called an *ion*. What kind of charge is on the ion in Fig. 6?

A negative charge, brought near end A of the conductor in Fig. 7, will force electrons to the other end of the conductor, leaving many positive ions—that is, atoms deficient in electrons. Hence, the charge at end A is positive.

The liberated electrons in turn repel those adjacent, forcing them out of their orbits. Those behind take the place of those in front, filling the vacant places. At the far end, B, we find a surplus of electrons corresponding to the dearth of electrons at end A, and the charge at end B is therefore negative.

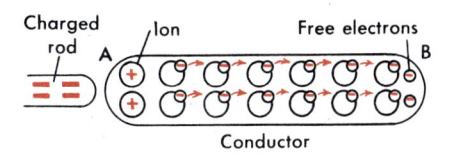

Fig. 7. Electron flow in a conductor. Account for the charge at A and B.

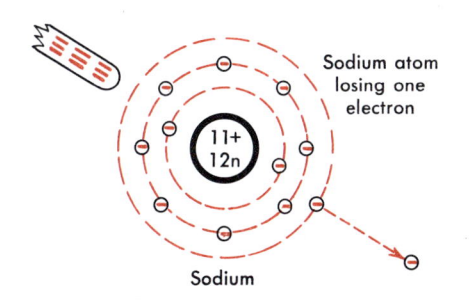

Fig. 6. Why is sodium a good conductor?

Difference in electrical potential. If we pour water on a concrete walk, it runs to the lowest points on the walk, to positions where it has the least possible potential energy. Similarly, a ball, or marble, placed on an inclined plane will do the same thing. The forces acting on it are such that its final position will be one in which its potential energy is the least possible.

Likewise, water in a pipe or stream flows from the position of highest potential energy to one of lower potential energy; it flows from a higher energy level to a lower energy level. The same is true of electricity.

How is electrical potential developed? To build up the potential energy of water we must do work on it. We can do this by increasing its height, as is done when water is pumped into a standpipe.

Similarly, if electrical potential is to be built up, work must be done. The electrical potential of a neutral body is said to be zero. One way of changing its potential is to take electrons away from it, causing its charge to be positive. The potential of the body is then said to be increased. But remember that work had to be done in order for the electrons to be removed from the body. Explain.

Another way of changing the potential of a body is to add electrons to it. Here again work must be done, but in this case the potential of the body is said to be de-

358 STATIC ELECTRICITY

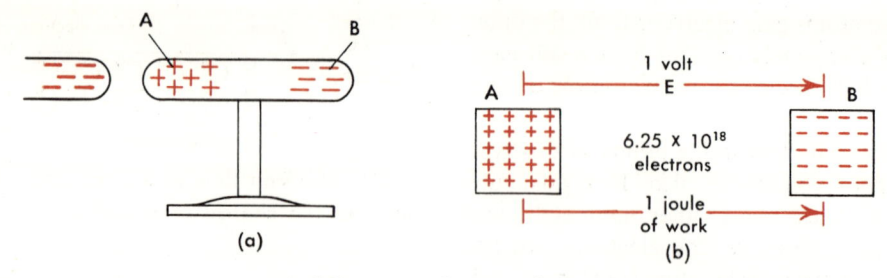

Fig. 8. How is a potential difference of one volt between A and B determined?

creased and is negative if the charge on the body is negative.

The unit of electrical potential. In (a) of Fig. 8, the potential of end A is positive and that of end B is negative. In order for a difference of potential to be built up, electrons had to be moved from end A to B; charges had to be separated. This required work, which was done by the experimenter. This work increased the potential energy of the charges, which will be released when the charges flow back together.

In case 6.25×10^{18} electrons (one coulomb* of electricity) are transferred from point A to B, as in (b) of Fig. 8, and one joule of energy is required to make the transfer, then the difference in potential between A and B is said to be 1 volt. That is, *the **volt** is the difference in potential between two points when one joule of work is required to transfer 6.25 $\times 10^{18}$ electrons from one point to the other.* You will recall that the joule is 10^7 ergs and that an erg is a dyne-centimeter of work. See page 195.

How much work in joules, J, would be done in case the quantity of electricity, Q, transferred from A to B in Fig. 8, were 2 coulombs? 3 coulombs? 4 coulombs? Q coulombs?

In case the difference in potential between A and B in Fig. 8 were E volts, how much work would be done if the number of coulombs transferred were 1? 2? 3? Q?

In conclusion, we may say that the work, J, needed to transfer Q coulombs of electricity from A to B, whose potential difference is E volts, equals $Q \times E$ joules. That is,

Work in joules (J) = quantity in coulombs (Q) $\times$ difference in potential in volts (E)

or,

$$J = QE$$

*The coulomb is the unit quantity of electricity: 6,250,000,000,000,000,000 electrons.

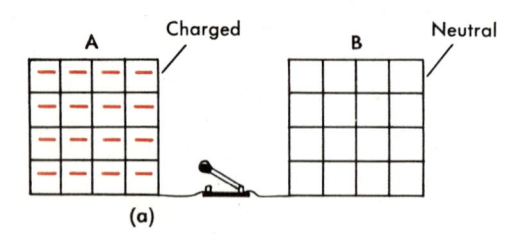

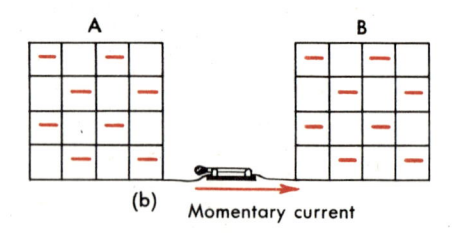

Fig. 9. (a) Charged and uncharged plates. (b) Same plates after being connected.

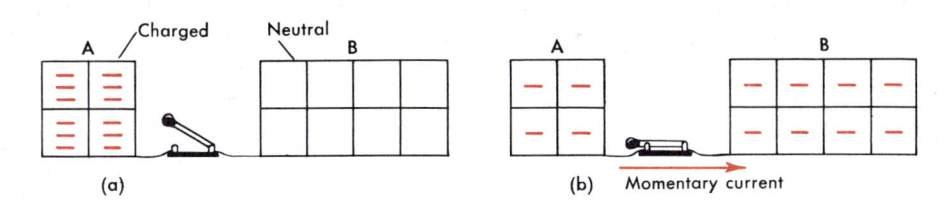

Fig. 10. Distribution of charges before and after the switch was closed.

PROBLEM: How much work is done in transferring 5 coulombs of electricity from A to B when the difference in potential is 10 volts? 50 volts? 80 volts?

Discharging a body by grounding it. Suppose we charge the metal plate A, shown in Fig. 9, and then connect it with a neutral plate B, of the same size. Because of the difference in potential and the mutual repulsion of electrons, we would expect the electrons to distribute themselves as shown in (b).* Thus, the two plates would have the same number of surplus electrons, which would be uniformly distributed over them. Also, we would expect the potentials of the two plates to be the same. What would happen if they were not the same?

Now suppose the neutral plate B is larger than the charged plate A, as shown in Fig. 10, and that the charges again distribute themselves uniformly over the two plates when they are connected. We should now expect a greater number of charges to be on the larger than on the smaller plate and the electrical potentials of the two plates to be the same.

Also, when a charged plate, such as A, Fig. 11, is grounded by being connected to the neutral earth, the charges on A, because of repulsion, tend to distribute themselves uniformly over both bodies. But since the earth is so many times larger

*No claim is made by the authors that the charges take the exact positions shown.

than the plate, the chances are that, as far as can be detected by a measuring instrument, all the charges on plate A will run to the earth and the plate will become neutral. When the switch is closed, what will happen to the extra electrons on A? What will happen to the potential on A? On the earth?

A convenient way of grounding a body is to connect it to a water pipe or some other conductor which leads to the earth. If a charge is small, like that on an electroscope, you can ground it simply by touching your finger to the object.

The rate of flow and the quantity of electricity. In signifying the rate of flow of water in a pipe, we might say that so many gallons of water flow per second. The unit rate of flow then would be one gallon, the unit quantity, flowing per second.

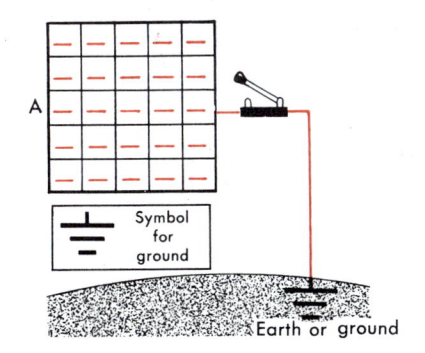

Fig. 11. Discharging a body by grounding it. Explain why all the charge leaves the plate.

Similarly, the unit rate of flow of electricity is the unit quantity, one coulomb, flowing per second. This unit is called the *ampere*. An **ampere** is one coulomb of electricity flowing per second past a given point. See Fig. 12.

Thus, if two amperes of electricity flowed for one second, the quantity Q transferred would be equal to 2×1, or 2 coulombs. And if two amperes flowed for three seconds, then the quantity $Q = 2 \times 3$, or 6 coulombs. That is,

$$Q = It$$

where Q stands for the quantity in coulombs, I for the rate of flow in amperes, (coulombs per second), and t for time in seconds.

PROBLEM: What current is required so that 100 coulombs of electricity flow in 20 seconds?

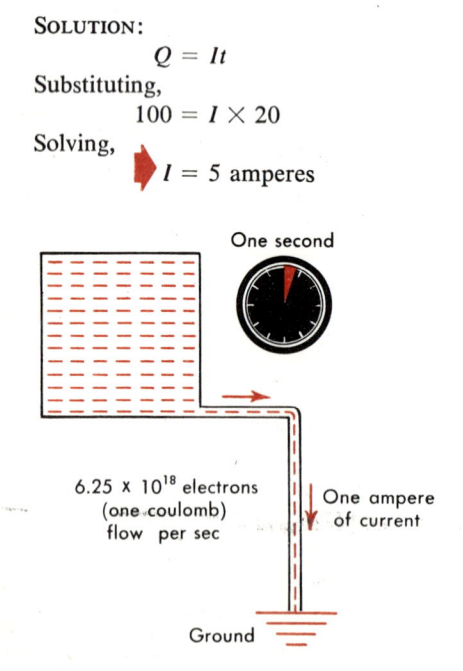

SOLUTION:
$$Q = It$$
Substituting,
$$100 = I \times 20$$
Solving,
$$I = 5 \text{ amperes}$$

Fig. 12. A current of one ampere.

Electron flow and electric current. In all our discussion so far we have seen that the electrons flow from a negative body to one that is less negative, to one that is neutral, or to one that is positive. On the other hand, perhaps many of you know from experience that the direction of electric current is said to be from positive to negative. This situation is a very unfortunate one. It all goes back to Benjamin Franklin (see page 345), who said that electricity can flow only from where it is in excess to where it is lacking, or from positive to negative. Through the years, electrical measuring instruments have been built on this assumption, and it has become firmly established in the thinking of practical electricians. However, in this book it will be assumed that current is from negative to positive and that it is the flow of electrons.

SUMMARY AND CONCLUSIONS

1. Atoms consist of neutrons, and of an equal number of electrons and protons, except for the ordinary hydrogen atom, which has one electron and one proton. The neutrons and the protons are all found in the nucleus, whose charge is positive. The number of protons in the nucleus is the atomic number of the atom or element, and the sum of the number of neutrons and protons is the mass number of the atom. The atomic weight of an element is its weight relative to the weight of oxygen, whose atomic weight is 16.

2. The electrons are in motion outside the nucleus and in orbits about it. The electrons in the nearly empty outer orbit of a metallic atom are held loosely. Electrons in migration constitute an electric current. An atom which has lost or gained one or several electrons is called an ion.

3. The volt is the difference in potential between two points when one joule of work is required to carry 6.25×10^{18} electrons from one point to the other. This number of

electrons is a unit quantity of electricity called the coulomb.

Work in joules (J) = quantity in coulombs (Q) × difference in potential in volts (E)

$$J = QE$$

4. The ampere is the unit rate of current flow: one coulomb flowing per second.
5. Quantity (Q) = Amperes (I) × time (t).

$$Q = It$$

QUESTIONS FOR REVIEW

1. What is an electron? A proton? A neutron?
2. What is the essential difference between the atoms of conductors and of insulators?
3. Make diagrams of the following atoms: (a) helium, (b) calcium, (c) sodium, (d) aluminum, and (e) neon. Explain which would be good conductors; good insulators. See Table 1.
4. Make a diagram to show what happens in the atoms of a piece of sodium when a charge is induced on it by a negative charge.
5. Is it possible to unlock the forces that hold the nucleus of a heavy atom together? What would happen if this were done?
6. For the uranium atom, $_{92}U^{235}$, what is the atomic number? Mass number? Number of electrons?
7. For each of the following atoms state the number of protons, neutrons, and electrons. (a) $_7N^{14}$, (b) $_6C^{13}$, (c) $_{93}Pu^{239}$.
8. What is meant by the transmutation of elements? (See an encyclopedia.)
9. What is meant by an isotope?
10. What is meant by difference of potential?
11. What is the potential of a body which has a surplus of electrons? A deficiency of electrons? Of a neutral body?
12. If a body is grounded, what is its potential? If a large plate and a small plate (both conductors) are both charged and then connected, compare their potentials.
13. What is a volt? A coulomb?

PROBLEMS

1. The difference in potential between two points A and B is 25 volts. Between these two points, how much work is required to transfer 4 coulombs? 10 coulombs? 20 coulombs?
2. Ten joules of work are required to transfer 2 coulombs of electricity from A to B. What is the difference in potential between A and B?
3. If there is a current of 10 amperes in a circuit for 10 minutes, what quantity of electricity flows in the circuit?
4. How much current in amperes must there be in a circuit if 100 coulombs flow past a point in the circuit in 4 seconds?
5. How much time is required for 10 coulombs of electricity to flow past a point if the difference in potential causing the flow is 20 volts and the rate of flow is 2 amperes? 5 amperes?
6. Fifty joules of work are required to transfer 500 coulombs of electricity from A to B. What is the difference of potential?
7. If there is a current of 100 milliamperes in a circuit, how much time is required for 20 coulombs to flow? 10 coulombs? 40 coulombs?
8. The difference in potential between points A and B is 100 volts.
   (a) What quantity of electricity would be transferred from A to B by the expenditure of 400 joules of energy in 2 seconds?
   (b) How much current would there be in the circuit?
9. The difference in potential between A and B is 25 volts. There are 10 amperes of current in the circuit for 20 seconds.
   (a) What quantity of electricity flows in the circuit?
   (b) How much work is done?
10. One hundred joules of work are done in transferring 200 coulombs of electricity from A to B in 5 seconds.
    (a) What is the average rate of flow of electricity?
    (b) What is the difference in potential between A and B?

11. Since $J = QE$ and $Q = It$, write another formula for finding work in joules.

12. If 100 volts cause a current of 5 amperes in a lamp for 20 seconds,
   (a) What quantity of electricity flows through the lamp?
   (b) How much energy is used?

13. Which one of the following choices specifies a potassium ion? See Table 1.

	Nuclear composition		Electron distribution			
			K	L	M	N
(1)	18p	20n	2	8	8	0
(2)	19p	20n	2	8	8	0
(3)	18p	20n	2	8	8	1
(4)	19p	20n	2	8	8	1
(5)	19p	21n	2	8	8	0

14. Which one of the following choices specifies a bromine ion?

	Nuclear composition		Electron distribution			
			K	L	M	N
(1)	36p	44n	2	8	18	7
(2)	44p	35n	2	8	18	8
(3)	35p	44n	2	8	18	7
(4)	36p	44n	2	8	18	8
(5)	35p	44n	2	8	18	8

READING YOU WILL ENJOY

1. Bayles, E. E., and A. L. Mills, *Basic Chemistry*, pp. 241-254. The Macmillan Company, New York, 1947. Gives an excellent explanation of the electron theory.

2. Beauchamp, W. L., and J. C. Mayfield, *Basic Electricity*. Scott, Foresman and Company, Chicago, 1943. Unit II, The Electric Current, discusses the electron theory.

3. Grimes, Davis, *Meet the Electron*. Pitman Publishing Corporation, New York, 1944. A fascinating story of the place of the electron in modern science.

4. Needham, Joseph, and Walter Pagel, *Background of Modern Science*. The Macmillan Company, New York, 1938. Chapter 5, "Forty Years of the Atomic Theory," contains a clear exposition of the growth of this theory.

5. The General Electric Company has published several booklets: *The Invisible World and Other Stories; Electronics—A New Science for a New World; A Primer of Electronics; The Romance of Electricity*, and *The Story of Research*.

Chapter 32

How Does the Electron Theory Explain Leyden Jars, Condensers, and Lightning?

The problem. Until about 1650, when interest in electricity and other sciences increased greatly in Europe, no easy method for producing a large charge of electricity had been invented. But as interest and the number of experimenters increased, it was to be expected that easier and better ways of producing electrical charges would be found.

Otto von Guericke, the inventor of the vacuum pump, fashioned the first electrostatic machine. To make it, he poured melted sulfur into a glass globe and then, after the sulfur had solidified, he broke the glass from the ball, little realizing that the glass globe alone would have served his purpose just as well. He then mounted the globe as shown in Fig. 1 so that it could be turned with a crank. To produce the charge, the experimenter turned the crank with one hand and held a piece of leather against the sulfur ball. The friction produced enough potential on the ball so that sparks several inches long could then be drawn from it.

This electrostatic machine of Guericke's was a real boon to experimental work in electricity, but the still more difficult problem of storing and retaining a large charge had yet to be overcome before experimentation could advance very far. Powerful charges could be built up on a body with Guericke's electrostatic machine, but these charges soon escaped. The loss of charge was believed to be due to evaporation. Our problem is to discover how these machines work and at the same time put the electron theory to still further tests.

The jar that shocked Western Europe. To prevent "evaporation," someone proposed putting the object to be charged in a closed container made of an insulating material. Naturally, a glass bottle was chosen as the container and water was chosen as the substance to be charged because it could be easily poured in and out of the bottle. In order that the water might be charged without the bottle being opened, a nail was driven through the cork stopper and into the water. The plan and the theory were fine; but for some reason unknown at that time, the apparatus was not much of a success.

Finally, however, it was discovered that if the charged bottle were held in one hand and the nail were touched with the other hand, according to pioneer investigators, a severe *shock* was received through the arms and shoulders. One investigator, who used a small glass bowl instead of a bottle, claimed that the shock was so severe that it took his breath away and it was days be-

STATIC ELECTRICITY

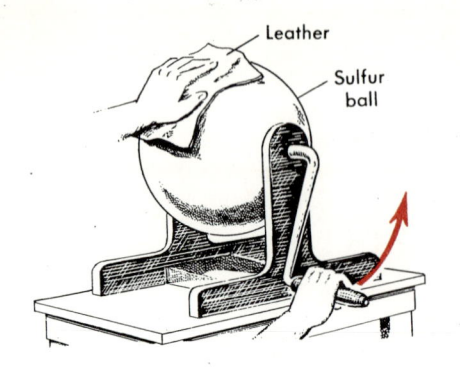

Fig. 1. An early electrostatic machine.

fore he recovered. Another said that he would not take another shock for the Kingdom of France. That the severity of the shock was greatly exaggerated can be verified if we repeat the experiment. However, the shock was severe enough so that news of the experiment spread like wildfire, and soon hundreds in Germany, France, and Holland were "shocking" their friends by means of this simple apparatus. See Fig. 2(a).

As a result of the increased experimentation, someone soon discovered that the stored charge, and hence the shock, could be increased greatly if the outside and the inside of the bottle were both covered with a conducting material such as a thin sheet of tinfoil. Moreover, if the nail were connected with the metal layer on the inside of the bottle by a good conductor, the water could be dispensed with. This new storehouse of electricity was invented in 1745 and was named a *Leyden jar* in honor of its place of origin, Leyden, Holland. See Fig. 2(b).

To gain firsthand knowledge of a Leyden jar, ground the outer plate and connect the inner plate to one terminal of an electrostatic machine as shown in Fig. 3(a). Turn the crank of the machine for one or two minutes until the jar is charged and then disconnect it. Then with the discharge tongs, discharge it as shown in Fig. 3(b).

When the knob on the tongs is about 2 centimeters or so from the "nail" head on top of the jar, a spark will jump the gap, producing a loud crackle. In dry air, if the terminals are pointed, roughly about 8000 volts are necessary to produce a spark 1 centimeter long. If the terminals are rounded and not too small, about 27,000 volts are required. Why are the terminals on a spark plug pointed?

It was discovered also that the "fatness" of the spark could be increased if the size of the bottles were increased or if two of them were connected together.

Benjamin Franklin connected two six-gallon Leyden jars together and electrocuted turkeys and other fowl with them. Once he accidentally discharged the bottles through his body and was unconscious for several hours afterward.

How does the electron theory explain the Leyden jar? To explain a Leyden jar, let us say that the inner metal coat or plate is connected with the negative terminal of a static machine. Since like charges repel, during the charging process, electrons are added to the inner plate, leaving it negative. These negative charges repel nega-

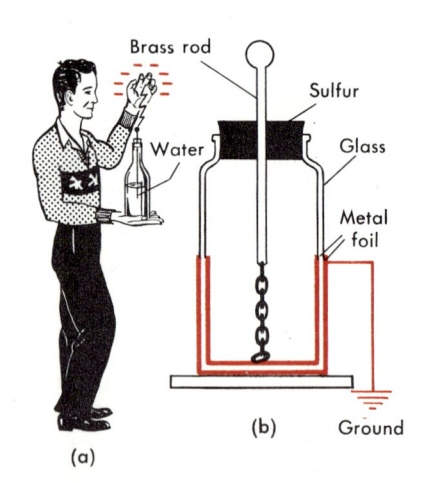

Fig. 2. (a) Early bottle used to store electrical charges. (b) A Leyden jar.

LEYDEN JARS, CONDENSERS, AND LIGHTNING

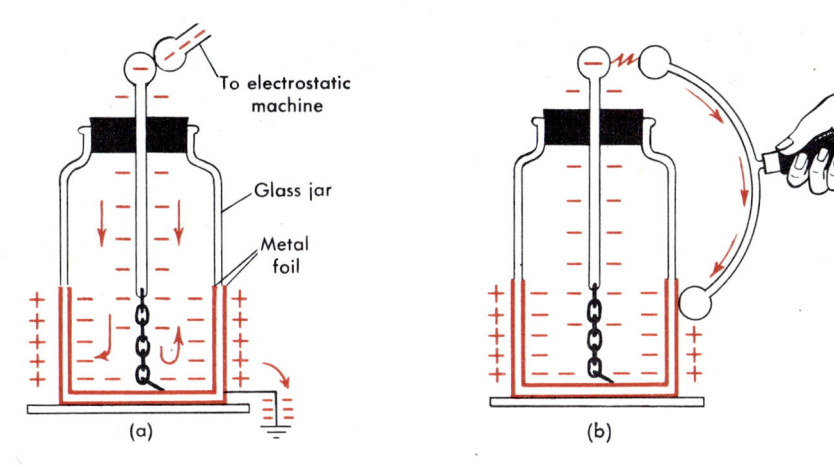

Fig. 3. A Leyden jar is being charged in (a) and discharged in (b).

tive charges from the outer plate down to the ground through the ground wire on the outer plate, causing it to have a positive charge.

When the jar is discharged with the tongs, the surplus electrons jump from the inner negative to the outer positive plate. Explain how a Leyden jar is charged and discharged when the inner plate is connected with the positive terminal of an electrostatic machine.

The condenser. The Leyden jar, since it can store an electric charge, is a type of *condenser* or *capacitor*. Benjamin Franklin modified the Leyden jar by substituting a pane of glass for the glass jar which separated the metal foil or plates. Later he found that air, mica, and other insulating materials could be used to separate them. Any material used for this or other electrical insulating purposes is called a *dielectric*.

Franklin found that the quantity of electricity that can be stored in a condenser depends (a) directly upon the area of the plates; (b) directly upon the voltage across the plates; and (c) inversely upon the distance between the plates. If the plates are brought too close together the electrons may puncture the dielectric or discharge through it. This often happens to a condenser in a radio.

The capacitance of a condenser. The quantity of electric charge which can be stored in a condenser, under conditions stated below, is called its *capacity* or *capacitance*. The capacity of a condenser, at least in two respects, might be compared with the capacity of a steel cylinder for holding air. This as you know depends not only upon the size of the cylinder, but also upon the work available for cramming air into it. Likewise, the quantity of electrons which can be stored in a given condenser is dependent upon the area of its plates as well as upon the voltage, or work per coulomb, to push the electrons in. For this reason, unit of capacity is defined not solely in terms of how much a condenser can hold but in terms of how much it holds when one volt is applied across its plates.

The *unit of capacitance* is the *farad*, named after Michael Faraday. *The* **farad** *is the capacity of a condenser in which 1 volt will store 1 coulomb (6.25×10^{18} electrons); or, vice versa, the farad is the capacity of a condenser whose potential is raised 1 volt when it is charged with 1 coulomb (6.25×10^{18} electrons) of electricity.* Because of its great size the farad

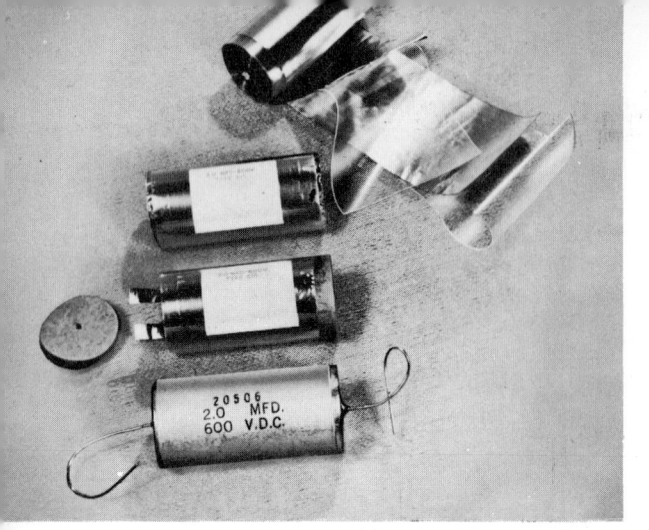

Fig. 4. (a) Fixed capacitor consisting of a roll of "Mylar" polyester film as an insulator and aluminum foil as a conductor wound up tightly and sealed.

Courtesy E.I. du Pont de Nemours and Co., Inc.

Fig. 4. (b) Variable tuning capacitor consisting of a set of fixed plates and a movable set that can be adjusted to vary the capacitance.

Courtesy Radio Condenser Co.

is an impractical unit and so the *microfarad* (millionth of a farad), abbreviated *mfd.*, is the unit commonly used.

Fixed and variable condensers. Condensers constructed so that their capacitances cannot be changed are called *fixed condensers;* those whose capacitances can be changed are called *variable condensers.*

Fixed condensers are made in many different shapes and of different materials. But those most common are the small cylindrical ones that are used so lavishly in modern radios. The plates are made of long, thin sheets of tinfoil or aluminum foil separated by an oiled, high-grade linen-paper or plastic dielectric. See (a) of Fig. 4.

Variable condensers are also constructed in several different ways. A very common type is the variable, air dielectric condenser found in the tuning circuit of a radio. This usually consists of two sets of plates: the *stator* plates, which are stationary, and the *rotors,* which can be moved in and out between the stators without touching them. The capacitance is varied through changes made in the actually effective area of the plates, as shown in (b) of Fig. 4. More uses of condensers are discussed on pages 458 and 472.

Lightning, and how Benjamin Franklin identified it and took it from the realm of the supernatural into the scientific fold. Perhaps there are no other natural phenomena which have caused, and still cause, as much awe, fear, and wonder as lightning and thunder. In Greek and Roman times, shafts of lightning were believed to be the thunderbolts of Jove (or Jupiter), and were thought to be hurled by the god of gods at anything which incurred his anger. Even today, in our so-called enlightened age, many persons are in mortal fear during an electrical storm. Consequently, as with many other matters about which people are ignorant but vitally concerned, superstitions galore have grown up about the causes of lightning and how to avoid being struck.

Early scientific investigators of electricity had proposed that lightning, except that it is on a larger scale, is exactly the same as the spark which jumps between the plates of a condenser when it is discharged across an air gap. But only by catching some of this death-dealing stuff in a Leyden jar could investigators prove or disprove the hypothesis.

Dalibard and Delor in France, at the suggestion of Benjamin Franklin, were the first to perform such experiments. To catch it they both put up metal rods, Dalibard's being forty feet high and Delor's ninety-nine, and each drew sparks at disances up to an inch and a half from his rod. The experiment was dangerous and foolhardy, to say the least, though it is doubtful that at the time the full danger was realized. Neither Dalibard nor Delor experienced any ill effects, but later a countryman of theirs was killed in performing the same experiment.

Franklin was not satisfied with the experiments of Dalibard and Delor because the rods did not extend into the clouds and hence failed to prove that the sparks from their rods originated there. Franklin puzzled over how to improve on the experiments of the Frenchmen. Finally, he hit upon the idea of flying a kite into a thundercloud. So one summer afternoon, as a storm cloud approached, he and his son did this, fully realizing the danger involved. This experiment is very dangerous. *Do not try it.*

As soon as the string attached to the kite became wet, the loose fibers on it suddenly stood out, indicating that the kite and string were charged. Standing under a shed and holding the kite string by means of a dry silk thread, Franklin performed the first crucial test, no doubt wondering whether it would be his last act and whether it would cause him to be the laughingstock of his neighbors and friends, most of whom made fun of or frowned upon his "foolish" experiments. He moved his finger toward a metal key which he had attached to the wet string. Before his finger reached the key a spark jumped from it to his finger, making the same crackling noise which he had heard so many times in discharging his Leyden jar.

But the final, crucial test was yet to come. Would this electricity charge a condenser, as would electricity from a friction machine? To answer this question he lowered the key so that it touched one of his Leyden jars, and then he discharged the jar in the usual way. Thus ended one of the greatest, possibly *the* greatest, and certainly the most educational, of all experiments in electricity. Lightning, which for ages had "put the fear of God into the hearts of men," had been identified and taken from the realm of mystery into the domain of science.

What causes lightning? There are several different theories concerning the cause of lightning and some authorities make little attempt really to explain it.

Usually, the lower part of a cloud is negatively charged and the upper part is positively charged. When the electrical potential becomes great enough a dis-

Fig. 5. An artist's representation of Benjamin Franklin's famous, although dangerous, kite experiment.

Courtesy The Franklin Institute

charge known as *lightning* will take place, either between the earth and the cloud or between two parts of the cloud.

The electrical discharge between the lower part of a cloud and the earth can be explained as follows. If this part of the cloud is negatively charged, then high points on earth directly below the cloud will possess an induced positive charge. And if the potential difference between the two is great enough, a discharge takes place between them. The exchange of electricity between cloud and earth (Fig. 6) takes the form of several swift, two-way impulses, of which the strongest are usually from the earth to the cloud. The light is produced by the ionization (see page 357) of molecules of air in the path of the bolt, in somewhat the same way that light is produced in a neon tube lighting fixture. Since several thousands of volts are necessary to cause a spark to jump an air gap of one centimeter, millions of volts are necessary to produce most flashes of lightning. In what way is the combination of the earth, a cloud, and the air between the two similar to a condenser?

Fig. 7. Notice the greater concentration of electric charges on the pointed end of the conductor than on the rounded end.

When the air dielectric separating the earth and a charged cloud is punctured, we would expect the puncture to be where the air dielectric is thinnest. In other words, lightning should take the path of least resistance, which in most cases is the shortest distance between the cloud and the earth. Church steeples, flagpoles, skyscrapers, and the lone trees on either plains or hilltops are some of the things which provide these shortest paths.

Another reason why lightning is likely to take such paths is that the closer an object is to a cloud, the greater the charge induced on the object; hence, the greater the attraction between the charges. Also, because of the geometrical relationships, the charge is greater on a point or sharp corner of a charged object than on a flat or rounded surface (see Fig. 7).

Lightning protection. Benjamin Franklin's lightning rod was the first scientific device invented for protection against lightning. It consisted of a metal rod, one end of which was a sharp spike, or better still, a bundle of sharp spikes, which protruded well above the building that it protected. The rod passed down the side of the building deep into the ground, where it was attached to a buried copper plate.

Not only did it furnish the path of least resistance for the lightning to follow, but

Fig. 6. Lightning is essentially an electrical discharge.

it also provided opportunity for the induced charge on the building to leak off as it formed, thereby preventing the charge from building up as much as it otherwise would, and lessening the attraction between cloud and building. This leakage from pointed objects may be seen, especially at night. For hundreds of years during electrical storms sailors have seen it take place at the top of the masts of their ships. It is referred to as *St. Elmo's fire*.

In recent years several spectacular experiments have been performed in the study of lightning control. In one, a man sat inside a closed automobile while death-dealing, man-made lightning more than a yard long poured down over the steel top of the car without harm to the man.

How can this be? Since the charges on a charged object repel each other, they spread out as far as possible. In the case of a hollow metal sphere or cylinder, this means that they spread over the outside of the object. Likewise, when a bolt of lightning strikes the top of a metal car, since the electrons repel each other, they too spread out as far as possible while being conducted by the car to the earth. Therefore, they pass along the surface of the car and not through it. For the same reasons one is perfectly safe from lightning in a metal cage.

Therefore a place that is very safe from lightning is the interior of an all-metal-frame building that is well grounded, such as any modern hotel or large office building. Here it is virtually impossible for lightning to strike you. The next safest place is inside dwellings or other buildings protected by lightning conductors. But if neither of these two types of building is

Fig. 8. High-voltage electricity produced by a surge generator jumps 16 feet across a spark gap in a laboratory test. Spark gaps on a smaller scale are used in protective devices to safeguard power transmission systems from high voltages produced by lightning.

Courtesy Westinghouse Electric Corp.

Fig. 9. As a result of bombarding the car with three million volts of artificial lightning, the voltage of the car and the man's body rose to about 200,000 volts. Yet the man did not experience even the slightest shock because there was no difference in potential across his body.

Courtesy Westinghouse Electric Corp.

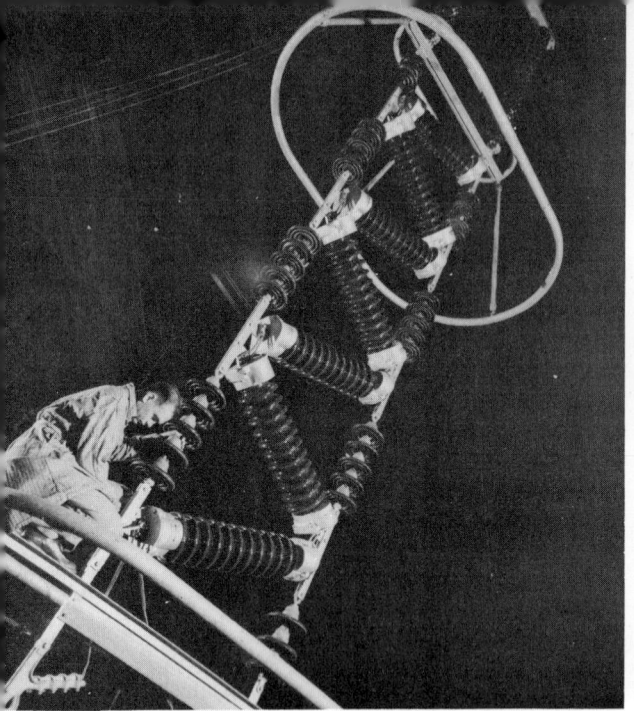

Fig. 10. (*l.*) A 258,000-volt lightning arrestor unit capable of protecting electrical systems up to 330,000 volts. (*r.*) The world's three largest lightning arrestors designed to protect transformers in an electric power substation.

available, one should seek shelter in as large an unprotected building as possible. When inside, stay away from fireplaces, stoves, and other possible conductors of electricity.

If you have to stay outside, you should avoid hilltops, haystacks, lone trees, flagpoles, fences, and other metallic objects. By all means *do not* play golf, fish, or participate in other activities which involve the use of metallic instruments in open spaces. A dense wood, a cave, and the foot of a steep hill or cliff are all good places to take refuge.

SUMMARY AND CONCLUSIONS

1. The Leyden jar is used to store electrical charges. It consists of two thin metal plates separated by an insulator.
2. The capacity of a condenser (modified Leyden jar) varies directly as the area of the plates and inversely as the distance between the plates.
3. The unit of capacitance of a condenser is the farad, which is the capacity of a condenser in which one volt will store one coulomb of electricity (6.25×10^{18} electrons).
4. Lightning is a phenomenon very similar to the discharge of a condenser. The earth and a cloud, or two clouds, act as the plates, and the air serves as the dielectric.
5. Lightning rods protect a building from lightning in two ways. (a) They allow any induced charge on a building to leak off. (b) They conduct lightning to the ground if it strikes the building.
6. During an electrical storm, avoid lone trees, hilltops, fences, and open spaces.

QUESTIONS FOR REVIEW

1. What was the original purpose of the Leyden jar and how was it constructed? Make a diagram.
2. The outside plate of a Leyden jar is grounded and a positive charge is placed on the inner plate. Show, by means of a dia-

gram, the kind of charge on the outer plate and explain where it came from.

3. Explain how a Leyden jar, a fixed condenser, and a variable condenser differ from one another.

4. Name two factors which affect the capacity of a condenser and three factors which affect the quantity of electricity in a condenser.

5. Define capacity of a condenser.

6. The capacity of a water bucket is stated in terms of the quantity of water it can hold. Why is the capacity of a condenser defined in terms of both quantity and voltage applied across the plates?

7. Is there any similarity between a condenser and a charged cloud, the earth, and the atmosphere? Explain.

8. If a cloud has a positive charge, what is the charge on the earth directly below?

9. Why is lightning more liable to strike tall trees, church steeples, and tall buildings than other things?

10. Explain how Benjamin Franklin proved that lightning is the same kind of electricity as that which jumps between two bodies charged by friction.

11. Why are the "points" on a spark plug pointed rather than spherical in shape?

12. Why are the top ends of lightning rods pointed?

13. Does a lightning rod increase or decrease the probability of a house being struck by lightning? Give reasons.

14. What places and what activities should be avoided during an electrical storm?

PROBLEMS

1. What is the current in amperes in a circuit if 20 coulombs of electricity flow through it in 4 sec.? 2 sec.? 10 sec.?

2. What quantity of electricity passes through a circuit if 6 amperes flow for 5 sec.? 8 sec.? 10 sec.?

3. How much work in joules is done when 20 coulombs of electricity are transmitted between two points whose potential difference is 30 volts? 10 volts?

4. The voltage across an electric lamp is 100 volts. Through the lamp 4 coulombs of electricity flow each second.
   (a) What is the current through the lamp?
   (b) How much work is done in 10 sec.?
   (c) What quantity of electricity flows through the lamp in 20 sec.?

5. An electric motor does 12,000 joules of work in $1/3$ minute. The current is 4 amperes. What is the voltage across the motor terminals? Assume no loss.

6. If 100 joules of work are required to transfer 20 coulombs of electricity from point A to point B in 4 sec., then:
   (a) What is the difference in potential between A and B?
   (b) What is the current?

7. The voltage across a lamp is 100 volts. Through the lamp 10 coulombs of electricity pass in 5 sec.
   (a) What is the current?
   (b) The energy consumed by the lamp is how many joules during $1/3$ minute?
   (c) What quantity of electricity passes through the lamp in 100 sec.?

PROJECTS AND EXPERIMENTS

1. Make the electrostatic machine pictured in Fig. 11.

2. Do experiments E-62 to E-75 in Sutton's *Demonstration Experiments in Physics*.

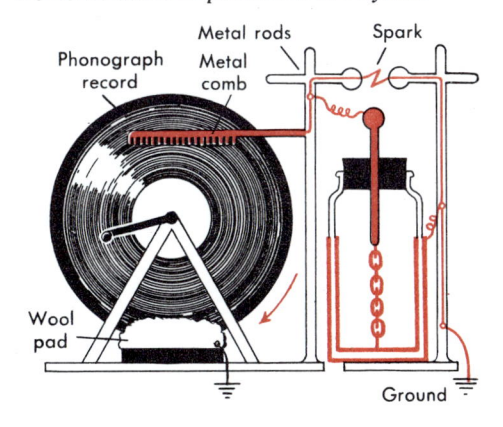

Fig. 11. A homemade electrostatic generator.

READING YOU WILL ENJOY

1. Caverly, Don, *Primer of Electronics and Radiant Energy*, pp. 1-26. McGraw-Hill Book Company, Inc., New York, 1952. Very readable and covers much of what we have studied thus far in electricity.

2. Franklin, Benjamin, *Experiments and Observations on Electricity*. Harvard University Press, Cambridge, Massachusetts, 1941. A new edition of a very old book. Shows that Franklin had not only an open mind but a very imaginative one because he thought of and did about every imaginable experiment concerning static electricity. To this day very few new ones have been added to his long list. His experiments by which he demonstrated the kind of charge on an overhead thunder cloud are particularly pertinent to this chapter.

3. Skilling, Hugh H., *Exploring Electricity*, pp. 15-28. The Ronald Press Company, New York, 1949. Tells of Franklin's successes and failures, as well as of the antagonism to his work.

4. Sutton, R. M., *Demonstration Experiments in Physics*. McGraw-Hill Book Company, Inc., New York, 1938.

Unit 12

Magnetism

From the lodestone of ancient lore to large industrial lifting magnets—that is the scope of this unit on magnetism. It will help to answer such questions as why compasses in airplanes often show inaccurate readings, why watches are often enclosed in nickel cases, and what happens when a magnet is broken into pieces. But most important of all, this unit will introduce you to a principle discovered by a young Dane early in the nineteenth-century—a principle that prepared the way for the age of electricity.

In the unit photograph, you see how the magnetic effect of an electric current is being used to magnetize a steel bar.

33. WHAT IS MAGNETISM?
34. WHAT IS THE CONNECTING LINK BETWEEN MAGNETISM AND ELECTRICITY?

Unit Photograph Courtesy General Electric Co.

Chapter 33

What Is Magnetism?

The problem. Magnetism, like frictional electricity, has been known about for centuries. There were early legends concerning its discovery. One of these, found in a Greek manuscript written several centuries before Christ, recounts the wonders performed by a roving band of ironworkers called Cabiri. One of their astounding feats was to cause an ironlike stone, now known as *lodestone,* to attract and hold several iron rings one below the other without any visible means of attachment.

We, of course, know that the lodestone of the Cabiri was a natural magnet which magnetized the rings and thus held them together by an invisible force. But many questions still come to mind. For example, what is the secret of magnetic attraction? Is magnetism electricity? If so, can it be explained in terms of the electron theory? These and many other related questions will be considered in this unit.

Magnetic attraction. The fact most commonly known about a magnet is that it attracts nails, needles, tacks, iron filings, and other things made of steel or iron. But it does not attract bits of paper, straw, hair, and lint as an electrified body does. Furthermore, a magnet will attract cobalt, nickel, and alloys (mixtures) of copper, tin, silicon, and manganese, even though none of these alloy metals is attracted by itself. Is a nickel coin attracted by a magnet? Explain.

Another surprising thing about magnetic attraction is that when a magnet is dipped into iron filings, tacks, or paper clips, they cluster around the ends of the magnet, known as *poles,* but not around the middle. See Fig. 1. Seemingly the magnetism is concentrated at the poles.

The magnetic compass. Another thing very commonly known about magnetism is that when a bar magnet, magnetized needle, or lodestone is mounted as shown in Fig. 2 so that it is free to rotate about a vertical axis in a horizontal plane, it will point north-and-south. Such an instrument is called a *compass*. The end of a compass needle which points north is called the *north-seeking pole* (*N-pole*); the other end is called the *south-seeking pole* (*S-pole*). Can an electrified glass or rubber rod be used to make a compass? Test your answer by experiment.

Fig. 1. Magnetism is concentrated at the poles of the bar magnet.

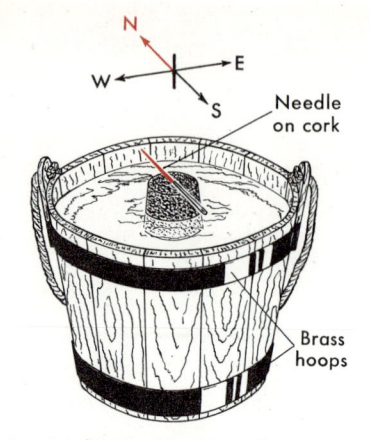

Fig. 2. Making a compass by mounting a magnetized needle on a vertical axis.

Why does a compass point in a north-south direction? When we bring the N-pole of a magnet near the N-pole of a freely suspended magnet (see Fig. 3a), the two poles repel. When two S-poles are brought together, they too repel. But when an N-pole and an S-pole are brought together, they attract (see Fig. 3b). Thus,

like poles repel and unlike poles attract.

The fact that unlike poles attract may be the clue to why a compass points in the direction that it does. Since the N-pole points north, possibly there is an unlike magnetic pole in that direction. Similarly, since the S-pole of a compass points south, possibly there is an unlike magnetic pole in that direction. But if these poles exist, where are they located?

For a long time it was thought that the source of magnetic attraction for the compass resided in the North Star. But if this were true, contrary to observation, the direction of the compass should vary as much as one degree every twelve hours because of the apparent circular motion of the star.

The part that the compass played in the discovery of America. That the compass does not everywhere point toward the Pole Star is shown in a letter written by Columbus to the king and queen of Spain:

When I sailed from Spain to the West Indies, I found that as soon as I had passed 100 leagues west of the Azores . . . the needle of the compass, which hitherto had turned toward the northeast, turned a full quarter of the wind to the northwest, and this took place from the time when we reached that line.

This erratic behavior of the compass caused much alarm among Columbus' sailors because they thought that the compass should always point toward the Pole Star. Columbus believed this, too; however, he was able to convince his sailors that the Pole Star, not the compass, was misbehaving. Thus he prevented his sailors from causing him to turn back, and was able to complete a noble experiment which, had it failed, might have delayed the discovery of America for several decades.

Does the source of magnetic attraction of the compass reside in the earth? William Gilbert (1544-1603), an Englishman, was one of the first to propose that the earth is a magnet. To test this hypothesis, he built a large magnetic iron globe which he called the "little earth" and placed the magnetic poles at its geographic

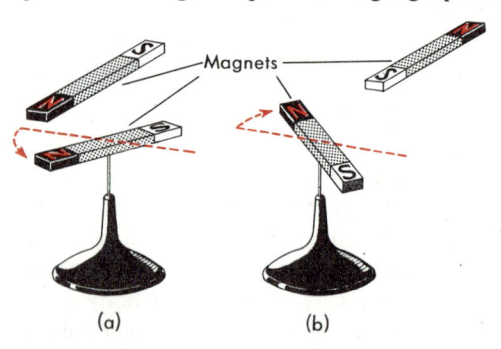

Fig. 3. (a) Repulsion of like magnetic poles. (b) Attraction of unlike magnetic poles.

WHAT IS MAGNETISM? 377

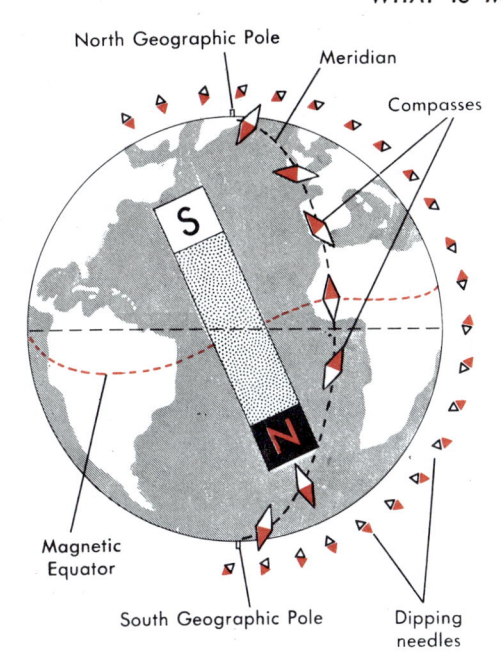

Fig. 4. The earth's magnetic field.

poles. See Fig. 4. Then he explored his model with a compass and found that at all points on it, except at the poles, the compass pointed due-north-and-south, just as it did where he lived in England, and as he thought it did at all other points on the earth.

To compare still further the magnetism of his globe and the earth, Gilbert used a *dipping needle,* which is a compass needle mounted so that it is free to rotate about a horizontal axis in a vertical plane. Over the magnetic poles, the dipping needle pointed straight up and down. Halfway between the poles, at the *magnetic equator,* the dipping needle pointed horizontally, parallel with the surface of the earth. The angle that a dipping needle makes with a horizontal plane is called the *angle of dip* or *angle of inclination.* At the magnetic equator the angle of dip was zero; at the poles it was 90 degrees; and between the magnetic equator and each pole it varied progressively from zero to 90 degrees. See Fig. 5.

When Gilbert tested corresponding parts of his globe and parts of the earth to which he had access, he found that the dip agreed very closely for both.

Where are the earth's magnetic poles located? Since the discovery of America explorers have found that north of Hudson Bay, in approximately latitude 73 degrees north and longitude 96 degrees west, the N-pole of a dipping needle points straight down, indicating that the earth's north magnetic pole is directly below that point. On the south polar continent (Antarctica), in latitude 72 degrees south and longitude 155 degrees east, the earth's south magnetic pole is located. And at points about halfway between the two magnetic poles is found the magnetic equator. See Fig. 4.

Connecting the two magnetic poles is a line which encircles the globe, known as the *line of zero declination* or the *agonic* (no angle) line, on which the compass points due north and south. A portion of this line extends in a general north-south direction through Canada and the United States, skirting the western boundary of Michigan and striking the Atlantic Ocean from the coast of Georgia. East of this line the compass points west of north; west of this line the compass points east of north. *The angle at which a compass deflects*

Fig. 5. A dipping needle.

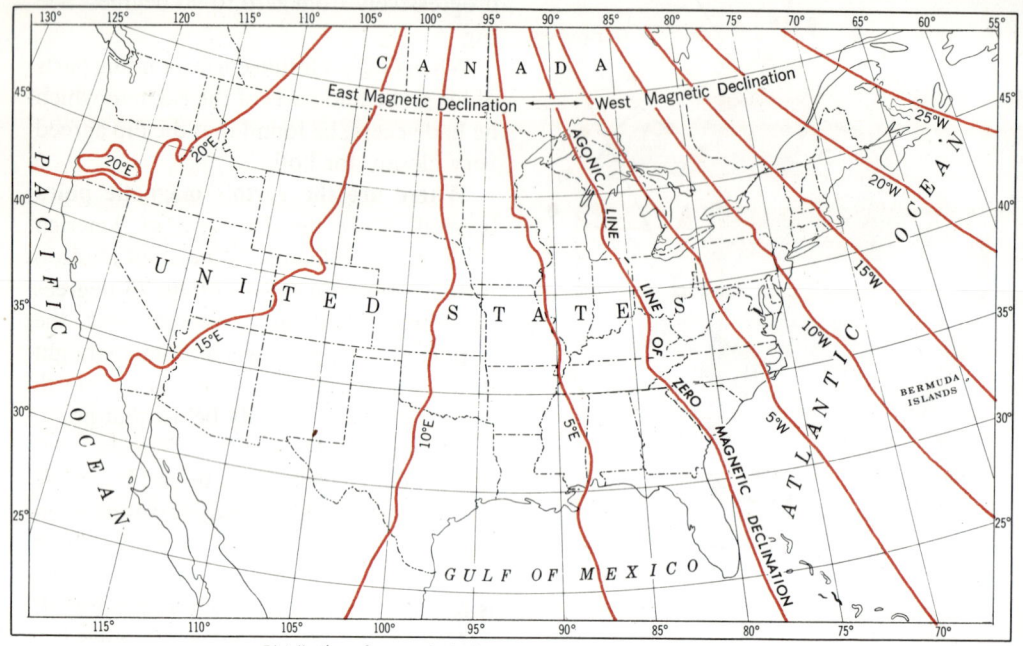

Distribution of magnetic declination in the United States for 1955.

Courtesy U.S. Coast Geodetic Survey

Fig. 6. Map of magnetic declination in the United States. Explain why this map must be revised yearly.

from geographic, or true, north and south is called magnetic **declination,** *or* **variation.** If the deflection is west of north, it is called *west* declination; if east of north, it is called *east* declination. For example, in upper Maine the declination is about 24 degrees west; in upper Washington State it is about 24 degrees east. What is the approximate declination in your community? See Fig. 6.

Through the cooperative efforts of all nations, magnetic declination and dip and the intensity of the earth's magnetism have all been carefully surveyed and are continually checked. Available maps show the declination for all parts of the world. The lines drawn through points having equal declination are known as *isogonic* (equal-angle) *lines.* Charts showing such lines are necessary for marine and air navigation by compass. Is the agonic line an isogonic line?

Induced magnetism. When a magnet and a piece of iron are brought close together, they attract each other, just as the unlike poles of two magnets attract one another. Furthermore, end *A* of the soft iron bar becomes an S-pole and end *B* becomes an N-pole which repels the N-pole of a compass (see Fig. 7). Moreover, when the piece of iron is turned around, end *A* repels an N-pole, which shows that the iron is again magnetized but that its poles have been reversed.

Magnetism caused in a body when it is brought *near* a magnet is called *induced*

WHAT IS MAGNETISM?

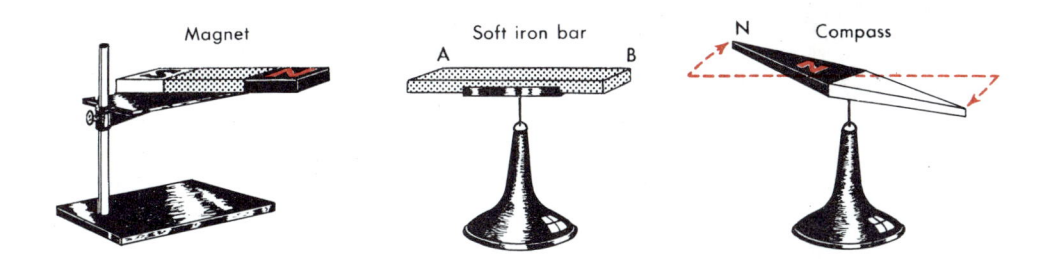

Fig. 7. Magnetizing an iron bar by induction.

magnetism. If a body is magnetized by being *touched* with a magnet, it is called *magnetism by contact.* See Fig. 8.

Soft iron and certain alloys magnetized in this manner quickly lose most of this induced magnetism after the permanent magnet is removed. Such magnetism is said to be temporary and the magnets are called *temporary magnets.* But harder pieces of iron (steel) and certain alloys are slow about losing induced magnetism. We can increase the rate at which the magnetism is lost, however, by heating or hammering the magnet.

We can make a *permanent* magnet by placing a piece of steel, such as a piece of clock spring or a knitting needle, near or in contact with a strong magnet. Or the steel can be stroked, in one direction only, with one pole of a strong magnet. If the steel is hammered during either process, the magnetization is increased. Why this is true we will endeavor to explain later.

Fitting our findings into a theory. So far, we have found that a freely suspended magnet points north and south; that a magnet has two unlike poles, an N-pole and an S-pole; that like poles repel and unlike poles attract; that a magnet attracts iron, steel, nickel, cobalt, and certain alloys; that when these magnetic substances are brought near or in contact with a magnet they become magnetized by induction;

that when they are removed from near a magnet they lose some or most of their magnetism; that steel and certain alloys retain their magnetism much longer than soft iron; that we can permanently magnetize steel and a few other substances by pounding them when they are near a magnet or are being stroked with one pole of a magnet; and that the earth is a magnet with two poles. How can these findings be explained?

You will recall that we explained electricity by assuming it to be two kinds of charges which we were able to isolate one from the other. Likewise, let us now temporarily assume that there are two kinds of magnetism, north-seeking and south-seeking. Also, let us assume that in a magnet the two kinds of magnetism are concentrated each at one of the respective poles. Therefore, we should be able to separate or isolate the two kinds by cutting the magnet in half.

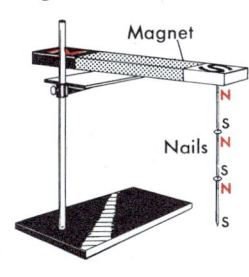

Fig. 8. Magnetizing nails by contact.

Fig. 9. Each half becomes a magnet.

But when a magnet is cut in two, the result is surprisingly different from what we just anticipated. From one magnet we obtain two new complete magnets, each with an N-pole and an S-pole. And if we cut each of these in two, we get two more magnets. This can be repeated again and again with the same results, but in every case two new magnetic poles appear at the middle, where no poles existed before. All of this seems to indicate that magnetic poles exist in pairs and one cannot be isolated from the other. The result also casts doubt on our assumption that magnetism is matter. However, it indicates that a large magnet is made up of a multitude of small magnets, which, if true, means that we should be able to make a large magnet by putting smaller magnets together.

Thus, if we fill a test tube (see Fig. 10a) half full of unmagnetized iron filings distributed uniformly in depth, the tube will show none of the properties of a permanent magnet. But if we then stroke the tube with one pole of a magnet so as to magnetize the filings and cause them to arrange themselves as shown in (b) of Fig. 10, then the test tube consisting of hundreds of small magnets, each with two poles, should have the properties of a single magnet. And, therefore, one end of the tube should be repelled by the N-pole of a magnet and the other end should be repelled by the S-pole.

Another theory of magnetism. From the preceding discussion, we see that a magnet acts as if it is made of a number of very tiny magnets. The tiniest possible magnet is likely to be the smallest particle into which the magnetic substance can be broken and still retain its identity. Probably this particle would be a molecule.

Evidently, then, when iron is magnetized, the molecules behave as do the bits of iron filings in the above experiment. Consequently, magnetism is not created. The magnetic molecules are aligned in an orderly manner. When all the molecules are aligned, maximum magnetization results and is known as *saturation*. Hence, magnetism seems to be an effect due to the arrangement and organization of the molecules of a body. And when this special arrangement is destroyed, the magnetism is lost. Does the fact that a magnet can be demagnetized by pounding or heating agree with this theory?

What forces exist around a magnet? We have observed the magnetization of soft iron when it is placed near a magnet. We have also observed the behavior of iron

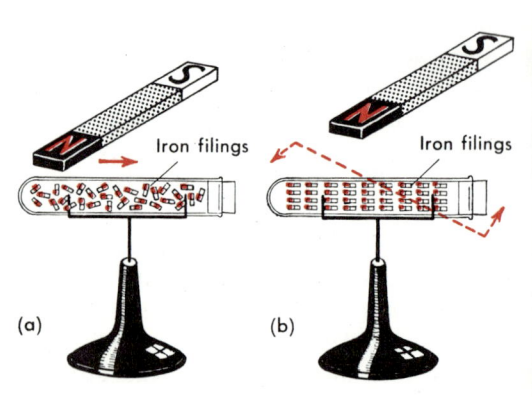

Fig. 10. (a) An unmagnetized substance. (b) A magnetized substance.

WHAT IS MAGNETISM?

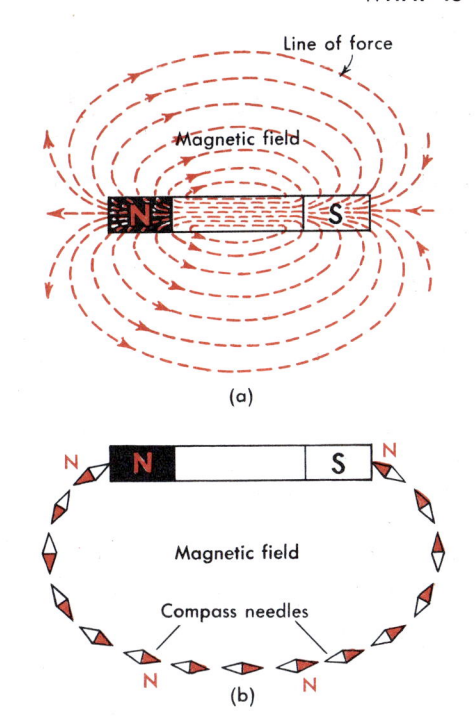

Fig. 11. Iron filings magnetized by induction indicate the direction of lines of force about a bar magnet.

filings in a test tube when a magnet is brought near them. All these observations indicate that there exists in the vicinity of a magnet some force which causes particles of nearby magnetic materials to align themselves systematically with respect to the magnet.

Consequently, if we place a bar magnet on a table, lay a pane of glass or sheet of paper over the magnet, and, while tapping the glass or paper gently, sprinkle iron filings over it, we should expect the iron filings to be magnetized by induction and to align themselves in a pattern. This is what actually happens when we do this; the filings fall into curved lines, as shown in Fig. 11. The lines marked out by the filings are called *lines of force*. The space where these lines of force exist may be called the *magnetic field*.

In the magnetic field near the poles the filings stick straight out from the poles. Equidistant between the poles, the filings align themselves parallel to a straight line connecting the two poles. A compass needle will behave in the same way that an iron filing does, which is further proof that the iron filings are magnetized. The direction in which the compass needle points is the same as the direction of the lines of force in that part of the magnet's field. *A* **line of force** *is defined as an "imaginary" line that indicates the direction, or path, in which a single magnetic pole would be urged if placed on that line.*

What is the direction of a magnetic line of force? Among scientists it was arbitrarily agreed that *the direction of a line of force, and hence the direction of the magnetic field, is the direction in which an N-pole in the field is urged. That is, it is the direction in which the N-pole of a compass points when it is in the field.* The direction of a line of force is indicated by an arrow. See Fig. 11(a). Do lines of force extend out of, or into, an N-pole?

The paths and distribution of lines of force. If you study the pattern of iron filings in a magnetic field, you may find that they never cross. They seem to be concentrated near the two ends or poles of the magnet and to thin out as the distance from the magnet increases. Furthermore, they seem to make a complete circuit through the magnet, extending out of the N-pole and into the S-pole. When two magnets are placed with like poles end to end, the lines of force take the pattern shown in Fig. 12; they apparently try to remain apart. But when unlike poles are placed end to end, the lines of force seem to bridge the gap, much as a handshake

Fig. 12. Distribution of lines of force between two like poles.

bridges the gap between two persons. See Fig. 13.

Permeability. In case a piece of soft iron is placed in a magnetic field, and iron filings are sprinkled over a piece of paper laid on top of the iron, the filings fail to align themselves, which shows the absence of lines of force in the region. This means that the lines of force in this part of the field extend through the iron rather than through the air around the iron. In other words, iron seems to offer an easier path for the lines of force than does air. This *lack of resistance* to magnetic lines of force, or the *ability to concentrate* them, is called *permeability*. The more permeable a substance is, the more highly magnetized it will become when placed in a given magnetic field.

A rather spectacular test for the permeability of a substance can be performed by the insertion of thin sheets of the material in question between a strong horseshoe magnet and a sewing needle suspended as in Fig. 14. If the material furnishes little resistance to the lines of force, they pass through it instead of through the air. The material thus shields the needle from the lines of force, and consequently the needle will fall. If the substance in question does not "gather in" the lines of force, the needle will remain in the position shown in the figure. Explain why watches are sometimes encased in soft iron.

If an *armature,* or *keeper,* made of soft iron is placed across the poles of a horseshoe magnet, as in Fig. 15, we would expect most of the lines of force to pass through the keeper and very few to pass through the air around it. We can test this theory by sprinkling iron filings over a piece of paper that is placed over a horseshoe magnet having a keeper. But, despite the almost complete absence of lines of force outside the magnet and keeper, the magnet is just as strong when the keeper is removed as it was before the keeper was put on. A horseshoe magnet loses its mag-

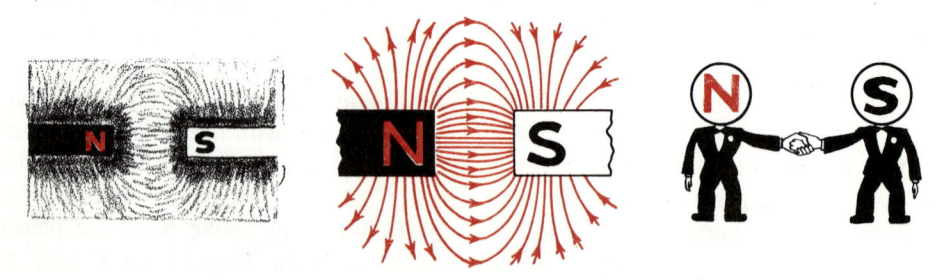

Fig. 13. Distribution of lines of force between two unlike poles.

WHAT IS MAGNETISM?

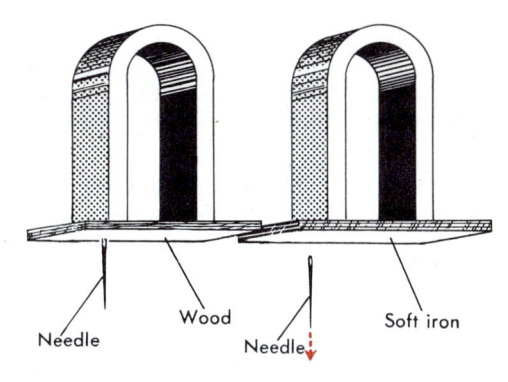

Fig. 14. Testing the permeability of materials. Is wood permeable?

netism much faster without a keeper than with one. This seems to indicate that a closed or complete circuit for the lines of force is necessary to keep the molecules inside a magnet in proper alignment.

And the same has been found to hold true with bar magnets. They will retain their magnetism much longer than otherwise if they are always stacked in pairs with *unlike poles together,* and with a soft iron keeper *across each end of the pair.*

SUMMARY AND CONCLUSIONS

1. A magnet attracts iron, steel, nickel, cobalt, and certain alloys.
2. Each magnet has an N-pole and an S-pole.
3. Like poles repel and unlike poles attract.
4. The earth behaves like a huge magnet.
5. Declination is the number of degrees which the N-pole of a compass points away from true north.
6. Dip is the angle which a dipping needle makes with a horizontal plane.
7. Surrounding a magnet is a magnetic field that is made up of so-called magnetic lines of force.
8. The direction of a magnetic line of force, or of a magnetic field, is the direction in which the N-pole of a compass points or is urged in that field.
9. Permeability is the ease with which lines of force may be established in a substance as compared with air.
10. A magnet is believed to be made up of many smaller magnets (molecules) which are properly aligned. Saturation exists when all small magnets are in alignment.

QUESTIONS FOR REVIEW

1. What substances are attracted by a magnet?
2. Compare the substances attracted by a magnet with those attracted by an electrified body.
3. Does the N-pole of a magnet attract a body with either a negative or a positive charge?
4. Does attraction and repulsion furnish any clue to the relationship between magnetism and electricity?
5. What is the law of magnetic attraction and repulsion?
6. What is declination? Magnetic variation? Dip?
7. What is the magnetic variation where you live? At New York City? Detroit? Los Angeles? St. Louis? Miami? Dallas?
8. What proof do we have that the earth's geographic and magnetic poles do not coincide?
9. The N-pole of a compass is the same kind of pole as the earth's south magnetic

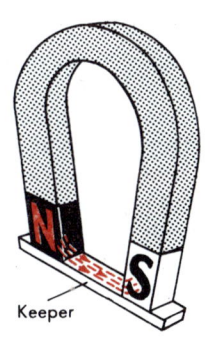

Fig. 15. Effect of a keeper on a magnet.

pole; the S-pole of a compass is the same kind as the earth's north magnetic pole. How do we know this to be true?

10. When a small bar magnet is placed on a cork and floated in a still pool of water located in the northern hemisphere, why is the magnet not attracted to the north side of the pool?

11. Account for the fact that the magnetic variation, from west to east, shown by Columbus' compass took place far to the east of the present agonic line.

12. When a steel ship is made, it becomes magnetized. Explain what causes this.

PROJECTS

1. Using a short piece of an old clock spring, or an old steel file, make a number of magnets. See page 379. Cut a few of them in two to see if two magnets are produced.

2. Will an ordinary compass work inside an automobile? Test by experiment.

3. Hold a steel rod three or four feet in length in a north-and-south direction so that its angle with the horizontal plane makes it parallel with the earth's magnetic lines of force. Then give it several sharp blows with a hammer. Next test it to see if it is magnetized. If it is, mark the N-pole and the S-pole. Now turn the rod end for end and repeat the experiment. Finally, hold the rod at right angles to the direction of the earth's magnetic field and repeat the pounding. Explain the results.

4. Determine whether the "brass" door knobs, lamp stands, and so on in your home are brass plated on iron.

5. In an early chapter we defined physics as a study of matter and motion. This is the basis of what is known as the *mechanistic* point of view and it has had tremendous influence on all fields of thought.

In this last chapter we have explained magnetism in terms of what Einstein and others call the *field theory*. In their book, *The Evolution of Physics*, Einstein and Infeld explain the breakdown of the mechanistic point of view in physics and the emergence of the field theory. The results in science have been unbelievable, but in education, philosophy, and other fields we are still clinging to mechanistic points of view. Why not read about the breakdown of the mechanistic point of view and the emergence of the field theory in physics? This study could be the beginning of a life work. Or better still, carry your study of the field theory over into other fields such as psychology, education, economics, or religion. Many great uncharted and unexplored intellectual fields will be opened to you. Furthermore, the fields are not crowded.

READING YOU WILL ENJOY

1. Caverly, D. P., *Primer of Electronics and Radiant Energy,* pp. 38-44. McGraw-Hill Book Company, Inc., New York, 1952.

2. Einstein, Albert, and Leopold Infeld, *The Evolution of Physics.* Simon and Schuster, Inc., New York, 1938.

3. Richardson, J. S., and G. P. Cahoon, *Methods and Materials for Teaching General and Physical Science,* pp. 214-222. McGraw-Hill Book Company, Inc., New York, 1951. Gives a number of simple projects and useful experiments that can be performed.

4. Sutton, R. M., *Demonstration Experiments in Physics,* pp. 280-285. McGraw-Hill Book Company, Inc., New York, 1938. Contains a number of simple experiments on magnetism.

5. Swezey, K. M., *After-Dinner Science.* Whittlesey House, McGraw-Hill Book Company, Inc., New York, 1948. "A Compass in a Minute," pp. 106-107; "Magnetism from the Earth's Field," p. 108; "A Magnetic Coin Rejecter," p. 109; "Magnetism May Be Molecular," pp. 110-111.

6. Taylor, L. W., *Physics, the Pioneer Science,* pp. 577-598. Houghton Mifflin Company, Boston, 1941. Explains elementary magnetism in a very interesting manner.

Chapter 34

What Is the Connecting Link between Magnetism and Electricity?

The problem. From the time that both magnetism and electricity were first seriously studied, it was suspected that some connecting link existed between the two. You probably suspect the same thing because you know that electric trains, bells, generators, motors, and many other electrical machines all run on electricity and contain magnets. Also you know that every study of electricity includes magnetism. What is the connecting link between the two?

Searching for a clue. To find the relationship between electricity and magnetism we should recall what we know about both. We already know that there are two kinds of electricity, positive and negative, and that like charges repel and unlike charges attract. Magnets, too, exhibit similar characteristics. Every magnet has two poles, an N-pole and an S-pole; and like poles repel and unlike poles attract. Furthermore, when an electrically charged body is brought near a pith ball, the latter becomes charged by induction. Likewise, when a magnet is brought near a piece of iron, the iron is magnetized by induction.

But beyond these there are few similarities. Neither an N-pole nor an S-pole shows any repulsion for either a positive or a negative electrical charge. A freely suspended, electrically charged rod will not point in a north-south direction, as does a compass needle. And neither an N-pole nor an S-pole will exist by itself, as will a positive or a negative electrical charge. Magnetic poles always exist in pairs.

Other differences are that electricity is believed to be matter. There are two kinds, positive protons and negative electrons. Magnetism is believed to be an effect due to the arrangement of matter: of molecules in a body. Hence it seems that magnetism and electricity are more unlike each other than alike. Nevertheless, we are faced with the unquestionable facts that they do occur together in many practical electrical devices, and that every study of electricity includes magnetism.

How Oersted discovered the connecting link. Near the close of the eighteenth century the identification of electricity and magnetism loomed high on the agenda of unsolved scientific problems. Many experimenters were "hot on the trail," but the secret for which they searched eluded them.

Finally there came upon the scene a young professor of physics in Copenhagen, Hans Christian Oersted (1778-1851), who made the world-changing discovery.

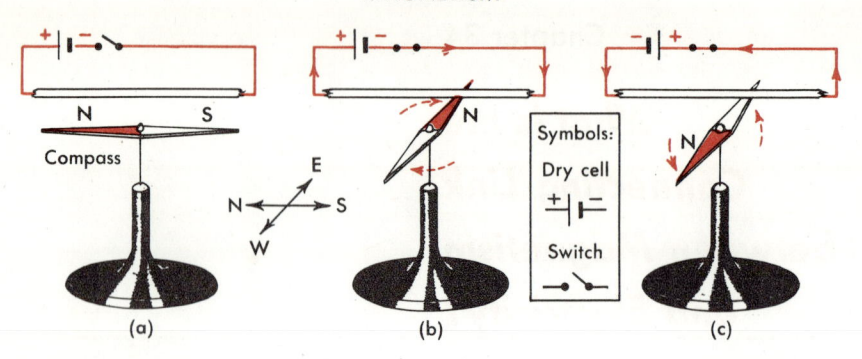

Fig. I. Oersted discovered that a magnetic field surrounds a wire carrying a current. Why is the compass needle not deflected in (a)? Account for the direction in which the compass needle is deflected in (b) and (c).

This was one of the few discoveries in science which might be classed as accidental, for Oersted happened upon it much as one finds a penny lying on the sidewalk or mushrooms growing in a pasture. Yet, had Oersted not been looking for the connecting link he might never have recognized it when he saw it.

We can repeat Oersted's experiment by connecting a dry cell, switch, and wire together; by holding the wire above and parallel to a compass needle in a north-south direction; and by then closing the switch. When the direction of the current is south, the north-seeking pole of the compass is made to swing west, as shown in Fig. 1. If the direction of the current is reversed, the north-seeking pole of the compass points east.

If the wire is next held below the compass instead of above it and the direction of the current is south, the north-seeking pole swings toward the east. And again, if the current is reversed, taking the direction of south to north, the north-seeking pole of the compass swings west. What Oersted discovered was that

every conductor which carries an electric current is surrounded by a magnetic field.

This was the connecting link for which scientists had searched so long. In terms of modern thought, Oersted's discovery meant that an electron or other charged particle, if moving, could produce a magnetic field which exerted a force on a magnetic pole, but could not do so if it were standing still.

What is the direction of the magnetic field about a wire that carries a current? To study the field about a conductor, pass a wire through the center of a sheet of paper and place the wire and paper in the position shown in (a) of Fig. 2. Then pass a current through the wire and at the same time sprinkle iron filings on the paper and tap it gently. As a result, the filings arrange themselves in concentric circles around the wire. This pattern indicates that lines of force extend around the wire in concentric circles which never cross each other.

To determine the direction of the field, place several small compasses on the paper about the wire and observe the direction in which each north-seeking pole points. When you look downward at the paper while current is passing down through the wire, as in (b) of Fig. 2, the north-seeking poles all point in a counter-

THE LINK BETWEEN MAGNETISM AND ELECTRICITY

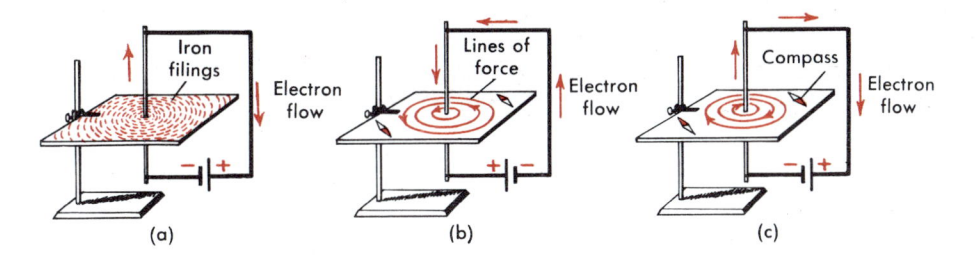

Fig. 2. In (a) the iron filings show the pattern of the magnetic field. In (b) and (c) the compasses show the direction of the field around the vertical wire. In which direction do the lines of force encircle the wire in (a) and (b)?

clockwise direction. When the current is reversed, as in (c) of Fig. 2, so that it passes upward, the lines of force are in a clockwise direction. And in all cases, whether the current passes upward or downward, the north-seeking poles of the compasses point *perpendicular to the path of electric current.*

The left-hand rule for determining direction of the magnetic field about a wire carrying a current. Using the foregoing data, we can make a very convenient "rule of thumb" with which we can quickly find the direction of the field when the direction of the current is known, or, vice versa, find the direction of the current when the direction of the field is known. See Fig. 3. The rule is:

Grasp the wire in the left hand, so that the thumb points along the wire in the direction of the current. The fingers then point around the wire in the direction of the magnetic field.

With the aid of a compass, how could you determine the direction of the current in a conductor? How could you locate an underground wire that is carrying a current?

What is the nature of the magnetic field about a coil carrying electric current?

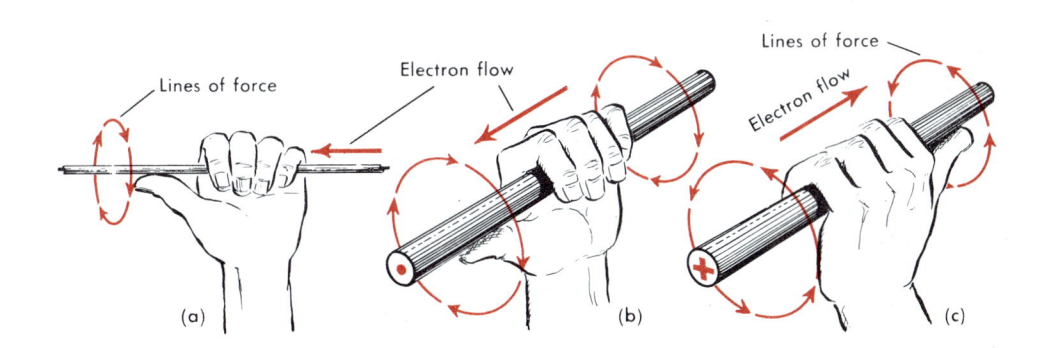

Fig. 3. The left-hand rule for a current-carrying conductor is shown in (a). Current moving away from the reader is indicated by a cross; toward the reader by a dot.

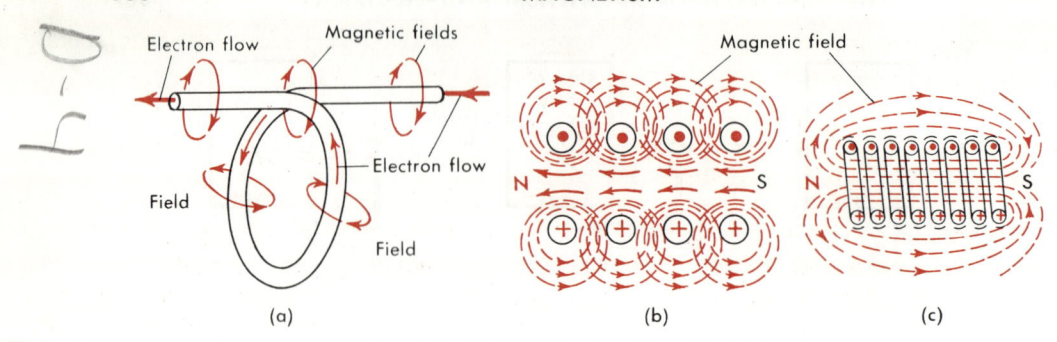

Fig. 4. (a) The field about a single loop of wire. (b) Cross section of the magnetic field about four turns of wire carrying a current. (c) Cross section of a magnetic coil.

Since we can determine the direction of the magnetic field about a single straight wire carrying electric current, we should be able also to predict the nature of the field about a coil of wire. In (b) and (c) of Fig. 4 are represented cross sections of a coil carrying a current. In the upper section of the coil the direction of the current in each wire is out of the paper toward you. In the lower section the direction of the current is into the paper away from you. Using the left-hand rule, check the direction of the field about each wire as shown by the arrows.

Inside the coil, the lines of force all have the same direction and extend lengthwise through it, and out one end, around the outside, and back into the other end, just as in a bar magnet. See (c) of Fig. 4. And as in a bar magnet, a north-seeking pole should be where the lines of force leave the coil, and a south-seeking pole should be where the lines of force enter the coil. Consequently, the coil acts like a magnet. When an iron core is placed inside such a coil we have an *electromagnet*.

Left-hand rule for a coil. Another convenient rule shows how to determine the polarity of an electromagnet when the direction of the current around the coil is known. (See Fig. 5.) Or, vice versa, the rule may be used to find the direction of the current if the polarity of the electromagnet is known. The rule is as follows:

If we grasp the coil in the left hand so that the fingers point in the direction of the current, then the thumb points toward the north-seeking pole.

A new clue to the cause of permanent magnetism. Since a magnet can be produced by a current in a coil of wire, it is only natural to suspect that magnetism in iron and other magnetic substances is caused by electric current. But where does the current come from in a magnet? We already have cause to believe that a magnet is made up of innumerable smaller magnets, perhaps atomic or molecular in size.

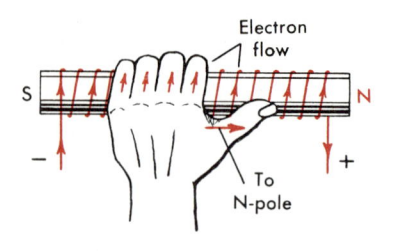

Fig. 5. The left-hand rule for a coil.

THE LINK BETWEEN MAGNETISM AND ELECTRICITY

Furthermore, we know that every atom has one or more planetary electrons revolving about its nucleus in regular orbits. Therefore, since electrons flowing in a circular coil cause it to be a magnet, then electrons which move in an orbit in an atom should cause the atom to be one, too. One end of each atom should be an N-pole and the other end an S-pole (see Fig. 6a), just as in the case of the coil (Fig. 6b). This explains the small magnets within a magnet which we talked about on page 380. The parts of our jigsaw puzzle, it seems, all are falling into place. Or are they? No, for immediately a question comes to mind which we must answer to prove our hypothesis. Since all matter is composed of atoms and molecules, why are not all substances magnetic?

One reason why some substances are magnetic and others are not is shown in (c) of Fig. 6. When the electrons all revolve in the same direction, either clockwise or counterclockwise, in parallel planes, a substance is magnetic. But if the planes of revolution are in helter-skelter positions, the magnetic effect of one moving electron cancels that of another. Only when the planes of revolution are oriented as shown in (d) of Fig. 6 will a substance have magnetic properties.

What is the effect of placing an iron core inside a coil? If an iron core is placed inside a coil of an electromagnet, the core should become magnetized by induction. Consequently the electron orbits in the core should all line up in parallel planes. In addition, if the revolutions of the electrons in the atoms and in the wires of the coil are in the same direction, then the magnetic strength of the coil and core should be greater than that of the coil alone. Design an experiment to test the effect of putting an iron core inside a coil.

What is the effect of increasing the number of turns of wire on an electromagnet? The first electromagnet was made in 1823 by William Sturgeon (1783-1850). It consisted only of a single layer of bare copper wire wound on a varnished core of iron. Since the wires were not insulated, they evidently were not wound closely enough to touch each other. Why would this have to be true? What was the purpose of the varnish on the iron core?

On October 10, 1827, Joseph Henry of Princeton University, the first American

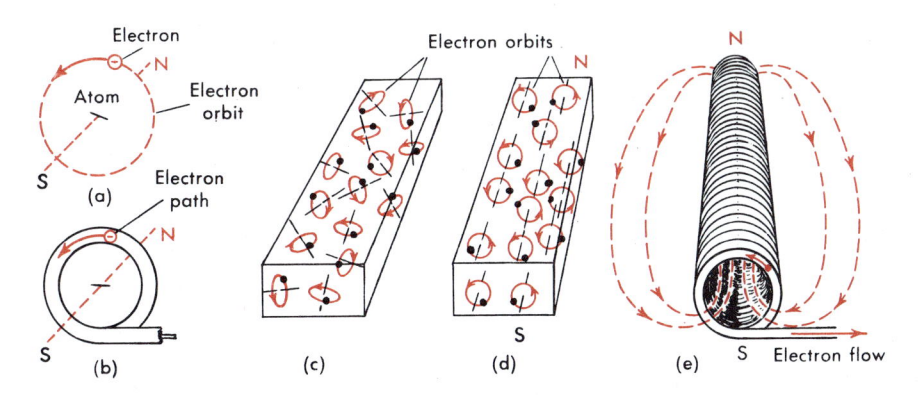

Fig. 6. Electron orbit in atom (a) and in one turn or loop of wire. (b). Electron orbits in unmagnetized piece of steel (c), in magnetized piece of steel (d), and in a coil carrying a current (e).

after Benjamin Franklin to make a major contribution to physics, improved the electromagnet by winding several layers instead of only one around the iron core. Henry's real contribution was to insulate the wire instead of the core as Sturgeon had done with varnish. By winding more and more wire on his electromagnets he made them stronger and stronger. In 1831 he constructed one which could lift 750 pounds.

What is the effect of increasing the current through an electromagnet? It is possible to design two electromagnets, having identical cores, which produce the same field strength, but with different currents. For example, in one coil there are, say, 1600 turns of wire, through which 1.5 amperes flow. In another coil with an identical core there are, say, 40,000 turns of wire, through which .06 ampere flows. In both cases the product of number of amperes and number of turns equals a given number, which may be designated as *ampere turns*.

$$1,600 \times 1.5 = 2400 \text{ ampere turns}$$
$$40,000 \times .06 = 2400 \text{ ampere turns}$$

Evidently the field or magnetic strength produced by an electromagnet having a given core is determined by the product of the number of amperes flowing through the coil and the number of turns of wire in the coil. It is neither amperes alone nor turns alone that determine magnetic strength; it is the product of the two: ampere turns. Therefore, the strength of an electromagnet may be increased, either by an increase in the electric current through the coil or by an increase in the number of turns of wire in the coil, or both.

In case the core becomes saturated, an increase in ampere turns does not give the same increase in strength as when the core is not saturated. Therefore, we could expect to increase the total strength of a given magnet by increasing the size of the magnet; that is, by increasing not only the number of ampere turns of the coil, but also the effective mass of the core. This does not increase the concentration of lines of force, but does increase the total number. Thus, a big magnet may not have greater lifting force per unit area of pole face, but it can lift much greater total loads than a small one.

Thus, we can increase in four ways the magnetic strength of a coil carrying electric current: (1) by inserting a core of material having high magnetic permeability, (2) by giving the magnetic core an advantageous shape, (3) by increasing the number of ampere turns in the coil, and (4) by increasing the mass of the magnet; that is, its cross-sectional area.

Fig. 7. A giant electromagnet is used in loading railroad rails for shipment.

Courtesy United States Steel Corp.

Uses of electromagnets. *Lifting.* Electromagnets have many more uses than permanent magnets because, first, they can be made very much stronger, and, second, since the electric currents can be started or stopped at will, the magnets may be magnetized or demagnetized as desired. Soft iron, permalloy, and certain other materials have the capability not only of taking on magnetism almost instantaneously but also of losing most of it just as quickly. Consequently, the use of electromagnets for lifting purposes is widespread. Large magnets are used to hoist scrap iron from one place to another, both because they take hold and let go quickly and at exactly the right times, and also because the odd shapes and sizes of the pieces have no deterrent effect on the lifting process. Moreover, by means of electromagnets iron and steel scrap may easily be separated from other metals which are non-magnetic.

Producing permanent magnets. Electromagnets are used extensively for manufacturing permanent magnets. For example, a piece of steel (Why is steel necessary?) shaped like a horseshoe magnet is placed so that the two ends rest on the poles of an electromagnet. The electric current is turned on and, while the magnetic lines of force are extending through the steel horseshoe, the horseshoe is struck sharply with a hammer in order to assist in the realignment of its molecules.

The strength of the electromagnet which does the magnetizing should be great enough to saturate the metal being magnetized. After magnetization, a keeper is placed across the poles of a permanent magnet to furnish a short path of low magnetic resistance and thereby aid in retaining the magnetization. See page 382.

The telegraph. Electromagnetism was discovered at a time when methods of transportation in most of the civilized world were undergoing a revolution. The great railway systems that were being built in the United States were greatly in need of a means of sending messages quickly over long distances. The discovery that we can produce magnetic attraction by closing an electric circuit and destroy it by opening the circuit again suggested a way in which messages might be sent across a continent in the twinkling of an eye.

The earliest telegraph consisted of a battery, wire for the circuit, a tapping key, and a magnetic compass (see Fig. 8) which was held over or under the wire.

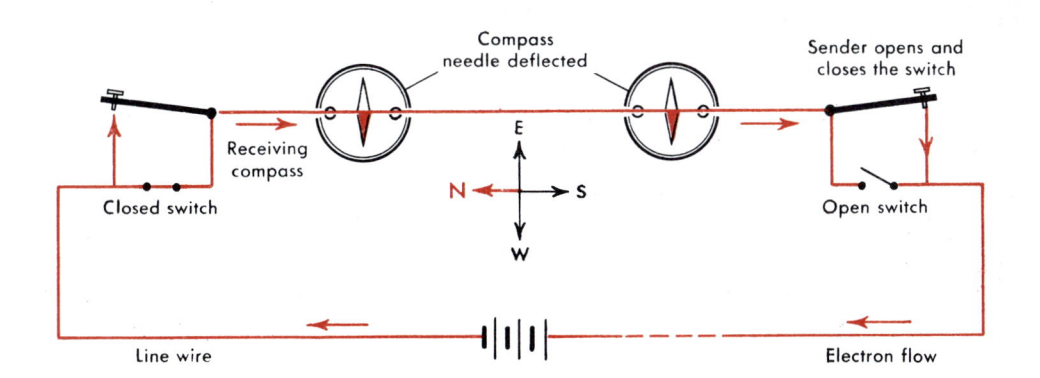

Fig. 8. An early telegraph. How do the compass needles act when both keys are closed? When both keys are opened?

When the key was closed the compass needle was deflected; when it was opened, the needle returned to zero position. Can you work out a code for sending messages by this method?

Later, Samuel F. B. Morse (1791-1872) of this country invented, in 1848, a receiver called a *sounder,* and a system of signaling by long and short taps which replaced earlier systems. The principle of the Morse sounder can be easily understood through study of Fig. 9. When the key is closed, current moves through the circuit and magnetizes the core of the electromagnet. The electromagnet, in turn, pulls down the soft-iron armature against the core, producing a click.

When the key is opened, the core then ceases to be a magnet and the armature is pulled back by a spring, producing a second click. In a modern sounder, the armature is a rather heavy bar which makes the click easily audible. At each station along the line is a key and a sounder. Messages are generally sent in a dot-dash code known as *Morse code.* The *international code,* which is a variant of Morse, is so called because it is used by the people of all nations.

Since, in order to make a circuit, two electrical paths, one outgoing and the other incoming, must be provided, one of the early improvements in telegraphy came with the discovery that the ground will serve very well as the second wire. Therefore, if each station is grounded by the attachment of one wire to a metal rod driven several feet into the ground, only one line wire is needed between stations. See Fig. 10.

One of the shortcomings of these early telegraph systems was that over long distances the signals were very weak, often too weak to be received at all. Can you explain the reason for this? To remedy this difficulty, the *relay* was invented.

The relay. A relay is an instrument very much like a sounder, except that the armature bar is very light, and a very light spring is used. Thus, the electrical circuit may be opened and closed by a much smaller electric current than with a sounder, but with insufficient sound for the dots and dashes to be heard plainly.

In order to operate an audible sounder, the relay merely acts as a switch to open and close the local electric circuit, which contains a battery and a sounder. The energy needed to operate the sounder comes from the local battery and not from the line.

The telegraphic relay has turned out to be a widely useful invention. More and more it is coming into use in automatic

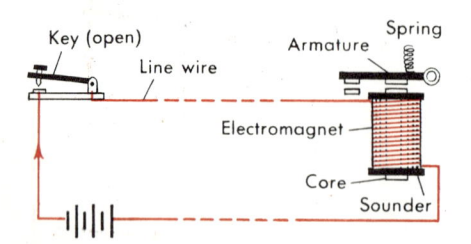

Fig. 9. A telegraph sounder, key, and battery. How does the sounder work?

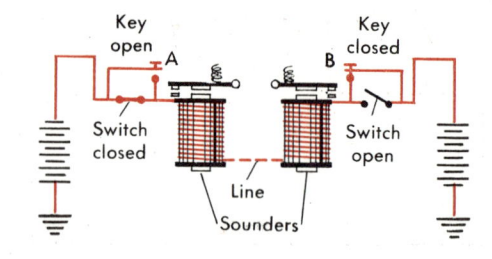

Fig. 10. A simple telegraph circuit. Station *A* is fixed to receive; station *B* to send.

THE LINK BETWEEN MAGNETISM AND ELECTRICITY

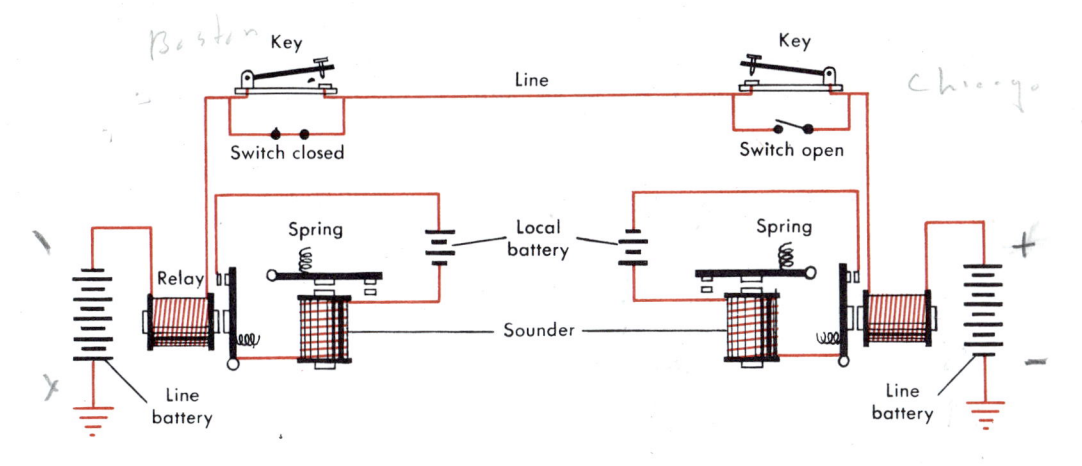

Fig. 11. A two-way telegraph system. Note that the earth serves as one conductor between the stations. Explain how the relay is used to control a large current by means of a feeble current.

machines. The relay, along with photoelectric cells, condensers, and vacuum (radio) tubes, has enabled scientists to create machines which will do almost everything but think for themselves. Such machines we shall discuss later.

The electric bell. Another invention that is an outcome of Oersted's discovery of the magnetic effect of an electric current is the electric bell. It works on exactly the same principle as the telegraph sounder described above. There are a few minor differences in structure, in that a gong is added, the armature bar is extended, and a hammer and contact spring have been attached to the bar. See Fig. 12.

Thus, when the circuit is closed by means of a pushbutton, the electromagnet pulls the armature, causing the hammer to strike the gong. At the same time, however, the contact spring is pulled away from the contact screw so that the circuit is broken, causing the core of the electromagnet to lose its magnetism and allowing the armature bar to spring back to its original position. Thus, the circuit is again closed

and the process is rapidly repeated as long as the push button is held down.

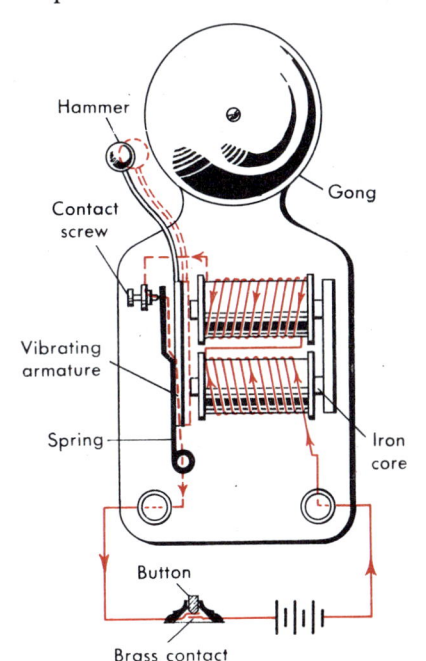

Fig. 12. The electric bell. Describe its operation.

At the point of contact between armature spring and adjustable contact screw, a small spark usually occurs each time contact is broken. Corrosion is therefore very likely to occur, and such points are usually tipped with silver, platinum, tungsten, or some other noncorrosive material. But even with such materials, some corrosion does occur. Most of the trouble which causes such bells to get out of order results either from poor contact at this point or from poor adjustment of the adjustable screw.

Electric buzzers, used in offices and elsewhere, are made like an electric bell except that the gong and hammer are omitted and the armature is made very light.

SUMMARY AND CONCLUSIONS

1. The relationship between magnetism and electricity is that an electron in motion produces a magnetic field. The direction of the field is always at right angles to the direction of motion.
2. The rule of thumb relating the direction of current and direction of field is to grasp the wire in the left hand so that the thumb points in the direction of the current. Then the fingers encircle the wire in the direction of the magnetic field.
3. A coil of wire carrying a current has the properties of a magnet and is known as an electromagnet. Its strength is dependent upon the permeability of its core, the shape and diameter of the core, the current through the coil, and the number of turns of wire.
4. The strength of two electromagnets having identical cores is dependent upon the product of the number of turns and the current. That is, the strength is dependent on the number of ampere turns.
5. The rule for a coil is to grasp the coil in the left hand so that the fingers point in the direction of the current. The thumb then points toward the north-seeking pole.

QUESTIONS FOR REVIEW

1. Explain two different ways of proving that a magnetic field exists around a conductor which is carrying a current.
2. Make a diagram of an electromagnet which is connected with a battery. Show the windings, the direction of the current, the N-pole and the S-pole, and the direction of the lines of force in the magnetic field produced.
3. Make a diagram of a horseshoe electromagnet having a soft iron core. Show how each pole is wrapped so that one is an N-pole and the other an S-pole.
4. Explain, by means of the electron theory of magnetism, just what is believed to happen when the core of an electromagnet is magnetized.
5. A horseshoe electromagnet is to be used to magnetize a steel bar. Show how you would place the steel bar on the electromagnet and show which end of the bar would be the N-pole and which would be the S-pole.
6. If you had to wind a coil so as to make an electromagnet as strong as possible with a given fixed amount of current, would you use many turns of fine wire or only a few turns of coarser wire? Explain.
7. Explain how you could locate a wire, carrying a current, which is buried in the ground or in a concrete floor.
8. Make a diagram of an electric bell and explain why the hammer does not strike the bell and stay there.
9. What is the essential difference between an electric bell and a telegraph sounder?
10. Explain the action of a relay.
11. How was one wire eliminated in completion of the circuit for a telegraph system?
12. How many wires are required for a streetcar? How is the circuit completed?

PROBLEMS AND EXERCISES

1. If the direction of a current of electricity in a conductor is toward the reader out of this page, is the direction of the magnetic field (choose the correct answer): (a) along the conductor toward the reader? (b) clock-

wise around the conductor? (c) counterclockwise around the conductor? (d) along the wire into the page?

2. If the direction of a current of electricity in a conductor is away from the reader into the page, then what is the direction of the magnetic field? Choose one from the four answers to Question 1 above.

3. If a copper wire *AB* is held in a north-south direction (see Fig. 13) and an electric

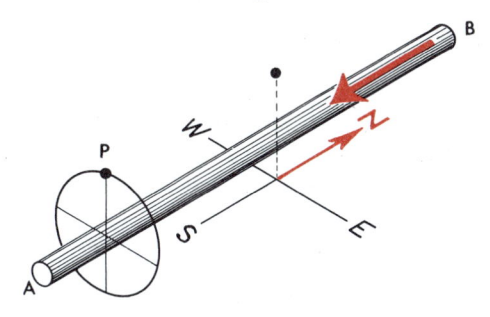

Fig. 13

current is passed from *B* to *A*, the direction of the magnetic field above the wire at the point *P* is which of the following? (1) D, down; (2) N, north; (3) S, south; (4) E, east; (5) W, west; (6) U, up.

4. In Fig. 14, at the point *P*, the direction

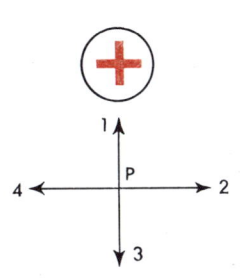

Fig. 14

of the magnetic field is indicated by which arrow: 1, 2, 3, or 4?

5. Fig. 15 shows the cross section of a coil of wire which is carrying a current. At the top of the coil the symbols indicate that the direction of the current is away from the reader. At the bottom, the symbols indicate that it is toward the reader.

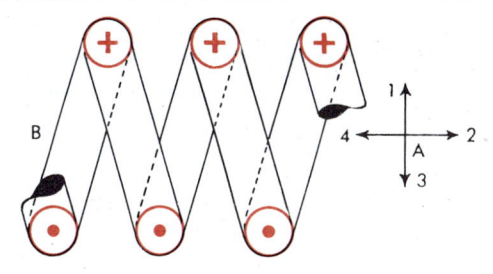

Fig. 15

(a) At point *A*, the direction of the magnetic field is indicated by which arrow: 1, 2, 3, or 4?

(b) Is end *B* of the coil an N-pole, an S-pole, or not any kind of pole?

6. We can increase the lifting force of an electromagnet by (a) increasing the number of turns of wire; (b) increasing the current; (c) increasing the cross-sectional area of core; (d) making the core of glass instead of soft iron. (Choose the one answer that is not correct.)

7. Two electromagnets, *A* and *B*, are identical except that *A* has 100 turns of wire and operates on a current of 50 amperes. *B* has 200 turns and operates on 20 amperes. Which is the stronger magnet, *A* or *B*? Why?

8. An electromagnet conducts 100 amperes of electricity for 1 minute. The potential is 20 volts.

(a) What energy is consumed in joules?

(b) What quantity of electricity is conducted?

PROJECTS

1. Place a magnetized piece of watch spring or a large magnetized needle on a cork stopper that is floating in water. Then hold a wire that is conducting a current over the magnet and observe the behavior of the magnet. Change the direction of the current and again observe.

2. Pass a current of several amperes through a bare copper wire and then dip the wire in iron filings or small iron tacks and small nails.

3. Using #18 or #22 wire, wrap about 100 turns around a cardboard tube which is about ½ inch in diameter. Lay it flat on the table,

pass a current through the coil, and (a) determine the maximum distance from one end that a compass will be deflected; (b) double the current and see what happens to the distance; (c) double the number of turns of wire and determine how this factor alone affects the distance; (d) place a soft iron core in the coil and determine its effect.

4. Suspend two straight flexible wires about ½ to ¾ inch apart, making each a part of a different electric circuit. Observe what happens when both are conducting current, first in the same direction and then in opposite directions. Make a sketch showing the ends of the wires and the direction of the magnetic field about each wire. Explain the behavior of each wire in terms of the magnetic fields produced. See Fig. 2, in which magnets are used in a somewhat similar manner.

5. Make an electric bell.

6. Set up a relay and show how it can control another circuit with a small current.

READING YOU WILL ENJOY

1. Fraser, Charles G., *Half-Hours with Great Scientists,* pp. 449-455. Reinhold Publishing Corporation, New York, 1948.

2. Martin, Thomas, *Faraday's Discovery of Electromagnetic Induction.* Edward Arnold and Company, London, 1949. A very interesting book which can be read in a few hours. Tells the story of the discovery of most of the principles of electricity that are yet to be discussed in this book.

3. Richardson, J. S., and G. P. Cahoon, *Methods and Materials for Teaching General and Physical Science,* pp. 218-219. McGraw-Hill Book Company, Inc., New York, 1951. Contains a number of interesting experiments on electromagnetism.

4. Suffern, M. G., *Basic Electrical Principles,* pp. 99-127. McGraw-Hill Book Company, Inc., New York, 1949. Contains exercises that make good demonstrations and projects.

5. Taylor, L. W., *Physics, the Pioneer Science,* pp. 631-641. Houghton Mifflin Company, Boston, 1941. Tells of Oersted's and Ampere's early work with electromagnetism and of how Sturgeon made the first electromagnet.

6. Williard, L. R., *Fundamentals of Electricity,* pp. 156-180. Ginn and Company, Boston, 1943. Contains exercises that make good demonstrations and projects.

Unit 13

**Production of Electric Current
and Electrical Measurement**

Today, the production of electric current is a vast enterprise that employs the skills of thousands of persons all over the world. Yet, like many other human enterprises, it had extremely humble beginnings. In fact, it was only the convulsive jerking of a dead frog's leg in a biological laboratory that initiated an inquiry into the methods of producing an electric current.

In stark contrast to such primitive experiments of generating an electric current is the control board of a modern electrical generating station shown in the unit photograph. Here is also an interesting example of the use of television in industry, as all parts of the generating station are operated by remote control from this panel which acts as the nerve center of the entire plant. In the center panel, a TV screen shows whether the stacks are smoking, while the two screens at the right indicate the condition of the boiler flames.

35. THE PRODUCTION OF ELECTRIC CURRENT BY CHEMICALS
36. HOW OERSTED'S DISCOVERY OPENED THE WAY FOR MEASURING ELECTRICITY

Unit Photograph Courtesy Consolidated Edison Co. of New York

Chapter 35

The Production of Electric Current by Chemicals

The problem and Galvani's experiment. The first to discover how to produce electric current otherwise than by friction was Luigi Galvani (1737-1798), who was primarily a biologist but who worked in a laboratory where electrical experiments were conducted.

Galvani had observed what many others already knew; namely, that the leg of a dead frog will jerk when a spark from an electrostatic machine is applied to the nerve in the leg. But one day he saw the leg move when the machine was started and a scalpel (steel knife) was touching the nerve. The peculiarity was that there was no conductor connecting the electrostatic machine and the scalpel. This disturbed Galvani to the extent that he set out to discover the origin of the current.

One of his experiments was for the purpose of determining whether the same motions would be produced by the electricity of a thunderstorm. To do this, he hung several frog legs out in the open against an iron lattice by means of brass hooks. And he discovered, contrary to what he had anticipated, that the contractions took place rain or shine, regardless of the state of the weather.

He found, too, that any two unlike metals could be used in place of the iron and brass, but that copper and zinc worked better than others. Glass, rubber, resin, stone, and dried wood produced nothing. Still the mystery of the origin of the current remained. Did the current originate solely in the frog tissues, in the unlike metals, or in the combination of metals and tissues?

Unfortunately for himself, Galvani concluded that the current originated solely in the tissues of the frog. At that time "animal electricity" was believed to be far more real than any other kind.

But this conclusion would not have been such a calamity had Galvani been willing to admit his error after much evidence had been accumulated that proved him wrong. Instead, he and his followers stanchly maintained Galvani's original conclusion, and in 1798 he died, a tragic figure filled with disappointment and bitterness. For more than a century "battery" current was called *galvanic* current. *Galvanize* and *galvanometer* we recognize as survivals of the term.

How Volta disproved Galvani's conclusion. It was Alessandro Volta (1745-1827), another Italian scientist, who proved conclusively, when he substituted certain liquid solutions for the frog legs, that galvanic current did not originate in the tissues of a frog. He found that ordi-

399

nary spring or well water could be used, but that when acid, salt, or lye was added to the water, much better results were obtained. Zinc and copper in a dilute solution of sulfuric acid seemed to work best (see Fig. 1). *A cell consisting of two unlike metal plates immersed in a water solution of lye, acid, or salt is called a* **voltaic cell.**

Table 1
ELECTROMOTIVE SERIES OF ELEMENTS
Zinc (Zn)
Iron (Fe)
Tin (Sn)
Lead (Pb)
Copper (Cu)
Silver (Ag)
Platinum (Pt)
Carbon (C)

When any two of these elements are used in making a voltaic cell, the one higher in the table has the lower potential; the element that is lower in the table is positive with respect to the one that is higher.

The kinds of charges on the plates of a voltaic cell. According to Table 1, if a copper plate and a zinc plate are used to make a voltaic cell, the copper is positive

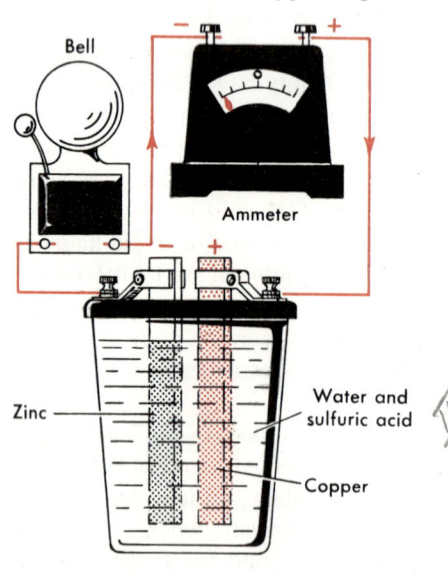

Fig. 1. A simple voltaic cell.

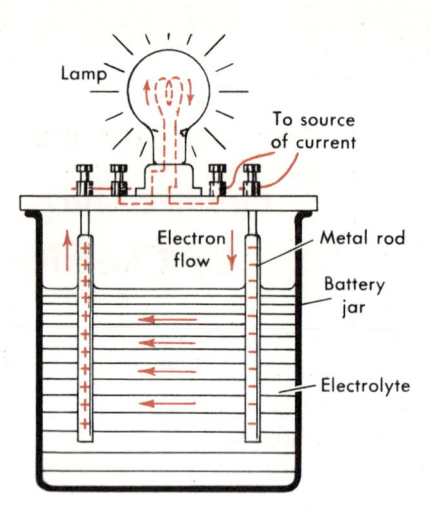

Fig. 2. Apparatus to test the conductivity of solutions. The lamp glows if the solution being tested is an electrolyte.

and the zinc is negative. The difference of potential is about 1.1 volts, regardless of the size of the plates. However, the larger the plates, the greater the current available.

Liquid conductors and the part they play in voltaic cells. With the apparatus pictured in Fig. 2 it can be shown that distilled water, glycerine, alcohol, alcohol in distilled water, glycerine in distilled water, and sugar dissolved in distilled water are all poor conductors of electricity. On the other hand, acid, lye, and salt in distilled water are all good conductors of electricity. Substances which in water solution conduct electricity are called *electrolytes*.

Are the liquid solutions used in voltaic cells electrolytes?

Electrolysis of water and its relation to voltaic cells. In 1800, when the conductivity of solutions was being tested, it was noticed that an electric current between two wires dipped in a dilute sulfuric acid solution produced hydrogen gas on the *cathode*—the wire connected with the negative terminal of the battery—and pro-

THE PRODUCTION OF ELECTRIC CURRENT BY CHEMICALS 401

duced oxygen on the other terminal, called the *anode* (see Fig. 3). According to chemistry, the following takes place:

$$2 H_2O \rightarrow 2 H_2 + O_2$$
Water yields hydrogen + oxygen

These symbols state that water, when decomposed, yields hydrogen gas and oxygen gas. *The decomposition of a substance by means of an electric current is called* **electrolysis**. The apparatus used is called an *electrolytic cell*.

These findings agree perfectly with what had been discovered thirty years before, when hydrogen gas had been caused to unite with oxygen gas to form water.

$$2 H_2 + O_2 \rightarrow 2 H_2O$$
hydrogen + oxygen yields water

These were pioneering experiments in that they opened up a whole new field in science known as *electrochemistry*.

Dissociation. Since, when current passes through a dilute water solution of sulfuric acid, hydrogen is produced at the cathode and oxygen at the anode, then it is logical to assume that either the water (HOH) or the sulfuric acid (H_2SO_4) breaks up or *dissociates* into hydrogen and oxygen particles, or ions. And since hydrogen is released at the cathode and unlike charges attract, then the hydrogen ion must have a positive charge. Logically, what should be the charge on the oxygen ion or on the ion which contains oxygen? See (b) of Fig. 3.

Furthermore, since, in the electrolysis of water, the amount of sulfuric acid does not diminish, some scientists, although not all, believe that the acid assists in what takes place but undergoes no change itself except for dissociation into ions. Only the water is believed to be decomposed. The water molecule is believed to slightly dissociate into a positive ion, H^+, and a negative ion, OH^-. The hydrogen ion possesses a single positive charge and the hydroxyl ion OH^- possesses a single negative charge. That is,

$$HOH \rightarrow H^+ + OH^-$$
water molecule → hydrogen ion + hydroxyl ion

The positive hydrogen ion migrates to the negatively charged cathode and picks

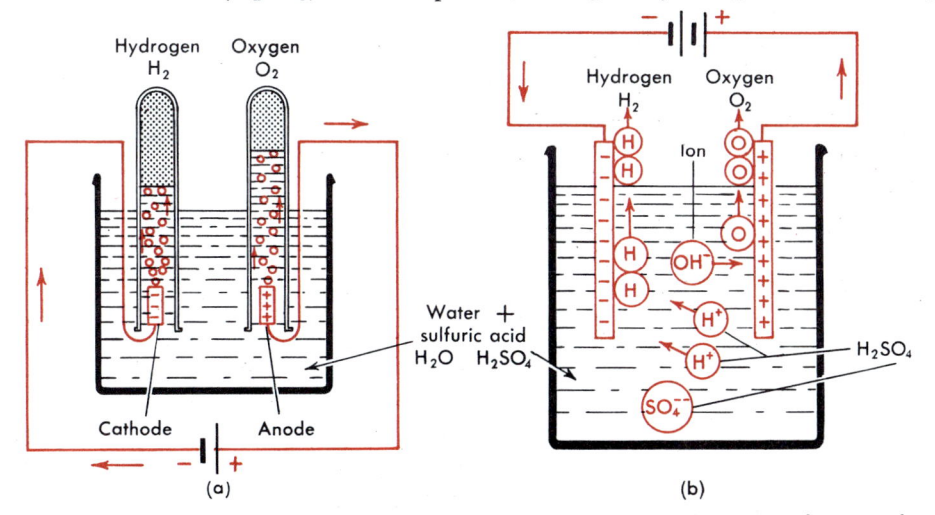

Fig. 3 (a) In the electrolysis of water, two volumes of hydrogen and one volume of oxygen are produced. (b) The migration of ions toward the cathode and anode.

up one electron, which neutralizes the ion and causes it to be a neutral atom of hydrogen. Then two hydrogen atoms unite to form a molecule of hydrogen gas. Finally, several molecules unite to form a bubble of hydrogen gas which displaces the solution in the tube above the cathode (Fig. 3a).

The negative hydroxyl ion migrates to the anode, where it loses its extra single electron. The loss of this causes the hydroxyl ion to become momentarily neutral. Then four OH particles unite to form water and oxygen.

$$2\ OH + 2\ OH \rightarrow 2\ H_2O + O_2 \uparrow$$

Finally, the oxygen collects in bubbles on the anode, rises, and displaces the liquid in the tube above the anode. The results are that the positive hydrogen ions take electrons off the cathode and the negative hydroxyl ions put electrons on the anode. This action is the same as though the solution conducted electrons from the cathode to the anode. The migrating charged ions in a solution accomplish the same result that is brought about by the migrating electrons in a solid conductor.

But unless a substance ionizes or dissociates when put in solution, the solution will not conduct current. The ionization enables a solution to conduct. However, ionization is not caused by the current; it takes place as soon as the substance goes into solution.

Electroplating. If we substitute copper sulfate, $CuSO_4$ (see Fig. 4a), in the place of the H_2SO_4, each copper sulfate molecule ionizes thus:

$$CuSO_4 \rightarrow Cu++ + SO_4--$$

to form one positive ion, $Cu++$, and one negative ion, SO_4--. The water also ionizes slightly, as already explained:

$$HOH \rightarrow H+ + OH-$$

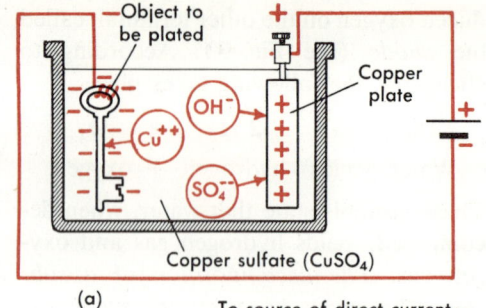

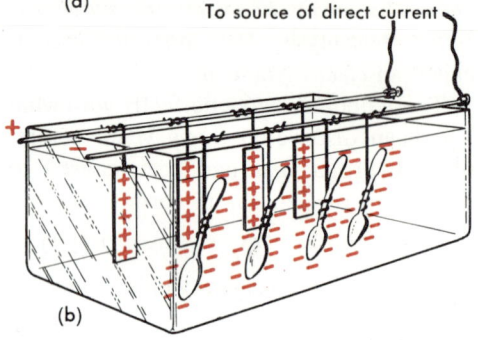

Fig. 4. In copper plating, copper ions go to the cathode where they gain electrons, forming atoms.

One negative sulfate ion, SO_4--, unites with two positive hydrogen ions,

$$2\ H+ + SO_4-- \rightarrow H_2SO_4$$

to form H_2SO_4, leaving copper ions $Cu++$ and hydroxyl ions $OH-$.

The negative hydroxyl ions migrate to the anode, where each loses its single charge and then unites with the other OH particles to form oxygen and water:

$$2\ OH + 2\ OH \rightarrow 2\ H_2O + O_2$$

The oxygen collects as bubbles on the anode and escapes.

Each free $Cu++$ migrates to the cathode and there receives two electrons to form an atom of copper, which is deposited on the cathode. This process is known as *electroplating*.

Unless copper sulfate, $CuSO_4$, is continually added to the solution, the copper

THE PRODUCTION OF ELECTRIC CURRENT BY CHEMICALS 403

ions soon will all be displaced. In commercial work, rather than add more copper sulfate the anode is made of copper. The negative ions SO_4^{--} cause this anode to dissolve as fast as the metal ions are deposited on the cathode. As a result, the amount of copper sulfate remains the same.

The object to be plated is always the cathode. When silver, gold, or other kinds of plating are done, the anode is made of the kind of metal that is to be plated on the cathode, and the solution is a salt solution of the metal that is being plated. In silver plating, for example, the cathode is the object to be plated, the anode is a piece of silver, and the solution is a salt of silver. See Fig. 4(b).

Faraday's laws of electrolysis. In 1834, Michael Faraday, an Englishman, found that over a certain definite time a given current always deposits the same amount of a given element from solution. For example, one coulomb of electricity (6.25×10^{18} electrons) always deposits 0.000010 gram of hydrogen, 0.000329 gram of copper, or 0.001118 gram of silver. These are known as the *electrochemical equivalents* of these elements.

Faraday formulated his findings into the laws of electrolysis:

1. **The mass, M, of an element deposited by electrolysis is directly proportional to the quantity of electricity which passes; or to the current, I, and time, t, which it flows.** That is, $M \propto It$.

2. **The weights of different elements liberated during electrolysis by a given current in the same time are proportional to their electrochemical equivalents, Z.** That is, $M \propto Z$, and the two laws combined give $M = ZIt$.

Values for Z are given in grams per coulomb and in grams per ampere-hour in Table 1.

PROBLEM 1: How many grams of copper can be deposited from a copper electrolyte in 5 hours by a current of 2 amperes?

SOLUTION:
$$M = ZIt$$
$$M = 1.18 \times 2 \times 5$$
$$M = 11.8 \text{ grams}$$

PROBLEM 2: How many hours would it take 2 amperes of current to deposit 49 grams of gold on a loving cup?

This furnishes an extremely accurate method for establishing the **international ampere**, which is defined as *the rate of flow of current that will deposit 0.001118 gram of silver in 1 second*.

How does a voltaic cell produce current? In our study of the polarity of the terminals of a voltaic cell, we found that the zinc in the acid acquired a negative charge, indicating an excess of electrons, and that the copper acquired a positive charge, indicating a deficiency of electrons. But how can this be true when both are put in the same liquid?

If you have ever observed a used voltaic cell, you know that the copper lasts much longer than the zinc. This indicates that the zinc dissolves much faster than the copper. When the atoms of a metal dissolve in the solution they leave one or more electrons behind, producing an excess of electrons on the metal itself, and the dis-

Table 1
ELECTROCHEMICAL EQUIVALENTS OF ELEMENTS

Element	Grams per coulomb	Grams per ampere-hour
Chromium	0.000179	0.6467
Copper	0.000329	1.1857
Gold	0.000681	2.4522
Hydrogen	0.000010	0.0376
Nickel	0.000304	1.0947
Oxygen	0.000082	0.2984
Silver	0.001118	4.0245
Zinc	0.000338	1.2195

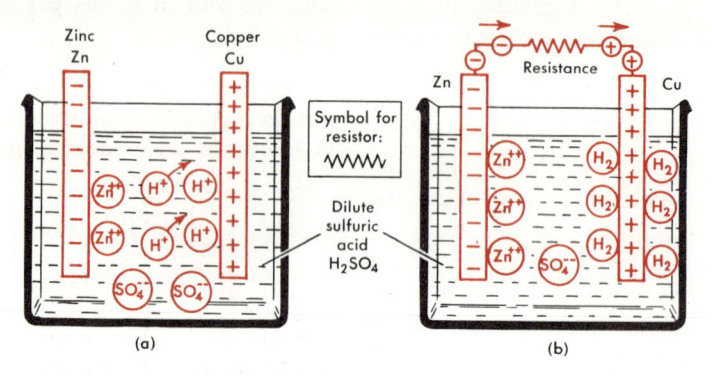

Fig. 5. Zinc ions repel the hydrogen ions toward the cathode where they gain electrons, forming hydrogen atoms. The hydrogen atoms unite to form molecules.

solved atoms become positively charged metal ions. This accounts for the negative charge on the zinc but not for the positive charge on the copper. Why, in a voltaic cell, does not the copper acquire a negative charge as the zinc does?

As we have already seen, the electrolyte, sulfuric acid (H_2SO_4) in water, ionizes, forming two H+ and one SO_4^{--} ions.

$$H_2SO_4 \rightarrow 2\,H^+ + SO_4^{--}$$

Sulfuric acid → hydrogen ions + sulfate ions

The positive zinc ions (Zn++) which enter the solution repel the positive hydrogen ions and force them against the copper plate. (Fig. 5(a).) Here each hydrogen ion H+ receives one electron, making a neutral atom, which unites with another hydrogen atom to form a molecule of hydrogen gas. After several molecules collect, a bubble is formed. Since the copper plate loses electrons, its charge is positive. But where do these electrons which are lost by the copper plate come from?

A few of them are acquired, when copper dissolves in the cell solution, in the same manner that the zinc acquires electrons when it goes into solution. But release of only these electrons to the hydrogen ions would cause the copper plate to be not much more than neutral. For the copper plate to become positive, it must lose some of the electrons within itself to the hydrogen ions.

What causes the action to stop when the cell is not in use? As soon as the charge on the copper plate begins to be positive, it begins to repel the approaching positive hydrogen ions. These in turn repel the positive zinc ions, making it more difficult for the zinc ions to go into solution. Also, the negative zinc plate attracts the positive zinc ions. When the forces become balanced, which happens very quickly if the cell is not in use, the action stops.

In the balanced condition there is an excess of electrons on the negative zinc plate. These repel each other. The positive copper plate is deficient in electrons. The positive charges on the copper attract the negative charges on the zinc plate. As a result, a potential difference of about 1.1 volts is developed. This is dependent solely upon the kinds of metals used in the cell and not upon the size of the plates. An increase in the size of the plates does, however, increase the available current. When the two plates are connected with a conductor, the electrons on the negative zinc plate flow through the conductor to the positive copper plate. These tend to neutralize the positive charge on the copper plate. See Fig. 5(b).

As a result of this, we should expect the voltage, or potential difference between the plates of a cell, when it is in use, to be less than the voltage across the plates when the cell is not in use. When a cell is tested under these circumstances, our prediction proves to be true. This of course tends to confirm our theory.

Local action. So far, our theory accounts for the negative charge on the zinc, the positive charge on the copper, the hydrogen bubbles on the copper plate, the current, and so on. But it does not explain why hydrogen is often, though not always, liberated at the zinc plate. Perhaps the clue is found in the fact that hydrogen is not liberated at the zinc electrode when pure zinc is used; it happens only when impure zinc is used.

Evidently the liberation is due to impurities such as carbon in the zinc. Each impure particle, of which there may be millions, along with the zinc plate and acid solution constitutes a small voltaic cell. And the zinc not only acts as one of the plates but also serves as a conductor between the plates. See Fig. 6. As a result,

each of the myriad of cells is short circuited and the reaction never stops until all the zinc is used up. The formation of hydrogen on the zinc plate, due to impurities in the zinc, is called *local action.*

As indicated, local action can be prevented through the use of pure zinc, or the impurities can be covered up through the coating (amalgamating) of impure zinc with mercury. Explain why it is unwise to put metal scraps into a lead sink into which acid, salt, and lye solutions are poured.

Polarization. Because of chemical action, hydrogen gas accumulates at the copper plate. The formation of this gas is quite detrimental because it cuts down electron flow. The gas acts as an electrical insulator and as a result the rate at which the hydrogen ions reach the copper plate is reduced. *The accumulation of gas on the copper plate, which prevents a cell from delivering the maximum amount of current, is called* **polarization.** See Fig. 7.

In early days, ingenious devices were used to prevent polarization. "Rocking chairs" run by water motors were used to rock the cells, thereby agitating the solution so that the gas bubbles were washed off the plates. Today, chemicals called

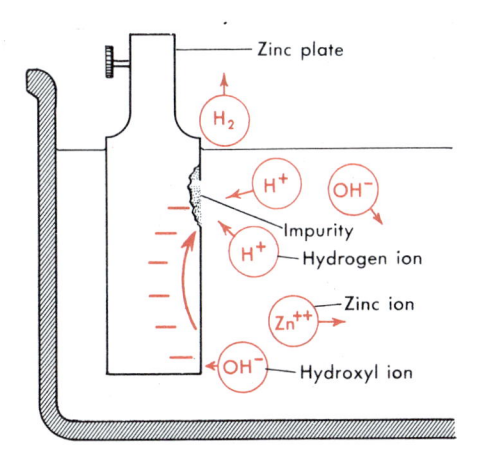

Fig. 6. Local action in a voltaic cell.

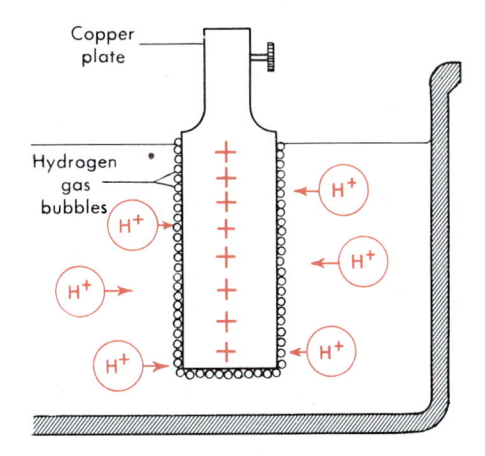

Fig. 7. Polarization of a voltaic cell.

oxidizing agents are placed in the cells. These furnish oxygen, which unites chemically with the hydrogen, forming water. Manganese dioxide and potassium dichromate are both commonly used.

A good way to show the depolarizing effects of such a chemical is to connect an electric bell with a voltaic cell. At first the bell will ring loudly, but its intensity soon begins to decrease, until finally the bell can barely be heard. Then, if a solution of potassium dichromate is poured around the copper plate, or if the cell is shaken, the bell sounds loudly again.

The dry cell—is it really dry? A dry cell is really a voltaic cell. The cylindrical zinc container not only holds the contents of the cell but also serves as the negative plate. And too, this container is not so easily broken as is glass.

The zinc cylinder is lined with a thin porous material resembling blotting paper, which is coated with a thick paste consisting of plaster of Paris, water, and ammonium chloride (NH_4Cl), a salt, commonly known as sal ammoniac. Standing at the center of the zinc container is a carbon rod (see Fig. 8), which is the positive plate. The remaining space completely surrounding the rod is filled with a mixture of granulated carbon and manganese dioxide which is saturated with a solution of sal ammoniac. Sealing wax covers the top, sealing it so that the contents cannot escape. Is the dry cell really dry?

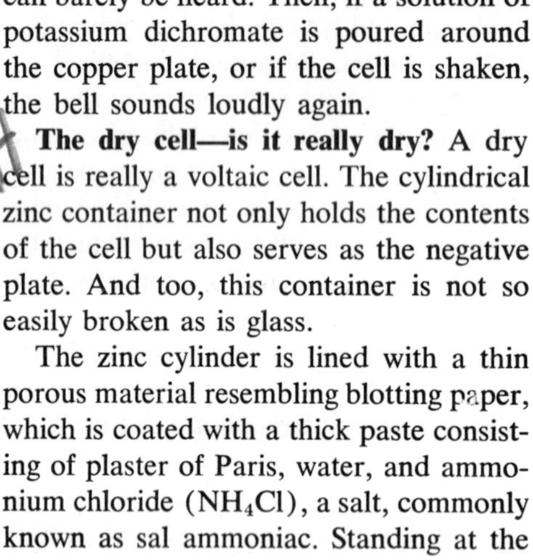

Courtesy National Carbon Co., A Division of Union Carbide and Carbon Corp.

Fig. 8. A cutaway view of a dry cell.

The outside of the cylinder is usually covered with a thick layer of paper. As the cell is used, the zinc gradually dissolves until holes appear in the sides.

The use of dry cells. Dry cells have innumerable uses. They are used for flashlights, doorbells, buzzers, and other intermittent circuits. They are also used in radio "B" and "C" batteries, where a steady voltage but little current is necessary. In spite of the fact that the cell is provided with a liberal amount of oxidizing agent, it will become polarized if very much current is drawn from it for any length of time. However, if the circuit is broken for a few minutes, the cell is soon depolarized.

Testing a dry cell. A good dry cell should have a voltage of about 1.5 volts on open circuit, and, when an ammeter is connected momentarily across its terminals, there should be between 25 and 30 amperes of current. When the voltage of a dry cell drops much below one volt, it should be discarded. Cells that have been used little and have deteriorated by drying out inside may, to a certain extent, be revived if nail holes are punched near the top of the zinc container and the cells are soaked in water for one or two days. A dry cell should never be "shorted" for any length of time.

Storage cells. If much current is needed for any length of time, dry cells are an expensive source because the zinc is used up rapidly and there is no way of restoring it. The cell simply must be junked. If, by some method, the chemical processes in a

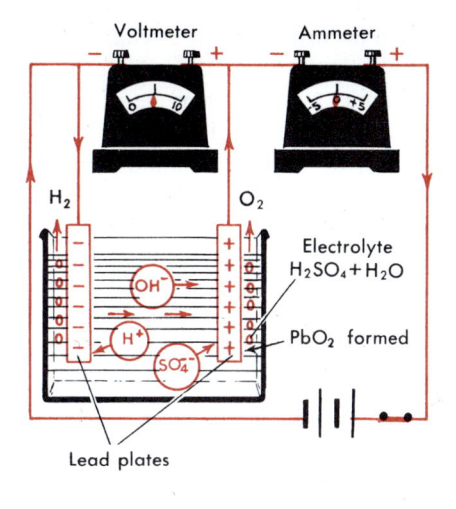

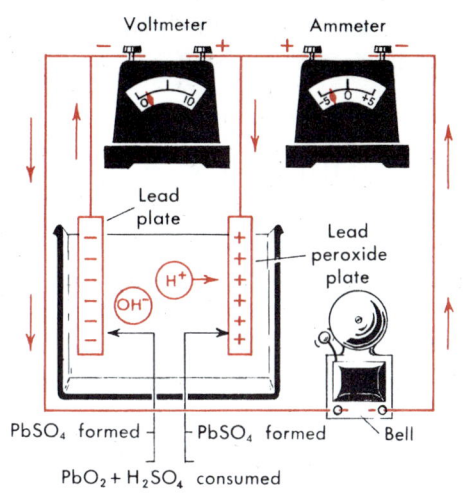

THE PRODUCTION OF ELECTRIC CURRENT BY CHEMICALS

Fig. 9. Charging a storage cell.

Fig. 10. Discharging a storage cell.

cell could be reversed so that the chemicals that are used up were replaced, perhaps the cost could be reduced. In the storage cell an attempt was made to do this. We can make such a cell in a way similar to that in which we made a voltaic cell, using two 6" x 2" lead plates, as in Fig. 9. The solution should consist of one part sulfuric acid and five parts water by volume.

To charge the cell, send a current from two storage cells in series through it and on through an ammeter in series with the cell you are charging. The setup is very similar to the one used in the electrolysis of water (page 401), and the chemical action is much the same.

As the current starts into the cell you will see quantities of hydrogen bubbles rising from the cathode. At the anode, as you might expect, oxygen is liberated, but this is not all that happens. The anode plate begins to turn dark brown because of a coating of lead peroxide (PbO_2). Some of the oxygen unites with the lead anode. When the PbO_2 begins to form, the charging current reduces, showing that the resistance of the cell has increased. Why this is true we shall consider later. When the cell is fully charged a voltmeter will show its voltage to be slightly over 2 volts.

If, after the cell has been charged for several minutes, it is removed and attached to a bell and ammeter in series, the bell will ring and the ammeter will show a current in the opposite direction from that of the "charging" current. The current in the circuit will decrease rapidly as the energy is expended in ringing the bell. Study Fig. 10 carefully.

The results are that, in the charging, one plate is changed so that the cell then consists of two dissimilar plates, one of lead and one of lead peroxide. The lead peroxide plate becomes positive, corresponding with the copper plate of the ordinary voltaic cell. The lead plate becomes negative, corresponding with the zinc plate.

The voltage produced by the charging is in opposition to the charging voltage. It is for this reason that the charging current drops as soon as the charging begins. The chemical reaction in a storage cell is as follows. For the charging process, read the reaction from left to right; for discharging, from right to left.

$$\text{CHARGING} \rightarrow$$
$$\leftarrow \text{DISCHARGING}$$

2PbSO_4	$+$	$2\text{H}_2\text{O}$	$\rightleftarrows$	PbO_2	$+$	Pb	$+$	$2\text{H}_2\text{SO}_4$
Both plates		Water		Positive plate		Negative plate		Electrolyte
Lead sulfate	$+$	Water	$\rightleftarrows$	Lead peroxide	$+$	Spongy lead	$+$	Sulfuric acid

The commercial lead storage battery. In the manufacture of the commercial cell, the positive plate is provided with a very thick coat of lead peroxide. The negative plate is made of spongy porous lead. The areas of the plates are also many times those of the experimental cell described. But increasing the area of the plates does not increase the voltage of the cell which, when fully charged, is slightly more than 2 volts. Increasing the size of the plates increases the amount of chemical energy stored, which increases the amount of electrical energy that the cell will give.

The voltage of the ordinary storage battery, which usually consists of three cells in series, is a little over 6 volts. The efficiency of a storage battery is about 75 per cent. That is, about 75 per cent of the energy used in charging a battery is available on discharge. Batteries are usually rated according to the available energy on discharge in terms of *ampere hours*. For example, a battery may be rated 120 ampere hours. This means that the battery, when fully charged, should furnish 1 ampere of current for 120 hours or 2 amperes for 60 hours, and so on. Storage batteries have very low internal resistance. This is one reason why a very sizable current can be drawn from them.

Care of a storage battery. Since water decomposes as a battery is charged, some water must be added from time to time in order to keep the electrolyte at the proper level. But because ordinary water may contain metal salts in solution, to avoid local action only distilled water should be added.

At all times a battery should be kept well charged by frequent charging, even when not in use. The amount of charge can be determined with a hydrometer. This is because, as the cell is discharged, the proportion of water (specific gravity 1) to sulfuric acid (specific gravity 1.84) is increased. That is, the specific gravity of the electrolyte is decreased. When a battery is fully charged, the specific gravity of the electrolyte is almost 1.30. When it is fully discharged it is as low as 1.15 or 1.13. On many hydrometers these respective readings would be 1300, 1150, and 1130.

Fig. 11. A cutaway view of a lead storage battery.

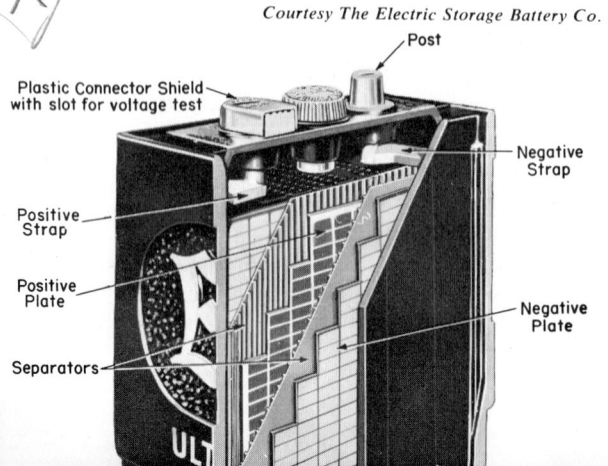

Courtesy The Electric Storage Battery Co.

Fig. 12. Testing the specific gravity of the electrolyte of a lead storage battery.

Courtesy Shell Oil Co.

The battery terminals should be kept clean and smeared with vaseline, which helps to prevent corrosion. A battery should not be allowed to freeze. It should be handled with care because usually the container is made of glass or hard rubber. If the acid solution is spilled where it will do damage, pour on plenty of water. If ordinary baking soda is available, put some of it in the water. This will neutralize the acid.

Uses of the storage battery. The chief use of storage batteries is in starting automobile and similar engines. Since a storage battery has low internal resistance, a large amount of current, which is needed by a starter, can be drawn from the battery. Fortunately this can be done without injury to the battery. Think of other uses of a storage battery, particularly in connection with an automobile.

The Edison storage cell. Thomas A. Edison developed and perfected the nickel-iron-caustic potash storage cell. The electrolyte is a 21 per cent solution of caustic potash (KOH) in water. The negative plate consists of an iron powder securely held in perforated flat rectangular capsules, and the positive plate consists of nickel peroxide held in perforated cylinders. The Edison cell is about half as heavy as a lead storage cell of the same volume. Its advantage is that it will stand a tremendous amount of abuse without being damaged. For this reason, Edison cells are often used in laboratories, where they must be handled a great deal and where students are likely to make mistakes in using them. But because of their high internal resistance they are not used for starting engines or in driving electric trucks and automobiles as are lead storage batteries.

The nickel-cadmium battery. Some of the disadvantages of the lead storage battery, such as noxious fumes, corrosive spray, damage due to overcharge and loss

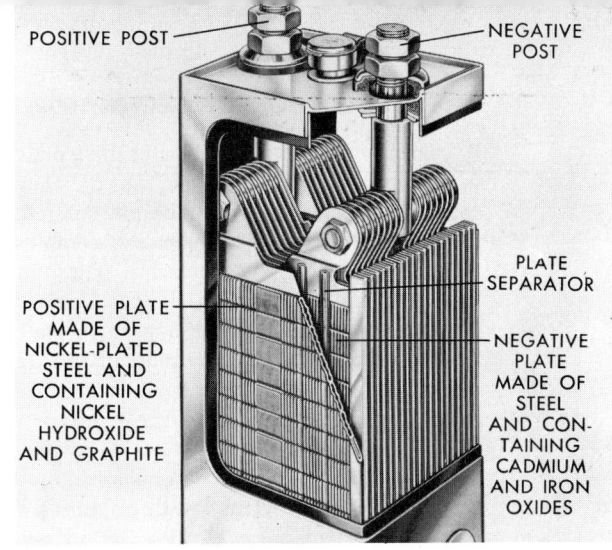

Courtesy Nickel Cadmium Battery Corp.

Fig. 13. A cutaway view of the nickel-cadmium storage battery. Unlike the lead storage battery, the specific gravity of the electrolyte, a solution of potassium hydroxide, does not change. The electrolyte simply serves to transfer hydrogen ions from one electrode to the other during charge or discharge.

of water, have been overcome in the nickel-cadmium battery. The plates of this battery are made of nickel hydroxide and cadmium and are immersed in an electrolyte of potassium hydroxide. Although the initial cost of this battery is relatively high, it will stand up under severe operating conditions and is supposed to last fifteen to twenty years. In addition the nickel-cadmium battery has other advantages. It holds charge when idle, cannot freeze, uses an unbreakable steel case, and has a low internal resistance.

SUMMARY AND CONCLUSIONS

1. A cell with plates of two unlike materials immersed in a water solution of lye, salt, or acid is called a voltaic cell.
2. Polarization is caused by the accumulation of hydrogen on the positive plate.
3. Local action is due to short-circuited little cells caused by chemical impurities in the zinc plate.

4. The dry cell is not dry. The positive plate is carbon, the negative is zinc, and the electrolyte is a solution of ammonium chloride in the form of a paste which also contains manganese dioxide, the depolarizer. The voltage is 1.5 volts.
5. A lead storage cell has a positive plate of lead peroxide, a negative plate of spongy lead, and an electrolyte of dilute sulfuric acid. The voltage is slightly over 2 volts.
6. The Edison storage cell has a positive plate of nickel peroxide and a negative plate of iron. The electrolyte is caustic potash (potassium hydroxide).
7. Water solutions of salts, acids, and bases are all good conductors of electricity. These substances are all known as electrolytes.
8. In the electrolysis of water, the electrolyte is sulfuric acid. Hydrogen is released at the ($-$) cathode and oxygen is liberated at the ($+$) anode.
9. The international ampere is the rate of flow of current which will deposit 0.001118 gram of silver in 1 second.

QUESTIONS FOR REVIEW

1. What influenced Galvani to believe that the current in his frog experiment was animal electricity that was generated by the frog?
2. Explain how Galvani's conclusion was proved to be erroneous. Did Galvani err because of his reasoning or because of the basic beliefs on which he based his reasoning?
3. What are the essentials of a voltaic cell?
4. What is an electrolyte? Non-electrolyte?
5. Explain the electrolysis of water.
6. How does an ion differ from an electron?
7. In the electrolysis of water, what is the purpose of the sulfuric acid? What evidence is there that the acid is not decomposed?
8. When copper sulfate is dissolved in water, explain how it ionizes and show the charge on each ion. What evidence do we have that the copper ion has this charge?
9. Explain why, in copper plating, oxygen is liberated at the anode.
10. Describe the internal construction of a dry cell and explain why it must be discarded when it is used up.
11. What is meant by local action? Polarization? How can they be prevented?
12. Why are dry cells not used where considerable steady current is needed for several hours?
13. What is the difference in principle between a voltaic cell and a storage cell?
14. Describe the internal construction of a lead-acid storage battery.
15. Why can the amount of charge of a lead-acid storage battery be determined by a hydrometer?
16. What is the hydrometer reading for a fully charged storage cell? A discharged cell?
17. Find the effect on a storage battery of (a) continued overcharging; (b) charging at a very high rate; (c) allowing water level to get very low; (d) allowing battery to stand idle when it is totally or nearly totally discharged.
18. What is meant by ampere-hour capacity of a storage battery?
19. Explain the construction of the Edison cell. What are its advantages? Why can it not be used for starting automobiles?
20. What is the difference between a battery and a cell?

PROBLEMS

1. In the electrolysis of copper, 0.000329 gram of copper is deposited by 6.25×10^{18} electrons, and two electrons are required to deposit one atom of copper. How many atoms are there in 0.000329 gram of copper? In 1 gram of copper? How much does an atom of copper weigh?
2. Find in the same manner the number of atoms in 0.000010 gram of hydrogen. Remember that only one electron is required to liberate one atom of hydrogen.
3. What weight of copper will be deposited by 2 amperes of current which passes through a copper electrolyte for 6 hours?
4. What time in hours is required to liberate 29.8 grams of oxygen in the electrolysis of water when 2 amperes of current are used?
5. What current in amperes is needed to deposit 20.12 grams of silver on a serving tray in 10 hours?

6. Copper and silver are being plated by the same current in separate containers. While 40.24 grams of silver are being plated, what weight of copper will be plated?

7. A storage battery is rated 120 ampere-hours. For how many hours could it deliver ½ ampere? Why could it not deliver 120 amperes for 1 hour?

PROJECTS

1. Make a simple storage cell as described on page 407, then discharge it through an electric bell or an incandescent lamp. Using a voltmeter, determine its voltage on open circuit and on closed circuit.

2. Storage batteries are given a "quick" charge while you wait. Find out when this is advantageous and whether or not it shortens the life of the battery.

3. Connect two copper wires with a dry cell. Then dip the ends of the wires in a solution of salt water and notice what happens at the ends of the wire. Next connect each wire with a nickel coin and dip the coins into a copper sulfate solution. Notice what happens and explain.

4. Make a water solution of one part sulfuric acid by volume and five parts water. Using the type of apparatus shown in Fig. 3a, observe what happens when current passes through the sulfuric acid solution. Next, stir and slowly add a water solution of barium hydroxide to the sulfuric acid solution and notice what happens. Then continue to add more barium hydroxide solution and observe. Explain briefly the observations in terms of the theory of ionization.

READING YOU WILL ENJOY

1. Bayles, E. E., and A. L. Mills, *Basic Chemistry,* pp. 281-303. The Macmillan Company, New York, 1947. Gives an excellent explanation of why some water solutions conduct electricity and others do not.

2. Field, S., and A. D. Weill, *Electroplating.* Pitman Publishing Corporation, New York, 1938. Those interested in electroplating will want to read this book.

3. Jaffe, Bernard, *Crucibles.* Simon and Schuster, Inc., New York, 1930. Contains the story of Arrhenius, who proposed the theory of ionization. It shows the struggle and difficulties that Arrhenius had to overcome before his theory was accepted.

4. Jaffe, Bernard, *New World of Chemistry,* pp. 239-248. Silver Burdett Company, New York, 1952. Explains very vividly the story of the origin of the theory of ionization.

5. Skilling, Hugh H., *Exploring Electricity,* pp. 29-62. The Ronald Press Company, New York, 1949. Tells in a very dramatic manner of the tragic story of Galvani and of the triumph of Volta.

6. Swezey, K. M., *After-Dinner Science.* Whittlesey House, McGraw-Hill Book Company, Inc., New York, 1948. "Volta, Volts, and a Penny Battery," pp. 112-113; "How Metals Change Places," pp. 136-137; "Clean Your Silver by Electrolysis," p. 151; "Electricity Produces Pure Copper," p. 166.

Chapter 36

How Oersted's Discovery Opened the Way for Measuring Electricity

The problem. No study can ever become highly scientific until the quantities dealt with are measured. We have already mentioned the coulomb, ampere, volt, and other electrical quantities.

There is no easy, direct method of measuring electricity as there is for measuring water, gasoline, potatoes, and similar things. However, there is the possibility that one or several of the electrical effects, such as light, heat, and electrochemical or magnetic effects can be measured.

The electrochemical effect when measured gives a very precise measure of current; but it is not commonly used because the apparatus necessary is not practical. See page 403. In certain circumstances the heat effect is used. See Fig. 1. However, the effect that is most commonly measured is the magnetic effect, which, you will recall, was discovered by Oersted. See page 386. In this chapter our chief problem is to discover how this effect is used to measure the different quantities of electricity.

How is the magnetic effect used to measure electric current? We know from Oersted's experiment that there is a magnetic field about a wire carrying a current and that the larger the current, the stronger the field. Therefore, if a wire were held a fixed distance above or below and parallel with a compass needle, then, if a current were passed through the wire, the compass needle should be deflected from its north-south direction, and the greater the current, the greater the deflection. See Fig. 2. When properly calibrated, such an instrument actually can be used to measure current in spite of its crudeness and lack of sensitiveness. In order to make the device more sensitive, the wire can be wrapped in the form of a circular coil and the compass can be set inside the coil. See Fig. 3. Such an instrument is called a *tangent galvanometer*. But this instrument also has its shortcomings because, before it is used, the coil must be lined up with the earth's magnetic field, whose strength and direction are affected by the presence of iron and steel or by electric power lines. All these influences tend to cause errors in measurement when a tangent galvanometer is used.

D'Arsonval galvanometer. Jacques d'Arsonval (1851-1940), a French physicist, made a great improvement over the tangent galvanometer. For the moving part of his instrument he used a coil instead of a permanent magnet in the form of a compass needle. He suspended the coil by a wire between the poles of a horseshoe magnet. See Fig. 4. Inside the rotating coil he placed a stationary soft iron core

MEASURING ELECTRICITY

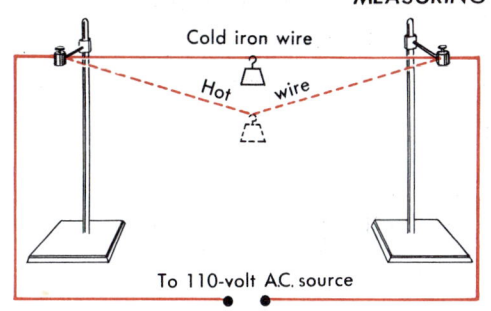

Fig. 1. The heating effect of an electric current used to measure electricity.

Fig. 2. The magnetic effect of an electric current is used to determine its strength.

which helped to strengthen the field between the poles of the permanent magnet. Note that d'Arsonval merely reversed the parts of the tangent galvanometer. His moving part was a coil and his stationary part was a permanent magnet, the field of which could be made much stronger than that of the earth. With the tangent galvanometer the moving part was a permanent magnet and the fixed part was a coil.

When electrons flow through the coil of a d'Arsonval galvanometer, the coil acts like an electromagnet, the poles being at the front and back of the coil as shown in (b) of Fig. 4. The attraction between the unlike poles of the coil and those of the permanent magnet causes the coil to rotate, in this case clockwise when we are looking down on it. The amount of deflection is approximately proportional to the current.

The tendency of the coil to rotate is opposed by the twisting of the suspension wire, but the rotation continues until the rotation tendency caused by the magnetic field equals the opposing tendency caused by twisting of the suspension wire.

To measure the deflection of the coil, which, as noted, is indicative of the current, a pointer can be attached to the coil and a scale be placed in front or in back of the pointer. The instrument can then be calibrated as known currents are passed through it.

Although the d'Arsonval galvanometer is quite an improvement over the tangent galvanometer in that it is more sensitive and is not affected by changes in the earth's magnetic field or local magnetic attractions, it nevertheless has several defects. First, it is bulky and therefore inconvenient to handle. Second, unless the coil is suspended vertically it is liable to drag on the stationary iron core inside it. The second defect can be overcome through leveling of the base, but this requires time and is inconvenient.

The Weston movement. About 1890 Dr. Edward Weston, an English-born American scientist, made several improve-

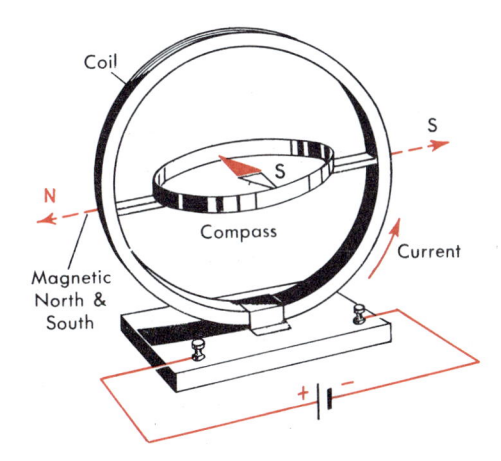

Fig. 3. A tangent galvanometer. The amount of deflection varies directly as the current in the circuit.

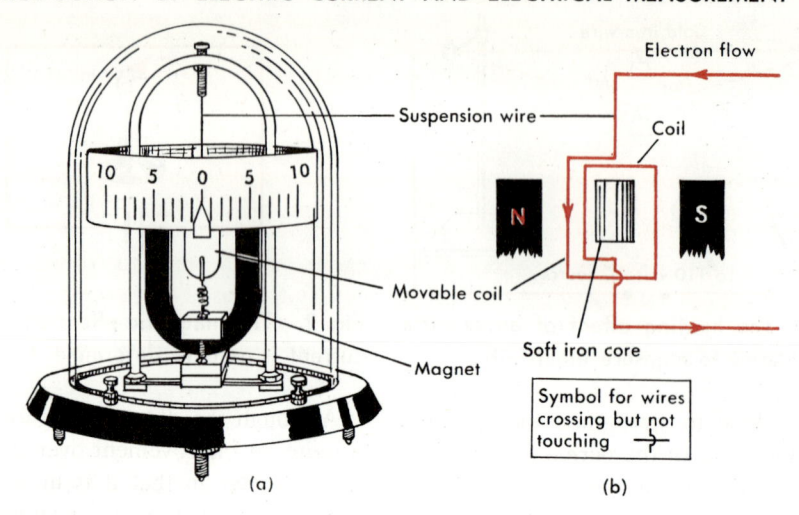

Fig. 4. In the D'Arsonval galvanometer, the coil rotates within the magnetic field until its rotational tendency is equally opposed by the torque of the suspension wire.

ments in the d'Arsonval movement that made it accurate, rugged, portable, compact, small in size, and better in practically every way. His improved instrument is known as the *Weston movement* and is widely used today in measurement of D.C. (direct current) electricity.

Dr. Weston retained the stationary permanent magnet, the moving coil, and the soft iron core inside the coil. See Fig. 5. His major change was in the design of the coil and method of supporting it.

The movable coil in the Weston movement consists of a thin, light, aluminum-alloy frame on which many turns of fine insulated wire are wound. At each end of the coil are hardened steel pivots which rest on sapphire bearings. The current is conducted to and from the coil through two light spiral hair springs which serve also to return the coil to the zero position. Fixed to the coil is an aluminum pointer under which a scale is placed. The instrument is calibrated by comparison of the readings with those of a standard precision meter when the same amount of current passes through both meters.

Due to the almost negligible friction in the bearings, the lightness of the movable coil, and the extreme sensitivity of the springs, the current which is required to deflect the pointer full scale is very small, the average being a very few milliamperes (thousandths of an ampere). The current which is required to deflect the pointer

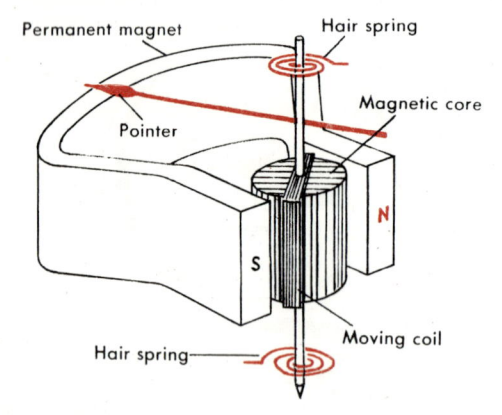

Fig. 5. Magnet and coil of a Weston galvanometer. Compare its method of operation with that of the D'Arsonval galvanometer.

full scale is indicative of the sensitivity of the instrument; the smaller the current the more sensitive the instrument. And as a rule, the more sensitive the instrument, the greater its accuracy. Such galvanometers are excellent for measuring small currents but are inadequate for large currents.

How are large currents measured? One possible way to increase the range of a Weston galvanometer without decreasing its sensitivity is to make the scale longer, but at best this would increase the range but a small amount. Another alternative is to divide up the current so that only a fractional part goes through the movable coil. The rest can be "shunted" or "detoured" around the coil. For example, suppose that the current deflects full scale the pointer in (a) of Fig. 6. But if half the current is shunted, or detoured, around the coil, then the pointer is deflected only half scale and the range is doubled.

In order to shunt half the current around the coil a *shunt resistor* is used (see (b) of Fig. 6) whose resistance is exactly the same as that of the galvanometer coil. Half the current then goes through the shunt and half through the coil.

To increase the range still further another shunt resistor can be used, as shown in (c) of Fig. 6. If its resistance is the same as that of the other resistor, then only one-third of the current will go through the galvanometer. As a result, the pointer will deflect only one-third of the full scale and the range of the instrument will be increased three times. Explain how the range of a galvanometer could be multiplied four times.

The direct current ammeter. We could carry the addition of shunts on and on indefinitely, thereby making the fraction of the current flowing through the coil smaller and smaller and the range of the instrument greater and greater. Galvanometers with built-in shunts such as these are called *ammeters* and are designed to measure only direct current.

Most ordinary D.C. ammeters are the Weston type of galvanometer with a built-in shunt. They are designed to measure currents ranging ordinarily from a few milliamperes up to about 30 amperes, though some will measure much higher than this.

Connecting an ammeter in a circuit. When connecting an ammeter in a circuit, one should first make sure that the range of the instrument is sufficient for the

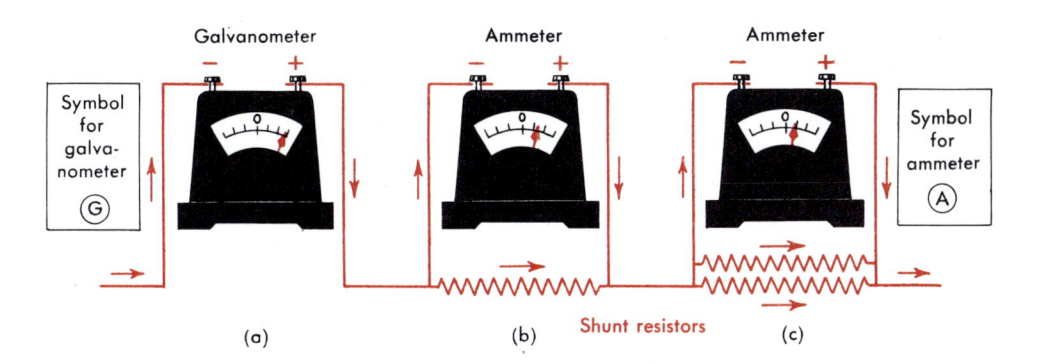

Fig. 6. When large currents must be measured, the range of the Weston galvanometer is multiplied by connecting a low-resistance shunt in parallel with the coil. The galvanometer then becomes an ammeter.

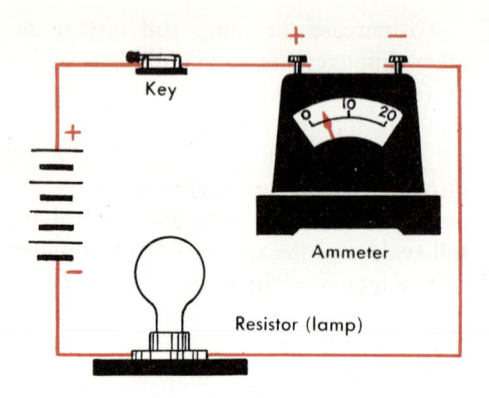

416 PRODUCTION OF ELECTRIC CURRENT AND ELECTRICAL MEASUREMENT

Fig. 7. An ammeter must be connected directly (in series) with the lamp, because the ammeter has such a low resistance.

current. Also, because the pointer on most ammeters can deflect in but one direction, it is necessary that the current go in the negative and out the positive terminal; otherwise the pointer is deflected backward.

In order to measure the current through, for example, an electric lamp, the ammeter must be connected directly in the circuit, as is illustrated in Fig. 7, so that all the current that goes through the lamp also goes through the ammeter. The lamp and the ammeter are then said to be connected in *series*. Because an ammeter has such a low resistance, one precaution must be taken: *an ammeter must be connected in series with a resistance*. Otherwise the coil in the ammeter may be burned out.

An exception to the general rule for connecting ammeters. Maybe at some time or other you have seen an ammeter used to test a dry cell without a resistance in the circuit. One reason why this can be done is that the dry cell itself possesses some resistance. If the range of the ammeter is 30 amperes or more, it can be connected directly across a dry cell.

But the ammeters ordinarily used for this purpose are of neither the d'Arsonval nor the Weston type. They consist of a small stationary electromagnet and a movable soft iron plunger to which a hand is attached. See (a) of Fig. 8. The greater the current through the electromagnet, the stronger the induced magnetism in the plunger and the more it deflects the hand of the ammeter. The hand is returned to the zero point by means of a spring. This same type of ammeter is used on the dashboards of some automobiles. A hot-wire ammeter is shown in (b) of Fig. 8. Explain its action.

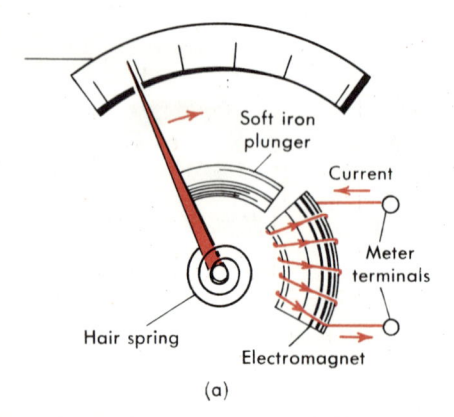

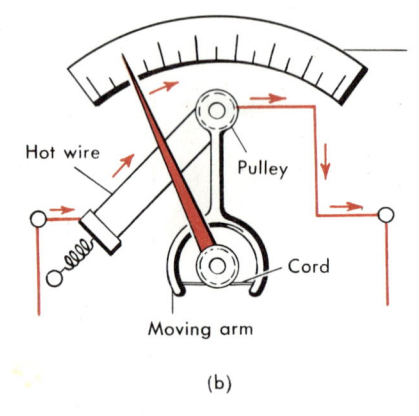

Fig. 8. (a) Sucking-coil ammeter. The magnetic strength of the electromagnet is made to measure the current which passes through the coil. (b) Hot-wire ammeter.

Electrical resistance and the unit of resistance. All conductors offer some opposition to the passage of current; there are no perfect conductors. The unit of resistance commonly used is the *ohm,* named in honor of G. S. Ohm, a German physicist. By international agreement, *the* **ohm** *is the resistance of a column of mercury at zero degrees centigrade, 106.3 centimeters long, of uniform cross section, and weighing 14.4521 grams.* Its cross-sectional area is almost exactly one square millimeter. Ten feet of No. 22 iron wire or sixty feet of No. 22 copper wire offer approximately one ohm of resistance.

Usually the resistance in ohms is computed from the current measured in amperes and the potential difference measured in volts. But before using this method we must first learn how to measure volts and must learn the relationship among volts, amperes, and ohms.

How is difference in potential measured in volts? We have already defined the volt as that difference of potential between two points when one joule of work is required to transfer one coulomb of electricity from the point of lower to that of higher potential.

As you may already suspect and as will be shown by experiment in the next few pages, the greater the difference of electrical potential between two points, the greater the flow of electricity (current) through a conductor having a fixed resistance connecting the two points.

We already have the galvanometer (Fig. 5) for measuring the current through the fixed resistance. The remaining problem is to discover the amount of the resistance that should be connected in series with the galvanometer coil (see Fig. 9).

Perhaps you see one difficulty in measuring in this manner the voltage of, say, a dry cell. Just as soon as the electrons begin to flow from one plate to another, the potential difference between the plates decreases, and the greater the current the greater the decrease. Ideally, then, for measuring voltage we should have an instrument which permits no current to pass. But since a no-current Weston-type voltmeter is impossible, we can do the next-best thing, which is to connect a high resistance in series with a sensitive galvanometer coil. Of course, for measuring low voltages the resistance cannot be so high as for measuring high voltages. In fact, the range of a voltmeter is controlled by the amount of resistance in the instrument. If its total resistance, which includes the sum of the fixed resistance and the resistance of the galvanometer, is doubled, its range is doubled. How could we triple the range of a voltmeter?

How is a voltmeter connected in a circuit? We have seen that an ammeter, which is connected directly in a circuit, has a very low resistance; consequently, it interferes only slightly with the current. On the other hand, a voltmeter, with its high resistance, if connected in series with

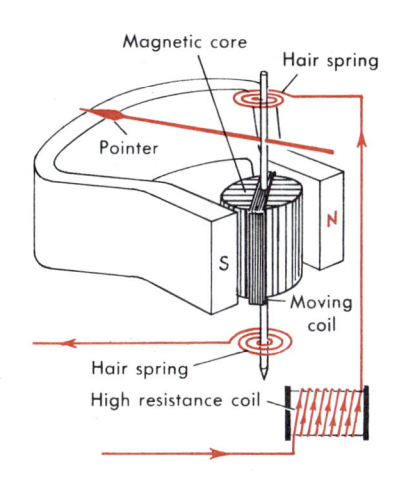

Fig. 9. Making a voltmeter out of a Weston galvanometer and a resistance coil. Compare its construction with that of the ammeter.

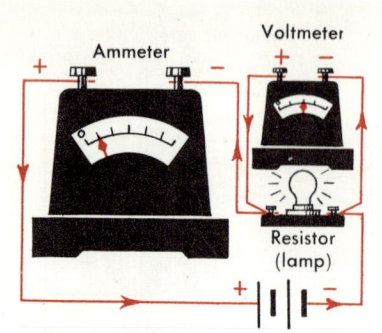

418 PRODUCTION OF ELECTRIC CURRENT AND ELECTRICAL MEASUREMENT

Fig. 10. Explain why a voltmeter must always be connected in parallel in a circuit.

an electric lamp or other resistor would allow very little current to pass. For this reason it must always be connected in *parallel,* as shown in Fig. 10. In this way the voltage is measured with the minimum of interference in the main circuit.

How is resistance measured? We have already indicated that resistance is sometimes computed from the mathematical relationship among amperes, volts, and ohms. To find this relationship a student placed a known resistor of 5 ohms in series with a battery and an ammeter. The circuit was similar to that in Fig. 10. In parallel with the resistor he placed the voltmeter. He read the ammeter and voltmeter, and recorded his findings in trial 1 of Table 1. Then he changed the voltage, E, by using more cells in the battery.

Table 1

Trial	Voltage (E)	Current (I)	Resistance (R)
1	1 volt	0.2 ampere	5 ohms
2	2 volts	0.4 ampere	5 ohms
3	3 volts	0.6 ampere	5 ohms

Study of the data obtained shows that the product of the current (I) in amperes and the resistance (R) in ohms equals the voltage (E). By experiment, test this statement further by allowing the resistance (R) to vary. In conclusion, then,

$$E = IR, \text{ or } I = \frac{E}{R}$$

The relationship $I = \dfrac{E}{R}$ was first discovered by Ohm and is known as **Ohm's Law.** He stated it as follows:

The current, I, through a resistor varies directly as the voltage, E, and inversely with the resistance, R.

PROBLEM 1: The voltage across a lamp is 10 volts. The current is 2 amperes. What is the resistance in ohms?

PROBLEM 2: The current through a lamp is 10 amperes. The resistance of the lamp is 20 ohms. Find the voltage across the lamp.

Computing the work done by electricity. Electric motors transform electrical energy into mechanical energy to run streetcars, buses, washing machines, vacuum cleaners, and hundreds of other machines. What is the relationship between electrical and mechanical energy?

You will recall that the volt is defined as the difference in potential between two points required to transfer one coulomb of electricity from the point of lower to the point of higher potential. Since, according to the law of conservation of energy, energy is not created or destroyed, then when one volt sends one coulomb (6.25×10^{18} electrons) of electricity through a circuit, one joule of work is done by the electricity. In case two coulombs flow, then two joules of work are done.

On page 358 we showed that

$$\text{Joules} = \text{volts} \times \text{coulombs}$$

or $\qquad J = E \times Q \qquad (1)$

But we learned on page 360 that $Q = It$ where I represents amperes and t represents time in seconds. Hence, substituting in (1), we may write:

$$J = E \times I \times t. \text{ Why?} \qquad (2)$$

or **Joules = volts × amperes × seconds**

MEASURING ELECTRICITY

PROBLEM: A motor on a 110-volt circuit takes 5 amperes for 10 minutes (600 sec.). How much energy is used?

SOLUTION:
$$J = E \times I \times t$$
Substituting,
$$J = 110 \times 5 \times 600$$
Multiplying,
$$J = 300,000 \text{ joules}$$

Express this energy in foot-pounds. (One joule equals approximately ¾ foot-pound.)

Since $E = IR$, another way of writing formula (2) is as follows:

$$J = I^2Rt \qquad (3)$$

Electrical energy and heat. We already know that 1 calorie = 4.19 joules (see page 276). Hence, heat in calories,

$$H = \frac{I^2Rt}{4.19} \text{ calories}$$

or $H = .24 \, I^2Rt$ **calories.** Explain.

Does experiment verify the formula, $H = .24 \, I^2Rt$? In order to test the formula that heat in calories $H = .24 \, I^2Rt$, a student resorted to experiment. First he placed an electric lamp in a calorimeter filled with water, as shown in Fig. 11. The water equivalent of the water and the calorimeter was 1000 grams. Then he attached an ammeter in series with the lamp. These he connected with a 100-volt direct-current source. The data obtained for one trial were as follows:

Weight of water.........	1000 g.
Temperature increase	10 C°
Number of calories......	10,000
Current (I)	2 amp.
Resistance (R) of lamp...	25 ohms
Time (t)	416 sec.

The results were checked as follows:

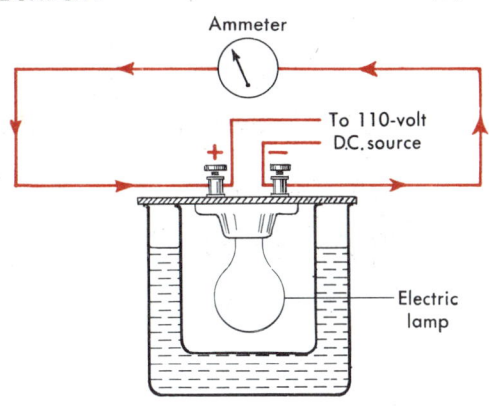

Fig. 11. Apparatus for determining the amount of heat produced by the passage of an electric current through a resistance.

Heat (H) = $0.24 \, I^2Rt$
$1000 \times 10 = 0.24 \times 2 \times 2 \times 25 \times 416$
10,000 cal. = approximately 10,000 cal.

Hence, in conclusion, we see that

heat energy is produced by the passage of electricity through a resistance, and the amount of heat varies:
  directly as the square of the current, I;
  directly as the resistance, R;
  directly as the time, t.

Changing electrical energy to heat energy. That the amount of heat produced varies with the resistance we can show better by connecting six inches of copper wire with an equal length of German silver wire, both of about No. 30 gauge, and by connecting these with a storage battery, as shown in Fig. 12. As a result, the German silver wire will become red hot and probably will melt, whereas the copper wire may be no more than uncomfortably warm. Since the same current passes through both wires and the resistance of the German silver wire is many times that of the copper wire, we see again that the

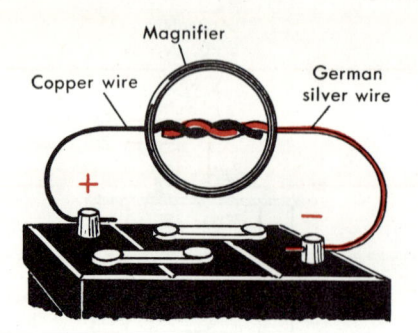

420 PRODUCTION OF ELECTRIC CURRENT AND ELECTRICAL MEASUREMENT

Fig. 12. German silver wire becomes very hot, while the copper wire remains relatively cool. Explain.

heating effect is dependent upon the resistance.

This same sort of arrangement of wires is used in electric stoves, heating pads, heaters, lamps, and certain other electrical appliances. Usually, large copper wire with low resistance carries the current to the instrument, and then smaller high-resistance wire is used for the heating element. In an ordinary 25-watt lamp the heating element (usually made of tungsten) is very small in diameter and only a few centimeters in length; yet its resistance is about 400 ohms.

Electrical power. On page 196, we defined power as the rate of doing work, or the work done per unit of time. Also we have learned that electrical work in joules is given by the formula:

$$J = EIt = I^2Rt$$

Dividing this formula by time in seconds, we have:

$$\text{Power } (W) = \frac{J}{t} = \frac{EIt}{t} = \frac{I^2Rt}{t}$$

The unit of electrical power is called the **watt**, which is defined as *one joule of work done per second*. Hence, in conclusion:

Power in watts = joules per second
= volts × amperes.

That is,

$$W = \frac{J}{t} = EI = I^2R$$

PROBLEM: The resistance of an electric lamp is 100 ohms. The current through the lamp is 1 ampere. (a) What is the power of the lamp? (b) What is the voltage across the lamp? (c) How much energy is used if the lamp operates for 20 seconds?

SOLUTION:

(a) $W = I^2R$
$W = 1 \times 1 \times 100$
$W = 100$ watts

(b) $E = IR$
$E = 1 \times 100$
$E = 100$ volts

(c) $J = EIt$
$J = 100 \times 1 \times 20$
$J = 2000$ joules

Check the answer to (c), using the formula $J = I^2Rt$.

The power utilized by an ordinary electric lamp may be 40, 75, or 100 watts; but an electric toaster may use as much as 500 watts or more. Also:

1000 watts = 1 kilowatt
746 watts = 1 horsepower
1 kilowatt = 1.34 or 4/3 horsepower

Commercial unit of electrical energy. Electric energy is sold by the kilowatt-hour, K.W.H., which is equivalent to the use of 1000 watts for 1 hour.

$$\text{K.W.H.} = \frac{\text{watts} \times \text{hours}}{1000} = \frac{E \times I \times T}{1000}$$

How does this *T* differ from the *t* used in the above formulas?

How is electrical energy measured? The electrical energy used by the consumer of electricity is measured by a watt-hour meter, which is usually placed near where the main wires lead into the building. The

MEASURING ELECTRICITY 421

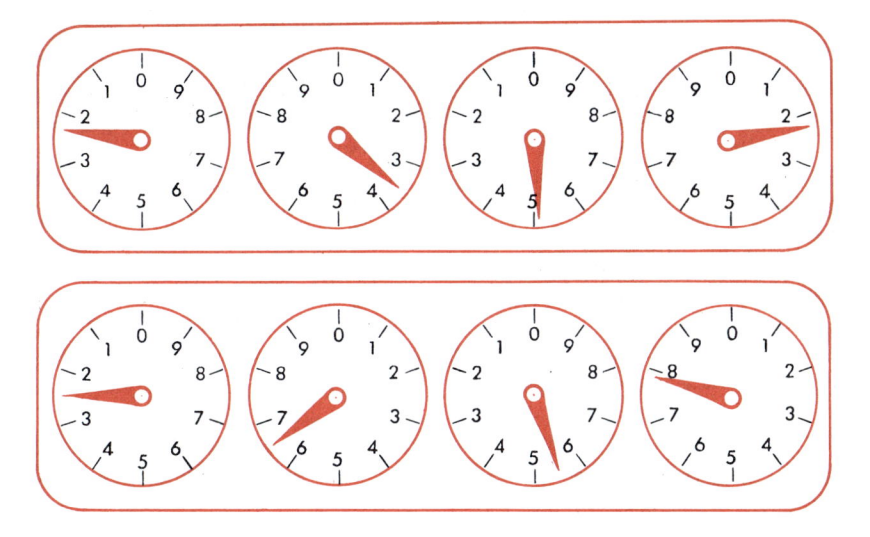

Fig. 13. Two readings of a kilowatt-hour meter taken a month apart. How much electric energy was used during the month? A kilowatt-hour meter measures the rate at which electrical energy is used and the length of time it is used.

instrument is really a small electric motor whose speed is proportional to the power used.

The rotating part of this motor is geared to the pointers of the dial and the instrument is calibrated so that it registers the number of kilowatt-hours used. Fig. 13 shows two readings taken a month apart. The top reading is 2352 K.W.H.

How is the consumer's electric bill calculated? In many places the rate charged depends upon the amount used. For example, the first ten K.W.H. used may cost ten to twelve cents each, and from there on the rate may be two, three, four, or five cents per K.W.H. In other sections a flat rate ranging from a fraction of a cent to several cents may be charged. In any case, however, if the cost per K.W.H. is known, an electric bill is easy to calculate. For example, the cost (C) of running a 5-ampere toaster on a 110-volt circuit for 20 minutes a day at the rate of 6 cents per K.W.H. for 30 days is,

$$C = \frac{\text{watts} \times \text{time (hrs.)} \times \text{cost/K.W.H.}}{1000}$$

Substituting,

$$C = \frac{110 \times 5 \times 1/3 \times 6 \times 30}{1000},$$

or 33 cents.

SUMMARY AND CONCLUSIONS

1. The coulomb (6.25×10^{18} electrons) is the unit quantity of electricity.
2. The ampere (I) is the rate of flow of electricity. It is one coulomb flowing per second.
3. The ohm is the resistance (R) of a column of mercury 106.30 centimeters long and one square millimeter in cross-sectional area at 0°C.
4. The volt is the difference of potential between two points when one joule of energy is required to transfer one coulomb of electricity between the points. Also, the volt is the difference in potential needed to send a current of one ampere through one ohm of resistance.

5. Ohm's Law, I (amperes) $= \dfrac{E \text{ (volts)}}{R \text{ (ohms)}}$, is that the current through a resistor varies directly as the voltage across the resistor and inversely with the resistance of the resistor.
6. A galvanometer is used to measure very small currents.
7. An ammeter measures current in amperes; it is a shunted galvanometer; it has low resistance; it is connected in series with the resistance in a circuit.
8. A voltmeter measures difference in potential in volts. It is a high-resistance galvanometer, and is connected in parallel with the device whose voltage is measured.
9. Work in joules $(J) = EIt$, or I^2Rt.
10. Heat in calories $(H) = 0.24\ EIt$, or $0.24\ I^2Rt$.
11. The unit of electrical power is the watt.
12. One watt is one joule of work done per second.
13. Watts $= EI$, or I^2R.
14. One kilowatt $= 1.34$ H.P. (approx. $\tfrac{4}{3}$ H.P.). One H.P. $= 746$ watts (approx. $\tfrac{3}{4}$ kilowatt).
15. A kilowatt-hour is the energy produced by 1000 watts used for one hour.

$$\text{K.W.H.} = \frac{E \times I \times T}{1000}$$

QUESTIONS FOR REVIEW

1. What is a coulomb? Ampere? Volt? Watt? Kilowatt hour?
2. Make a sketch of a galvanometer and explain the principle of its construction.
3. Make a sketch of the essential parts of an ammeter and point out the essential differences between it and a galvanometer.
4. Make a sketch to show how an ammeter is connected with an electric lamp in order to measure the current which flows through the lamp.
5. Make a sketch of a voltmeter and point out the essential differences between it and a galvanometer. Also, in the sketch in Question 4, connect a voltmeter so as to determine the voltage drop across the lamp.
6. Explain the principle upon which a voltmeter is constructed and explain the essential differences between it and an ammeter. Why must a voltmeter have a relatively high resistance?
7. Make a diagram to show how a voltmeter is connected with a lamp in a circuit in order to measure the potential difference across the lamp.
8. By definition, what is the relationship between a watt and a joule?
9. A kilowatt-hour is how many joules?
10. A joule is how many calories?
11. A kilowatt is how many H.P.?
12. A kilowatt-hour is how many calories?
13. How is electrical energy changed into heat?
14. Upon what factors does the heating effect of an electric current depend?
15. If the current through a resistance is doubled, how is the amount of heat produced affected? If the resistance is doubled and the current is not changed, how is the amount of heat affected?

PROBLEMS

1. What difference of potential is needed to send a current of 3 amperes through a resistance of 15 ohms? 10 ohms? 60 ohms?
2. If the resistance of a galvanometer is 30 ohms, what is the resistance of a shunt which would be used to double the range of the galvanometer? What is such an instrument called?
3. If the resistance of a voltmeter is 106 ohms and a 10-volt source deflects it full scale, how much resistance must be added to double the range of the voltmeter?
4. The voltage across a lamp is 100 volts. Three amperes flow through the lamp. What is the resistance of the lamp?
5. The voltage across a lamp is 100 volts. The resistance of the lamp is 75 ohms. What is the current through the lamp?
6. If a lamp has a resistance of 110 ohms and draws 1 ampere of current, what is the voltage across the lamp? What is the power of the lamp?
7. A 40-watt lamp is designed to be used

on a 120-volt line. How much current does this lamp use?
8. What is the resistance of a 60-watt lamp designed to be used on a 120-volt line?
9. What is the resistance of a 100-watt lamp which is designed to be used on a 220-volt circuit?
10. If a 100-watt motor were operated for 10 minutes, how many joules of energy would be used?
11. Five amperes flow through a heater coil for 2 seconds. What quantity of electricity passes through it?
12. The voltage across a lamp is 40 volts. There is a current of 2 amperes through the lamp for 10 minutes. How many joules of energy are used?
13. If the resistance of a lamp is 220 ohms and the current through it is 0.5 ampere, how many calories of heat will be produced during 60 seconds?
14. A 600-watt electric iron operates on a 120-volt circuit. How great is the current through the iron? What is the resistance of the iron? How much time is required for it to develop 288,000 calories of heat?
15. A 2-kg. flatiron uses 5 amperes of current when operated on a 120-volt circuit. What time is required to heat the iron from 20°C to 200°C, if no heat is lost by the iron? (The specific heat of iron is .113.)
16. The output of an electric motor is 1120 watts. What is its horsepower?
17. What is the output in watts of a 10-H.P. motor?
18. How much work in foot-pounds could be done by a 1000-watt motor in 10 seconds?
19. The input of an electric motor is 1 kilowatt. Its output is 1 horsepower. What is its efficiency?
20. A 600-watt electric iron is operated 1 hour per day, and a 200-watt toaster is operated 20 minutes per day. At 5 cents per K.W.H., what is the total cost of operation for 30 days?
21. An electric lamp is connected in a circuit. The voltage across the lamp is 100 volts. Through the lamp 4 coulombs of electricity flow each second. Choose one answer for each.

(1) The current through the lamp, measured in amperes, is:
(a) 25; (b) 400; (c) 100; (d) 4; (e) data insufficient.
(2) The work in joules done on the lamp in 10 seconds is:
(a) 400; (b) 25; (c) 4000; (d) 10; (e) 1000.
(3) The power of the lamp, measured in watts, is:
(a) 400; (b) 25; (c) 4000; (d) 40; (e) 1000.
(4) The quantity of electricity, measured in coulombs, which passes through the lamp in 10 seconds is:
(a) 100; (b) 25; (c) 4000; (d) 40; (e) 1000.
(5) The heat developed, measured in calories, during 10 seconds is:
(a) 400; (b) 100; (c) 1000; (d) 960; (e) 4000.
(6) The horsepower of the lamp is approximately
(a) 400; (b) ⅓; (c) ½; (d) 4000; (e) data insufficient.

PROJECTS

1. *How to measure the power of an electrical appliance.* In your home, turn off all the electrical appliances except one 100-watt or two 60-watt lamps. Then watch the aluminum disk on the watt-hour meter and determine the time required for it to turn around 25 times. Next, turn off the lamp and switch on your radio or some other device. Again determine the time for the disk to make 25 turns. By proportion, find in watts the power of the appliance tested.

2. *How to make a galvanometer.* Using a cork stopper, horseshoe magnet, and about 10 feet of #22 wire, make a galvanometer similar to that shown in Fig. 5. Wrap 15 to 20 turns of wire on the cork to form a rectangular coil of wire. Then, using a dry cell in series with a variable resistance, pass a current through the coil. Increase and decrease the current and note the effect. Also, change the direction of the current through the coil and note the effect.

3. Modify the galvanometer so as to make it into an ammeter. Also demonstrate how to vary the range of the ammeter.

4. Make the galvanometer into a voltmeter. Also show how to increase the range of the voltmeter.

5. Give an argument or proof as to why a bird is not electrocuted when it sits on a high-voltage line.

READING YOU WILL ENJOY

1. Bragg, W. L., *Electricity*, pp. 105-108. The Macmillan Company, New York, 1936. Explains voltmeters and ammeters simply.

2. Siskind, Charles S., *Electricity: Principles, Practice, Experiments*, pp. 57-68. McGraw-Hill Book Company, Inc., New York, 1947. Solves several mathematical problems similar to the ones in this chapter.

3. Skilling, Hugh H., *Exploring Electricity*. The Ronald Press Company, New York, 1949. Chapter 8, "Men Who Measured Electricity."

4. Suffern, M. G., *Basic Electrical Principles*, pp. 362-394. McGraw-Hill Book Company, Inc., New York, 1949. Gives a very complete development of electrical measurement for beginning students.

Unit 14

Electric Circuits

The maze of electric wires shown in the electronic computer in the unit photograph is a far cry from the simple electric circuits you will meet in this unit. Nevertheless, the basic principles of electric circuits apply to all electric circuits no matter how complex they are. After studying the laws of series and parallel circuits, you will be able to appreciate the advantages and disadvantages of each type of wiring. Furthermore, you will understand why cells are connected in series in a battery-powered radio and why parallel circuits are used in wiring a house.

37. LAWS GOVERNING ELECTRIC CIRCUITS

Unit Photograph Courtesy NACA

Chapter 37

Laws Governing Electric Circuits

The problem. We already know that if a battery sends a current through a resistor, such as a lamp, there must be a complete continuous path (circuit) from the negative to the positive terminal of the battery.

Basically, there are only two different kinds of electric circuits, unless you call a combination of the two a third kind. One of these is shown in (a) of Fig. 1. Starting with the battery, the current leaves the negative terminal, passes through the first lamp (or resistance, r_1), passes on through lamp r_2, then through lamp r_3, and back to the positive terminal. This type of circuit is called a *series circuit.* Its distinguishing characteristic is that it provides but one path around the circuit. If one lamp in a series circuit burns out, do the others continue to operate? Explain your answer.

The second type, known as a *parallel circuit,* is shown in (b) of Fig. 1. Here a wire leads from the negative terminal of the battery to the point M, where the circuit splits into three paths or branches. One contains lamp r_1; the second, lamp r_2; and the third, lamp r_3. At S, the paths again merge into a single wire which leads back to the positive terminal of the battery. The distinguishing characteristic of a parallel circuit is that it provides more than one conducting path. If one lamp in the parallel circuit burns out, do the others continue to function? Why?

Naturally, the question arises, "When should electrical devices be wired in parallel, when in series, and when in a series-parallel combination?"

What are the laws governing series circuits? Fig. 2 shows a series circuit consisting of three resistances (r_1, r_2, and r_3) connected with battery, voltmeters, and ammeters. The currents through the various resistances are designated i_1, i_2, and i_3 respectively, and the voltages across the resistances are designated e_1, e_2, and e_3 respectively. E_t represents voltage across the battery terminals, and I_t represents the current from the battery. See Table 1.

Table 1

Resistance or source	Voltage	Current in amperes	Resistance $\frac{E}{I}$
r_1	$e_1=20$	$i_1=2$	$r_1=10$ ohms
r_2	$e_2=30$	$i_2=2$	$r_2=15$ ohms
r_3	$e_3=50$	$i_3=2$	$r_3=25$ ohms
Battery	$E_t=100$	$I_t=2$	$R_t=50$ ohms

Examination of column 2 shows that the sum of the separate voltages (20 + 30

ELECTRIC CIRCUITS

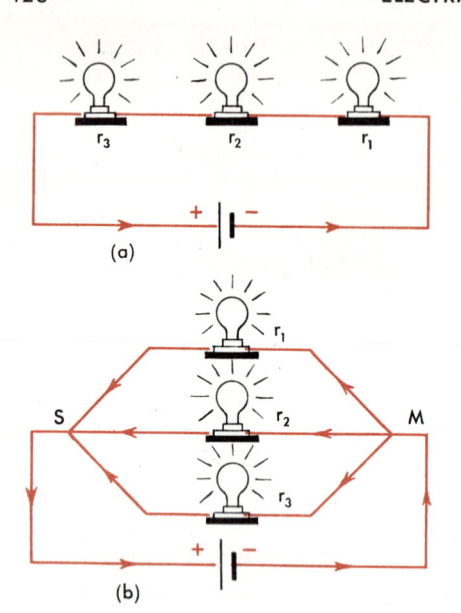

Fig. 1. (a) In a series circuit, there is a single path for the current. (b) In a parallel circuit, the current is divided.

+ 50 = 100) equals the voltage across the battery, E_t. That is,

$$E_t = e_1 + e_2 + e_3$$

Column 3 shows that the current i_1 (2 amperes) through r_1 equals that through r_2, and also that through r_3. Moreover, i_1 equals the current I_t furnished by the battery. In other words, the current through all parts of the circuit is the same. Hence,

$$I_t = i_1 = i_2 = i_3$$

Column 4, which has been calculated by Ohm's Law from the data in columns 2 and 3, shows that the sum of the separate resistances (10 + 15 + 25 = 50) also equals the total resistance, obtained by division of the total voltage (E_t) by the total current (I_t). Thus:

$$R_t = r_1 + r_2 + r_3 = \frac{E_t}{I_t}$$

Since the foregoing observations are for a typical series circuit, we may conclude that the laws governing a series circuit are as follows:

1. The voltage across the battery equals the sum of the voltages across the separate resistances.

$$E_t = e_1 + e_2 + e_3$$

2. The current through all parts of the circuit is the same.

$$I_t = i_1 = i_2 = i_3$$

3. The total resistance of the circuit equals:
   (a) the sum of the separate resistances, or
   (b) the voltage across the source divided by the current.

$$R_t = r_1 + r_2 + r_3$$

or

$$R_t = \frac{E_t}{I_t}$$

What are the laws governing parallel circuits? Fig. 3 shows a parallel circuit consisting of three resistances, r_1, r_2, and r_3, connected with a battery. The currents through the resistances are designated i_1, i_2, and i_3 respectively, and the voltages across them are designated e_1, e_2, and e_3 respectively. See Table 2.

Table 2

Resistance or source	Voltage	Current in amperes	Resistance $\frac{E}{I}$
r_1	e_1=120	i_1=6	r_1=20 ohms
r_2	e_2=120	i_2=4	r_2=30 ohms
r_3	e_3=120	i_3=2	r_3=60 ohms
Battery	E_t=120	I_t=12	R_t=10 ohms

Examination of the voltages in column 2 shows that the voltages across all branches of the circuit are equal. That is,

$$E_t = e_1 = e_2 = e_3$$
$$120 = 120 = 120 = 120$$

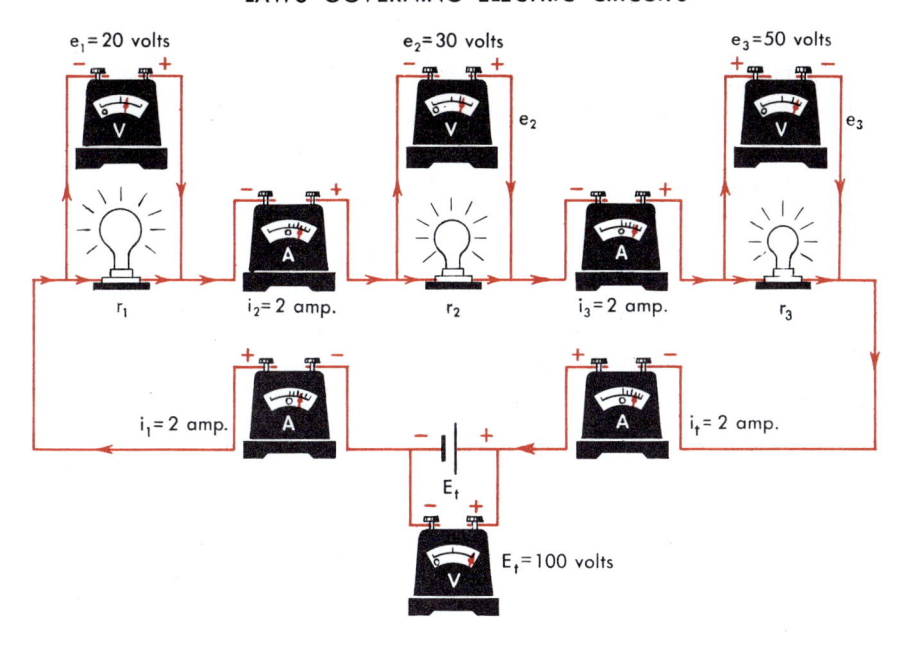

Fig. 2. A series circuit. How much current passes through each resistance?

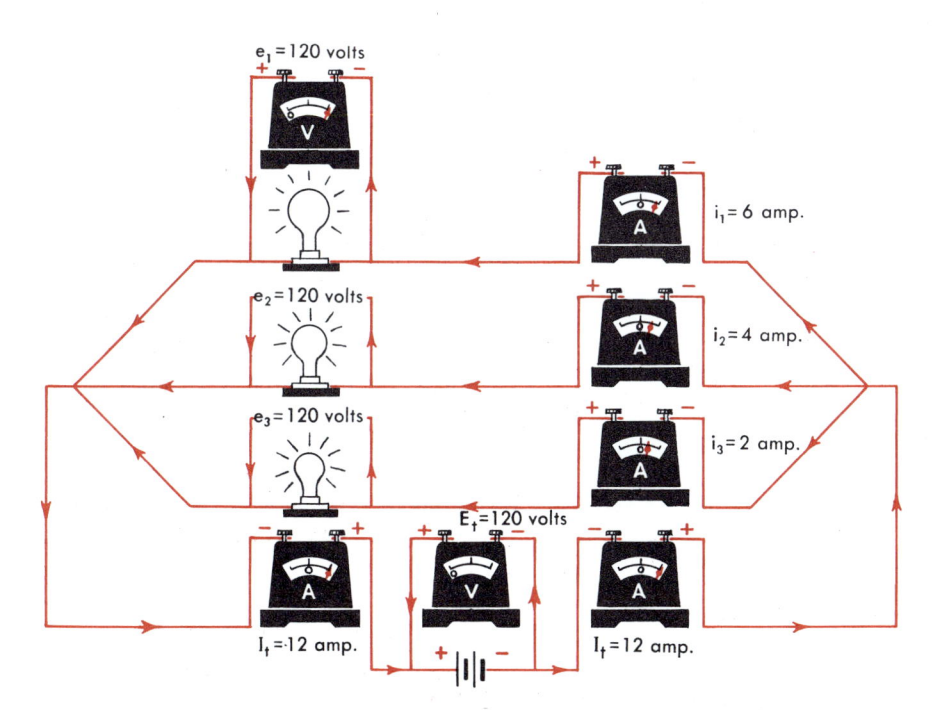

Fig. 3. A parallel circuit. How many amperes pass through each resistance?

Column 3 indicates that only a portion of the current from the battery flows through each path or resistance. But the sum of the currents flowing through the three resistances equals the current furnished by the battery; that is, the total current,

$$I_t = i_1 + i_2 + i_3$$
$$I_t = 6 + 4 + 2 = 12 \text{ amperes}$$

Column 4 shows that *the combined resistance of the three resistances in parallel is less than any single resistance.* On first thought, this may seem impossible. But if we recall that in a parallel circuit several paths are provided, and that increasing the number of paths is the same as making the conducting wire larger, then it is easy to see that the total resistance should be less than any single resistance.

In column 4, we obtain the total resistance (R_t) by the formula

$$R_t = \frac{E_t}{I_t}$$

Substituting,

$$R_t = \frac{120}{12} = 10 \text{ ohms}$$

Can the total resistance, R_t, be obtained directly from the separate resistances, r_1, r_2, and r_3?

We already know that:

The voltages,
$$E_t = e_1 = e_2 = e_3$$

The total current,
$$I_t = \frac{E_t}{R_t}$$

Current,
$$i_1 = \frac{E_t}{r_1}. \quad \text{Why?}$$

Current,
$$i_2 = \frac{E_t}{r_2}. \quad \text{Why?}$$

Current,
$$i_3 = \frac{E_t}{r_3}. \quad \text{Why?}$$

Also,
$$I_t = i_1 + i_2 + i_3$$

Hence,
$$\frac{E_t}{R_t} = \frac{E_t}{r_1} + \frac{E_t}{r_2} + \frac{E_t}{r_3}. \quad \text{Why?}$$

Dividing by E_t, we have,
$$\frac{1}{R_t} = \frac{1}{r_1} + \frac{1}{r_2} + \frac{1}{r_3}$$

Using this formula for finding the total resistance of the three parallel resistances above, where $r_1 = 20$ ohms, $r_2 = 30$ ohms, and $r_3 = 60$ ohms, we have,

$$\frac{1}{R_t} = \frac{1}{20} + \frac{1}{30} + \frac{1}{60}$$
$$\frac{1}{R_t} = \frac{3}{60} + \frac{2}{60} + \frac{1}{60}$$

or,
$$\frac{1}{R_t} = \frac{6}{60}$$

Hence, $6R_t = 60$
and, $R_t = 10$ ohms

This result shows that the total resistance of a combination of resistances in parallel can be obtained from the formula,

$$\frac{1}{R_t} = \frac{1}{r_1} + \frac{1}{r_2} + \frac{1}{r_3}$$

as well as the formula

$$R_t = \frac{E_t}{I_t}$$

In the light of the foregoing, the laws governing parallel circuits may be summarized as follows:

1. The voltage is the same across all the parallel resistances of the circuit.

$$E_t = e_1 = e_2 = e_3$$

2. The total current equals the sum of the currents through the separate resistances.

$$I_t = i_1 + i_2 + i_3$$

LAWS GOVERNING ELECTRIC CIRCUITS

3. **The total, or combined, resistance is less than any single resistance. The combined resistance can be obtained by the formula,**

$$\frac{1}{R_t} = \frac{1}{r_1} + \frac{1}{r_2} + \frac{1}{r_3}$$

or by the formula

$$R_t = \frac{E_t}{I_t}$$

Voltage distribution in a circuit. As water flows along a horizontal pipe, there is a drop in water pressure along the pipe, due to friction. If the resistance of the pipe per unit length is greater in one section than in another, then the drop in water pressure per unit length in that portion is increased accordingly.

Is the same true of electricity? Does the electrical potential (voltage) fall along a wire of uniform resistance in the same way that, for flowing water, the potential pressure falls along a pipe of uniform size and construction?

To answer this question we connect a 12-volt battery and a 12-foot wire having 3 ohms resistance as shown in Fig. 4. A voltmeter connected across the source shows a fall, or a potential difference, of 12 volts across the wire between positive and negative terminals. The ammeter, in agreement with Ohm's Law, shows there are 4 amperes of current.

If the drop in potential along the wire is uniform, as we have suggested, then when the positive terminal of the voltmeter is connected with the one-foot mark on the wire (Fig. 4), the voltmeter should read 11 volts, indicating a drop in potential of one volt along one foot of wire. Shifting the positive terminal of the voltmeter to the two-foot mark should cause a reading of 10 volts, thereby indicating a voltage drop of two volts along two feet of wire.

Experiment shows that these results are true. How great a voltage drop would there be along three feet of wire? Four feet? Six feet? Ten feet?

The resistance of a wire depends on what factors? The resistance of a wire depends upon four things: the material, length, cross-sectional area, and temperature. Experiments show that the resistance of a wire varies directly as its length and inversely as the area of its cross section. That is, $R = \frac{KL}{A}$. Before we use the formula, several aspects of it need to be explained.

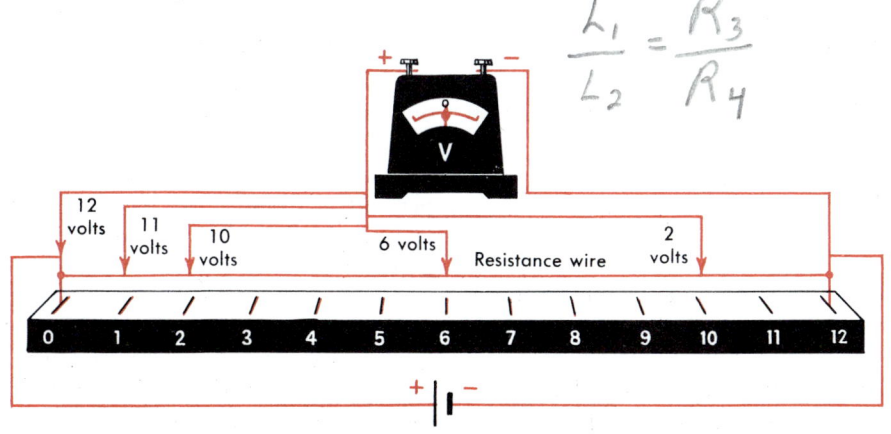

Fig. 4. Is the voltage drop uniform along a wire of uniform resistance?

Since wire is usually round, it is inconvenient to compute its cross-sectional area in square inches because π (3.14) must be used. To avoid this, engineers use the *mil* to measure the diameters of wires and the *circular mil* to measure the cross-sectional areas.

The mil is one-thousandth (0.001) inch and the circular mil is the area of a circle whose diameter is one mil. Because the areas of circles vary as the squares of their diameters, the area of a wire expressed in circular mils is equal to the square of its diameter expressed in mils.

Therefore, if the diameter of a wire is 2 mils, its cross-sectional area is 4 circular mils, and so on. If its diameter is 0.025 inch, then in mils its diameter is 25 and its area is $(25)^2$, or 625 circular mils.

PROBLEM: What is the area of cross section of a wire which is 10 mils in diameter?

SOLUTION: $A = (10)^2 = 100$ circular mils in cross section. What did we say is the advantage of finding the area in circular mils?

What is the area of cross section of a wire whose diameter is 20 mils? 40 mils? 1/10 inch?

When the diameter of a wire is doubled, how is the area affected? How is its resistance affected?

Since the square of the diameter d in mils equals the area in circular mils, then the formula $R = \dfrac{KL}{A}$ can be written as follows:

$$R = \frac{KL}{d^2}$$

By definition, K is said to be the resistance in ohms of a piece of wire one foot long and one circular mil in area of cross section. Such a piece of wire is called a *mil-foot* of wire. The resistance of a mil-foot of wire is called its *specific resistance,* or *resistivity.* In Table 3 the specific resistances are given in ohms per mil-foot for the more commonly used conductors at 20° C.

Table 3
SPECIFIC RESISTANCES OF CONDUCTORS

Material	Ohms per mil-ft.	Material	Ohms per mil-ft.
Aluminum	17.0	Nichrome	602
Copper	10.4	Platinum	60
German silver	198	Silver	9.6
Iron	60	Piano Wire	71
Manganin	266	Tungsten	33

PROBLEM: What is the resistance of a piece of aluminum wire 34 mils in diameter and 1700 feet long?

SOLUTION:

$$R = \frac{KL}{d^2}$$

$$R = \frac{17 \times 1700}{34 \times 34}$$

$R = 25$ ohms

Effect of temperature on resistance. Heating increases the resistance of most metals and metal alloys. For pure metals there is about a 4 per cent increase in resistance for every 10 C° increase in temperature. The resistance of a piece of copper wire of 1 ohm resistance at 0° C increases .00426 ohm for each degree of temperature rise. In the careful measurement of the resistance of a wire when it is hot or cold, we have an electrical method of measuring temperature.

PROBLEM: At 0°C the resistance of a copper wire is 1 ohm. After the wire is heated its resistance is 1.426 ohms. What is its temperature?

How do fuses protect against line overloads? The size of line wire used in wiring most older homes was No. 12 gauge, which until recently was large enough for most lighting circuits. But today, as more and more electrical devices such as vacuum cleaners, refrigerators, irons, TV sets, radios, hair curlers, and air conditioners are used in homes along with electric lights, the amount of current used is much greater than the circuit wires were designed to carry.

The overloading of circuits not only causes voltage (IR) drop in the line but also causes overheating of wires, which leads to fire. To protect the wires from overheating, fuses are used. The essential part of a fuse is a short, low-melting-point wire which will melt and break the circuit when more than the rated number of amperes flows through it. See Fig. 5.

The use of fuses of the proper size in electric circuits will protect against fires from overloaded lines. But it does not solve all the householder's problems, because fuses usually "blow," if at all, at the most inconvenient times, such as during a party, when the radio and all the lights are on.

The remedy for overloaded circuits is either to install larger-sized wires or to install more circuits. By all means resist the temptation of putting in oversized fuses; otherwise you may read some morning of a fire in your own home. But in the newspaper account the blame will probably be improperly placed on "defective" wiring rather than overloaded circuits.

Once a house is built, the installation of new wiring is quite costly. Hence, during the building of a new home a little foresight concerning future wiring needs could save hundreds of dollars later on.

The resistance of a cell and its effect on the terminal voltage of the cell. If a high-resistance voltmeter is connected with, say, a dry cell only, the voltmeter will read about 1.5 volts. But when a resistance of about 0.1 ohm is connected across the cell, the voltmeter will read about 1 volt instead of 1.5 volts. See Fig. 6.

From this experiment, it is evident that the terminal voltage of a cell which is de-

Courtesy Westinghouse Electric Corp.

Fig. 5. Testing high-voltage electric fuses that have been designed to protect power lines against lightning strokes and other rampant electrical surges.

livering little or no current is greater than the voltage across the cell when it is delivering current. *The terminal voltage of a cell which is not delivering current is the* **electromotive force (e.m.f.)** *of the cell.*

With the *internal resistance* of a dry cell known to be 0.05 ohm, the difference in voltmeter readings can be explained when a resistance of 0.1 ohm is connected with the cell. The internal resistance of the cell plus the resistance of the resistor is 0.15 ohm. Through this combined resistance an e.m.f. of 1.5 volts sends $\frac{1.5}{0.15}$, or 10 amperes. This means that across the internal resistance of the cell there is a voltage drop ($I \times R$) of 10 × 0.05, or 0.5 volt. Across the external resistance there is a voltage drop of 10 × 0.1, or 1 volt. That is, 0.5 volt is the voltage drop across the internal resistance of the cell and 1 volt is the drop across the external resistance. The voltmeter registers only the potential difference across the external circuit.

The e.m.f. = terminal voltage + volts used on the internal resistance

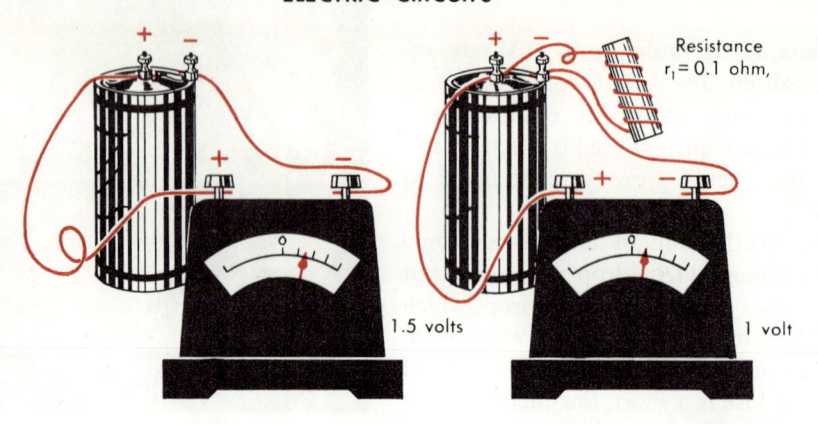

Fig. 6. Account for the difference in the voltmeter readings.

PROBLEM 1: The e.m.f. of a dry cell is 1.5 volts and its internal resistance is 0.06 ohm. What is the terminal voltage when the cell is delivering 5 amperes?

SOLUTION:
Volts across the internal resistance =
    5 × 0.06, or 0.3
Terminal voltage =
    e.m.f. − internal voltage drop
Terminal voltage =
    1.5 − 0.3 = 1.2 volts

Think of another solution and check this answer by means of it.

PROBLEM 2: The e.m.f. of a dry cell is 1.5 volts and its internal resistance is 0.1 ohm. What is the terminal voltage when the cell is delivering 5 amperes?

When should cells be connected in series? As with resistances, so with cells. When two or more cells are connected in such a way as to make the entire current go through each cell, the connection is in *series*. A series connection of cells, therefore, is one in which the lead wires extend from the negative of one cell to the positive of the next, and so on.

As shown in Fig. 7, when three dry cells are connected in series, the total voltage equals about 4.5 volts, which equals the sum of the separate voltages. That is, 1.5 + 1.5 + 1.5 = 4.5.

On the other hand, as shown in Fig. 8, when three dry cells are connected in parallel (wires go from + to + to + and from − to − to −) the total voltage is only 1.5 volts, the same as that for only one cell. The question is, when should cells be connected in series and when in parallel?

Naturally, when large voltages are needed (for example, as in the B-battery circuit of a battery-powered radio), the cells are put in series. In fact, thirty small dry cells are connected in series in a 45-volt B-battery. Also, if the maximum current is needed through a large resistance, then the maximum voltage is necessary, so the cells should be connected in series.

Cells are usually connected in parallel when the external resistance is low and considerable current is needed. In this way, all the current does not pass through each cell, and each cell furnishes its share of current. If enough cells are used, the current furnished by each can be made quite small so that polarization is low. In parallel, the e.m.f.'s of all cells should be about equal; otherwise the cells with high

LAWS GOVERNING ELECTRIC CIRCUITS

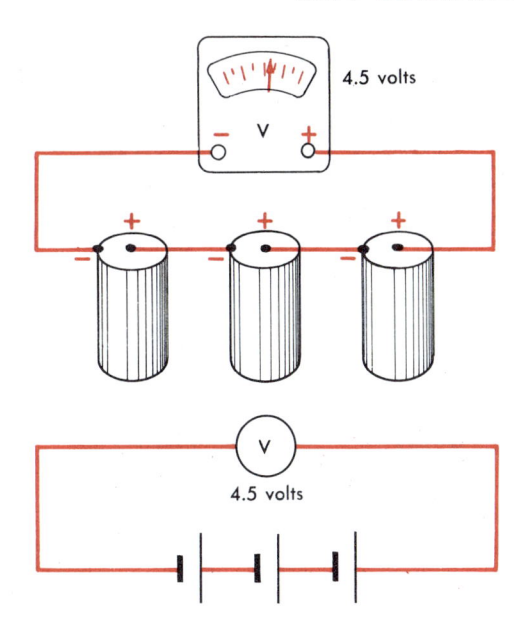

Fig. 7. Cells are connected in series when the external resistance is large. Maximum voltage is then obtained.

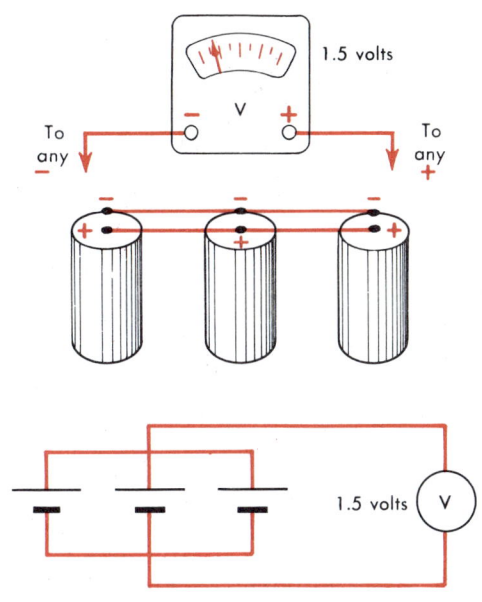

Fig. 8. Cells are connected in parallel when the external resistance is very small. Maximum current is then obtained.

e.m.f. will discharge through those of low e.m.f. Explain.

For the transmission of the maximum power, although this is not necessarily the most efficient arrangement, cells should be connected so that the internal resistance of a battery is about equal to the resistance of the circuit. A good example of a place where maximum power is needed with a "minimum of battery" is the starter on an automobile. Since storage batteries have very low internal resistance, a starter must likewise have a low resistance if it is to draw enough power to start a large engine.

PROBLEM: Each of twenty old radio B-battery cells has a resistance of 0.1 ohm and an e.m.f. of 1 volt. What current will result when a 10-ohm resistor is connected with these cells arranged in series? In parallel?

Series-parallel connection of resistors. Often it is impossible to avoid combined, series-parallel connections. See Fig. 9.

The following problem and its solution will illustrate the application of the series and parallel laws to such a circuit.

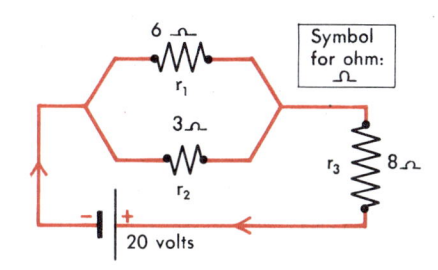

Fig. 9. Series-parallel connection.

PROBLEM: Referring to Fig. 9, a 6-ohm and a 3-ohm resistor are connected in parallel, and these are connected in series with an 8-ohm resistor. Find (a) the combined resistance of the resistors in parallel; (b) the total resistance R_t of the circuit; (c) the current I_t from the 20-volt battery; (d) voltage drop across each resistor; (e) current through each resistor.

SOLUTION:

(a) $\dfrac{1}{R} = \dfrac{1}{r_1} + \dfrac{1}{r_2}$

$\dfrac{1}{R} = \dfrac{1}{6} + \dfrac{1}{3}$

$\dfrac{1}{R} = \dfrac{1}{6} + \dfrac{2}{6} = \dfrac{3}{6}$

$R = 2$ ohms

(b) $R_t = 2 + 8$

$R_t = 10$ ohms

(c) $I_t = \dfrac{E_t}{R_t}$

$I_t = \dfrac{20}{10} = 2$ amperes

(d) $e_3 = i_3 \times r_3$

$e_3 = 2 \times 8 = 16$ volts

$e_2 = E_t - e_3$

$e_2 = 20 - 16 = 4$ volts

$e_1 = 4$ volts. Explain.

(e) $i_1 = \dfrac{e_1}{r_1} = \dfrac{4}{6} = \dfrac{2}{3}$ ampere

$i_2 = \dfrac{e_2}{r_2} = \dfrac{4}{3}$ amperes

$i_3 = \dfrac{e_3}{r_3} = \dfrac{16}{8} = 2$ amperes

The Wheatstone bridge. As shown in Fig. 10, a *Wheatstone bridge* consists of a battery connected with a series-parallel type of circuit that is designed to find electrical resistance.

At A the circuit divides into two parallel circuits, ACB and ADB. Resistances X and R are in series and resistances r_1 and r_2 are in series. Usually, r_1 and r_2 consist of a straight wire, and the resistance of each varies with its respective length. Connecting C and D is a galvanometer. X is the unknown whose resistance is to be found, R is a resistance whose value is known, and r_1 and r_2 can be varied by changing the position of the contact at D.

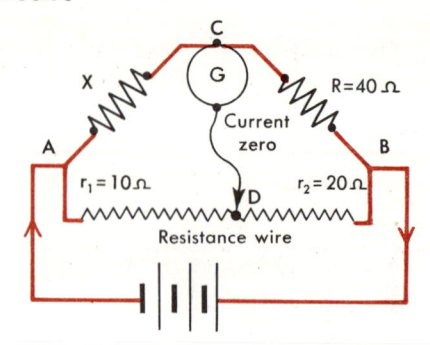

Fig. 10. A Wheatstone bridge.

When the four resistors are of proper proportions in size so that the voltage drop across X is the same as that across r_1, then the difference in potential between C and D is zero (explain), and therefore there will be no current between C and D. Also under these circumstances the voltage drop across R equals the voltage drop across r_2. Explain. What about the current through r_1 and r_2? Through X and R?

Experiment will show that when the bridge in Fig. 10 balances—that is, when there is no current through the galvanometer—then X must equal 20 ohms. Therefore we may write that:

$$\dfrac{20}{10} = \dfrac{40}{20}$$

or

$$\dfrac{X}{r_1} = \dfrac{R}{r_2}$$

PROBLEM: In case $R = 10$ ohms, $r_1 = 4$ ohms, and $r_2 = 5$ ohms when the bridge is balanced, then what is the resistance of X? See Fig. 10.

SUMMARY AND CONCLUSIONS

1. There are two different distinct electrical circuits: (a) parallel, and (b) series.
2. The laws governing series circuits are:

$$E_t = e_1 + e_2 + e_3 \ldots\ldots + e_n$$
$$I_t = i_1 = i_2 = i_3 =$$
$$R_t = r_1 + r_2 + r_3 = \dfrac{E_t}{I_t}$$

3. The laws governing parallel circuits are:

$$E_t = e_1 = e_2 = e_3$$
$$I_t = i_1 + i_2 + i_3 \ldots\ldots + i_n$$
$$\frac{1}{R_t} = \frac{1}{r_1} + \frac{1}{r_2} + \frac{1}{r_3} \ldots\ldots + \frac{1}{r_n}$$
$$R_t = \frac{E_t}{I_t}$$

4. The resistance of a wire varies directly as its length and inversely as the area of its cross section, or the square of its diameter in mils. $R = \frac{KL}{d^2}$. K is the specific resistance, which is the resistance of a wire 1 foot long whose diameter is 1 mil.

5. For identical cells in series,

$$E_t = e_1 + e_2 + e_3$$

6. For identical cells in parallel,

$$E_t = e_1 = e_2 = e_3$$

7. The e.m.f. of a battery or cell equals the voltage on open circuit, or the sum of the terminal voltage and voltage drop in the cell on closed circuit.

8. A Wheatstone bridge is used to measure resistance. The formula is:

$$\frac{X}{r_1} = \frac{R}{r_2}$$

QUESTIONS FOR REVIEW

1. What are the two kinds of electrical circuits?
2. Make a diagram showing each type of circuit and a combination of the two.
3. Why are lamps for general lighting purposes seldom connected in series?
4. How many 10-volt Christmas tree lamps should be connected in series on a 110-volt line?
5. State the laws governing series circuits.
6. State the laws governing parallel circuits.
7. What is the e.m.f. of four cells, each with an e.m.f. of 1.5 volts, when these cells are connected in parallel? In series?
8. Why is the e.m.f. of a cell more than the terminal voltage when the cell is delivering current?
9. What is the general rule for connecting cells (series or parallel) when the maximum power is to be delivered?
10. To renew the battery for a 6-volt-bulb flashlight, how many dry cells would be needed and how should they be connected?
11. What is a mil? A circular mil?
12. What is the cross-sectional area, in circular mils, of a wire whose diameter is 0.1 inch?
13. What is meant by specific resistance?
14. What metals have the lowest specific resistance?
15. How is the resistance of a wire affected if we double its length? Its diameter? Its cross-sectional area?
16. How is the resistance of a wire affected if both its length and its diameter are doubled?
17. Are the headlights on your car connected in series or in parallel? How can you prove your answer?

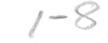

PROBLEMS

1. Three resistors having resistances of 10, 20, and 30 ohms, respectively, are connected in series.
    (a) Draw a diagram showing the connections.
    (b) Find the total resistance of the combination.
    (c) How much current will there be if the group is connected with a 60-volt source?
2. Find the combined resistance of a 15-ohm coil and a 25-ohm coil connected in parallel.
3. The resistances in Problem 1 are connected in parallel.
    (a) Draw a diagram showing the connections.
    (b) Find the total resistance of the group.
    (c) How much current will there be if the group is connected with a 60-volt source?
4. Find the combined resistance of resistors of 4, 5, 10, and 20 ohms: When the resistors are connected (a) in series; (b) in parallel.

5. Three resistors, 15, 20, and 25 ohms, are connected in series, and the combination is connected with a voltage source. As a result, there are 2 amperes of current in the circuit.
   (a) Find the voltage across each resistance.
   (b) Find the voltage of the source.
   (c) Find the total resistance of the combination.
   (d) Find the current, using the formula
   $$I_t = \frac{E_t}{R_t}$$

6. A 33-volt lamp has a resistance of 11 ohms. Find the resistance which must be used in series with it, if it is to be used on a 115-volt line.

7. In order for a certain automobile headlamp not to burn out, it must be limited to 4 amperes. When this lamp is connected with a 12-volt battery, tests show that a 1-ohm resistor must be connected in series with it. What is the resistance of the lamp?

8. Three resistances of 20, 30, and 60 ohms are connected in parallel, and the combination is then connected with a 120-volt line. Find:
   (a) The voltage across each resistance.
   (b) The current through each resistance.
   (c) The total resistance of the combination.
   (d) The total current in the circuit, using two different methods.

9. Three dry cells, each with an e.m.f. of 1.5 volts and an internal resistance of 0.05 ohm, are connected in series. Find:
   (a) The total e.m.f. of the cells.
   (b) The total or combined resistance of the cells.

10. Five dry cells, each with an e.m.f. of 1.5 volts and an internal resistance of 0.05 ohm, are connected in parallel. Find:
    (a) The combined internal resistance of the cells.
    (b) The total e.m.f. of the battery.
    (c) The total terminal voltage of the cells when they are delivering 10 amperes of current.

11. The open-circuit voltage (e.m.f.) of a dry cell is 1.5 volts. When momentarily shorted it delivers 30 amperes. What is its internal resistance? What would be the terminal voltage of this cell if it were connected with a 1-ohm coil?

12. What is the internal resistance of a 6-volt storage battery which delivers 300 amperes through a cable of negligible resistance? What would be the terminal voltage if this battery delivered 100 amperes to an automobile starter whose resistance is 0.04 ohm?

13. Two dry cells, each having an e.m.f. of 1.5 volts and an internal resistance of 0.05 ohm, are connected (a) in series and then with a 1.4-ohm resistor; (b) in parallel and then with a 1.4-ohm resistor. Find the current in each circuit.

14. A wire 50 feet long has a resistance of 10 ohms. What is the resistance of 200 feet of the same kind and size of wire?

15. A piece of wire 100 feet long has a resistance of 20 ohms. Its diameter is 0.04 inch. What would be its resistance if its diameter were 0.02 inch?

16. How many feet of German silver wire of No. 20 gauge ($K = 198$) are needed to make a resistance spool of 100 ohms?

17. A student wants to make a 50-ohm resistance coil from a piece of manganin wire for which K is 266. The gauge number is 24. How many feet of wire does he need? The diameter of 24-gauge wire in mils is 20.10. (See Appendix.)

18. A 60-ohm and a 30-ohm resistor are connected in parallel. This combination is then connected in series with a 40-ohm resistor. The voltage across the circuit is 120 volts. Find (a) the total current, I_t; (b) the voltage across each resistance; (c) the current through each resistance.

19. A Wheatstone bridge is balanced when $r_1 = 5$ ohms, $r_2 = 15$ ohms, and $R = 20$ ohms. Find the unknown resistance, X.

READING YOU WILL ENJOY

Rinde, Charles A., *Electricity*. Harcourt, Brace and Company, New York, 1943. "The Two Main Types of Electrical Connections," pp. 117-127.

Unit 15

Electric Machines

Motors and generators are essentially energy converters that do opposite things. The motor converts electrical energy into mechanical energy, while the generator converts mechanical energy into electrical energy. The exact means by which these energy transformations take place is the subject of this unit.

Although all of you have had some experience with motors, most of you have probably never seen a generator, much less tinkered with one. However, every automobile has a small generator to supply electrical energy to the ignition system, headlights, heater, and radio while the engine is in operation. After you have completed the study of this unit, you should be able to analyze the energy relationships that exist among the engine, the generator, and the storage battery in the family automobile.

Meanwhile, examine the unit photograph to get an idea of how large a motor can be. Silhouetted against the sky is the 75-ton stator, or outer frame and coils, of the world's most powerful motor. When assembled, the rotor will fit into the space where the man is standing. The entire motor, which contains 31 miles of copper windings, will be used to drive the vanes in the world's largest wind tunnel at the Air Force's Arnold Engineering Center at Tullahoma, Tennessee.

38. HOW AN ELECTROMOTIVE FORCE IS PRODUCED BY MECHANICAL MEANS
39. INDUCTION COILS AND TRANSFORMERS

Unit Photograph Courtesy Westinghouse Electric Corp.

Chapter 38

How an Electromotive Force Is Produced by Mechanical Means

The problem. If friction, and chemical action in cells, were the only means for producing an electromotive force, the cost of electricity needed to operate most electrical machines would be so high that only the very rich could afford them. In fact, it is doubtful that many modern electrical devices would ever have been invented.

Our problem in this chapter is to find how an electromotive force can be produced cheaply by mechanical means and how such machines are built and operated.

Faraday makes a world-changing discovery. Oersted, you will recall, opened up a whole new vista in electricity when he discovered that a magnetic field surrounds a conductor which carries a current. In 1831, Faraday made a discovery that was equal in importance to Oersted's. Faraday found (see Fig. 1) that

when relative motion causes a conductor of electricity to cut the lines of force in a magnetic field, there is induced in the conductor an e.m.f. which will cause a current in a circuit of which the conductor is a part.

The galvanometer indicates the strength of current that results. And since the resistance of the circuit is constant, the strength of current is indicative of the induced e.m.f. You will recall that according to Ohm's law, when the resistance is constant, the current varies directly as the e.m.f.

On what factors does an induced e.m.f. depend? If the conductor in Fig. 1 is moved slowly (up or down) across the magnetic field, the induced e.m.f. is less than if it is moved rapidly. Hence the e.m.f. seems to vary with the speed of the conductor. Also, if the field strength is increased by use of a stronger magnet, or two magnets, as shown in (a) of Fig. 2, the e.m.f. and current are increased. Compare with Fig. 1. And if the number of conductors is increased, as shown in (b) of Fig. 2, the e.m.f. and current are increased accordingly.

In conclusion, we see that the induced e.m.f. varies directly as the speed of the conductors, the field strength, and the number of conductors. That is, the induced e.m.f. varies directly as the number of lines of force across which the conductor moves per unit of time. *When a conductor is moved across 100,000,000 lines of force per second, the induced e.m.f. is 1 volt.*

Direction of the induced current. Furthermore, when a wire in a closed circuit is pushed downward between the poles

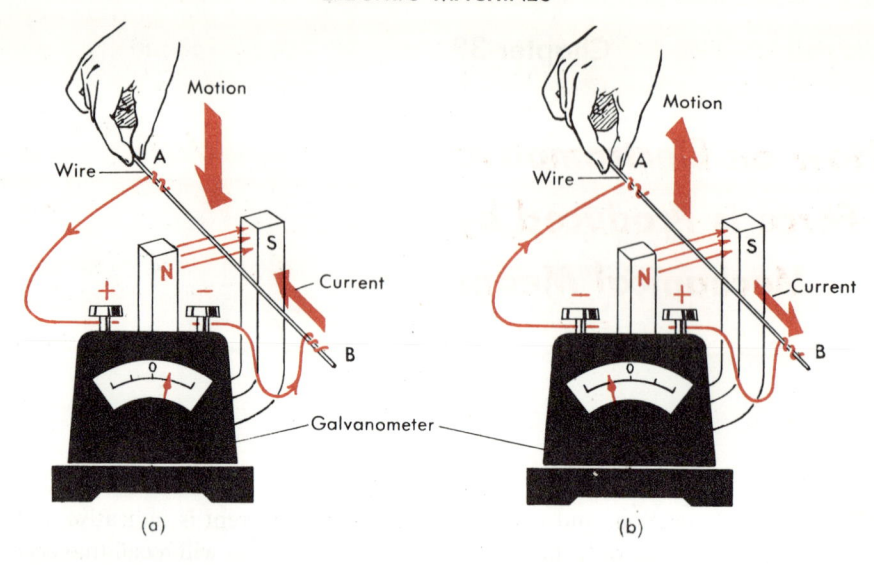

Fig. 1. When the wire cuts lines of force, an e.m.f. is induced in the wire.

of a horseshoe magnet in the position shown in (a) of Fig. 1, the induced current causes the galvanometer needle to deflect to the right. This means that the current enters the negative terminal of the galvanometer. Therefore the induced current in the wire *AB* must be in the direction shown. When the wire is moved upward, as shown in (b) of Fig. 1, the induced current travels in the opposite direction. Hence, *we can reverse the direction of the induced e.m.f., as well as the current, by reversing the direction of the motion of the conductor.*

What would happen if we changed only the direction of the field? Both the direction of the field and the direction of the motion of the conductor? It should be noted

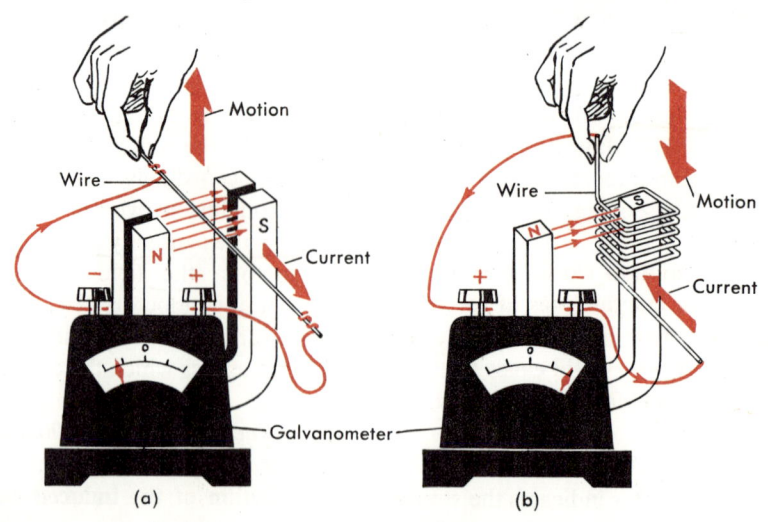

Fig. 2. What are the factors upon which an induced e.m.f. depends?

PRODUCING AN ELECTROMOTIVE FORCE BY MECHANICAL MEANS

that when the conductor is moved parallel with the lines of force, so that the conductor does not cross them, no e.m.f. is induced in the conductor. Why?

The direction which the induced current takes (see Fig. 3) can be determined by the following **left-hand generator rule:**

Extend thumb, forefinger, and center finger of the left hand so that they form right angles with one another. If the thumb points in the direction of the motion of the wire, and the forefinger in the direction of the magnetic field, then the center finger will point in the direction of the current.

As an aid to recalling this rule, note that field and forefinger, and current and center finger, respectively, begin with the same letters.

Fundamental principles of electric generators. We could not produce large currents by moving a single wire, or a coil of wire, by hand across a magnetic field. A far more effective way is to wrap the wire on a large spool or drumlike affair which

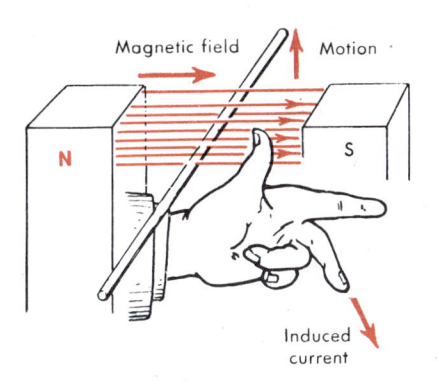

Fig. 3. The left-hand generator rule.

is mounted on an axle so that the coil may be turned between the poles of a magnet by steam or water power. This, in essence, is an *electric generator,* the principles of which are shown in Fig. 4. The magnets produce what is known as the *field* of the generator. The rotating drum with its wire windings is called the *armature.*

In order to lead the current from the coil, each end of the wire is attached to a separate brass ring which fits snugly to the axle. These two *slip rings, R* and *R'* (connected to *H* and *D* respectively), are to-

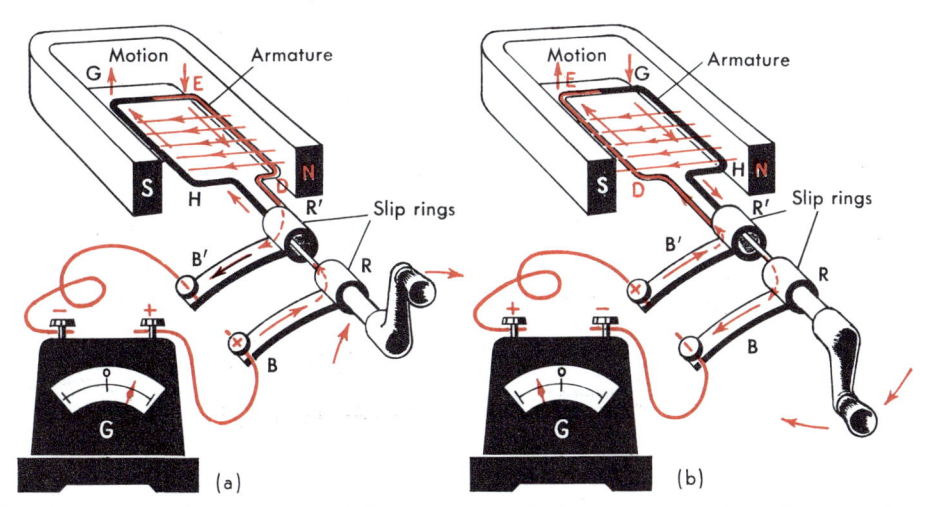

Fig. 4. An e.m.f. is generated in the wire of the armature when the armature is rotated.

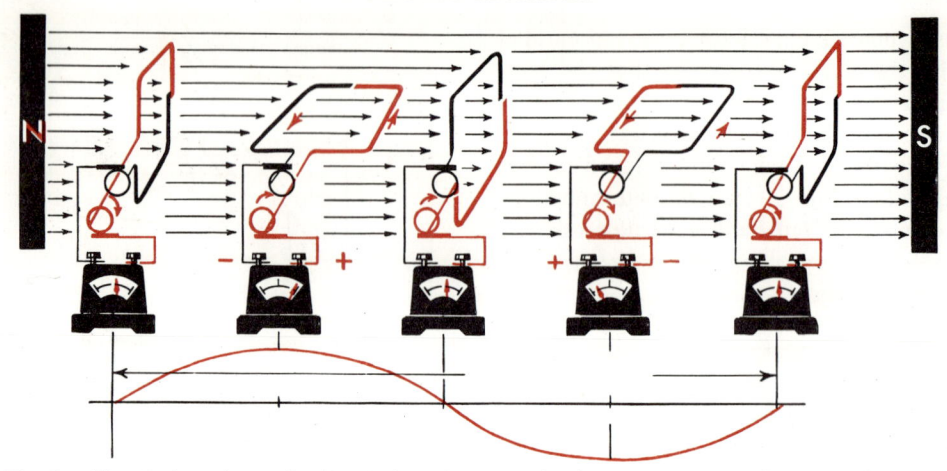

Fig. 5. The induced e.m.f. (or induced current) during one complete revolution of the armature.

tally insulated from each other. In contact with these rings are two *brushes, B* and *B'*, made of carbon, copper, or some other good conductor.

To understand what happens in one loop of the rotating armature during one complete revolution, let us start with the plane of the loop vertical, with side *DE* at the top, and then turn it clockwise to the position shown in (a) of Fig. 4, and at the same time observe the deflection of the hand of the galvanometer. As the one side, *DE,* of the wire loop moves across the field and down during the first half of the turn, the current that is induced goes from *E* to *D,* in accordance with the left-hand rule. At the same time in the other side of the loop the current is traveling from *H* to *G*, so that in the loop as a whole the current flows in the direction *HGED*. As a result, the current comes out of the slip ring that rubs on the negative brush *B'*. From here the current goes through the galvanometer and back into the generator through the positive brush *B* and slip ring *R* and thereby completes the circuit.

As shown in (b) of Fig. 4, during the second half turn of the loop (armature), in accordance with the left-hand rule, the induced current moves in the direction *DEGH* and comes out of brush *B,* making this brush negative. Then the current passes through the galvanometer, entering at the negative terminal and leaving through the positive terminal. Finally, it returns to the generator through brush *B'*, which should be positive. That the current takes this direction in the circuit is shown by the galvanometer, whose needle moves to the left of the zero position during this half turn.

What takes place in the armature during one complete revolution is shown in Fig. 5. When the coil is in the vertical position (a), the induced e.m.f. is zero; after it is turned through 90 degrees (b), the e.m.f. is a maximum; when the coil is turned through 180 degrees the e.m.f. drops to zero; at 270 degrees the e.m.f. is again a maximum; and at 360 degrees, back at the starting position, the e.m.f. is again zero. Explain why it is zero and a maximum at the positions indicated.

A complete revolution of the loop (360 degrees) in a generator that possesses only two *poles,* one N-pole and one S-pole, produces what is known as a *cycle* of current. During a cycle the current is

PRODUCING AN ELECTROMOTIVE FORCE BY MECHANICAL MEANS

zero twice and a maximum twice. In a four-pole machine the coil must be turned but one-half of a revolution to complete one cycle. In most generators the current alternates 120 times per second, producing 60 cycles per second. Explain why this does not cause incandescent lamps to fluctuate in intensity. Is this noticeable in fluorescent lamps? Explain.

The number of cycles completed per second is called the **frequency** *of the alternating current.* How many revolutions would the armature have to make per minute in a 60-cycle A.C. generator having two poles? Four poles? Eight poles?

Direct current (D.C.) generators. For many purposes, such as refining metals by electrolytic processes, charging storage batteries, electrolysis of water, and metal plating, alternating current cannot be used. It can be used in an arc lamp but it does not work so well as direct current.

To obtain direct current from a generator a most ingenious device, known as a *commutator,* or reversing switch, is used. The commutator is really a split ring, as shown in Fig. 7. Each half of the split ring, C_1 and C_2, is attached to a different end of the armature coil. The brushes $B+$ and $B-$ are usually set on opposite sides of the commutator (split ring) so that each brush is connected first with one end of the coil and then with the other as the armature revolves.

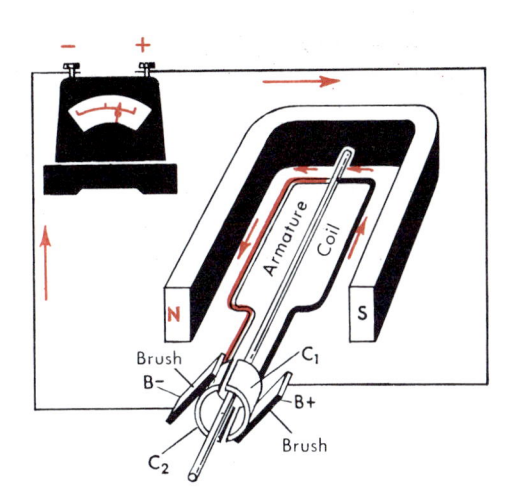

Fig. 7. A D.C. generator.

Fig. 6. These men are pulling the magnet out of the stationary part of the generator. As the magnet rotates with the turbine spindle to which it is attached, electricity is generated in the wires in the shell around the magnet.

Courtesy Consolidated Edison Co. of New York

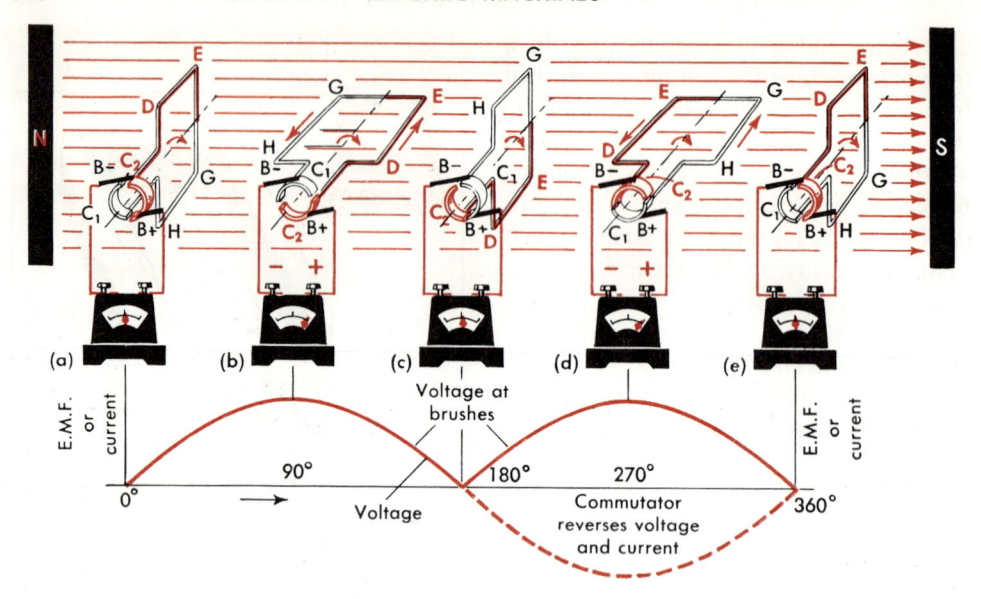

Fig. 8. Curve showing pulsating D.C., e.m.f., and current delivered to the commutator.

If the brushes are properly set and the plane of the coil is vertical, as shown in (a) of Fig. 8, then, when the coil is revolved clockwise, the current should take the direction indicated in (b) of Fig. 8 during the first half of the revolution, varying in magnitude from zero to a maximum and back to zero again. The current should leave the generator through the C_1 half of the commutator and the brush $B-$.

In the next portion of the cycle, as shown in (c) and (d) of Fig. 8, when the direction of the wires crossing the lines of force changes, the direction of the current in the loop should also change so that the current must come out of the loop through the other half of the commutator, C_2. But as the current changes direction the C_2 half of the commutator comes in contact with brush $B-$,' so that the current once more is led out through the brush, $B-$. Hence, although the current reverses twice in the armature coil during every cycle, the current in the external circuit does not change direction. This is shown by the galvanometer pointer, which deflects to the right twice and returns to the zero position twice during each cycle. Outside the generator the current always travels in the same direction, and because of its fluctuations, it is said to be *pulsating*. A generator with a commutator for delivering direct current is called a *direct-current* (D.C.) generator.

For many purposes the pulsations make no difference, but in some instances—for example, in a radio where direct current is needed—the pulsations, for one thing, cause a hum. One way of smoothing out the pulsations is to put more coils on the armature, but for every coil added two more segments must be put into the commutator. A graph of the current as well as the e.m.f. produced by an armature having two coils wrapped at right angles to each other is shown in Fig. 9b. As one coil is generating a minimum e.m.f. the other one is producing a maximum, and vice versa. The greater the number of coils the smoother the top of the curve becomes and the less the current fluctuates. Condensers and other devices which will be

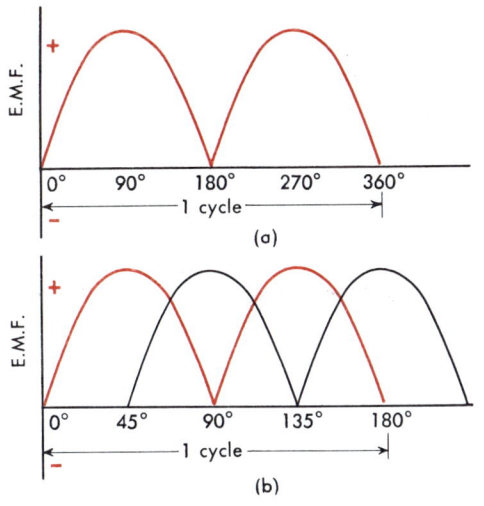

PRODUCING AN ELECTROMOTIVE FORCE BY MECHANICAL MEANS 447

Fig. 9. (a) The sine curve for a one-coil D.C. generator. (b) The curve will be smoother if another coil is wrapped at right angles to the first.

discussed later can be used to smooth the top of the curve still more.

The construction of armatures. There are several different types of armatures, but the most common is the drum type shown in Fig. 10. The core of this type of armature is made up of soft-iron disks insulated from one another by shellac or some other substance. These disks are mounted in such a way that they form grooves in which the insulated wires are wrapped. The soft iron offers little opposition to the lines of force between the pole faces. As a result, the field is stronger than it would be if the core were made of nonmagnetic material. Why the core is not one solid piece will be discussed on page 462.

Various kinds of field magnets. In the electric generator used in early telephones and the first automobiles, and in those used today on motor bicycles, motorcycles, and similar engines which do not use a storage battery for ignition purposes, the field is produced by several permanent magnets. Such a generator is called a *magneto.*

In larger generators, electromagnets are excited by a storage battery or direct current furnished by the generator itself is used to excite the field. In the case of an A.C. generator, or *alternator,* a direct-current generator may be attached to the same shaft as that of the A.C. generator. By this means a steady current is applied to the field poles, and if the speed of the armature is kept constant, the voltage generated will be constant. Such generators are said to be *self-excited*. To start a new self-excited generator, the field must be magnetized by an outside source of current. Thereafter, however, the iron cores of the electromagnets will retain enough residual magnetism so that some current will be induced in the armature coils when the armature is turned.

Types of self-excited (D.C.) generators. There are three different types of self-excited generators: (a) the series wound, (b) the shunt wound, and (c) the compound wound. Each has its deficiencies as

Fig. 10. Winding the rotating armature for a 300-watt, 125-volt compound D.C. generator. Note the commutator segments.

Courtesy General Electric Co.

448   ELECTRIC MACHINES

[handwritten at top: increase R, take one or more lamps away if connected in ∥]

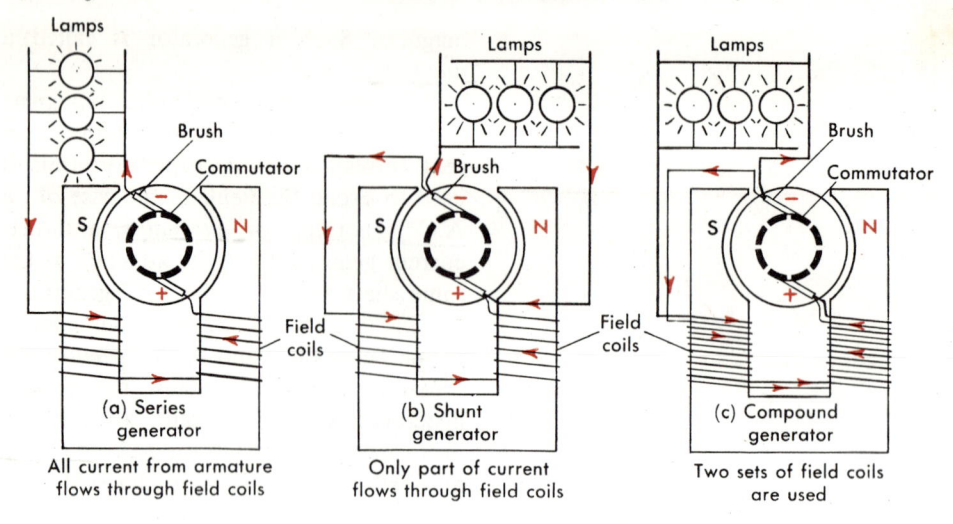

Fig. 11. (a) Series-wound generator. (b) Only part of the current flows through the field coils. (c) Two sets of field coils are used.

well as its good points. When to use one in preference to another is our problem.

The *series-wound* generator is shown in (a) of Fig. 11. The current, after leaving the brush, passes through the windings on the field magnet, then on into the external circuit. Consequently, if the resistance of the external circuit is increased, the amount of current decreases, which weakens the field strength. As a result, the voltage drops because fewer lines of force are crossed per second. Such a generator is satisfactory if the load on it is fairly constant. If the load is not constant, another type of generator should be used unless a steady source of current can be found to supply the current to the field coils.

The *shunt-wound* generator is shown in (b) of Fig. 11. Starting with the negative brush, one wire leads out to the external circuit and returns to the positive brush. Another circuit parallel with the external circuit conducts the current through the field magnets. Thereby only part of the current is used to energize the field in the shunt-wound generator. In case the resistance of the load increases, then more current goes through the field circuit and as a result the voltage is increased. But if the load resistance decreases—for example, if more lamps in parallel are turned on—then less current goes through the field, hence the voltage drops just when it is needed most.

The *compound-wound* generator is shown in (c) of Fig. 11. The field is both series wound and shunt wound. An increase in the resistance of the load decreases the current in the series coil but causes it to increase in the shunt coil. As a result, it is possible to keep the voltage fairly constant with a varying load.

Large commercial generators. In large commercial generators (see Fig. 12) which induce large currents, the armature, called a *stator,* is stationary. The field poles rotate inside the stator. One reason for this arrangement is that no brushes are needed to lead the current from the stator to the external circuit. Thus, the very troublesome sliding contacts, which always heat, wear away, and become corroded, are eliminated.

The generator principle operating in

Courtesy General Electric Co.

Fig. 12. An armature winder is inspecting the stationary armature, or stator, of a generator. The generator rotor, or field windings, will be placed inside the stator.

reverse—the electric motor. It was on Christmas Day in 1821 that Faraday made another world-changing discovery; namely, that *mechanical motion can be produced if a wire carrying a current is placed in a magnetic field,* as shown in Fig. 14. When

Fig. 13. A cutaway view of a turbine-generator team. Note that the field rotor is connected to the turbine rotor.

Courtesy General Electric Co.

STEAM ADMISSION VALVES
HIGH-PRESSURE ROTOR
NOZZLE DIAPHRAGM
TURBINE ROTOR
WINDINGS
LAMINATED CORE
EXCITER
STEAM INLET (UPPER)
FIELD
GENERATOR TERMINAL
STEAM INLET (LOWER)
CONDENSER

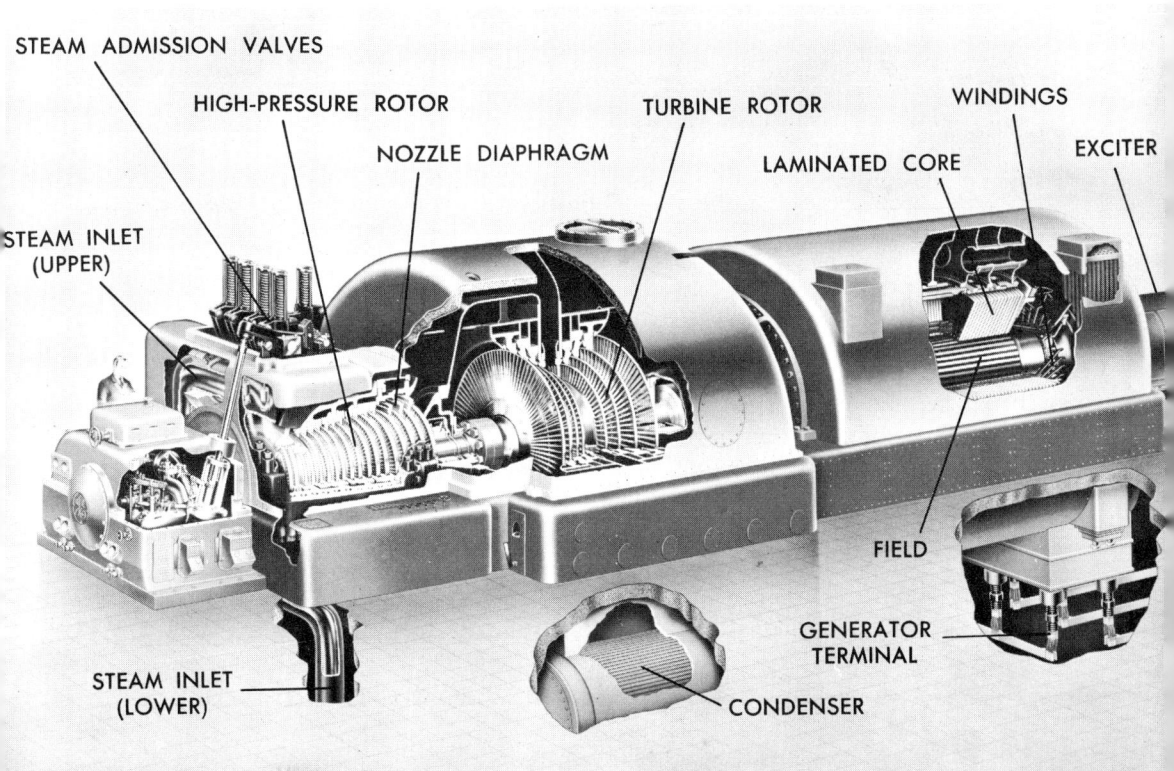

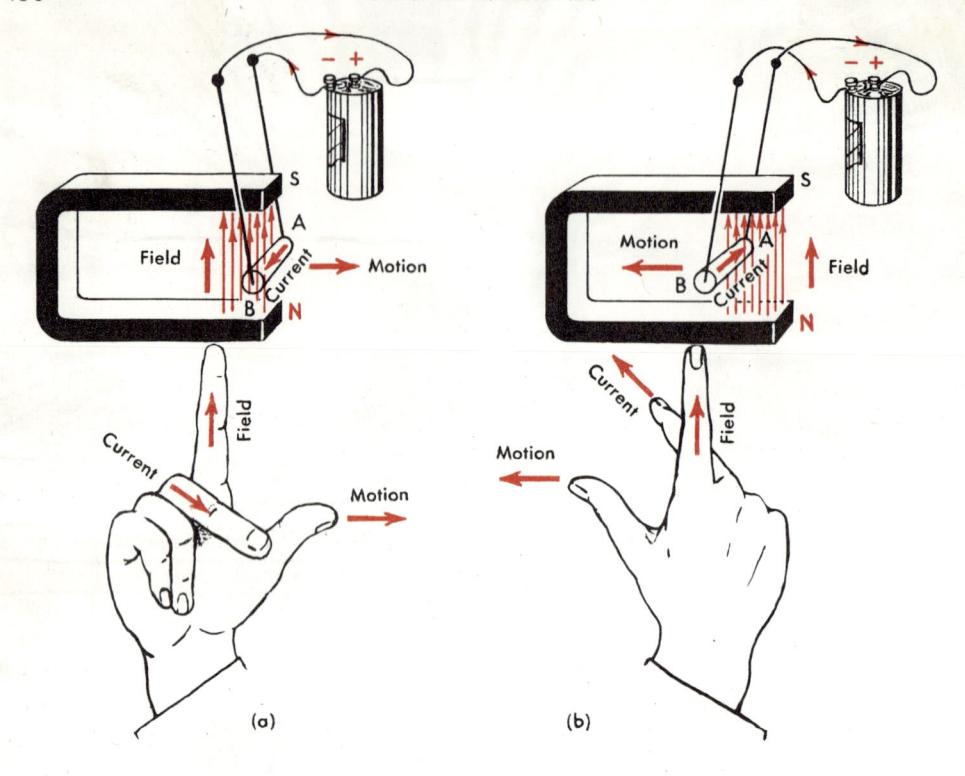

Fig. 14. Applying the right-hand rule to the electric motor.

the current in (a) of Fig. 14 is from A to B, the wire is forced outward. When it is from B to A, as in (b) of Fig. 14, the wire is forced inward. Thus the direction of the motion is reversed by reversal of the direction of the current.

Faraday found, too, that if the field was reversed in direction, the direction of motion was reversed. But if the directions of both the field and the current were reversed, the direction of the motion did not change. This latter fact should be remembered because it explains why a direct-current motor will run on alternating current.

Furthermore, it was discovered that, as in a generator, the directions of the motion, current, and field were at right angles to one another. However, you will find that the left-hand rule of the generator does not work out for the motor. Instead, the **motor right-hand rule** is used to determine the relative directions, as follows:

If we extend the thumb, forefinger, and center finger of the right hand, as shown in Fig. 14, so that they form right angles, and point the center finger in the direction of the current and the forefinger in the direction of the field, then the thumb will point in the direction of the motion.

Essentials of an electric motor. The electric motor, like a generator, consists of an armature and a field. See Fig. 15. The field may consist of either permanent magnets or electromagnets. The direct-current motors have a commutator and brushes. Most A.C. motors have slip rings and brushes. In *induction* motors, however, slip rings are used only in starting the armature.

The action of the direct-current motor. The armature of many electric motors, like that of a generator, consists of a loop of wire wrapped on a soft-iron core. The loop alone is pictured in Fig. 16, together with the magnetic poles and field. When the plane of the loop is horizontal and the current goes into the brush ($B-$) and around the loop, as shown by the arrows, then, in accordance with the right-hand motor rule, side DE of the loop is forced down and side GH is forced up until the loop is in the vertical position. But at this point the current in the loop is reversed in direction because the other segment of the commutator is now in contact with the brush $B-$. The reversal of current in the loop reverses the forces, so that the side of the loop which was being forced up is now forced down and the side which was being forced down is forced up. The loop therefore rotates through half a turn more, when the current again reverses. Then the process is repeated, causing a continuous rotation of the coil.

Back e.m.f. in a motor. In all motors, whether D.C. or A.C., conductors cross lines of force which induce an e.m.f. in the conductors. That is, all motors act as generators. The e.m.f. induced, in accordance with the right-hand rule and with experiment, is opposite in direction to the e.m.f. which causes the motor to run. For this reason the induced e.m.f. is called *back* e.m.f. And, as in a generator, the faster the armature turns, the more back e.m.f. there is generated. Generally the back e.m.f. of a motor, when it has acquired full speed, is about 90 per cent of the e.m.f. causing the motor to run. That is, on a 100-volt line, the back e.m.f. at full speed would be about 90 volts. This means that only $100 - 90$, or 10 volts, actually cause the motor to run.

Courtesy Westinghouse Electric Corp.

Fig. 15. The rotor of an 83,000-horsepower motor is being inserted into the stator.

Starting rheostat. The resistance of the coils in the armatures of most large motors is quite small, often being only one or two ohms. Assuming that the resistance of the armature is one ohm and the motor runs on a 100-volt line, then when the motor is

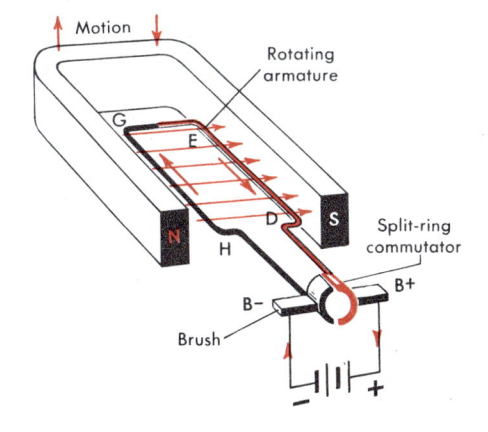

Fig. 16. The D.C. electric motor.

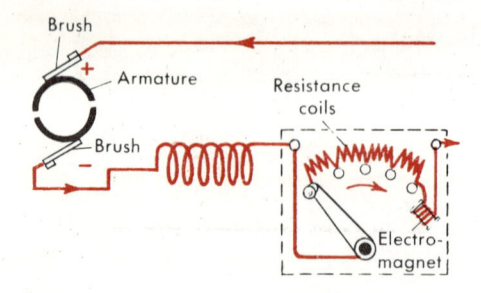

Fig. 17. The starting box adds resistance to the armature until its speed increases.

first started 100 amperes of current would surge through the armature, which would likely produce enough heat to cause serious damage. To avoid this, the motor is given a variable starting resistance called a *rheostat*. This consists of resistance coils which are thrown into series with the motor on starting and are thrown out again gradually as the speed, and hence the back e.m.f., increases. See Fig. 17. An example is the streetcar. When the motorman starts it, he gradually reduces the resistance as the armature gains speed and builds up back e.m.f.

Upon what factors does the force which turns the armature in a motor depend? When a conductor carrying a current is in a magnetic field, the force exerted on the conductor depends upon three things: the strength of field, the current, and the length of wire. In a motor, the force which turns the armature is dependent upon the same three factors: (a) the strength of field, (b) the current through the armature, and (c) the effective length of the turns of wire, which is approximately twice the length of the armature times the number of turns of wire.

Series, shunt, and compound field-magnet windings for D.C. motors. The field magnets, as in the case of a generator, are wound in any one of the three different ways with respect to the armature and each causes a motor to behave differently.

In the series-wound D.C. motor, all the current passes through both the armature and the field coils. Hence, the turning force (torque) on the armature is going to vary as the square of the current, because the force depends upon the current through the armature and upon the field strength. The latter, you will recall, varies as the current through the field coils.

As a result, when a heavy load slows down the armature of a series-wound motor, so that the back e.m.f. is low, then a large current passes through both the armature and the field coils. This condition produces a tremendous force for turning the armature. Series-wound motors are used in streetcars, electric locomotives, automobile starters, and other places where heavy loads are thrown suddenly upon them. Usually series motors are geared, not belted, to their load because they "race" dangerously if the load becomes disconnected from the motor when it is running.

In shunt-wound motors the current divides, one part going through the armature and the other part through the field coils. The total current through both is the same as that which enters the motor. As a result, the force which turns the armature varies as the current, whereas in a series motor the force varies as the square of the current.

When the armature in a shunt-wound motor is slowed down by a heavier load, a larger current traverses the armature but less passes through the field, and as a result the turning force is not changed. Consequently, the motor will not regain its normal speed as long as the load remains on the motor. Shunt-wound motors will not respond to heavy loads. For this reason they are usually used where a constant speed is required and the load is steady. Examples are electric fans, blowers, water pumps, and so on.

The compound-wound motor will not race if the load is detached and it will also respond to heavy loads. Why this is true we leave to the student to explain. These motors are used on elevators, punch presses, and other machines where a large initial force is necessary in starting. After starting, the series winding, in many cases, is cut out when the machine reaches a certain speed.

SUMMARY AND CONCLUSIONS

1. An induced e.m.f. is set up in a conductor when it is moved across lines of force. The e.m.f. generated depends upon the strength of the field, length of conductor, and speed of conductor; that is, upon the number of lines of force the conductor moves across per second.
2. The essentials of both a generator and a motor are a magnetic field and an armature. Most A.C. generators have slip rings and brushes. D.C. motors and generators have commutators and brushes.
3. An induced e.m.f. of 1 volt is produced in a conductor when it moves across 100,000,000 lines of force per second.
4. On either a generator or an electric motor, the field and the armature may be connected in series (series wound), in parallel (shunt wound), or in a combination of the two (compound wound).
5. An electrical generator changes mechanical energy into electrical energy; a motor changes electrical into mechanical energy.
6. A motor has all the essentials of a generator and produces an e.m.f. which opposes the applied e.m.f. The armature of a motor has very little resistance. For this reason a starting box is used which puts resistances in series with the armature until the armature gains speed and develops a back e.m.f.

QUESTIONS FOR REVIEW

1. Is an e.m.f. being induced in a closed loop of wire that is revolving on a vertical axis in the earth's magnetic field?
2. Upon what factors does the e.m.f. induced in a closed loop of wire depend? What is necessary so that one volt of e.m.f. will be induced in a coil or loop?
3. Explain how a wire can be moved in a field so that no e.m.f. is induced in it.
4. What kind of current flows in the armature of an A.C. generator? D.C. generator? What kind of current flows in the external circuit of each?
5. Explain by means of diagrams what is meant by (a) steady direct current; (b) pulsating direct current; (c) alternating current.
6. What are slip rings? For what are they used? Is the polarity of the rings constant or alternating?
7. What is the purpose of a commutator? Describe its action, using sketches.
8. Show by means of diagrams the changes in the e.m.f. and the external current during one cycle for (a) an A.C. generator; (b) a D.C. generator.
9. How many revolutions per minute must the armature of an A.C. generator make to generate 60-cycle current for a generator which has two poles? Four poles? Six poles?
10. Show by means of diagrams the three different ways in which the armature and the field of a generator can be connected. Also state the conditions for which each type of connection is best suited.
11. What is back e.m.f. in a motor? Why is it a problem in starting a large motor?
12. If more coils are wound on the armature of a D.C. generator, what other changes must be made and what is the effect produced?
13. Make a list of as many household appliances as you can that make use of an electric motor. What do they all have in common?

PROBLEMS

1. The coil of wire on the armature of a generator moves across lines of magnetic force at the rate of 10 billion per second. What e.m.f. is developed in the armature?
2. A motor operating on a 100-volt circuit develops a back e.m.f. of 90 volts. If the re-

sistance of the armature is 2 ohms, how much current flows in the armature?

3. How many watts of power would be delivered by the above motor? What would be the cost of operating this motor continuously for a month (30 days) at a cost of five cents per kilowatt-hour?

4. The motor in an electric refrigerator is rated at 200 watts. What is the horsepower of this motor? If the motor ran for an average of 10 hours per day, what would be the cost of operating it for 30 days at five cents per kilowatt-hour?

5. A motor operating on a 100-volt circuit develops a back e.m.f. of 80 volts. The motor draws 5 amperes. What is the resistance of the armature? What current would flow through the armature if the armature were not rotating? How much heat in calories would be generated in the armature in one minute if it were not turning?

6. One kilowatt of electrical power is used to run a 1-horsepower motor. What is the efficiency of the motor?

7. An electric motor furnishes 5 horsepower to a water pump. Assuming an efficiency of 100 per cent, (a) how many kilowatts are developed by the motor? (b) How many amperes does the motor draw from a 100-volt line?

8. The armature of a shunt motor has a resistance of 0.25 ohm and it operates on a 100-volt line. (a) If the armature is standing still, how much current passes through the armature? (b) If, when the motor is running, it takes 20 amperes, what is the back e.m.f.?

9. The voltage across the armature of a motor is 115 volts. The back e.m.f. is 112.4 volts. The current is 20 amperes. What is the armature resistance?

ANS.: 0.130 ohm.

PROJECTS

1. *How to make a metal rod roll up hill.* Place three brass or copper rods as shown in Fig. 18, so that the one that rests on the other two is between the poles of a horseshoe magnet. Connect rods *A* and *B* with a dry cell or other D.C. source, as shown, then close the switch. Note the behavior of wire *C*. It can be caused to roll up hill.

2. Connect the two ends of a 40- or 50-foot piece of copper wire to a sensitive galvanometer. Then let two students hold and stretch as much of the loop as possible, horizontally, in an east-and-west direction about six feet above the floor. Next have them bring the wire straight down toward the floor as quickly as possible and observe the galvanometer. Have them move the wire up, horizontally, and in other directions, and note the galvanometer. Also let them stretch the wire north and south and in other directions, and repeat the experiment. Explain.

3. Do experiments E-142, E-143, E-146 and E-147 in Sutton, *Demonstration Experiments in Physics*, pp. 308-310.

READING YOU WILL ENJOY

1. *Motors Make the World Go Round.* General Electric Company, Schenectady, N. Y. This brief pamphlet tells graphically what makes an electric motor run and how you can make one out of a tin can.

2. Skilling, Hugh H., *Exploring Electricity*, pp. 93-138. The Ronald Press Company, New York, 1949.

3. Sutton, R. M., *Demonstration Experiments in Physics*. McGraw-Hill Book Company, Inc., New York, 1938.

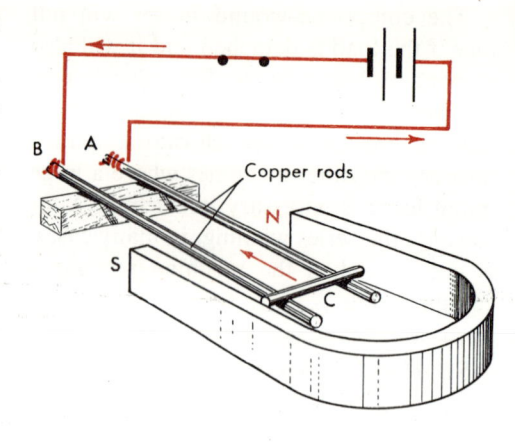

Fig. 18

Chapter 39

Induction Coils and Transformers

The problem. Suppose we wrap an insulated wire around a cardboard tube, connect the ends of the coil to a galvanometer, and then suddenly thrust the N-pole of a bar magnet into one end of the coil, as shown in (a) of Fig. 1. The needle on the galvanometer will deflect to the right, indicating that a current enters its negative terminal and that an e.m.f. has been induced in the coil.

When the N-pole is pulled out of the coil, as shown in (b) of Fig. 1, the needle is deflected in the opposite direction. This shows that the directions of the current and the induced e.m.f. are the opposite of what they were when the N-pole was pushed into the coil.

When the S-pole of the magnet is shoved into the coil, the needle deflects in the direction opposite to the deflection when the N-pole was introduced. And when the S-pole is pulled out, the deflection and hence the current and e.m.f. are opposite to that noted when the N-pole is pulled out of the coil.

The amount of e.m.f. induced in the coil is dependent upon the strength of the magnet, the number of turns of wire in the coil, and the speed with which the magnet is moved. If the magnet and coil are at rest with respect to each other, no e.m.f. is induced in the coil. Evidently, as in a generator, the e.m.f. induced in the coil is dependent upon the number of magnetic lines of force which move across the wire per unit of time. Or we can say that *the e.m.f. is dependent upon the rate of change of lines of force inside the coil.*

Our problem in this chapter is to study these phenomena further and to consider a few of their hundreds of applications.

What is the source of the electrical energy in the coil? In order to induce an e.m.f. which will cause a current and deflect the hand of a galvanometer, we know that work has to be done. Electrical energy, like any other energy, is not created. It must come from another form of energy.

If work is done when the magnet is pushed into a coil, then a force must be exerted for a distance. But if a force is exerted on the magnet, then the coil must exert an equal and opposite force on the magnet, because forces always exist in pairs that are equal and opposite. Where does this resisting force come from? Is there developed at the end of the coil a like pole which resists the pole entering the coil?

If the answer to the last question is yes, it means that the e.m.f. induced in the coil must be in such a direction as to cause

456 ELECTRIC MACHINES

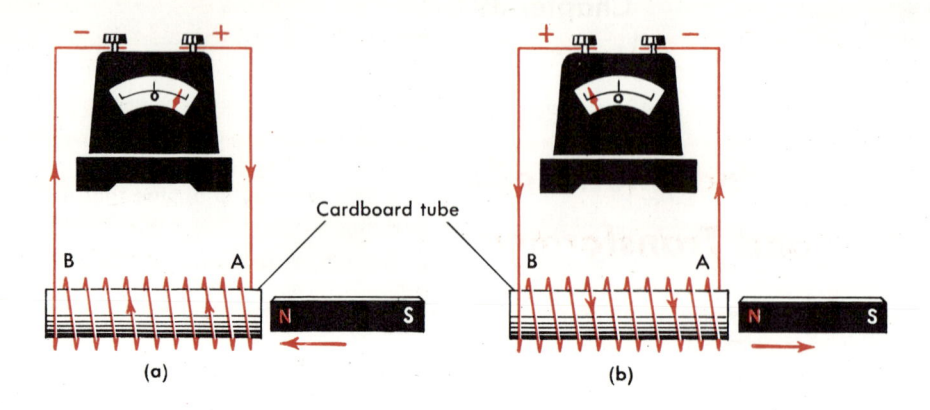

Fig. 1. An e.m.f. is induced in a coil when a magnet is pushed into or pulled out of the coil. (a) N-pole is being pushed into a coil. (b) N-pole is being pulled out.

the end into which an N-pole, for example, is inserted, to become an N-pole. Will experiment prove this to be true?

Direction of induced current in a coil. In accordance with our reasoning above, experiment will show that when the N-pole is shoved into end *A* of the coil in (a) of Fig. 1, the induced current is in such a direction that end *A* is an N-pole.

When the N-pole of a magnet is pulled out of end *A*, the induced current in the coil is in such a direction that end *A* is an S-pole. It attracts the N-pole and opposes its motion, so that work must be done in

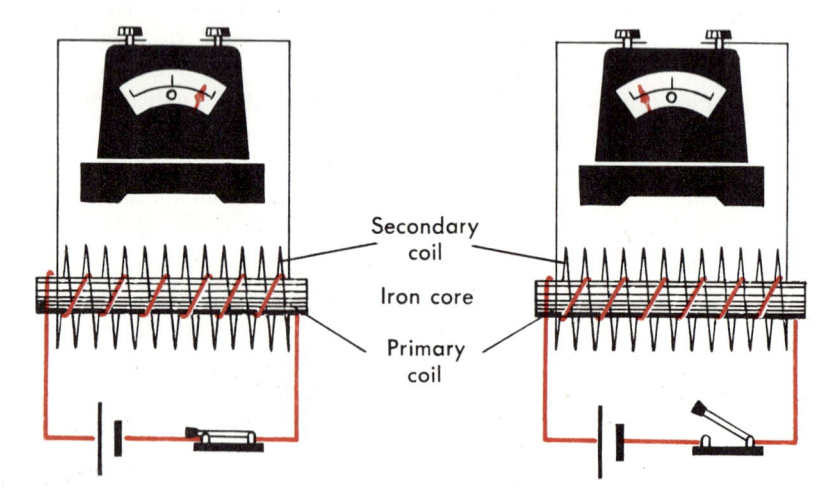

Fig. 2. When the key is closed, an e.m.f. and current are induced momentarily in the secondary coil. Current from the battery flows only through the primary coil. (b) What happens momentarily when the key is opened?

INDUCTION COILS AND TRANSFORMERS

pulling the magnet out. Find by experiment the polarity of a coil when an S-pole is inserted; is pulled out. Hence, knowing the kind of pole which enters or leaves a coil, we know the polarity of the coil, and, using the left-hand rule given on page 388, we can determine the direction of the current in the wires of the coil. In conclusion, we say that:

an induced current in a coil has such a direction that it produces a magnetic field which opposes the motion of the magnetic field by which the current is produced.

The law stated above is known as **Lenz's Law**.

How can electric current induce an e.m.f. in a coil? When an electromagnet is shoved into a coil, an e.m.f. is induced in the coil in the same manner as when a permanent magnet is used.

Also, as shown in Fig. 2, when an electromagnet, known as a *primary coil,* is placed inside a coil, known as the *secondary coil,* and the key is closed so that there is current in the electromagnet, then the galvanometer needle is deflected momentarily. This shows that an e.m.f. is momentarily induced in the secondary coil. If the key is kept closed, the needle of the galvanometer returns to the zero position.

Evidently, when the key is closed, the current in the primary coil produces lines of force around this coil and inside the secondary coil. See (a) and (b) of Fig. 3. This formation of lines of force inside the secondary coil evidently induces an e.m.f. in it. When the current becomes constant the number of lines of force becomes constant, as shown in (c) of Fig. 3.

When the key is opened, the field collapses. And the number of lines of force inside the secondary coil decreases so that an e.m.f. is again induced in the secondary coil, in such a direction that the current takes the opposite direction from that taken when the primary circuit is closed. (See (d) of Fig. 3.)

Hence, we may conclude that upon our "making" or "breaking" the circuit, which causes the number of lines of force in the field of the primary coil to increase or decrease, an e.m.f. is induced in the secondary coil.

The induction coil. It would indeed be tiresome to open and close a switch as just described for any length of time. To avoid this, we might use a circuit breaker which automatically opens and closes the circuit in the primary coil. We have already studied what amounts to a circuit breaker; namely, the moving armature of an electric bell. When such an automatic breaker is used in the primary circuit, we have the essentials of an *induction* or *spark coil.*

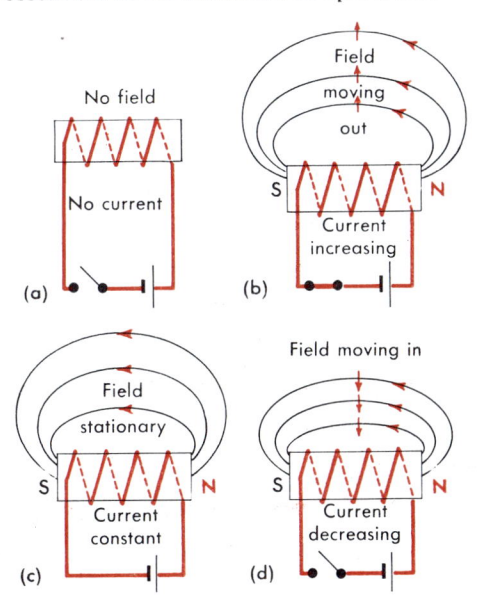

Fig. 3. The changing magnetic fields surrounding the primary coil of an induction coil as the circuit is closed and opened.

When several thousand turns of wire are wound around the secondary coil and relatively few on the primary, the e.m.f. induced in the secondary is many times greater than that in the primary, whose voltage is often that of a 6-volt storage battery.

There is a rough rule that about 15,000 volts are required to make a spark jump between sharp points one centimeter apart in air, and more in proportion for longer sparks. With the rather small induction coil found in many laboratories a 2-inch (5-cm.) spark is not uncommon between sharp points. This means that the e.m.f. would have to be well above 50,000 volts. Induction coils are used commercially to fire the spark plugs in the gasoline engines of automobiles, trucks, and buses, and in many other places.

How does an induction coil work? When the current from the battery goes through the primary coil, the iron core of this coil is magnetized. See Fig. 4. This pulls the armature A to the end of the core, and at the same time breaks the primary circuit at F. Then the core loses most of its magnetism, the armature is pulled back by a spring to its starting position, and the primary circuit is again closed. This process is repeated over and over. The armature oscillates back and forth like the hammer in an electric bell, continually starting and stopping the current in the primary coil. The e.m.f. is induced in the secondary as already described.

The magnitude of the e.m.f. in the secondary depends upon the rate at which the lines of force inside the secondary coil increase or decrease and upon the number of turns on the secondary.

If a condenser is put across the gap where the break is made, as shown in Fig. 4, the break in particular can be made much more sudden. Current which otherwise would surge across the gap as the break occurs, surges instead into the condenser. Then the condenser, immediately after the break is made, discharges back through the primary coil in reverse direction. This speeds up the loss of magnetism in the primary coil, which causes the field in the primary coil to change faster than it otherwise would. As a result the efficiency of the coil as well as the e.m.f. is increased greatly.

It should be noted that *in an induction coil, electric energy is transmitted across space from the primary coil to the secondary coil by means of an expanding and then collapsing magnetic field, a changing field.* This is somewhat similar to what occurs when energy is transmitted between the aerial of a broadcasting station and your radio aerial. See page 587.

The transformer and its construction. In operating an induction coil it is necessary to make and break the direct current in order to set up an expanding and collapsing field about the primary. If, however, alternating current is used to operate an induction coil, there is no need for the circuit breaker. This is because alternat-

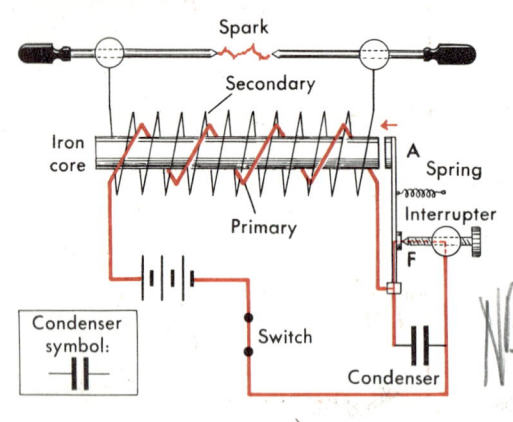

Fig. 4. An induction coil is a means of producing a high-voltage D.C. from a low-voltage source.

ing current is repeatedly rising from zero to a maximum in one direction, then falling back to zero and rising to a maximum in the opposite direction, and finally decreasing to zero again. These four steps are respectively equivalent to (1) closing the circuit, (2) opening the circuit, (3) reversing the polarity of the battery and closing the circuit, and (4) opening the circuit again.

As a consequence of this behavior, the field around the primary coil varies in strength and direction and induces an alternating e.m.f. in the secondary. Each time the primary circuit reaches a maximum, the direction of the e.m.f. induced in the secondary changes. Can you explain why the direction of the induced e.m.f. changes when the primary current is just past a maximum rather than when it is zero?

Another modification of the induction coil, found on a transformer, is the shape of the silicon-iron core and the way in which it is utilized. Usually the core is rectangular in shape, as shown in Fig. 5. It is put together in sheets, or sections, which are electrically insulated from one another. The construction of the core is such that it makes a continuous magnetic circuit for the magnetic lines of force. Around part of this iron core are wound a primary and a secondary coil, usually one over the other, although sometimes they are apart, as in the figure. The latter construction is less efficient than the other, but it is much easier to observe in our study.

Principle of the A.C. transformer. When an alternating current passes through the primary it magnetizes the iron core, causing lines of force to pass through the core first in one direction and then in the opposite direction. Since these lines of force pass through the secondary coil as well as the primary coil, an alternating e.m.f. is induced in the secondary coil. In case the number of turns of wire on the secondary coil is greater than the number on the primary, the transformer *steps up* the voltage. See Fig. 5. Vice versa, if the number of turns of wire on the primary is greater than the number on the secondary, the transformer *steps down* the voltage.

In case the number of turns on the secondary is two, three, or four times the number of turns on the primary, then the e.m.f. of the secondary is respectively two, three, or four times the e.m.f. of the primary. Therefore, *the voltage in the primary coil is to the voltage in the secondary coil as the number of turns on the primary is to the number of turns on the secondary.* That is:

$$\frac{\text{Voltage in primary}}{\text{Voltage in secondary}} = \frac{\text{Turns on primary}}{\text{Turns on secondary}}$$

or

$$\frac{E_p}{E_s} = \frac{N_p}{N_s} \quad (1)$$

PROBLEM: A transformer has 88 turns of wire on the primary and 880 turns on the secondary. The voltage of the primary is 110 volts. What is the voltage of the secondary coil?

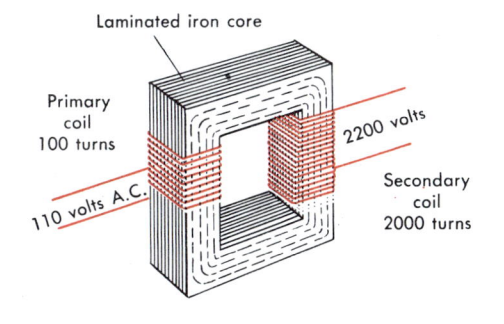

Fig. 5. In a step-up transformer the secondary has more turns than the primary.

Laminated iron core
Primary coil 100 turns
110 volts A.C.
2200 volts
Secondary coil 2000 turns

SOLUTION:

$$\frac{E_p}{E_s} = \frac{N_p}{N_s}$$

Substituting,

$$\frac{110}{x} = \frac{88}{880}$$

or

$$\frac{110}{x} = \frac{1}{10}$$

and

$$x = 1100 \text{ volts}$$

Do we get something for nothing from a transformer? In the operation of every machine studied so far, it was necessary to put more energy into the machine than was obtained from it. Is the step-up transformer a violation of the law of conservation of energy?

To answer this question, let us refer back to the problem above and assume that there is a current of 20 amperes in the primary circuit. This means that the power in watts (EI) put into the primary coil is 110×20, or 2200 watts. Assuming no loss, then, according to the law of conservation of energy, the secondary coil should furnish 2200 watts of power at 1100 volts. This e.m.f. was found in the solution of the problem above. But since power in watts equals EI, then $2200 = 1100\ I$, and I equals 2 amperes. This will be found by experiment to be true. Thus, when a transformer steps up the voltage, the current is stepped down so that, neglecting small heat losses, there is no increase in either power or energy.

In other words, as the voltage increases the current decreases, and as the voltage decreases the current increases. That is, the current varies inversely with the voltage:

$$\frac{E_p}{E_s} = \frac{I_s}{I_p} \quad (2)$$

This equation, like equation (1) above, is only approximately true.

PROBLEM: The current in the primary coil of a transformer is 10 amperes and the voltage is 110 volts. The voltage on the secondary is 11,000 volts. What is the current in the secondary?

SOLUTION:

$$\frac{E_p}{E_s} = \frac{I_s}{I_p}$$

Substituting,

$$\frac{110}{11,000} = \frac{I_s}{10}$$

Solving,

$$I_s = 0.1 \text{ ampere}$$

What power in watts is delivered by this transformer? How many times as many turns of wire are there on the secondary as on the primary?

Uses of transformers in the transmission of electrical power. In the transmission of electricity, the loss along the line due to heat varies directly as the *square* of the current, I. See page 419. That is, if the current is doubled, the heat loss is four times as great as before, and so on. Hence, in transmitting electricity, it is wise to keep the current low. How is this done?

As we have seen, if the voltage is stepped up by a transformer, the current drops proportionately. This is our clue. To keep the current low, step up the voltage. At the power plant this is done by a step-up transformer, which may raise it as high as 120,000 volts or more. Near a city into which the transmission line leads, the voltage is stepped down to about 2200 volts and it is transmitted up the alleys at this voltage. Near your home, however, you will find a transformer which steps it down to about 110 or 115 volts, which can be safely used in the home.

Other uses of transformers. An important use of step-down transformers is to furnish large currents at very low voltage for electric furnaces and electric welding.

Fig. 6. (a) Alternating current is transmitted at high voltages and low amperage on these power lines to reduce heat losses.

Courtesy Westinghouse Electric Corp.

Fig. 6. (b) This step-down transformer reduces the high voltage from the transmission lines to a safe value for home use.

Monkmeyer

For the transformer setup for welding, see Fig. 7. Only a very few turns of large wire are used on the secondary, whereas a relatively high number is used on the primary.

The telephone. The telephone is another device in which transformers are used. The essential parts, however, are the transmitter, into which we speak, and the receiver, over which we hear.

The most essential part of the transmitter is a thin soft-iron disk, about two inches in diameter, on the back of which is fastened a carbon button, as shown in Fig. 8. Behind this button and insulated from it is a carbon box. In between the button and the box, grains of carbon are packed. These will conduct a direct current from the button to the box. A battery furnishes this current, which also goes through the primary coil of a small transformer.

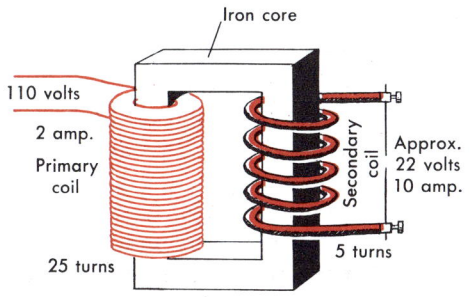

When a sound wave strikes the disk in the transmitter, the condensations push in the flexible disk and press the grains of carbon in the box more closely together. This reduces the resistance in the circuit, which results in an increase of current in the primary of the transformer. The rarefactions lessen the pressure on the flexible disk; this increases the resistance in the circuit and reduces the current. Hence there is a pulsating direct current in the primary coil. This induces an alternating current in the secondary, which alternates with every rarefaction and condensation of the voice sound wave. This secondary coil is connected into the circuit containing the receiver. See Fig. 8.

The receiver consists of a permanent horseshoe magnet, as shown in this figure, and a flexible iron diaphragm mounted with its center near the poles but not

Fig. 7. Why is a step-down transformer used for welding?

(Diagram labels: Iron core; 110 volts, 2 amp., Primary coil, 25 turns; Secondary coil, 5 turns; Approx. 22 volts 10 amp.)

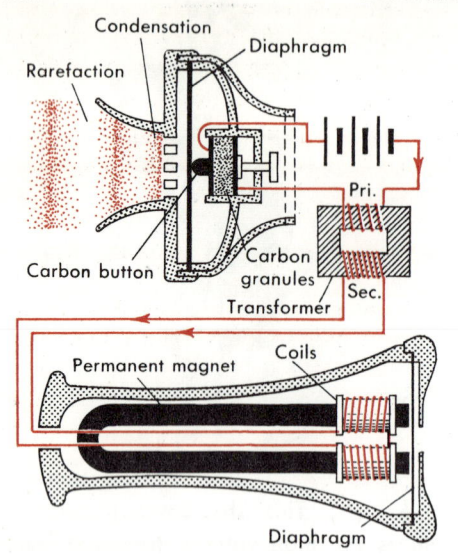

Fig. 8. A cross section of a telephone transmitter (top), battery, transformer, and receiver (bottom).

touching them. Around each pole end of the permanent magnet is wrapped a coil of wire which is connected in series with the secondary coil of the transformer described above.

When the alternating current takes one direction through the coils in the receiver —for example, during a condensation— it strengthens the magnet and pulls the diaphragm toward the magnet. But when the current reverses, as during a rarefaction, the magnet is weakened and the diaphragm springs back to its original position. As a result the vibrator in the receiver sets up in the air a series of sound waves very much like those produced by the voice in the transmitter.

The dial telephone makes use of many ingenious circuits, but to a large degree its basis for operation· is that of the earlier telephone already described.

Eddy currents. We have seen that the cores of transformers and the armatures of motors and generators are not solid iron but are made up of thin sheets (called *laminations*) of iron. The cores of induction coils are made of soft-iron wires put together in bundles. In all cases the sheets or wires are insulated from one another by shellac. Why are these all constructed in such a manner?

In the study of generators we saw that when a conductor in a closed circuit moves across magnetic lines of force, there is induced in the conductor an e.m.f. which causes current. In the generator, not only is an e.m.f. induced in the wires on the armature provided for this, but one is also induced in the iron core of the armature. This e.m.f. causes currents known as *eddy currents* through the armature. These heat and magnetize the armature, thereby retarding its motion and wasting energy.

To reduce the eddy currents and to prevent those induced in one part of the armature from flowing through another part, the core is *laminated*—built up in insulated sections—in such a way that the plane of each section is perpendicular to the direction of the current. See Fig. 9.

The jumping ring. One way of showing the effects of eddy currents is by means of a coil, aluminum ring, and iron core (Fig. 10). A strong alternating current is passed through the coil. As a result, rapid reversals in the magnetic field about the iron core are produced and large eddy currents are induced in the aluminum ring. These rush first in one direction and then in the other with the same frequency as the current in the primary coil. And in accordance with Lenz's Law, the current in the ring produces at the bottom of the ring a magnetic pole which opposes the pole of the iron core. If about 220 volts are used, the ring will be thrown several feet into the air when the circuit is closed.

How to fry hamburgers on ice. At your science "open house" a very spectacular stunt which makes use of eddy currents is to fry hamburgers on ice. To do this, a

INDUCTION COILS AND TRANSFORMERS

Then, when the current passes through the coil, a rapidly reversing magnetic field is produced above the coil. As a result, strong eddy currents are induced in the bottom of the skillet. These heat the skillet hot enough to fry hamburgers.

SUMMARY AND CONCLUSIONS

1. An induced current is caused when the number of lines of force in a coil or around a wire is changing.
2. The direction of an induced current in a coil is such that it produces a magnetic field which opposes the motion of the magnetic field by which it is produced. This is Lenz's Law.
3. The induced e.m.f. depends upon the rate of change in the number of lines of force which pass through a coil.
4. In a transformer,

$$\frac{E_p}{E_s} = \frac{N_p}{N_s}$$

Also,

$$\frac{E_p}{E_s} = \frac{I_s}{I_p}$$

5. In long-distance transmission, the line losses are reduced by high voltage and low amperage.
6. The cores of transformers and armatures of motors are laminated to prevent energy losses due to eddy currents.

QUESTIONS FOR REVIEW

1. Explain at least three methods for inducing an e.m.f. How does an induced e.m.f. differ from an induced current?
2. The S-pole of a permanent bar magnet is plunged downward into a wire coil. Make a diagram showing the direction of the induced e.m.f. and current and show the magnetic poles of the coil. Explain Lenz's Law.
3. Other than for lifting and lowering the magnet against gravity, explain why work needs to be done in Question 2.
4. Make a diagram which shows the essentials of an induction coil.

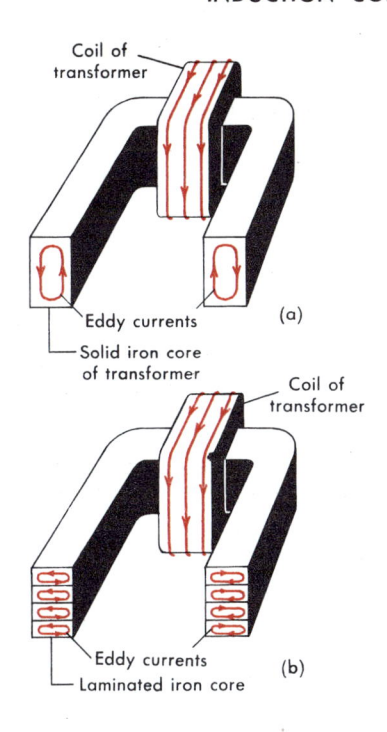

Fig. 9. Eddy currents are set up in the iron core of a transmitter.

coil like that shown in Fig. 10 is hidden from view under a wooden box on which there is a glass tray containing cracked ice. The iron core is pushed into the coil until the top end of it is flush with the top of the coil. On top of the ice is set an iron skillet in which the hamburgers are placed.

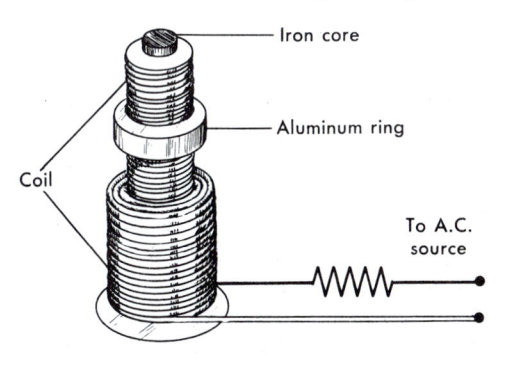

Fig. 10. The jumping ring or coil.

464 ELECTRIC MACHINES

5. Explain why, in an induction coil, an e.m.f. is developed in the secondary coil on both the "make" and the "break" of the primary circuit.

6. What is the purpose of a condenser in an induction coil?

7. For what are induction coils used?

8. What is the essential difference between an induction coil and a transformer?

9. What is the purpose of a transformer? Give several uses of it.

10. What are eddy currents?

11. Explain heating by induction. For example, explain how hamburgers can be fried in an iron skillet standing on ice.

12. Explain what causes "cross-talk" on telephone lines which run parallel with each other. Would crossing the wires from one side of the poles to the other every mile or so help to decrease cross-talk?

13. A bar magnet is moved up and down 100 times per minute in a coil having 100 turns. State three ways by which the induced e.m.f. could be increased.

14. How does the frequency of the current induced in the secondary coil of a transformer compare with the frequency in the primary?

15. Why is soft iron rather than steel used in the cores of transformers?

16. Explain why a transformer core is made up of sections (laminated) instead of being made up of one piece of solid iron.

PROBLEMS

1. The primary coil of a step-up transformer has 100 turns of wire and the secondary coil has 1000 turns. The voltage on the primary coil is 120 volts. Assuming no loss of electrical energy, what is the voltage on the secondary coil?

2. A step-down transformer is used to change 22,000 volts on the primary to 110 volts on the secondary. The secondary has 100 turns. How many turns are there on the primary?

3. A step-down transformer delivers 20 amperes at 120 volts. The primary voltage is 22,000 volts. Assuming no loss of power,

(a) what is the primary current? (b) What is the power output of the transformer? (c) What is the power input?

4. A step-up transformer delivers 2 amperes at 2200 volts. The voltage on the primary coil is 110. Assuming no loss of power, (a) what is the current through the primary coil? (b) What is the power output of the transformer? (c) Power input?

5. A toy transformer is connected with a 110-volt line. On the primary coil there are 440 turns of wire. The transformer supplies 4, 6, 8, and 10 volts at its output terminals. (a) What is the total number of turns on the secondary? (b) How are taps arranged on the secondary coil?

6. The voltage on the primary coil of a step-down transformer is 2200. The current through the primary coil is 2 amperes. There are 1000 turns of wire on the primary and 100 turns on the secondary. Assuming no loss of electrical energy, (a) what would be the voltage on the secondary coil? (b) Current through the secondary coil? (c) Power supplied to the primary coil? (d) Power delivered by the secondary coil? (e) Energy delivered by the secondary coil in one minute?

7. A certain generator is capable of delivering 2000 watts of power. It delivers power to a consumer through a transformer and then through a transmission line whose resistance is 5 ohms. When the 2000 watts are delivered to the transmission line at 100 volts, (a) what is the current through the transmission line? (Use $W = EI$.) (b) What is the drop in voltage along the line? (c) What is the voltage supplied the consumer? (d) How much power is lost in the line? (e) What is the efficiency of the transmission line?

8. If, in Problem 7, the 2000 watts of power are delivered to the transmission line at 200 volts, then what would be (a) the current in the transmission line? (Use $W = EI$.) (b) Drop of voltage in the transmission line? (c) The voltage supplied the consumer? (d) Power lost in the line? (e) Power supplied the consumer? (f) Efficiency of the transmission line?

Unit 16

Alternating Current

The designation "60 cycles A.C." is a familiar term to those of you who have ever examined the name plates of such electric appliances as fans, washing machines, or vacuum cleaners. Perhaps you have a rough idea of what this term means from your study of the previous chapter, but you will gain a clearer understanding of its significance after completing this unit. You will discover why it is relatively more difficult to measure current and voltage in A.C. circuits and what it means to have current and voltage "in," or "out of," phase.

The latter terms are not entirely new to you, as you had some contact with them when you studied sound. You will also renew your acquaintance with vectors which you used in mechanics. They will prove useful in applying Ohm's Law to A.C. circuits. Although alternating current may seem harder to understand than D.C., you cannot ignore A.C. as more and more generators are being built to supply alternating current for domestic and industrial use. The generators in the unit photograph are cases in point.

40. ALTERNATING CURRENT

Unit Photograph Courtesy TVA

Chapter 40

Alternating Current

The problem. We have already seen that in a 60-cycle A.C. circuit the direction of both the voltage and the current changes 120 times per second. Also, during each cycle both current and voltage start out at zero, gradually increase to a maximum, and then decrease to zero. Then both current and voltage reverse direction, reach a new maximum in the negative direction, and finally again reach zero. The cycle is repeated again and again. In Fig. 1 the variation of an alternating current is shown.

Knowing these facts brings several questions to mind. How can these ever-changing currents and voltages be measured? Can the volt, ampere, and other D.C. units be used to measure A.C.? Can D.C. meters be used to measure A.C.? Furthermore, since A.C. seems much more complicated than D.C., why use A.C.?

How is A.C. measured? An ordinary D.C. meter cannot be used for measuring A.C. The reason is that the pointer (hand) would have to move back and forth past the zero point on the meter dial with each change in direction of the current. For ordinary A.C. this would mean 120 times per second, which is too fast for the pointer to follow. Instead it would stand still. Even so, most A.C. meters, like most D.C. meters (see page 412) operate by measuring the electromagnetic effect of the current.

Units for measuring A.C. Alternating current quantities, like D.C. quantities, are measured in volts, amperes, ohms, and so on. But since A.C. quantities vary from zero to the maximum and then back to zero, the problem is to know which one of these many values can be chosen as an equivalent D.C. value. See Fig. 1. Also, what is the relationship between A.C. volts and D.C. volts, amperes, and so on?

The fact that both A.C. and D.C. can be used equally well for heating gives us a clue. The amount of heat produced by one ampere of D.C. when it is passed for a given time through an unchanging fixed resistance is first found. Then the A.C. required to produce an equivalent amount of heat in the same time is found. The two currents are said to be equivalent: both are equal to one ampere. See Fig. 1. The equivalent alternating current is called the *effective current*, I_{eff}.

The relationship between effective current and maximum current. Experiment shows that there is a simple, definite relationship between the effective alternating current, I_{eff}, and the maximum current, I_{max}. See Fig. 1.

468 ALTERNATING CURRENT

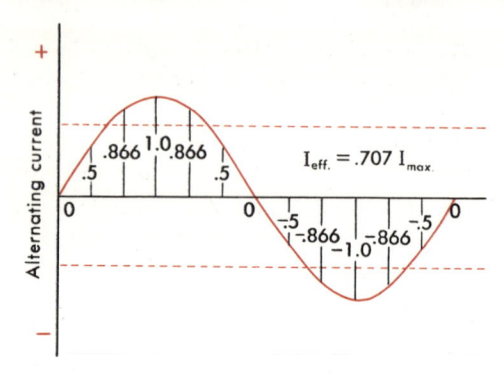

Fig. I. A complete cycle of A.C.

$$\text{Effective } I = \frac{\text{Maximum } I}{\sqrt{2}}$$

Or, $I_{\text{eff.}} = 0.707\, I_{\text{max.}}$ Why?

Similarly, the *effective voltage*, $E_{\text{eff.}}$, is 0.707 times the maximum voltage. That is,

$$E_{\text{eff.}} = 0.707\, E_{\text{max.}}$$

Furthermore, if only resistance is in an A.C. circuit, Ohm's Law applies the same as it does in a D.C. circuit. That is,

$$I_{\text{eff.}} = \frac{E_{\text{eff.}}}{R}$$

Also, if only resistance is in a circuit, power in watts equals the effective voltage times the effective current. That is,

$$W = E_{\text{eff.}} \times I_{\text{eff.}}$$

Hereafter in this book, current, voltage, and other A.C. quantities will mean effective amounts unless stated otherwise.

What is the effect of a coil in an A.C. circuit? When the coil having 20 ohms of resistance, shown in Fig. 2, is connected with an ammeter and into a 100-volt D.C. circuit, the ammeter reads 5 amperes.

On the other hand, when the 20-ohm coil is connected with an A.C. ammeter and to a 100-volt A.C. source, the ammeter reads about 0.05 ampere. Therefore, the resistance of the coil seems to be about $\frac{100}{0.05}$, or 2000 ohms for A.C., whereas it is 20 ohms for D.C. Furthermore, if a soft-iron core is placed in the coil the current is lessened still more, showing that the resistance of the coil is increased still more. Besides this, if the frequency of the A.C. is increased the current decreases, and if the frequency is decreased the current increases, showing that the current varies inversely with the frequency of A.C.

These data show that in an A.C. circuit containing a coil, more than just *ohmic* resistance opposes the current. The total opposition to alternating current is called *impedance*. The symbol for impedance is Z and the unit of impedance is the ohm. For A.C. circuits, Ohm's Law becomes:

$$I = \frac{E}{Z}$$

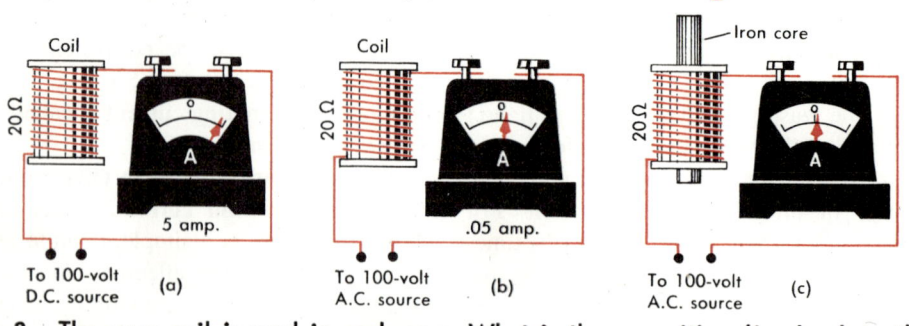

Fig. 2. The same coil is used in each case. What is the opposition (in ohms) to the flow of current in (a)? In (b)? In (c)?

ALTERNATING CURRENT

PROBLEM 1: A D.C. voltage of 30 volts is connected across a long *straight* wire. The current through the wire is 15 amperes. What is the ohmic resistance of the wire?

ANS.: 2 ohms.

PROBLEM 2: An A.C. voltage of 30 volts is connected across the *straight* wire in Problem 1. The current through the wire is 15 amperes. What is the impedance of the wire?

SOLUTION:

$$Z = \frac{E_{\text{eff.}}}{I_{\text{eff.}}}$$

Substituting,

$$Z = \frac{30}{15}$$

$$Z = 2 \text{ ohms}$$

In Problems 1 and 2, does the ohmic resistance of the straight wire equal the impedance?

PROBLEM 3: When the wire in Problem 1 is wound into a *coil* and 30 A.C. volts are applied across its terminals, the current is now 1.20 amperes. What is the impedance of the coil?

SOLUTION:

$$Z = \frac{E}{I}$$

$$Z = \frac{30}{1.2} = 25 \text{ ohms}$$

Compare the pure ohmic resistance and the impedance of the coil.

What causes impedance? We have just seen that when alternating current goes through a straight wire the impedance is the same as the ohmic resistance. However, when the wire is wound into a coil, the impedance increases sharply. Also, if an iron core is put inside the coil, the impedance is still greater. What causes this increased opposition?

We have already found (see page 386) that whenever an electric current passes through a conductor, lines of force (a magnetic field) are produced around the wire. If the current increases, the number of lines of force increases and the field expands. And if the current decreases, the number of lines decreases and the field shrinks.

Also, we found in the study of the transformer (Chapter 39) that with any increase or decrease in the number of lines of force in the primary coil, an e.m.f. is induced in the secondary coil.

Knowing this, we might suspect that an e.m.f. would be induced in the primary coil at the same time. And if this is true, we could expect that an e.m.f. is induced in a single coil in an A.C. circuit when the current increases or decreases. Furthermore, if the direction of the e.m.f. is in opposition to the applied voltage, then this opposing induced voltage would account for the fact that the A.C. is smaller than the D.C. for the same voltage. Also, knowing that this opposing induced e.m.f. should be greatest when the field changes most rapidly, we can explain why the impedance is greater for high-frequency than for low-frequency A.C.

Suppose that this theory is correct, and that an increase in the current in a coil sets up an e.m.f. which opposes the applied voltage and the increase in current. Then a decrease in the current should produce in the coil an e.m.f. whose direction should cause the current to continue to flow momentarily after the applied voltage is decreased, even though the applied voltage drops to zero.

To test this hypothesis, connect a resistor (a 6-volt lamp), coil, switch, and battery as shown in Fig. 3. Then close the switch. Nothing peculiar appears to happen. But open the switch, and the lamp burns very brightly momentarily afterward.

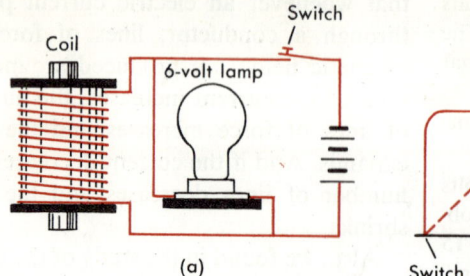

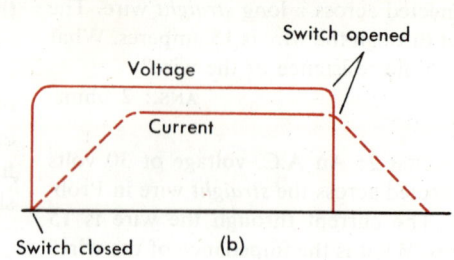

Fig. 3. (a) Apparatus to show self-induction in a coil. (b) When the key is closed, the current lags behind the voltage. When the key is opened, the current continues to flow after the applied voltage of the battery becomes zero.

This experiment indicates, as we predicted, that when a circuit is broken so that the amount of current changes, there is induced in the coil an e.m.f. which causes the current to continue after the applied e.m.f. is cut off.

Seemingly these results show that the induced e.m.f. caused by a changing current is in such a direction as to oppose any change of current. The e.m.f. developed in a coil, or other conductor, by a changing current is called *self-inductance* or *inductance*. The opposition it offers to the flow of electricity is called *inductive resistance*, or *inductive reactance*. It should be understood that a straight wire does offer inductive reactance to an alternating current. Unless, however, the wire is quite long, or the frequency is very high, the reactance is so small that it is usually neglected.

The unit of inductance. The unit of inductance is called the *henry* in honor of the American scientist, Joseph Henry. A coil having an inductance of 1 henry is one in which a change of current of 1 ampere per second produces an e.m.f. of 1 volt. The symbol for inductance is L.

The more practical unit is the *millihenry*, which is one thousandth of a henry.

Inductive reactance. As we have said, the resistance caused by inductance is called inductive reactance, and it is measured in ohms. Its symbol is X_L. Since the inductive reactance increases with the frequency and also with the amount of inductance L,

then $\qquad X_L \propto f \times L$

or $\qquad X_L = KfL$

The constant K is found by theory and experiment to be 2π.

Substituting,

$$X_L = 2\pi fL$$

Remember that X_L is measured in ohms; f is the frequency, and L is the inductance measured in henries.

PROBLEM: What is the inductive reactance for a 60-cycle circuit containing a coil with an inductance of 14 millihenries?

SOLUTION:

$$X_L = 2\pi fL$$

Substituting,

$$X_L = 2 \times \frac{22}{7} \times 60 \times \frac{14}{1000}$$

$$X_L = 5.28 \text{ ohms}$$

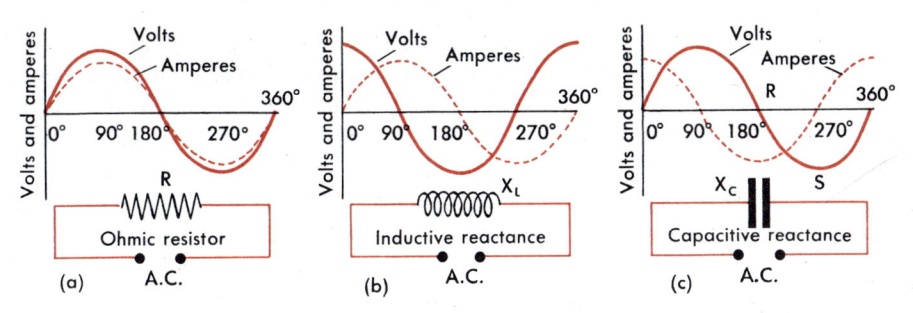

Fig. 4. Describe the phase relations in each of the following A.C. circuits: (a) with resistance only; (b) with inductive reactance only; (c) with capacitive reactance only. In which case does the voltage lag behind the current?

Inductance and current lag. When a battery is connected to the ends of a long straight copper wire containing only resistance, the current rises immediately to the value given by Ohm's Law. But when the same wire is wound into a coil, the current rises more slowly, as shown in (b) of Fig. 3. The maximum current in the circuit is not reached as soon as the maximum voltage is reached. The current lags behind the voltage. The cause of this lag, we have said, is the inductance in the circuit; the e.m.f. induced in the coil opposes an increase in the current to a point where the current actually lags behind the voltage imposed by the battery on the circuit.

Similarly, once the direct current is established in the coil and the circuit is broken, the current continues to flow after the voltage impressed on the circuit by the battery ceases to exist. See Fig. 3b. Again we see that the current lags behind the applied voltage.

In an A.C. circuit containing resistance only, with no inductance, the current and the voltage are in step; the current does not lag behind the voltage. See (a) of Fig. 4.

In an A.C. circuit containing inductance only, the alternating current lags behind the applied voltage by one-quarter of a cycle, or 90 degrees. See (b) of Fig. 4. Consequently, the current and the applied voltage are said to be *out of phase,* or out of step, by 90 degrees.

Finding the impedance of a circuit containing resistance and inductance. You will recall that impedance is the total opposition, or resistance, to the flow of current. Since the impedance in a circuit containing inductance and resistance con-

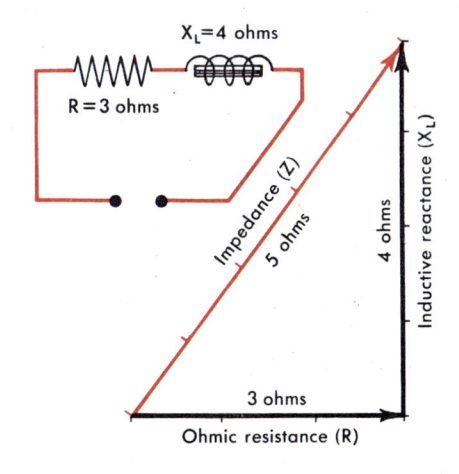

Fig. 5. Finding impedance using vectors.

sists of ohmic resistance and inductive reactance, we might suppose that the total impedance would equal their arithmetical sum. However, if we have in series an ohmic resistance of 3 ohms and an inductive reactance of 4 ohms, the impedance is not 7 ohms but 5 ohms.

One way of combining 4 and 3 so as to obtain 5 is shown in Fig. 5, where the ohmic resistance R is represented by one side of a right triangle, the inductive reactance X_L is represented by the other short side, and the impedance Z is represented by the hypotenuse. That is:

$$\text{Impedance} = \sqrt{\left(\begin{array}{c}\text{Ohmic}\\ \text{Resistance}\end{array}\right)^2 + \left(\begin{array}{c}\text{Inductive}\\ \text{Reactance}\end{array}\right)^2}$$

or,

$$Z = \sqrt{R^2 + X_L^2}$$

PROBLEM: What is the impedance of an A.C. circuit whose ohmic resistance is 5 ohms and inductive reactance is 12 ohms?

$$C = \frac{Q}{E}$$

The condenser in an A.C. circuit. You will recall that a condenser consists essentially of two conducting plates separated by an insulator called a dielectric. The unit of capacity is the *farad*. *The* **farad** *is the capacity of a condenser in which an applied e.m.f. of 1 volt will store 1 coulomb of electricity (6.25 × 10¹⁸ electrons)*. A *microfarad* is one millionth of a farad.

If a condenser with a capacity of a few hundred microfarads is connected in series with an incandescent lamp to a 110-volt D.C. line, the lamp is not lighted because the circuit is not complete between the plates of the condenser. See Fig. 6a.

But when the condenser and lamp are connected to a 60-cycle 110-volt A.C. line the lamp lights, even though the circuit is not complete between the plates. If the capacity of the condenser is increased the lamp burns brighter. Also, if the frequency of the A.C. is increased the intensity of the light increases. However, if the frequency is decreased the lamp glows less and less intensely, ceasing to glow entirely when the frequency becomes zero, as in D.C. See Fig. 6b.

Because of the dielectric in a condenser, it is impossible for current to travel through the condenser. It is possible, however, for alternating current to pass in and out of a condenser. When one terminal of the A.C. source becomes positive, the plate of the condenser to which the positive terminal is attached also becomes positive. This is because electrons are caused to flow from this plate toward the positive terminal. The other plate of the condenser becomes negative and electrons flow onto it. But when the A.C. voltage reverses, the charges on the plates reverse. In the ordinary 60-cycle A.C. the reversals take place 120 times per second. Thus, the cur-

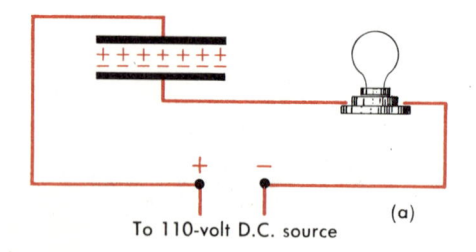

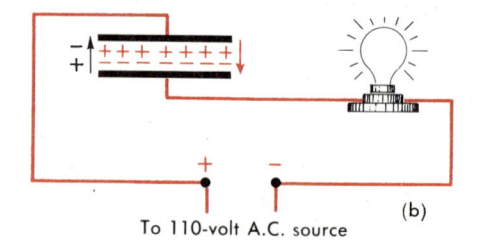

Fig. 6. (a) On D.C. the lamp does not burn. (b) On A.C. the lamp burns brightly.

rent moves first in one direction and then in the opposite direction 120 times per second in the circuit outside the condenser.

With 120-cycle A.C. the number of reversals takes place twice as often as for 60-cycle A.C., and the current is about twice as great. Evidently, then, the current varies directly as the frequency, and the impedance (resistance) due to the condenser varies inversely with the frequency.

Condenser "resistance"—capacitive reactance. The "resistance" offered by a condenser is called *capacitive reactance*. It is measured in ohms and is represented by the symbol X_C.

Since the capacitive reactance, X_C, varies inversely with the frequency, f, and inversely with the capacity, C, in farads, of the circuit, then

$$X_C \propto \frac{1}{fC}$$

or,

$$X_C = K \frac{1}{fC}$$

Experiment shows that $K = \frac{1}{2\pi}$. Hence, by substitution,

$$X_C = \frac{1}{2\pi fC}$$

PROBLEM: What is the capacitive reactance of a condenser which has a capacitance of 30 microfarads (0.00003 farad) and is in a 60-cycle A.C. circuit?

SOLUTION:

$$X_C = \frac{1}{2\pi fC}$$

$$X_C = \frac{1}{2 \times 3.14 \times 60 \times 0.00003} = 88.5 \text{ ohms}$$

Capacitive reactance and current lead. When a condenser (see (c) of Fig. 4) is connected with an A.C. voltage source and the voltage starts at zero, then electrons flow from one plate, making it positive, and onto the other plate, making it negative. As more electrons are forced onto the negative plate and off the positive plate, the counter, or back, e.m.f. in the condenser increases. This continues until the applied voltage reaches a maximum at 90 degrees. Then the counter e.m.f. and the applied voltage are equal, hence all current ceases to flow into or out of the condenser. The current then becomes zero.

At this moment, however, the applied voltage begins to decrease, but it has not reversed its direction. And as it decreases still more, the greater counter e.m.f. across the condenser plates causes the current to flow in opposition to the decreasing applied voltage. At R, in (c) of Fig. 4, the applied voltage has reached zero and the current has reached its maximum. Then the applied voltage reverses, but the current has already reversed its direction 90° or ¼ cycle previous to this. For this reason the current is said to lead the applied voltage by 90°.

The reversed applied voltage reaches a maximum at point S and again the current goes to zero. Explain what next happens to the voltage and the current.

Finding the impedance of a circuit containing ohmic resistance and capacitance. You will recall again that impedance is the total resistance to the current in an A.C. circuit. To find the impedance in a circuit containing both ohmic resistance and capacitive reactance in series, we must combine the two.

We might expect that the total combined resistance would be the arithmetical sum of the ohmic resistance and the capacitive reactance. However, if the ohmic resistance is 4 ohms and the capacitive react-

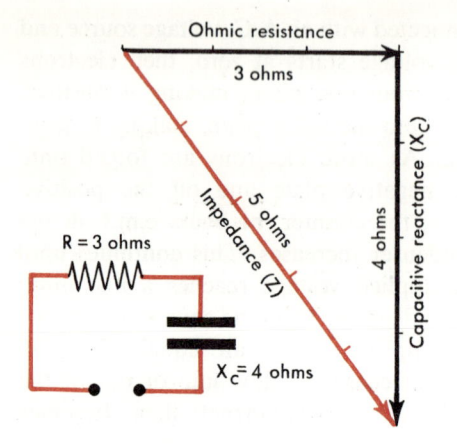

Fig. 7. Combining ohmic resistance and capacitive reactance to find impedance.

ance is 3 ohms, the combined resistance is not 7 ohms; it is 5 ohms.

Here again we can find the impedance by combining 3 and 4 graphically, as shown in Fig. 7, where the ohmic resistance R is represented by the base of a right triangle, the capacitive reactance X_C is represented by the other short side of the triangle, and Z is represented by the hypotenuse of the triangle. That is,

$$Z = \sqrt{R^2 + (X_C)^2}.$$ Explain.

PROBLEM 1: The ohmic resistance of a circuit is 6 ohms and the capacitive reactance is 8 ohms. What is the impedance?

SOLUTION:

$$Z = \sqrt{R^2 + (X_C)^2}$$
$$Z = \sqrt{36 + 64}$$
$$Z = \sqrt{100} = 10 \text{ ohms}$$

PROBLEM 2: The ohmic resistance of a 60-cycle A.C. circuit is 10 ohms. In series with the resistance is a condenser having a capacity of 30 microfarads. What is the impedance of the circuit? (See problem on page 473.)

Finding impedance in an A.C. series circuit which contains a resistance, a coil, and a condenser. We know that the combining of ohmic resistance with inductive reactance is as shown in Fig. 5. The combining of ohmic resistance with capacitive reactance is done as shown in Fig. 7. Thus it appears that, if the two figures were combined, the capacitive reactance, X_C, could be subtracted either graphically or arithmetically from the inductive reactance, X_L. As a result, the formula for impedance in the series circuit shown in Fig. 8 would be as follows:

$$Z = \sqrt{R^2 + (X_L - X_C)^2}$$

The power factor. When the current is out of phase, or step, with the voltage, the power, P, is not effective volts times effective current. Instead it is equal to $\frac{R}{Z}$ times EI. And $\frac{R}{Z}$ is known as the *power factor*, P.F. Hence, power is given by the formula:

$$P = \frac{R}{Z} \times EI$$

PROBLEM: If the resistance in an A.C. series circuit is 40 ohms, the inductive reactance is 50 ohms, the capacitive reactance is 20 ohms, and the voltage across the circuit is 100 volts:

(a) What is the total impedance?
(b) What is the current in the circuit?
(c) What is the power factor?
(d) How much power is used?

SOLUTION:

(a) $Z = \sqrt{R^2 + (X_L - X_C)^2}$

$Z = \sqrt{(40)^2 + (50 - 20)^2}$

$Z = \sqrt{1600 + 900} = 50$ ohms

(b) $I = \dfrac{E}{Z}$

$I = \dfrac{100}{50} = 2$ amperes

(c) P.F. $= \dfrac{R}{Z}$

P.F. $= \dfrac{40}{50} = \dfrac{4}{5}$

(d) $P =$ P.F. $\times EI =$

$\dfrac{4}{5} \times 100 \times 2 = 160$ watts

High-frequency current produced by a Leyden-jar condenser. When the Leyden jar was in its early stages of development, one of its few practical uses was in the making of magnets out of needles and other pieces of steel by discharge of a charged jar through a wire coil that was wound around an object such as a needle. Peculiarly, it was found that sometimes one end of the needle was made the N-pole and sometimes the other end, even though the jar was always charged and discharged in the same manner.

Also, when the discharge from a condenser was used in the electrolysis of water, both hydrogen and oxygen came off at both electrodes, totally unlike what happened when direct current from a battery was used.

Both of these phenomena were explained by the assumption that in the discharge of a condenser the current reverses back and forth between the plates, finally dying out, as shown in Fig. 9. The direction in which a needle is magnetized depends upon which way the current flows last. In the electrolysis of water, hydrogen comes off first one electrode and then the other, reversing every time the current reverses. Oxygen does the same thing, so that a mixture of both gases can be collected at either electrode.

At a later stage a mathematician showed that mathematically the current must be oscillatory, back and forth. His prediction was subsequently verified by experiment, and the time of one complete oscillation

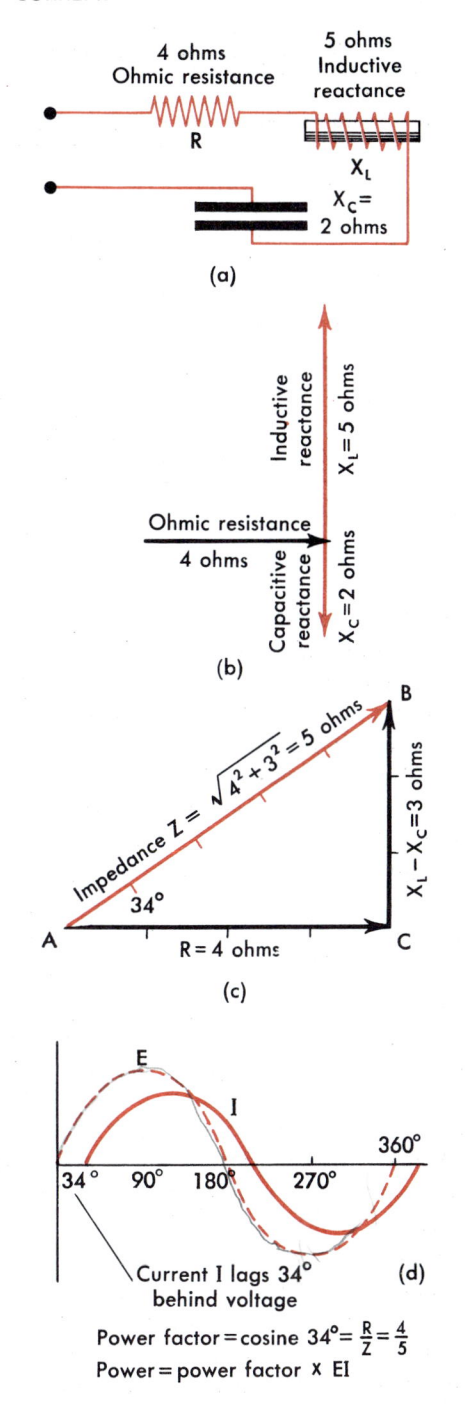

Fig. 8. Finding impedance, current lag, and power factor in an A.C. circuit.

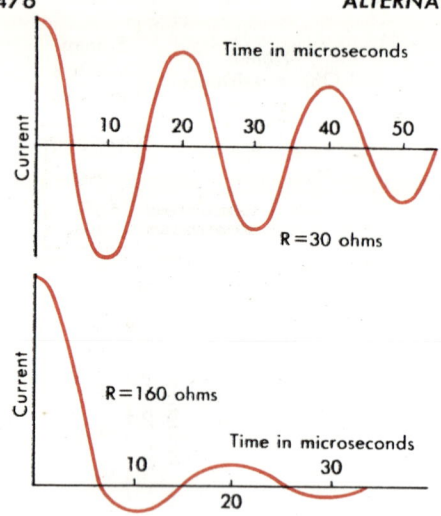

Fig. 9. Electrical oscillations.

was found to vary from one thousandth to one ten-millionth of a second.

It was also found that the length of time that the oscillations continued after discharge was shortened with ohmic resistance in the circuit (Fig. 9). The energy of the oscillating circuit was changed to heat. On the other hand, it was found that if the ohmic resistance was made small and the capacity of the Leyden jar was matched properly with the inductance of the coil, the length of time that the oscillations continued was very greatly increased.

Furthermore, suppose one Leyden jar is attached to an induction coil and discharged through such a circuit near another Leyden jar with the same capacitive and same inductive reactance in its circuit. The energy from the jar that is being discharged seems to be radiated out into space, and it causes oscillating current to flow in the other circuit nearby. Figure 10 shows how this experiment can be done. No coil is shown in the receiving circuit because the capacitive reactance of the circuit is so small that the inductive reactance of the wire is sufficient to equalize it. The inductance of the receiving circuit *ABCD* can be changed by sliding the wire *CD*. The circuits are thereby tuned. The spark gaps *XY* and *MN* are very small. This experiment was the forerunner of wireless telegraphy and radio.

Resonance. When the circuit *ABCD* picks up or absorbs the energy from the oscillating circuit *EFGH*, we have what is known as *electrical resonance*. One clue to electrical resonance is the fact that when the inductance and the capacity of a Leyden jar circuit are properly adjusted, the oscillations from a discharged condenser continue for a much longer time than otherwise.

We know too that inductance causes the current to lag behind the voltage, and that capacitance causes the current to lead the voltage. Therefore, if both are present in the proper amounts, the capacitive reactance cancels the inductive reactance, leaving only ohmic resistance to stop the oscillations. If the ohmic resistance is very small, it allows the oscillations to continue for some time before dying out.

"Tuning in" a radio. As we have already said, a coil (inductance) in a circuit causes the current to lag behind the e.m.f.

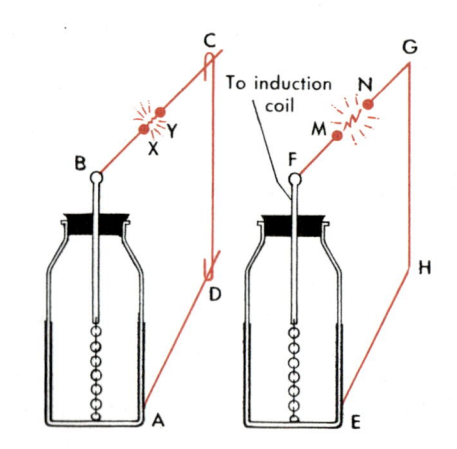

Fig. 10. A spark appears across the gap *XY* when the two circuits are tuned.

Fig. 11. This high-speed synchronous motor derives its name from the fact that the motor runs synchronously with its generator. Alternating current is supplied to the armature, but direct current to the field. Synchronous motors are used for all types of constant-speed machinery such as fans, blowers, compressors, pumps, and motor-generator sets.

Courtesy Westinghouse Electric Corp.

and resists high-frequency currents. It "chokes" the high-frequency currents.

On the other hand, a condenser (capacitance) causes the current to lead the applied e.m.f., and resists low-frequency currents. It "chokes off" the low frequencies. Hence the tuning of a radio, so as to pick out a single frequency from among many frequencies, amounts to nothing more than adjusting either the inductance of the circuit or the capacitance of the circuit so that their respective effects, inductive reactance and capacitive reactance, are equal and cancel each other for that frequency. That is, when a circuit is tuned:

$$X_C = X_L$$

Substituting,

$$\frac{1}{2 \pi fC} = 2 \pi fL$$

Or,

$$f^2 = \frac{1}{4 \pi^2 LC}$$

Hence, in a tuned circuit, the frequency

$$f = \frac{1}{2 \pi \sqrt{LC}}$$

How is the circuit in Fig. 10 tuned: by adjustment of capacitance or by adjustment of inductance?

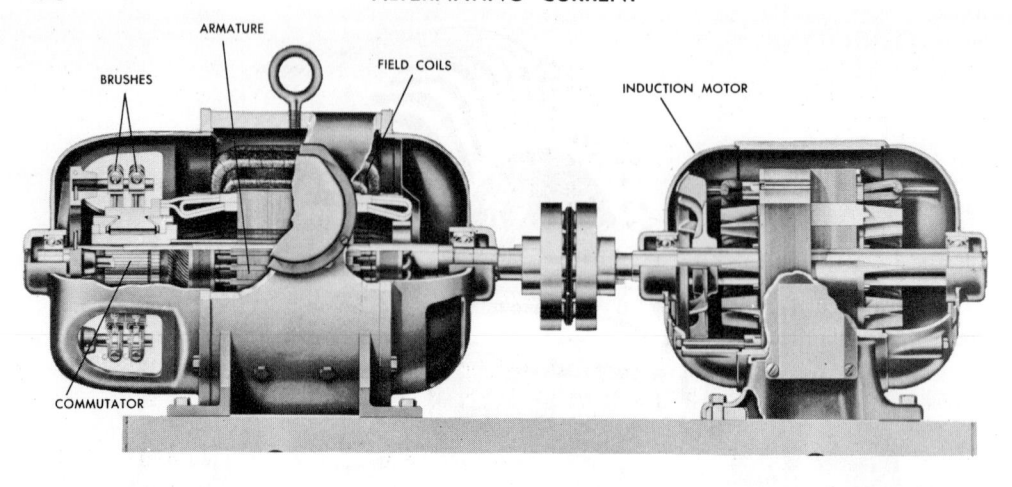

Fig. 12. This motor-generator set, which consists of an A.C. motor and a D.C. generator, is used to change alternating current to direct current.

SUMMARY AND CONCLUSIONS

1. The effective value, $I_{\text{eff.}}$, of an alternating current is that value in amperes which will produce the same heating effect as a direct current of the same number of amperes.

2. Effective currents and voltages = 0.707 of the respective maximum values.

3. A.C. voltmeters and ammeters indicate effective values.

4. A coil having an inductance of 1 henry is one in which a change of current of 1 ampere per second induces an e.m.f. of 1 volt. A millihenry is $\frac{1}{1000}$ henry.

5. A farad is the capacitance of a condenser in which an e.m.f. of 1 volt will store 1 coulomb of electricity (6.25 × 10^{18} electrons). A microfarad is $\frac{1}{1,000,000}$ farad.

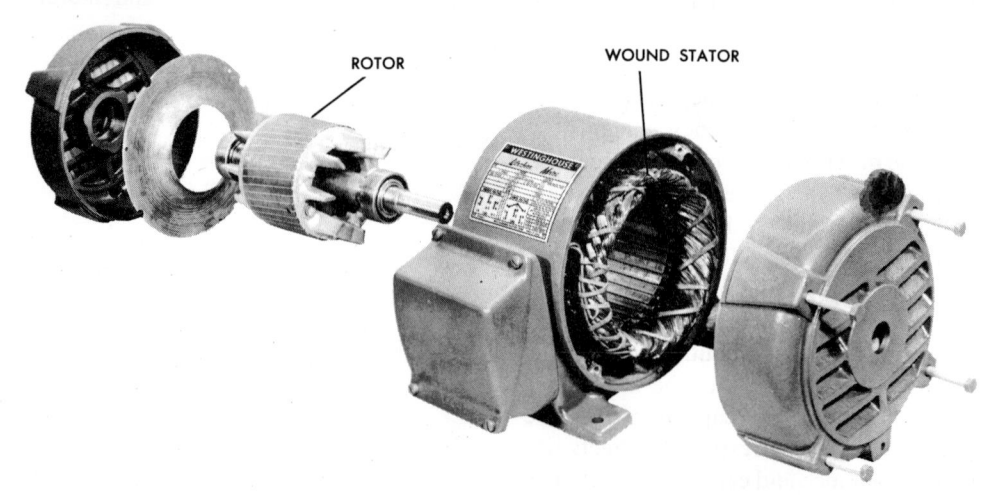

Fig. 13. Cutaway view of an A.C. induction motor.

ALTERNATING CURRENT

6. Inductive reactance, $X_L = 2\pi f L$ (ohms).
7. Capacitive reactance, $X_C = \dfrac{1}{2\pi f C}$ (ohms).
8. Impedance is the total opposition to alternating current. Thus, it is the combination of the reactance and resistance and is measured in ohms.
9. Reactance, X, in a circuit containing inductive reactance and capacitive reactance in series is found as follows:

$$X = X_L - X_C$$

10. Impedance, Z, in a circuit containing resistance and reactance is found by substituting in the following formula:

$$Z = \sqrt{R^2 + (X_L - X_C)^2}$$

11. A circuit is in tune with a given frequency when:

$$X_C = X_L$$

or

$$f = \dfrac{1}{2\pi\sqrt{LC}}$$

12. The power factor equals $\dfrac{R}{Z}$.
13. Power $= \dfrac{R}{Z} \times EI$.

QUESTIONS FOR REVIEW

1. When a wire is straight, why does it offer less opposition to A.C. than it does when it is coiled compactly?
2. Why does a condenser offer more opposition to D.C. than to A.C.?
3. What is impedance? Unit of impedance?
4. What is inductance? Unit of inductance?
5. What is inductive reactance? Unit of inductive reactance?
6. What is capacitive reactance? Unit of capacitive reactance?
7. The effective A.C. is what part of the maximum?
8. Explain why the current variations lag behind the voltage variations in an A.C. circuit which contains inductance and resistance.
9. Explain why the current variations lead the voltage variations in an A.C. circuit which contains capacitance and resistance.
10. What conditions exist when resonance exists in a circuit?
11. What is meant by the power factor?

PROBLEMS

1. The maximum voltage in an A.C. circuit is 141 volts. What is the effective voltage?
2. The effective current in an A.C. circuit is 10 amperes. What is the maximum current?
3. If a change of current of 1 ampere per second in a coil induces an e.m.f. of 1 volt in a coil, what is the inductance of the coil?
4. What is the reactance, X_L, of a coil which has an inductance of 0.14 henry and is used in a 60-cycle circuit?
5. What is the reactance of a choke coil which has an inductance of 2.1 henries and is used in a 60-cycle circuit?
6. The reactance of a coil in a million-cycle circuit is 6280 ohms. What is its inductance?
7. What is the capacitive reactance, X_C, of a condenser which has a capacity of 0.0001 farad and is used in a 100-cycle A.C. circuit?
8. What is the impedance, Z, of an A.C. series circuit that contains 8 ohms of resistance and 6 ohms of inductive reactance, X_L? Make a diagram.
9. What is the impedance of a circuit that contains 39 ohms of resistance and a capacitive reactance of 52 ohms? Make a diagram.
10. A coil has an ohmic resistance of 68 ohms and an impedance of 85 ohms. What is its reactance?
11. A circuit has 20 ohms of inductive reactance. How much capacitive reactance must it have in order that the circuit may have resonance?
12. (a) What is the impedance, Z, of a circuit whose ohmic resistance is 12 ohms and whose capacitive reactance, X_C, is 9 ohms? (b) What is the power factor of the circuit?
13. A coil of 0.2-henry inductance and 25-ohm resistance is connected with a 220-volt 60-cycle line. (a) What is the reactance? (b)

ALTERNATING CURRENT

The impedance? (c) The current? (d) The power factor? (e) The power used in the coil?

14. In a certain circuit the ohmic resistance is 15 ohms, X_L is 10 ohms, and X_C is 30 ohms. The A.C. voltage across the circuit is 100 volts. Find:
   (a) The total impedance, Z.
   (b) The effective current.
   (c) The power factor.
   (d) The power utilized.
   (e) Whether the current leads the voltage or lags behind it.

15. A Leyden-jar condenser with a capacity of 0.0001 farad is connected to a single turn of wire about 6 inches in diameter having an inductance of 0.0001 henry. Calculate the natural frequency of the circuit.

PROJECTS

1. Do the experiment pictured in Fig. 6.
2. Connect in series a coil and a lamp similar to those in Fig. 3 and show how the current varies as the inductance in the circuit is changed. The inductance is changed by removal of the iron core from inside the coil.
3. Set up an apparatus similar to that in Fig. 10 and show how you can tune a circuit by changing the inductance of the circuit.
4. Place a clear glass electric lamp, with a straight filament that is one or more inches long, in an A.C. circuit and then bring a horseshoe magnet near the lamp so that the field is perpendicular to the conducting filament. Note the behavior of the filament. Explain.
5. Stretch a No. 24 wire about 5 feet long between two insulated supports and connect it in an A.C. circuit with a rheostat. Then bring one end of a strong bar magnet near the wire. Explain.

READING YOU WILL ENJOY

1. Leonard, J. N., *Loki: The Life of Charles Proteus Steinmetz*. Doubleday, Doran and Company, Inc., Garden City, N. Y., 1929. Tells the life story of Steinmetz, who was badly deformed at birth in Germany and who later emigrated to this country. What he lacked physically was compensated for mentally. Almost single-handed he revolutionized the electrical industry by developing a fruitful mathematical theory of alternating current machines. As a result, most of the guesswork was taken out of building them.
2. Siskind, Charles S., *Electricity: Principles, Practice, Experiments*, pp. 92-142. McGraw-Hill Book Company, Inc., New York, 1947. Material is well written and well illustrated. Covers the same material that this chapter does. Contains a number of well-planned experiments.

Unit 17

The Riddle of Light

In this unit, you will discover that scientists themselves do not have all the answers to the question, "What is light?" As you seek to understand the nature of light, you will study the contributions of such intellectual giants as Newton and Einstein to the solution of this fascinating riddle. In addition to following the work of scientists at the frontiers of knowledge, you will also gain insight into many practical problems. You will discover the answers to such puzzles as what causes a mirage, how glare can be eliminated, how we see, how photographers measure light, and why no two people see exactly the same rainbow.

How a knowledge of the principles of light can contribute to human safety is strikingly shown in the unit photograph. The top photograph shows how auto headlights appear when no polarizing filter is used over the camera lens. When a suitably oriented polarizing filter is placed over the camera lens, automobile headlight glare is eliminated as in the bottom photograph. The same effect would be obtained if each auto had its headlamps and windshields fitted with polarizing screens.

41. WHAT IS LIGHT?
42. INTERFERENCE, POLARIZATION, AND THE SPEED OF LIGHT
43. IMAGE FORMATION AND MIRRORS
44. LENSES AND IMAGES
45. OPTICAL INSTRUMENTS
46. THE EYE
47. ILLUMINATION AND BETTER SEEING
48. THE RIDDLE OF COLOR
49. SPECTRA AND THE EMISSION AND ABSORPTION OF LIGHT

Unit Photograph Courtesy Polaroid Corp.

Chapter 41

What Is Light?

The problem—one of the darkest in physics. From even before the days of the ancient Greeks, when, according to legend, Apollo drove his flaming chariot across the sky, down to the present day of the bright lights of Broadway, man has been puzzled and fascinated by light. Nothing in nature, however, has been more elusive or has guarded its secret of reality more closely. For these reasons light is sometimes called the "darkest" subject in physics. But despite this darkness, light has revealed more to us through our sense of sight than we have learned through all our other senses put together.

Because there is so much yet to be learned about light, study of it affords many opportunities for beginners in science. Already several scientists, while still young men, have made names for themselves through its study. It was at the age of sixteen that Albert Einstein began a study of light that resulted in a complete revolution in physics and led civilization to the brink of a new age, the Atomic Age.

The mere realization that light exists is enough to bring forth a torrent of questions about it. For example, does light have weight? Does it occupy space? Does light jar anything when it strikes it? Is light hot or cold? How fast does it travel? If it cannot pass through a thin piece of cardboard, how can it pass through a thick piece of glass? These are only a few of the questions which we shall endeavor to answer in our study of light.

Early theories of the nature of light. The ancient Greeks advanced several theories about the nature of light. One of them is of particular interest. According to this theory, light is something that streams out of the eyes much like water out of a hose, the idea being that we see a thing by directing this stream of light to hit it. Thereby we learn what it looks like, much as we learn what a thing feels like by feeling it with our hands. A blind man's eyes emit no light; for this reason he cannot see.

According to this theory, should one see as well at night as in the daytime? Could a blind man take a picture with a camera in the absence of a seeing person? Do you accept or reject this theory? Explain why.

Until the intellectual awakening in Europe, known as the Renaissance, this theory was never seriously challenged. Sir Isaac Newton was one of the first to advance a consistent theory of light based upon observation and experiment.

Newton's theory of light. In formulating a theory of light, Newton considered two

Fig. 1. Corpuscles travel in straight lines in all directions from a luminous body.

hypotheses: one, that light is matter; the other, that it is wave energy. Knowing the ability of sound and water waves to bend around a corner, which light seemingly does not do because we cannot see around a corner, Newton rejected the theory of waves in favor of the theory of matter.

According to Newton, light consists of small particles (corpuscles) of matter emitted in all directions in straight lines, or *rays,* by a luminous body such as the sun, a burning candle, or a red-hot coal. See Fig. 1. If these rays consisting of corpuscles strike our eyes, we see the source of them. According to Newton's theory, should one be able to see in a totally dark room? Could a blind man take a picture in the absence of a seeing person? Should light have weight and momentum?

The wave theory of light. About the same time that Newton proposed the corpuscular theory, Christian Huyghens (1629-1695), a Dutch astronomer and physicist, advanced the wave theory of light. Fig. 2 illustrates how light, according to the wave theory, radiates from a source. The straight lines drawn from the source are called *rays* and are perpendicular to the circles called *wave fronts.*

The farther a wave front is from the source, the more nearly a short section of it—for example, the section AB—approaches a straight line, and the more nearly two wave fronts become parallel. Such waves are known as *parallel waves.*

Light waves coming directly from a source, or from a body which reflects them, cause the sensation of sight, just as Newton claimed for the corpuscles.

Newton objects to Huyghens' wave theory. Newton* would not accept the wave theory. He argued that "Sound,

*Much of the argument given here is taken with modification from *The Evolution of Physics,* by Albert Einstein and Leopold Infeld. The argument is presented as it might have occurred. No claim that it actually happened is made here.

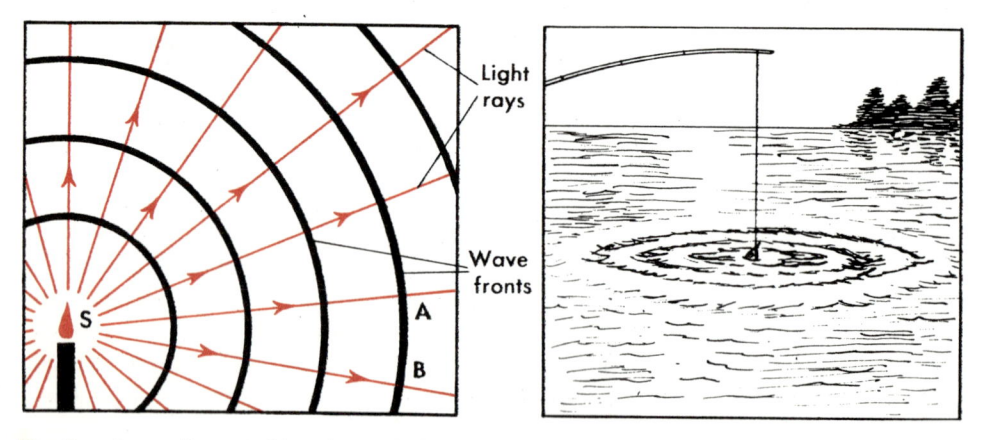

Fig. 2. According to Huyghens, light consists of waves. Light waves travel in much the same way as water waves produced when a stone is dropped into still water.

which is a wave motion, will travel through a crooked hollow pipe, bend around a hill or other obstruction and be heard. If light is a wave, it too should do the same, but experiment proves that it doesn't."

In reply Huyghens said, "That is not a convincing argument. Take short water waves on a river striking the side of a ship; the waves originating on one side will not be seen on the other. However, if the waves are large and the obstacle is small, the waves will bend around the obstacle and be seen on the other side." Huyghens even went so far with this line of reasoning as to predict that a very small obstruction would cast no shadow in light.

Still Newton objected. "Every wave," he said, "must have something in which to travel. Light travels through a vacuum, whereas sound does not. Corpuscles, like a thrown ball, need nothing to travel in; but waves do. What do light waves travel in as they pass through a vacuum or across the vast empty space between the sun and the earth?" Newton and his followers could no more think of a light wave without something for it to travel in than they could think of an ocean wave without an ocean.

In what do light waves travel? To answer this question, Huyghens did what pseudo-scientists and good scientists had done before him and have done since in like situations. Fully realizing its implications and the storm of criticism that it would bring, Huyghens assumed the existence of a substance which he called *ether*. Logically, this meant that glass, air, water, and even a vacuum, along with every other thing that transmits light, contains ether. Huyghens believed that ether is a fluidlike substance, perhaps more like jelly than air, which fills all space and permeates all matter.

Again Newton objected. "What is this ether?" he asked. "I cannot see, feel, taste or smell it," he said. "Does it stand still or does it 'blow' like the wind? Is it frictionless? If it is not," he said, "then what prevents the earth and other planets, which are rotating and moving about in it, from running down as a spinning top does?"

Newton vigorously assailed the wave theory, and as a result few scientists accepted it. To doubt Newton was to doubt "the" scientific authority of the world. It was the "Age of Newton." However, the test of a theory is not who proposes it but whether it can be used to predict and explain all data pertaining to it. Which theory of light does this best?

Does light actually travel in straight lines? One of the pillars supporting the corpuscular theory was the assertion that light travels in straight lines. The question is, does it?

If we place a cross, as shown in Fig. 3, between a small source of light and a screen, we see that the shadow cast is sharp. And if we stretch a string, or draw a line, from a very small light source (*point source*) to a point on the very edge of the shadow, the string touches a corresponding part of the cross and is not bent.

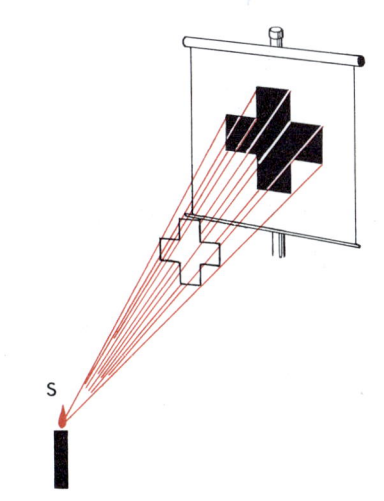

Fig. 3. A sharp shadow appears on the screen. What does this demonstrate?

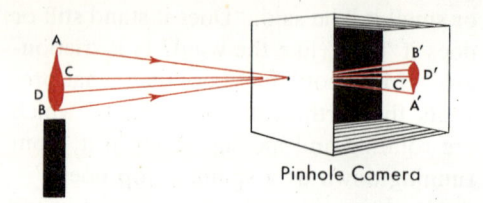

Fig. 4. What does a sharp image in the camera tend to prove about the nature of light?

Also, suppose we place a source of light, such as a candle flame, in front of a pinhole camera in a dark room, as in Fig. 4. If light travels in straight lines, then light from point A in the flame should pass straight through the pinhole and strike the screen of the camera at the point A′ and at this point only. Likewise, light from points B, C, and D should strike the screen at the respective points B′, C′, and D′ and at these points only. Therefore, when the light from the camera screen enters the eye, a sharp reproduction of the flame, called an *image*, should be seen on the screen. But if light bends around corners, then light from several different points on the flame should strike any point, such as A′, on the image. Thus, a blurred image would appear on the screen. Since the image is sharp, again it appears that light travels in straight lines. What would be the effect on the image if the pinhole were enlarged? Made smaller?

These experimental findings, however, do not necessarily prove the corpuscular and disprove the wave theory of light. For if we assume, as Huyghens did, that short waves cast sharp shadows and that a light wave has a very short wave length, then our findings do not favor either theory at the expense of the other.

Umbra and penumbra. Fig. 5 shows two shadows that are not sharp or uniform in intensity. The center part of each is sharper than the outer edges. Does this mean that light does bend around corners?

Further investigation shows that in (a) of Fig. 5 there are two small sources, two candles, instead of one small source. The dark part of the shadow, which is distinct and sharp, is called the *umbra*, which means *shadow*. The less dense part is called the *penumbra*, meaning *almost shadow*. If you place one eye in the umbra and close the other eye, you will not see either source. In the penumbra you can never see more than one source at a time. That parts of the shadow are light and dark is due to the fact that light from neither source shines in the umbra, whereas light from one source shines in the penumbra. Outside the shadow, light shines from both sources. Explain (b) of Fig. 5.

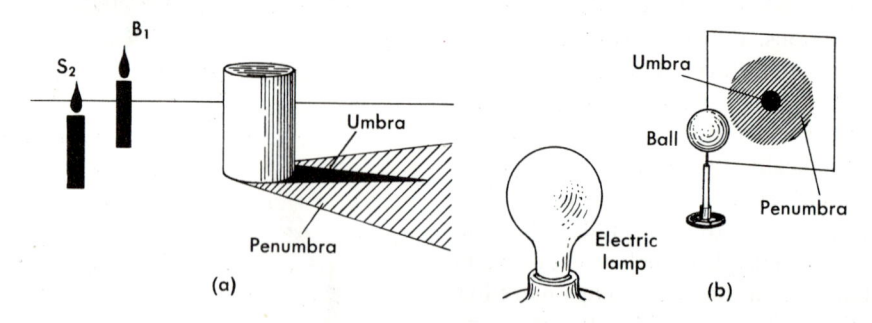

Fig. 5. (a) The shadow formed by a relatively large object when two relatively small sources of light are used. (b) One source, relatively large in comparison with the object, is used to form a shadow.

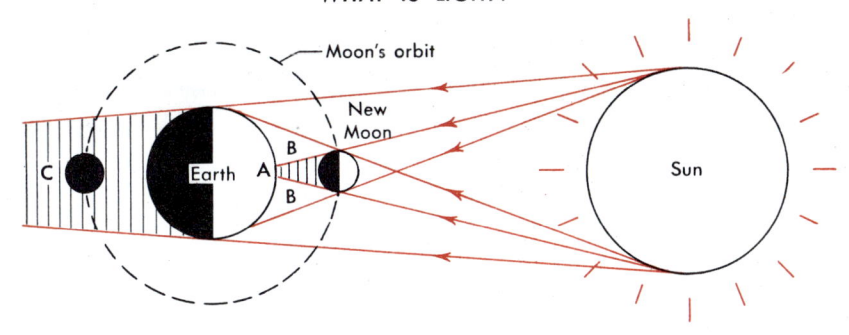

Fig. 6. A solar eclipse occurs when the moon passes between the earth and the sun in such a way that the three bodies are in a straight line. In the area within the umbra, the eclipse is total; in the area within the penumbra, the eclipse is partial.

Eclipses. In eclipses, such as those of the sun and the moon, nature itself furnishes some good examples of umbra and penumbra. Fig. 6 shows an eclipse of the sun during which the umbra, *A*, cast by the moon falls on the earth's surface. Inside this umbra it is impossible to see the sun; consequently, darkness reigns. For an observer in this part of the moon's shadow, the eclipse is *total*. An observer outside the umbra in the penumbra, *B*, sees only part of the sun. In this region the eclipse is only *partial*.

In case the moon is too far from the earth for the umbra to reach the earth, as is often the case, an *annular,* or ring-shaped, eclipse is seen by an observer near the center of the shadow. A penny held in front of one eye when a person is observing the sun demonstrates total and annular eclipses very well. When the penny is very close to the eye, the whole sun is obscured by it. When the distance of the penny from the eye is increased, the center of the sun is obscured but the outer edge appears as a ring. Very dark glasses should be worn during this demonstration. Why?

Eclipses of the sun are of special interest to astronomers because they afford opportunities to study the light coming from distant stars past the edge of the sun. At other times the stars are not visible when the sun is overhead. If light is matter, should it be bent by the gravitational attraction of the sun as it passes the edge of the sun?

The laws of reflection: which theory explains them better? One of the most commonly known facts about light is that it is reflected from mirrors, pools of water, shop windows, car windshields, polished metal, and other objects. In fact, every nonluminous body that we see reflects light. Which theory, the wave or the corpuscular, predicts what actually takes place? Which gives the better explanation of what happens?

If light consists of corpuscles, we might expect it to be reflected in the same way that a billiard ball is reflected when it is shot against the side of a billiard table, as shown in (a) and (b) of Fig. 7. For example, when the ball is shot along a line perpendicular to the side of the table it rebounds along the same line. If, however, the ball is shot so that its path is at an angle with the side of the table, it rebounds so that the *angle of incidence* (i) equals *the angle of reflection* (r).

As shown in (c) and (d) of Fig. 7, light behaves in this manner. The *angle of incidence* is the angle between the *nor-*

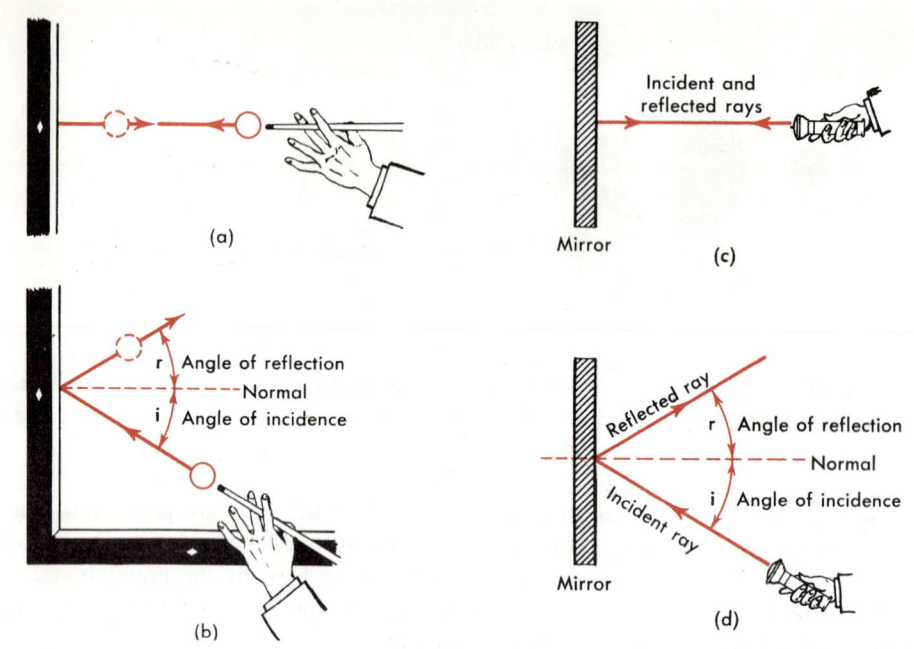

Fig. 7. The laws of reflection explained according to the corpuscular theory by a billiard-ball demonstration. The angle at which the billiard ball (light corpuscle) strikes the side of the table is equal to the angle at which the ball rebounds.

mal, a line perpendicular to the surface at the point where the light strikes the mirror, and the *incident* path, the one along which the light enters the mirror. The *angle of reflection* is the angle between the normal and the *reflected* path. The incident and reflected paths, the normal, and the angles are all in the same plane. These relationships are known as the **laws of reflection.** They are:

1. **The angle of incidence (i) equals the angle of reflection (r).**

2. **The incident ray, the normal, and the reflected ray all lie in the same plane.**

Thus, we see that reflected light behaves exactly as predicted by the corpuscular theory. Will the wave theory explain reflection as well?

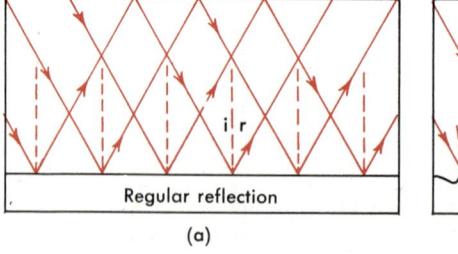

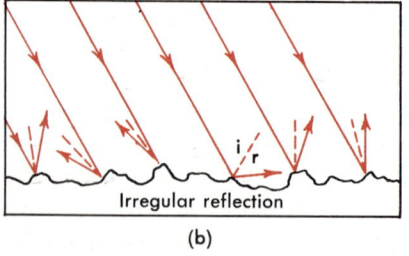

Fig. 8. (a) Rays striking a smooth surface are reflected parallel to one another. (b) Rays striking a rough surface are scattered in all directions.

WHAT IS LIGHT?

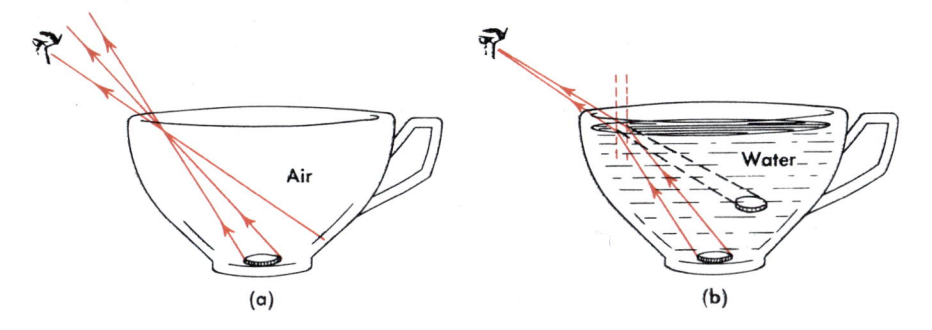

Fig. 9. (a) The coin is not seen by the eye when the cup is empty. (b) When the cup is filled with water, the coin is seen. Explain why the coin becomes visible.

Study of Fig. 8(a) will show that a beam of light consisting of parallel wave fronts is reflected according to the laws of reflection, and that the wave theory explains reflection just as well as the corpuscular theory does.

If the reflecting surface is rough, the reflection is *irregular* and the light is scattered, or *diffused*. See Fig. 8(b). Irregular reflection is far more restful to the eye than reflection by a smooth surface, which is called *regular* reflection.

What happens when light passes from air into another substance, such as water or glass? One of the oldest yet most amazing tricks performed by fakirs and magicians is done with a coin placed in the bottom of an empty cup so that when the cup is viewed from the side, as shown in Fig. 9, the coin can not quite be seen over the edge of the cup. When the cup is filled with water, then, to the surprise of the observer, a coin appears in the cup where no coin appeared before.

All of us have observed similar phenomena. The bottom of a tank filled with water appears to be nearer the surface than it actually is. And those who have speared fish know that they must aim below the apparent position of a fish in order to hit it. When viewed from the side, the stick in the container (Fig. 10) appears to be broken at the surface in such a way that the part under water seems to bend downward. What is the explanation of these phenomena?

The performance of a simple experiment may give us the answer. Fill a rectangular jar about three-fourths full of water to which a little fluorescein or mercurochrome in solution has been added. Cover the jar with a cardboard in which there is a slit, as shown in Fig. 11. Then pass a beam of light through the slit so that it strikes the water surface obliquely, passes through the water, strikes a mirror, and is reflected back out of the water and container.

The beam of light, when viewed from the side, is luminous and is bent, or *re-*

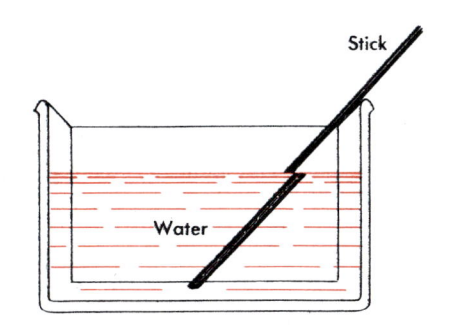

Fig. 10. How a stick appears when one part of it is in water and the other part in air. How does refraction explain the result?

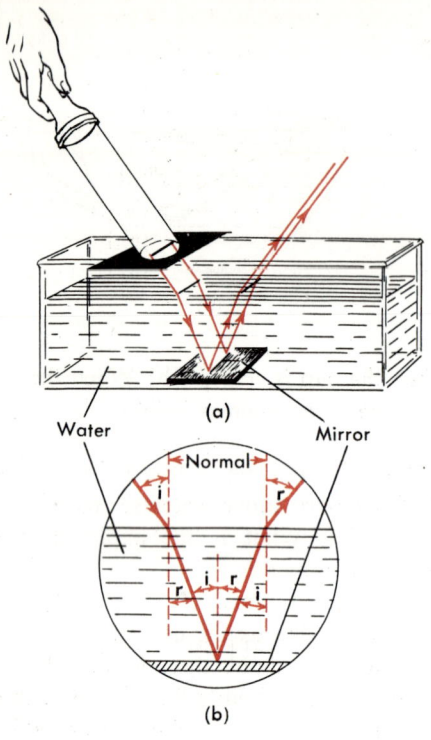

Fig. 11. The refraction of light in passing from air to water. The straight-line ray is bent toward the normal.

fracted, where it enters and leaves the water. *The abrupt change in direction of a beam of light as it passes obliquely from one substance into another of different optical density is called* **refraction.**

Does refraction explain the coin trick? In the trick above (Fig. 9), the coin could be seen after water was poured into the cup because light coming from the coin was bent sufficiently at the water surface so that it reached the eye. When the cup was empty the light was not bent, hence it could not reach the eye.

Since an object always appears to be in the direction of the incoming ray of light which enters the eye, the coin, when it is under water, appears to be above its real position. Likewise, the bottom of a tank filled with water appears to be higher than it actually is. Explain the apparent break in the stick in Fig. 10.

Laws of refraction. If we make a sketch (see (b) of Fig. 11) of the apparatus and beam of light in (a) of Fig. 11, and draw normals to the water surface at each point where the light enters and leaves the water, we see that:

1. **A beam of light which enters perpendicularly from one medium to another of different optical density passes through unrefracted.**

2. **A beam of light which passes obliquely from one medium into another medium of greater optical density is bent** *toward* **or closer to the normal.**

3. **A beam of light which passes obliquely from one medium to another medium of lesser optical density is bent** *away* **from the normal.**

The angle (i) between the normal and the incident ray is called the *angle of incidence*. The angle (r) between the normal and the refracted ray is called the *angle of refraction*.

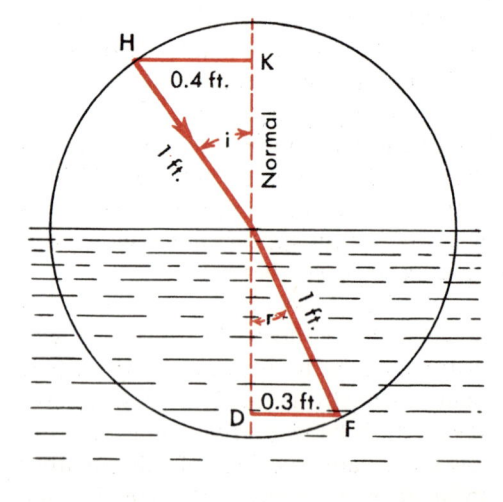

Fig. 12. Finding the index of refraction.

WHAT IS LIGHT?

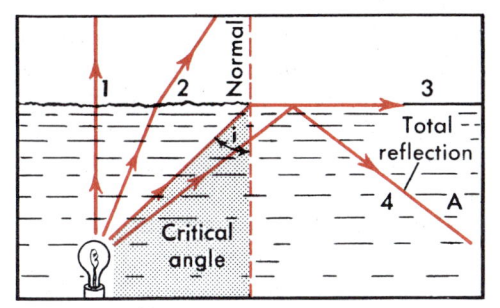

Fig. 13. When the critical angle is exceeded, the lamp appears to be above the water. Explain.

Index of refraction. Referring to Fig. 12, in which the radius of the circle is 1 foot, the line *HK*, measured in feet, is equivalent to what is known as the *sine* of the angle of incidence (*i*). And the line *DF*, measured in feet, is equivalent to the sine of the angle of refraction (*r*). When the sine of the angle of incidence is divided by the sine of the angle of refraction, the quotient is called the *index of refraction*. The index is always a constant for any two given materials, regardless of the sizes of the angles of incidence and refraction. Find from Fig. 12 by calculation the index of refraction for water.

The indices (plural for index) of refraction of various substances when light passes into them from a vacuum* are as follows:

Table 1
INDICES OF REFRACTION OF VARIOUS SUBSTANCES

Water	1.33
Alcohol (ethyl)	1.36
Crown glass	1.52
Carbon disulfide	1.63
Flint glass	1.65
Diamond	2.42

Materials with high indices of refraction refract (bend) light more than do those with low indices of refraction.

*Since the index of refraction for air is very small, ordinarily we can use the sine of the angle of incidence in air rather than in a vacuum.

Total reflection. If a light source is placed under water, as shown in Fig. 13, an observer whose eye is at *A* can see the image of the light source above the water in much the same way that he could see it if the water surface were a mirror.

We can explain this phenomenon by tracing a few of the rays emitted by the light source. Ray 1 passes out of the water and is not bent. Ray 2 is bent (refracted) slightly. And finally, when the angle of incidence is about 48°, the refracted ray 3 is parallel to the water surface. If the angle of incidence is now made larger, light from the source, such as ray 4, does not escape into the air at all but is reflected back into the water, and the reflection is called *total*. *The angle at which the effect changes from refraction to total reflection is called the* **critical angle.** Thus, because of total reflection, when the eye is placed in the water, for example at *A*, the lamp

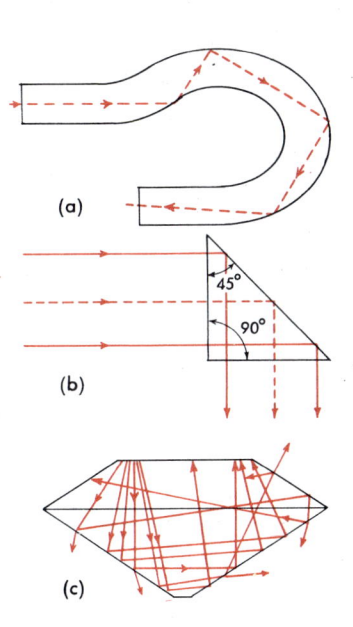

Fig. 14. (a) Light is piped through a bent tube. (b) An image is inverted. (c) Why does a diamond sparkle?

fraction. Such rods are used by dentists and surgeons to pipe light into body cavities. Determine by experiment whether or not light will follow a crooked stream of water, such as that shot horizontally from the end of a hose.

Other uses of total reflection. In the diamond, whose index of refraction is very high, the critical angle is only 24°. As a result, when the diamond is cut properly, much of the light which enters it from all sides is totally reflected and so emerges from the top side. For this reason, a diamond appears to be very brilliant. When lead is added to glass during its manufacture, the index of refraction is greatly increased. Such glass is used to make cut-glass dishes. The higher the index of refraction, the more total reflection and hence brilliancy can be produced.

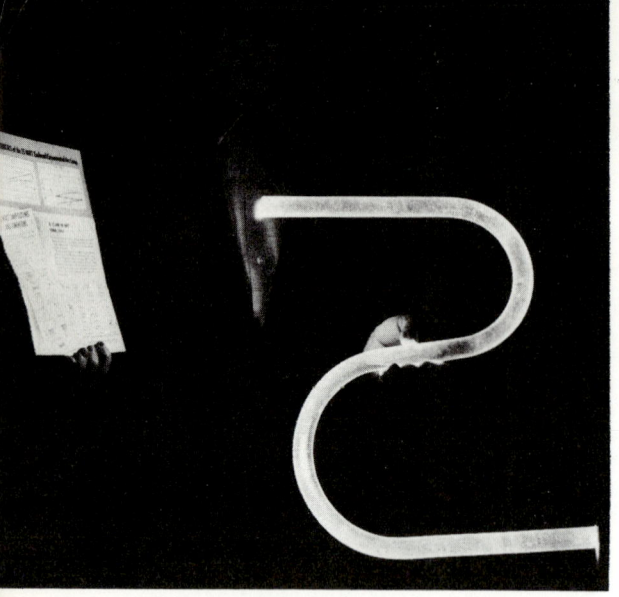

Courtesy E.I. du Pont de Nemours Co., Inc.

Fig. 15. The principle of total reflection is applied in the "Lucite" rod.

can be seen above the water surface. Explain why it appears above the water.

How to pipe light through a crooked transparent rod. Suppose a beam of light is passed in at one end of a plastic rod, as shown in Fig. 14a, and that the beam everywhere strikes the sides of the rod so that the angle of incidence is greater than the critical angle. The light will be reflected back into the rod and as a result will travel the entire length of the rod and out the other end.

If the turns in the rod are sharp, the material must have a high index of re-

Mirages. The mirage, as we might suspect, is due to atmospheric refraction. In (a) of Fig. 16. A represents a treetop viewed across hot sand. Over the hot sand is hot air, above which is a layer of cooler air. This is an unstable condition, but one that occurs quite often.

The light ray (m) from A travels through the cool air straight from the treetop to the observer. But the ray (n) is refracted as it passes downward from the cooler to the hotter air. Therefore, when it enters the observer's eye, it appears to

(a)

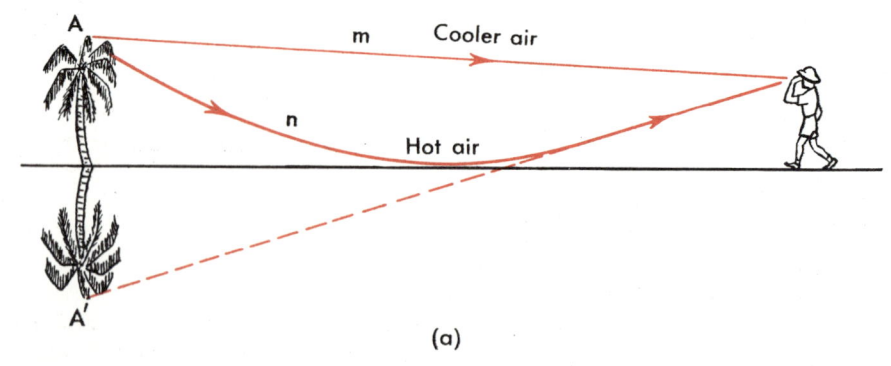

Fig. 16. (a) A distant treetop is seen inverted as if reflected in a mirror.

WHAT IS LIGHT?

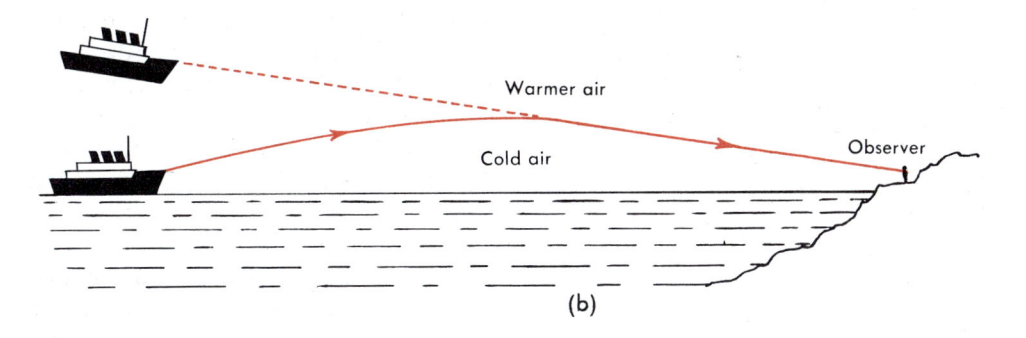

Fig. 16. (b) Since the cold air close to the surface of the water is denser and hence more refracting than the less dense warm air layers above, the apparent position of a distant ship on the horizon is much higher than its actual position.

come from A' instead of from A. But when the mirrored image is approached it disappears.

Similar effects can be seen on a clear hot day by a motorist as he looks down a stretch of paved highway from the top of a hill. Light from the distant sky is refracted by the hot air right above the pavement, so that the sky appears to be reflected by a pool of water ahead. And since the air, as it rises from the hot pavement, is not all of the same temperature and hence density, its indices of refraction vary. The result is a quivering distortion resembling water waves, which makes the water mirage appear all the more realistic.

Over water the process may be reversed. Near the water may be a layer of cold air, above which there is a layer of hot air. As a result, a distant ship at sea may appear to be floating in the sky, as shown in (b) of Fig. 16.

Another rather important phenomenon caused by atmospheric refraction is the increased length of days, which are seven to eight minutes longer than they would be otherwise. That is, the sun appears a few minutes earlier in the morning and disappears a few minutes later in the evening than it would without this refraction. Can you explain why? See Fig. 17.

How did Newton explain refraction?
To explain refraction, Newton said that the corpuscles of light approaching water are attracted by it in a direction perpendicular to the surface of the water, in accordance with the law of universal gravitation. See Fig. 18(a). Since the force of attraction is slight until the corpuscles are right at the surface, the beam is not bent until it reaches the surface, where it is bent toward the normal.

Because of this attraction of the water for the corpuscles, Newton predicted that light would be speeded up as it entered the denser medium and hence would travel faster in it. This, of course, is not the case when one tries to throw a ball through water, and it seemingly does not make sense. But in spite of this, Newton's followers, most of whom basked in the shade of his greatness, accepted it and were ready to condemn anyone who dared to question it.

How did Huyghens explain refraction?
In Fig. 18(b) is pictured a beam of light made up of parallel rays and parallel wave fronts passing from air to water. Each wave front may be thought of as a rigid pole carried by two men, one at each end. All the waves in air may be thought of as two men walking on dry land while carrying

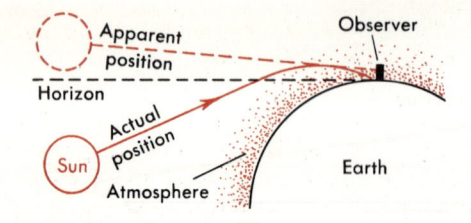

Fig. 17. Because of atmospheric refraction, the sun is visible a few minutes before it rises and after it sets.

the pole; those in water may be thought of as men walking in mud.

As *A* and *B* advance toward the mud, *B* will step in it first and will be slowed up. And during the time interval in which the speeds of *A* and *B* are different the direction of the pole will change. But once both men are in the mud their speeds will not differ and the column of marching men will again form another straight line. According to this theory, does light travel faster in water or in air?

The crucial differences between the corpuscular and wave theories. After the death of Newton and Huyghens, the argument still waxed hot, with the consensus of scientists being in favor of the corpuscular theory. One reason for this was that it explained all known phenomena as well

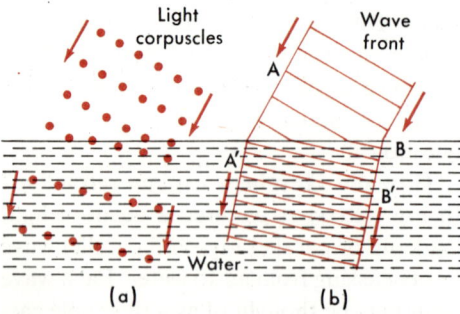

Fig. 18. How refraction of light was explained (a) by the corpuscular theory and (b) by the wave theory.

as, if not better than, the wave theory did. Many had their doubts about the wave theory because it postulated a medium, ether, whose existence was not proved. And too, like Newton, they thought that if light is a wave, it should bend around corners.

Another factor that favored the corpuscular theory for a long time was that Newton had tremendous scientific prestige and lived in a nation whose political, economic, and military might surpassed that of any other nation. In contrast, Huyghens was a relatively unknown Dutchman whose country ranked far below the British Empire in world prestige.

Although these factors might have had an influence on opinion for a time, only scientific research would determine which theory, if either, was correct. The final decision would hinge around the answers to the following four questions:

1. Does light actually travel in straight lines?
2. Is there an ether?
3. Does light travel faster in a medium of greater optical density than it does in one of lesser density?
4. Does light have mass and momentum?

What would be the outcome? Would one of the most brilliant and most renowned men ever to live, the pride of all England, prove to be correct? Or would Huyghens, the comparatively unknown Dutchman, emerge victorious from this controversy?

SUMMARY AND CONCLUSIONS

1. Light is reflected in accordance with the laws of reflection. These are:
    (a) The angle of incidence (*i*) equals the angle of reflection (*r*).
    (b) The incident ray, the normal, and the reflected ray all lie in the same plane.

2. Laws of refraction:
   (a) When a beam of light passes perpendicularly from one medium to another of different optical density, it is not refracted.
   (b) When a beam of light passes obliquely from one medium to another of greater optical density, the beam is bent toward the normal.
   (c) If the path is reversed, the beam is bent away from the normal.
3. The sine of the angle of incidence divided by the sine of the angle of refraction is a constant for any two given materials and is known as the index of refraction.

QUESTIONS FOR REVIEW

1. Why did Newton object to the wave theory of light?
2. How did Huyghens explain Newton's objections?
3. Below are listed several light phenomena which we have just studied. Examine each of these and state whether it supports (a) the wave theory only; (b) the corpuscular theory only; (c) both theories equally well.
   I. Reflection of light.
   II. Light travels in straight lines in a substance having uniform optical density or in a vacuum.
   III. In light radiated by a point source, opaque objects cast sharp shadows.
   IV. Light passes through a vacuum.
   V. Refraction.
   VI. In a vacuum, the speed of light is 186,000 miles per second.
   VII. The formation of an image in a pinhole camera.
4. Make a diagram to show how light passes obliquely through a thick piece of glass.
5. What is meant by a ray of light? A wave front?
6. Make a diagram to show where the rising sun would appear to be to a fish in a lake.

PROJECTS

1. Make a pinhole camera and explain how the image is formed. Also, explain the effect on the image of making the hole small and of making it relatively large.
2. Do the coin trick pictured on page 489.
3. Consult a diamond expert and ask him to explain to you how a diamond is cut so that the total reflection causes a well-illuminated mounted diamond to appear so brilliant. Make a large diagram showing the path of light as it enters the diamond, passes through the diamond, and leaves the diamond. Explain why glass will not appear so brilliant.
4. Project a pencil of colored light into and parallel with a curved stream of water that is about ¼ inch in diameter. Observe. Change the curvature of the stream and observe. Explain your observations.
5. *Mirages.* Do experiment L-32 in Sutton's *Demonstration Experiments in Physics.*

READING YOU WILL ENJOY

1. Bragg, W. H., *The Universe of Light,* pp. 67-87. The Macmillan Company, New York, 1933. Deals with refraction, including a good treatment of the brilliance of gems.
2. Einstein, Albert, and Leopold Infeld, *The Evolution of Physics,* pp. 94-126. Simon and Schuster, Inc., New York, 1938. This little book is not only written like a detective story but is written as simply and as interestingly as many "whodunits." Here is told the story of the search to solve one of nature's greatest mysteries. Any student interested in a further study of physics would want to read the whole book.
3. Sutton, R. M., *Demonstration Experiments in Physics.* McGraw-Hill Book Company, Inc., New York, 1938.
4. Swezey, K. M., *After-Dinner Science.* Whittlesey House, McGraw-Hill Book Company, Inc., New York, 1948. "Clear Water Is Sometimes Opaque," pp. 100-101; "Now You See It!" pp. 102-103.
5. Trattner, Ernest R., *Architects of Ideas.* Carrick and Evans, Inc., New York, 1938. Chapter 6, "Huyghens . . . Theory of Light," is a very interesting, simple, and thought-provoking story of the riddle of light.

Chapter 42

Interference, Polarization, and the Speed of Light

"Phenomenon" Young rocks the intellectual world. It was not until 1801 that the corpuscular theory of light was seriously challenged. In that year, Thomas Young (1773-1829), a most brilliant young English physicist who had been nicknamed "Phenomenon" Young at Cambridge, performed an experiment which shook the centers of learning all over the civilized world.

This simple but astounding experiment can be understood easily by reference to (a) of Fig. 1. X is a source from which light of one color diverges. S is a screen, and B and C are very narrow slits one or two millimeters apart.

According to Newton's theory, two lines should appear on the screen. Instead, however, several bright and dark lines appear there, as shown in (b) of Fig. 1. Still more surprisingly, a line of light, P_0, appears directly behind the part of the screen separating the openings B and C, thus proving conclusively that light will bend around an obstacle, somewhat as Huyghens predicted. See page 485.

How are the several bright lines explained? In the study of sound, you learned that when two sound waves of the same amplitude are superimposed, one on the other, there is interference. When the waves are in phase—that is, rarefaction on rarefaction and condensation on condensation—the result is constructive interference, or increased loudness. When the two waves are completely out of phase—that is, rarefaction on condensation—the result is destructive interference, or silence.

If we assume that light consists of waves, we can account for the bright and dark lines in a similar manner. The bright lines P_0, P_2, etc., are caused by light waves from C reinforcing those coming from B. See (c) of Fig. 1. The two dark lines P_1, P_1 are caused by light waves from C interfering destructively with those coming from B. See (d) of Fig. 1.

Since Newton's corpuscular theory would not explain interference, and since the wave theory explained everything else just as well as the corpuscular theory did, one would expect, as Young expected, that the wave theory would be loudly acclaimed. But such was not the case.

Unable to understand Young's work, Lord Brougham, editor of the Edinburgh Review, made a vicious attack upon it. Brougham asserted that he could find in Young's scientific papers nothing "which deserves the name either of experiment or of discovery," and he took the Royal Society to task for printing such "paltry and unsubstantial papers." Of course, the tragedy was that few people had a chance to read Young's papers, but they did have a chance to read the Edinburgh Review, and they read it. Do such journalistic practices still exist?

An interference experiment. Another simple way of demonstrating interference is as follows: Place two pieces of rectangular plate glass, about 4 x 8 cm. each, one on top of the other. Put a rubber band around one end of them to hold them together as illustrated in Fig. 2(a); and between the other ends, put a piece of tissue paper to hold them apart. There is thus formed a wedge of air between the two plates. Now hold this apparatus so that light of one color, produced, for example, by the burning of common table salt (sodium chloride) in a Bunsen flame, is reflected in the plates. As a result, you will see an image of the flame, crossed by a series of parallel dark and bright lines.

These lines can be explained by reference to Fig. 2(b). The air wedge is represented by the space between AB and AC. When the light strikes each surface of the glass, it is partly reflected; the rest is transmitted. To explain the dark and bright lines, we need consider only what happens at the surfaces of the air wedge.

Let ED (full line) represent the wave train of light reflected at E. Now if the distance from E' to E is one-half of a wave length, then half the wave trains ED and $E'D$ are completely out of phase, with crest on trough; consequently, destructive interference (darkness) is produced.

Determination of the wave length of light. If light is a form of wave energy, we should be able to measure its wave length. The above interference experiment furnishes a clue to a way of doing this. Those who have studied geometry know that the triangles CAB, $F'AF$, and $E'AE$ are similar. Consequently, if the dimensions of the large triangle CAB and the side FA of triangle $F'AF$ are known, then

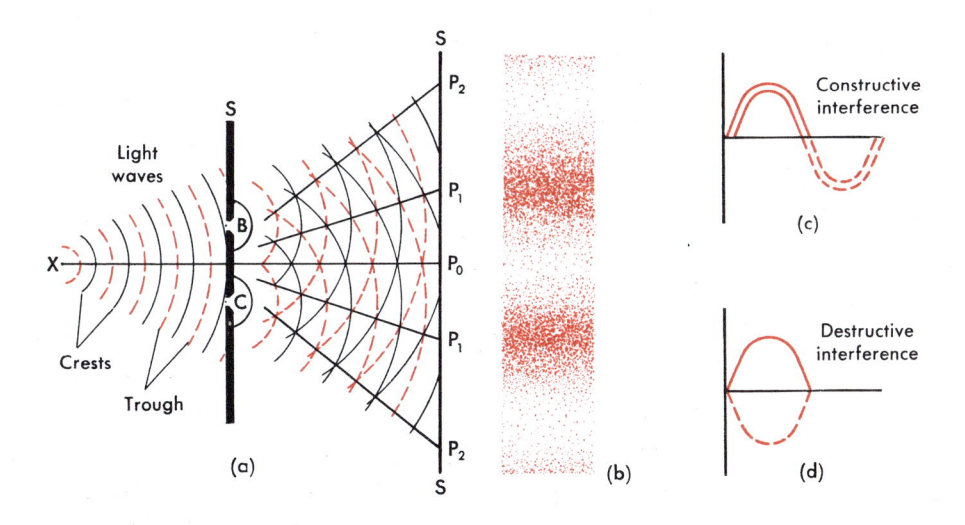

Fig. 1. Young's interference experiment. Does it tend to prove the wave or corpuscular theory of light? The bright lines are caused by waves meeting in the same phase, while dark lines are caused by waves meeting in opposite phases.

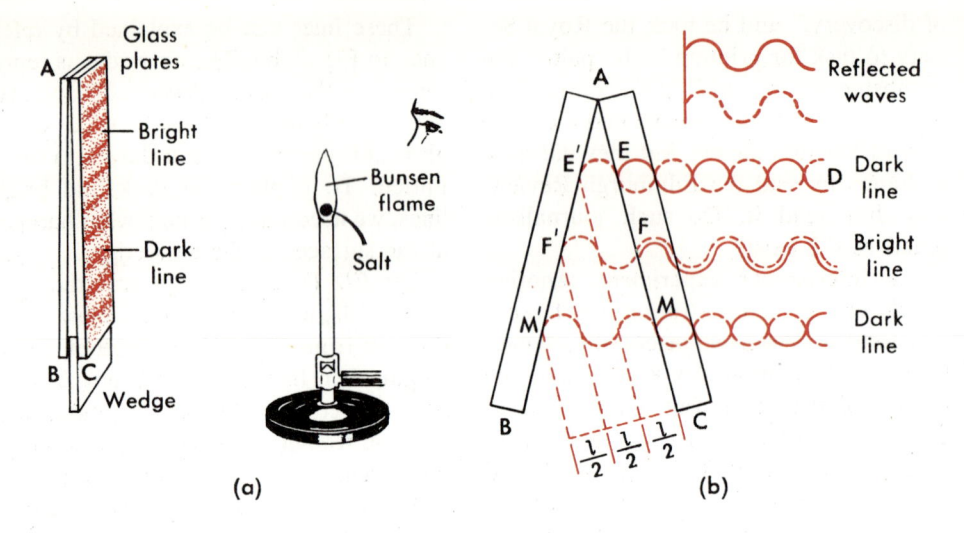

Fig. 2. An interference experiment which can be used to measure the wave length of light. In the one-colored sodium light, alternate dark and bright bands are formed perpendicular to the edges of the wedge of air between the glass plates.

the length of the side $F'F$, which equals the wave length of sodium light, can be calculated from the proportion:

$$\frac{CB}{F'F} = \frac{CA}{FA}$$

Surprisingly accurate results can be obtained by this crude method. The wave lengths of different colors are given on page 567.

The nature of light waves. In our study of sound we found that there are two different types of wave motion: longitudinal and transverse. In the longitudinal wave, such as a sound wave, the particles in the medium through which the wave train is transmitted vibrate to and fro, parallel to the direction in which the wave travels. In a transverse wave, such as the wave in a rope shown in Fig. 3, the particles vibrate perpendicularly to the direction in which the wave travels.

Knowing the distinguishing features of each type of wave, we should be able to determine the exact nature of any wave.

We know that a longitudinal wave, such as a sound wave, should pass right through a picket-fence type of obstruction. Of course, a decrease in loudness would be expected, but otherwise it would not be affected. Likewise, a transverse rope wave should pass right through a picket fence, provided the to-and-fro motions of the rope particles are up and down, parallel to the slits between the pickets, as shown in (a) of Fig. 3.

However, if the pickets are turned horizontally, as shown in Fig. 3(b), then they will stop a vertical transverse wave. It should be noted particularly that stoppage takes place only when the wave is transverse and the to-and-fro motions of the particles in the medium are perpendicular to the slits in the fence.

In order to determine whether a light wave is longitudinal or transverse, a *Polaroid* filter or a tourmaline crystal can be substituted for the picket fence. In a tourmaline crystal the molecules are arranged in layers, much like the pages in this book,

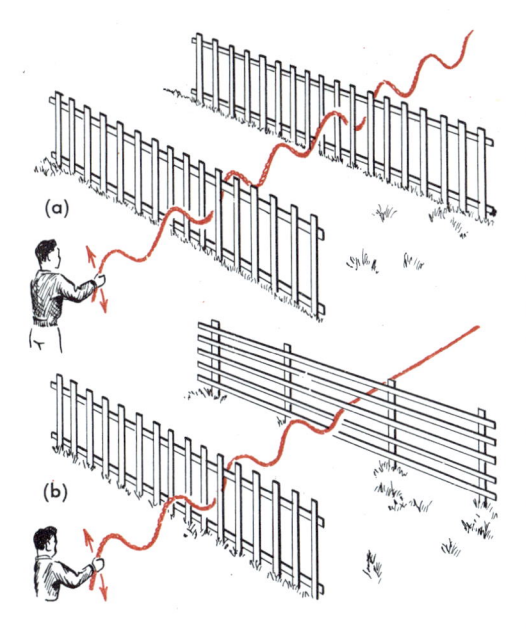

INTERFERENCE, POLARIZATION, AND THE SPEED OF LIGHT 499

Fig. 3. The transverse wave in (a) passes through the fence, but is stopped in (b).

and between two adjacent layers it is as if there were a very, very narrow space through which light can pass. These layers are always parallel to the axis of the crystal. Polaroid filters contain a plastic film composed of lined-up molecules that have the same effect as the tourmaline crystal. You can think of a Polaroid filter as being a picket fence, with its axis parallel to the slits between the pickets.

When ordinary light strikes a Polaroid disk, it appears to pass right through, regardless of the direction in which the axis is turned. See (a) of Fig. 4. Only the intensity, or brightness, is decreased. This seems to indicate that a light wave is longitudinal. And if a second disk is placed behind the first, as in (b) of Fig. 4, so that their axes are parallel, the light passes right through both of them. However, if the axes are perpendicular, as in (c) of Fig. 4, the second disk prevents passage. This stoppage, as we saw above with the rope, indicates that the light waves which strike the second crystal must be transverse, and the to-and-fro vibration in the waves must be at right angles to the axis of the second crystal. But if a light wave is transverse, why did not the first disk prevent passage when its axis was held perpendicular to the plane of polarization?

Evidently the to-and-fro motions of the medium transmitting ordinary waves are not all in one plane. Instead, they must vibrate to and fro in several planes perpendicular to the direction in which the wave travels, as shown in Fig. 5. Consequently, when such waves strike a disk whose axis

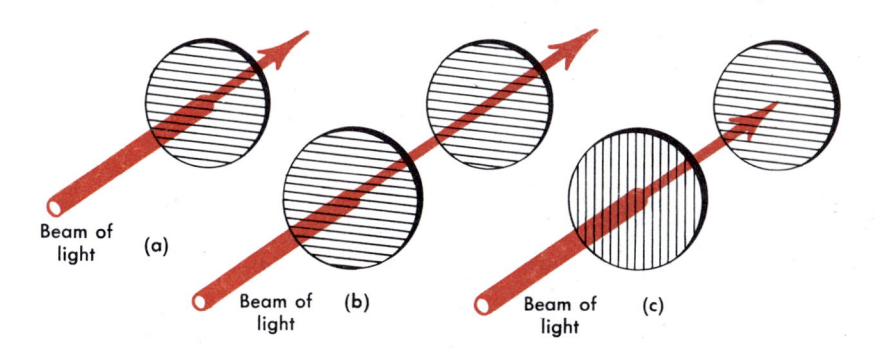

Fig. 4. (a) Ordinary light passing through a Polaroid disk. (b) When the slits are parallel, the beam of light passes through both Polaroid disks. (c) When the slits are held perpendicular to each other, the second disk stops the light.

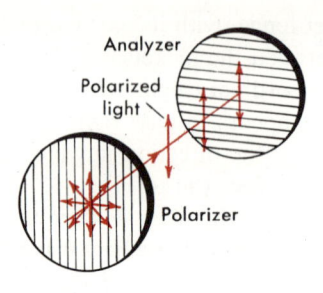

Fig. 5. Polarized light stopped by an analyzer.

is vertical, only the vertical vibrations pass through. Such light is called *polarized* light, and the crystal disk is called a *polarizer*.

Whether or not light is polarized we can determine by allowing it to strike a Polaroid disk and slowly turning the axis of the disk (Fig. 5). If the light is polarized, then, when the axis of the disk is at right angles to the to-and-fro motion (plane of polarization), the passage of the light is prevented. The crystal or Polaroid disk is, in this case, called an *analyzer*.

Fig. 6. When the axes of rotation of the Polaroid disks are at right angles, the light is blocked. When the axes are at slight angles, some light is stopped.

Courtesy The Polaroid Corporation

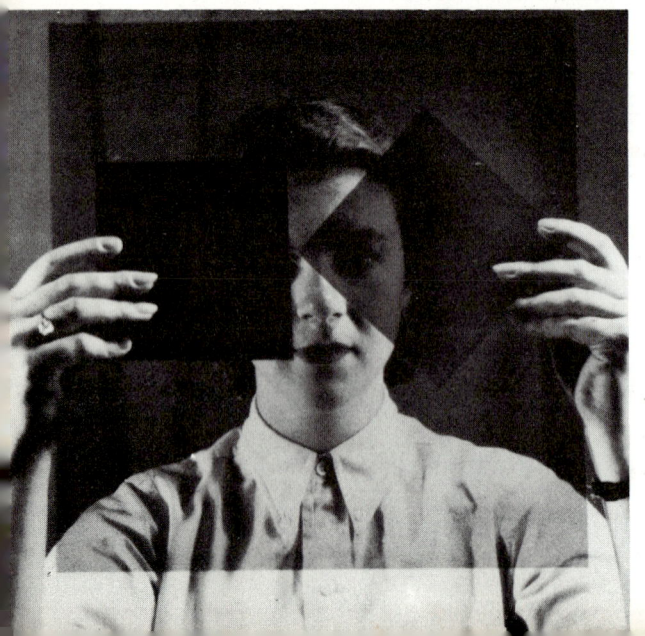

Polarization by reflection. There may be hanging in your room a picture which, when you view it from certain angles, is blurred by the glare of the glass. But if you view the picture through a polaroid disk while slowly rotating the axis of the disk, you can find a position at which the glare completely disappears.

This, of course, indicates that reflected glare is composed of polarized light. To demonstrate how glass polarizes light by reflection, place a piece of ordinary glass on a flat table top and view, through an analyzer, a beam of light reflected from the glass. As a result, you will find that the light is polarized, and the plane of polarization is perpendicular to the axis of the Polaroid disk shown in Fig. 7. When the angle of incidence for the glass is about 57°, the maximum amount of polarized light is reflected.

Knowing that reflected glare is polarized light, and knowing the direction of the plane of polarization for a flat horizontal reflector, we can counteract glare from the highway, the street, and flat water surfaces by the use of polarized sun glasses whose axes are vertical.

It should be understood that not all reflected light is polarized. Glossy paper, glass, water, and other highly polished nonconductors of electricity polarize light by reflection. Strangely, metal reflectors and other good conductors of electricity do not. Paper with a rough finish, as you know, produces little glare and consequently is not a good polarizer of light. And, as has been pointed out, the amount of reflected polarized light depends upon the angle of incidence and angle of reflection.

Uses of polarized light. If a piece of glass, plastic, or other transparent material is compressed, stretched, bent, twisted, or otherwise put under stress, and it is viewed

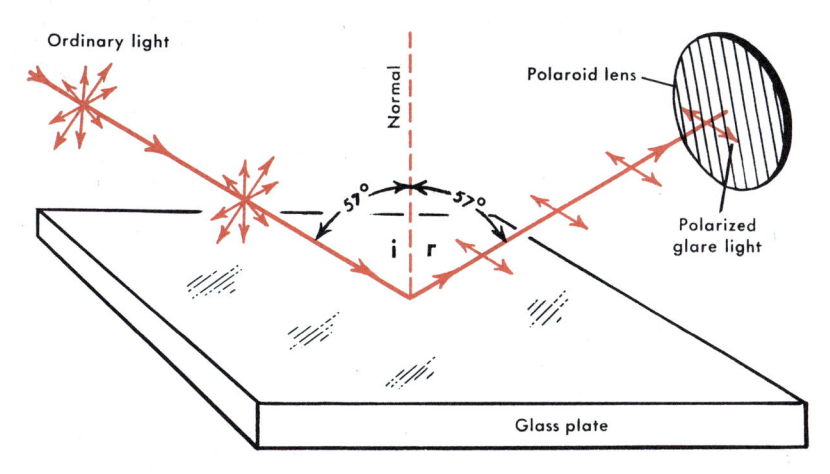

INTERFERENCE, POLARIZATION, AND THE SPEED OF LIGHT

Fig. 7. The fact that the reflected light does not pass through the Polaroid lens shows that the light is polarized.

between light polarizers, the body will exhibit colors at the points of stress (see Fig. 8). The effect is the same whether the stress is produced mechanically or by rapid and unequal cooling. Therefore, polarized light can be used to determine whether a glass bottle or other transparent body is under stress due to improper cooling. If, when it is viewed between polarizers, color patterns appear, the piece in question can be reheated or rejected.

Polarized light is also used in the study of the distribution of stresses and the discovery of strong and weak points in cogwheels, gear teeth, drive shafts, and similar objects. If transparent models are made of plastics and subjected to the same stresses that the finished products will experience, the weak points can be discovered when the models are viewed between polarizers. The weak points can then be strengthened. Also much material can be saved through the use of minimum quantities at points where the stress is shown to be the least.

Polarized light can also be used to prevent glare from automobile headlights.

Polarizing lenses in the headlight polarize the light, and a polarizing section in the windshield reduces the glare.

The speed of light. In the argument over waves versus corpuscles, we have answered one of the crucial questions, "Does light bend around a corner?" in favor of Huyghens' wave theory. Another question remaining for us to answer concerns the speed of light.

Courtesy Dr. W. M. Murray, M.I.T.

Fig. 8. Stress patterns about a hole.

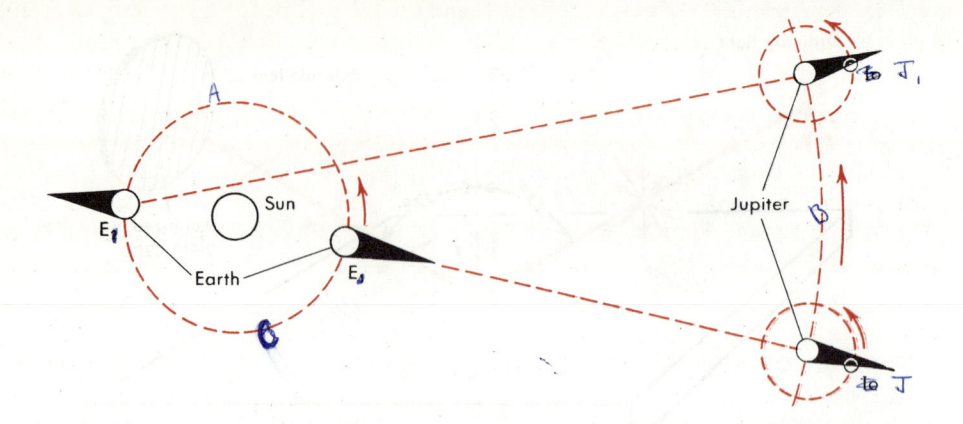

Fig. 9. Roemer's method of determining the speed of light. Roemer observed that the eclipse of Io occurred 1000 minutes later when the earth was at E_2 than at E_1.

Aristotle believed that light travels instantaneously from one point to another. Both Newton and Huyghens opposed this theory. Neither thought it possible for either a particle or a wave to travel instantaneously.

Galileo performed the first known experiment to measure the speed of light. He placed two observers, A and B, several miles apart, each with a lantern. A uncovered his lantern and at the same instant noted the time. When B saw the light from A's lantern, he uncovered his lantern. When A saw the light from the lantern of B, he again observed the time. The speed of light was calculated by dividing twice the distance between the observers by the difference between the two observed times. Needless to say, the times for various trials varied so greatly that no reliable speed was obtained. Explain what could have been done so that observer B would have been unnecessary.

In 1676 Olaus Roemer, a Danish astronomer, observed slight variations in the time periods between the eclipses of one of the moons of Jupiter, Io, which traverses its orbit around Jupiter in the direction shown in Fig. 9.

Since the orbits of the sun, earth, Jupiter, and Io lie in about the same plane, at times when Io and the earth are on opposite sides of Jupiter, Io is eclipsed and cannot be seen from the earth. (See Fig. 9.) When the earth was near E_1, Roemer determined the time intervals between the eclipses. He used this position because, when the earth is near this point, it is moving neither toward nor away from Io; consequently the light travels from Io to the earth through the same distance for each of the eclipses.

Roemer found this time interval between eclipses to be 42 hours, 28 minutes, and 36 seconds, and he used it to predict the times of occurrence of future eclipses. If an eclipse occurred on Wednesday at 2:45 P. M., when should the next one occur? The next after that?

When, however, the earth was near E_2, the eclipses occurred 996 (approximately 1000) seconds later than when the earth was at E_1. The time intervals between the eclipses did not change.

Roemer knew that when the earth is near E_1, it is 186,000,000 miles closer to Io than it is at E_2. Why? He reasoned that the delay was the time required for light

INTERFERENCE, POLARIZATION, AND THE SPEED OF LIGHT 503

to travel the 186,000,000 miles. Therefore, to find the velocity of light, he divided the number of miles (distance) by the number of seconds (time), $\frac{186,000,000}{1000}$, and found the speed of light to be *186,000 miles per second*, or approximately 300,000,000 meters per second. For practical purposes this is the velocity usually used.

Other measurements of the speed of light. Not until 1849 was the velocity of light measured over a short distance. The French physicists Foucault and Fizeau, working independently and using different methods, both patterned after Galileo's method, succeeded in measuring the speed of light in the same year. Fizeau substituted a revolving toothed wheel, and Foucault substituted a revolving mirror for Galileo's observer *A*, who took the cloth off and put it back on the lantern. Both substituted a mirror for observer *B*. Foucault's method was very similar (see Fig. 10) to that used by Michelson, an American, in 1880 and again in 1927.

Fizeau found the speed of light to be 186,900 miles per second, Foucault found it to be 185,800 miles per second, and Michelson found it to be 186,281 miles per second in a high vacuum. All are very close to the approximate value of 186,000 miles per second found by Roemer. Michelson's value is considered to be the most reliable one.

Foucault measured the velocity of light in water. He found light to take 1.33 times as long to travel a certain distance in water as in air. Since 1.33 is the index of refrac-

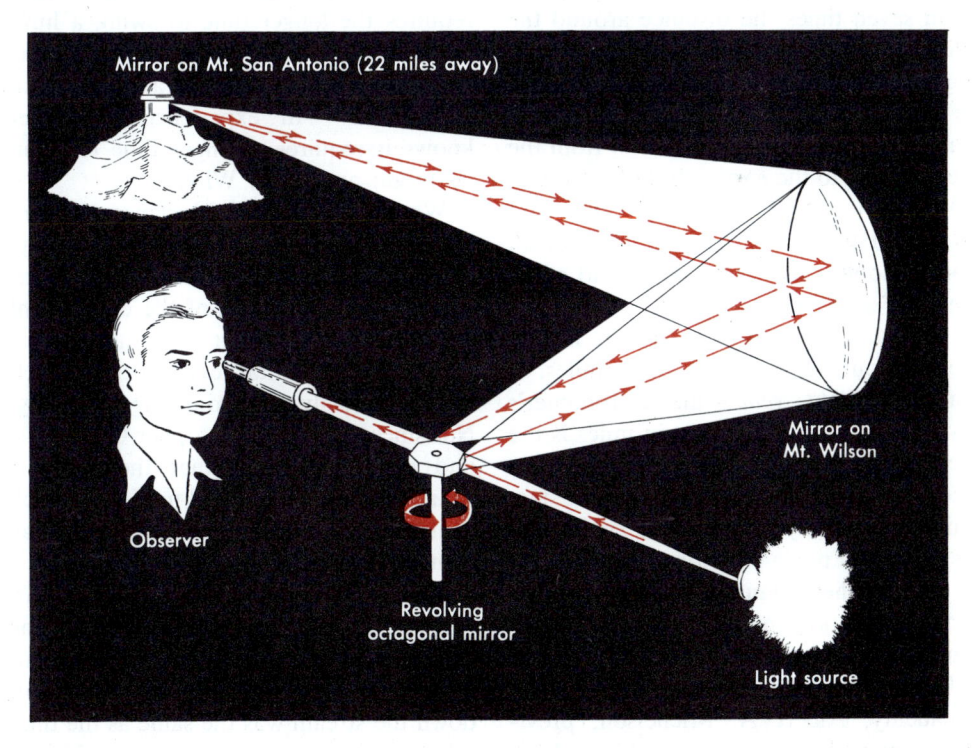

Fig. 10. Michelson's measurement of the speed of light. He determined the amount of time it took for the reflected light to make the 44-mile round trip during $\frac{1}{8}$ of a revolution of the rapidly rotating octagonal mirror.

tion for water, it appears that the index of refraction of a substance may be defined as *the ratio of the speed of light in a vacuum to the speed of light in the substance.*

These findings for the speed of light in water were contrary to Newton's predictions but agreed perfectly with Huyghens' wave theory. As a result, one might expect the corpuscular theory to have been completely discredited and the wave theory firmly established. However, we should remember that old beliefs die hard in spite of the evidence contrary to them.

The astronomer's "yardstick." The velocity of light is so enormous that it is almost beyond our conception. A simple calculation shows that in one second light will travel a distance somewhat greater than seven times the distance around the earth at the equator. The time required for light to travel from the moon to the earth is about 1.3 seconds; from the sun to the earth, a little over eight minutes; from the nearest star to the earth, about four years; from Polaris, our North Star, about 44 years. If Polaris were destroyed, how much longer could sailors use its light to guide ships at sea?

The distance that light travels in one year, about six million million miles, is called a *light year*—the astronomer's "yardstick." How far away in miles is the nearest star? Polaris? With modern telescopes astronomers are now studying stars millions of light years distant. Explain why astronomers use such a long yardstick.

Does ether actually exist? Another crucial question in the wave versus corpuscle controversy was whether or not an ether exists. While a student at the Naval Academy, Albert A. Michelson, previously mentioned, began thinking about this question. Like other physicists of his day, Michelson assumed that the ether is the one thing in the universe which is standing still. Therefore he reasoned that the moving earth should cause apparent ether currents parallel to the direction in which the earth moves, just as a moving train or automobile causes apparent air currents in still air.

In 1881 Michelson, assisted by Morley, attempted to measure the velocity of light with respect to the ether by timing the passage of light a certain distance up the ether stream and back, and the same distance across the stream and back. In case an ether exists and is standing still, then the time required for the light to travel up the stream and back should be greater than the time taken by the light to travel across the stream and back. Why this should be the case can best be explained by our considering the question, "Which requires the longer time to swim, a hundred yards upstream and back in a flowing river or a hundred yards across stream and back?" An experienced swimmer knows it requires a longer time to swim upstream and back. Why?

When the Michelson-Morley experiment was performed, to the surprise of everyone, the two times were found to be exactly equal. Repetition of the experiment with the most precise instruments showed that the experimental results were correct. This was really an astounding discovery. Not since Galileo, Christopher Columbus, and others proposed that the earth is round, instead of flat, had man faced such a situation. It did not make sense and was contrary to the physics of that time.

Another mystifying discovery was that, when light from the sun or other star was used in the Michelson-Morley experiment, the time taken by the light to travel up and down the stream was the same as the time taken to travel across the stream and back, regardless of whether the earth was turning so that the apparatus was traveling toward the light source or away from it.

This was about like saying that when two cars approach each other at 50 miles per hour their relative passing speed is not 50 + 50, or 100 miles per hour, but is 50 miles per hour instead. Their speeds are not additive.

One way of explaining the results was to assume that the earth is standing still. This however was unthinkable. Another explanation, just as unthinkable, was that there is no ether. But this is about like telling modern New Yorkers that there is no water in the Hudson river on which boats there float.

Einstein's special theory of relativity. It was Albert Einstein who brought order out of chaos by making two simple basic assumptions.

1. **Everything in the universe is in motion and hence there is no way of distinguishing absolute motion.** In other words, **all motion is relative.**

2. **The velocity of light in empty space is constant, regardless of the motion of the source or the observer of light.**

Although any good theory ought to make sense, this alone is not a complete test of any idea. Time and time again we have seen in our studies that a seemingly logical theory may be completely out of agreement with experiment. A more important test of a theory is whether it can be used to predict new data which agree with experiment, and to bring into agreement all the seemingly diverse and contrary data pertaining to it. Would Einstein's new theory, which he called the *special theory of relativity,* meet these tests?

Starting with his two basic assumptions, Einstein began deducing their logical consequences and thereby predicting what the universe is like. The results so far are that not one false prediction has been made.

Furthermore, by means of these two simple basic assumptions, Einstein and others brought into harmony all the seemingly contradictory facts pertaining to the Michelson-Morley experiment. But most important of all was that Einstein's new theory of relativity opened up a whole new vista for scientific investigation, a vista even greater than the one opened up 300 years earlier by Galileo and Newton. Einstein's special theory was really the beginning of the Atomic Age.

Most important for the present study is that Einstein's special theory cast doubt on the wave theory of light. Without ether, how could a light wave travel through empty space? In spite of Young's interference experiment, could it be that Newton's corpuscular theory was going to win in the long run? These questions will be considered again after mirrors and lenses have been studied.

SUMMARY AND CONCLUSIONS

1. According to Young's interference experiment, light appears to be a wave phenomenon.
2. Experiments show that light consists of transverse waves.
3. Light which has passed through a tourmaline crystal, or polaroid disk, is said to be polarized. The crystal, or disk, is called a polarizer. The particles in the medium transmitting the polarized light vibrate in planes parallel with the axis of the polarizer.
4. If polarized light strikes the surface of a crystal or polaroid disk whose axis is parallel with the plane of polarization, the light passes through. If the axis is perpendicular to the plane of polarization, the light is not transmitted.
5. Light is partially polarized when reflected by most highly polished or smooth nonmetallic substances, such as the surface of a lake, paper, or glass.
6. Glare is caused by light polarized by reflection. Glare from water, highways, pa-

per, and other things can be counteracted by the wearing of polarizing lenses.

7. Glare from headlights can be reduced by polaroid lenses on headlights and polaroid strips on windshields.

8. The speed of light is approximately 186,000 miles or 300,000,000 meters per second.

9. The index of refraction of a substance may be defined as the ratio of the speed of light through air (or a vacuum) to the speed of light through the substance.

10. The Michelson-Morley experiment tended to prove that ether does not exist.

QUESTIONS FOR REVIEW

1. Explain the formation of the alternate dark and bright lines in Young's interference experiment.

2. What was the full significance of the discovery of the polarization of light?

3. What are the meanings of the terms polarizer and analyzer?

4. For what angle of incidence will reflected polarized light be a maximum? What kinds of reflectors are the best polarizers?

5. Make a list of as many uses of polarized light as you can.

6. Describe Roemer's method of determining the speed of light. Compare it with Galileo's method.

7. Define the index of refraction of a substance in terms of light speeds.

8. Calculate the number of miles in a light year.

9. From your own experience, cite as many incidents as you can which have indicated to you that motion is relative.

10. What was the purpose of the Michelson-Morley experiment? What did the results seem to prove?

11. What experiments tended to prove the wave theory of light? Why? Did the Michelson-Morley experiment tend to prove or to disprove this theory?

12. What are the assumptions underlying Einstein's special theory of relativity?

13. Since time is measured in terms of motion, would you say that it is relative or absolute? Explain.

PROJECTS

1. Do Young's interference experiment as explained at the beginning of this chapter.

2. To demonstrate Young's findings more easily, scratch two very fine lines, about 1 millimeter apart, in the emulsion of an undeveloped photographic plate. Hold the slits just in front of one eye. Do not use a screen. A lamp with a vertical filament and a green filter in front of it may be used as the light source.

3. *How to polarize light by reflection.* Make the apparatus described in experiment L-125 of Sutton's *Demonstration Experiments in Physics.*

4. *How to demonstrate photoelasticity* (show strains in materials by the use of polarized light). See experiment L-134 in Sutton.

READING YOU WILL ENJOY

1. *Encyclopaedia Britannica,* Vol. 23, "Velocity of Light."

2. Gamow, G., *Mr. Tompkins in Wonderland.* The Macmillan Company, New York, 1940. Mr. Tompkins, having attended some scientific lectures, dreams of a universe of relativity phenomena.

3. Sutton, R. M., *Demonstration Experiments in Physics.* McGraw-Hill Book Company, Inc., New York, 1938.

4. Taylor, L. W., *Physics, the Pioneer Science,* pp. 549-564. Houghton Mifflin Company, Boston, 1941. After reading this discussion of polarized light, discuss why such a long period of time has elapsed between the discovery of polaroid lenses and their application to automobile headlights.

Chapter 43

Image Formation and Mirrors

The problem. Did you ever see the look of wonder and bewilderment on the face of a small child when he first recognized his own image in a full-length mirror? And did you notice that perhaps he tried to walk behind the mirror in search of his mysterious second self? Also, have you ever seen the startled action of a wild animal when he lowered his head to drink from a pool of water and suddenly saw his own image staring him in the face?

Image formation plays a varied and important part in our lives. Without it we could not see or be seen. And without sight, man probably could not exist on the earth. The problem in this chapter is to discover how images are produced by use of mirrors.

Image formation. We have already considered image formation in a pinhole camera. See page 486. Here light comes from an object through a pinhole onto a screen. This light is then reflected from the screen to the eye, and an image of the object is seen on the screen. You will recall that the reproduction is far more faithful and the details are much sharper when the pinhole is comparatively small than when it is large. This, we explained, is due to the fact that, as light passes in straight lines from a point on the object to the screen, it can cover but a very small surface on the screen provided the hole is small. Likewise, light from other points does the same. Consequently, light from one point on the object does not overlap the light from other points in forming the image. As a result, the light reflected by a point on the image is almost identical with that reflected by a corresponding point on the object. It is for this reason that an image is produced. In case the pinhole (aperture) is large, the light from several different points overlaps at one point on the screen, causing an indistinct, blurred image.

How is an image formed by a plane mirror? You look daily into a plane (flat) mirror, and perhaps wonder why you can see yourself and why you appear to be behind the mirror. The deception of the direction is due to the fact that when we see an object we determine its location primarily by the direction from which light enters the eye. Since the light entering the eye is reflected from the mirror, your face appears to be in that direction. However, this does not explain why your face appears to be behind the mirror instead of at its surface.

As shown in (a) of Fig. 1, when an object is placed in front of a mirror, millions of light rays pass from each point on

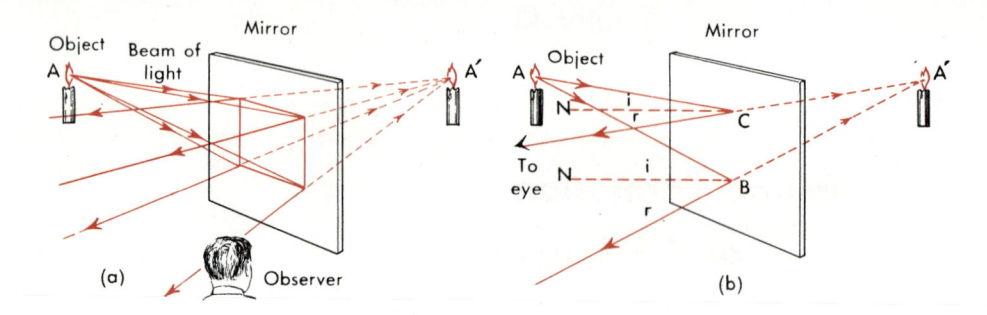

Fig. 1. (a) Why the image of A appears at A' and how A' is located according to the laws of reflection. (b) A simpler method of locating the image A'.

the object, such as point A, to the mirror. A small percentage of these are reflected from the front surface of the mirror, but most of them are reflected by the silver-coated back surface, according to the laws of reflection which we studied on page 488. As a result, the eye in the figure sees the image of A at point A' behind the mirror. Why the image of A appears to be at point A' can be shown better if the reflected rays are extended backward on themselves behind the mirror, where they all meet at point A', exactly where the image appears to be. Notice, however, that the light does not really radiate from point A'; it only appears to do so.

However, as shown in (b) of Fig. 1, to locate the image of A, or the point of apparent divergence, we need to extend but two reflected rays backward behind the mirror, though a third will serve as a check. But regardless of how many reflected rays are extended behind the mirror, they should all converge at one point, which will be found to be as far behind the mirror as the object A is in front of the mirror.

Virtual and real images. When light

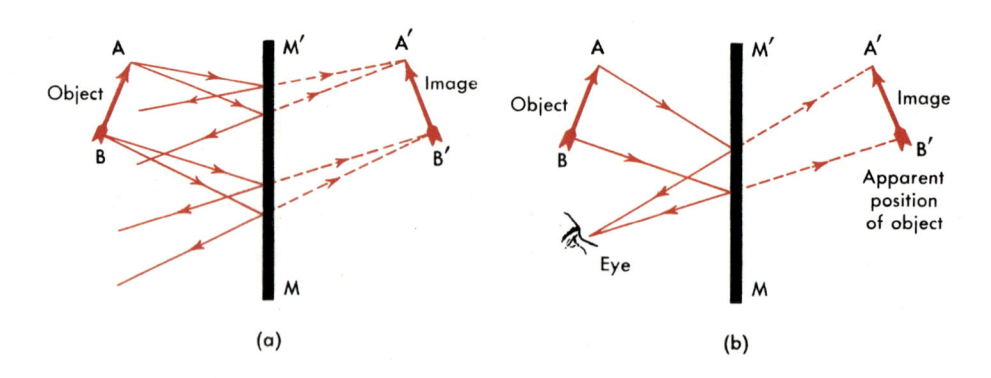

Fig. 2. (a) How the image of AB is located in a plane mirror. (b) Why the image appears to be behind the mirror. The image produced by a plane mirror is called a virtual image, since light does not actually come from the image.

does not actually diverge from where an image appears to be, as in the case of the image formed by a plane mirror, the image is said to be *virtual,* or *unreal.* In contrast with a virtual image is the *real* image formed by the pinhole camera on page 486. From a real image, light rays actually diverge and strike the eye. A real image can be caught on a screen, whereas a virtual image cannot be. Virtual images are "optical ghosts," whereas real images actually exist. Name at least one virtual image and two real images other than those already mentioned.

How is the complete image of an object located in a plane mirror? The image of a straight line, *AB,* can be determined if the images of the two end points, *A* and *B,* are located, then connected by a straight line. Fig. 2 (a) shows how to do this. Here the plane mirror *MM'* reflects light coming from *A* and *B*. Two incident rays are drawn from each point to the mirror and are reflected according to the laws of reflection, as shown. Both pairs of reflected rays are then extended behind the mirror. The reflected pair coming originally from *A* converge at *A'*, which locates the image of *A*, and the reflected pair coming from *B* converge at *B'*, which locates the image of *B*. If the points *A'* and *B'* are connected by a straight line, we have the complete image of *AB*. Part (b) of Fig. 2 shows the paths of the rays of light necessary for an eye to see the image. Measurement will show that the image is as far behind the mirror as the object is in front of the mirror, and the size of the image is the same as that of the object. Locate the image of a triangle by means of a diagram. Is the image of the triangle reversed?

That in a plane mirror the image is reversed is better shown in Fig. 3. Here the letter *F* reads backward. Is the image of your face reversed in a similar manner?

In conclusion, we see that

the image formed by a plane mirror is the same size as the object; it is the same distance behind the mirror as the object is in front of the mirror; the image is reversed; and it is virtual.

Characteristics of an image. Every image has several different characteristics, and in every study of images these should be considered. (1) Is it real or virtual? (2) Larger or smaller than the object? (3) In front of or behind the mirror? (4) Inverted or erect? What are the characteristics of an image formed in a plane mirror?

Curved mirrors. The number of things that can be done with a plane mirror is limited, so perhaps it was for this reason that men early began to investigate other shapes. One of the first forms studied was the spherical mirror—that is, one consisting of a portion of the surface of a sphere. There are two types of such mirrors. If the hollowed-out portion is used, it is called a *concave* mirror. See Fig. 4. If the opposite side is used, the mirror is called *convex*. The center of the sphere of which the curved surface is a part is called the *center of curvature (CC)*, and its radius is called the *radius of curvature*. A line drawn from the center of curvature to the exact center of the mirror surface is called the *principal axis*.

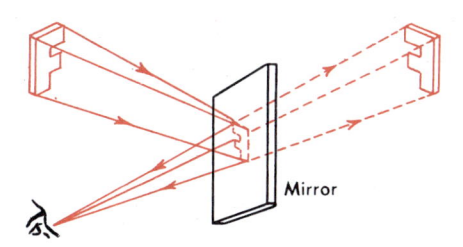

Fig. 3. Describe the characteristics of the image F in the plane mirror.

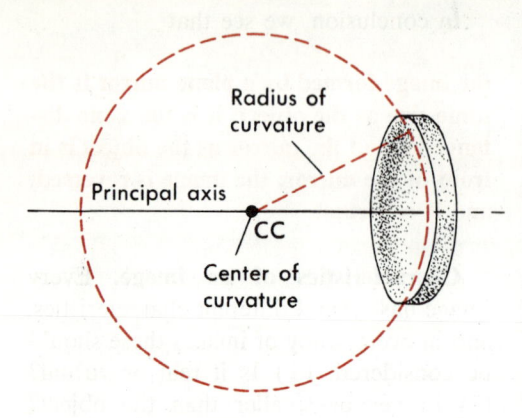

Fig. 4. Concave-convex spherical mirror. Which side is concave?

Reflection from curved mirrors when the source of light is far away. As you may know, when a concave mirror is held toward the sun, the rays of light parallel to the principal axis are reflected so that they converge to one point on the principal axis, as shown in (a) of Fig. 5. This point, F, is known as the *principal focus* of the concave mirror. The distance from the center of the mirror to F is called the *focal length*. Measurement will show that the principal focus, F, lies halfway between the mirror and the center of curvature of the mirror.

If a convex mirror is used, as in (b) of Fig. 5, rays parallel to the principal axis are reflected so that they all appear to come from a single point behind the convex mirror. This point is the *virtual focus point*.

Reflection from curved mirrors when the source of light is at or near the principal focus. Regardless of the kind of mirror, light is always reflected according to the laws of reflection. When the light source is placed at the principal focus of a spherical concave mirror, the light rays striking the mirror near its center are reflected parallel to the principal axis, as shown in (a) of Fig. 6. The rays of light striking the edge of the mirror are reflected so that they diverge, that is, spread out. This can be corrected if the curvature of the mirror is changed to make it parabolic in shape, like the small end of an egg. See (b) of Fig. 6. How are the rays of light caused to converge in (c) of Fig. 6?

Images formed by a spherical convex mirror. When you look at yourself in a convex mirror, your image appears to be

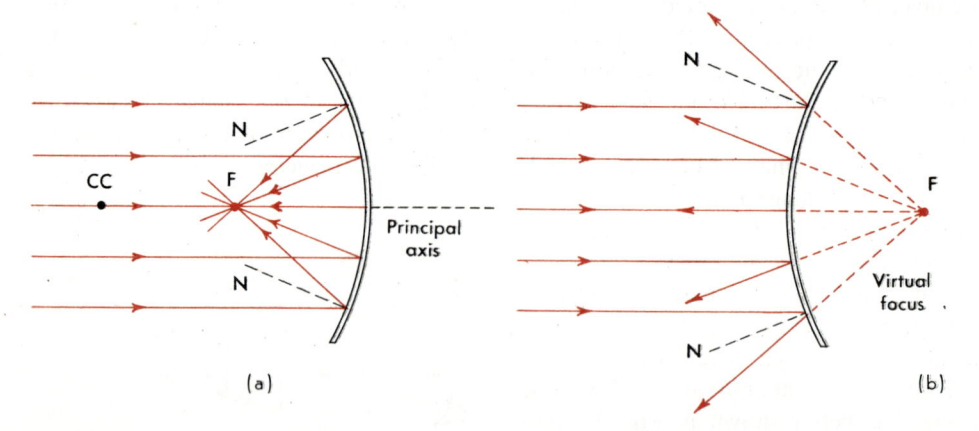

Fig. 5. (a) Reflection from a concave mirror. (b) Reflection from a convex mirror. Note that in both cases the incident rays are parallel with the principal axis.

IMAGE FORMATION AND MIRRORS

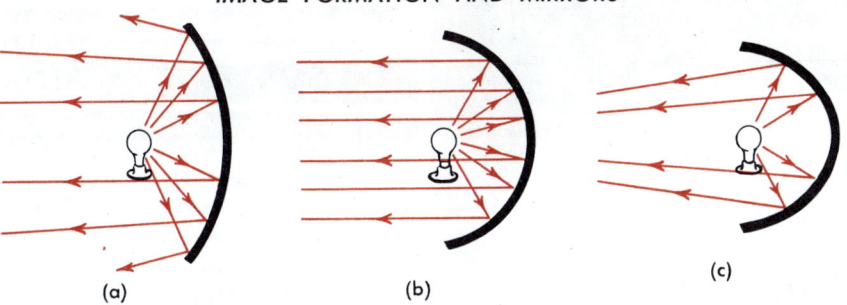

Fig. 6. (a) Rays striking the mirror near its center are reflected parallel to the principal axis. Rays striking near the outside of the mirror are caused to diverge from the principal axis. (b) By changing the curvature of the mirror, all the rays are reflected parallel to the principal axis. In (c) the curvature is still sharper.

virtual and behind the mirror, erect, smaller than yourself, and closer to the mirror than you are. These characteristics of an image in a convex mirror seem to be true regardless of the object distance, D_O, which is the distance from the mirror to the object. Could you use the diagrammatic scheme developed for plane mirrors to locate and study images in a convex mirror?

To answer this question, draw two incident rays AD and AGC from the point A, and two rays BEC and BH from point B, as shown in Fig. 7, so that they are reflected from the convex mirror MM' according to the laws of reflection. Note that C is at the center of curvature and that AG and BE are perpendicular to the mirror. Next, extend behind the mirror the two reflected rays coming from A until they meet at point A'. Likewise, extend the reflected rays coming from B backward behind the mirror until they meet at B'. Now connect the points A' and B' with a straight line. This should be the location of the image of the line AB. Study of the diagram shows that $A'B'$ is smaller than AB, is closer to the mirror than AB, is erect, and is a virtual image behind the mirror. Since these characteristics all agree with the observations above, it appears that the diagrammatic scheme applied to plane mirrors also applies to convex mirrors.

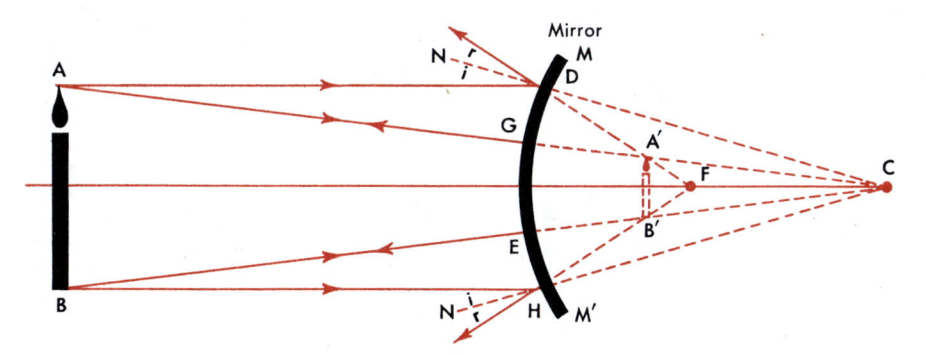

Fig. 7. Image produced by a convex spherical mirror.

Courtesy General Dynamics Corp.

Fig. 8. (a) By focusing this concave searchlight mirror at the sun, it becomes an efficient solar furnace for testing metals.

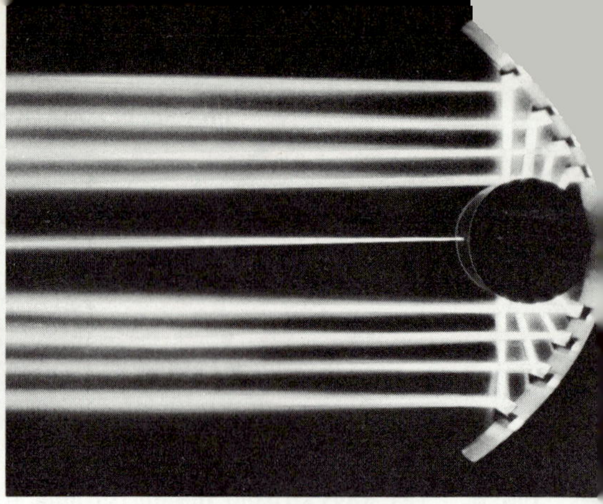

Courtesy General Motors Corp.

Fig. 8. (b) A parabolic reflector is used in automobile headlamps to cause the rays of light to emerge parallel.

Convex spherical and convex cylindrical mirrors are often used as rear-view mirrors in automobiles because they will reflect a much larger view than a plane mirror of the same size can reflect.

Image formation and construction when a concave mirror is used. We have seen that the general scheme for constructing and locating images in a plane mirror can be used with a convex mirror. Can the same method be used with a concave mirror?

To answer this question, let us consider how the image of point A in (a) of Fig. 9 is found. First, a single ray of light AD is drawn from A to D on the mirror parallel with the principal axis. At D the ray is reflected in accordance with the laws of reflection. What do we call the point at which the reflected ray DA' crosses the principal axis?

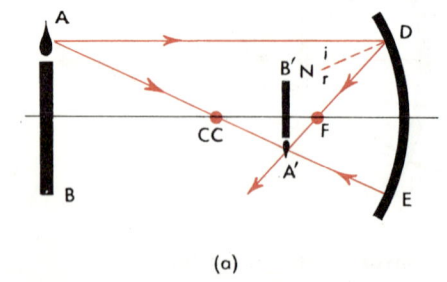

Next, we draw a second ray from A to the mirror so that it strikes the mirror at E and is perpendicular to it. We can do this by drawing the second ray from A through the center of curvature, CC, of the mirror. When this ray strikes the mirror it is reflected back on itself, intersecting at point A' the other reflected ray originally coming from A. This point, A', should be the image of A. If A' is the image, however, then all the other rays of light that originate at A and are reflected by the mirror must pass through A'. That this is true is shown in (b) of Fig. 9, which is drawn so that all the incident rays entering the mirror are reflected according to the laws of reflection.

The image of B, the other end of the candle in (a) of Fig. 9, can be located in the same manner as the image of A was located. As a result the image of B, lettered

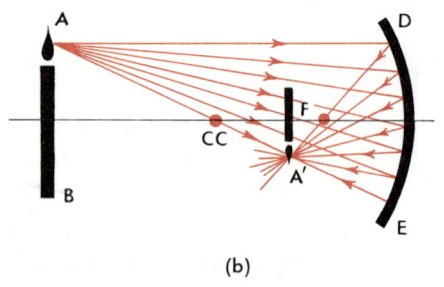

(a)   (b)

Fig. 9. The location of the image A' of the object-point A in a concave mirror.

IMAGE FORMATION AND MIRRORS

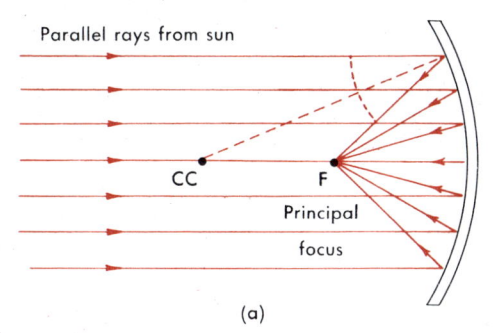

Fig. 10. (a) When the object distance is very great, the image formed is located at the principal focus and is real, inverted, and very small.

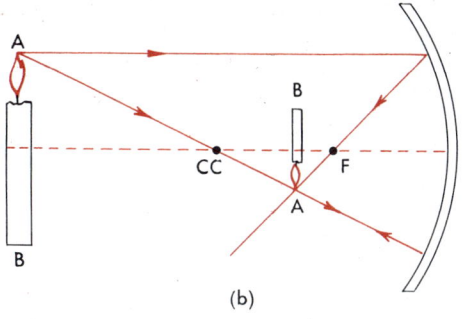

Fig. 10. (b) When the object distance is beyond the center of curvature, the image formed is located between the principal focus and the center of curvature.

B', will be found directly above A', the same distance above the principal axis as A' is below the principal axis. Explain. And when these two points, A' and B', are connected as in (a) of Fig. 9, the complete image $A'B'$ is thereby located. In most of the diagrams that follow, only the image of A is found, but the student is expected to know how to find the image of B.

Does a concave mirror produce more than one image? We have found that a convex mirror produces only a virtual image, regardless of where the object is placed. Is this true of a concave mirror? To answer this question (see Fig. 10), we must resort to experiment by placing the object at all possible distances in front of the concave mirror in the following manner.

(a) Make the object distance very, very great, infinitely great, so that all rays from it incident to the mirror are parallel. At this distance, the object is said to be at *infinity*. The sun can serve as the object in this case.

The image can be caught on a translucent screen located at the principal focus of the mirror, and it is real, inverted, and very small. Give a practical example of a concave mirror used in this manner.

(b) Place the object between infinity and the center of curvature, CC. The image is located between the principal focus and the center of curvature CC; it is real, inverted, and smaller than the object. Compare the object distance and the image distance.

(c) Place the object at the center of curvature. The image is now found to be right at the center of curvature, and the object distance and image distance are equal. The image is real, inverted, and the same size as the object. Note that when the object was moved all the way from infinity to the center of curvature, the image moved only from the principal focus to the center of curvature.

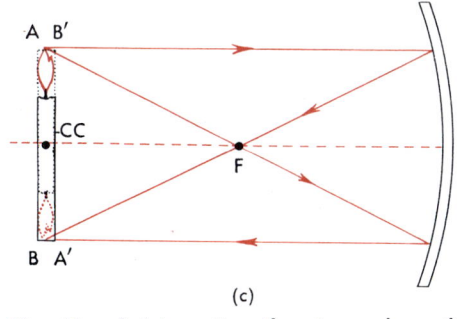

Fig. 10. (c) Locating the place where the image is formed when the object is placed at the center of curvature of a concave mirror.

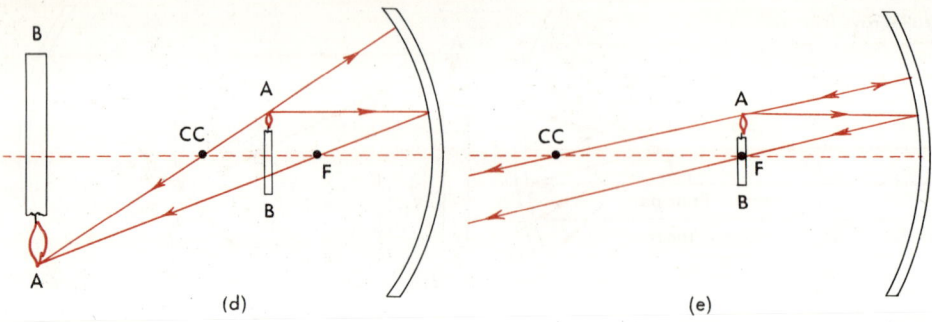

Fig. 10. (d) Locating the image when the object is placed between the center of curvature and the principal focus.

Fig. 10. (e) When the object is placed at the principal focus, no visible image is formed.

(d) Place the object between the center of curvature and the principal focus. The image is now found beyond the center of curvature. Note again that as the object approaches the mirror in the successive cases illustrated, the image is found farther from the mirror. The image distance in this case is greater than the object distance. The image is real, inverted, and larger than the object.

(e) Place the object at the principal focus. In this case the rays originating at A are reflected so that they are parallel, and no image can be found. But we have already noted that, as the object is brought toward the mirror and approaches the principal focus, the image distance and magnification both increase tremendously. We can therefore assume that the image approaches infinity as the object approaches the principal focus. Also note that as the object moved from the center of curvature to the principal focus, the image moved all the way from the center of curvature to infinity, and its size increased in a similar manner.

(f) Place the object between the principal focus and the mirror. In this position the image appears behind the mirror. The image is virtual, erect, and larger than the object, and the image distance is greater than the object distance. The closer the object comes to the principal focus, the greater the image distance as well as the magnification. Where is the image and what is its size when the object is right on the principal focus? The shaving mirror is designed so that one's face, when placed about ten inches in front of it, is between the mirror and the principal focus. Thus the image is magnified.

Concave mirror used in a telescope. As we have seen, the image of a distant object formed by a concave mirror is inverted, real, and much smaller than the object. The smallness of the image can be remedied by magnifying lenses and the image can be studied in detail at close range. Attachments may also be made which photograph the image. The largest such *reflecting telescope* is shown in Fig. 11.

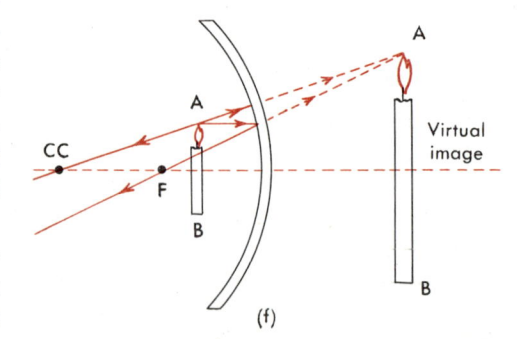

Fig. 10. (f) Locating the image formed by a concave mirror when the object is between the principal focus and the mirror.

Fig. 11. The Hale telescope showing the observer in the prime-focus cage and the reflecting surface of the 200-inch concave mirror. Light rays coming down the tube from a star are reflected 55 feet by the mirror to the prime-focus cage, where photographs are taken. Contrary to popular notion, the large mirror is not designed to achieve greater magnification, but rather to increase the light-gathering ability and resolving power of the mirror.

Pepper's Ghost. When an object is placed at the center of curvature of a concave mirror, a real image will fall upon the object and its size will be the same as that of the object. However, the image will be inverted. In case a lighted lamp is hidden from sight and placed in front of a concave mirror and below the principal axis, as shown in Fig. 12, an image "ghost" of the lamp will be formed above the principal axis. Also, if an empty light socket is placed directly above the image, it can be made to appear all the more realistic. The real image looks so real that people who stand at a distance will say that a lamp is actually burning in the socket. An image of this kind has long been known as "Pepper's Ghost."

Magnification by use of mirrors. The relation of the size of the image to the size of the object is called *magnification*. Fig. 13 shows an object, AB, and the constructed image, $A'B'$, in which two triangles are formed, AOB and $A'OB'$. Since angle (i) equals angle (r), then the two right-angled triangles are similar, and consequently:

$$\frac{A'B'}{AB} = \frac{OB'}{OB}$$

But since $A'B'$ equals the size of the image, S_i; AB equals the size of the object, S_o; OB' equals the image distance, D_i; and OB equals the distance, D_o, then:

$$\frac{S_i}{S_o} = \frac{D_i}{D_o}$$

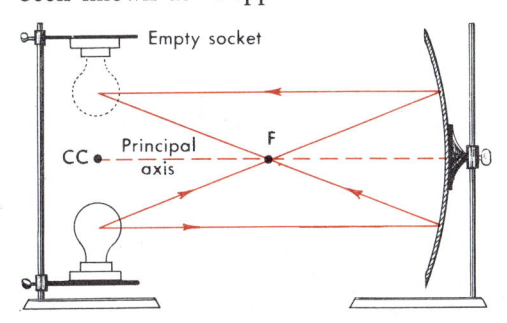

Fig. 12. Demonstration of "Pepper's Ghost" with a concave mirror.

Fig. 13. Magnification with a concave mirror. Where is the image formed?

Also, since the ratio of the size of the image, S_i, to the size of the object, S_o, is the magnification, M, we have:

$$M = \frac{S_i}{S_o} = \frac{\text{Size of image}}{\text{Size of object}}$$

or

$$M = \frac{D_i}{D_o} = \frac{\text{Image distance}}{\text{Object distance}}$$

In what positions, if any, can the object be placed so that the image formed by (a) a concave mirror and (b) a convex mirror is larger than the object? See Figs. 7 and 10.

How are object distance and image distance related to focal length? The relationship among the object distance, D_o, the image distance, D_i, and the focal length, f, is given by the formula

$$\frac{1}{D_o} + \frac{1}{D_i} = \frac{1}{f}$$

This formula applies for concave mirrors as well as convex mirrors. It is a very valuable relationship because it makes it possible to find the distance to a faraway object by indirect measurement. Only two quantities need to be known, the image distance and the focal length, both of which can be easily measured. Also, if the object and image distances are known, the focal length can be calculated.

PROBLEM: The image of a distant object is 100 inches from a concave mirror whose focal length is 98 inches. What is the object distance?

SOLUTION:

$$\frac{1}{D_o} + \frac{1}{D_i} = \frac{1}{f}$$

Substituting,

$$\frac{1}{D_o} + \frac{1}{100} = \frac{1}{98}$$

Or

$$\frac{1}{D_o} = \frac{1}{98} - \frac{1}{100}$$

$$\frac{1}{D_o} = \frac{100}{9800} - \frac{98}{9800}$$

$$\frac{1}{D_o} = \frac{2}{9800}$$

$$2\,D_o = 9800$$

Or

$$D_o = 4900 \text{ inches}$$

$$D_o = 408\tfrac{1}{3} \text{ feet}$$

In concave mirrors, D_o and f are always considered to be plus ($+$). For real images, D_i is $+$. These are always in front of the mirror and on the same side of it as the object is. For virtual images, D_i is minus ($-$).

PROBLEM: An object stands 8 feet in front of a concave mirror whose focal length is 12 feet. (a) Where is the image located? (b) Is the image real or virtual?

SOLUTION:

$$\frac{1}{D_o} + \frac{1}{D_i} = \frac{1}{f}$$

Substituting,

$$\frac{1}{8} + \frac{1}{D_i} = \frac{1}{12}$$

And

$$\frac{1}{D_i} = \frac{1}{12} - \frac{1}{8}$$

$$\frac{1}{D_i} = \frac{2}{24} - \frac{3}{24} = -\frac{1}{24}$$

Therefore

$$D_i = -24 \text{ feet}$$

Since D_i is negative, the image is virtual and is behind the mirror.

In convex mirrors, since the image and virtual focus always appear behind the mirror, D_i is always negative and f is always negative.

PROBLEM 1: A candle is placed 18 inches in front of a convex mirror having a focal length of 9 inches. Where is the image formed?

IMAGE FORMATION AND MIRRORS

SOLUTION:

$$\frac{1}{D_o} + \frac{1}{D_i} = \frac{1}{f} \text{ and } \frac{1}{18} + \frac{1}{D_i} = -\frac{1}{9}$$

Also,

$$\frac{1}{D_i} = -\frac{1}{9} - \frac{1}{18} = -\frac{2}{18} - \frac{1}{18} = -\frac{3}{18}$$

Hence

$$-3 D_i = 18$$

And

$$D_i = -6 \text{ inches}$$

The image is therefore formed 6 inches behind the mirror and is virtual. Is it erect or inverted?

PROBLEM 2: A baby 24 inches tall stands 18 inches in front of a convex mirror. The image appears to be formed 12 inches behind the mirror. What is the image height?

SOLUTION:

$$\frac{S_i}{S_o} = \frac{D_i}{D_o}$$

Substituting,

$$\frac{S_i}{24} = \frac{12}{18}$$

$$S_i = 16 \text{ inches}$$

SUMMARY AND CONCLUSIONS

1. Mirror Image Characteristics

D_o (Object distance)	D_i (Image distance)	Image characteristics
PLANE MIRROR		
Any distance	Always equals object distance	Virtual, erect, true size, behind mirror, and reversed
CONVEX MIRROR		
Any distance	Between virtual focus and mirror	Virtual, erect, smaller, and behind mirror
CONCAVE MIRROR		
Very distant (at infinity)	At principal focus	Real, inverted, smaller
Beyond center of curvature (finite distance)	Between principal focus and center of curvature	Real, inverted, smaller
At center of curvature	At center of curvature	Real, inverted, true size
Between center of curvature and principal focus	Beyond center of curvature	Real, inverted, enlarged
At principal focus	No visible image	
Between principal focus and mirror	Behind mirror	Virtual, erect, enlarged

2. The formula $\frac{1}{D_o} + \frac{1}{D_i} = \frac{1}{f}$ applies in all cases to both convex and concave mirrors. D_o is always positive for both convex and concave mirrors.

In convex mirrors:
    f is always negative
    D_i is always negative

In concave mirrors:
    f is always positive
    D_i is positive for real images
    D_i is negative for virtual images

QUESTIONS FOR REVIEW

1. What does the fact that a sharp image is formed by a pinhole camera tend to prove?
2. Name two effects on the image:
   (a) When the hole in a pinhole camera is enlarged.
   (b) When the hole is made smaller. Explain.
3. What are the laws of reflection?
4. Locate the image of a point which is in front of a plane mirror.
5. Why does the image in Question 4 appear to be behind the mirror?
6. Distinguish between a virtual and a real image and give one example of each.
7. What are the four characteristics of an image?
8. What are the characteristics of the image formed in a plane mirror?

9. Make a diagram of a spherical concave mirror and show its principal axis, radius of curvature, center of curvature, and principal focus.

10. How can the principal focus of a spherical mirror be located by experiment? Explain.

11. What is the relationship between the focal length and radius of curvature of a spherical mirror?

12. By means of diagrams, locate and state the characteristics of the image formed by a spherical concave mirror when the object is placed:
   (a) Far beyond the center of curvature
   (b) At the center of curvature
   (c) Between the center of curvature and the principal focus
   (d) At the principal focus
   (e) Between the principal focus and the mirror

13. Where must the object be placed in front of a spherical concave mirror in order that the image will be magnified?

14. If in using the mirror formula, $\frac{1}{D_i} + \frac{1}{D_o} = \frac{1}{f}$, to solve a problem, we find the image distance to have a minus (negative) value, is the image real or virtual?

PROBLEMS

1. The focal length of a concave mirror is 25 centimeters. What is its radius of curvature?

2. An object is 15 inches from a concave mirror whose focal length is 6 inches. Calculate the image distance.

3. Make a sketch to locate the image in Problem 2. Is the image real or virtual?

4. A boy 5 feet tall stands 20 feet in front of a concave mirror. His image is located 2 feet in front of the mirror. What is the height of the image?

5. What is the focal length of the mirror in Problem 4?

6. Make a sketch of the object and image in Problem 4.

7. A convex rear-vision mirror has a focal length of 18 inches. An automobile is 30 feet from the mirror. At what distance from the mirror is the image formed? Is it in front of or behind the mirror?

8. A man, who is 18 inches wide across the shoulders, stands 10 feet in front of a convex spherical mirror. The focal length of the mirror is 5 feet. See Fig. 7. (a) What is the image distance? (b) What is the width of the image? What are the advantages of such a mirror? Disadvantages?

9. A man placed a concave mirror 4 inches from his face. The focal length of the mirror was 6 inches. If the man held his mouth so it was 2 inches wide, what width was its image? Was the image in front of or behind the mirror? Solve graphically and mathematically.

10. If in Problem 9 the man had placed the mirror 6 inches from his face, where would the image have been and what would have been its size? Solve graphically and mathematically.

11. How far from your face should you hold a concave spherical shaving mirror of focal length $f = 50$ cm. in order to magnify your face five times?

PROJECTS

1. Secure a blank piece of glass of the kind that is used in grinding the reflecting surface of a mirror telescope. This, along with the materials needed, can be obtained from certain scientific companies. Then grind the glass, silver it, and mount it as a telescope. For a few dollars you can make an excellent astronomical telescope. Consult your teacher for more information. Also, see Thompson's *Making Your Own Telescope*.

2. Make the apparatus needed to demonstrate Pepper's Ghost. It is always a source of wonderment at any science demonstration, such as an open house.

3. Demonstrate the principle of a reflecting telescope, using the concave surface of a highly polished tablespoon. Use an overhead lamp for the object. Also demonstrate the principle of the shaving mirror, using the same side of the spoon.

4. Make a report on the reflecting telescope that is located at Mt. Palomar, California.

READING YOU WILL ENJOY

1. *Optics and Wheels*. General Motors Corporation, Department of Public Relations, Detroit, Michigan. A pamphlet that deals with the light control of automobile headlights.
2. Stokely, James, *Stars and Telescopes*. Harper & Brothers, New York, 1936. A story of the telescope and the part it has played in astronomical discoveries.
3. Swezey, K. M., *After-Dinner Science*. Whittlesey House, McGraw-Hill Book Company, Inc., New York, 1948. "Where Is the Image in the Looking Glass?" p. 95; "See Yourself as Others See You," pp. 96-97; "Shaving Mirror Produces Phantom Flowers," pp. 98-99.
4. Thompson, Allyn J., *Making Your Own Telescope*. Sky Publishing Company, Cambridge, Mass., Reprint 1951. Tells how to grind mirrors, polish them, and mount them at very low cost.
5. Wright, Helen, *Palomar*. The Macmillan Company, New York, 1952. Tells the story of the world's largest telescope, which is located at Mt. Palomar, California.

Chapter 44

Lenses and Images

The problem of lenses and human welfare. The microscope of the microbe hunter, the camera of the motion picture producer, the sextant of the navigator, the telescope of the astronomer, and the eyeglasses of millions of ordinary citizens are but a few of the instruments using lenses upon which the life and comfort of modern man extensively depend. The development of these has been due largely to the direct application of the laws of reflection and refraction. In this chapter we shall consider lenses and how they produce images.

Kinds of lenses. Most lenses are made of glass, plastics, or some similar transparent material. Usually their surfaces are portions of either spheres or cylinders. Lenses whose surfaces are portions of spheres are called *spherical lenses,* and those with cylindrical surfaces are called *cylindrical lenses.* Hereafter, though, the term *lens* will mean *spherical* lens unless otherwise stated. As shown in Fig. 1, lenses may also be classified as:

1. *Converging* (convex) lenses, thicker at their centers than at their edges; and
2. *Diverging* (concave) lenses, thinner at their centers than at their edges.

Meanings of some terms. Most lenses have two surfaces, both or one of which is spherical or cylindrical. The center of the sphere, or cylinder, of which a lens surface is a part is called the *center of curvature*. In case one surface is flat, it too is considered part of a spherical surface having a center of curvature at *infinity*. Thus, each lens has two centers of curvature, *CC* and *CC'*, and two *radii of curvature,* as shown in Fig. 2.

A straight line joining the two centers of curvature is called the *principal axis,* and it is perpendicular, or normal, to the surfaces where it passes through them.

What happens when light passes through a lens? A converging lens, such as the one in (a) of Fig. 1, being thicker at the center than at the edge, is analogous to two prisms placed base to base. Fig. 3 (a) shows parallel rays of light falling on two such prisms placed base to base. It would be well for us to trace the ray *AO,* which is incident upon one face of the upper prism. First, however, we should recall that when a ray of light passes obliquely from a medium of lesser to one of greater optical density, its speed is decreased and it is bent toward the normal. Conversely, when a ray of light passes obliquely from a denser to a rarer medium,

520

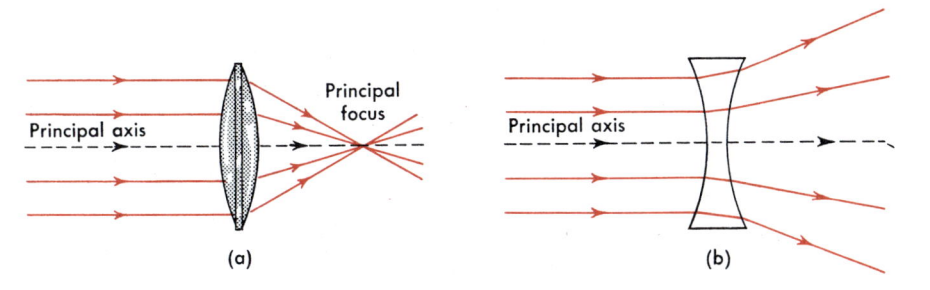

Fig. 1. How are the parallel rays of light refracted upon entering (a) a convex lens? (b) A concave lens?

its speed is increased and it is bent away from the normal.

At O the ray AO is refracted toward the normal NF. As it leaves the prism at B it is refracted away from the normal BE along the line BC. The feature we should note is that the light is bent toward the base, that is, toward the thicker part of the prism. Consequently, the two prisms placed base to base converge the light because each refracts the light toward its base.

Similarly, when light rays parallel to the principal axis fall on a converging lens, the rays are refracted toward the thick part of the lens, and they all converge at a point called the *principal focus*. See (b) of Fig. 3. The distance from the *optical center* (discussed below) of the lens to the principal focus is called the *focal length*. For very thin lenses, the only kind we shall consider, the focal length is the distance along the principal axis measured between the lens surface and the principal focus.

A diverging lens such as a double concave lens is analogous to two prisms placed as shown in (a) of Fig. 4. Again the rays of light parallel to the principal axis are refracted toward the thick part of each prism and hence are caused to diverge instead of converge. Similarly, with a diverg-

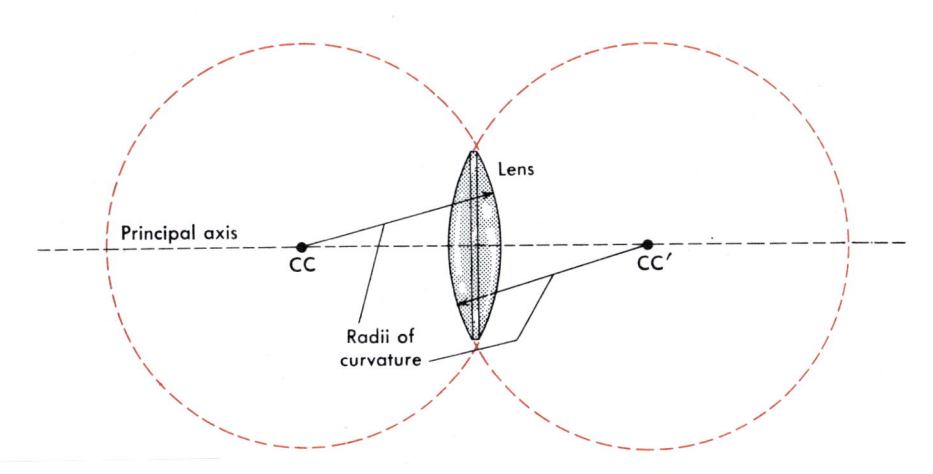

Fig. 2. Each surface of the lens may be considered part of a spherical surface. Points CC and CC' denote the respective centers of the spherical surfaces.

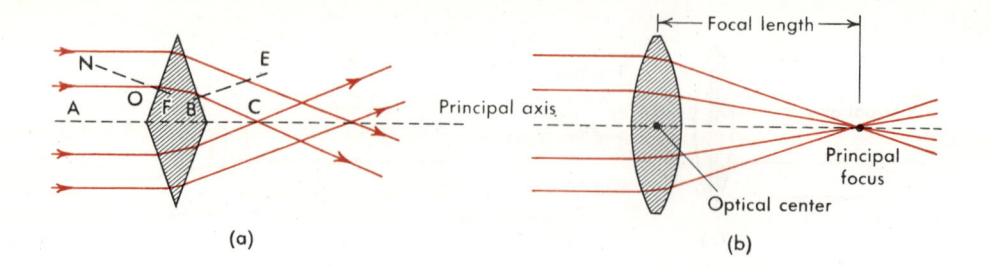

Fig. 3. The bending of light rays by two prisms placed base to base is similar to the bending of light rays by a converging, or convex, lens.

ing lens, rays parallel to the principal axis are bent away from the principal axis. After passing through the lens they appear to diverge from a point, *F,* on the opposite side. This point *F* is called the *virtual focus* because the refracted rays of light do not pass through it; they only appear to have come from this point. See (b) of Fig. 4.

Neither the converging nor the diverging lens bends light that passes through what is known as the optical center of the lens. These light rays pass straight through the lens. In symmetrical lenses, the optical center coincides with the geometic center. This fact should be kept in mind.

When two or more rays from a point, *A,* intersect after passing through the lens, this point of intersection is called the *refracted image* of *A*.

With a converging lens, where is the image when the object is at infinity? The first image we shall consider is that of a distant object far enough away so that the light rays from it, incident to the lens, are parallel or nearly so. The sun is such an object, and its distance is considered to be *infinitely great*. As you would expect, its image is located at the principal focus of a converging lens, as shown in (a) of Fig. 5. The image is real, inverted, very small, and can be caught on a screen. Care should be taken not to set the screen on fire. Since the image is at the principal focus, the image distance is also the focal length. Suggest an easy way for finding the focal length of a converging lens.

Where is the image when the object is between infinity and a place twice the focal length from the lens? As we have seen, the image of a very distant object is

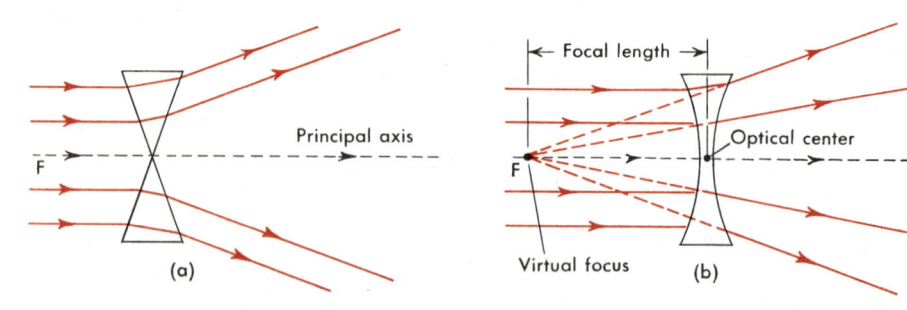

Fig. 4. Bending of light rays by two prisms, bases out, is similar to the bending of light rays by a diverging, or concave, lens.

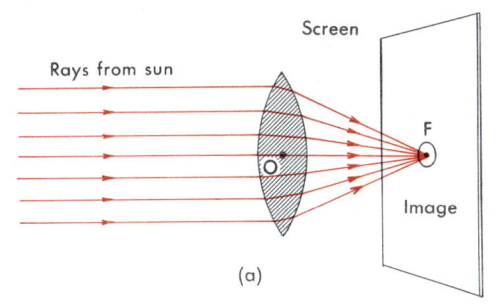

Fig. 5. (a) Locating the image formed by a convex lens when the object is at infinity.

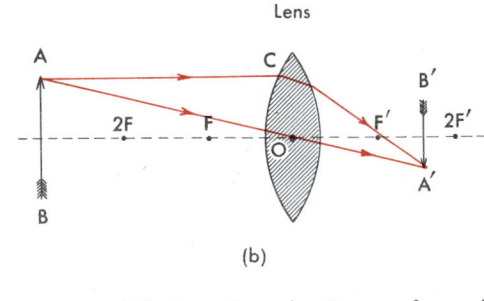

Fig. 5. (b) Locating the image formed when the object is between infinity and 2 f.

right at the principal focus. And as a distant object is brought closer to a converging lens, a great change in the object distance is needed to cause even an extremely small increase in the image distance. In fact, when the object is moved from infinity to a place twice the focal length from the lens, the image distance increases from the focal length to twice the focal length. Hence, if the focal length of the lens is very short, as it is in a box camera, the object distance can vary greatly with little variation in the image distance and with little change of sharpness of the image on the photographic plate.

The graphical construction of the image of an object placed between infinity and twice the focal length (2f) is shown in (b) of Fig. 5. From point A, light rays diverge in all directions. Many of them fall upon the lens, and it can be shown experimentally, as illustrated, that these rays are refracted so that they all converge at A', which is the image of A. To locate the image of A by the graphical method, it will be necessary to trace the paths of only two rays rather than of all of them. Explain why.

One of the two rays whose paths we know is AC. It, you will note, is parallel to the principal axis. Upon emerging from the lens, it passes through the principal focus, F'. The other ray is AO. This ray passes unrefracted through the optical center of the lens. The point A' where these two rays converge is the image of A. The image of B, marked B', can be found in the same manner. But since it is directly above A', the same distance above the principal axis as A is below the principal axis, the construction is not shown here. A line joining the two points A' and B' marks the position of the image of AB. As can be shown by experiment and construction, the image is real, inverted, smaller than the object, and more than once but less than twice the focal length from the lens. It is real because the light which passes from each point on AB through the lens actually converges at a point and then diverges. Millions of point images make up the whole image. Note that, for lenses, a real image is always on the opposite side of the lens from the object.

Where is the image when the object is twice the focal length from the lens? When the object is close enough so that its distance is twice the focal length, the image is found by both graphical construction and experiment to be *real, inverted, and the same size as the object; and the image distance, like the object distance, is twice the focal length.* See (c) of Fig. 5.

This arrangement is used in field telescopes to turn inverted real images right side up without changing their size.

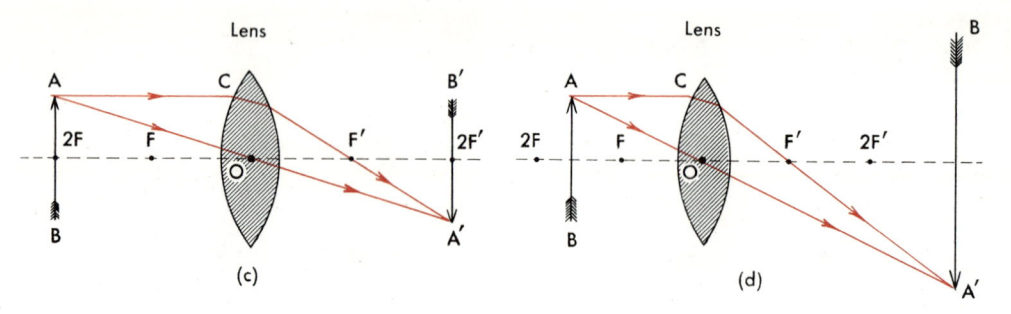

Fig. 5. (c) Locating the image formed by a convex lens when the object is at 2 f.

Fig. 5. (d) Locating the image formed when the object is between F and 2 f.

Where is the image when the object is between the focal point and 2f? As the object is moved from twice the focal length still closer to the lens, a very little change in the object distance causes a tremendous increase in the image distance as well as in the size of the image. This arrangement is used in the motion picture projector and magic lantern slides. The film or slide, strongly illuminated from behind, is located just outside the focal point of the projection lens. The image is formed many feet away and is much magnified on the screen. The film or slide must be inverted if the picture on the screen is to be right side up. Fig. 5(d) shows the graphic construction of the image, which is real, inverted, larger than the object, and more than two focal lengths from the lens.

Where is the image when the object is at the principal focus? If the object is now brought so close to the lens that it is at the principal focus, the distance to the image and its size are both infinite. This situation is the converse of the first one considered, where the object was at infinity and the image was at the principal focus. When a light source is placed at the principal focus of a lens, the rays from it incident to the lens are refracted so that they are parallel. Name at least one optical instrument in which such a condition exists.

Where is the image when the object is between the lens and the principal focus? Finally, let us suppose that the object is brought inside the principal focus. Again the rays diverge from each point on the object so much that the lens cannot bend them enough to converge them. Instead

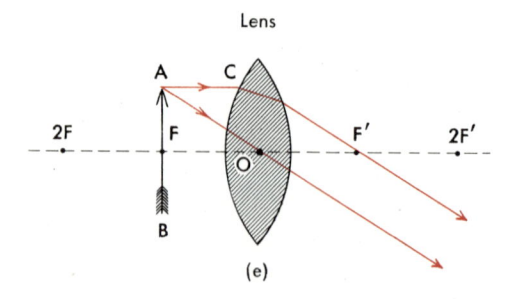

Fig. 5. (e) Explain why no image is formed when the object is at F.

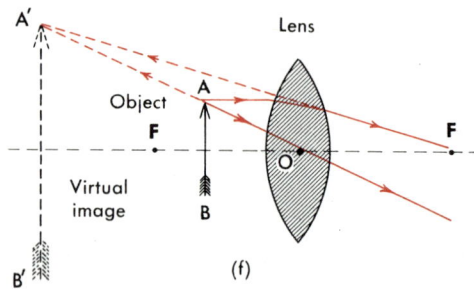

Fig. 5. (f) Locating the image formed by a convex lens when the object is inside F.

they continue to spread, or diverge, after passing through the lens. Consequently an image cannot be formed on that side of the lens. However, if the rays are projected backward after they emerge from the lens, they will converge on the same side of the lens as the object and should form a virtual image there. And sure enough, if you place your eye close to the lens and look through it at the object on the other side, you will see a virtual image which is erect and larger than the object. Its graphical construction is shown in (f) of Fig. 5. A lens employed in this way makes a very good magnifying glass or reading glass.

How do diverging lenses form images? Since diverging lenses cause refracted rays to diverge, it would be safe to predict that such a lens would never produce a real image. However, if the refracted rays were projected to the opposite side of the lens, a virtual image should be produced on the same side of the lens as the object. Experiment will show that, regardless of where you put an object with respect to a diverging lens, this prediction will be true. Fig. 6 shows the graphical construction of the virtual image. State the characteristics of the image formed.

What is the relative size of the image and the object? Referring to Fig. 6, we note that the triangles ABO and $A'B'O$ are similar. Explain why. Hence:

$$\frac{AB}{A'B'} = \frac{OB}{OB'}$$

Since OB is object distance, OB' is image distance, AB is height, or size, of object, and $A'B'$ is height, or size, of image, then:

$$\frac{\text{Height of object}}{\text{Height of image}} = \frac{\text{object distance}}{\text{image distance}}$$

This relationship is often written:

$$\frac{S_o}{S_i} = \frac{D_o}{D_i}$$

S_o represents the size of the object and S_i represents the size of the image. This formula is used to compute the magnification or the reduction in size of the image. It can also be used to calculate either image distance or object distance when one of these is unknown and the other three quantities are known.

PROBLEM: A tree 10 feet high forms a real image 5 inches high 2 feet from a converging lens. What distance is the tree from the lens?

SOLUTION:

$$\frac{S_o}{S_i} = \frac{D_o}{D_i}$$

Substituting,

$$\frac{120}{5} = \frac{D_o}{2}$$

$$5 D_o = 240$$

$$D_o = 48 \text{ feet}$$

Note that the height of the object was changed to inches. Why?

The relationship among the image and object distances and the focal length—the lens equation. The relationship among object distance, image distance, and the focal length is expressed by the same equation for lenses as for mirrors and is often called the *lens equation*. The lens equation is:

$$\frac{1}{D_o} + \frac{1}{D_i} = \frac{1}{f}$$

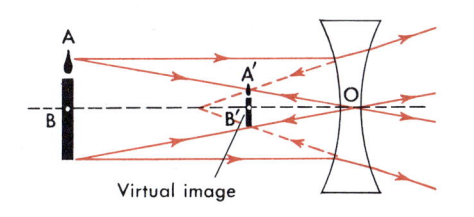

Fig. 6. The image formed by a concave lens is virtual, erect, and smaller than the object.

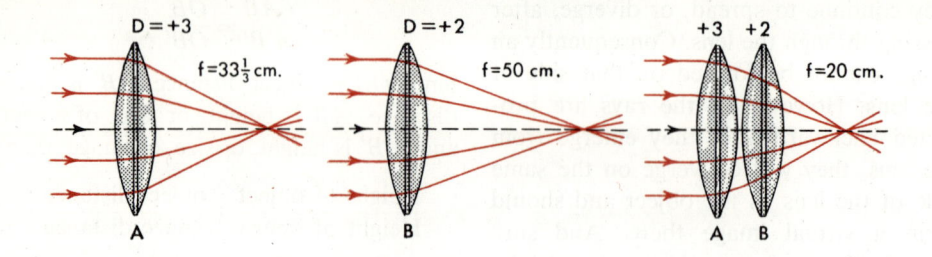

Fig. 7. By definition, the power of a lens whose focal length is one meter is one diopter. Power in diopters (D) is equal to the reciprocal of the focal length in meters.

The focal length f is always positive for a converging lens and negative for a diverging lens. If, in solving for the image distance D_i, a negative value is obtained, it means that the image is virtual.

PROBLEM 1: An object is placed 75 cm. from a thin converging lens whose focal length is 50 cm. Where will the image be located?

SOLUTION:
$$\frac{1}{D_o} + \frac{1}{D_i} = \frac{1}{f}$$

Substituting,
$$\frac{1}{75} + \frac{1}{D_i} = \frac{1}{50}$$

Transposing,
$$\frac{1}{D_i} = \frac{1}{50} - \frac{1}{75}$$

or
$$\frac{1}{D_i} = \frac{3}{150} - \frac{2}{150} = \frac{1}{150}$$

Clearing of fractions,
$$D_i = 150 \text{ cm.}$$

PROBLEM 2: In the preceding problem, where will the image be when the object is placed 25 cm. from the lens?

SOLUTION:
$$\frac{1}{D_o} + \frac{1}{D_i} = \frac{1}{f}.$$

Substituting,
$$\frac{1}{25} + \frac{1}{D_i} = \frac{1}{50}$$

Solving for D_i,
$$\frac{1}{D_i} = \frac{1}{50} - \frac{1}{25}$$

$$\frac{1}{D_i} = \frac{1}{50} - \frac{2}{50} = -\frac{1}{50}$$

and
$$D_i = -50 \text{ cm.}$$

This means that the image is virtual. Is it on the same side of the lens as the object or on the opposite side?

What is meant by the power of a lens? A thick lens with sharply curved surfaces bends light rays much more than does a thinner and flatter lens. The thicker lens with sharper curvature also has a shorter focal length than a thinner one. The more converging or diverging a lens is, the shorter its focal length, and the higher its bending power, or *power* for short. That is, the power varies inversely as the focal length. If D is the power, and f is measured in meters, the relation between focal length and power is given in the formula:

$$D = \frac{1}{f}$$

The power of a lens is usually measured

LENSES AND IMAGES 527

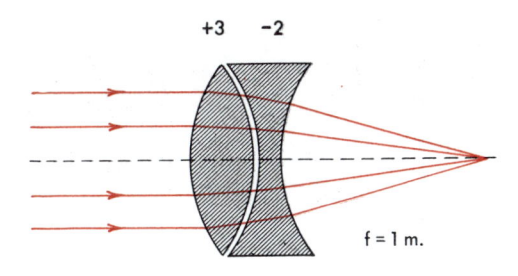

Fig. 8. What is the algebraic sum of the powers of the individual lenses?

in *diopters*. The power of a lens whose focal length is 1 meter is 1 diopter. The power is 2 diopters when the focal length is ½ meter and is 4 diopters when the focal length is 25 centimeters. What is the power of a lens whose focal length is 2 meters? 1/3 meter? 12½ centimeters?

The powers of spectacle lenses are usually measured in diopters. The power of a converging lens is *positive* and of a diverging lens is *negative*.

The power of two lenses when placed in contact. Fig. 7 shows a converging lens with a focal length of 33 1/3 cm. and a power of plus 3 diopters in contact with another converging lens having a focal length of 50 cm., or a power of 2 diopters. The focal length of the combination, as shown by experiment, is 20 cm., which means that the combined power is 5 diopters. Since $2 + 3 = 5$, the power of the combination (D_C) must equal the algebraic sum of the powers of the individual lenses. That is:

$$D_C = D_1 + D_2$$

A further test of this formula is shown in Fig. 8. Here a plus-3 diopter, converging lens is in contact with a minus-2 diopter, diverging lens. The focal length of the combination is shown by experiment to be 1 meter, which means that the power of the combination is plus 1 diopter. This agrees with the result, $-2 + 3 = +1$, obtained by the formula. What would be the combined power of a plus-2 lens and a minus-2 lens? Would the combination bring about either convergence or divergence?

Thus, we see that two converging lenses have greater converging power and shorter focal length than either one alone. Also, two diverging lenses have greater diverging power than one. And a diverging lens can be used to neutralize the effect of a converging lens, and vice versa.

Spherical aberration. In Fig. 9(a) the images near the outer edge of the lens are blurred; near the center of the lens they are not. Experiment shows that light rays refracted by such a spherical lens near its center and those refracted through the outer edges of the lens do not intersect at a single focal point. The outer rays, as shown in Fig. 9(b), intersect closer to the lens than the more central ones in converging lenses; the opposite is true of diverging lenses. This defect, which is known as *spherical aberration*, is the cause of the blurred images. It is more pronounced in thick lenses with short focal lengths than in thin lenses with long focal lengths.

Fig. 9. (a) Photograph taken with a lens having spherical aberration.

Courtesy Bausch and Lomb Optical Co.

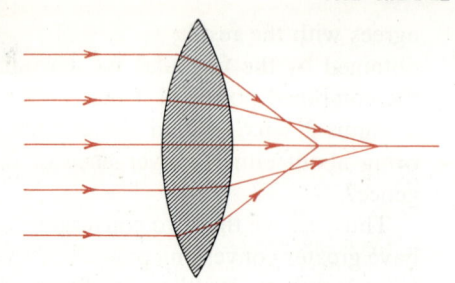

Fig. 9. (b) Why spherical aberration in a lens causes blurred images.

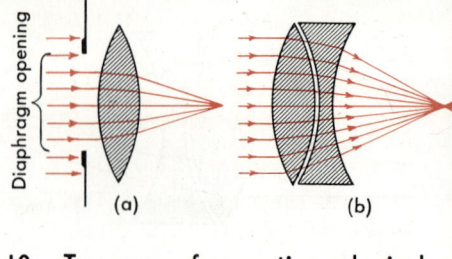

Fig. 10. Two ways of correcting spherical aberration.

One way to avoid spherical aberration is to use only the center part of the lens. Another is to grind the surfaces of the lenses so as to compensate for the greater refraction near the edges, but this method is very costly. A third method is to cement a converging and a diverging lens together into a compound lens, each individual lens having a different refractive index.

Chromatic aberration. When white light is refracted, light rays of different colors are dispersed as shown in Fig. 11(a). The red rays undergo the least refraction and the violet rays the most. This same dispersive effect exists in a lens and is known as *chromatic aberration*. The violet rays focus nearer the lens than the red rays, and the rays of other colors focus at intermediate points. Thus, each lens has a different focal length for each different color, and the image is fringed with color. Chromatic aberration, unless corrected, causes much difficulty in telescopes, microscopes, and similar instruments.

Chromatic aberration is usually corrected by a compound lens. Fortunately, the same compound lens can be used to correct both spherical and chromatic aberration. A lens designed to correct chromatic aberration is called an *achromatic lens*.

SUMMARY AND CONCLUSIONS

1. Lenses whose surfaces are portions of spheres are called spherical lenses, and those whose surfaces are portions of cylinders are called cylindrical lenses.
2. All lenses can be classified into two classes: diverging (concave), which are thicker at the edges than at the center; and converging (convex), which are thicker at the center than at the edges.
3. The center of the sphere of which the curved surface of the lens is a part, is called the center of curvature. Each lens has two

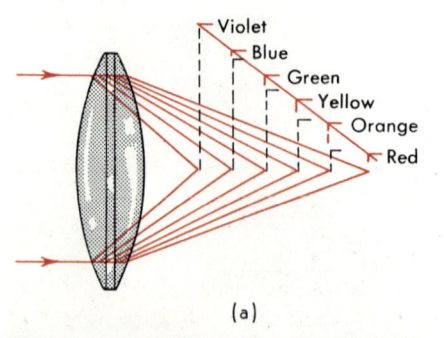

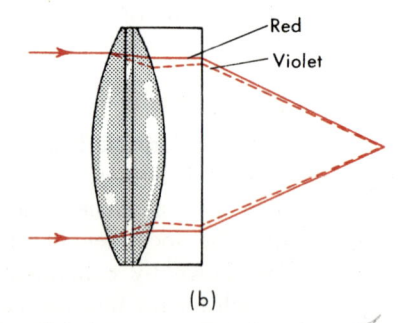

Fig. 11. (a) The cause of chromatic aberration. (b) Its correction by the use of a compound lens.

centers of curvature, and a line connecting these is called the principal axis of the lens.
4. Rays of light parallel with the principal axis upon passing through a converging lens are caused to converge at a point called the principal focus of the lens. The distance from the lens to the principal focus is called the focal length of the lens. With concave lenses, rays of light parallel with the principal axis are caused to diverge so that they all appear to come from a point, called the virtual focus, on the same side of the lens from which the rays enter the lens.
5. In lenses the relative positions of the object, lens, and image are as follows:

D_o	D_i	Image characteristics
CONVERGING LENSES		
Very distant (at infinity)	At principal focus	Real, inverted, smaller (theoretically a point)
More than twice the focal length	Between principal focus and twice focal length	Real, inverted, smaller
At twice the focal length	At twice the focal length	Real, inverted, same size
Between twice focal length and principal focus	Beyond twice focal length	Real, inverted, enlarged
At principal focus	No visible image (at infinity)	
Between principal focus and lens	Greater than object distance (same side of lens as object)	Virtual, erect, enlarged
DIVERGING LENSES		
Any distance	Less than object distance	Virtual, erect, smaller than object

6. The relationship among object distance, image distance, and focal length of a lens is given in the formula

$$\frac{1}{D_o} + \frac{1}{D_i} = \frac{1}{f}$$

For converging lenses:
f is always positive and on the opposite side of the lens from the object.
D_o is always positive.
D_i is positive when the image is real and on the opposite side of the lens from the object.
D_i is negative when the image is virtual and on the same side of the lens as the object.
For diverging lenses:
f is always negative.
D_i is always negative.
D_o is always positive.
7. The relationship among size of object, size of image, object distance, and image distance is

$$\frac{S_o}{S_i} = \frac{D_o}{D_i}$$

8. The power of a lens is measured in diopters. A lens having a focal length of 1 meter has a power D of 1 diopter. The diopter power of a converging lens is positive, $+$; of a diverging lens, negative, $-$.

$$D = \frac{1}{f \text{ (meters)}} = \frac{100}{f \text{ (cm.)}}$$

9. The power of a combination of lenses is given by the formula:

$$D_c = D_1 + D_2 + D_3 + \ldots D_n$$

QUESTIONS FOR REVIEW

1. What is the nature of the surfaces of a spherical lens? Cylindrical lens?
2. Make a sketch of a double convex lens, showing the two centers of curvature, two radii of curvature, the principal axis, and the two principal foci (one on each side of the lens).
3. Repeat Question 2, sketching a double concave lens.
4. Make a sketch showing how rays of light parallel to the principal axis pass through (a) a double convex lens; (b) a double concave lens.
5. What is the point called at which the refracted rays in Question 4(a) converge? In Question 4(b) diverge?
6. Explain what is meant by (a) focal

length; (b) image distance; (c) object distance.
7. Explain the path of a ray of light which passes through the optical center of a lens.
8. Explain an easy experimental way of finding the focal length of a converging lens.
9. With respect to a converging double convex lens, where is the location of the image of a distant object? Of an object which is located between the focal point and twice the focal length?
10. In finding the image of a point on an object, we draw two rays from the point to the lens. These rays are refracted by the lens. The image is located where they intersect. Explain the path of the two rays of light. Are they the only ones that pass from the point on the object to the lens?
11. What is meant by the term diopter?
12. What is the difference between a positive and a negative lens?
13. Will one-half of a lens produce a complete image of an object? Test your answer by covering half of a lens with a paper or cardboard.

PROBLEMS

1. An object is placed 10 ft. from a converging lens. The image distance is 3 ft. What is the focal length of the lens? Make a sketch showing position of object, image, and lens.
2. If the object in Problem 1 is 12 in. high, what is the height of the image?
3. The focal length of a converging lens is 24 in. An object is placed 60 in. from the lens. What distance is the image from the lens? Make sketch.
4. The focal length of a converging lens is 14 cm. What is the image distance when an object is placed 10 cm. from the lens? Make sketch.
5. In Problem 4 the length of the object is 5 cm. What is the length of the image?
6. What are the characteristics of the image in Problem 4?
7. A child 3 ft. tall stands 15 ft. from a camera lens whose focal length is 18 in. How far from the lens should the photographic plate be placed?
8. What would be the height of the child's unenlarged photograph in Problem 7?
9. The focal length of a lens is 12 cm. Where must a candle 4 cm. high be placed so that the image is real and 8 cm. high?
10. The focal length of a lens is 18 cm. What distance from the lens must an object be placed so that a real image is formed and is three times the size of the object? Hint: Let $D_i = 3D_o$. Why?
11. The focal length of a double convex lens is 50 cm. What is its power in diopters?
12. The power of a lens is 5 diopters. What is the focal length? Is the lens diverging or converging?
13. What is the focal length of a combination of lenses of 3 and −1 diopters? Of 3 and 1 diopters?
14. Match the objects I, II, III, IV, V, and VI with their respective images found among a, b, c, d, e, f, and g, Fig. 12.

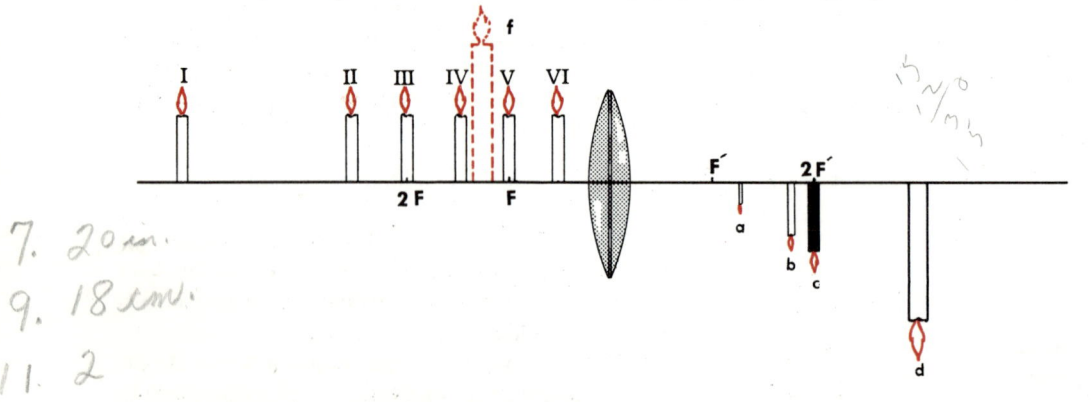

Fig. 12. Match the object positions with the respective images.

Chapter 45

Optical Instruments

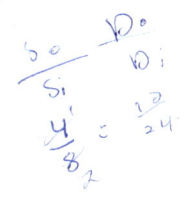

The problem. Optical instruments are designed in accordance with the known laws of lenses. In this chapter our problem is to discover how optical instruments are constructed and used to man's advantage.

The camera. Since the photographic camera employs but a single lens, or lens unit, it may be considered one of the simplest of all optical instruments. As illustrated in Fig. 1, a camera consists of a converging lens, usually of short focal length, which forms a real and inverted image on the film. If the object is distant the image will be formed close to the *focal plane,* which is the plane through the focal point perpendicular to the principal axis. If the object is close up, the image is formed beyond the focal plane.

In order that either distant or close-up objects may be photographed clearly with the same camera, the lens is set in the end of a bellows. This allows the image distance to be changed in accordance with the object distance. This changing of the position of the lens so as to make the image sharp and distinct on the film is called *focusing.*

In the box camera no such provision is made for focusing, yet fairly clear pictures can be made of both distant and fairly near objects. This discrepancy between theory and practice is accounted for in two different ways. First, in the box camera the focal length of the lens is quite short, being only a very small fraction of the distance to the nearest object which such a camera will photograph distinctly. As a result, even the images of the closest objects (about 10 feet in distance) are so near the focal plane and the film that any increase in the object distance can cause very little decrease in the image distance. Second, in the box camera the diaphragm opening is usually small, so that only the center of the lens is used. This reduces spherical aberration to a minimum and helps to sharpen the image (see page 527). Of course the small diaphragm opening increases the time of exposure, which limits picture-taking to still objects unless the intensity of illumination on the object being photographed is very great.

How to develop a photographic film and print a picture. When a picture is taken, the light that strikes the film causes a change in the silver bromide with which the film is coated. To be developed, the film is put in a solution known as developer. This removes the bromine from the silver bromide that was exposed to light,

532   THE RIDDLE OF LIGHT

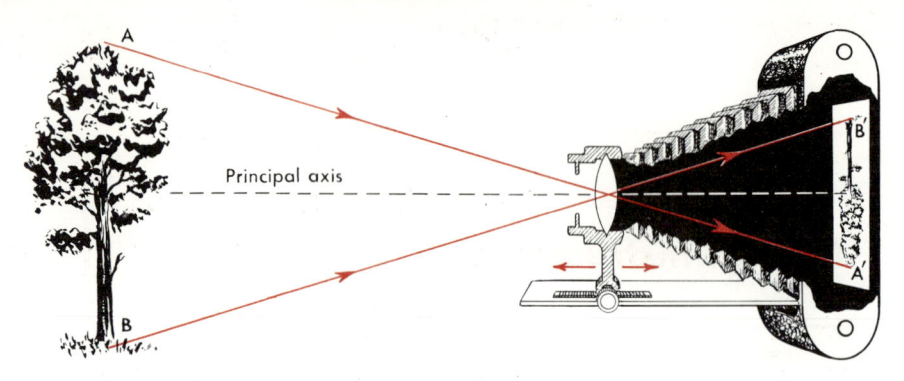

Fig. 1. A camera is focused by altering the distance between the lens and the film.

leaving the silver on the film. To "fix" the picture, the film is put in a "fixing" solution. This dissolves all the silver bromide not exposed to light but leaves the exposed silver on the film in the form of a black image. See (a) of Fig. 2. The treated film is now known as a *negative* and should be washed thoroughly and then dried.

To print the picture, the negative is laid on a sheet of paper coated with silver bromide and is then exposed to light. As a result, the darker image on the negative will shield the silver bromide beneath it, and all the rest of the coated paper will be exposed to light.

Consequently, when the print is developed the unexposed silver bromide will dissolve and the exposed silver bromide will remain as a black silver deposit. This is the finished positive picture. See (b) of Fig. 2.

The projecting lantern. The projecting lantern is essentially a camera in which the positions of the object and the image have been interchanged. The object, a lantern slide in Fig. 3, is placed a little farther from the objective lens L_1 than its focal length so that an enlarged inverted image is formed on a screen S placed several feet from the objective lens L_1.

The object, or lantern slide, is illuminated by a very bright source, such as a carbon arc or high-powered incandescent lamp, C, which is placed at the principal focus of the condensing lenses L_2. These concentrate the light upon the lantern slide.

In the moving-picture projector, the object is a long film made up of separate pictures. Sixteen to twenty-four of these distinct separate pictures are thrown on the screen per second, thus giving the

Fig. 2. A negative and a positive of the same scene.

Courtesy Standard Oil Co. (N. J.)

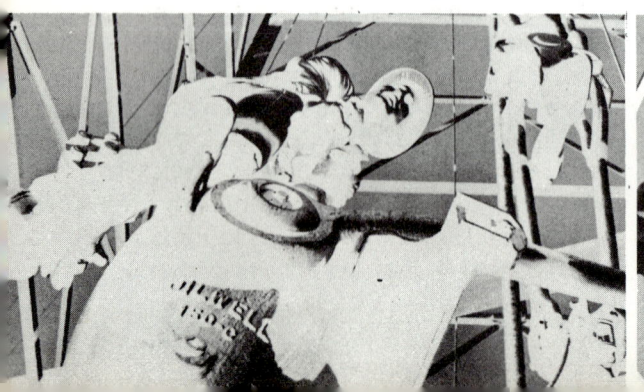

OPTICAL INSTRUMENTS

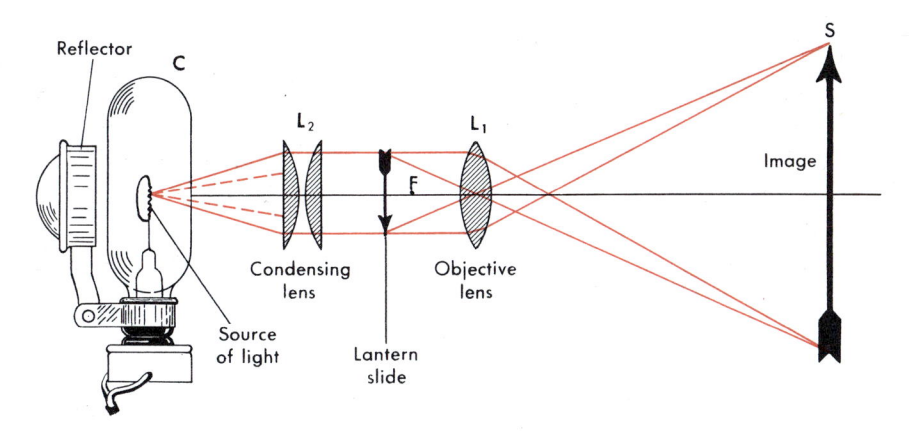

Fig. 3. The projecting lantern. Why is the object, or lantern slide, placed upside down in the slide carrier?

impression of continuous motion. (See page 542.

Magnifying glass. As we have already learned, there are two places where objects may be placed relative to a converging lens in order to produce magnification. First, when the object is between f and $2f$, a real, magnified image is produced on the opposite side of the lens. This type of magnification is used in projecting and magic lanterns. The image, of course, is real, and is projected on a screen.

With respect to what is generally called a *magnifying glass* (see Fig. 4), the object is usually placed inside the focal length of the converging lens practically at the principal focus, so close that the object distance, D_o, may be said to equal the focal length, f, and so that the image distance equals 25 centimeters. This image distance is used because the eye sees distinctly when 25 centimeters from the image. As a result the image is magnified, virtual, and on the same side of the lens as the object. The image is seen when the eye is close enough to the lens to see the object through the lens.

Since the magnification of a lens equals $\frac{D_i}{D_o}$ (see page 525), then a magnifying lens having a focal length of 5 centimeters has a magnifying power of $\frac{25}{5}$, or 5. Remember that $D_o = f$ and $D_i = 25$. What is the magnifying power of a lense whose focal length is 1 centimeter?

The refracting telescope and how to build one. The purpose of a refracting telescope is to enable us by means of lenses to see distant objects better. Logically, we can think of two ways in which a telescope might do this. First, it might cause the bodies to appear closer; secondly, it might

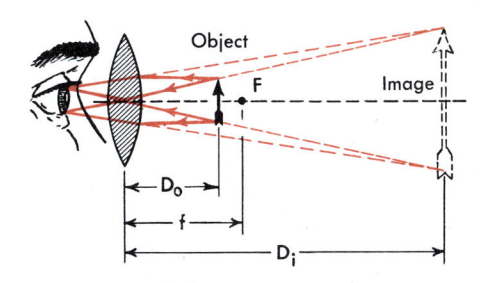

Fig. 4. A magnifying glass. Note that the object is placed inside the principal focus very close to the principal focus, F.

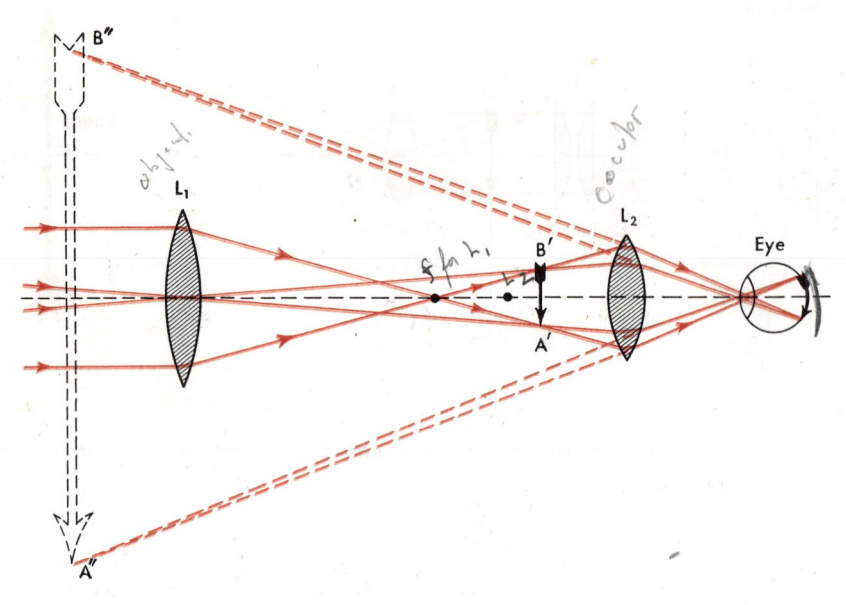

Fig. 5. A refracting telescope. The distant object is not shown.

cause them to appear larger. How can lenses be used to do these things?

We already know that a converging lens, which is used as the objective lens, L_1, in the telescope shown in Fig. 5, will form the image of a distant object as close to the eye as we may desire. Usually, however, this is of no advantage because the image is so small that the details cannot be recognized. But since the image is real, there is no reason why we cannot magnify it. We do this, as shown in the figure, by placing a converging lens, L_2, of short focal length, called the *eyepiece*, near the inverted real image $A'B'$. The eyepiece is placed so that $A'B'$ is between it and its principal focus. As a result, a magnified image $A''B''$ is produced. The image is inverted, but this is of no disadvantage as long as only heavenly bodies are viewed.

To secure an erect image when earthly bodies are viewed, another converging lens may be placed between the objective lens and the eyepiece so that the image $A'B'$ is at twice the focal length of the second lens. As a result an erect, real image of the object is formed at twice the focal length on the other side of this second lens. This image is then magnified by the eyepiece. The disadvantage of making the image erect in this manner is that the length of the telescope is increased. How this disadvantage can be overcome by another method will be shown in the study of the opera glass.

The opera glass. Galileo constructed a comparatively short telescope that did not invert the image. See Fig. 6. The same principle is used today in the *opera glass*. The objective in Galileo's type of telescope, as in the opera glass, is a converging lens, the same as in the telescope above. The difference is in the eyepiece, which is a diverging lens. This is placed so close to the objective that the real image which the objective would form at A' is not formed at all, because the diverging eyepiece bends the converging light rays from

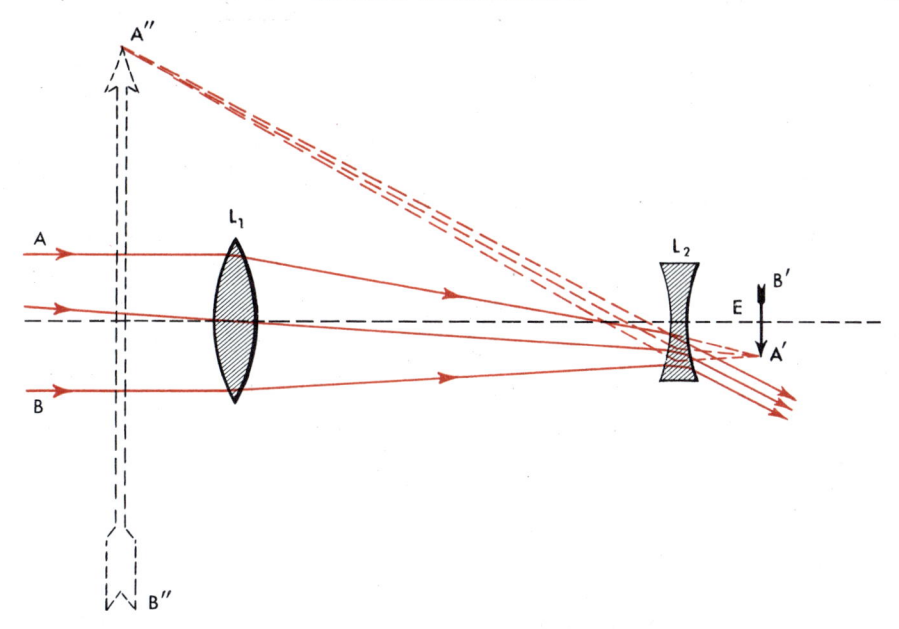

Fig. 6. Galileo's telescope. When the eye is placed at E, the image A"B" is seen.

A so that they appear to be coming from A''. In the same manner, rays coming from B appear to be coming from B''. Such construction not only magnifies the image and keeps it erect but also reduces the length of a telescope. This design is utilized in opera glasses. Galileo made a telescope of this kind and with it saw, before anyone else, the moons of Jupiter.

Prism binoculars. Fig. 8 shows the arrangement of parts in the common military and field glasses known as *prism binoculars*. They are quite short in length but still give magnification and erect images in spite of the fact that the objectives and eyepieces are converging lenses, as in the astronomical telescope of much greater length diagrammed in Fig. 5. The compactness and

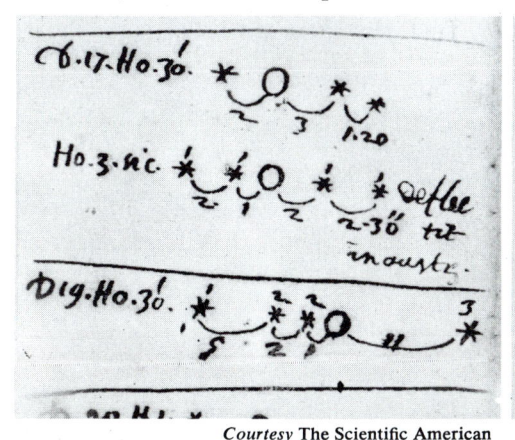

Fig. 7. Galileo's sketches of the moons of Jupiter that he saw with his telescope.

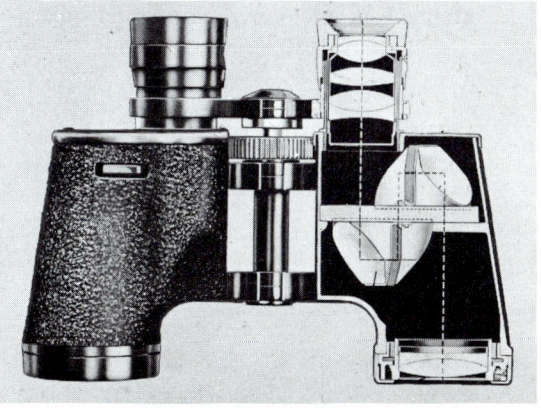

Fig. 8. Cutaway view of prism binoculars. The prisms produce an erect image.

magnification are due to the use of the reflecting prisms. These not only invert the image but cause the light rays to double back on themselves. They make possible objectives with greater focal length, obtaining greater magnification.

The microscope. The purpose of the microscope is to enable us to magnify small objects. Since lenses with the shortest focal length give the greatest magnification, it was no wonder that small glass spheres were used in the first successful microscope. Van Leeuwenhoek used lenses of this kind to discover the red corpuscles in the blood.

The *compound microscope* was invented by Galileo. Like his telescope, it consisted of an objective lens and an eyepiece. However, the objective of the microscope has a short focal length and the object is placed between its principal focus and twice the distance of its focal length, as shown in Fig. 9. This lens forms an inverted, magnified, real image in front of the eyepiece. The eyepiece has a greater focal length than the objective and is used as a magnifying glass. It forms a virtual magnified image of the already inverted and magnified real image of the object.

Only fairly low magnifying power was attained in the early compound microscope. Today's high-powered microscope overcomes this deficiency by using an objective with as many as ten lenses and an eyepiece with two or more lenses. With such lenses, magnifying powers as high as 2000 diameters are commonly attained.

Factors that limit magnification. Ordinarily we might think that there would be no limit to the amount that an image could be magnified and hence no limit to the minuteness of the object that could be seen through a microscope, provided perfect enough lenses could be made. There are, however, other limiting factors that exist, regardless of the degree of perfection of the lenses.

Huyghens predicted one of these other limiting factors. You will recall he said that if a body were small enough in comparison with the wave length of light, the body would not reflect the light wave. He believed that a light wave would pass right over and around a minutely small object without being reflected, in much the same way that a large wave passes over and around a small boulder on the ocean beach. As a consequence of this, Huyghens reasoned that if a body could not reflect light it could not be seen, regardless of the magnifying power of the microscope.

That Huyghens predicted correctly is

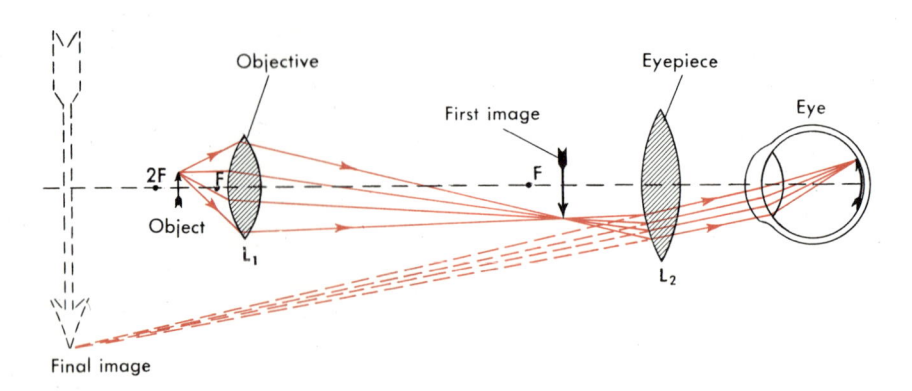

Fig. 9. A diagram of the optical parts of a compound microscope.

OPTICAL INSTRUMENTS

beam can be refracted and condensed as a light beam can be refracted and condensed (brought to a focus).

As we have already learned, there are two ways to refract or bend a stream of electrons. One method is to pass the stream through an electrostatic field. Negatively charged bodies would repel the stream and positively charged bodies would attract the stream.

Another method of bending a stream or beam of electrons is to pass it through a magnetic field. You will recall from your study of electric motors that a wire carrying moving electrons (current) through a magnetic field is pushed at right angles to the direction of the field. Fig. 10 shows

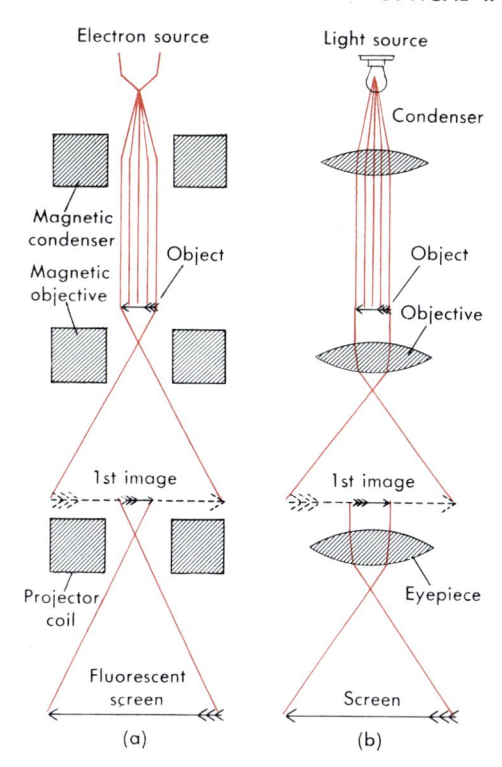

Fig. 10. Comparison of the principle of operation of an electron microscope and an ordinary visible light microscope.

Fig. 11. Specimens as small as one ten-millionth of an inch may be magnified 30,000 times with this electron microscope.

Courtesy Radio Corporation of America

shown by the fact that greater magnification can be obtained with short-wave ultraviolet light than with ordinary light, which has much greater wave length. Of course, such images cannot be seen directly because ultraviolet light is invisible. Usually such images are photographed or focused on a fluorescent screen, similar to a television screen.

The amazing electron microscope. Since electrons striking a photographic plate will have the same effect as light, it is logical to suppose that electrons reflected from a body will produce an image of the body, much as reflected light does. Furthermore, it is logical to suppose that the image can be magnified, provided that an electron

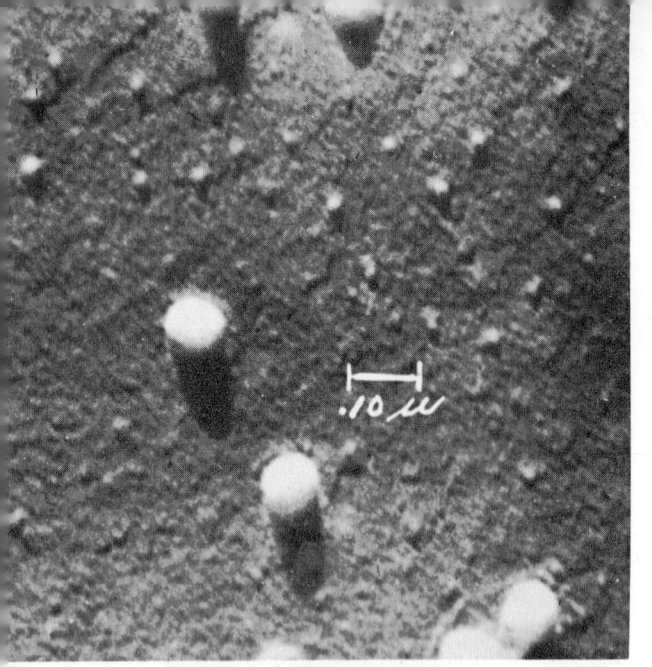

Courtesy Radio Corporation of America

Fig. 12. Influenza virus as revealed by electron microscope. The symbol μ represents one micron, which is the thousandth part of a millimeter.

how a magnetic field is used to condense a stream of electrons much as a converging lens condenses a beam of light.

Fig. 11 is a picture of an electron microscope. The source of electrons is a white-hot filament heated by an electric current. The heat causes the electrons to swarm out of the atoms of the metal. These electrons are speeded in the direction shown by an electrostatic field, not shown here, of 45,000 or more volts. The specimen is placed as shown and the electrons either pass through it or glance off it. Then they pass through the first *magnetic lens,* which produces the first image. This image is then magnified by a second magnetic lens, after which it can be projected onto a photographic plate or onto a fluorescent screen. In this manner, magnification of as much as 30,000 diameters can be obtained. Often the photographs are so distinct and sharp that they can be magnified still more, giving an over-all magnification of 120,000 to 250,000 diameters!

SUMMARY AND CONCLUSIONS

1. The camera consists of a converging lens which forms a real and inverted image on the film.
2. The focal plane of a lens is the plane through the focal point perpendicular to the principal axis.
3. The lens of a box camera has a short focal length to accommodate it to both distant and near objects without focusing.
4. The "object" for a projecting lantern or movie projector is the lantern slide or movie film, which is placed a little more than the focal length from the projection lens, thus giving a magnified image on the screen. In motion pictures the illusion of continuous motion is obtained by the projection of 16 to 24 "stills" per second on the screen.
5. The magnifying power of a lens =

$$\frac{25 \text{ cm.}}{\text{focal length (cm.)}}$$

6. The use of the electron microscope depends upon the facts that electrons affect a photographic plate as light does, and that they can be focused by electrostatic and magnetic fields.

QUESTIONS FOR REVIEW

1. Explain how a bellows camera is focused so as to obtain a distinct photograph of a distant object; a near object.
2. Explain why we can obtain distinct images of distant objects as well as fairly near objects with a box camera.
3. What is spherical aberration and how can it be reduced in a camera?
4. What is the effect on a photograph of making the diaphragm opening small? Explain.
5. How does a small diaphragm opening limit the variety of photographs that can be taken? Explain.
6. What is the effect on the photograph of making the diaphragm opening large?
7. Under what conditions should the diaphragm opening be large? Small?
8. What type of converging lens has the greatest magnifying power?

OPTICAL INSTRUMENTS 539

9. Where is the object placed with respect to the focal point of a simple magnifying lens?
10. Why should the image distance appear to be 25 cm. (10 inches) from a magnifying lens?
11. Make a diagram of a telescope in which a converging lens is used as the objective and one is also used as the eyepiece. Show the positions of both images relative to the lenses.
12. What are the shortcomings of the telescope in Fig. 5?
13. Make a diagram of Galileo's telescope. What are its advantages over the one in Fig. 5?
14. Make a diagram of a compound microscope, showing object and images.
15. Why can ultraviolet light be used to photograph smaller objects than can be photographed with ordinary visible light?

PROJECTS

1. Using two converging lenses and a cardboard tube into which the lenses can be fitted, make a telescope.
2. Using a diverging lens, a converging lens, and a cardboard tube into which the lenses can be fitted, make a telescope like the one which Galileo made. See Fig. 6.
3. Using two converging lenses, make a compound microscope. The lighted filament of a 1.5-volt flashlight lamp makes a good object.
4. Originate a method of showing that a drop of water can be used as a magnifying glass.

READING YOU WILL ENJOY

1. Ashcroft, E. B., *Eyes for Little Worlds*. School Service, Westinghouse Electric and Manufacturing Company, Pittsburgh, Pennsylvania. A pamphlet which tells the story of the microscope.
2. Neblette, C. B., F. W. Brehm, and E. L. Priest, *Elementary Photography,* Third Revised Edition. The Macmillan Company, New York, 1945. Chapter 1, "Making a Pinhole Camera," is not only an interesting but a very practical introduction to the subject.

Chapter 46

The Eye

The problem of safe seeing. If you were standing on a busy street corner in any American city and suddenly people's eye defects were turned into leg defects, over 50 per cent of the pedestrians would begin limping or would be unable to get about without crutches or wheel chairs. In case the scene were changed to a college campus, the number would be about 40 per cent, while in a garment factory as many as eight out of ten would be afflicted. Modern civilization has lightened many of our daily tasks and has taken much of the drudgery out of life, but the work of the eyes has been multiplied many fold.

Studies show that over 95 per cent of all babies are born with normal vision and without eye defects. But, as shown in Table 1, a very small percentage of them will reach old age with anything like normal vision. A heavy toll is being levied on man's eyesight. As a result, America is rapidly becoming a nation of spectacle wearers. The wholesale impairment of human eyesight is one of the most serious defects of modern civilization.

Part of the toll on eyesight is due to the fact that man is using his eyes under conditions entirely foreign to those under which the eye originally developed and adapted itself. Primitive man used his eyes almost entirely out-of-doors for distant vision in bright sunlight: for hunting, fishing, and fighting. When the sun went down, his tasks were done. He certainly did not work all day at close tasks and then attend a three-dimensional motion picture, watch television for several hours, or read a book far into the night.

Since many eye defects are seemingly caused by the tasks imposed and the conditions under which they are done, the situation can be greatly improved. This, however, demands scientific action on the part of many different groups and every individual. For us to do our part we should

Table 1
APPROXIMATE PERCENTAGE OF IMPAIRED EYESIGHT AMONG PEOPLE OF VARYING AGES*

Age group	Percentage with eye defects
At birth	0-5
Grade school	20
Through college	40
40 years	60
60 years	95

*Data assembled from statements made by M. Luckiesh in *Light, Vision, and Seeing*. D. Van Nostrand Company, Inc., New York, 1944.

have a knowledge of the eye, of how it functions, of eye defects, and of the working conditions causing the toll. First let us make a study of the eye.

The eye as a living camera. Many have called the eye a living camera, but like most analogies this one is only partially true. The eye is infinitely more delicate and complicated than the finest camera, but in principle they are the same.

In the camera, as is shown in Fig. 1. there is a simple converging lens, or a system of lenses, which acts like the converging *crystalline* lens in the eye. The sensitized film inside the camera corresponds to the light-sensitive *retina* in the back of the eye, and both receive inverted, real images, which are smaller than the object. The diaphragm, or "stop," regulates the amount of light that enters the camera; the *iris* regulates the amount of light that enters the eye. In the dark the *pupil*, or opening in the iris, may be as much as one centimeter in diameter, whereas in bright sunlight it is about the size of a pinhead.

The interior of the camera is blackened so that the walls will absorb any stray light rays. The interior of the eye is similarly surrounded by a black coat that also absorbs light. Outside the black coat of the eye there is a tough white coat which preserves the shape of the eyeball and protects the eye from injury.

In most respects the eye is superior to the camera, but it is not so in every way. The camera gives us a lasting picture with all details of the object, whereas the image in the eye persists for only about $\frac{1}{16}$ of a second before another distinct image is formed. Details on the retina are often not sensed, and one image may overlap and blend with the one that follows. It is for this reason that two truthful observers may disagree on the winner of a close race or a decision at home plate. Photographs do not have these defects and consequently in such circumstances are given precedence over mere observation.

The persistence of the image in the eye results in other interesting phenomena. It causes the blurred appearance of the spokes of a rotating wheel and the trail of light which appears behind a glowing light when it is moved rapidly in the dark. And it causes the optical illusion of motion

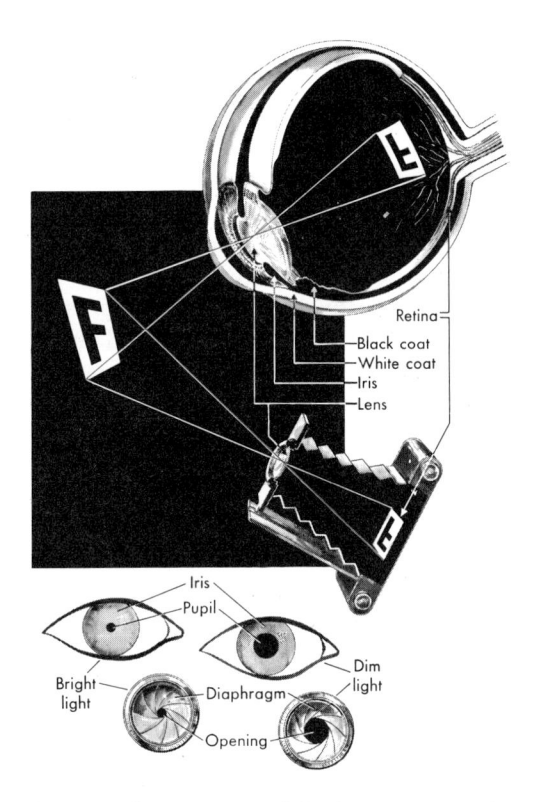

Fig. 1. Comparison of the human eye and a camera. To regulate the amount of light entering a camera lens, the diaphragm must be adjusted manually while this adjustment is made automatically by the iris of the eye.

when we view the so-called motion picture. What one really sees in motion pictures is sixteen to twenty-four still pictures flashed on the screen per second. After each picture and before the next, the screen is darkened by a shutter in the projection machine. But the eye carries over the impression from one picture to the next, blending the separate images into an illusion of continuous motion.

How does the eye focus? In an instant the normal eye is able to bring a distant object as large as a mountain into sharp focus on the retina, and a fraction of a second later to form an equally sharp image of a printed page, or an automobile speedometer, only a few inches away. Without this ability we would have difficulty in driving high-speed automobiles and airplanes without many more accidents than we already have. How is the eye focused so quickly?

Theoretically, there are several possible ways. A fish focuses its eye by changing the distance between the lens and the retina, just as a bellows-type camera is focused. But as you know, the human eye does not focus in this manner. Instead, the lens merely changes shape. As the object distance increases, causing the image distance to decrease, the muscles attached to the outer edges of the eye lens permit the lens to become thinner and flatter. Thus, its focal length is increased enough so that the image is focused sharply on the retina. See (a) of Fig. 2.

In case the object is brought closer to the eye, causing the image distance to increase, the lens is caused to become rounder and thicker. Its focal length is thus shortened, so that the image distance is kept constant and the image is kept on the retina. See (b) of Fig. 2. The process which accomplishes the same result as focusing in the camera, is called *accommodation*.

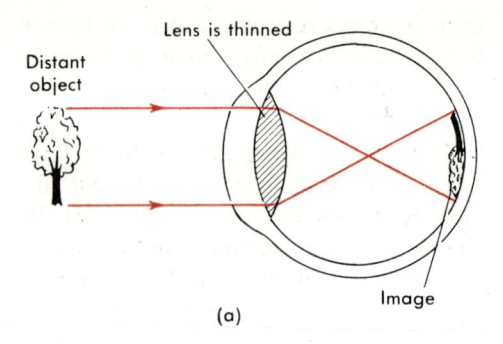

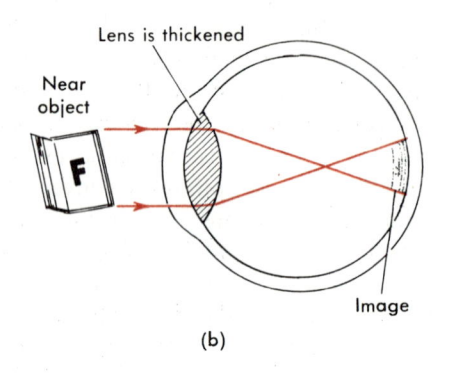

Fig. 2. How the lens of the eye focuses (a) on a distant object and (b) on a near object.

Near point and far point. When the eye muscles are perfectly relaxed, as when a person is looking at a distant object, the lens has its greatest focal length and is said to be adapted to the *far point*. When the object is so near that the lens has its

4 Point

The only accurate way to measure sight is by means of letters or c distance of twenty feet. Quite a variety of such cards have been types are used to determine the patient's ability to see to read at th is not in general use for books or papers, except where lack of sp

5½ Point

The terms used by printers to designate the different examples given of the customary use of each. Spacin bility, therefore, the "leading" has been made to conf Newspapers are usually printed in 5½ and 7 point. M

Courtesy Better Vision Institute

Fig. 3. Test for reading near point.

shortest possible focal length, the object is said to be at the *near point*. You can determine your near point by bringing the small print in Fig. 3 slowly toward your eye. Test one eye at a time. The shortest distance at which the type shows no sign of blurring is your near point. Measure this distance for each eye and compare it with what it should be as shown in Table 2.

Table 2
APPROXIMATE NEAR POINTS FOR AVERAGE EYE AT VARIOUS AGES

Age	Near point in inches	Age	Near point in inches
10	2.7	40	9
15	3	45	12
20	4	50	16
25	5	55	20
30	6	60	40
35	7	65	80

Presbyopia. As we grow older, the power of accommodation gradually decreases. This is due to the decrease in the elasticity of the lens and the lessened ability of the eye muscles to increase the roundness of the lens. This inability is called *presbyopia*. As this takes place, the near point moves farther from the eye and the power of accommodation is decreased. Table 2 shows that for a person of 65 the near point is 80 inches. What would be the nearest approximate distance at which a person of 65 could read this page without the aid of spectacles?

At this distance, 80 inches, it is doubtful that the words can be recognized because of the smallness of the image on the retina. There is no ideal distance for reading and other close work, but, when all factors are considered, the best distance is 13 to 15 inches. However, if this distance is roughly less than 1.5 times the near-point distance, the tension on certain eye muscles needed to converge the light to form a sharp image on the retina is so great that eyestrain is likely to result.

At the age of 35 and below it is fairly easy to comply with this rule. After the age of 40 (see Table 2) this is generally difficult to do. At the age of 45, the minimum distance is 1.5×12, or 18 inches, which is farther away than the object should be if the image is of proper size for ease of seeing.

After the age of 40, the average eye lens needs help in converging light for near vision. This is accomplished when a converging lens of the proper power is placed in front of the eye. But with such a lens it may be impossible to see distant objects. To remedy this, the glasses may be taken off or *bifocal* lenses may be fitted. With these, the lower part of the lens is used for the near point and the upper part is used in viewing distant objects. Although presbyopia seems to be a natural and unavoidable deficiency, it has been found that higher intensity of illumination on close tasks does much to defer "reading glasses." Higher illumination causes greater contraction of the pupil. This causes a sharper and more distinct image on the retina, just as, in a camera, the smaller the aperture the sharper the image. See page 531.

Nearsightedness. In case the distance between the retina and the crystalline lens is abnormally long, or the lens is so round and thick that its focal length is abnormally short, then the image of a distant object will fall in front of the retina, as shown in Fig. 4. This eye defect is quite common and is known as *nearsightedness* or *myopia*. Nearsightedness is the eye defect which takes the greatest toll among school and college students. According to an authority, at birth, about 3 children out of 100 are afflicted; in grade school the number is about 10 out of 100; in high school the appalling number of 24 out of 100 has been reached, and in college 31 out of 100 are afflicted. Among uncivilized tribes, who live and work mostly out-of-doors, nearsightedness is almost unknown. Also, among farmers and out-of-doors workmen, few are afflicted with nearsightedness unless they developed it in school or working at other close tasks.

The cause of much nearsightedness seems to be that in childhood the eye is quite yielding, and the convergence of light rays when close work is done tends to lengthen the eyeball so much that the eye lens cannot flatten and thin itself enough to focus the image of a distant object on the retina without undue strain. Compare the length of the nearsighted eye in Fig. 4 with the length of the farsighted eye in Fig. 6.

Test for myopia or nearsightedness. One test for myopia is made with a Snellen chart. Fig. 5 shows a Snellen chart reduced in size. If your vision is normal, you should be able to read line 7 on a chart of standard size with either eye at 20 feet when the chart is well lighted. Inability to do this does not necessarily mean that you are nearsighted, because the inability might be due to another cause. But in case a negative (diverging) spherical lens improves your vision—start with a low-diopter lens and gradually increase the strength—the chances are that you are nearsighted.

Nearsightedness can be corrected, not cured, by means of eyeglasses. A diverging spherical lens is used, as shown in Fig. 4(c). It causes the nearly parallel light rays from distant objects to diverge enough so that the image is thrown onto the retina, behind the point where it would otherwise be.

Hyperopia, or farsightedness. In case the distance between the retina and the crystalline lens is abnormally short, or the lens is abnormally thin and flat, so that the focal length is abnormally long, images formed by objects that are close will fall behind the retina, as shown in Fig. 6.

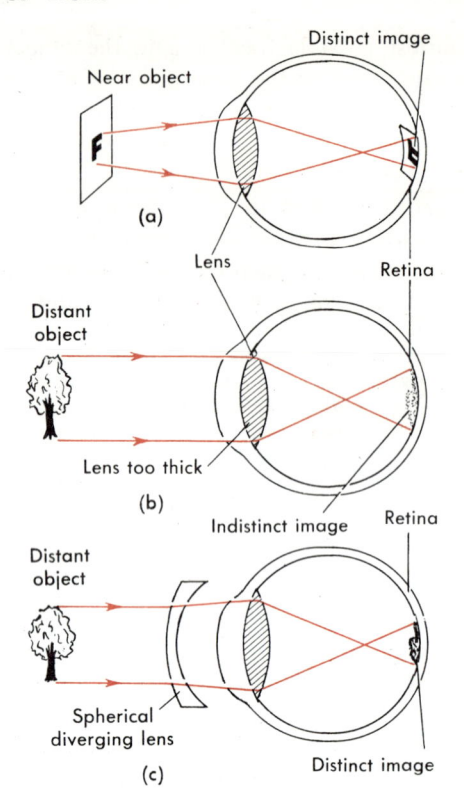

Fig. 4. A nearsighted eye. What causes nearsightedness? How is this condition corrected?

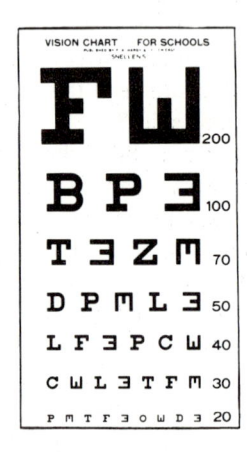

Fig. 5. Snellen chart.

THE EYE 545

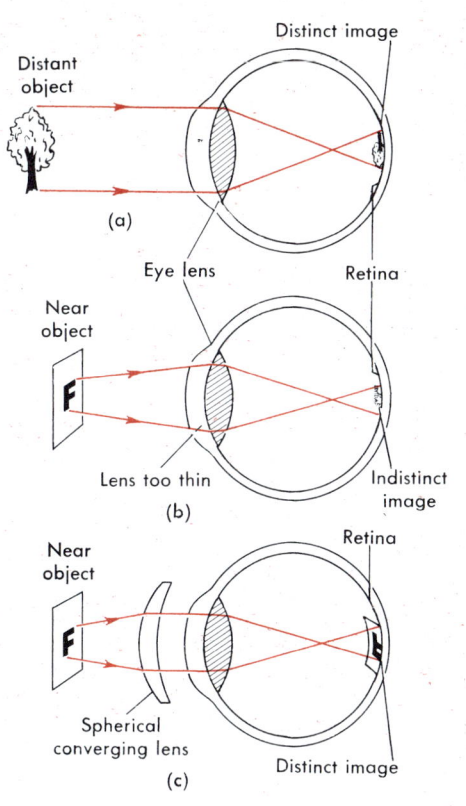

Fig. 6. A farsighted eye. What causes farsightedness? How is this condition corrected?

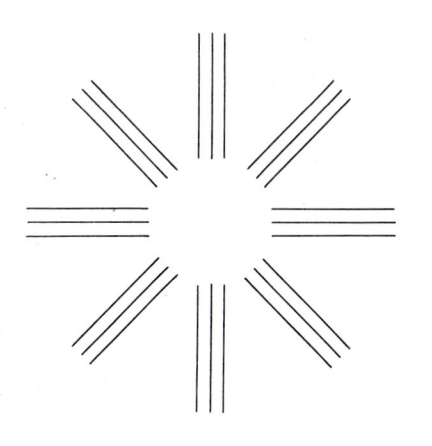

Fig. 7. An astigmatism chart.

Consequently, nearby objects cannot be seen plainly without eyestrain.

If you are farsighted and have no other eye defect, you can very likely read with ease line 9 on the Snellen chart, but your near point may be farther out than normal.

To correct hyperopia, the image distance for near objects at the near point must be decreased. This requires a converging (positive) lens of proper strength, as shown in Fig. 6(c).

Astigmatism. Normally the surface of the cornea, the somewhat bulging front portion of the eyeball, and the surfaces of the eye lens are portions of nearly perfect spheres. However, it is not uncommon for the curvature of one or both of these to be more in one plane than in any other. This defect, which may cause indistinct vision, is called *astigmatism*.

Astigmatism can be detected by means of Fig. 7. With normal eyes the sets of radiating lines will be seen with equal distinctness at all distances from the eyes. In case either eye is astigmatic (test one eye at a time), the vertical or horizontal lines, or those in between, will appear black and distinct, whereas the lines at right angles to the distinct ones will be less black and perhaps blurred.

Astigmatism is likely to cause headaches and blurred vision, especially when one reads for any prolonged length of time. Astigmatism is corrected by a cylindrical lens instead of a spherical one, as shown in Fig. 8. Note especially that the direction of curvature in the spectacle lens must coincide with the proper curvature in the eye lens. *Consequently, if an astigmatic lens comes out of the eyeglass frame, care must be taken in replacing it because it is absolutely necessary that the proper curvatures coincide.* Explain what happens if they do not.

Characteristics of binocular vision. If the head is erect and we look at a distant

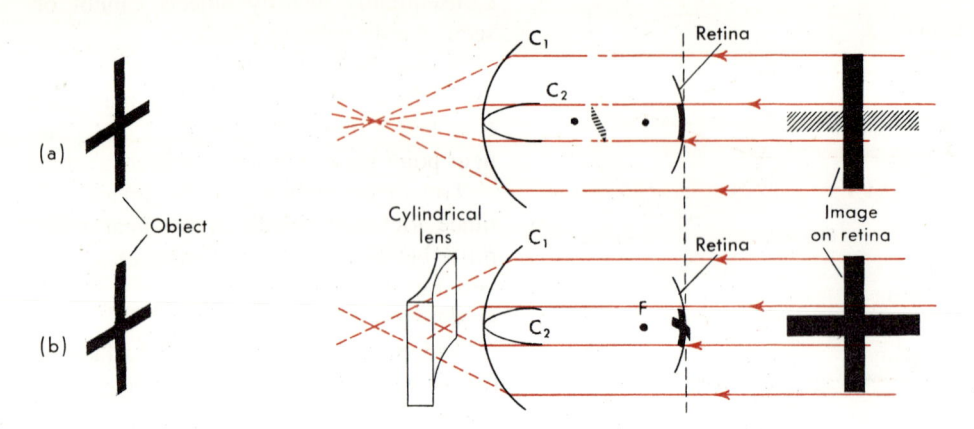

Fig. 8. (a) Astigmatic eye and the image formed on the retina. The vertical curvature, C_1, of the eye lens differs from the horizontal curvature C_2. (b) This condition is corrected by the use of a diverging cylindrical lens.

object, duplicate images are formed on identical parts of the retina of each eye, if our eyes are normal, and the two images are received and fused by the brain as one. This is known as *binocular vision*.

In case the images are focused upon noncorresponding parts of the retinas, the brain may be unable to fuse the images, and consequently one may see double. Nor will the images be fused if they are appreciably dissimilar or one is larger than the other. First one will dominate and then the other; rivalry ensues. In case the images are not fused, nature soon suppresses the image in one eye, so that only one image is sensed by the brain. One eye just ceases to function. If the favored eye is covered or fails to function, in many instances the other eye takes over the task. As a result the patient normally sees with only one eye but never becomes aware of the fact. People with crossed eyes, unless the condition is corrected, see with one eye only.

You can illustrate binocular vision by placing the edge of a small card on the center line of Fig. 9, so that the card is perpendicular to the page. Then place your nose on the upper edge of the card so that each eye views only half of the total picture. As a result you should see one three-dimensional picture with depth as well as length and width. Do you?

The old-fashioned *stereoscope* is another good device to illustrate binocular vision. Two pictures of the same thing are

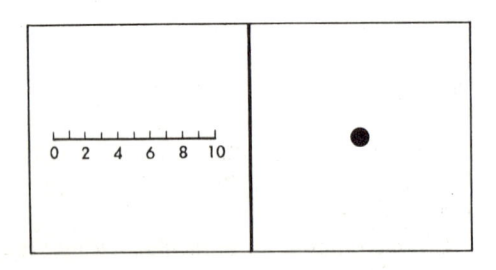

Fig. 9. Demonstrating binocular vision.

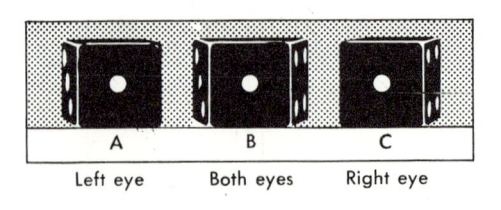

Fig. 10. Two eyes perceive depth better than one. Explain.

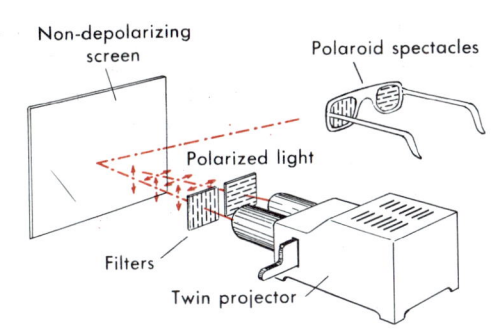

Fig. 11. How three-dimensional pictures are projected and seen.

taken simultaneously by two cameras placed a few inches apart, and the finished photographs are mounted side by side on a piece of cardboard. This card is inserted in the stereoscope so that each picture is in front of a prismatic positive lens, and so that each eye sees only one, not both, of the pictures. Because of the positive lenses, the pictures are somewhat enlarged, and because of the prisms they are merged. The effect is that the two pictures appear as a single three-dimensional picture possessing depth and all the characteristics of a real scene. The appearance of depth is caused by the fact that the picture on the left shows a little more of the left side of a three-dimensional body, and the one on the right, a little more of the right side. It is also probable that a little more of the top, or bottom, is shown on the one than on the other. When these two slightly different pictures are fused, the effect of depth or distance is produced.

Three-dimensional motion pictures and binocular vision. Three-dimensional motion pictures (3D) are an outgrowth of the principles of binocular vision and the methods of stereoscopic photography. Instead of one picture of each scene, as in ordinary motion-picture photography, two pictures are taken by two different cameras that are placed a few inches apart.

When the pictures are shown, both are projected simultaneously onto the screen by two different projectors. Both projectors polarize the light so that the plane of polarization of one projector is perpendicular to that of the other. See Fig. 11.

Consequently, when the screen is viewed through polarizing lenses, as shown in Fig. 11, one eye views one picture on the screen and the other eye views the other picture. As a result, when both pictures are fused by the brain, one picture having depth as well as width and height is observed, as explained above.

Importance of ability to judge distance and to see sidewise. To be successful in many sports and other activities in which the highest acuity of vision is demanded, one must be able to judge distance and depth and at the same time be able to see sidewise with both eyes. For example, in basketball or football, a passer's ability to judge distance is tested to the utmost when he passes the ball to a speeding teammate far down the court or field. And at the same time the passer must see clearly and distinctly at an angle of 90 degrees to either side in order to guard against an opponent coming in from the side to break up the pass.

A good automobile driver must have these same abilities. At busy intersections the good driver will look straight ahead without altering the focus of his gaze either

Fig. 12. A modern stereo camera that takes two photographs of the same scene simultaneously. When viewed, the two pictures have a three-dimensional quality.

Courtesy Eastman Kodak Co.

to the right or to the left. With his head and eyes in this position, he can detect a moving object to either the right or the left of him and at the same time can easily avoid striking a car in front of him. By using this principle in driving, one has a vision of 180°, or 90° to each side. Does an airplane pilot need to be able to judge distance and depth well? Explain.

Athletes who lack the ability to judge distance cannot spot their teammates well, they cannot "hit" well in baseball, and they have trouble "hitting the basket" in basketball. Likewise, an automobile driver who cannot judge distance and see sidewise well, will meet with more accidents than he would otherwise.

Various ways in which distance is judged. Distance is judged in a variety of ways. Looking at Fig 13, you see what appears to be a long row of telephone poles which stretch far into the distance, yet they are all the same distance from your eye.

The secret of this optical illusion is that as the object distance from the eye increases, the size of the image decreases. In the diagram, the pole which appears the most distant is the smallest one and its image on the retina is likewise the same. Since the heights of the poles are drawn in the proper proportion and in correct relative positions, there is produced on the retina an image which gives the illusion of distance, even though all the objects are equidistant from the eye. Thus you see that if we view several objects that are all equal in size, we judge their relative distances by the relative sizes of the images in the eye. Through experience we learn to judge the distance of a *single* object by the size of the image. Fig. 14 shows a very simple apparatus which can be used to judge distance.

One reason why you can judge distance better with two eyes than with one is that when you sight both eyes on some point, *D,* as illustrated in Fig. 14, a certain amount of muscular effort is necessary to pull the eyes inward. The eyes are set a constant distance apart, and by experience we learn to estimate distance to *D* by the muscular effort necessary to do this. In order to see a closer point, *B,* still more muscular effort is required to sight both eyes on *B*. Military range finders function in a very similar way. A constant *base line* separates two telescopes, each of which is focused on the distant object. The smaller the angle of convergence, the more distant is the object.

Improper muscle balance. As we have said, in case the two images are not focused on identical parts of the two retinas, the afflicted persons will see double in extreme cases. With milder cases, eye-muscle strain is the result. This defect is caused by the

Fig. 13. Account for the apparent size of the distant telephone poles.

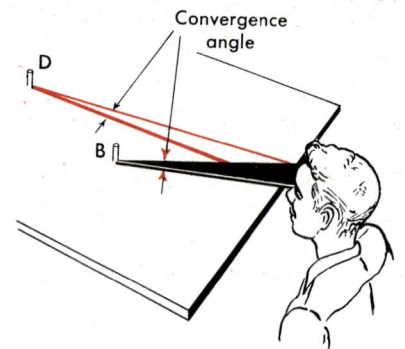

Fig. 14. Apparatus for testing the ability to judge distances.

fact that the muscles of the two different eyes do not work together as they should. The muscles are not in balance.

A rough test of your eye balance can be made by means of the old-fashioned stereoscope.* Fig. 9 shows a homemade card which can be viewed in the stereoscope to make the test. For normal eyes the ball should appear to be at about the center of the line, somewhere between 4 and 6, and the line should cut through the center of the dot.

What defect is present if:
(a) The ball is not seen?
(b) The line is not seen?
(c) The ball appears to be at 1 instead of near 5?
(d) The ball appears to be at 8 instead of near 5?
(e) The ball appears to be above the line?
(f) The ball appears to be below the line?

Find out from an oculist how the defects indicated by (c), (d), (e), and (f) are corrected.

SUMMARY AND CONCLUSIONS

1. Many eye defects, other than presbyopia, are caused by the tasks imposed on the eye and by the conditions under which the tasks are done.
2. Accommodation is the ability of the eye lens to focus the image of either distant or nearby objects plainly on the eye retina.
3. Presbyopia is caused by the loss of accommodation due to old age. The elasticity of the lens decreases and the eye muscles lose their ability to increase the roundness and thickness of the eye lens.
4. Nearsightedness (myopia) is due to either too long an eyeball or inability to flatten the eye lens. It is corrected by a diverging (negative) lens.
5. Farsightedness (hyperopia) is due to either too short an eyeball or inability of the muscles to thicken the eye lens. It is corrected by a converging (positive) lens.
6. Vision is most distinct and reading is done most comfortably at a distance of 13 to 15 inches.
7. Astigmatism is due to the fact that the surface of the eye lens or the cornea is not a portion of a perfect sphere. It is corrected by a cylindrical lens.

QUESTIONS FOR REVIEW

1. Make a diagram of the eye showing the lens, retina, and iris.
2. What is accommodation?
3. How is accommodation achieved with a bellows-type camera? By the eye?
4. As the object distance increases, what happens to the image distance in the eye?
5. Why is it easier to see a near object than a distant one?
6. What is the near point? What happens to one's near point as one grows older?
7. What is presbyopia and what is its cause?
8. How is presbyopia corrected?
9. If an object is held too close to the eye, why is it difficult to see it plainly?
10. What is myopia?
11. What is hyperopia?
12. Make a diagram to show how myopia is corrected. Also make one to show how hyperopia is corrected.
13. What is astigmatism and what causes it?
14. What are the symptoms of astigmatism?
15. What are some of the symptoms when the two eyes do not work together?
16. Explain how one judges distance. Why is this ability extremely important?

PROJECTS

1. Build an apparatus for measuring the ability to see sidewise. Such equipment is often found in police departments that give eye tests for drivers' licenses. Also consult the Readers' Guide in your library.

---

*The results of the tests given in this book should not be considered conclusive. In case eye defects are suspected, an ophthalmologist should be consulted.

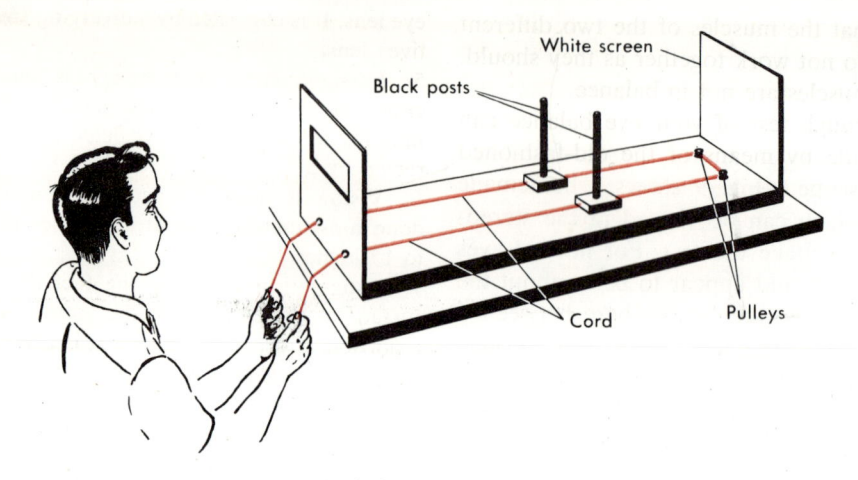

Fig. 15. With this apparatus, the object is to get the images of the two upright posts to coincide, first using one eye and then the other. Finally, use both eyes together.

2. Build and demonstrate the equipment shown in Fig. 15 for determining the ability to judge distance.

3. Using a stereoscope, make appropriate cards for determining deficiencies of binocular vision and muscle balance.

4. If you live near the seashore, obtain a nautilus, the lowly sea animal made famous by Oliver Wendell Holmes, and examine its organ of sight. You will find that it is very similar to a pinhole camera.

5. Do the experiments on the eye listed in Sutton's *Demonstration Experiments in Physics*, pp. 393-395. L-58, which demonstrates the blind spot, and L-61, which demonstrates eye fatigue, are of particular importance.

READING YOU WILL ENJOY

1. Gibson, James J., *The Perception of the Visual World,* page 235. Houghton Mifflin Company, Boston, 1950. Explains by means of many diagrams why things look as they do.

2. Luckiesh, Matthew, and Frank K. Moss, *The Science of Seeing.* D. Van Nostrand Company, Inc., New York, 1937. Chapters I and II are of particular importance to everyone, and Chapter VII, which deals with conservation of sight, is still more important. These chapters could furnish material for several important reports to the class.

3. Sutton, R. M., *Demonstration Experiments in Physics*. McGraw-Hill Book Company, Inc., New York, 1938.

Chapter 47

Illumination and Better Seeing

The problem. The advertisements of power and light companies urge us to use more light. The question which concerns us is whether our homes, schools, factories, and other buildings actually need more light and whether the light being used is properly used to curtail the toll on eyesight studied in the preceding chapter. To answer these questions, we must know something about luminous intensity of light sources, illumination, and methods of measuring these. Then we will be ready to attack the bigger problem of illumination and better seeing.

Luminous intensity and its units. One factor which determines the amount of light available for seeing is the brightness (*luminous intensity*) of the source of light. The unit of luminous intensity is the *candle power*. Originally this was the intensity of light given off by a particular kind of candle burning at a specified rate—approximately the intensity of light given off by the ordinary candle. As you may surmise, such a source was very unreliable as a standard.

Today the *new international candle* is the standard unit. It is defined as one-sixtieth of the luminous intensity provided by one square centimeter of a "black body" at the temperature of melting platinum (1755° C). A black body is a body that is black when it is cold. When it is at the required temperature, it is white hot. Surprisingly, the blacker the body is when cold, the brighter it is when heated to incandescence.

Illumination and units for measuring it. Illumination refers to the amount of light in the region where it is needed; for example, the amount that falls on the page of a book. Naturally the illumination depends upon the brightness of the source and the distance from it. The unit of illumination is the **foot-candle,** which is *the illumination one foot distant from a source having a luminous intensity of one candle power.*

This definition is based on the assumption that the source is a point source and that the surface is perpendicular to a line connecting the source and the surface. Also, this definition implies that if the intensity of the source is doubled, then at a given distance the illumination is doubled.

The illumination varies directly as the intensity of the source.

How does the illumination vary with the distance from the source? In Fig. 1,

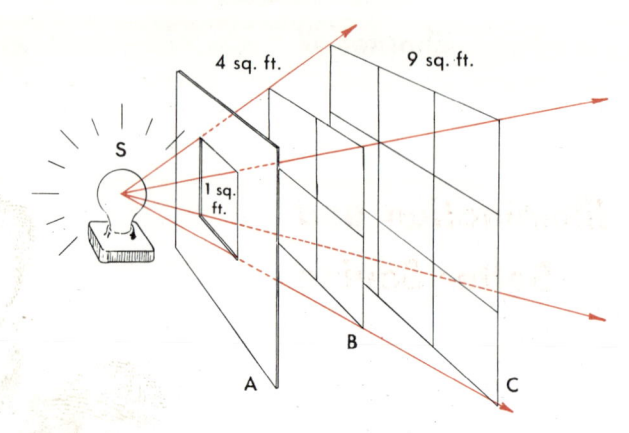

Fig. 1. The illumination varies directly as the intensity of the source and inversely as the square of the distance.

one foot from the light source, S, is a screen, A, in which there is a hole one foot square. Two feet from the source is a second screen, B, and three feet from the source is a third screen, C.

Light from the source which passes through one square foot one foot away, covers four square feet two feet away and covers nine square feet three feet away. That is, at a distance of two feet the light is spread over four times as great an area as at one foot, and it is spread over nine times as great an area at three feet. What area should it spread over at four feet from the source?

This illustration shows that when the distance from the source is doubled (made two feet instead of one) the illumination is reduced to one-fourth of what it was at one foot; and when the distance is tripled the illumination is reduced to one-ninth. At four feet, how will the illumination compare with the illumination at one foot?

Hence, it appears that

the intensity of illumination, E, varies directly as the candle power, cp, of the source and inversely as the square of the distance, d^2.

That is,

$$E \propto \frac{cp}{d^2}$$

Or,

$$E = K \frac{cp}{d^2}$$

K is 1 when E is measured in foot-candles, d in feet, and cp in candle power. Hence,

$$E = \frac{cp}{d^2}$$

PROBLEM: What is the illumination 3 feet from a 90-candle-power source?

SOLUTION:

$$E = \frac{cp}{d^2}$$

Substituting,

$$E = \frac{90}{9} = 10 \text{ foot-candles}$$

What would be the illumination 6 feet from the source? 1½ feet from the source?

Photometry—the measurement of the intensity of light sources. Two light sources can be compared in intensity by the balancing (making equal) of the illumination they produce. In this way, if the intensity of one is known, the intensity of the other source can be determined. This procedure is called *photometry* and the instrument is called a *photometer,* of which there are several different kinds.

The simplest photometer is the Joly photometer. The one shown in Fig. 2 consists of two blocks of paraffin separated by tinfoil. The light on either side is transmitted by the paraffin, but not by the foil. You can tell when the illumination is the same on both sides by looking at the edges of the paraffin blocks. In practice, the distances to the known and unknown sources are adjusted so that both edges appear to be illuminated the same.

Under such circumstances, we know that the illumination E_A caused by source A equals the illumination E_B caused by source B.

That is,
$$E_A = E_B$$

Also,
$$E_A = \frac{(cp)_A}{d^2_A}$$

And,
$$E_B = \frac{(cp)_B}{d^2_B}$$

Therefore,
$$\frac{(cp)_A}{d^2_A} = \frac{(cp)_B}{d^2_B} \quad \text{Why?}$$

PROBLEM: A photometer shows equal illumination when a 20-cp lamp is 10 cm. distant from it and an incandescent lamp is 60 cm. distant from it on the opposite side. Find the candle power of the unknown lamp.

SOLUTION:
$$\frac{(cp)_A}{d^2_A} = \frac{(cp)_B}{d^2_B}$$

Substituting,
$$\frac{20}{100} = \frac{x}{3600}$$

Solving,
$$x = 720 \text{ cp}$$

Bunsen photometer. The Bunsen photometer is the one most commonly used. It differs from the Joly photometer only in that a greased paper is substituted for the paraffin blocks. Usually the greased paper is placed in a box containing mirrors which are arranged so that both sides of the paper can be conveniently seen at once. See Fig. 3.

Foot-candle meters. Foot-candle meters are often used to determine illumination. They may be so graduated that they show the amount of illumination by comparison, or they may be calibrated to read in foot-candles directly. Photographers make use of such meters to determine the brightness of light both indoors and outdoors. We suggest that you obtain one and determine the illumination in various parts of your schoolroom at regular intervals for a period of several days.

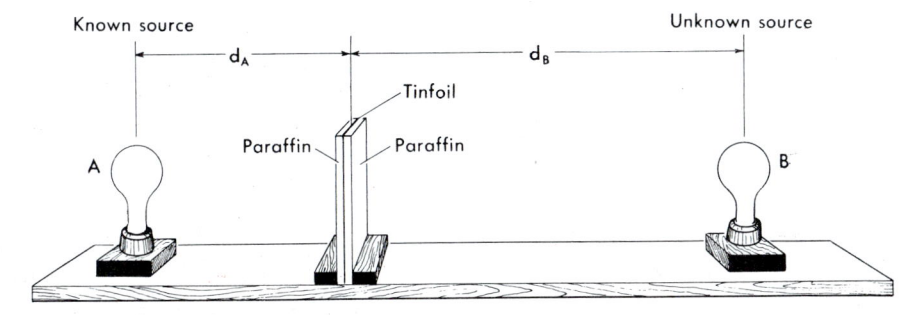

Fig. 2. The Joly photometer for determining the intensity of illumination.

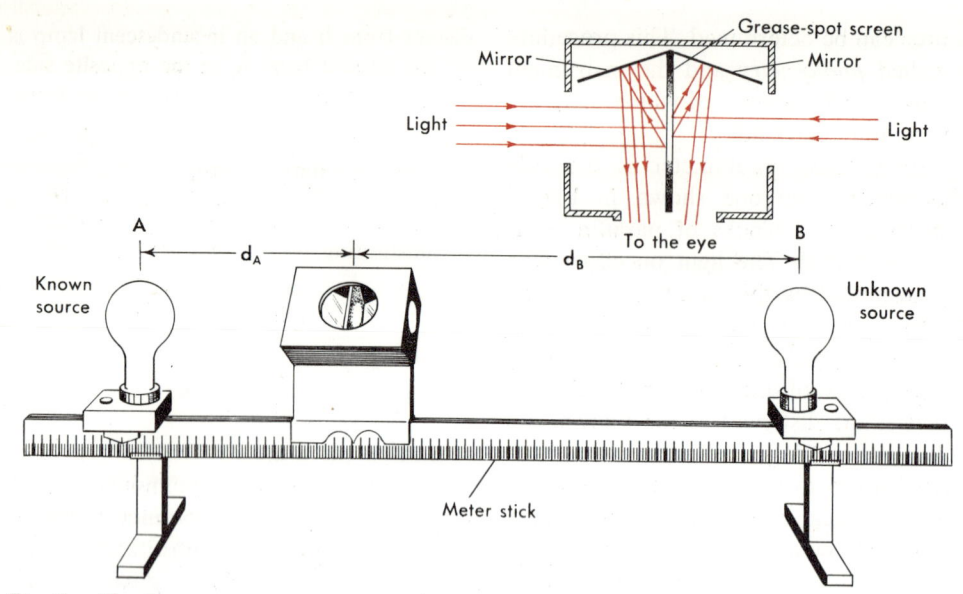

Fig. 3. The Bunsen, or grease-spot, photometer is used for comparing the intensities of two light sources.

Electric lamps vary in intensity. Modern tungsten lamps give approximately 1 candle power per watt. Fluorescent lamps give between 4 and 5 candle power per watt. Only about 3 per cent of the power consumed by an incandescent lamp is converted into light, and only about 11 per cent in case of a fluorescent lamp.

What conditions are necessary for sight-saving when one is reading and perform-ing other close tasks? As we pointed out in the previous chapter, it is not necessary to accept defective eyes as inevitable when less than 5 per cent of them are inherited. What can be done to remedy the defects?

A study of Fig. 4 shows that the right-hand column can be read more easily than the left because the print is larger in the right-hand column. Also, it is easier to read the print at the top of the page than

Fig. 4. What effect does increasing the contrast between the type and paper have on readability?

at the bottom because there is more contrast between the color of the paper and the color of the print at the top.

Furthermore, if we place the page in bright light, we will find it easier to read, particularly the fine print, than when the page is in less intense light. Another factor which determines ease of seeing is the time available for looking at the body. Hence, in conclusion, we see that ease of seeing can be improved, particularly for close tasks, by our:

(a) Making the print or other material adequately large.
(b) Making the contrast between the background and the body as great as possible.
(c) Making sure that the intensity of illumination is great enough.
(d) Making the time for seeing long enough.

In many situations, it may be difficult to improve the size of the object and the contrast between the object and its background. For example, in sewing, it is often necessary to use thread of a certain size and of the same color as that of the cloth being sewed. But even under such adverse circumstances, the task of seeing can be made measurably easier by the proper intensity of illumination.

In school, where heavy toll is taken on eyesight, there is little excuse for improper contrast between reading matter and the paper on which it is printed, and still less excuse for the type being too small. Perhaps the worst offense in school against ease of sight is improper illumination. The proper intensities of illumination for various tasks are shown in Table 1. A very interesting project would be to test the intensities of illumination in your classrooms and other rooms in your school and your home with a foot-candle meter (Fig. 5) and compare them with the intensities found in Table 1.

Courtesy Westinghouse Electric Corp.

Fig. 5. (a) A foot-candle meter. When light falls on its photoelectric cell, an electric current is generated, causing the deflection of a galvanometer needle in the circuit.

Fig. 5. (b) With this spherical photometer, it is possible to measure the intensity of illumination with great accuracy.

Courtesy General Electric Co.

Table 1

Task	Foot-candles recommended
Excellent printing 8-point type	10
Excellent printing 6-point type	17
Own handwriting in pencil	23
Newspaper—text matter	33
Typing on dark blue paper	76
Steel scale—1/64-inch divisions	166
Distinguishing black thread on dark cloth	540

The foot-candles recommended in Table 1 are taken from the work of Luckiesh and Moss. Compared with the foot-candles often found in school and factories, these may seem quite high. But compared with the illumination under a shade tree, commonly about 1000 foot-candles, these intensities are very low. In most schools, homes, offices, and factories, the intensities are far below those recommended in the table, and far below the outdoor intensities to which human eyes have become adapted through thousands of years of living outdoors.

Distribution of light. The proper distribution of light for ease of seeing is almost as important as proper intensity. Out-of-doors on a clear day about 80 per cent, or four-fifths, of the light comes directly from the sun, and 20 per cent, or one-fifth, is scattered or diffused by the atmosphere.

Experts believe that indoors about the same relation between direct lighting and diffused lighting should exist as out-of-doors. This means that for a close task, such as sewing or studying, four-fifths of the light should come directly from the source and one-fifth should be reflected onto the object from the ceiling, walls, and other surroundings.

Harsh contrasts between the direct lighting and surroundings should by all means be avoided. Great contrast between a brightly lighted page and dark surroundings causes the eyes to adjust themselves every time they glance out into darkened parts of the room, which they do very often without our being aware of it. If harsh contrasts exist, a severe strain is put on our eyes and on our nervous system as well. Furthermore, the surroundings should not be illuminated more brightly than the task being performed. Does the lighting in your home comply with these recommendations?

The outstanding violation of sharp contrasts is found in the moving picture theatre. There is still a mistaken belief that motion pictures must be viewed in a dark theatre in order to be seen. Perhaps the cost of the production of one motion picture, if spent on research, would greatly increase the ease of seeing in theatres.

Glare—misplaced light. Even when the size of the object, the intensity of light, contrast of object with background, and the time for seeing the object are all adequate, seeing may still be difficult. All of us at some time or other have tried to read a metal ruler or glossy printed page and have found it impossible until the angle at which the light struck the object was changed. This poor vision is due to glare, which causes not only poor vision but much discomfort.

Fig. 6 shows the waste of light from glare. Two light sources were used. One gave a background illumination of 10 foot-candles and little or no glare; the other, of 5 foot-candles, was the glare source. When light from the glare source made an angle of 5 degrees with the line of vision, the visibility was only 16 per cent of the 10 foot-candles which illuminated the object. Eighty-four per cent of the 10 foot-candles was wasted due to glare. As the glare source was raised, the waste due to glare was decreased. Glare can be reduced even more if the light is allowed to come from over one of the shoulders. By elimination of glare in factories, production has been known to increase as much as 35 per cent.

ILLUMINATION AND BETTER SEEING

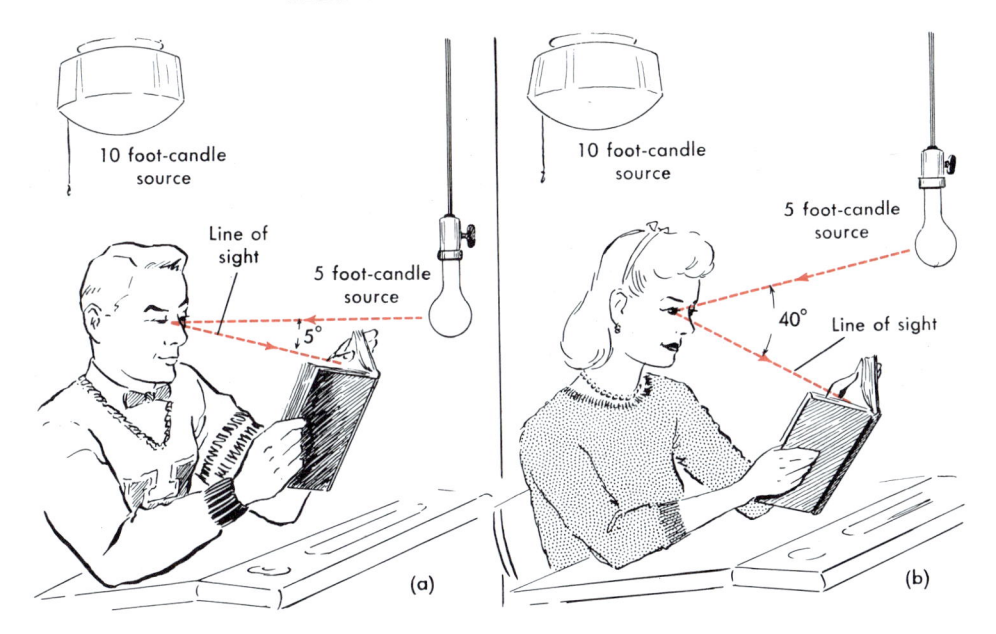

Fig. 6. As the angle that the glare source (the 5 foot-candle lamp) makes with the reader's line of sight increases, the waste due to glare decreases. In (a) 84 per cent of the 10 foot-candle source is wasted; in (b) only 40 per cent is wasted.

SUMMARY AND CONCLUSIONS

1. The unit of luminous intensity is the new international candle, which is one-sixtieth of the luminous intensity provided by one square centimeter of a black body heated to incandescence at the temperature of melting platinum (1755°C).
2. The unit of intensity of illumination, or foot-candle, is illumination due to a one-candle-power lamp one foot away.
3. Illumination (E) (in foot-candles) =

$$\frac{\text{candle power (cp)}}{\text{distance (ft.)}^2}$$

4. For better vision there should be:
   (a) Adequate illumination (see Table 1).
   (b) No glare.
   (c) Greatest possible contrast between background and body observed.
   (d) Plenty of time for seeing.
   (e) Proper distance between eyes and body observed. For children, work at the near point should be kept at the minimum.

QUESTIONS FOR REVIEW

1. How is the illumination affected when the distance from the source is doubled? Tripled? Halved?
2. What is the unit of luminous intensity? Of illumination?
3. What is meant by a black body, and what peculiar characteristic does it have when hot that it does not have when cold?
4. Name two things that can be done with light sources to reduce glare.
5. Name four things that you possibly could do in order to improve the ease of seeing when you read and study.
6. Does the lighting in your room meet with the other conditions necessary for good vision?
7. What is the wattage and approximate candle power of the lamp in your room and what is its distance from your book when you sit and read? Also, what is the intensity of illumination on your book?
8. In what way is the frosted electric light bulb superior to the clear glass bulb?

PROBLEMS

1. What is the intensity of illumination 5 feet from a lamp whose luminous intensity is 100 candle power? Is this sufficient for reading this book?
2. What is the luminous intensity of a lamp which gives an intensity of illumination of 5 foot-candles 10 feet from the lamp?
3. What is the illumination on a book held 5 feet from a 50-candle-power source?
4. What is the approximate candle power of a 25-watt incandescent electric lamp? Of a 25-watt fluorescent lamp?
5. When an electric lamp is 8 feet away, the illumination is only one-fourth of that needed for good vision. What distance should the lamp be moved in order for proper illumination to be attained?
6. For doing certain work, 8 foot-candles of light are needed. Nothing but a 60-candle-power lamp is available. How far away from the worker must the lamp be placed?
7. At one end of a meter stick a 1-cp source is placed. At the other end of the stick there is a lamp of unknown candle power. A screen is equally illuminated on both sides when it is 20 cm. from the 1-cp source. Calculate the candle power of the lamp.
8. At one end of a meter stick is a 16-cp lamp and at the other end a 9-cp source. Where must a screen be placed between the two to be equally illuminated? Hint: Let x equal one distance and 100 minus x equal the other distance.

PROJECTS

1. Borrow from the camera club in your school an exposure meter, which is a foot-candle meter calibrated in lens openings. Or perhaps the school's Science Department has a foot-candle meter which you can borrow. Using one of these, make a survey of the lighting conditions in your classroom, auditorium, shop, and library. Do your readings compare favorably with the standards indicated on the meter?
2. Write to the Lamp Department of the General Electric Company, Schenectady, N. Y. Ask for literature and visual aids on how the candle power of lamps is measured.
3. Make and use photometers as described in Sutton's *Demonstration Experiments in Physics*, L-13 and L-14, or Swezey's *After-Dinner Science*, pp. 88-89.

READING YOU WILL ENJOY

1. Luckiesh, Matthew, *Light, Vision, and Seeing*. D. Van Nostrand Company, Inc., New York, 1944.
2. Luckiesh, Matthew, and Frank K. Moss, *The Science of Seeing*. D. Van Nostrand Company, Inc., New York, 1937.
3. Sutton, R. M., *Demonstration Experiments in Physics*. McGraw-Hill Book Company, Inc., New York, 1938.
4. Swezey, K. M., *After-Dinner Science*. Whittlesey House, McGraw-Hill Book Company, Inc., New York, 1948.

Chapter 48

The Riddle of Color

Newton's color experiment stirs the ire of poets and artists. For several hundred years before the time of Newton, poets, artists, philosophers, and others had delved into the nature of color, and most of them were convinced that they knew all there was to be learned about it. But in the year 1666 Newton performed an experiment which contradicted practically all the color theories of that time. The news of his discovery spread rapidly, but it met with the most violent opposition and condemnation.

For the sake of brevity and clarity we shall quote Newton's own description of his famous experiment:

In the year 1666 (at which time I applied myself to the grinding of optick glasses of other figures than spherical) I procured me a triangular glass prism, to try therewith the celebrated phenomena of colors. And in order thereto, having darkened my chamber and made a very small hole in my window-shuts to let in a convenient quantity of the sun's light, I placed my prism at its entrance, that it might thereby be refracted to the opposite wall. It was at first a very pleasing divertisement, to view the vivid and intense colours produced thereby.

You, too, can perform this same experiment very easily. If direct sunlight is not readily available, white light from a carbon arc or incandescent electric lamp can be used. For best results the wave fronts should be parallel. Newton used a round incident beam of such light. Much to his surprise, it emerged from his prism as an oblong beam that consisted of a band of colors containing violet, blue, green, yellow, orange, and red, as shown in Color Plate 2(c). A band of colors formed by light passing from a source through a prism is known as a *spectrum* of that source.

Two features of this experiment puzzled Newton. Why did the white light that entered the prism emerge as a band of colors? And why was the round incident beam oblong after refraction? Comparing its length with its width, he found the length to be five times greater.

At first Newton tried to explain the oblongness as being due to refraction, but he gave up this idea because he thought the light was bent entirely too much to be explained in this way. After rejecting several other theories trying to account for the oblongness, Newton finally separated each different color of the sun's spectrum from all the others and passed each through a second prism. As a result he found that orange light by itself was refracted more than red, yellow more than orange, green more than yellow, blue more than green, and finally violet more than any of the others. Why this was true Newton did not know, but it did explain why the refracted beam was longer one way than another.

The experiment indicated too that white light actually consists of six different colors. It was this conclusion that many opposed. The crucial test of it was simple. Would these six colors of light, when recombined, again produce white light? When Newton recombined them by placing a second prism beyond the first, he found that white light resulted. See Color Plate 2(d).

For Newton, his experiment was enough to prove his theory. But his opponents were not convinced. For more than a hundred years they were antagonistic. As late as the nineteenth century, the poet Goethe, whose word carried tremendous prestige, challenged Newton's theory of color. His most convincing argument was that every colored light is darker than white light. And brightness cannot be compounded out of darkness. How would you disprove this argument? Contrast Newton's method of finding truth with Goethe's method in this instance.

Complementary colors. Newton's discovery that white light would result from the mixing of the colors of the sun's spectrum prompted a horde of new experiments, many of which you can perform with the relatively simple apparatus shown in Fig. 1. Examples are: What color of light will result if red, violet, green, yellow, or any other single color is cut out before the colors of the sun's spectrum are recombined? And what color will result if any two, three, or more colors are combined?

If red is cut out of the sun's spectrum, the resulting light will be bluish-green; if blue is removed, the result will be yellow; and if green is removed, the result will be magenta. See Color Plate 1. On the other hand, if blue-green and red are recombined, the result will be white light again. Similarly, yellow plus blue light produces white light. What will be produced when green and magenta light are com-

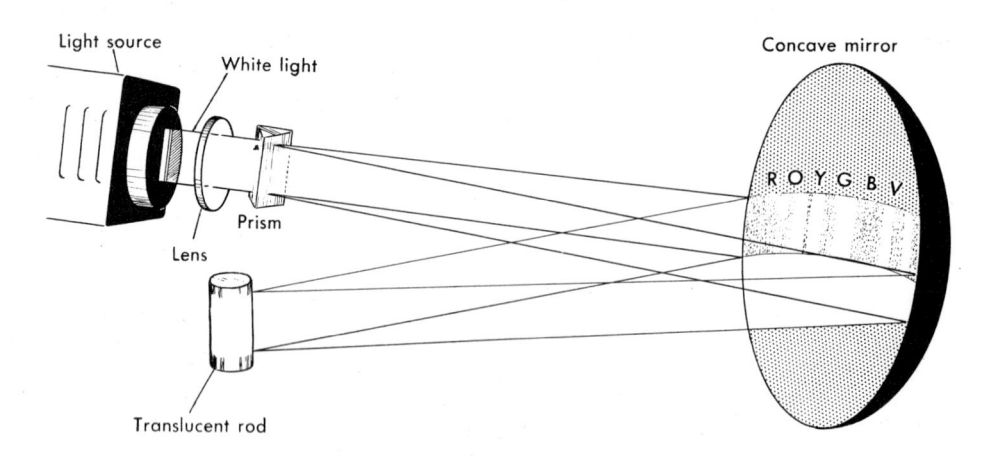

Fig. 1. Experimental arrangements for mixing pure spectrum colors.

bined? See (b) of Color Plate 1. Newton called two colored lights which produce white light when combined, *complementary colors*.

Primary colors. The crowning achievement of Newton's experiment was that he proved white light to be a combination of all the visible colors of light. But in 1807, a discovery just as important as Newton's was made by Thomas Young. You will recall that it was this youthful genius who discovered light interference and really established the wave theory of light.

Young found that white or grey light could be produced by the combination of red, green, and blue lights, and that all the other colors of the visible spectrum could be produced by various combinations of these three. Red, green, and blue were called *primary* light colors. None of the primary colors, however, could be produced by any combination of other colors.

We can easily verify these discoveries by projecting three spots of blue, green, and red light onto a white screen so that they overlap. See (a) of Color Plate 1. Where all three colors overlap, white is produced; where red and blue overlap, magenta is produced; where red and green overlap, yellow is found; and where blue and green overlap, blue-green is produced.

The color triangle. In order to show what color would be produced when any two colors of light were combined, Newton made a chart which revealed at a glance what the resultant color would be. Many modified forms of it are in use today. See (b) of Color Plate 1.

Two colors of light at the corners of the triangle, when combined, give the color in between. Colors opposite each other on the triangle are the complementary ones; that is, the pairs blue and yellow, green and magenta, and blue-green and red all give white light when combined. See (c) of Color Plate 1.

The colors of objects. If white light strikes a sheet of white paper or a book, as shown in (a) of Fig. 2, the object appears white. But why? To answer this, let us assume that the color sensation produced in the eye is the same as the color of the light reflected from the object to the eye. Therefore a book appears white because it reflects white light. And since white light consists of violet, blue, green, yellow, orange, and red, then a white object must reflect all these colors. Therefore, if only red light strikes a "white" paper, the paper must reflect red light and must appear red. Likewise, if only green light strikes a "white" object, the object must reflect green light and appear green. Experiment shows these predictions to be true. This tends to verify our assumption that the color of a body is the same as the color of the light, or of the combination of light colors, reflected by the body.

But what happens when a book appears to be red, for example, when white light illuminates it? What happens to the colors other than red? Evidently either the book must absorb them so that they are not reflected, or it must change them to red before they are reflected. In case, however, all the non-red colors are changed to red, then when only a green light illuminates a red book, the green should be changed to red and be reflected, so that the book appears red. But this is contrary to experiment. Instead the book appears black. See (i) of Fig. 2.

Since the red book does not change the green light to red and does not reflect it as green light, then the red book must absorb the green light so that no light is reflected. And evidently a body which reflects no light appears black. Furthermore, when white light illuminates a red book, the book must reflect only red light and must absorb all other colors. See (c) of Fig. 2. Actually, as shown, a red

additive mixing = adding colors

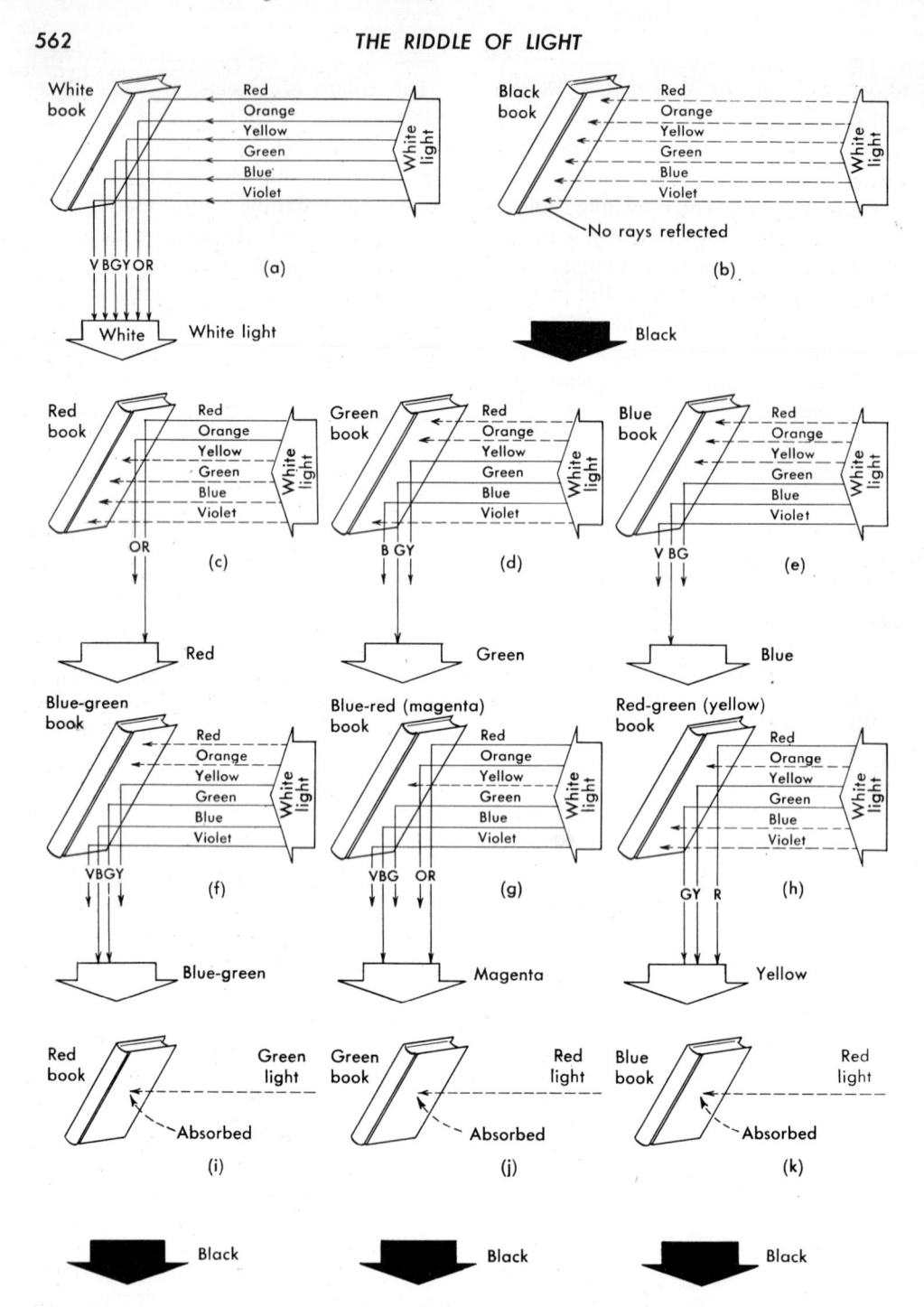

562   THE RIDDLE OF LIGHT

Fig. 2. The color of an object is determined by the color that is reflected. A short arrow indicates that very little of the respective color is reflected.

object reflects a little orange and a little violet because red pigments used in making objects red are never pure.

Likewise, a green book will reflect chiefly green and absorb all other colors, and a blue book will reflect chiefly blue and absorb all other colors. Remember that red, green, and blue are the primary colors of light. See Fig. 2 for what actually happens in each of these cases.

On the other hand, since yellow light consists of a mixture of red light and green light (see Color Plate 1b), then a yellow book should reflect both red and green light. It absorbs blue light, the complement of yellow. Similarly, a blue-green book should reflect green and blue light and should absorb red light, which is its complement. Also, magenta should absorb its complement, green, and reflect blue and red. See (f), (g), and (h) of Fig. 2 for what actually happens in each of these cases.

In conclusion, the color of a body is the result of absorption, a subtractive process, as well as a result of reflection. The subtractive process is explained more fully later in the study of color printing.

A few substances, such as clear glass and ice, absorb no colors from white light. The light passes right through both, and little light is reflected at the surfaces. Consequently, both appear almost as transparent as air itself.

On the other hand, snow and soapsuds appear white. Also, the foam on certain beverages, such as root beer, may appear white, even though the liquid which imprisons the air in the bubbles may have a different color. Seemingly, this foam is white because the bubbles reflect the light from their surfaces so that it does not penetrate far enough for any of it to be absorbed. Because of the reflection at the surfaces, soapsuds and snow also appear white and not colorless like ice and glass.

Color filters. If we allow white light to strike a piece of ordinary colorless transparent window glass, white light is transmitted. If the glass is red, light of the red end of the spectrum will pass through; the other colors are absorbed or filtered out. See Fig. 3. Likewise, a green glass or other green filter transmits chiefly green, or the green part of the spectrum, and a blue filter transmits chiefly blue light, or the blue part of the spectrum. If two filters of different colors are placed together, only the colors that are transmitted by both will pass through. Two filters, one red and one green, will transmit virtually no light. Explain. What other pairs will do the same? See Fig. 3. Thus, in photography and color printing it is possible to select, through the use of filters, the color of light desired.

Theatrical stage effects caused by light. Many of the amazing effects that we see on the theatrical stage are simply applications of the principles we have been studying. A masked figure appearing in red against a black background can be made to disappear almost entirely if the lights are switched from white to the correct shade of green. The red absorbs the green so that nothing is reflected. Consequently the figure appears black and shades into the background. Faces painted with red grease paint or covered with red rouge will appear natural in a red spotlight but will appear to be black in a green spotlight. The red will absorb the green so that nothing will be reflected. Likewise, red lips will appear black under the green or blue lights of the ballroom. A yellow costume will change to a bright red under crimson light. A crimson costume will appear to be blue under a blue-green spotlight. Scores of other color effects can be worked out by a study of the light-absorbing properties of the various pigments.

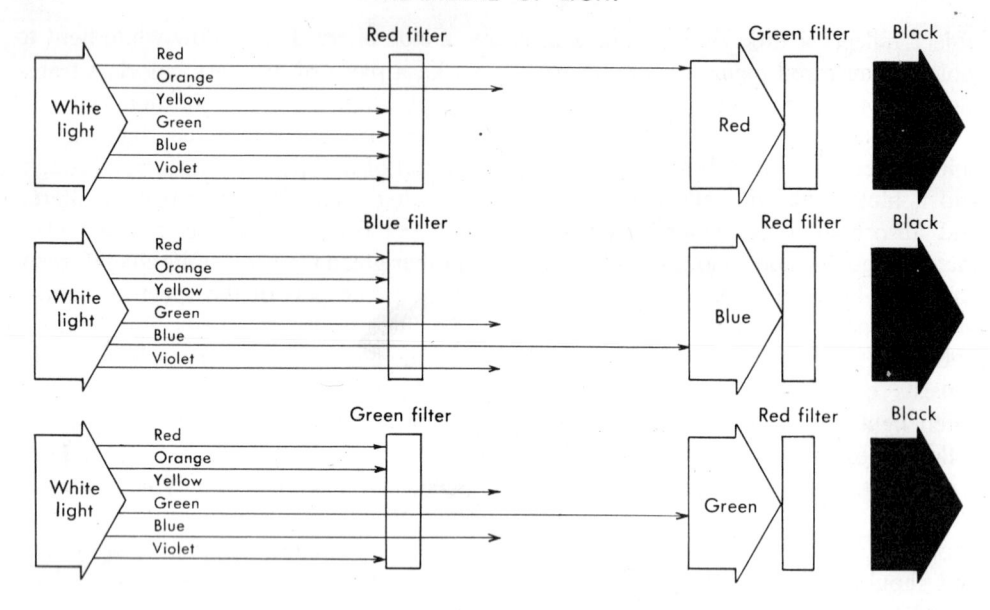

Fig. 3. By means of any two filters of the three primary colors of light, all visible light is absorbed. A short arrow indicates that only a very small amount of the respective color passes through the filter.

The artist's primary colors. Artists have long contended that the primary colors are red, blue, and yellow. What they refer to are *pigments,* which are vastly different from the colors of light with which Newton experimented.

Actually, the primary pigments used today by artists and printers are yellow, which reflects red and green light; blue-green, which reflects blue and green light; and magenta (red-blue), which reflects red and blue light. See (d), (e), and (f) of Color Plate 1. Note that these primary pigment colors are actually the complementary colors of the primary light colors.

Colors produced when pigments are mixed. When all three primary pigments—yellow, blue-green, and magenta—are combined, black is produced and not white as when the primary colors of light are combined. See (d) of Color Plate 1.

When equal amounts of two primary pigments are mixed, the colors in between are produced, as in (e) of Color Plate 1. For example, if yellow (red-green) and blue-green are mixed, green is produced. Both of these primary pigments, as shown in (e) of Color Plate 1, reflect green, and the red in the yellow absorbs the blue in the blue-green, whereas the blue in the blue-green absorbs the red from the yellow. As a consequence, only green light is reflected.

PROBLEM 1: What color is produced when magenta (red-blue) pigment is mixed with yellow (red-green)? Explain in terms of the colors reflected and those absorbed from white light.

PROBLEM 2: What color results when magenta (red-blue) pigment is mixed with blue-green? Explain in terms of the colors reflected and absorbed from white light.

Theoretically, when a primary pigment is mixed with its complement, black or

THE RIDDLE OF COLOR

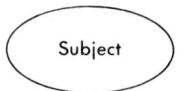

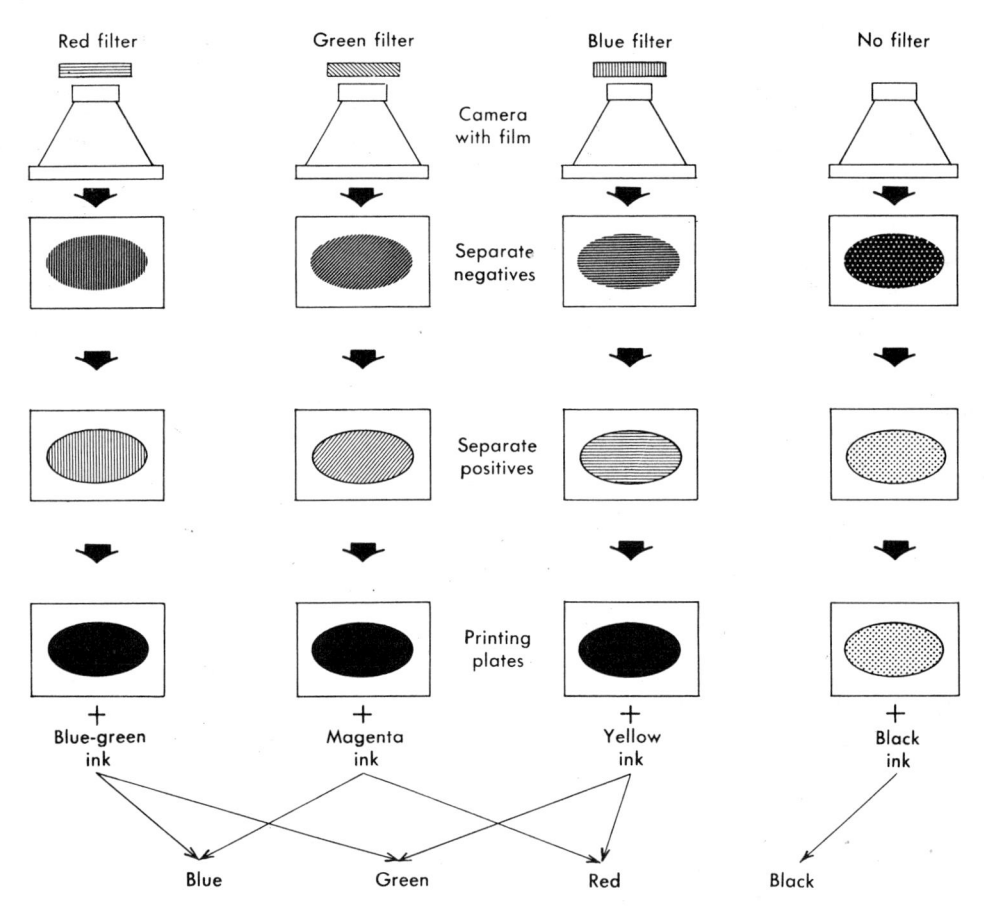

Fig. 4. In color printing, the primaries are produced by the subtractive mixture of the complementaries, while the complementary colors are produced by the additive mixture of primaries.

gray should be produced. However, because in practice no pigment is pure, this is found to be untrue.

Color printing. Color printing like that which you see in most magazines and books begins with four photographs of the subject. As shown in Fig. 4, one photograph is taken through a green filter, another through a red filter, and the third through a blue filter. No filter is used when the fourth photograph is taken. With the four plates produced from these photographs, and the primary colors of ink, yellow, blue-green, and magenta, along with black, all the colors of the spectrum as well as black and white can be printed in one picture.

As you know, the red filter allows only

transmitted light of the red end of the spectrum to strike the photographic film. Hence, when the film is developed, only those parts of the film which correspond with the red in the subject are darkened. Likewise, the darkened parts of the films taken through the green and blue filters correspond respectively with the green and the blue in the subject.

The next step is to develop positive films from the negatives by passing light through the negatives onto photographic film. As a result, little or no light strikes the positive film where the negative film is black. Consequently, when the positive film is developed, where the negative is black the positive is white, and where the negative is white the positive is black. The printing plate is then made. However, only the blackened part of the positive is printed.

But instead of red, blue, and green ink being used on the plates made through these respective filters, the complements of these inks are used. On the plate produced through the red filter, blue-green ink is used; on the plate produced through the blue filter, yellow ink is used; and on the plate produced through the green filter, magenta ink is used. Black ink is used on the fourth plate.

If, in the printing process, only blue-green ink is printed on white paper, then naturally the color is blue-green. But if a layer of yellow is superimposed on the blue-green, then, when white light strikes the mixture, the red and blue light are absorbed by the mixture so that only green, which incidentally will correspond with the green in the subject, is reflected. Similarly, when magenta (red-blue) is superimposed on yellow (red-green), the blue and the green are absorbed, and only the red, which corresponds with the red in the subject, is reflected. What colors of light are absorbed and reflected from white light when magenta is superimposed on blue-green?

Supposedly, when yellow, magenta, and blue-green pigments are mixed, all colors of white light should be absorbed and black should be produced. As you will recall, black is a mixture of all three of the primary pigments; but printers use a black-ink plate to print where these three overlap because the three superimposed layers do not absorb light sufficiently to give a good black.

In conclusion, when the three primary pigments (yellow, magenta, and blue-green) are printed on white paper, all six colors of the spectrum can be obtained, along with black and white. Four plates are necessary, one for each complementary color and one for the black. How is white obtained?

Proper and improper use of color. Homes, costumes, hats, suits, and dresses, even though very expensive, may look very common or border on the ridiculous if color combinations are used incorrectly. On the other hand, proper color combinations can add greatly to their charm and attractiveness. For most of us the question is, "What colors can be used together?"

Different tints and shades of any one color are sure to be harmonious when used in a costume or house decoration. But touches of white, black, or both will add interest. For example, a costume that has several shades of blue is very attractive but will be improved by the addition of white or black, or both. A blue suit of clothes looks well with a white shirt, white straw hat, and a black tie.

Colors that lie side by side in a color triangle and have one color in common usually combine well. An example is a combination of green, yellow, and orange, which all have yellow in common. A blue, blue-green, and green combination is another example. The blue and the green alone might clash, but with blue-green to blend them, harmony can be established.

Bright complementary colors with equal areas clash badly and are unpleasant. But if we subdue their intensity and give one of them a much smaller space than the other, one enriches its opposite and produces one of the best of harmonies.

There are two general laws of color harmony: (1) *The colors must be related in some definite way;* (2) *one color must dominate.*

Unless startling effects are desired, very bright colors should rarely be used and then should be combined with white, black, or gray. If we wish to paint the shutters of our house a bright green, then we should paint the house white or a very light gray.

Color blindness. According to theory, there are three sets of nerve endings distributed over the retina of the eye. One set responds chiefly to blue light, a second set to green light, and the third to red. If pure spectral yellow enters the eye, the red and the green sets respond equally, but the sensation is that of yellow light. And as we might expect, when pure spectral red and pure spectral green enter the eye, the red and the green sets again respond equally, which again gives the sensation of yellow.

Similarly, green and blue lights give the sensation of bluish-green, and red and blue give the sensation of magenta. In some people one set of nerve endings fails to respond to color stimuli. A person may be blind to red, green, or blue. Most common is blindness to red. About 4 per cent of the male population is color-blind, but only about 0.5 per cent of the female population is affected. However, it appears that color blindness is transmitted by heredity through women from one generation to the next.

Color and wave length. We know that the dispersion of white light caused by refraction is due to the fact that the colors at the violet end of the spectrum are refracted more than those at the red end. According to the wave theory, we explained the refraction of light as it passes obliquely to the surface from one medium to another as being due to the fact that the velocity of light is decreased in the medium of greater optical density. See page 494. Newton, who proposed the corpuscular theory, said the velocity would be increased. This was contrary to experiment.

Since violet light is refracted more than red light, then the velocity of violet light must be less than that of red light in the medium of greater optical density. One way of accounting for this is to assume that the wave length of violet light is less, and its frequency is more, than that of red light. Actual experiment shows this is the case.

Table 1

WAVE LENGTHS AND FREQUENCIES OF VISIBLE LIGHT

Color	Wave length		No. of waves per mm.	No. of waves per sec. (million million)
	Millimeter	*Angstroms**		
Violet	.00041	4100	2440	732
Blue	.00047	4700	2130	639
Green	.00052	5200	1920	576
Yellow	.00057	5700	1750	525
Orange	.00062	6200	1610	483
Red	.00071	7100	1410	423

The rainbow. One of the most commonly known spectra is the rainbow. We have all seen it in the morning in a cloud in the western sky and in the evening in the eastern sky. We have also seen rainbows in the spray of a fountain or of a garden hose. Standing on the ground, we never see one in a cloud if the sun is more than 54 degrees above the horizon, and

*An angstrom is $\frac{1}{10,000,000,000}$ meter.

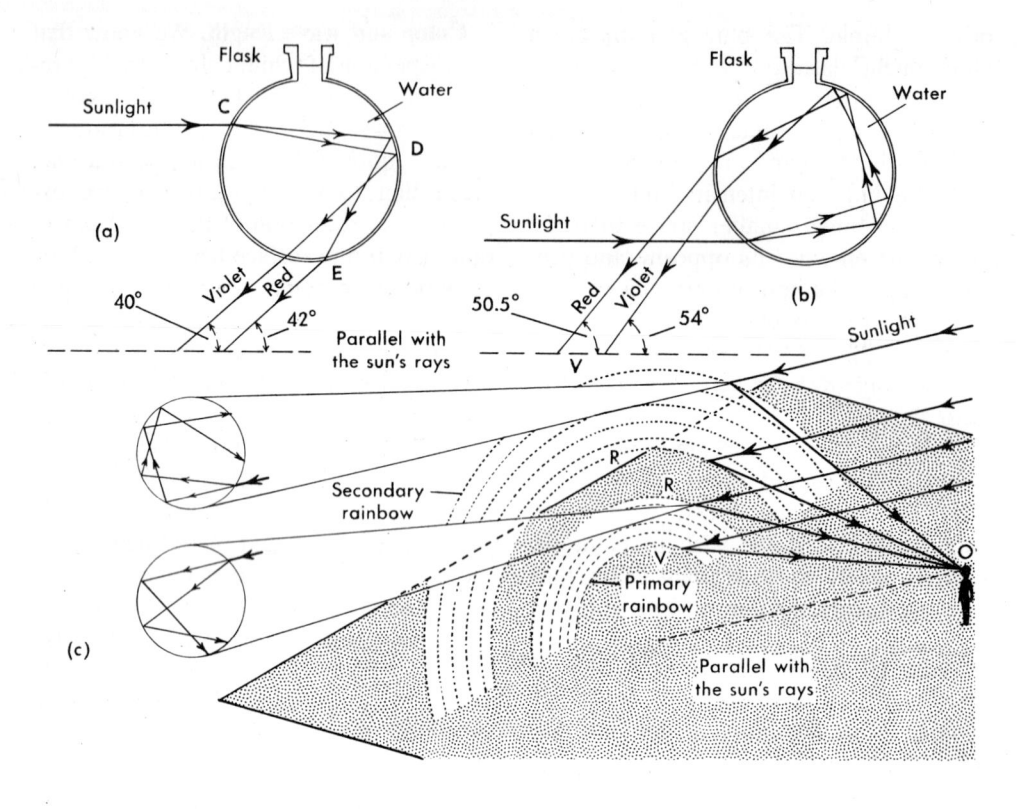

Fig. 5. (a) Demonstrating the total reflection of a light ray striking a water particle in the primary rainbow. (b) Showing the two internal reflections of light rays in the secondary rainbow. (c) Primary and secondary rainbows as seen by an observer at O.

we seldom see one from an airplane except when flying at low altitudes.

From these observations, it is evident that a rainbow must be caused by the dispersion and bending of light rays by raindrops or cloud particles. If this is true, we should be able to demonstrate what takes place when light passes through a spherical flask of water, as in (a) and (b) of Fig. 5.

A beam of light which enters the flask (a) at C is both refracted and dispersed. At D it is totally reflected, and at E it is again refracted and dispersed as it passes into the air. Since in both refractions the violet is bent more than the red, the violet must return nearer to the incident white beam than the red does. When the flask is a perfect sphere, the angle between the incident white ray and the violet is 40°; between the red and white it is 42°.

Consequently, when the sun, an observer, and a cloud consisting of spherical water particles are in the proper relative positions, the observer should see the *primary* rainbow in the cloud, as shown in (c) of Fig. 5. The red is on the top and the violet on the lower side of the bow.

A second bow (*secondary* rainbow) having the red on the lower and violet on the top side is often seen above the one just described. This bow is caused by rays that undergo two internal reflections. See (b) of Fig. 5.

THE RIDDLE OF COLOR

It should be remembered that no two people ever see the same rainbow, since the light that enters one person's eyes cannot enter another's. It should also be understood that the rainbow one sees is the result of the refraction and dispersion of sunlight, not from just one raindrop or cloud droplet, but from myriads of them.

SUMMARY AND CONCLUSIONS

1. When white light is passed through a prism, it is dispersed into a band of colors called a spectrum. The colors are red, orange, yellow, green, blue, and violet. When these colors of light are recombined, they reproduce white light.
2. Two colors of light which together produce white light are complementary colors.
3. The primary colors of light are red, blue, and green. None of these can be produced by the mixing of other colors. Any other color of light can be produced if the proper primary colors of light are mixed in the proper proportions.
4. The primary pigments are magenta, blue-green, and yellow. When mixed these give black; they neutralize each other. Black, gray, and white are called neutrals. Two pigments that neutralize each other are called complementary pigments.
5. The laws of color harmony are:
   (a) The colors must be related in some definite way.
   (b) One color must dominate.
6. A rainbow is caused by the internal reflection and the dispersion (by refraction) of sunlight by raindrops or droplets of clouds and fine spray.

QUESTIONS FOR REVIEW

1. What was the crucial experiment which Newton performed to show that white light is a combination of all the other colors?
2. What is a spectrum?
3. What causes white light which enters a prism to emerge as a band of colors rather than remain as one beam of white light?
4. What argument did Newton's opponents use to disprove his color theory of light? Upon what assumption was the argument based?
5. What are complementary light colors? Give several examples, making use of the color triangle.
6. What causes a body to appear to be black?
7. What are the primary light colors? Why are they called primary colors?
8. Explain why a white body appears to be white in white light, red in red light, and so on.
9. Explain why a green hat appears to be black in red light.
10. Why does the sun appear to be red at sunset and sunrise?
11. What causes the sky to appear to be blue?
12. Why does the sky appear to be black instead of blue to an observer high in the atmosphere?
13. What are the artist's primary colors?
14. What are the neutrals?
15. What are the artist's complementary colors?
16. Explain why, according to theory, yellow and blue-green pigments should give black or gray when mixed, but actually produce green instead.
17. Why is a rainbow never seen in the sky at noon by a low-altitude earthbound observer?
18. State the laws of color harmony. Apply them to various color combinations seen.
19. What is an angstrom?
20. Why is violet light refracted more than red light?
21. What color is produced when the following colors of light are combined?
    (a) Yellow and blue *white – gray*
    (b) Red and green *yellow – gray*
    (c) Blue and green *blue-green – gray*
    (d) Green and magenta *white – gray*
    (e) Blue and red *magenta – gray*
    (f) Red and blue-green *white – gray*
22. What colors are produced when pigments of the above colors are combined?

PROJECTS

1. Bring to class samples of clothing, wallpaper, linoleum, and similar products and discuss whether they have been designed in keeping with the laws of color harmony.
2. Ask your art teacher to discuss color harmony with your class.
3. If you owned a gasoline filling station, what colors would you paint it? Discuss.

READING YOU WILL ENJOY

1. Birren, Faber, *The Story of Color*. Crimson Press, Westport, Conn., 1941. Treats color from the time of ancient mysticism to the time of modern science. Is very readable and highly interesting.
2. Committee on Colorimetry, Optical Society of America, *The Science of Color*. Thomas Y. Crowell Company, New York, 1953. Gives a complete and authentic discussion of color. Contains several beautiful color illustrations.
3. Evans, Ralph M., *An Introduction to Color*. John Wiley and Sons, Inc., New York, 1948. Discusses virtually all aspects of color.
4. Judd, Dean B., *Color in Business, Science, and Industry*. John Wiley and Sons, Inc., New York, 1952. Contains many practical ideas concerning color.

Chapter 49

Spectra and the Emission and Absorption of Light

How good a detective are you? We have already learned that when white light is passed through a prism, as in Newton's famous color experiment, a continuous band of colors ranging from red to violet is emitted. The band is composed of color from end to end. See Color Plate 3(a). There is no break between the colors. Violet blends into blue, blue into green, green into yellow, and so on. Such a band of colors is known as a *continuous spectrum*. White light is produced by the heating of a solid, a liquid, or a gas under high pressure until each is white hot. A carbon arc, or an ordinary tungsten-filament electric lamp, is a good source of white light. A substance which is hot enough to give off light of any color is said to be *incandescent*.

Peculiarly, a gas, under low pressure, does not emit either white light or a continuous spectrum as solids and liquids do. A gas at low pressure emits a few lines or bands of color. For example, heated sodium vapor, as in the bright-line sodium spectrum, Color Plate 3(c), emits only two very narrow yellow lines, called D lines, that are so close together they look as one unless the spectrum is dispersed, or "spread," widely. The hydrogen spectrum shows the lines emitted by hydrogen. Each of the other elements emits lines that are characteristic of it alone.

Salts of different elements, when heated in an open fire, Bunsen flame, or exploding fireworks, are caused to vaporize and to emit the spectacular colors characteristic of the various elements of which they are composed. The spectrum of an incandescent gas or vapor is called a *bright-line spectrum*.

Although in Newton's famous color experiment the spectrum of the sun appeared continuous, further investigation by means of a *spectroscope,* an instrument designed especially to give more dispersion than the ordinary prism does, showed that the sun's spectrum is not continuous. Instead, as shown in Color Plate 3(b), it is crossed by dark lines called *Fraunhofer lines*. These dark lines were named after Joseph von Fraunhofer (1787-1826), a German scientist, who first discovered them. This spectrum is called a *dark-line* or *absorption spectrum*. Naturally these findings raise several questions. For example: Why is the sun's spectrum not continuous? Is it because the sun consists solely of low-pressure burning gases? Or is there another reason for the dark Fraunhofer lines? If you are a good detective, with one more clue and by careful study of the bright-line and dark-line spectra in Color Plate 3, you should solve the mystery.

The clue to the Fraunhofer lines. The clue to the Fraunhofer dark lines in the sun's spectrum was discovered by another German, Gustav Robert Kirchhoff. He found that *an element in the gaseous state absorbs the identical wave lengths of light that it emits when it is heated to incandescence.* For example, incandescent sodium vapor emits yellow light, as shown in the sodium bright-line spectrum. And sodium vapor absorbs light of this identical wave length, as shown in the sodium absorption spectrum, Color Plate 3(d). With these suggestions and clues, see if you can now explain the dark lines in the sun's spectrum.

How helium gas was discovered in the sun before it was discovered on earth. Study of the spectra (b) and (c) in Color Plate 3 shows that the bright lines emitted by sodium are missing in the solar spectrum. In their places are two dark lines, marked *D*. One explanation of these dark lines is that the solar spectrum is actually continuous, and that the *D* dark lines are caused by sodium vapor which exists in the outer atmosphere of the sun and absorbs the yellow lines from the continuous spectrum of the sun. The sodium vapor in the outer edge of the sun is not hot enough to emit its characteristic light. This hypothesis, if true, has important significance, because it means that for every dark line in the solar spectrum there must exist between the earth and the sun a vapor which absorbs light of the same wave length as that missing in the solar spectrum. Since each element in the gaseous form will emit the same wave length or wave lengths that it will absorb, then, if we know the element that emits the absorbed wave lengths, we can know all the gaseous elements between the earth and the sun. What a hypothesis, if it is true!

When the bright lines for all the known elements were matched against the dark lines in the solar spectrum, practically all the dark lines could be accounted for, showing that many of the same elements that exist on the earth also exist in the sun's atmosphere in vapor form. However, there were certain dark lines which could not be accounted for by early investigators. There was no earthly element which emitted the bright lines that corresponded to a few dark lines in the sun's spectrum. This indicated that there existed in the sun's atmosphere a gaseous element which, if it existed on earth, had never yet been discovered. This new gas was named *helium* (from *helios,* the Greek name for the sun).

Even before this, chemists and others had suspected the existence of such a gas. They had already computed its density and had predicted many of its actual characteristics. These new findings by the astronomers spurred on the search for it. Nearly a quarter of a century later helium was found in certain minerals, then in very minute quantities in the earth's atmosphere, and finally in natural gas in the gas wells of Texas, Kansas, and Oklahoma. Thus, again we see what the human mind is capable of accomplishing by using hypotheses as guides, and experiments to check and guide in the direction in which well-reasoned hypotheses lead.

"Gold from the sun"—and stars. The almost unbelievable news that scientists could determine the composition of the sun and other stars spread like wildfire.

Naturally, one of the questions asked by materialistic people was whether or not the findings revealed the presence of gold in the sun. Seeing no possibility of getting it, if it did exist in the sun, and seeing no practical application of such "nonsensical research," a banker remarked, "What do I care for gold in the sun if I cannot fetch it down here!" Shortly afterward Kirchhoff received from England a gold medal and gold cash prize for his brilliant work in the study of the sun's spectrum. When he handed the money over to this banker, he said, "Look here, I have succeeded at last in fetching some gold from the sun." How embarrassed the banker would have been had he lived to learn that Kirchhoff's discovery was part of the preliminary work that led to the discovery of how to release atomic energy.

What does the spectroscope tell us about the motions of the stars? Not only does the spectroscope enable us to determine the chemical composition of the sun and other stars, but it also detects their motions. The principle is one that we have already studied in sound. There we learned that if a sound source is approaching a listener, the pitch is raised, which is the same as increasing the frequency. Vice versa, if the source is moving away from the listener, the pitch is lowered, which is the same as decreasing the frequency.

Similarly, when a star is approaching a spectroscope the result is the same as though the frequency of the light were increased. This increases the refraction caused by the prism. You will recall that violet light has a higher frequency than red light, and it is for this reason that violet is refracted more than red. Hence, as a result, light from a star moving *toward* the earth is refracted more and shifted slightly toward the violet end of the spectrum. Light from a star moving *away* from

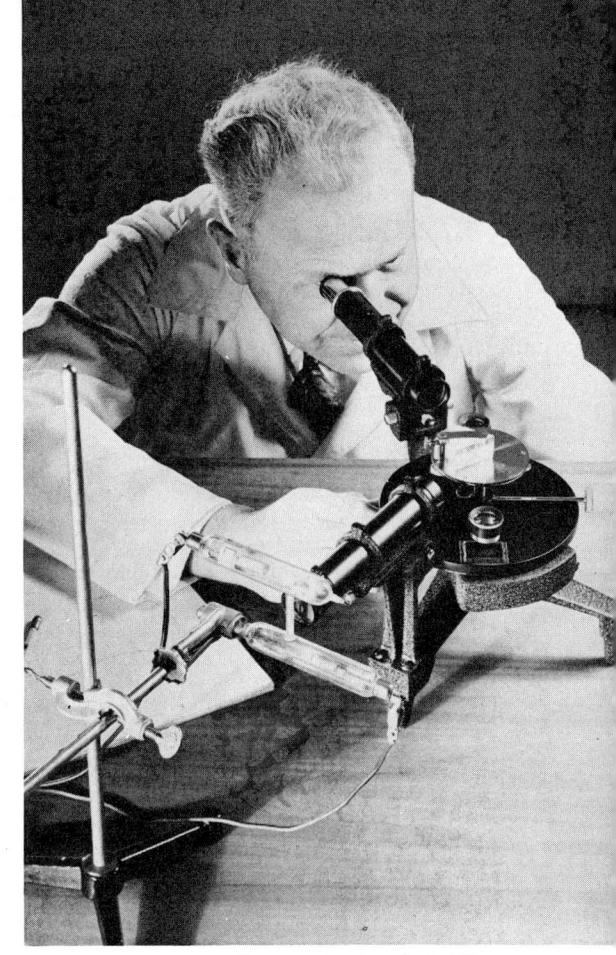

Courtesy American Optical Co.

Fig. 1. The spectroscope is an instrument for separating the spectrum colors produced by a light source so that they do not overlap as do those produced by a prism alone. The parallel rays dispersed by the prism are viewed through a telescope.

the earth is shifted slightly toward the red end of the spectrum. The lines in the spectrum of a star which is neither approaching nor moving away from the earth, match those of an incandescent source at rest on the earth.

How is the spectroscope used in chemical analysis? Not only does the spectroscope tell us the composition of the stars,

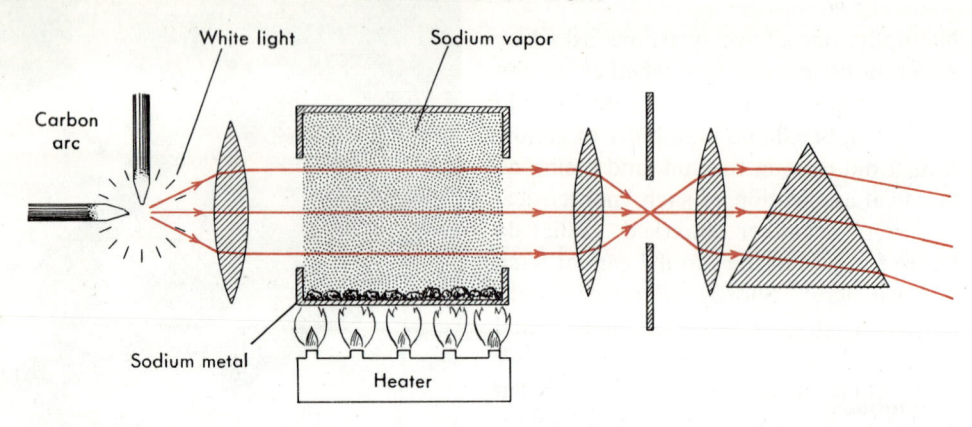

Fig. 2. An apparatus for studying the absorption spectrum produced by sodium vapor. Yellow is not produced, because the vapor absorbs light of the same wave length as the vapor itself would produce.

but it is also the chemists' readiest, quickest, and one of their most accurate means for analyzing chemicals of all sorts. For the detection of even the slightest impurities in foods, metals, and other substances, it is unsurpassed. As little as one part in a million of some chemicals can be detected. Also, by knowing the color emitted by a hot body it is possible for us to know its temperature.

How better photography enabled scientists to discover black light—the ultraviolet region of the sun's spectrum. Previous to about 1850 a visit to the photographer was quite an ordeal. Even when the face was dusted with a white powder to increase the reflection of light, the exposure time on the brightest day was about six minutes. In 1839 the sensitivity of photographic plates was increased greatly. Then Edmond Becquerel, French physicist, using the new type of plate, made a photograph of the sun's spectrum which extended far beyond the visible violet. This new region is totally invisible to the eye. It is called the *ultraviolet* (beyond violet) portion of the spectrum and it consists of wave lengths shorter than 4000 angstrom units. The angstrom, you will recall, is one 10-billionth part of a meter. Ultraviolet light behaves differently from ordinary light in many ways, one of these being its effects on the human body. A carbon arc is a good source of ultraviolet light. Make a detailed study of the nature and uses of ultraviolet light, and make a report to your class.

The discovery of the infrared region of the sun's spectrum. In 1799, Sir William Herschel placed a thermometer in different parts of the sun's spectrum and found that the temperature was higher at a certain distance beyond the red end than at any other point. He believed it to be caused by invisible heat rays coming from the sun and believed them to be the same as the invisible rays given off by a hot stove or other hot body. He called them *infrared* rays. Later research proved his hypothesis correct. Today the sun's spectrum has been extended from the visible red light, having a wave length of 7100 angstroms, to the invisible infrared light having a wave length of about 53,000 angstroms.

Electromagnetic theory of light. About 1860, Maxwell found that *electromagnetic waves* travel through a vacuum with the same speed as heat and light waves. This,

SPECTRA AND THE EMISSION AND ABSORPTION OF LIGHT

along with certain other observations, caused Maxwell to believe that visible light, radiated heat, ultraviolet, infrared, and electromagnetic waves are all electromagnetic in nature. And he predicted the existence of electromagnetic waves other than those already known at that time. About twenty-five years later, Hertz discovered these and called them *radio waves*.

Maxwell proposed, too, that the origin of light is a vibrating electrified particle which causes a disturbance in the ether similar to the disturbance caused by a vibrating tuning fork in air. At that time electrons were unknown. This electromagnetic theory of Maxwell's, like Huyghens' wave theory, was based upon the assumption that ether transmits electromagnetic waves.

The photoelectric effect. The twentieth century was ushered in by science with the discovery that when ultraviolet light strikes a polished metal, such as zinc, electrons are emitted by the metal. This phenomenon is called the *photoelectric effect*.

Knowing the cause of the photoelectric effect, it is logical for us to expect that an increase in the intensity of the light striking the metal would cause the velocities of the electrons to increase. This, however, is contrary to experimental findings. Increasing the intensity of light increases the number of electrons emitted, but the velocities of the fastest ones, like the velocities of the slowest ones and those in between, all remain the same. Naturally, a question arises as to whether these findings are in keeping with either the wave theory or the corpuscular theory.

To answer this question, we shall consider the wave theory first.

How adequately does the wave theory explain the photoelectric effect? In the study of sound, we found that an increase in the intensity of sound causes an increase only in the amplitude of the waves emitted.

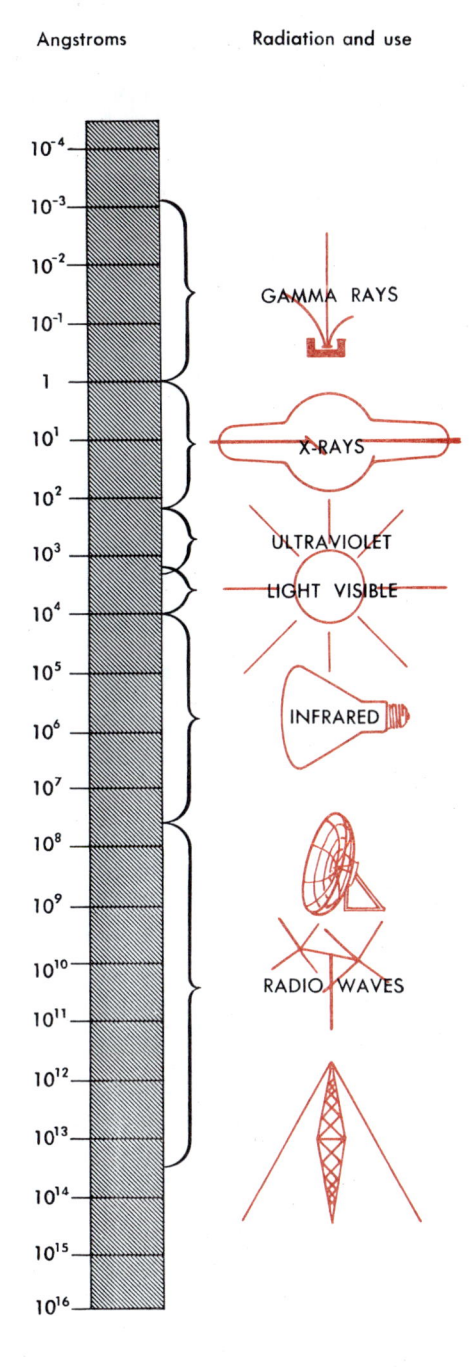

Fig. 3. A chart of the electromagnetic spectrum, showing the wave lengths in angstroms.

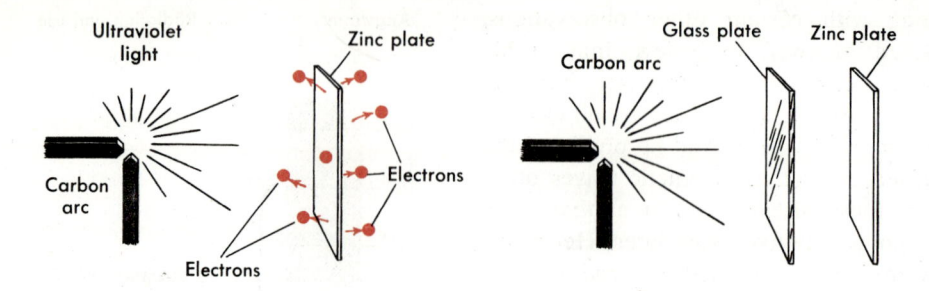

Fig. 4. (a) The emission of electrons as a result of light waves striking a metal plate is called the photoelectric effect. (b) The glass plate does not transmit ultraviolet.

If the same is true of light, then increasing the intensity should increase the amplitude of the waves; and hence, increasing the amplitude of a wave should increase the velocity of an electron tossed out by it for the same reason that a high ocean wave tosses spray higher than a low one does.

That is, increasing the intensity of light should increase the velocities of the electrons emitted by the metal. But this is not so. Increasing the intensity of light merely increases the number of electrons emitted, with no change in velocities. In other words, the wave theory and the experimental facts are not in agreement.

How adequately does the corpuscular theory explain the photoelectric effect? Now let us consider Newton's corpuscular theory. According to Newton, when the intensity of a light source is increased, the number of corpuscles emitted per unit of time is increased but the speeds of the corpuscles are not changed; they all travel with the same speed through empty space. Also, the corpuscles which make up light of one color are all alike.

Therefore, if two identical corpuscles were to strike two identical electrons direct, head-on blows, then the same amounts of energy should be transferred to each electron. Therefore, both should come out of a metal, as in the photoelectric effect, with equal velocities, provided that one electron can escape from the metal as easily as the other. Increasing the intensity of light should increase the number of electrons emitted by the metal but should not increase the velocities with which the electrons are emitted. This we find is the actual case.

On the other hand, if the corpuscular theory is correct, for every different possible glancing blow, of which there should be millions, an electron should be emitted having a corresponding speed. The situation is similar to shooting the cue ball in billiards into a nest of balls. Coming out of the nest, no two balls would have the same velocity. Likewise, with the photoelectric effect, there should be a wide variety of electron velocities. This, however, is not the case. The variety of velocities is actually much smaller than it should be. The corpuscular theory accounts in part for the photoelectric effect but not completely.

The quantum theory of light. In an endeavor to account for the photoelectric effect, a brilliant German physicist named Max Planck proposed the *quantum theory* in 1905. Instead of assuming that light consists of continuous waves, Planck assumed that it consists of bits of energy, of particles of energy, or of *quanta* of energy, which are also known as *photons*. Planck assumed too that photons or quanta

SPECTRA AND THE EMISSION AND ABSORPTION OF LIGHT

which make up light of a single frequency are identical, and that each photon has the same amount of energy. When a photon strikes an electron, the electron either absorbs all the energy or none of it. This accounts for the lack of variety of electron velocities explained above when light of one color strikes a metal body.

It seems that certain electrons absorb certain photons but not others. The electrons seem almost able to choose the photons that they absorb. To the German Academy of Science this did not make sense. Most members said, "Humbug. This is not science."

Doubtless you are thinking similar thoughts and are asking, "What does this quantum theory mean?" "Does it mean that Huyghens, Young, and Fresnel were wrong, and that consequently the wave theory is all wrong?" "Does it mean that Newton was more nearly correct than Huyghens?" To answer these questions, we must test the quantum theory further by determining, for example, how well it explains the emission of light.

The emission of light. Maxwell believed that light is produced by a vibrating electrical particle, very much as sound is produced by a vibrating tuning fork. But, if this were true, light, like sound, would be emitted as a continuous wave and not as quanta. Maxwell's theory meant also that the vibrating particles would have to be stationary all the time, except when the atom was emitting light; for in case the vibrating particles were in motion all the time, they would have to emit energy all the time, which is contrary to experience. However, that the electrons are at rest at any time disagrees completely with the electron theory advanced on page 346.

Going back to the electron theory, let us endeavor to account for the bright-line spectra emitted by different incandescent gases, assuming that light is emitted in quanta. According to the electron theory, the electrons in an atom revolve about a nucleus in definitely fixed orbits or *energy levels*. See page 355. Each electron possesses kinetic energy due to its motion, and potential energy due to its position or distance from the nucleus which attracts it. The farther an energy level is from the nucleus, the more potential energy an electron in it has. The potential energy of an

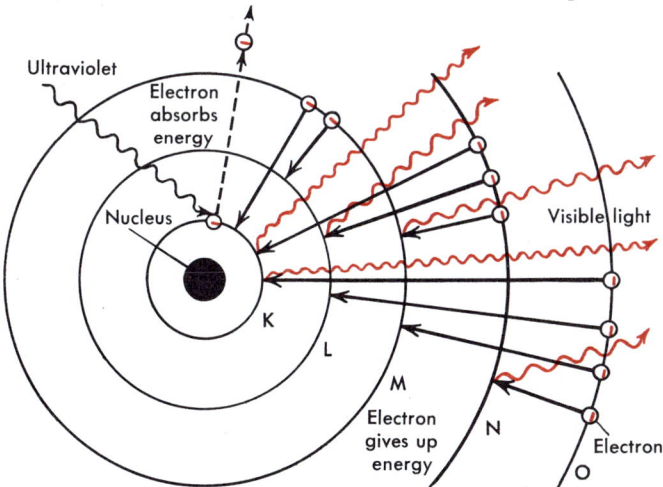

Fig. 5. In moving from a higher energy level to a lower one, electrons give off energy in the form of light or photons. When an electron is stimulated to travel to a higher energy level, it gains potential energy.

electron in an atom is very similar to that of a stone which is above the earth's surface; the greater the distance of the stone from the center of the earth, the greater its potential energy. And an electron which falls from a higher to a lower level loses potential energy, just as a stone does when it falls from a higher to a lower level.

If an electron drops from a higher fixed energy level to a lower fixed one, it loses a definite fixed amount of potential energy in the form of a light quantum. Conversely, it is logical to suppose that an equal quantity of energy would be required to lift an electron from this lower level back to the original energy level. Hence, according to theory, it is perfectly possible for light to be emitted in quanta and absorbed in quanta.

As a result, an element whose atoms possess several different energy levels should be able to emit several different quanta as well as colors of light. Hence, knowing the number of energy levels in an atom, we should be able to predict how many bright lines an incandescent gaseous element will emit. And vice versa, knowing the number of bright lines, we should know the number of different electron energy levels.

Study of the sodium atom (page 355) shows that it possesses only one electron in the outer shell or ring of electrons. The other rings are complete and stable. Hence it seems that the two bright D lines in the sodium spectrum are emitted by one electron.

This emission could take place provided that it were possible for the electron to occupy one of two orbits above the one that it ordinarily occupies when not heated or "excited" by other means. For example, when a sodium atom is heated, the outer electron is lifted to one of these two higher levels; it then falls back to the lower natural level. This would account for one bright line. In another atom, the outer electron might be lifted to the other higher orbit. Then, when it fell back again into the natural lower level, the other bright line should be emitted. Do you see any possibility of a third bright line being emitted? Why do you suppose the other electrons in the sodium atom do not emit light when the atom is excited?

How atoms are "stimulated" to radiate photons (quanta of energy). One way of causing an atom to radiate light and other forms of electromagnetic energy is to heat it. Another method is to bombard it with electrons or certain other atomic particles. When one of these "plows" through an

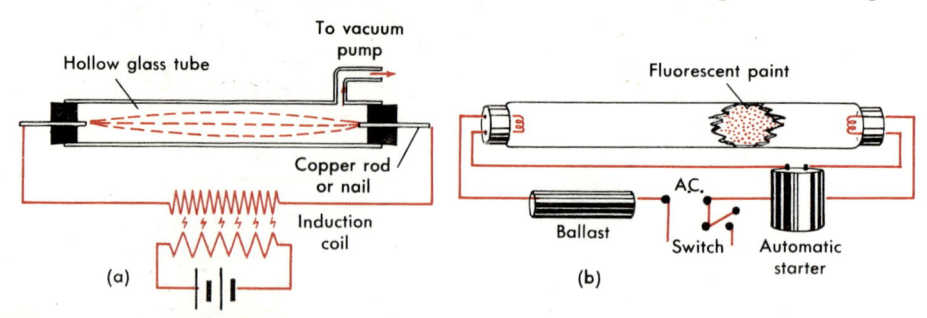

Fig. 6. (a) By applying a high-voltage across the terminals, a discharge of electrons occurs in the gas-filled tube. (b) Fluorescent lamp. When high-speed electrons strike atoms of mercury vapor, ultraviolet radiation is given off as a result of electron jumps. These radiations strike the phosphors, causing the emission of visible light.

COLOR PLATE I

ADDITIVE MIXTURE OF LIGHT

(a) Mixing the primary colors of light.

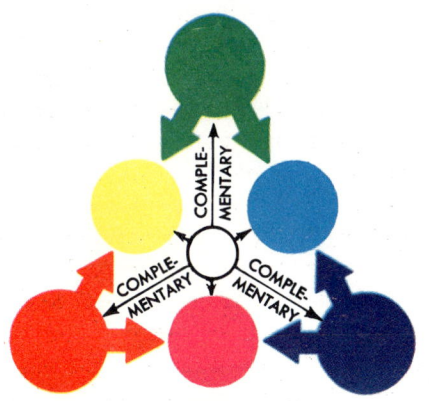

(b) Color triangle for light.

(c) Mixing complementary colors to produce white light.

SUBTRACTIVE MIXTURE OF PIGMENTS

(d) Mixing the primary pigments.

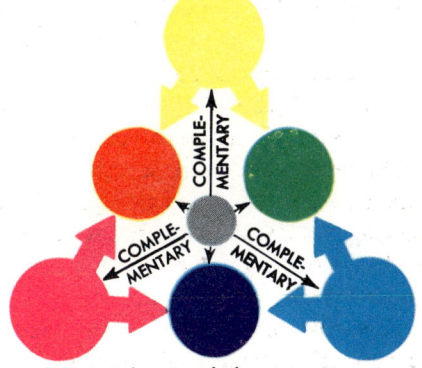

(e) Color triangle for pigments.

(f) Mixing a primary pigment and a complementary.

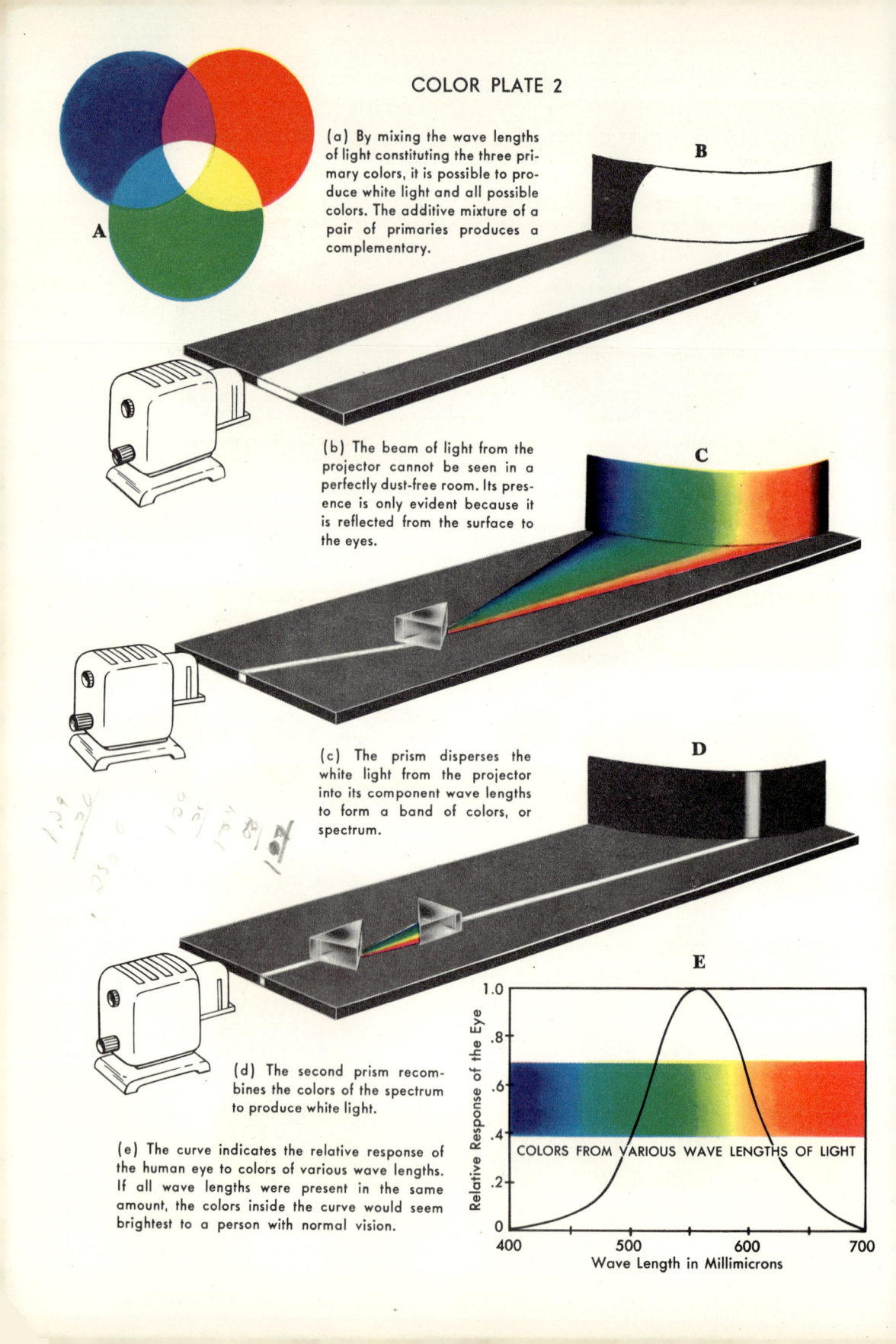

COLOR PLATE 2

(a) By mixing the wave lengths of light constituting the three primary colors, it is possible to produce white light and all possible colors. The additive mixture of a pair of primaries produces a complementary.

(b) The beam of light from the projector cannot be seen in a perfectly dust-free room. Its presence is only evident because it is reflected from the surface to the eyes.

(c) The prism disperses the white light from the projector into its component wave lengths to form a band of colors, or spectrum.

(d) The second prism recombines the colors of the spectrum to produce white light.

(e) The curve indicates the relative response of the human eye to colors of various wave lengths. If all wave lengths were present in the same amount, the colors inside the curve would seem brightest to a person with normal vision.

COLORS FROM VARIOUS WAVE LENGTHS OF LIGHT

Wave Length in Millimicrons

COLOR PLATE 3

SPECTRA

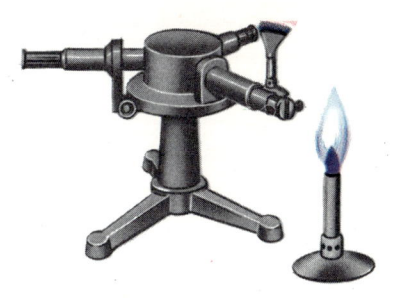

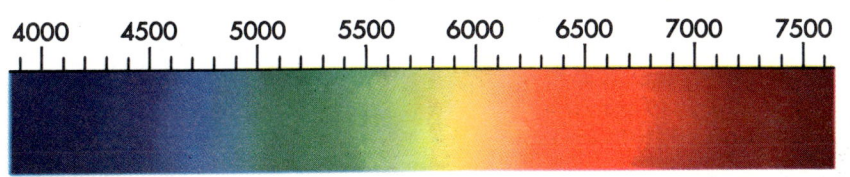

(a) White-light continuous spectrum. The wave lengths are indicated in angstrom units.

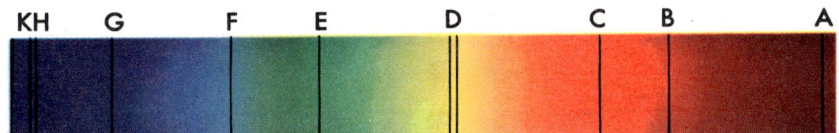

(b) Solar spectrum, showing Fraunhofer lines.

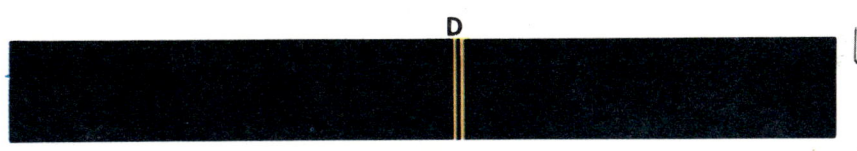

(c) Sodium bright-line spectrum.

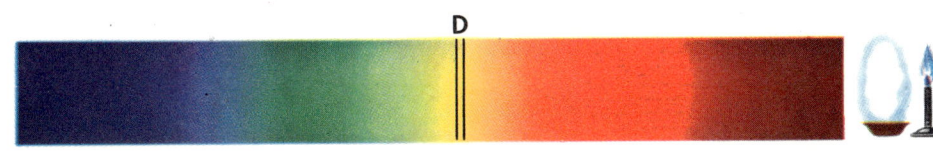

(d) Sodium absorption spectrum.

(e) Hydrogen bright-line spectrum.

COLOR PLATE 4

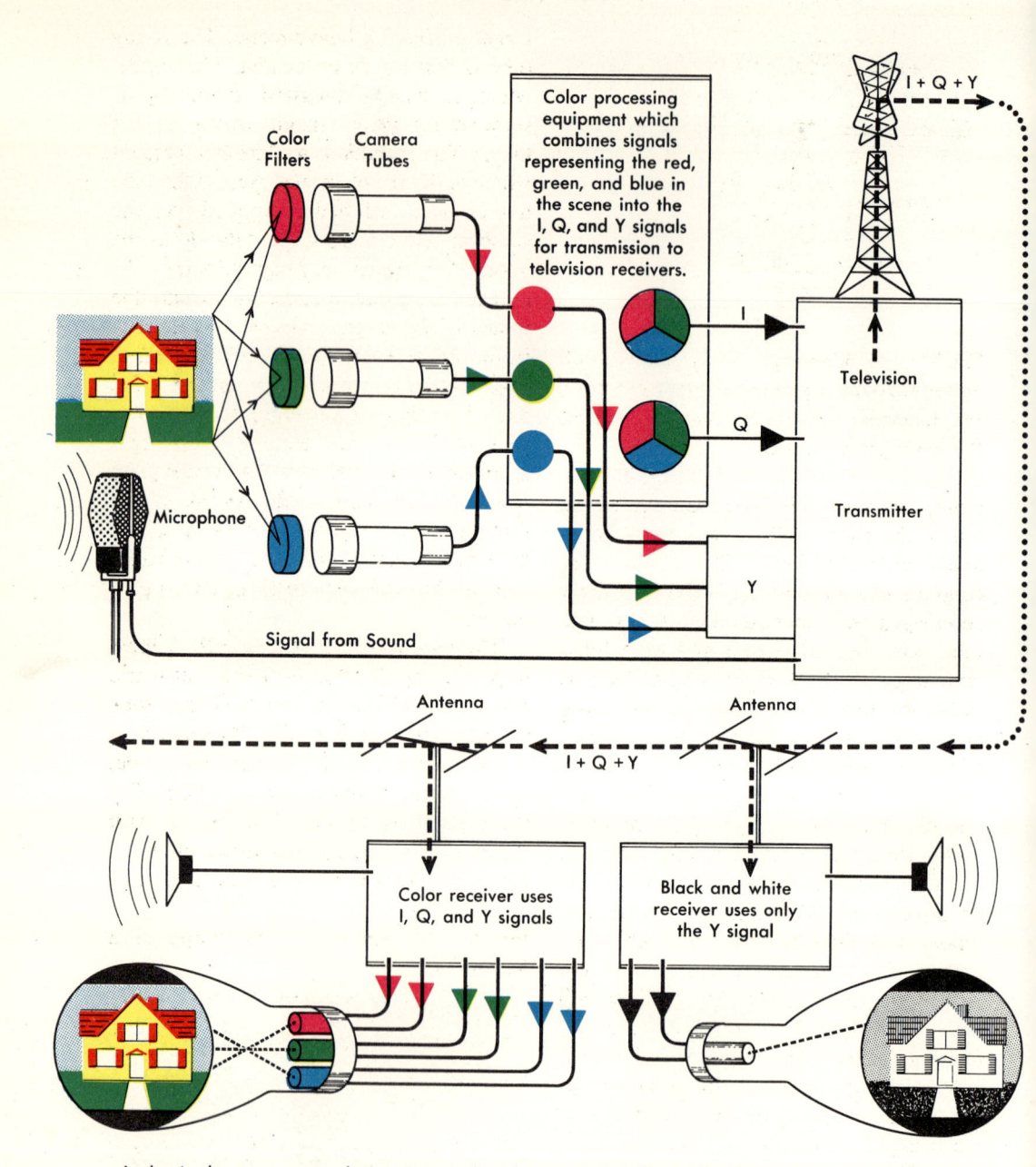

In the simultaneous system of transmitting color television, light reflected from the illuminated scene passes through primary color filters on its way to the camera tubes. Thus the signal from the top camera tube depends upon the red in the scene; that from the middle camera tube upon the green, while that from the lower camera tube depends upon the blue. The I and Q (chrominance) signals depend primarily upon the different *colors* in the scene, while the Y (luminance) signal depends upon the *brightness* of the colors. Thus, while the Y signal alone will operate a black-and-white receiver, all three signals are needed to operate a color receiver.

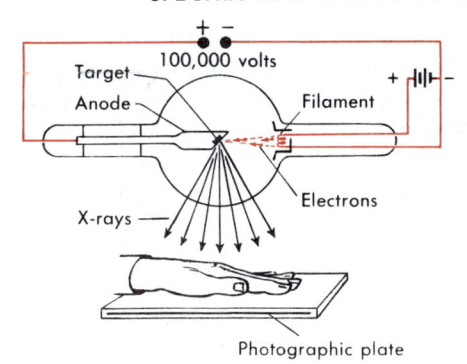

SPECTRA AND THE EMISSION AND ABSORPTION OF LIGHT

Fig. 7. (a) Coolidge X-ray tube. High voltage drives a stream of electrons from the tungsten coil to the anode, causing the emission of X-rays.

atom, it may actually knock some electrons out of the atom or lift others from lower to higher energy levels. One of the most common examples of this is the light from neon signs and other gas-filled tubes. The tubes are first evacuated and then filled with a gas such as neon, argon, etc., at rather low pressure. Across the tube a high voltage is applied, which causes an electrical discharge through the tube. See (a) of Fig. 6. This discharge excites the gas particles in the tube so that they emit light.

Another way of exciting a substance is to irradiate it with X-rays or photons. For example, if certain chemicals such as zinc oxide, strontium stearate, lead chloride, amber, and uranium glass are irradiated with ultraviolet (dark light), they will emit visible light. Such substances are said to be *fluorescent*. See page 580. Fluorescent lamps are based on this principle. In the lamp, photons are produced by an electrical discharge through the gas in the tube. The photons of light then strike a fluorescent substance which is coated on the inside walls of the lamp. As a result the fluorescent substance emits light. See (b) of Fig. 6.

How are X-rays produced? We produce X-rays by bombarbing with electrons a target made of a heavy metal. The X-ray tube is first highly evacuated. The anode, which is usually tungsten, platinum, or some other heavy metal, serves as the target. The cathode is a white-hot filament which emits the electrons. Across the tube a high D.C. voltage is applied. As the electrons stream from the cathode to the anode, they attain very high velocities. As a result they are plunged deep into the atoms of the target, causing the electrons in the lower energy levels to be lifted to higher energy levels. When electrons fall back into these lower energy levels, photons of X-rays are emitted. Very light atoms do not emit X-rays. Can you explain why? Fig. 7a shows a fluorescent screen that is being bombarded with X-rays which have been passed through a human hand. Explain how the picture (Fig. 7b) is produced.

The photoelectric tube or cell. A most important application of the photoelectric effect is made in the *photoelectric tube* or *cell*. This consists of a photosensitive metal surface, such as calcium oxide, which emits electrons when light strikes the metal surface. See S of Fig. 8. Also the tube contains another metal plate, C, called a *collector*, which is kept at a posi-

Fig. 7. (b) An X-ray photograph of a human hand.

Courtesy General Electric X-Ray Corp.

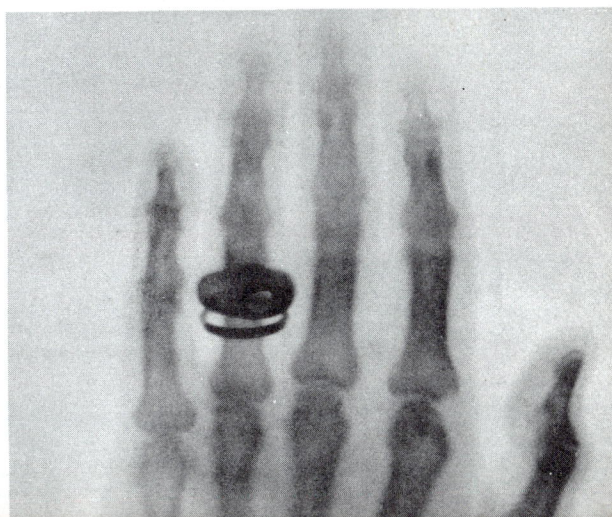

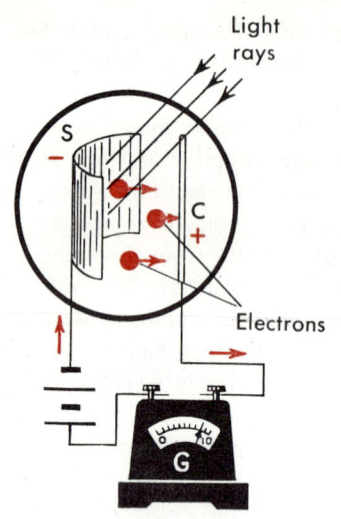

Fig. 8. A photoelectric cell.

tive potential with respect to S. Both the emitter and the collector are enclosed in an evacuated container. When light strikes the photosensitive metal surface, electrons are emitted by it which are attracted to and collected by the positive collector plate C. The result is that when light strikes the emitter, S, a current flows in the battery circuit through the galvanometer. By means of relays and other devices, the photoelectric tube can be used to set off a chain of mechanical events which cause doors to close or open and cause machines to count, select, weigh, wrap packages, and do hundreds of other things.

The cathode ray tube. One of the most important scientific developments in recent years is the *cathode ray tube,* the end of which is coated with a fluorescent substance that produces the picture in a television set.

The tube (see Fig. 10) is highly evacuated. Electrons are emitted from a heated filament or cathode, K. At P there is a positive anode. Between the cathode, K, and the anode, P, a difference of potential of several hundred volts is maintained.

When the electrons are emitted at K they are accelerated toward P. Most of the electrons strike P, but a narrow beam of electrons passes through a small hole in P. This much of the tube is sometimes referred to as an *electron gun.* After leaving the gun, the electrons continue on to the screen, S, which is coated with a fluorescent substance. This fluoresces when bombarded by the electrons, producing a small bright spot on the screen.

Fig. 9. (a) A telephone lineman in Americus, Georgia, adjusts a device to capture solar energy for rural power lines. Beneath the frame are over 400 disks of silicon, which are positive-negative junction transistors. When light strikes the transistor surfaces, electricity flows.

Courtesy Bell Telephone Laboratories

Fig. 9. (b) This bean-sized photocell consisting of a glass lens and a germanium wafer is more sensitive to light than vacuum photocells a hundred times larger. The cell can regulate heating devices, hunt targets for guided missiles, and substitute for a Geiger counter.

Courtesy General Electric Co.

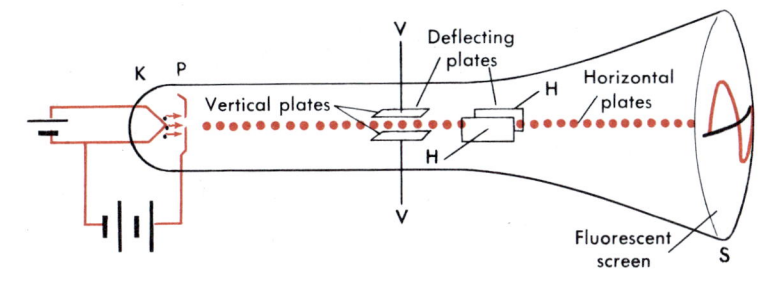

SPECTRA AND THE EMISSION AND ABSORPTION OF LIGHT

Fig. 10. A simplified drawing of a cathode ray tube. As the stream of electrons leave the cathode, it is deflected by the electromagnetic coils of the deflecting plates. Then the application of oscillating currents causes the stream to move up and down and right and left.

The electron beam may be deflected horizontally or vertically by two pairs of deflecting plates, marked H and V in the diagram. In most tubes the deflection is produced by magnetic fields set up by coils outside the tube.

When the tube is used as a television receiver, the spot at which the stream of electrons strikes the screen is caused to sweep over the screen, while its brightness is controlled in accordance with the brightness of points in the object that is being televised. Persistence of vision, as explained on page 542, along with persistence of screen fluorescence, creates the illusion of an image.

The dual nature of matter: waves vs. particles. In 1927 it was found that when very thin sheets of metal are bombarded with electrons and a photographic plate is put behind the metal, the electrons, which pass through the metal and strike the plate, cause interference bands similar to those formed by waves.

This indicated that high-speed electrons have the characteristics of waves. That is, an electron plays a dual role. At low velocities it exhibits the characteristics of matter. At high velocities it has the characteristics of wave energy. Also, this discovery indicated that matter and energy are interchangeable. If matter approaches the speed of light, we call it energy. And conversely, if energy congeals and becomes inert, we call it matter.

In 1905, Albert Einstein had already asserted that matter and energy were one and the same thing. The relationship between the two he expressed in his famous equation:

$$E = mc^2$$

where m is the mass and c is the velocity of light.

To compute the amount of energy in foot-pounds possessed by any pound of matter, we merely substitute as follows:

$$E = 1/32 \times (1 \times 186{,}000 \times 5280)^2$$

$$E = 3{,}000{,}000{,}000{,}000{,}000, \text{ or}$$
$$(3 \times 10^{16}) \text{ foot-pounds.}$$

The mass is divided by 32 so that the answer is in foot-pounds instead of foot-poundals. The velocity of light is in feet per second.

This formula provides the answer to many long-standing mysteries in physics. It explains how the sun and other stars can go on emitting light for billions of years without seemingly burning out; for if the sun were being consumed by ordinary burning processes, it would have burned out ages ago, and the earth would have become a cold dark planet.

Furthermore, Einstein's formula reveals the tremendous energy which lies bound up in the nuclei of atoms and enables scientists to determine how many grams of uranium atomic fuel must be used to power a ship across the ocean or a rocket ship to the moon. And, unfortunately, in many respects, it reveals how much atomic fuel must be used in a bomb to level a city.

Although the formula $E = mc^2$ resolved the conflict between matter and wave energy, no one theory of light is sufficient. The wave theory is not adequate when we want to explain the photoelectric effect, and neither the corpuscular theory nor the quantum theory explains interference. As a result, scientists use one theory to explain one phenomenon and another theory to explain another. Their plight is something like that described in the following account by the American physicist, Arthur Holly Compton.

Waves and Corpuscles in Hard Fought Game
Waves Lead, End of Third Quarter
(By Ray O. Light)

The big game opened with a kickoff by Galileo, veteran fullback of the "Waves." The ball was received by Isaac Newton, the strategic quarter of the "Corpuscles," who stiffarmed Huyghens, the giant tackle of the Waves, and carried the ball for a 45-yard gain. Then by a series of skillfully directed trick plays and forward passes, he led his team through to a touchdown at the end of the first quarter. LaGrange failed to kick goal. Score—Corpuscles 6, Waves 0.

Fresnel, captain of the Waves, elected to receive, and himself caught the ball. Tom Young organized an interference which completely overwhelmed the Corpuscles, and Fresnel ran the length of the field for a touchdown. The electric toe of Maxwell kicked the ball for a goal, giving Waves 7—Corpuscles 6.

At the beginning of the second half Maxwell was put in as quarter for the Waves, and with the help of the famous backfield consisting of Hertz, Kelvin, and Michelson they had things their own way, scoring two touchdowns. Score at the end of the third quarter, Waves 20, Corpuscles 6.

As the last quarter opened, Planck, of the Corpuscles, made a long kickoff to Jeans of the Waves, who was able to return the ball only a few yards. A forward pass was intercepted by Einstein, right end of the Corpuscles, who crossed the line with the velocity of light for a touchdown. The game during the next few minutes was very hard fought, neither side being able to make a first down. At the time this edition goes to press the Waves are in the lead by 7 points, but the Corpuscles seem to have the upper hand.

To some it may seem that science is hopeless because, after all these years of work and study, several conflicting theories are needed to explain the nature of light. Furthermore, is it not a weakness of science that scientists continually change their minds? To answer this latter question, we might ask where science would be today if scientists had lacked the ability to change their minds. The fact that several theories are needed to explain light is not a weakness of science but rather is a challenge to us to find one theory that explains and harmonizes all light phenomena.

Einstein's General Theory of Relativity. The chief purpose that Einstein had in life was to formulate one general theory, the *General Theory of Relativity,* which would explain all physical phenomena, including light. Finally in 1949, after nearly a half-century of work, Einstein announced that he had completed his work.

By means of the general theory, Einstein not only explained all light phenomena but also accounted for the mysterious forces which guide the whirling stars, galaxies, planets, meteors, molecules, atoms, electrons, neutrons, protons, and all other moving bodies. Some of these forces Newton called gravity. Others were called inertia as well as magnetic, electromagnetic, and electrostatic forces. And for years most of them were believed to be unrelated. Einstein, however, combined the ideas of gravity, inertia, electricity, heat, and light all into one harmonious theory which probably will prove to be the greatest mental accomplishment ever achieved by man. His famous equation $E = mc^2$, which is a part of his general theory and which has had such far-reaching consequences in peace and war, will probably seem small in comparison.

But formulation of Einstein's general theory does not mean that everything in physics has now been accomplished. Many years may be required to test many of the consequences of the theory. Like Galileo, Newton, and Oersted, Einstein opened up a vast new unexplored universe. Nevertheless, his general theory will almost certainly be modified; indeed, it may eventually give way to a theory that is even more comprehensive. That is the way of science.

SUMMARY AND CONCLUSIONS

1. The spectra of incandescent solids, liquids, and high-pressure gases are called continuous spectra.
2. The spectrum of an incandescent vapor or gas at low pressure is called a bright-line spectrum.
3. The spectrum of the sun is not continuous, but is nearly so. It is interspersed with dark lines. Such a spectrum is called a dark-line or absorption spectrum.
4. Every gas or vapor absorbs exactly those wave lengths of light which it is capable of emitting when heated to incandescence.
5. When light passes from the sun, or from other stars, gases surrounding the body absorb the same light which these absorbing gases are capable of emitting. Hence, the lines in a dark-line spectrum of a star indicate the gaseous elements which surround it.
6. The composition of earthly chemicals can be determined by the study of their bright-line spectra.
7. According to the quantum theory, light energy is emitted and absorbed in quanta or photons. This is explained by the assumption that the electrons in the atoms revolve in fixed spherical shells, and that any electron when in a particular shell has a definite amount of energy. When electrons fall from a higher energy level to a lower one, they lose energy in the form of light. The same quantity of energy, no more nor less, is required to lift them back again to the higher level.
8. Matter is dual in nature and may be changed into energy. Conversely, energy can be changed into matter. The relationship between the two is given by Einstein's famous equation:

$$E = mc^2$$

QUESTIONS FOR REVIEW

1. What is a continuous spectrum?
2. What is the nature of a substance which emits a continuous spectrum?
3. What is a bright-line spectrum?
4. What kind of spectrum is that of the sun?
5. Sodium vapor, when heated to incandescence, emits what color of light?
6. What color of light will sodium vapor absorb?
7. Explain how helium gas was discovered in the atmosphere of the sun before it was discovered on the earth.
8. Is theory playing a greater and greater or a smaller and smaller part in scientific research? Cite examples.
9. What is ultraviolet light? Infrared light?
10. What is the photoelectric effect?
11. Does the wave theory account for the photoelectric effect? Explain.
12. Does the corpuscular theory account for the photoelectric effect? Explain.
13. What is the quantum theory?
14. What is a photon?
15. Explain the emission and the absorption of light in accordance with the quantum theory.

16. Explain fluorescence.
17. How are X-rays produced?
18. Why will only the heavy atoms emit X-rays?
19. What is the dual nature of matter? Explain the experiment which tended to prove it.
20. How much atomic energy in ergs is available in one gram of matter if it is all converted into energy?

PROJECT

Make a photocell as shown in Fig. 11 A copper washer and a lead disk are each soldered to a length of wire. The copper must be cleaned with sandpaper, then oxidized by being held in a gas flame. Next it should be washed in dilute nitric acid to remove the black oxide. Then coat one side with ordinary nail lacquer. This reduces the "dark" current. Finally, put the metal disk and the washer in the solution of salt water, as shown in the figure.

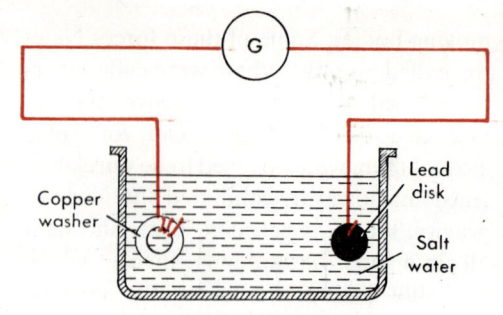

Fig. 1. A homemade photocell.

READING YOU WILL ENJOY

1. Gamow, George, *Mr. Tompkins in Wonderland*. The Macmillan Company, New York, 1940. Mr. Tompkins dreams about the lectures he has heard on the problems of the quantum theory and relativity.
2. Mills, John, *Electronics: Today and Tomorrow*. D. Van Nostrand Company, Inc., New York, 1944. Tells the story of the photoelectric cell.

Unit 18

Electricity in Communication

The story of electricity in communication is the story of harnessing the electron to transmit invisible radio waves at the speed of light to distant points. In television broadcasting, both the light reflected from a scene and the sounds produced must be transmitted simultaneously by means of a varying electric current. Radar employs even higher frequencies to transmit signals to points as distant as the moon. In this unit, you will see why radar plays such a vital part in our national defense as well as how it can be used to track approaching storms or to catch speeders.

In the unit photograph are shown two types of height-finder radar installations that are designed to detect enemy aircraft or missiles. The unit at the left is mobile, while the domelike structure in the center is designed to house radar equipment in Arctic climates. At the right is a fixed installation designed for use in temperate zones.

50. RADIO COMMUNICATION
51. SOUND MOVIES, TELEVISION, AND RADAR

Unit Photograph Courtesy General Electric Co.

Chapter 50

Radio Communication

The problem. It is scarcely necessary to emphasize the importance of the study of electronics in this day and age. Wireless telegraphy and telephony, hourly broadcasts of news, music, and drama throughout the world, radar and its contact with the moon, television—all these and more are the results of the application of the scientific method to problems that were vital to scientists and others who made their contributions to scientific living.

The problem of this chapter is not to produce radio technicians, but to present certain fundamentals of radio which can be used as the basis for further study. To start this chapter, let us concern ourselves with the generation and transmission of radio waves.

How are radio waves generated and transmitted? Let us imagine that A and B in Fig. 1 are cross sections of a sending and a receiving antenna respectively. A rapidly oscillating (alternating) current in A will produce rapidly changing magnetic and electric fields around it.

Let us assume, at the moment, that the direction of the electron flow in A is toward us, or "out." By the left-hand rule this will produce clockwise lines of force, as shown. As the current increases and then decreases in this direction, the field will build up to a maximum and then collapse. This will be followed by a build-up and collapse in the opposite direction when the electrons are flowing away from us, or "in." This changing magnetic field produces a changing electric field. At the velocity of light (300,000,000 meters per second) these fields sustain one another. The combined effect of their interaction is the kind of wave called a radio wave.

As these lines of force of the fields expand and collapse toward B with the speed of light, they induce in B an alternating current which is opposite in phase to that in A. The oscillating *carrier current* in the sending antenna produces waves called *carrier waves,* so named because they carry the transmitted message, or *signal,* to the receiving antenna. The current

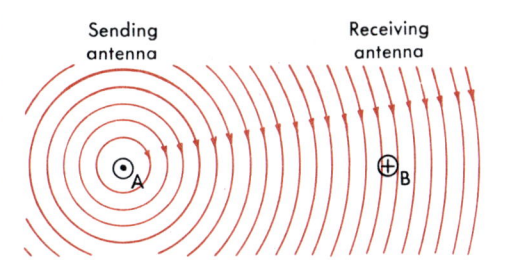

Fig. 1. The carrier waves from A induce a radio-frequency carrier current in B.

which is induced in the receiving antenna is also called a carrier current.

How is the carrier current modulated? A carrier current is of high, or *radio frequency* (r.f.), and of constant amplitude, and would appear as in Fig. 2(a). In fact, the frequency of the carrier current is so high that loud-speakers and earphones cannot respond to it because of inertia. Therefore it must be *modulated*, or changed, by the electrical impression of sound waves upon it.

(a) Carrier current

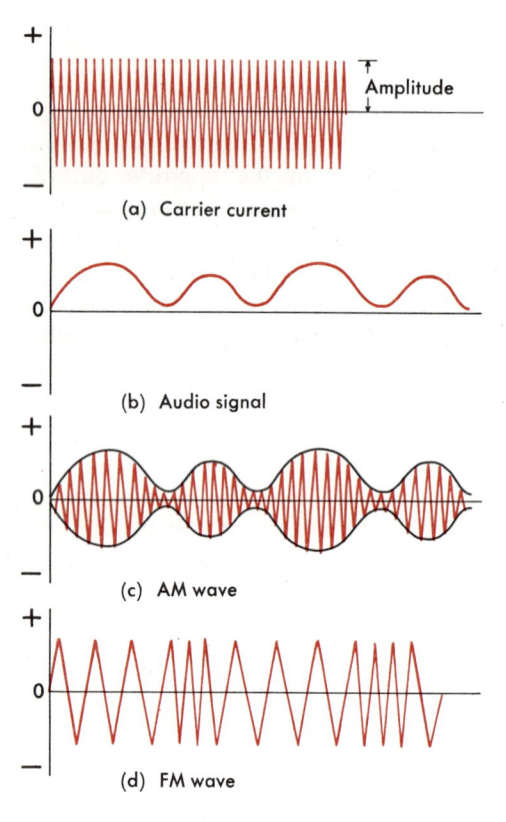

(b) Audio signal

(c) AM wave

(d) FM wave

Fig. 2. (a) Unmodulated alternating r.f. carrier current of constant amplitude induced in receiving antenna. (b) The "sound current" or audio signal (a.f.) generated by a microphone. (c) The carrier current as modulated by the sound current. (d) A frequency-modulated carrier current.

At the broadcasting station sound waves of *audio frequency* (a.f.), frequencies that are audible, are produced near a *microphone*. These are the signals which are to be transmitted to and reproduced by the receiving set. The microphone generates an electrical "sound current" called the *audio signal* (Fig. 2(b)), the varying amplitudes of which are impressed upon the carrier wave, and thence to the carrier current in the receiving antenna. Thus, the amplitude of the carrier current is modified, or controlled, by the audio-frequency current of the microphone. The effect of the modulation of the carrier current is shown in Fig. 2(c).

Note the effect of the a.f. current upon the amplitude of the carrier current. In this type of modulation, called *amplitude modulation* (AM), the amplitude is changed while the frequency remains constant. In another type of modulation, called *frequency modulation* (FM), the amplitude is held constant while the frequency is made to fluctuate in accordance with the frequencies of the audio waves, as shown in Fig. 2(d). Special receiving sets are necessary for the reception of FM broadcasting. Further discussion of FM is beyond the scope of this text.

What are the meanings of cycle, frequency, and wave length? In our study of sound waves we used the relationship, $n = \dfrac{V}{l}$, frequency = $\dfrac{\text{velocity}}{\text{wave length}}$. This also applies to radio waves. When the current in A of Fig. 1 flows in once and out once, one complete cycle has occurred and results in the sending out of one wave Frequency is the number of cycles produced per second. Because radio frequencies are so high, they are expressed in *kilocycles* or *megacycles* per second. A kilocycle is a thousand cycles; a megacycle is a million cycles. Two radio frequencies and their corresponding wave lengths are

RADIO COMMUNICATION

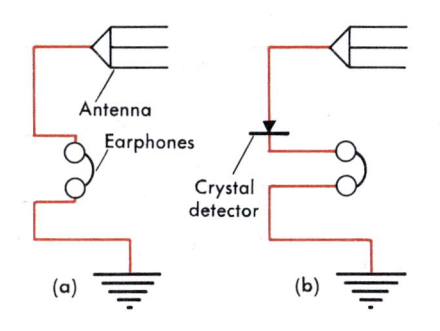

Fig. 3. (a) No reception can be obtained. (b) Reception from all nearby sending stations.

given below. The former is found in the *regular broadcast band,* while the latter is used in *short-wave* broadcasting.

Frequencies	Speed of waves / Frequency	Wave lengths (meters)
950 kilocycles per second	300,000,000 / 950,000	315.8
12 megacycles per second	300,000,000 / 12,000,000	25

How are selection and detection of radio waves accomplished? If we were to connect telephone receivers in series with the receiving antenna and the ground, as shown in Fig. 3(a), the high-frequency oscillations of the modulated carrier current would pass through the receivers. However, since the receiver diaphragms cannot vibrate as rapidly as the high-frequency current, no sound would be heard. If a *crystal detector* were connected in series with the receivers, as in Fig. 3(b), we should hear little but a jumbled mixture of sounds from all the nearby sending stations. This is because no provision has been made for *tuning in,* or *selection,* of the desired program.

A simple method of tuning consists in changing the length of the receiving antenna circuit. We can do this by inserting a tuning coil with a sliding contact (see Fig. 4). Time is required for the high-frequency oscillations of the modulated carrier current to travel back and forth through the antenna circuit; the longer the circuit the greater the time, and vice versa. Thus, to tune to lower frequencies, we lengthen the circuit by moving the sliding contact downward, or away from the antenna; moving the contact upward tunes to higher frequencies. In the early days of radio, receiving sets like the one shown in this figure were in common use. They were effective, however, only for sending stations that were relatively near.

Improved methods of tuning, using variable inductance and capacitance, have been discussed in Chapter 40. Using this as a reference, try to explain the operation of the receiving set in Fig. 5.

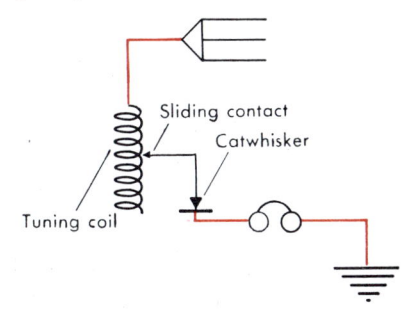

Fig. 4. Tuning by changing the length of the antenna circuit.

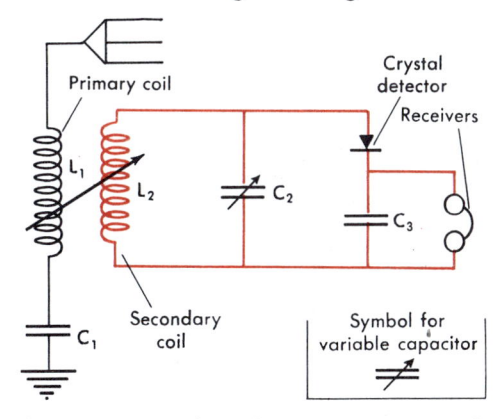

Fig. 5. A simple radio receiving set with a tuned antenna circuit, coupled with a tuned crystal detector and receiver circuit.

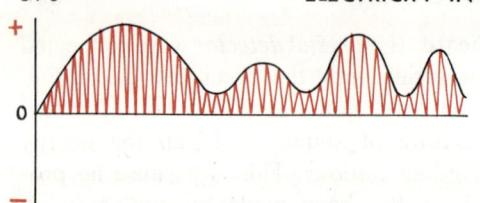

Fig. 6. Telephone receivers are sensitive to the variations in amplitude of the rectified, modulated carrier current, but not to the individual pulses.

How does the crystal detector work? Before further discussion of radio reception, we should understand the operation of the crystal detector. It is really a *rectifier,* which allows current to flow through it in only one direction. Early crystals were composed of the mineral *galena* (lead sulfide), but now either silicon dioxide or germanium crystals are used. Contact with the crystal was made by an adjustable fine wire called a *catwhisker.*

Since the high-frequency, modulated carrier current of Fig. 2(c) is alternating, only half of it, say the lower half, can pass through the crystal. Thus, the upper half (see Fig. 6) must flow through the receivers. Although the telephone receivers *cannot* respond to the individual pulses of this rectified current, they *can* and *do* respond to the variations in amplitudes of these pulses, shown by the solid, wavy line. Since this line has the same frequency as the original sound, this sound is reproduced in the receivers.

The development of the vacuum tube detector. The crystal detector, although widely used at first, was soon replaced by a much more sensitive detector, the *vacuum tube* detector. This device, so useful because of its many and varied forms and applications, is based upon a discovery made in 1883 by Thomas A. Edison. Because of an uneven blackening of the inside surfaces of his incandescent lamps, he sealed a wire into the side of one of them (see Fig. 7) in an attempt to discover the cause of the blackening.

Edison was somewhat surprised to find that, when the lamp was lighted, a small current flowed through this wire so long as it was maintained at a positive potential, but not when it was negative. Since electrons were unknown at the time, it was difficult to explain this current, and the phenomenon was simply called the "Edison effect." A few years later Sir J. J. Thomson (the discoverer of the electron) and other scientists showed that the heated filament of the bulb "boiled off" electrons, which were then attracted through the evacuated space to the positively charged, sealed-in wire.

These discoveries led to the development of the "Tungar" rectifier, a *diode* (two-electrode) tube, used to convert alternating current into direct current. Its two electrodes are the *filament,* which emits electrons when heated, and the *plate,* which attracts electrons to it only when positively charged. In other words, electrons can flow through the tube in only one direction, from filament to plate, and this can occur only when the plate is on the positive half-cycle of the alternating current. Thus, a pulsating direct current (D.C.) is produced, which can be used in charging storage batteries from A.C. (see Fig. 8). A diode is a *half-wave* rectifier because it lets through only one-half of each cycle of A.C.

The vacuum tube was first used as a radio detector tube by Joseph Fleming of England. The *Edison-Fleming* tube is still known in England as the "Fleming valve." But the improvement of the vacuum tube which gave radio development its greatest impetus was the one made by Lee DeForest in 1906. DeForest added a third electrode, called the *grid,* consisting of a mesh of fine wire placed between the filament and the plate, thus giving the world its first

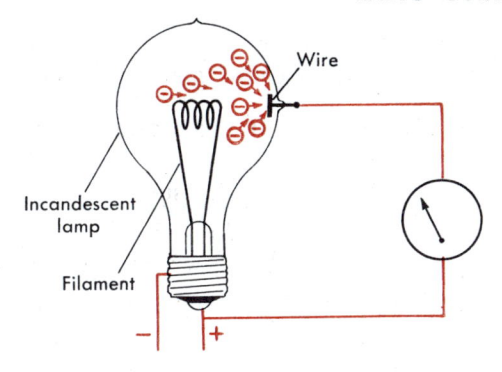

Fig. 7. The Edison effect. Electrons flow from the filament to the positive wire.

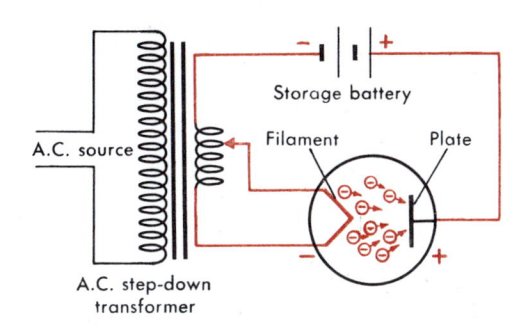

Fig. 8. The Tungar rectifier as used in charging storage batteries.

triode tube (Fig. 9). We cannot exaggerate the importance of this invention. Its effects upon radio communication, long-distance telephony, and other fields of electrical engineering have been most profound. New uses are constantly being found for the three-electrode vacuum tube.

What are the characteristics of the triode tube? Suppose that we connect a triode tube in a circuit as shown in Fig. 10. The rheostat, R, controls the *filament current*, I_f, which is furnished by the "A" battery and measured by the milliammeter, MA_f, in the filament circuit. The "B" battery holds the plate at a positive potential so it attracts electrons emitted by the heated filament. This current from filament to plate, the *plate current*, I_p, is measured by the milliammeter, MA_p, in the plate circuit. The hotter the filament, the more electrons it emits and the greater the plate current, until a point of saturation is reached.

If we plot the plate current against the corresponding filament currents, we obtain a curve like that of Fig. 11. The curve

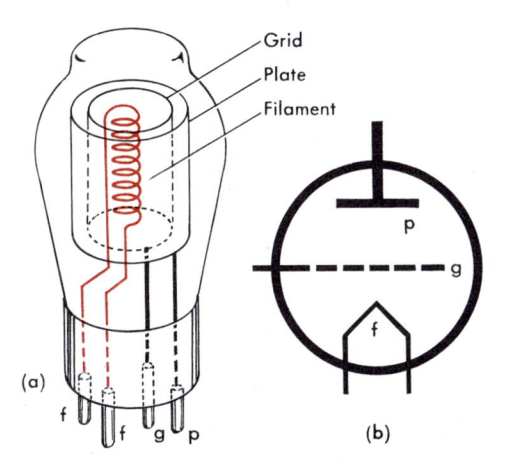

Fig. 9. (a) Drawing of triode tube with its filament, grid, plate, and external prongs. (b) Schematic drawing of the triode.

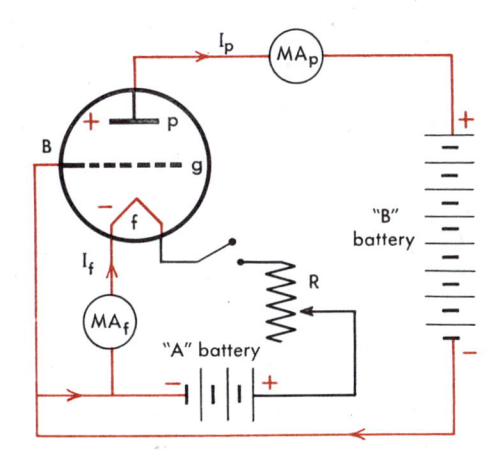

Fig. 10. Action of triode tube. The e.m.f. of the "B" battery should be 45-90 volts; that of the "A" battery about 6 volts, depending on the tube.

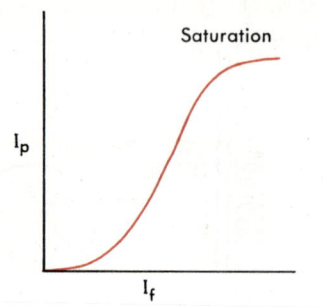

Fig. 11. Relation between plate and filament current.

levels off at the top because a sort of "electron cloud" forms around the filament. Why should this produce saturation?

In Fig. 10 the grid was kept at a constant potential. However, if we insert a voltage source between *A* and *B* of Fig. 10, we can vary the grid voltage while keeping the filament current and plate potential constant. Thus we can show the effect of changing grid voltage on the plate current. Figure 12 shows curves obtained in this manner, using two different plate potentials, 67.5 volts and 90 volts.

These curves show that a small increase in grid voltage increases the plate current as much as does a relatively large increase in plate voltage. *The ratio of the change in plate voltage to the change in grid voltage* which will produce the same change in plate current is called the **amplification factor** *of the tube*. In this case it is $\frac{22.5}{4}$, or about 5.6. It is this characteristic which makes the triode tube valuable as an amplifier. It is also valuable as a detector because electrons can flow through it in only one direction, the same as in a diode.

Using the triode as a detector and amplifier. You may have already realized that the diode tube might be used as a detector, replacing the crystal detector in circuits like the one shown in Fig. 5. However, the triode tube is much better because it can be made to amplify incoming signals at the same time that it detects or rectifies them. If we were to adapt the circuit of Fig. 5 for use with a triode detector, it would be like the circuit of Fig. 13.

The figure is designed to show two different methods of detection, the *grid-bias* method, and the *grid-leak and condenser* method. The "C" battery is used with the grid-bias method. The grid leak and grid condenser C_4 are shown merely to indicate where they belong in the input circuit, should the latter method be used.

In the grid-bias method of detection the "C" battery holds the grid at a negative potential of such value that, without a carrier current, the plate current is near zero. But when the modulated carrier current of Fig. 2(c) is impressed on the grid, the grid is made alternately more and less negative, and these changes in grid potential cause the plate current to vary in accordance with the signal variations. Since small changes in grid potential cause fairly large changes in the plate current, the audio-frequency signals are not only detected but amplified at the same time.

The grid-leak and condenser method, not discussed here, is more sensitive than the grid-bias method of detection and gives better results on weak signals. How-

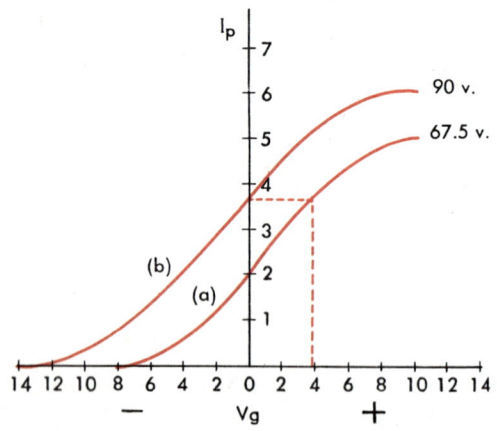

Fig. 12. Relation of *Ip* to *Vg* at two different plate voltages.

RADIO COMMUNICATION 593

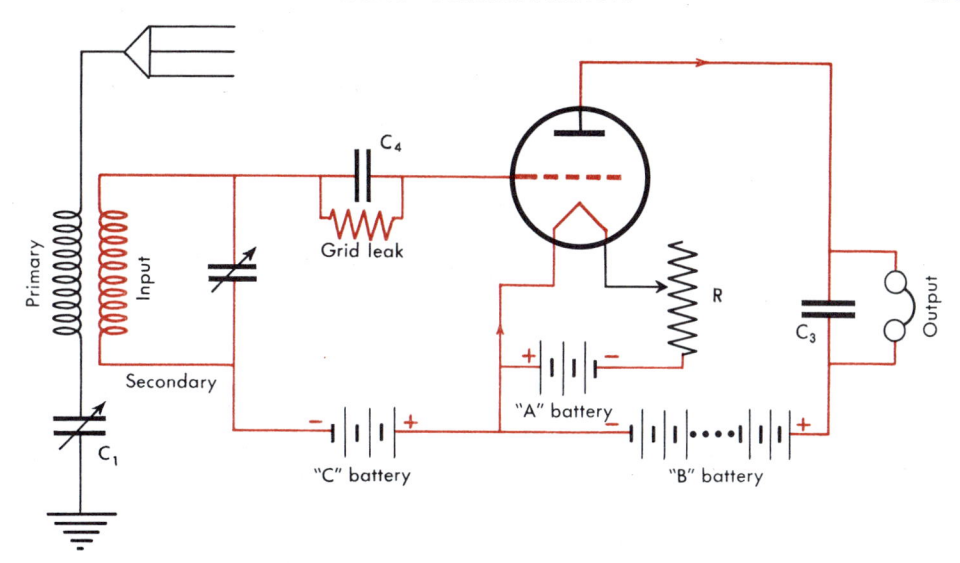

Fig. 13. The use of the triode tube as a detector and an amplifier in a simple radio receiving set.

ever, it permits less selective tuning than the grid-bias method.

We have shown telephone receivers in the output circuit, but these could be replaced with a loud-speaker, a transformer connected to another amplifying tube, or some other useful device. If an audio-frequency transformer is used in the output circuit and is properly connected to the grid and filament of a second tube, a second and greater plate current can be produced. Likewise, we may amplify the second plate current, producing a third and still greater plate current. This can be car-

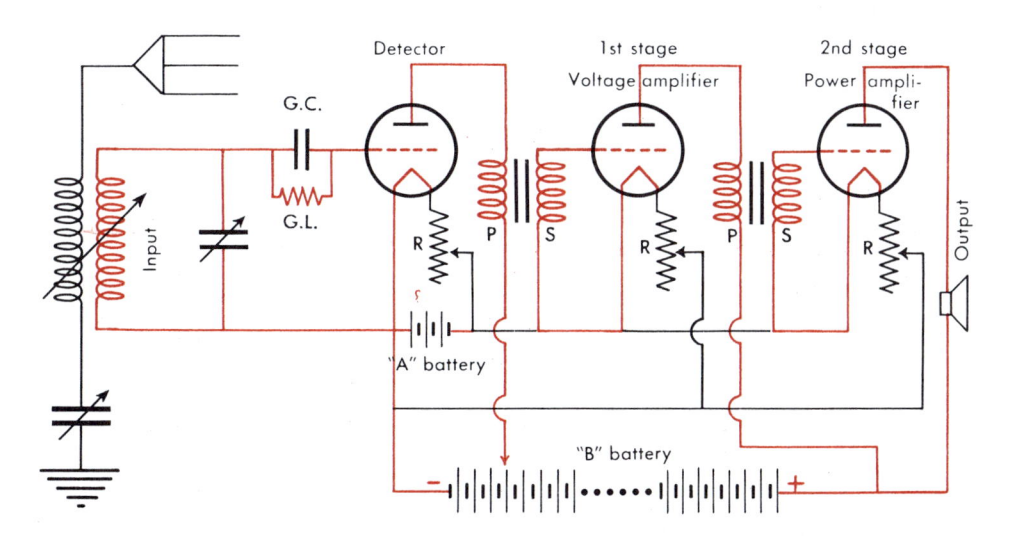

Fig. 14. A simple circuit for two-stage amplification.

594   ELECTRICITY IN COMMUNICATION

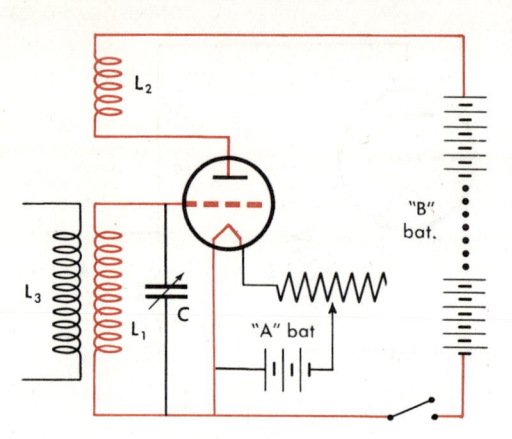

Fig. 15. Triode tube in a simple radio-frequency oscillator circuit.

ried on to as many stages of amplification as desired. Figure 14 shows a simple circuit for two-stage amplification. Generally not more than three stages are used.

How is the triode tube used as an oscillator? The use of the triode tube as a radio-frequency oscillator is one of its most important adaptations. Modern radio broadcasting would be impossible without it. By the employment of circuits similar to that shown in Fig. 15, the carrier waves from broadcasting stations are generated. By proper choice of the inductance L_1 and the capacitance C, continuous oscillations may be obtained, ranging from a few cycles to billions of cycles per second. Let us see how it works.

When we close the key, a current starts to build up in the plate circuit. Since this current flows through coil L_2, which is coupled with L_1 in the transformer, the increasing plate current induces an e.m.f. in L_1. But L_1 is so connected to the grid as to give it a positive potential in this case. This positive grid potential serves to further increase the plate current until it reaches its maximum value, corresponding to the upper portions of the curves in Fig. 12. When the plate current reaches

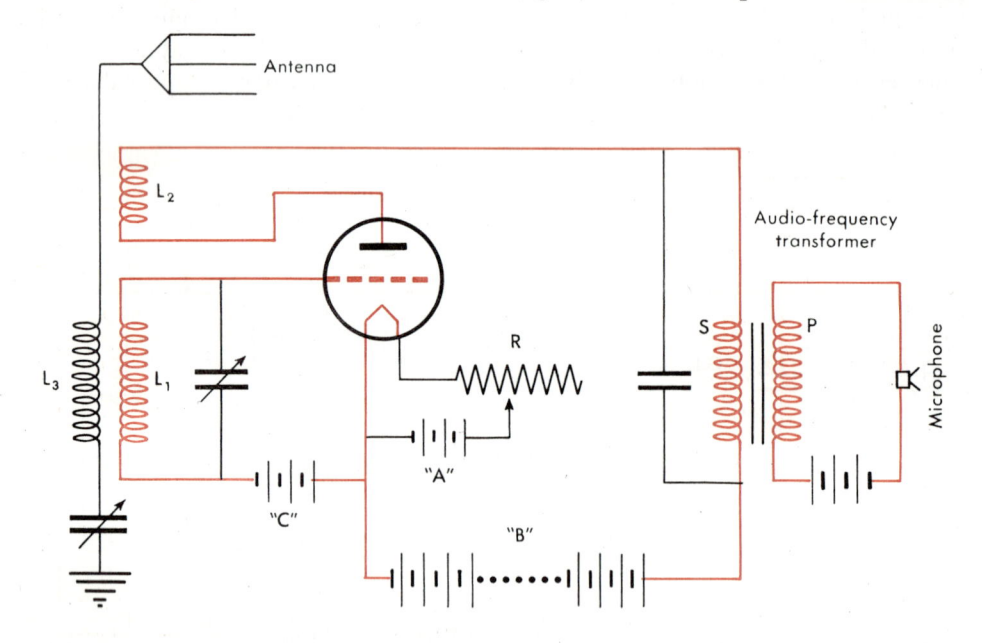

Fig. 16. A simple radio-transmitter circuit.

this maximum value, it no longer increases, and the inductive action of coil L_2 ceases, causing the grid to lose its positive potential, with a resulting decrease in the plate current.

This decreasing plate current induces an opposite e.m.f. in L_1, giving the grid a negative potential, which further decreases the plate current. This action continues until the moment when the plate current is zero, at which time there is no longer any inductive action between L_2 and L_1. Thus, the grid potential becomes zero and the whole action starts repeating itself. These increases and decreases of the plate current cause electric oscillations of the same frequency to occur in the L_1C circuit.

It should be noted that the plate current is not alternating, but pulsating D.C. However, the e.m.f. induced in L_1 and L_2 is alternating. Since L_1 is also coupled with L_3, it will induce in L_3 an alternating e.m.f. which is of the same frequency as the oscillations in the L_1C circuit. If L_3 is properly connected in an antenna circuit, the antenna will send out carrier waves of the same frequency.

This use of the vacuum tube is fundamental in radio circuits. One can make a simple transmitting set by properly connecting a microphone in an oscillating circuit like the one just described. A simple radio transmitter circuit is shown in Fig. 16.

How is power supplied to our modern radios? Throughout this chapter, batteries have been used for all the voltages necessary. As you know, however, in the majority of radio sets used today there are no batteries. Their source of power is the 120-volt, 60-cycle house current. You may wonder how high D.C. voltages and low filament voltages are produced for these radios.

At the beginning of this chapter we discussed the rectification of alternating current by means of a diode tube. This is called *half-wave rectification*, whose output wave form is illustrated in Fig. 17(b). This produces pulsating voltages and pulsating direct currents. If these voltages were used in a receiver set, a terrific *60-cycle hum* would be heard in the loudspeaker. Therefore, the pulsations must be filtered out to produce smooth-flowing D.C., as in Fig. 17(d). This is done with a filter circuit, sometimes called the *pi circuit* (in dotted rectangle, Fig. 18).

How does the pi circuit filter and smooth out the D.C.? To begin with, it must be explained that pulsating D.C. may be thought of as the result of adding a steady direct current and an alternating current. You will recall that condensers

(a) A.C. current

(b) Unfiltered, half-wave rectified pulsating D.C.

(c) Unfiltered, full-wave rectified pulsating D.C.

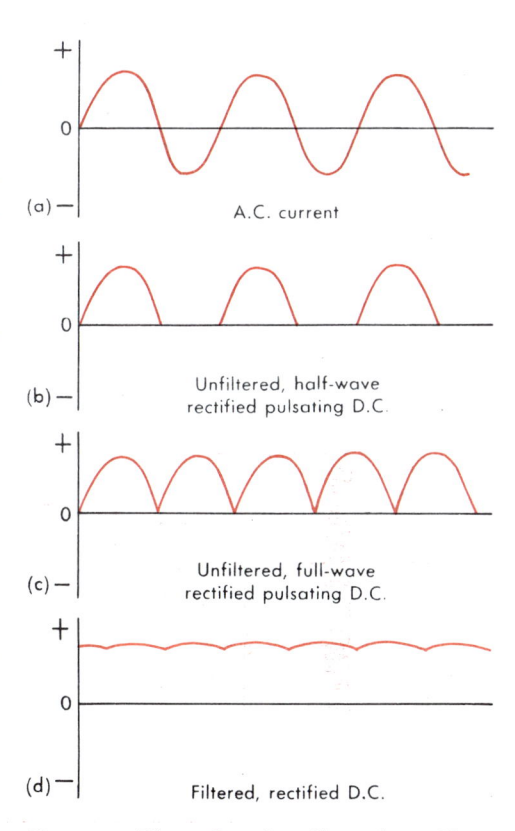

(d) Filtered, rectified D.C.

Fig. 17. Filtered and unfiltered rectification of alternating current.

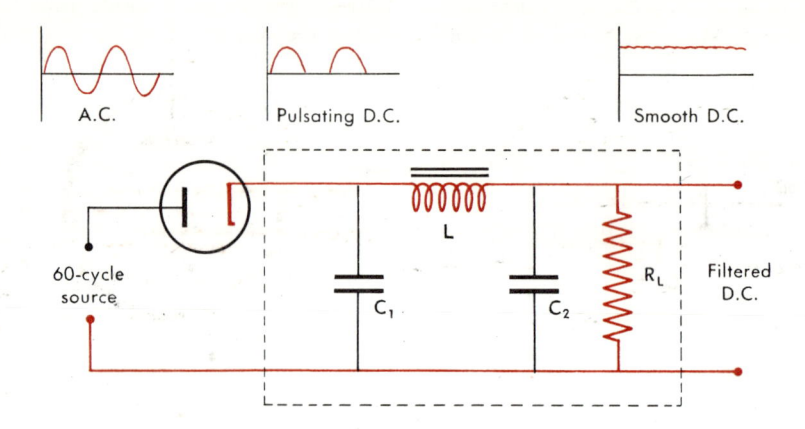

Fig. 18. Half-wave rectifier circuit with filter.

are capable of conducting A.C. but not D.C., and that choke coils offer little impedance to D.C. but great impedance to A.C. (Chapter 40).

Now look carefully at the pi circuit. As the pulsating D.C. enters, some of the A.C. component is shorted through C_1, while the D.C. component and the remaining A.C. part try to get through L. The choke lets the D.C. through easily but hinders the A.C. However, some A.C. gets through with the D.C., but this remaining A.C. is shorted through C_2, leaving pure D.C. to flow through the load resistance R_L. Therefore, a smooth voltage appears across R_L, and this voltage may be used for the plates of the radio's amplifier and detector tubes. The complete diagram of Fig. 18 shows a *power pack* using a half-wave rectifier.

Full-wave rectification may be obtained by means of two diodes, or with a single tube having two diodes in it, a *duodiode*. A circuit for full-wave rectification is shown in Fig. 19. The unfiltered output voltage from a full-wave rectifier may be seen in Fig. 17(c).

How does a full-wave rectifier work? The transformer T in Fig. 19 is a step-up transformer with a center-tapped secondary. The voltages of the ends of the

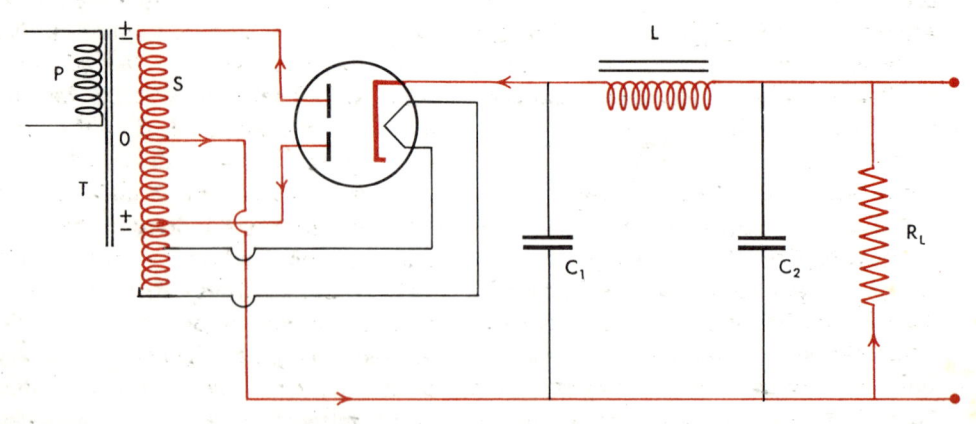

Fig. 19. Full-wave rectifier using duodiode with filter.

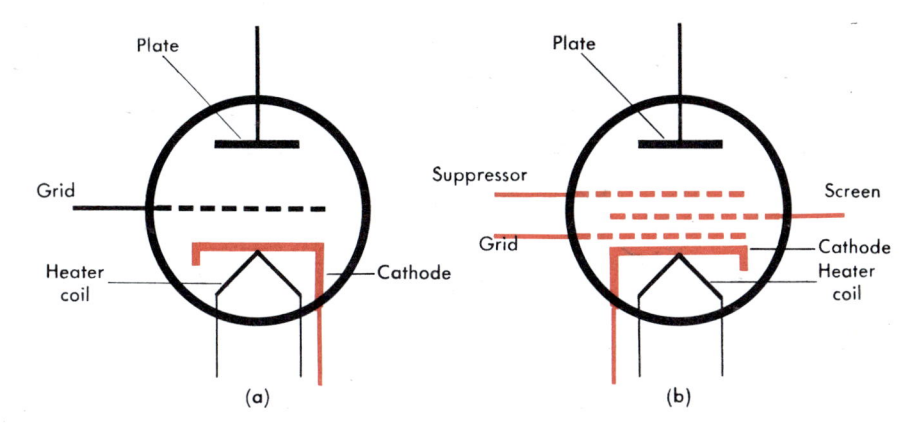

Fig. 20. Schematic drawings of (a) a modern triode tube and (b) a pentode tube.

secondary become alternately plus and minus, while the voltage of the center tap stays at zero.

Consider first the positive half-cycle when the upper plate of the duodiode is made positive and the lower plate negative. The electron flow must be up through R_L and from the cathode to the upper plate, then out through the center tap to R_L again. Now consider the negative part of the cycle when the upper plate is negative and the lower plate positive. Now the electron flow is up through R_L and from the cathode to the lower plate, and out of the center tap and back to R_L. Thus we have full-wave rectification. To furnish low voltages for tube filaments we can tap a small portion of the transformer secondary, as shown in the figure.

As you can see, it is less difficult to filter the pulsating D.C. from a full-wave rectifier than that from a half-wave rectifier. Both types of rectifiers are commonly used today. Half-wave rectifiers are generally used in the less expensive receiving sets which do not use transformers, while the full-wave rectifiers are employed in the larger sets and must have a center-tapped power transformer.

Modern radio tubes. The modern triode tube, and also *tetrode* (four-electrode) and *pentode* (five-electrode) tubes, have *indirectly* heated cathodes, each consisting of a thin metal sleeve coated with electron-emitting material. Inside the sleeve and insulated from it is a tungsten or tungsten alloy *heater coil* which can be operated on low voltage A.C. (see Fig. 20). A step-down A.C. transformer is used in operating these cathodes.

The majority of our modern tubes, regardless of type, except those used in battery-operated sets, have indirectly heated cathodes. This indirect heating has the advantage of eliminating the 60-cycle hum that would be heard in our receiving sets if the cathodes were heated directly with A.C. The plate voltages for these modern tubes are supplied by the sort of power-pack previously discussed.

What are transistors? A major development in the crystal detector has given the electronics industry a great impetus. This is the discovery that, if *two* catwhiskers, instead of one, are placed close together on a germanium crystal, the crystal can be used as a *crystal triode* amplifier, or *transistor*. The use of three catwhiskers produces a *crystal tetrode*, which can mix and amplify two signals simultaneously.

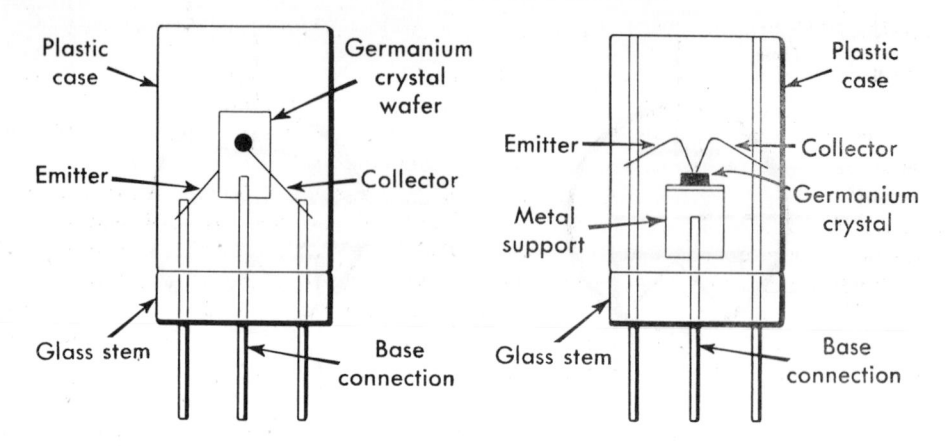

598 ELECTRICITY IN COMMUNICATION

Fig. 21. (*l.*) A positive-negative junction transistor. (*r.*) A point-contact transistor.

Courtesy RCA

Transistors have several advantages over vacuum tubes. They are very small and, since they require no heated cathodes, they can be operated on as little as a millionth of a volt. They are extremely rugged and require no "warm-up" period.

There are two general types of transistors: *point contact* and *junction* transistors. The junction type (Fig. 21a) can amplify a signal 10,000 times, whereas the point contact type (Fig. 21b) amplifies only 100 times.

The junction transistor looks like a plastic bead about the size of a kernel of corn. It contains a tiny crystal wafer of germanium, both sides of which are negative. The middle, or *base,* is positive. One side is called the *emitter,* the other side the *collector.* The emitter is connected through a wire lead in the input circuit; the collector, in the output circuit.

Transistors can serve as amplifiers in radio, telephone, and television circuits. Their uses sometimes parallel those of electron tubes and sometimes surpass them.

Fig. 22. (a) Using a single transistor and a matched circuit, this radio transmitter in the operator's hand uses the sound energy of the human voice. No additional power source is required.

Courtesy U.S. Army Signal Corps.

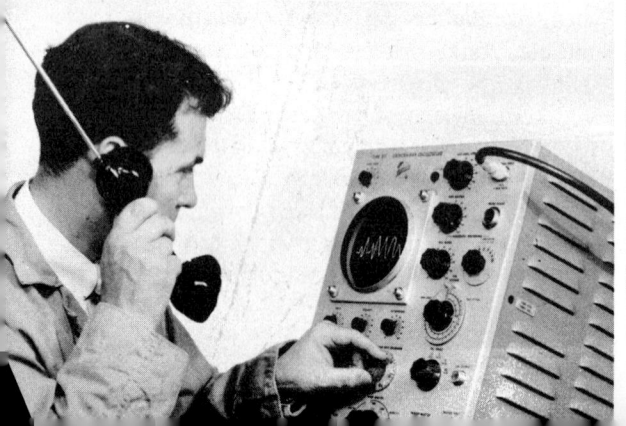

Fig. 22. (b) Miniaturization is the keynote in designing airborne electronic computers. Using 800 transistors instead of vacuum tubes, this computer requires less power than a 100-watt bulb.

Courtesy Bell Telephone Laboratories

SUMMARY AND CONCLUSIONS

1. Radio waves travel with the speed of light.
2. The velocity, frequency, and wave length of radio waves are related as shown in the equation $V = nl$.
3. Radio waves are of high frequency.
4. Carrier waves are modulated by the electrical impression of sound waves upon them.
5. Amplitude modulation consists in varying the amplitude of the carrier wave in accordance with the variations in amplitude of the sounds being broadcast.
6. Detection or rectification of radio signals is accomplished by crystal detectors or triode detectors.
7. Tuning a receiving set to a given frequency consists in putting it in resonance with that frequency.
8. Diode and triode tubes are used as rectifiers. The triode tube is also used as an amplifier.
9. The essential parts of the triode tube are the filament, grid, and plate.
10. The plate current can be increased in three ways: by increasing the filament current, increasing the plate voltage, and increasing the grid voltage.
11. A small change in grid voltage changes the plate current as much as does a relatively large change in plate voltage.
12. The grid-bias method of detection consists in maintaining the grid at a negative potential which is made to vary by incoming signals.
13. The triode tube may be used as an oscillator. This is one of its most important uses.
14. The pi circuit is used to filter out the A.C. components from the D.C. plate current, thus smoothing out the D.C.
15. Half-wave rectification can be accomplished by a single diode. Full-wave rectification is accomplished by two diodes or a duodiode.
16. Transistors can be used both as detectors and as amplifiers. They can amplify greatly and are very efficient.

QUESTIONS FOR REVIEW

1. What kind of waves are radio waves? How do they differ from light waves?
2. What is amplitude modulation? How is it accomplished?
3. What is the difference between audio-frequency and radio-frequency waves?
4. Why doesn't a telephone receiver respond to high-frequency carrier waves?
5. What is the length of the waves sent out by a broadcasting station operating on a frequency of 1400 kilocycles per second?
6. What is the operating frequency of a broadcasting station whose assigned wave length is 250 meters?
7. How is the filament heated in the diode tube of Fig. 8?
8. What are the characteristics of a triode tube?
9. Why does a triode tube detect and amplify at the same time?
10. What is meant by amplification?
11. What is the grid-bias method of detection?
12. What is meant by a filter circuit? Why is it used, and where?
13. Draw a diagram of a pi circuit and explain what it does.
14. Would the power supply of a modern radio work satisfactorily without the filter circuit? Why?
15. In radios which do not use power transformers, the tube filaments are all connected in series. Why is this necessary?
16. What is meant by half-wave and full-wave rectification? How are they accomplished?
17. How does the modern heater-type tube differ from the old type?
18. How are transistors apt to affect the radio industry?

PROJECTS

1. Find out what pioneering work Joseph Henry did that contributed to the field of radio. Make a report to the class.
2. Look up material on the works of Lord

Kelvin, Fedderson, and J. Clerk Maxwell that contributed to radio broadcasting and receiving. Make a report to the class.
3. Make a report on the life of Heinrich Hertz, with special emphasis on his work with radio waves.
4. Make a report on the contributions to radio made by Guglielmo Marconi.
5. Construct a one-tube or two-tube radio.
6. Construct a simple oscillator.
7. Build a power pack.
8. Look up material on tetrode and pentode tubes, and make a report.
9. Redraw figures 13 and 14, using tubes with indirectly heated cathodes (see Fig. 20(a)).

READING YOU WILL ENJOY

1. *Allied's Radio-Circuit Handbook.* Allied Radio Corporation, Chicago. This handbook shows and discusses many schematic and pictorial diagrams of different circuits, such as various types of oscillators, detectors, power packs, filters, amplifiers, AC-DC receivers, amateur broadcast and receiving sets, phonograph amplifiers, and others. Other ARC handbooks available for 10¢ each are: A Dictionary of Radio Terms, Radio Builder's Handbook, Radio Data Handbook, Radio-Formula and Data Book, and Manual of Simplified Radio Servicing.
2. *Everybody's Television and Radio Handbook.* Popular Science Publishing Co., Inc., New York. Distributed by Garden City Books, Garden City, New York. This book contains many discussions of practical gadgets for amateur enthusiasts.
3. Marcus, W., and A. Levy, *Elements of Radio Servicing.* McGraw-Hill Book Company, Inc., New York, 1947. A very thorough book covering the explanations of circuit fundamentals and practical servicing procedure.
4. *RCA Receiving Tube Manual.* Radio Corporation of America, Harrison, New Jersey. This manual lists all types of tubes and their characteristics, as well as showing circuits for detectors, amplifiers, oscillators, and many others.
5. Watson, H. M., H. E. Welch, and G. S. Eby, *Understanding Radio,* 2nd Ed. McGraw-Hill Book Company, Inc., New York, 1951. Written for students who have very little background in electricity. It covers laws of electricity and magnetism, principles of the vacuum tube, simple receiving sets, transmitters, F.M., oscillators, and amplified circuits. Many of the schematics have single drawings showing the actual hook-up of components.
6. Wellman, W. R., *Elementary Industrial Electronics.* D. Van Nostrand Company, Inc., New York, 1948. This book covers A.C. fundamentals, vacuum tubes, gas-filled tubes, symbols and terms; also industrial applications of kenotrons, rectifiers, amplifiers, high-frequency heating, motor and generator controls, welding controls, and photoelectric devices.

Chapter 51

Sound Movies, Television, and Radar

The problem. Both the electrons and what can be done with them are, indeed, amazing. This is an electronic age. Electronic devices are used to count highway traffic, open garage doors, turn on water fountains, detect flaws in machinery, solve complicated mathematical problems, and do many other useful tasks. An electronic device, set off by the light from a distant star, started the controls which opened the gates of the World's Fair in Chicago in 1932.

Without our knowledge of the electron and methods of controlling it we should still be without radios, sound films, television, and radar. We cannot hope to cover the whole field of electronics in a high school physics text. Our immediate problem is simply to study the fundamentals of sound movies, television, and radar.

How are sound motion pictures produced? The principles of the production of motion pictures are discussed in Chapter 46. The fact that the eye persists in seeing an object for about 1/16 second after it has left the field of vision makes motion pictures possible. For silent movies, 16 exposures per second are made of a moving object, and the film is then projected onto a screen at the same rate—16 frames per second.

For sound movies, the film is exposed at the rate of 24 frames per second, the greater speed making it possible to add a faithful sound track to the edge of the film. The essential steps in the production of this sound track are shown in Fig. 1(a).

The steps are as follows: 1. At the microphone, sound waves are changed into varying electric currents. 2. The amplifier increases the intensity of these electric currents and causes them to flow through the "light valve," which is composed of two strips of duralumin, spaced at about .001 inch. 3. The varying electric currents flowing through these strips cause them to be repelled and attracted by the poles of strong magnets, thus varying the width of the slit between the strips. 4. The slit variations permit corresponding variations of light intensity to pass through from the light source S. 5. These varying light intensities are focused upon the edge of the light-sensitive film F. 6. The film is then developed and a positive film is made from the negative. This film thus has a sound track consisting of light and dark bands whose varying intensities correspond to the original sound waves which were picked up by the microphone.

When this sound film is reproduced on the screen, a beam of light is caused to

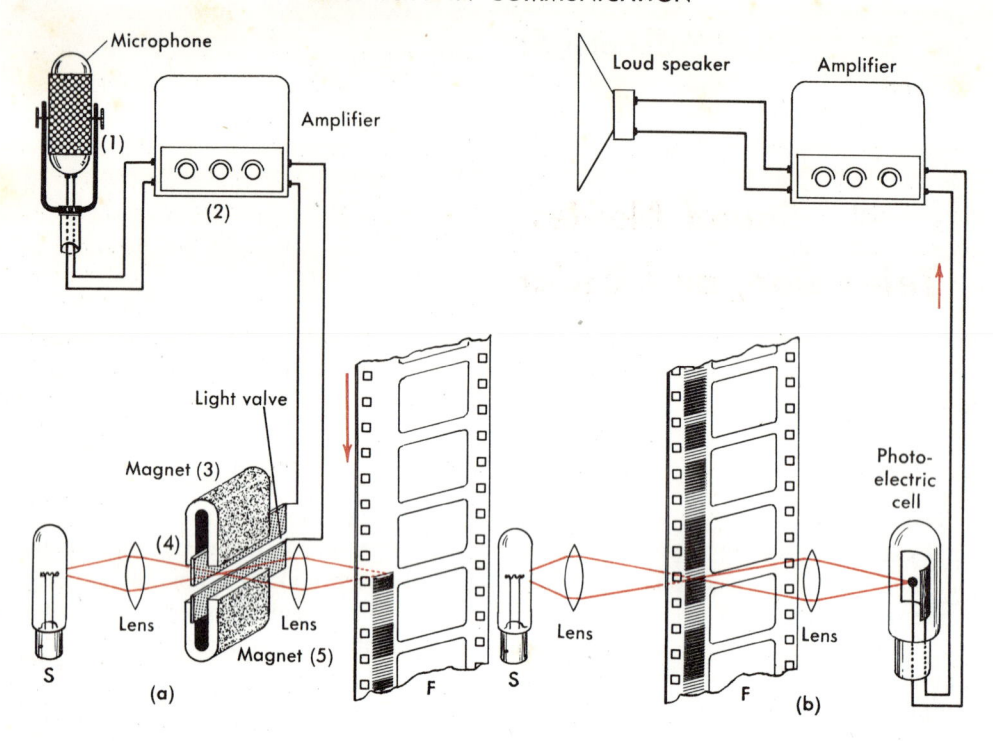

Fig. 1. The production and projection of a sound track on motion-picture film.

pass through the sound track and into a light-sensitive, or photoelectric, cell (Fig. 1(b)). This cell, in turn, produces an electric current which has the same variations and characteristics as the original sound. This current is amplified several million times its original strength and sent through a loud-speaker, where it is converted back into sound waves which correspond to those originally picked up by the microphone. Because light travels faster than sound, the sound track must precede the projected pictures by a few frames. Why?

What is the range of television broadcasting? The addition of pictures to accompany our radio programs is one of the marvels of modern science. One of the main problems confronting television engineers was long-distance transmission of television waves. Television frequencies are so high that the ionospheric layers, which reflect the relatively long radio waves, act like sieves for the short television waves. They pass right through these layers, and no energy is returned to the ground. Television waves therefore cannot be transmitted farther than the "vision" distance, because they are intercepted and absorbed by the curvature of the earth.

This problem was solved by the use of transmission relay towers and *coaxial cable,* in which one of the conductors is a tube and the other is a wire in the center of the tube and insulated from it. More than a hundred towers, strategically located across the continent, relay transmitted programs by microwaves beamed from tower to tower. Coaxial cable connects the towers to side broadcasting stations, where the programs are rebroadcast, making coast-to-coast programs possible.

How does modern television transmission work? The heart of one type of modern television camera is the *iconoscope*, which means literally "image observer." It is a special cathode ray tube (Fig. 3), the essential parts of which are the electron gun, a rectangular *scanning plate,* 3½ by 4¾ inches and about 0.001 inch in thickness, and the *collecting ring*. The electron gun is capable of shooting a stream of electrons which scans the scanning plate 60 times per second vertically and 15,750 times per second horizontally along 525 lines which are only a small fraction of an inch apart.

The scanning plate consists of a thin sheet of mica, the front surface of which is coated with myriads of microscopic particles of a cesium silver compound, a material sensitive to light. The back of the mica sheet is coated with a layer of colloidal graphite, an electrical conducting material, which is connected to an output lead; and the whole arrangement acts as many tiny condensers with a common lead through which they can be discharged. The collecting ring is metallic platinum and is for the purpose of collecting electrons emitted from the scanning area. The ring is also connected to an outside lead, which, together with the lead from the graphite, or *signal plate,* completes the signal circuit.

In the television transmission process, an image of the object to be televised is focused upon the scanning area of the iconoscope by a camera lens. Where the light is most intense, the light-sensitive particles will "leak off" the greatest numbers of electrons; where it is least intense, the smallest numbers of electrons will be emitted. Thus, there is produced a mosaic pattern of differences of positive potential, making an electron picture on the light-sensitive particles on the mica sheet.

When the electron beam scans this mosaic, the particles "soak up" enough elec-

Fig. 2. This huge antenna, 60 feet in diameter, is used in over-the-horizon transmission of telephone and television signals at ultra-high frequencies for distances as great as 200 miles without relay stations. The conventional antenna at the left is used for line-of-sight transmission for distances of 30 miles.

Courtesy Bell Telephone Laboratories

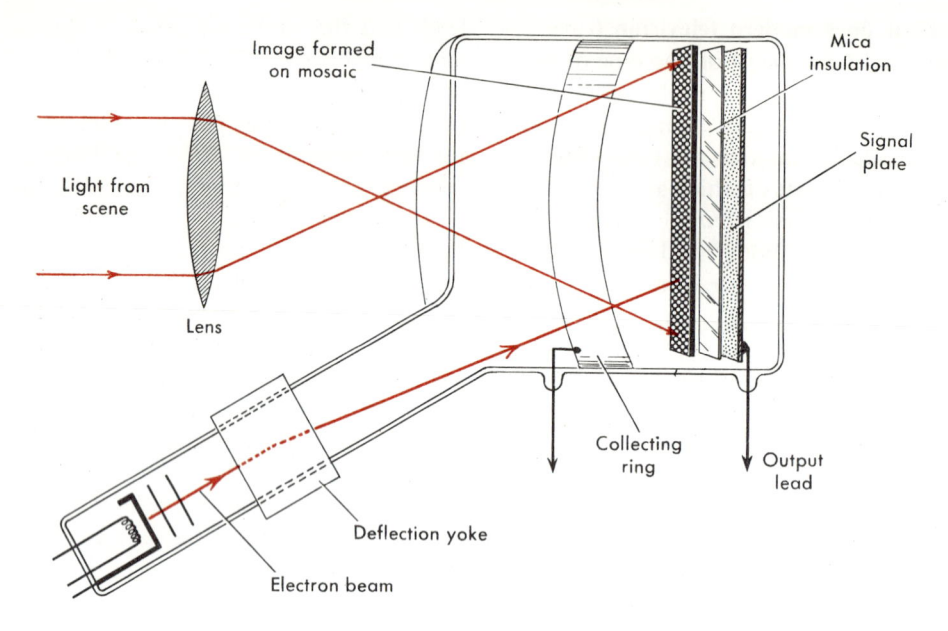

Fig. 3. Schematic drawing of the iconoscope.

trons to bring them back to what is called the *equilibrium potential*. Then the pattern starts all over again. Thus we have electrical impulses, known as the *video* signals, between the scanning plate and the collecting ring. These impulses are amplified and broadcast as in radio transmission. Since the camera lens inverts the image, the scanning must begin at the bottom of the scanning area. Why?

A more modern camera tube is the *image orthicon*. This tube is from 100 to 1000 times as sensitive as the iconoscope and can thus be used for scenes having very low illumination. It can see what the eye can see, but is not suited to intense illumination. The iconoscope can be used only for scenes having high illumination.

The arrangement of the essential parts of the image orthicon is shown in Fig. 4. It is very compact and differs from the iconoscope in several respects. (1) The light image is focused on a conducting semi-transparent light-sensitive surface, called the *photo cathode,* instead of on an insulated mosaic; and the resulting electron emission takes place on the *opposite* side of this cathode. (2) The scanning, by a lower-velocity electron beam than that used in the iconoscope, takes place on a separate plate called the *target,* not on the photosensitive surface. (3) The current, which is modulated by the image—that is, the video signal—is produced by the *reflected* electron beam, returning from the target toward the cathode (electron gun) from which it came.

In the operation of the image orthicon, the camera lens focuses the light image on the photo cathode just inside the face of the tube. The photo cathode is made of metal so thin that light passes through it as it would through tracing paper. The photo cathode, held at a potential of minus 600 volts, emits electrons in proportion to the amount of light which falls upon it. These emitted electrons, held on parallel courses by a focusing coil, are attracted to the

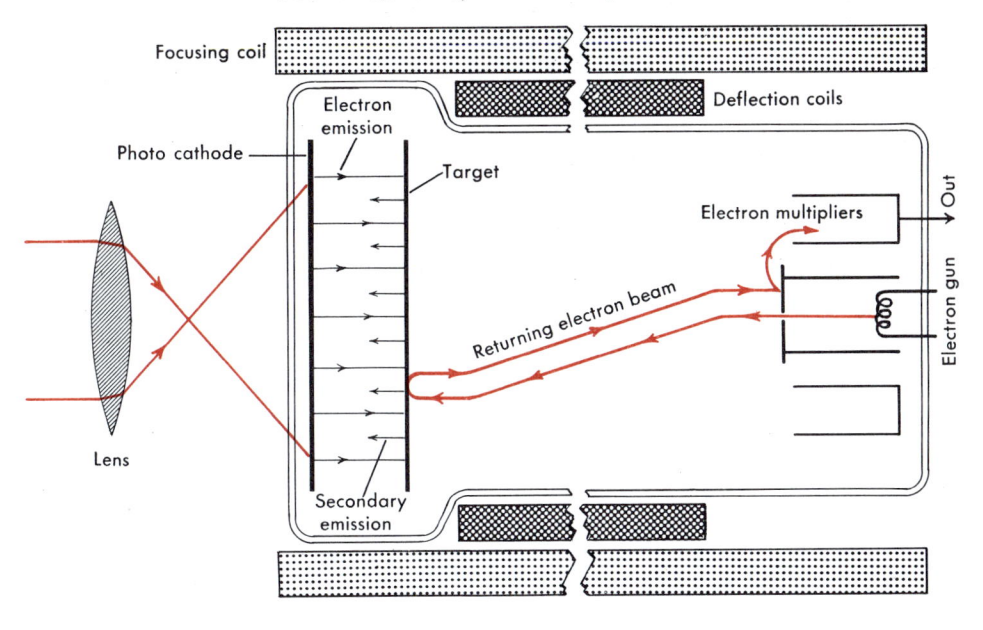

Fig. 4. Schematic drawing of the image orthicon.

target, because the target potential is zero, or 600 volts more positive than the photo cathode.

When the electrons strike the target, secondary electron emission is caused by their impacts, thus leaving on the target a pattern of varying positive charges which correspond to the varying light intensities of the televised scene. The back of the target is scanned by an electron beam from the electron gun, the beam being controlled by horizontal and vertical *deflection coils* (Fig. 5). The beam leaves enough electrons on the various parts of the target to bring the potentials back to zero.

The rest of the beam, carrying the picture information with it by virtue of its having lost electrons to the target, is reflected back to the first of a series of electron-multiplying phototubes, which, because of secondary electron emission, are capable of amplifying the video signals from 100 to 500 times their original strengths. From these electron multipliers the modulated current is conducted to the external circuit and then broadcast.

How does modern television reception work? At the receiving station the most essential piece of apparatus is the *kinescope,* which is essentially a cathode ray

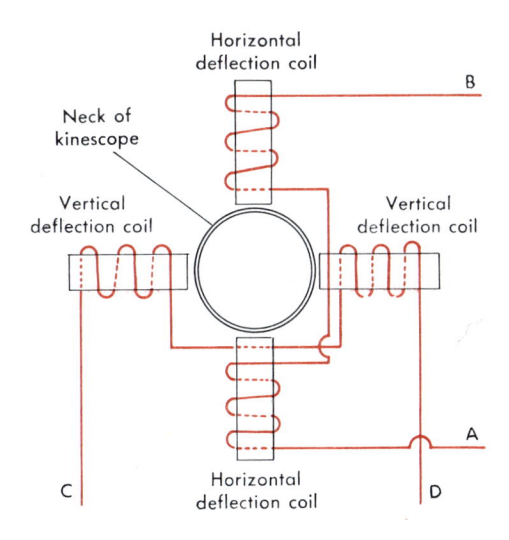

Fig. 5. Schematic of a deflection yoke.

oscilloscope (see page 336.) The modern kinescope, however, differs from the oscilloscope in that it uses deflection coils (Fig. 5), in the form of a yoke around the outside of the neck of the tube, instead of the usual interior deflection plates. The modern iconoscope also employs deflection coils.

The electrical impulses in the receiving antenna, caused by the broadcast waves, are amplified and conducted to the kinescope. Here an electron beam, synchronized with the one at the broadcasting station, is caused to scan the enlarged fluorescent end of the tube. Since this electron beam varies in accordance with the variations of light intensity from the originally televised object, the viewer sees a composite image of the object faithfully reproduced.

The fidelity of the image depends to a large extent upon the number of lines through which the electron beam sweeps across the fluorescent screen. At the present time the number of lines used in the United States is 525. The 525-line scanning is accomplished by two successive downsweeps of vertical scanning, the first sweep covering 262½ lines and the second sweep covering 262½ alternate lines. This is called *interlaced scanning* (see Fig. 6). Since each downsweep requires one-sixtieth of a second, the time required to produce the entire picture is one-thirtieth of a second. The picture frequency is thus 30 cycles per second, each picture being broken up into two projections to reduce flickering.

What are television channels? There are some eighty television channels in operation today, using frequencies from about 50 to 900 megacycles, with the exception of the range of 88-174 mc., which is reserved for FM broadcasting. Each TV channel is 6.0 mc. wide, only 4.5 mc. of which are used for transmission. The por-

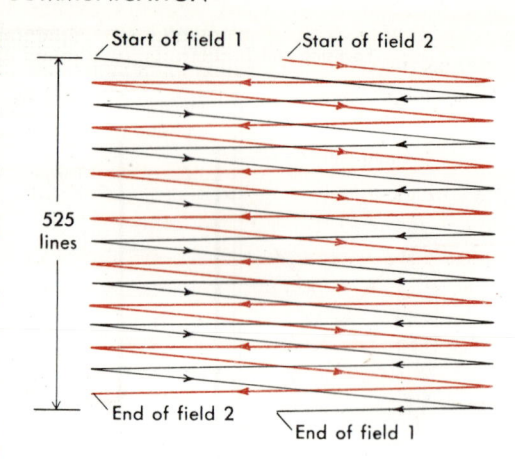

Fig. 6. Interlaced scanning. Note where the first and second scanning fields begin and end.

tion of a channel not used is reserved for *guard bands* to prevent interference with other channels.

Within the used portion of a television channel three signals are transmitted, one of which is the audio (sound) signal, transmitted by FM. Another one is the video (picture) signal, transmitted by amplitude modulation (AM), and the third is the synchronizing (sync) signal (also AM), which causes the scanning of the electron beam at the receiving station to "keep step" with the one at the transmitting station. Obviously two transmitters are necessary, one for the picture signals and one for the sound.

How is color television achieved? In our study of color we learned that all shades of color can be produced by proper mixing of the primaries, red, blue, and green. The problem of color television, then, is that of breaking down the light from a transmitted scene into its primary colors and recombining them at the receiving end. Several color TV systems have been developed, but the system accepted by the Federal Communications Commission (FCC) is a *simultaneous transmis-*

sion system developed by several companies in cooperation with the National Television System Committee. See Color Plate 4.

This system is compatible with the present black-and-white system; that is, at the receiving end it operates with 525-line interlaced scanning and a picture frequency of 30 cycles per second. This makes it possible to receive programs on our regular black-and-white receivers.

At the transmission end, three cameras, each using a primary color filter, are used. The channel width is 6 megacycles, as in black-and-white. Within this band a monochrome (one color) black-and-white carrier wave, called the *luminance signal,* is used. This signal, actually carrying information of relative brightnesses of red, green, and blue, is interlaced with a *color (chrominance) signal band* consisting of two *color difference signals* of blue and red.

The receiving tube requires three electron guns, one for each primary color. The tube has a *tri-phosphor* screen on which phosphor color dots are deposited in triangles, or *triads,* each triad being composed of a red, a blue, and a green dot (see Fig. 7). The tube also has an *aperture mask* which matches the curvature of the screen.

In the operation of this tube, all three electron beams from the three electron guns are directed through the same apertures of the mask at the same time as they sweep across its surface. They are thus convergent beams on their way to the mask, but between the mask and the phosphor-dot screen they diverge just enough so that one covers a red, one a blue, and one a green dot of one of the triads. Each beam is carrying information about the televised picture which it received from the transmitting station. Thus the picture is reproduced in its original colors.

Simpler and less expensive is the Lawrence color TV tube, or *chromatron*. In this there is a grid of wires, instead of a perforated aperture mask, between the picture screen and the electron gun. The electron beams are bent toward red, green, or blue phosphors on the screen by voltages which vary between the wires of the grid in accordance with the color signals received.

What is radar and how does it operate? Almost everyone has heard of radar and of how it was used in World War II to locate the positions of enemy planes, submarines, and ships. Fortunately, it is as useful in peace as in war—perhaps more useful. It is being used on trains to detect the presence of other trains on the tracks ahead of them. It is used on ships to guide them through narrow passages, and is extensively used in aeronautics as well. It is used by the U. S. Weather Bureau to track storms and to trace the flight of weather

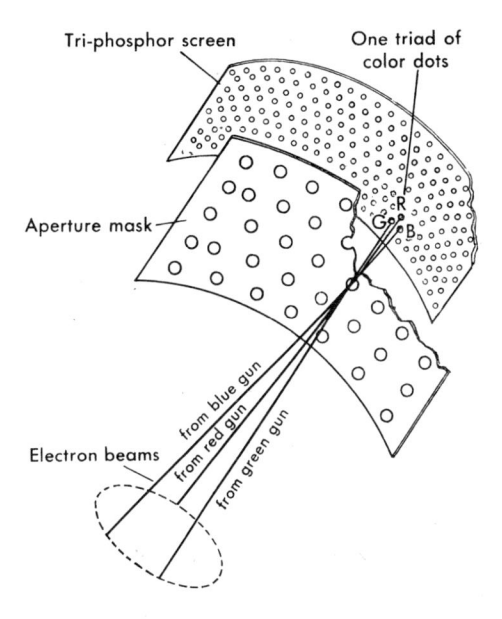

Fig. 7. Schematic drawing of a modern color TV receiver. Note how all beams reach the correct color dots through the same operture.

Fig. 8. With this antenna of a radio telescope, it is possible to receive radio signals from stars and galaxies that give off no light or insufficient light to be detected by an optical telescope.

Courtesy Harvard University News Office

balloons, which transmit complete weather data back to the station. Radar is an abbreviation for *RA*dio *D*etecting *A*nd *R*anging.

The principles of radar are very similar to those of television. Very short wave pulses of ultrahigh frequency (UHF) are generated by a *pulse oscillator*. These pulses are amplified and then transmitted by a transmitting antenna which sweeps back and forth across the horizon, or any desired area. Figure 9(a) is a block drawing of a radar transmitter and receiver.

The pulses sent out by the transmitting antenna are reflected back from the object whose distance is to be determined and are picked up by the receiving antenna. One antenna usually does both the sending and the receiving, in which case it will have an automatic switch to change from sending to receiving. These antennas are not solid but are netlike in appearance, and are so shaped that they can transmit very narrow beams of wave pulses whose wave lengths vary from about 3 to 10 centimeters. What would the frequency be if the wave length were 8 centimeters?

Figure 9(a) shows the sending and receiving equipment connected to a cathode-ray oscilloscope. At the moment a wave pulse is transmitted, a *pip*, or protuberance, appears on the horizontal line produced on the fluorescent screen of the oscilloscope by the sweep circuit. When the wave pulse is reflected back by the object and received by the antenna, another pip appears further along the line (see Fig. 9(b)). The distance between these pips is a measure of the time (t) required for the wave pulse to make a round trip to and from the object whose distance away is to be measured. Since the wave pulses travel with the speed of light (c), which is 186,000 miles per second, the distance (d) of the object can be calculated by

$$d = \frac{ct}{2}. \quad \text{Why?}$$

By a special sweep-circuit arrangement, the line along which the pips occur can be made to travel in a complete circle on the fluorescent screen (Fig. 9(c)). While the antenna scans the horizon through 360 degrees, the line travels once around the circle. Thus, a complete "map" of the surrounding territory can be seen on the screen. This device is especially valuable for short-range work, such as for guiding a ship through a canal, and for navigation, since radar beams are not affected by fog. What other applications of radar that are in use today can you cite?

SUMMARY AND CONCLUSIONS

1. The process of attaching a sound track to a motion picture film involves: (a) using a microphone to change sound waves into varying electric currents; (b) amplifying these electric currents and passing them through a

light valve composed of duralumin strips; (c) passing light from a light source through a slit between the duralumin strips which, because the width of the slit varies in accordance with the varying currents, permit corresponding variations of light intensity to pass through; (d) focusing these varying light intensities upon the edge of the light-sensitive movie film; and (e) developing the film and making a positive film from the negative.

2. In the projection of the sound film, a photoelectric cell is essential in changing the varying light intensities back to sound.

3. One type of modern television camera uses the iconoscope, a cathode-ray tube, whose essential parts are the electron gun, scanning plate, collecting ring, and deflection coils.

4. The image orthicon is a more modern camera tube. Its essential parts are the photo cathode, the target, the electron gun, the electron multipliers, and the deflection coils.

5. The present television receiving tube is the kinescope. Its essential parts are the electron gun, the deflection coils, and the fluorescent screen.

6. Television broadcasting uses channels and ultrahigh frequency waves. The width of a channel is 6 megacycles.

7. Color television is presently achieved by a simultaneous transmission system. This system uses three camera tubes for transmission and a three-electron-gun picture tube for reception.

8. Radar is much like television. It is useful in detecting and locating objects such as ships, submarines, airplanes, etc., as well as

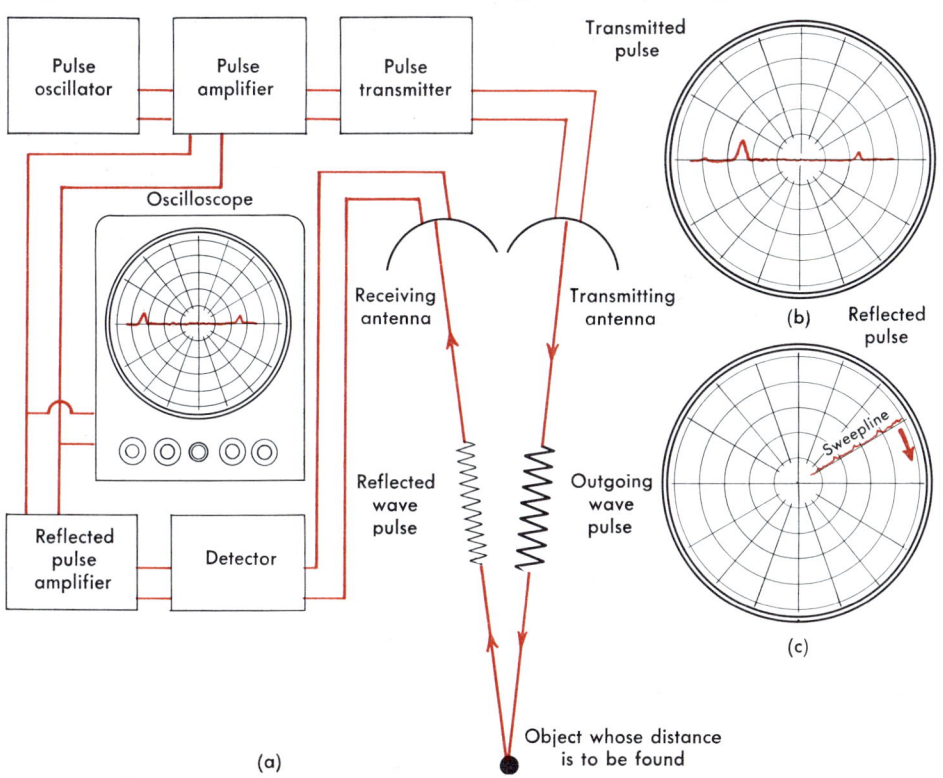

Fig. 9. (a) A block diagram of a radar unit. The first "pip" on the oscilloscope occurs at the time a wavy pulse is transmitted; the second one when it returns and is received (b) Is the time long or short between "pips"? (c) "Pips" on the sweepline show the outline of the surrounding territory.

in navigation. Over a short range it can show the essential details of the surrounding territory.

QUESTIONS FOR REVIEW

1. Upon what eye characteristic does our viewing of motion pictures depend?
2. Why are sound movies exposed at a more rapid rate than silent movies?
3. What are the essential steps in the production of the sound track for sound movies?
4. Explain the operation of a photoelectric cell.
5. Sometimes the inside of an iconoscope tube is coated with a conducting material. What could be the purpose of this?
6. What are the essential parts of the iconoscope and what are their functions?
7. Try to explain how a deflection yoke deflects an electron beam both vertically and horizontally.
8. What are the essential parts of the image orthicon tube? How does it differ from the iconoscope?
9. What signals are transmitted within a television channel? How wide is a channel?
10. What is the essential problem of color television?
11. What are the essential features of the color television picture tube?
12. In what ways is radar like television? How does it differ from television?
13. If the time elapsing between the transmission of a radar pulse and its reflection back to the station is 0.0001 second, how far away is the reflecting object?
14. Explain how it is possible to see a radar "map" of the surrounding territory on a radar scope.

PROJECTS

1. Ask your Latin teacher the literal meanings of the terms "video" and "audio" and report to the class.
2. Do some research on the iconoscope and make a report to the class on the parts and operation of the electron gun.
3. Do some research on the kinescope and report on the manner in which the electron beam is made to scan the fluorescent screen both horizontally and vertically.
4. Be on the lookout for an article on modern color television. If a suitable one is found, make a report on it to the class.
5. Look up material on early television methods and report to the class.

READING YOU WILL ENJOY

1. Anderson, Edwin P., *Television Service Manual.* Theodore Audel & Co., New York, 1951. Though parts of this book are quite technical, it contains much readable and interesting information on the theory and construction of television equipment and parts.
2. Bendick, Jeanne, and Robert Bendick, *Television Works Like This,* 2nd Ed. Whittlesey House, McGraw-Hill Book Company, Inc., New York, 1954. A very elementary book for children and high school students, discussing, with many hand-drawn illustrations, the whole topic of television from the studio, sets, props, rehearsals, etc., to some of the transmitting and receiving principles.
3. Hicks, H. J., *Introductory Radio Theory and Servicing.* McGraw-Hill Book Company, Inc., New York, 1949. A text prepared to fill the needs of small schools which wish to add a course in radio theory. The book contains principles of electricity, magnetism, construction soldering, vacuum tubes, amplifiers, power supplies, test equipment, television, and others.
4. *Radio & Television News,* a monthly magazine published by Ziff-Davis Publishing Co., Chicago. Carries articles on up-to-date developments and techniques in radio and television. Fairly technical.
5. *Television Principles and Practice.* General Electric Company, Schenectady, New York, 1949. A television course in lesson form.

Unit 19

Nuclear Physics
(Atomic Energy)

In their increasing efforts to unlock the secret of the forces within the nucleus of an atom, scientists have constructed this huge atomic "racetrack," or accelerator, called the cosmotron. The large "doughnut" on which the man is kneeling is a magnet of the cosmotron. In the vacuum chamber, which rests in the gap of the magnet, atomic particles make three million trips until they attain full energy of two to three billion volts. Then the accelerated particles are shot at targets of carbon or liquid hydrogen. When the cosmotron is in full operation, no one is allowed in the room except behind the shield of concrete blocks in the foreground. In this way, the personnel is protected from the high-energy rays and particles which are given off by the machine.

This unit will round out your knowledge of the fabulous world within the atom and provide you with a basis for understanding how nuclear energy is released. You will also learn how this energy is being applied in solving problems in industry, medicine, and agriculture.

52. THE CONQUEST OF ATOMIC ENERGY
53. THE ATOM IS HARNESSED AND CIVILIZATION IS CHALLENGED

Unit Photograph Courtesy Brookhaven National Laboratory

Chapter 52

The Conquest of Atomic Energy

One of the first clues to the existence of atomic energy. When Albert Einstein proposed his famous equation, $E = mc^2$, to many physicists it sounded more like the ravings of a madman than the work of a genius. This was a natural reaction because the equation was a violation of the tried and tested laws of conservation of energy and matter, it was based on assumptions that seemed almost completely divorced from matter, and it was arrived at by sheer logic untested by experiment.

Besides logic, only a few observable data, most of which were found in the sun, supported Einstein's equation. The spectroscope revealed that the temperature at the exterior of the sun is about 6000° C, and calculations showed that at its interior the temperature is as high as 20,000,000° C. Tests at the earth's surface, 93,000,000 miles from the sun, showed that one square centimeter of area exposed to the vertical rays of the sun receives approximately two calories of heat per minute. The total amount of energy received per minute by the whole earth is a staggering sum, but it is only a tiny fraction of the total energy radiated by the sun.

The burning of ordinary fuels would not account for either the high temperatures of the sun or the tremendous quantity of energy radiated. Nor would the electron theory of atomic radiation of heat and light proposed on page 577 account for these phenomena. The most promising explanation seemed to be that in the sun, matter is being changed to energy, and that a very small bit of matter produces a tremendous amount of energy, as Einstein's equation, $E = mc^2$, showed would be the case. See page 581.

Further observations with the spectroscope indicated still more definitely that Einstein might be right. They showed that the chemical composition of the sun is about the same as that of the earth, with the exception that the sun's atmosphere is made up largely of hydrogen and helium gas. This suggested that perhaps, under the extremely high pressures and temperatures in the sun, the hydrogen atoms are uniting to form helium, and that in the process some matter is being converted to energy.

The facts which support this clue we already know. You will recall that a hydrogen atom, with a single planetary electron, has a nucleus of one proton. A helium atom, containing two planetary electrons, has a nucleus which contains two neutrons and two protons. In other words, a helium atom consists of the equivalent of four hydrogen atoms, or four *mass units*.

NUCLEAR PHYSICS (ATOMIC ENERGY)

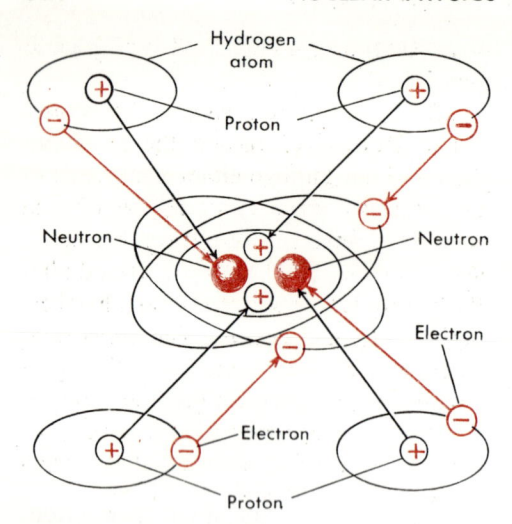

Fig. 1. The formation of a helium atom from four hydrogen atoms.

Accurate measurements show that the mass of a proton is 1.00758; of a neutron, 1.00893; and of a helium nucleus, 4.00280. The combined mass of two protons and two neutrons is found as follows:

$$2 \times 1.00758 = 2.01516$$
$$2 \times 1.00893 = 2.01786$$

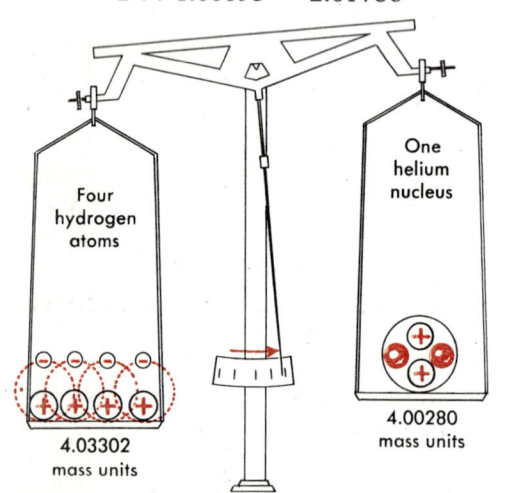

Fig. 2. A comparison of the mass of a helium nucleus with the mass of four hydrogen atoms reveals a difference of .03022 mass unit.

Calculated mass of
helium nucleus = 4.03302

Actual mass of helium nucleus = 4.00280
Difference = 0.03022

These results seem to show that in the formation of a helium nucleus, 0.03022 mass unit is converted to energy (Fig. 2).

Early workers on the conquest of atomic energy were totally unable to convert hydrogen into helium, and, as a consequence, turned their attention to other clues and modes of attack.

The discovery of radioactivity. Shortly after the discovery of X-rays in 1895, Henri Becquerel, in Paris, was studying phosphorescent substances (materials which glow softly after exposure to bright light). Among his materials was a mineral containing the heavy metal, uranium. Accidentally a little pile of this mineral was left on a photographic plate in his darkroom. Although Becquerel knew, when he saw the mineral on the plate, that the plate was wrapped so that no light could possibly strike it, he nevertheless developed the plate and found a dark spot on it right below where the pile of mineral had lain for several days. The spot was a silhouette of the pile of salt. That a substance could take a picture of itself was almost unbelievable.

Further study showed that this uranium was sending out radiations that were far more penetrating than X-rays. Also, like X-rays, they caused fluorescent substances to fluoresce, they ionized air and other gases, and they discharged a charged electroscope. Such minerals were said to be *radioactive*.

Strangely, these radioactive minerals radiated these new rays day after day and month after month. Like the energy in the sun, the supply seemed endless. Having discovered these facts, Becquerel turned these radioactive materials over to a young woman student by the name of Marie Sklodowska Curie, wife of Pierre Curie.

Madame Curie and her contribution to the quest. The story of the life of Madame Curie is a most dramatic one. It is one of triumph, tragedy, sorrow, and happiness, and it has been well told in both books and motion pictures. Here we will mention only her contribution to the conquest of atomic energy.

Soon after she began her investigations, Madame Curie found that a piece of pitchblende, a black mineral found in Bohemia, darkened a photographic plate far more extensively, and discharged an electroscope far more quickly, than it should in proportion to the amount of uranium found in the pitchblende. It was evident to her that another mineral, or perhaps several minerals, other than uranium were the cause. Madame Curie and her husband set themselves to the task of finding this unknown cause.

For three long, hectic years they labored feverishly, hardly stopping to eat or sleep. The search was like trying to find a needle in a haystack. From over a ton of the black pitchblende they were able to wrest only a small bit of highly radioactive material. Nevertheless, they found two new elements. The first discovered they named *polonium,* after Madame Curie's native Poland. The other, and the more abundant of the two elements, was called *radium.* Radium in particular seemed to be a limitless reservoir of energy, being about 1½ million times as radioactive as uranium.

As the news of the discovery of the new radioactive elements spread, scientists in different parts of the world turned their attention to radioactive minerals, and soon several more were discovered. Among these scientists was a young Englishman by the name of Ernest Rutherford (1871-1937), a native of New Zealand, who had come to England to study and who was later to become one of England's greatest physicists.

Alpha, beta, and gamma radiations. When Rutherford passed the radiations from radium through either a magnetic or an electrostatic field, he discovered that they were separated into three beams, as shown in Fig. 3. These were named after the first three letters in the Greek alphabet: *alpha, beta,* and *gamma.* The alpha rays, as shown, were deflected as if they possessed positive charges; the beta rays, as if they possessed negative charges. The gamma rays were not deflected, which showed that they were uncharged.

The alpha particles when collected proved to be ions of helium—helium atoms stripped of their two planetary electrons and with a positive charge of plus two. The beta particles proved to be high-speed electrons, and the gamma rays were found to be X-rays of very short wave length. These are shown in Fig. 4.

The alpha particle when emitted from radium had a speed of about 10,000 miles per second, but even so it would not penetrate more than eight centimeters of air at one atmosphere of pressure. The beta particle (an electron) had a speed close to that of light. It would penetrate several centimeters of air and pass through thin sheets of metal foil. The gamma rays were far more penetrating than X-rays, about four inches of lead being necessary to shield a body from them.

Radioactivity and the alchemist's dream. One of the dreams of the early chemists, known as *alchemists,* was to change cheaper elements to gold. As you know, none of them were successful. The change of one element to another is known as the *transmutation of the elements.*

But when Dalton said that matter consists of elements, that each element is made up of identical atoms which are unlike the atoms of other elements, and that atoms

616 NUCLEAR PHYSICS (ATOMIC ENERGY)

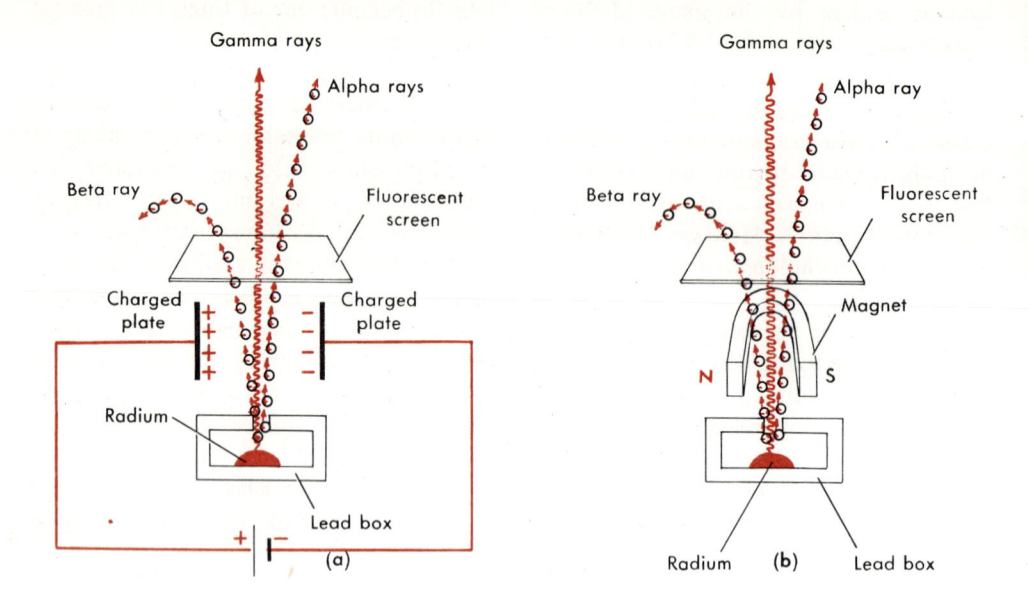

Fig. 3. Deflection of alpha, beta, and gamma rays.

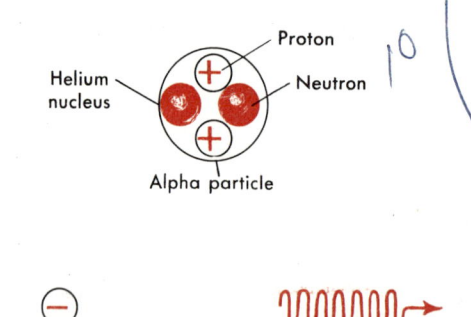

Fig. 4. Three kinds of atomic radiations.

are indestructible and everlasting, his followers gave up hope of changing one element into another.

Contrary to Dalton, we find that the nuclei of radium atoms are exploding spontaneously and that each exploding atom shoots out a helium nucleus (alpha particle). As a result a new atom of the element *radon* along with helium is formed. The emission of another alpha particle (helium nucleus) by a radon atom produces more helium and the atom of another element, *radium A*. The emission of a beta particle (an electron) from the nucleus produces *radium B,* and so on, as shown in Fig. 5. The final product is lead, which is not radioactive.

How a nucleus can emit an electron when supposedly it consists only of protons and neutrons is not clear. One answer is that a neutron splits into a proton and an electron. The electron is emitted by the atom, and the proton remains in the nucleus. Thereby the number of protons in the nucleus is increased by one, and an atom of a new element is formed.

Further study of Fig. 5 shows that radium is a product of ionium, which is a product of uranium II. Each element listed is the product of the one above; all originally came from uranium. Hence we see that what the old alchemists dreamed of is actually taking place among the radioactive elements, which are disintegrating, forming new elements, and giving off a continuous stream of energy.

How are radioactive elements used to calculate the age of the earth? In Column II of Fig. 5, the so-called *half life* of each radioactive element is given. This is the length of time needed for half of a sample to disintegrate. For example, in 1590 years 500,000 atoms out of a sample of a million atoms of radium would disintegrate. For half of the remaining 500,000 atoms to disintegrate, another 1590 years would be required. And for half of the remaining 250,000 original radium atoms to disintegrate it would take another 1590 years. And so the process continues. See Fig. 5 for the half lives of other elements in the uranium-radium family.

Incidentally, such information has proved very valuable in calculations of the age of the earth. By determining the percentage of uranium, radon, lead, and all the other products of disintegration in a natural deposit of uranium, it is possible for us to determine the age of the earth quite accurately. Such calculations show that the earth is about 2½ billion years old. This answer agrees very closely with results obtained by totally unrelated methods. When the same answer to a problem can be obtained by totally independent methods, what does this tend to prove about the answer?

Controlling the release of atomic energy from radioactive elements. The fact that radioactive atoms were exploding spon-

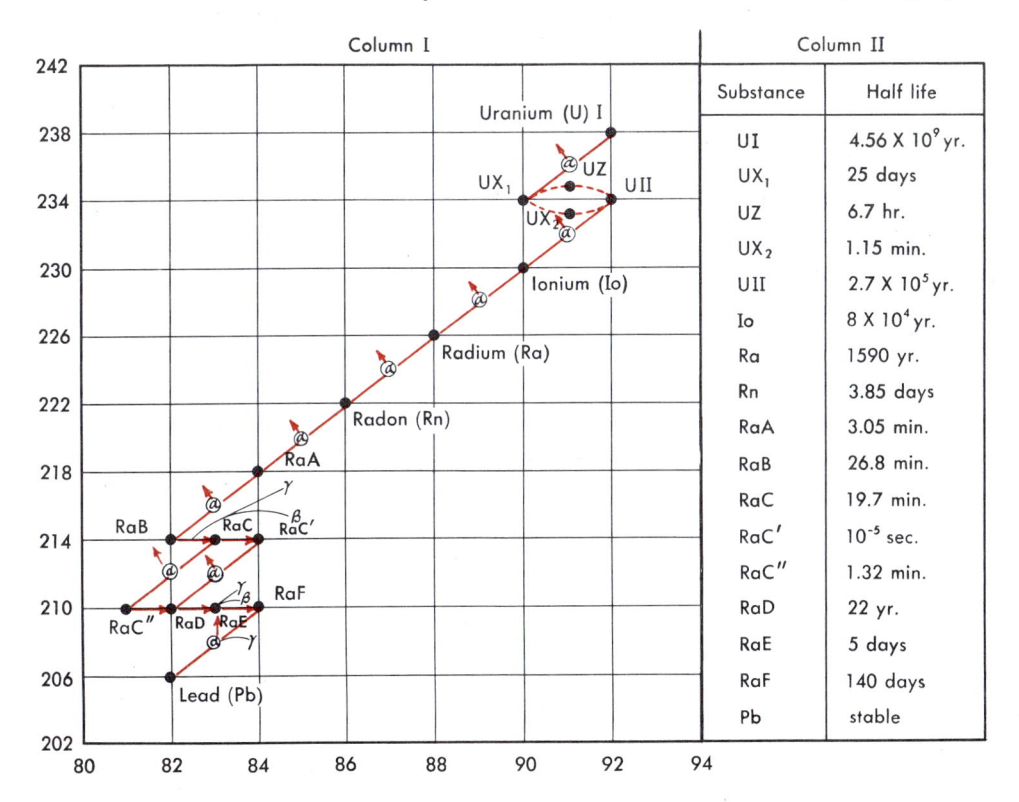

Substance	Half life
UI	4.56×10^9 yr.
UX_1	25 days
UZ	6.7 hr.
UX_2	1.15 min.
UII	2.7×10^5 yr.
Io	8×10^4 yr.
Ra	1590 yr.
Rn	3.85 days
RaA	3.05 min.
RaB	26.8 min.
RaC	19.7 min.
RaC'	10^{-5} sec.
RaC"	1.32 min.
RaD	22 yr.
RaE	5 days
RaF	140 days
Pb	stable

Fig. 5. Disintegration of uranium, showing the half lives of the various decay products. Mass numbers are shown on the y-axis; atomic numbers on the x-axis.

taneously and had been doing so for millions of years indicated to scientists that these elements were a source of an enormous amount of stored-up energy. The problem was how to speed up and control the rate of release.

Several methods, including exposure to heat, cold, and light, were used to no avail. Then it was proposed that the rate might be increased if protons, neutrons, or other particles were shot into the nuclei, causing them to explode, much as a stick of dynamite explodes when struck by a rifle bullet. What, though, could be used to shoot such particles?

Rutherford's gun for shooting nuclei. Nature itself not only provided the bullets to shoot atoms, but also supplied the gun for Rutherford. What better gun could he have wanted than a small bit of radium, which fires electrons at a speed close to that of light, and alpha particles at the speed of 10,000 miles per second? Of course, shooting invisible bullets at invisible targets was a strange way to hunt. How was Rutherford to know when he had hit an atom? And in case he did hit one, how was he to know whether it exploded?

Wilson's cloud chamber. Wilson's cloud chamber gave the answer to the questions just asked. It was based on the fact that when air is saturated with water and expanded suddenly, the cooling effect causes the formation of tiny drops of water. The vapor collects around the dust particles in the air. If, however, there is no dust, then no water vapor condenses and no fog particles are formed.

When the cloud chamber is used, the air is first rendered free of dust. Then the air is allowed to expand, with the result that its temperature is lowered; and in the absence of dust, no water vapor condenses. But if a charged particle—for example, a helium ion (alpha particle)—is shot through the air, millions of air molecules are ionized, and the water vapor collects on these ions. As a result, the path of the particle (bullet) is marked by a line of fog which appears white against a properly lighted black background. Alpha particles, beta particles (electrons), and protons all leave tracks. Each has different penetrating power, or range, and other characteristics which make it possible for each to be recognized by its "tracks." See Fig. 6. In fact, the *positron,* which is a positively charged particle with the same mass as an electron, and the *meson,* with a mass 300 times that of an electron, were discovered in this manner in the study of *cosmic rays.* The latter are rays of very short wave length and of unknown origin, coming from interstellar space.

Also, from cloud chamber photographs, the speeds of different particles can be calculated and the kinetic energy of each computed.

Rutherford shoots nitrogen nuclei. Armed with radium as his artillery, Rutherford directed atomic bullets (alpha particles) at nitrogen gas which was enclosed

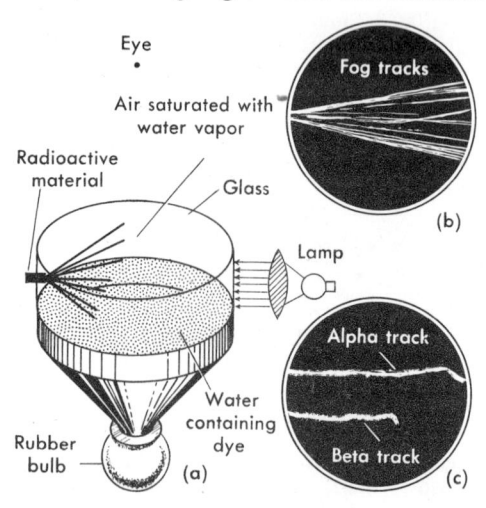

Fig. 6. (a) Wilson cloud chamber. (b) Fog tracks caused by alpha particles. (c) Alpha and beta tracks.

in a Wilson cloud chamber. First appeared the straight path produced by the atoms from which the alpha particle was literally tearing off the electrons. Then appeared a sudden break in this path as the alpha particle evidently met a nitrogen nucleus. Then two particles appeared, one of which had longer range and hence greater speed than the alpha particle had at its time of collision.

Investigation of the gas in the cloud chamber after bombardment showed the presence of hydrogen and oxygen, neither of which had previously been present. Where did these two new gases come from, and what was this new high-speed particle?

Rutherford concluded that the new high-speed particle was a hydrogen nucleus (a proton) which, when it joined up with a free electron, formed a hydrogen atom. This accounted for the presence of hydrogen. The oxygen, Rutherford believed, was formed by the union of a nitrogen nucleus with a helium nucleus. In the process the proton, which joined up with an electron to form hydrogen, was ejected. The formation of oxygen and hydrogen and the nuclear change can be shown as follows:

$$_7N^{14} + {_2He^4} \rightarrow {_8O^{17}} + {_1H^1}$$

Nitrogen nucleus + Helium ion → Oxygen isotope + Hydrogen nucleus (proton)

Rutherford's experiment was a landmark because it showed that one element can be changed into another by artificial methods; in other words, that artificial transmutation is possible.

Rutherford verifies Einstein's equation. The first measured test of Einstein's equation $E = mc^2$ came when Rutherford shot hydrogen nuclei at lithium, a light metal. The change is pictured in Fig. 8. An account of the mass units is as follows:

Courtesy Radiation Laboratory, University of California

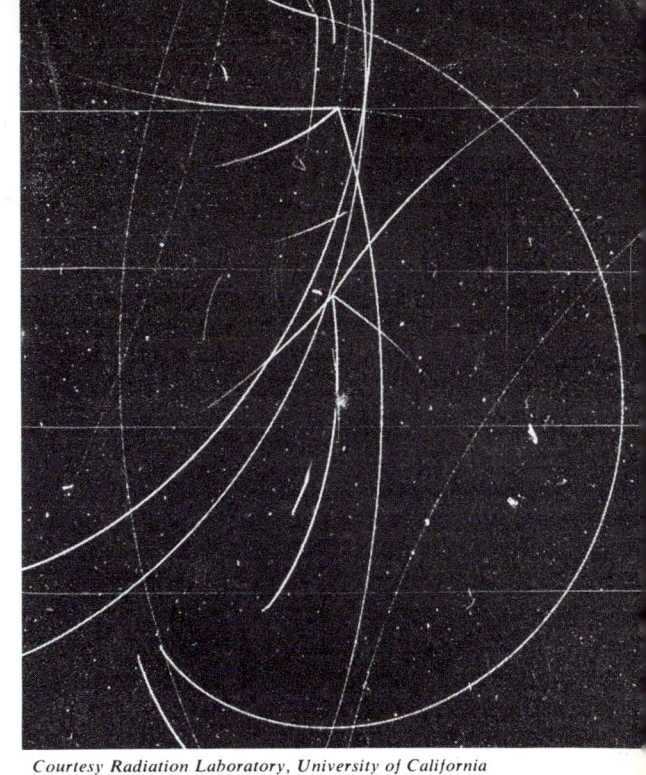

Fig. 7. Wilson cloud chamber photograph of atomic particles.

$$_1H^1 + {_3Li^7} \rightarrow 2{_2He^4} + \text{K.E. of helium nuclei}$$

One hydrogen nucleus + One lithium nucleus → Two helium nuclei + K.E. etc.

$$1.00758 + 7.0165 \rightarrow 2 \times 4.00280$$

Total mass on the left side = 8.02408
Total mass on the right side = 8.00560
Loss of mass = .01848

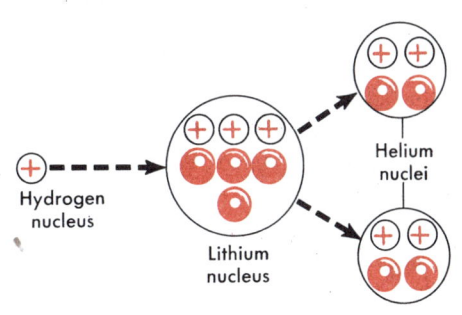

Fig. 8. How Rutherford verified Einstein's equation, $E = mc^2$, by shooting protons at a lithium nucleus.

NUCLEAR PHYSICS (ATOMIC ENERGY)

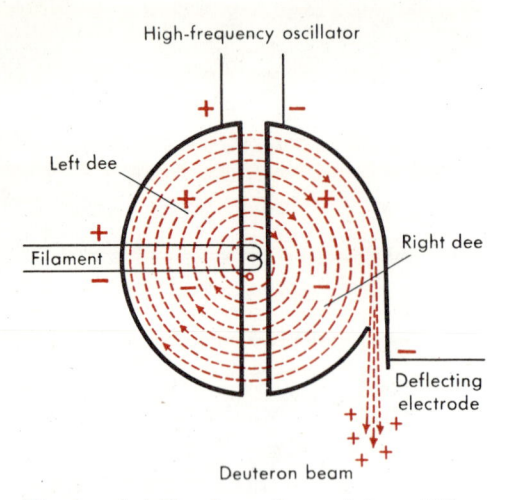

Fig. 9. (a) The dees of a cyclotron. When the deuterons travel a half circle, the voltage reverses, causing the particles to jump across the gap. The magnetic field keeps the atomic particles in a circular path.

From the cloud chamber, the speeds of the alpha particles (helium nuclei) were measured and their kinetic energies were computed. This total energy over and above the energy of the hydrogen nucleus was found to be equivalent to the vanished mass, in accordance with Einstein's formula, $E = mc^2$. Hence, it was proved that mass may disappear and energy may appear in its stead, but always the amount of one which is formed is equivalent to the amount of the other which vanishes, as Einstein had predicted many years before.

Bigger and better guns needed. It became apparent as research went forward that guns more powerful than radium were needed, guns which would fire any kind of bullets, such as electrons, neutrons, deuterons, alpha particles, and other particles that might be discovered.

The *betatron*, which fires beta particles (electrons), and the *cyclotron*, which fires a great variety of particles, are the two most famous guns. Here we will discuss only the cyclotron.

The cyclotron was used first by Dr. E. O. Lawrence at the University of California. It consists essentially of two semicircular hollow boxes called *dees*. The dees of the first cyclotron were a few inches in diameter. In modern ones the dees may be several feet in diameter. They are always separated by a gap, however, as shown in (a) of Fig. 9. Perpendicular to their sides is a very strong magnetic field produced by two very powerful magnets, as shown in (b) of Fig. 9. Both dees are in an

Fig. 9. (b) The magnets of this research cyclotron are clearly visible above and below the vacuum box in the center.

Courtesy General Electric Co.

airtight box which can be filled with any gas and can be evacuated to any degree of vacuum.

Between the dees is a high-voltage oscillator of 10,000,000 cycles which causes each dee to become alternately positive and negative.

An incandescent filament heated by a high-frequency current is placed at the center of the dees. Its purpose is to break up the atoms of the surrounding gas into ions. In the case of deuterium (heavy hydrogen) gas, it produces a *deuteron*, which consists of one neutron and one proton, with a positive charge of one.

When the right-hand dee is negative, a deuteron, which is positive, will be pulled and accelerated toward this dee. But at the same time the magnetic flux will cause the deuteron to move perpendicularly to this direction. The net result is that the positively charged deuteron moves in a half circle in the right-hand dee. Its speed is such that by the time it completes a half circle the oscillator has completed a half cycle. Hence, when it arrives at the boundary between the dees, the left-hand dee becomes negative, which with the magnetic field accelerates the deuteron along the path shown. As the speed increases, the centrifugal force causes the deuterons to spiral outward along the course, covering a greater distance in the same time. Finally they hit an opening in the right-hand dee, where they are guided by a deflecting electrode so that they strike the target.

The Geiger counter. The Geiger counter is another instrument which has proved to be of great value in atomic research. The counter consists of two electrodes, as shown in Fig. 10, across which a voltage is applied. The tube is filled with gas. If high-energy particles, X-rays, gamma rays, or cosmic rays enter the tube, the gas is ionized and the ions move to the electrodes. The result is a current in the electrical circuit to which the tube is connected. The effect (current) is amplified to operate a counting device or to make clicks in a radio loud-speaker. The Geiger counter is used to determine the intensity of radiation from a radioactive source.

The electron volt. In atomic work, a new unit of energy called *electron volt* was

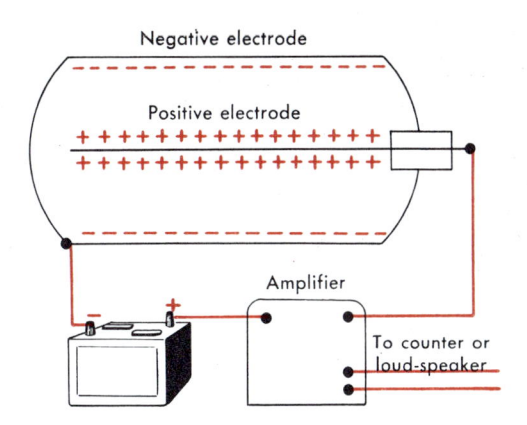

Fig. 10. A Geiger counter determines the number of ionization events caused by high-energy particles.

Fig. 11. The bevatron accelerates protons to an energy of 6 billion electron volts (bev).

Courtesy Radiation Laboratory, University of California

devised. It is the energy acquired when an electron falls through a difference of potential of one volt. Although we do not make use of it in our study, you will find it used in atomic energy literature.

Radioactive isotopes. In one experiment, high-powered atomic "guns" fired deuterons, heavy hydrogen nuclei, at rock salt (a compound of sodium), and a hitherto unknown isotope of sodium was formed. This isotope proved to be radioactive. In effect, the sodium nucleus absorbed a deuteron, which broke into a proton and a neutron. The proton was ejected from the nucleus, leaving the neutron behind. This neutron raised the mass of the sodium atom by one. The reaction is as follows:

$$_{11}Na^{23} + {}_1H^2 \rightarrow {}_{11}Na^{24} + {}_1H^1$$

Sodium atom + Deuteron → Sodium isotope + Proton

When the sodium target was removed from the deuteron beam, it was found to be radioactive; the nuclei of the atoms were emitting electrons and gamma rays. This radioactive element is an isotope of sodium and is called *radiosodium*. Having a half life of only fifteen days, it is not found in nature.

Upon the emission of an electron, the positive charge on the nucleus is raised one, from 11 to 12. When this happens a new element, $_{12}Mg^{24}$, is formed. By bombardment, isotopes of all the elements have been produced from other elements. In the future this may be a way of producing the scarce but much-needed elements. Many of the isotopes produced are being used in medicine, agriculture, industry, and other fields. More about this will be said later.

What binds the nucleus of a heavy atom together? Even after the structure of the atom was fairly well known in theory, several questions remained unanswered. It is estimated that the force of repulsion between two protons as close together as they are in a nucleus is about 40 pounds. Why do they not fly apart? What holds the protons together in a nucleus? Also, why is it that matter can be changed to energy by the union of the lighter elements, such as helium and lithium, as well as by the disintegration of heavy elements into the lighter elements, but not by union or disintegration of those of intermediate weight? Furthermore, why are the heavy elements spontaneously disintegrating into the lighter elements?

Evidently, when protons and neutrons are brought close enough together they cohere, much as two drops of water cohere and run together when one is brought very close to the other. And evidently the forces of cohesion among the protons and neutrons are greater than the forces of repulsion among the protons. This accounts in part for what holds the nucleus together.

This argument seems still more plausible when we realize that when protons and neutrons of the lighter elements come together to form heavier nuclei, part of the mass is converted to energy.

It is believed that part of this energy, before it is released, serves to hold the protons and neutrons together. The amount of mass lost per mass unit particle is called the *packing factor* or binding energy. The less the packing factor, the more unstable the nucleus is.

The packing factors of the elements, given in hundredths of one per cent of the mass converted per particle, when plotted against the atomic numbers of the same elements, help to explain why some atoms tend to break down spontaneously and give off energy, and why energy can be obtained when light atoms are put together.

As shown in Fig. 12, the packing factor of hydrogen is zero. Explain. The packing factor of iron, atomic number 26, is about

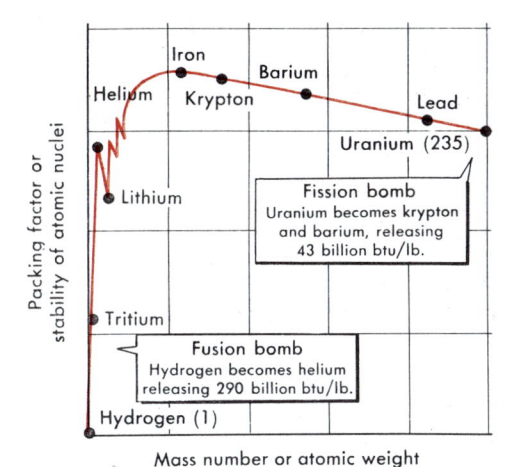

Fig. 12. Atomic mass versus the stability of atomic nuclei.

85 and is the greatest of all atoms. Its nucleus is therefore the most stable of all the nuclei. Among the heavy atoms, uranium (atomic number 92) has the least packing factor, about 70, and hence its nucleus is the least stable of the heavy nuclei.

If you turn Fig. 12 upside down and think of the curve as a cross section of a valley, you will see that iron is at the bottom of the valley in the most stable position, and that uranium and hydrogen are at the tops of the sides at the most unstable positions. Hence, if the unstable hydrogen atoms were to "roll" down the hill, and unite to form atoms having higher packing factors, then energy should be given off. For example, if four atoms of hydrogen were to unite to form helium, which has a higher packing factor than hydrogen, energy would be emitted, as explained on page 614.

Likewise, if a uranium atom were to tumble down into the valley, by exploding so as to form two atoms having packing factors about the same as iron, then energy would be emitted, with a corresponding loss in mass. Hence, theoretically at least, any element above or below iron in atomic number is a potential source of atomic energy. Of course, hydrogen and uranium are the two farthest up the hillsides and hence should be the best two sources.

Why was not atomic energy harnessed long before it was? With Einstein's theory confirmed and enormous quantities of atomic energy virtually waiting to be harnessed, why was not atomic energy harnessed soon after Rutherford's pioneer experiment? Why did a quarter of a century elapse before atomic energy was harnessed? Part of the answer is that, in splitting heavy atoms with atomic bullets, millions of shots had to be fired in order to hit the nucleus of one atom. The energy required to fire these millions of bullets was greater than the energy released when an atom was hit and caused to explode. Another part of the answer is that there was no way of keeping an explosion going once it was started. What scientists hoped to find was an element whose atoms, in exploding, would cause other atoms to explode until all had exploded.

Uranium fission—a new clue. In 1939, just before the outbreak of World War II, there came a most startling announcement from four European scientists, Otto Hahn, Fritz Strassman, O. R. Frisch, and Lise Meitner. They had bombarded atoms of the heavy metal uranium with neutrons and caused them to split into fragments, and had found that the energy released was tremendous in comparison with other nuclear explosions. The reaction is shown in Fig. 13.

But this was only part of the important discovery. Among the products of the reaction were neutrons, the same particles that were used to set it off. The possibilities of this discovery were breathtaking. This was what scientists had hoped they would

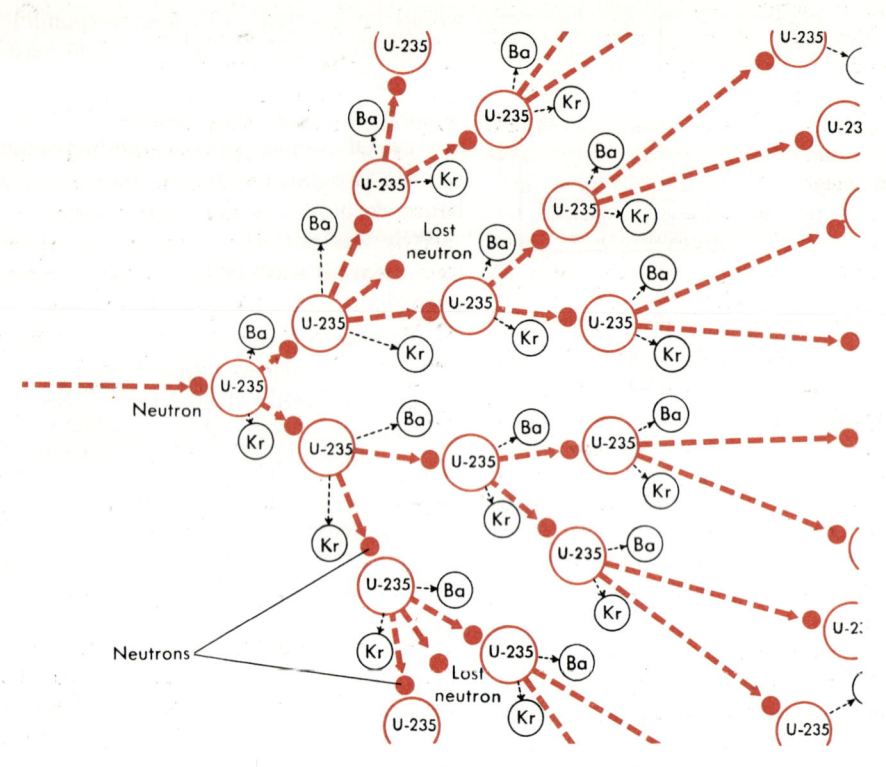

Fig. 13. A chain reaction, showing the result of bombarding U^{235} atoms with neutrons. In order to sustain a chain reaction, the number of neutrons released by fission must be greater than the number lost.

find. Under proper conditions, the neutrons emitted by one atom might cause several other atoms to explode. If they in turn emitted neutrons, they would cause many other atoms to explode, and so on; and thus the reaction would be maintained. This sort of reaction is called a *chain reaction,* and the splitting of atoms in this manner is known as *fission*.

Upon hearing the news, atomic research workers rushed to their atom smashers and verified the report. In a matter of a few hours a state of excitement and concern reigned in the world of science. And a few days later, when World War II broke out in Europe, this state of affairs was intensified even more.

An iron curtain falls on science. During peacetime, scientists of all countries had cooperated in trying to harness atomic energy for creative purposes. But with the coming of war, international cooperation ceased. Among scientists of opposing sides, a desperate race developed to see which could first produce an atomic bomb. At that time nuclear research went "underground," and it was conducted behind an iron curtain for years afterward. It was under such conditions that the atomic bomb was produced. This we shall consider in the next chapter.

SUMMARY AND CONCLUSIONS

1. In the sun, hydrogen atoms are joining together to form helium atoms, and in the process, a small percentage of the matter is

changed to energy in accordance with Einstein's equation, $E = mc^2$. This accounts for the seemingly inexhaustible supply of heat and energy radiated by the sun.

2. Radioactive elements such as uranium, radium, polonium, and others are spontaneously disintegrating and at the same time are emitting energy, alpha particles (helium nuclei), beta particles (electrons), and gamma rays (short-wave X-rays). These changes are also in accordance with Einstein's equation, $E = mc^2$.

3. Atoms are not indestructible, and, contrary to the laws of conservation of matter and energy, matter can be changed into energy and energy can be changed into matter.

4. One element can be changed into another. This change is known as the transmutation of elements.

5. Not all the atoms of an element are exactly alike. All atoms of an element do have the same chemical properties and the same number of protons in their nuclei, but they may differ in the number of neutrons in their nuclei and in their atomic weights.

6. Isotopes are atoms of an element all having the same chemical properties but different atomic weights.

7. Rutherford changed nitrogen to oxygen by shooting helium ions emitted by radium at nitrogen atoms. The nuclear reaction is as follows:

$$_7N^{14} + {}_2He^4 \rightarrow {}_8O^{17} + {}_1H^1$$

Nitrogen + Helium → Oxygen + Hydrogen

8. The electron volt is the energy acquired by an electron when it falls through a difference of potential of one volt.

9. Rutherford verified Einstein's equation, $E = mc^2$, by shooting deuterons (heavy hydrogen nuclei) at lithium atoms.

10. The packing factor is the amount of energy lost per mass unit particle when the protons and neutrons are packed together in the nucleus of an atom. The atoms with the highest packing factor have the most stable nuclei.

11. Among the light elements, hydrogen has the smallest packing factor. Uranium has the smallest packing factor among the heavy atoms. These elements also have the least stable nuclei. For this reason, they are considered the sources from which atomic energy can be most easily secured.

12. In 1939, it was discovered that a uranium 235 atom, when bombarded with neutrons, splits into the more stable barium and krypton atoms, and that in the process two more neutrons are emitted, along with considerable energy caused by the loss of matter in the explosion. These neutrons will cause other atoms to explode, and, in turn, to emit more neutrons, which will cause further explosions. This reaction is called a chain reaction. With fissionable materials, it is possible under proper conditions to make an atomic bomb or a controlled source of atomic energy.

QUESTIONS FOR REVIEW

1. Explain the theory of the production of heat and light in the sun. Does this mean that the sun is losing mass? If so, how much mass per day? For an answer to the latter question, see a modern encyclopedia.

2. Explain one relatively simple experimental test of one consequence of the theory explained in Question 1.

3. What is the approximate mass of an electron in comparison with the mass of a hydrogen atom?

4. Compare the mass of a proton with the mass of (a) a neutron; (b) a hydrogen atom.

5. Define an element.

6. How is the atomic number related to the number of protons in the nucleus of an atom? To the number of electrons in the atom?

7. What is an ion? Of what does a helium ion consist? Of what does a helium nucleus consist?

8. What is the mass number of an element?

9. Explain in terms of your definition of an element why an atom becomes an atom of a new element when (a) its nucleus loses or gains a proton; (b) its nucleus loses an electron.

10. Explain how the nucleus of an atom can lose an electron when it is supposed to consist only of protons and neutrons.

11. What is an isotope? Does the fact that isotopes exist agree with your definition of an element?
12. In the atom $_{92}U^{235}$, how many protons are in the nucleus? What is the mass number? How many neutrons are in the nucleus?
13. How many neutrons and protons are in the nuclei of the following atoms: (a) hydrogen? (b) Lithium? (c) Sodium? (d) Iron?
14. What is a radioactive element?
15. What is an alpha particle? Beta particle? Gamma ray?
16. What is fluorescence? Phosphorescence?
17. What is meant by the transmutation of the elements?
18. Why was Rutherford's experiment, in which he shot alpha particles into nitrogen particles, so important? Write the reaction.
19. Explain a Wilson cloud chamber and tell for what it is used.
20. Explain a Geiger counter.
21. What is a positron? Meson?
22. What is meant by the half life of a radioactive element?
23. Explain why, when an atom loses a neutron from its nucleus, it does not become an atom of another element.
24. In an atom of $_{92}U^{238}$ there are how many electrons? Protons? Neutrons?
25. What is the mass number of $_{92}U^{238}$?
26. What is meant by nuclear fission and chain reaction?
27. What is the packing factor? What is the relationship between the packing factor and stability of the nucleus of an atom?
28. Explain the graph in Fig. 12.
29. Explain how we compute the age of the earth by studying a sample of natural uranium ore.

READING YOU WILL ENJOY

The World Within the Atom. Westinghouse Electric Corporation, School Service, Pittsburgh 30, Pennsylvania. A 30-page pamphlet that tells how scientists explored the atom and learned to control and release its energy.

Chapter 53

The Atom Is Harnessed and Civilization Is Challenged

The problem. We have just learned that when uranium 235 is bombarded with neutrons, the uranium nuclei capture or absorb neutrons and then disintegrate. Each disintegrating nucleus breaks up into one atom of krypton and one atom of barium and, on the average, two high-speed neutrons are released. At the same time, a small proportion of the matter involved is converted to energy.

This reaction, when discovered, was one which scientists had hopefully sought for some time. The two neutrons released in the disintegration of the nucleus, they hoped, under proper conditions, could be caused to explode two more nuclei which would release four neutrons, which would cause four more nuclei to explode and thereby release eight more neutrons in the manner of a regular chain reaction. With this knowledge and a plentiful supply of uranium, provided the reaction could be controlled, the harnessing of atomic energy appeared to be a relatively simple matter.

Difficulties begin. Soon, however, it was discovered that only one particular isotope of uranium, U^{235}, is actually fissionable. It was also found that in natural uranium this isotope is quite scarce, only a single one out of every 140 atoms being U^{235}. Most of the other atoms in a uranium sample were found to be uranium 238 atoms, which are not fissionable. Moreover, in the presence of U^{238}, the U^{235} chain reaction would not continue when started; instead, it died out. The cause of this seemed to be that when a U^{235} atom exploded, the neutrons emitted seldom penetrated a U^{235} atom; they were absorbed or captured by the more numerous U^{238} nuclei. Neutrons, particularly before they lost their high speed, seemed to be easy prey for U^{238} atoms.

Thus, it became clear that if a chain reaction were to be produced, U^{235} would have to be separated from the other uranium isotopes. Separation of isotopes, except hydrogen isotopes, had never before been attempted on a large scale. This alone was a tremendous project. Nevertheless, commercial plants were set up which separated U^{235} in quantities. One method used was described in principle on page 172. As a project, make a report to the class about other methods. See a modern encyclopedia or consult a more advanced physics book.

Plutonium enters the picture. Although the presence of U^{238} seemed to be a barrier

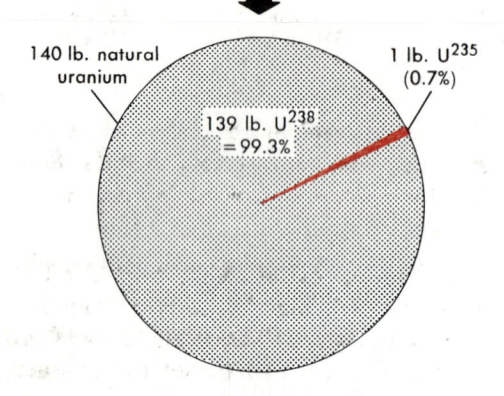

Fig. 1. Natural uranium is not fissionable because only 1 out of every 140 is U^{235}. The other atoms, U^{238}, capture neutrons, thereby stopping a chain reaction.

to harnessing the atom, in some ways it turned out to be a blessing in disguise. An atom of U^{238}, upon the absorption of a neutron, becomes another isotope of uranium, U^{239}.

$$_0n^1 + {}_{92}U^{238} \rightarrow {}_{92}U^{239}$$

Neutron + Uranium isotope 238 → Uranium isotope 239

Uranium 239 is a very unstable atom. Upon the emission of a beta particle (electron) from its nucleus, uranium 239 forms a new element, *neptunium*, $_{93}Np^{239}$, as follows:

$$_{92}U^{239} \rightarrow \text{electron} + {}_{93}Np^{239}$$

Neptunium likewise is very unstable. It breaks down immediately by the emission of another beta particle (electron) to form another new element *plutonium,* Pu. The change is as follows:

$$_{93}Np^{239} \rightarrow \text{electron} + {}_{94}Pu^{239}$$

Neptunium → electron + plutonium

Like uranium 235, plutonium is fairly stable, but when it is bombarded with neutrons, it explodes, sending out neutrons capable of sustaining a chain reaction. Here was a new clue to harnessing atomic energy and making a bomb. In many ways it appeared simpler to manufacture plutonium from uranium 238 than to separate uranium 235 from the other uranium isotopes. Both methods of making the bomb were used, in spite of the fact that the amount of scarce equipment, manpower, and other needs had to be doubled. It was a matter of playing safe. If one method failed, there was always a second one to fall back on. In a perilous situation, is such strategy wise?

The atomic bomb. Now let us assume that we have a piece of fissionable uranium 235, or fissionable plutonium. At all times there are a few stray neutrons about; in fact, it is estimated that about 1000 per second pass through one's body. Consequently, some will be going into the fissionable material and some will hit nuclei and produce isolated single explosions. When this happens, several more neutrons will be produced. But in case the piece of fissionable material is small, most of the neutrons will escape from the fissionable material before hitting a nucleus. And if enough escape, the chain reaction will die out.

If, however, we put another piece of fissionable material alongside the first, then neutrons from one piece will hit those of the other piece. As more fissionable material is added, the total amount finally becomes just enough for the neutrons to sustain reaction. This amount is called

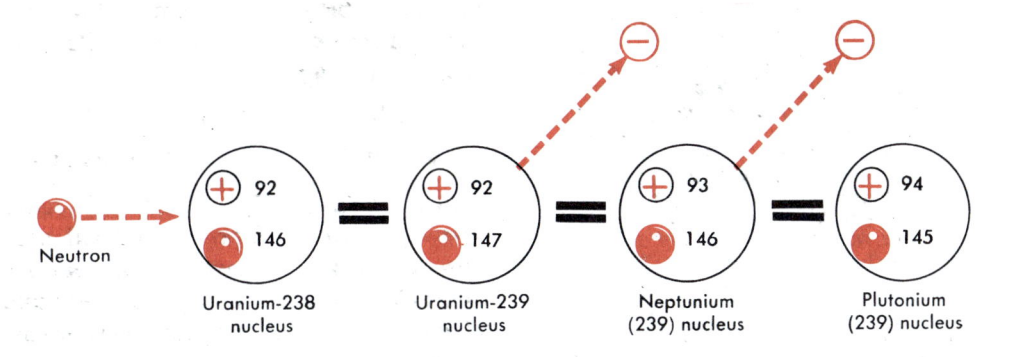

Fig. 2. Nonfissionable U^{238} captures a neutron to form radioactive U^{239} which emits a beta particle to form radioactive neptunium. Neptunium emits a beta particle, forming fissionable plutonium. Like U^{235}, plutonium can capture a slow-moving neutron.

the *critical mass*. In uranium 235, Heisenberg, the German physicist, calculated the critical mass to be about twenty pounds, or about the size of a baseball. If more than the critical mass of material is brought together, the reaction accelerates rapidly, and, as a result, a terrific explosion occurs. The actual critical mass is one of the secrets of the atomic bomb.

So, with plenty of either U^{235} or plutonium on hand, the problem of causing an atomic explosion is to take two pieces of these fissionable materials, each of which is slightly smaller than the critical mass, and bring them together very suddenly. One way of doing this is to shoot them together with highly compressed air. Of course the actual design, safety devices, and the fusing of the bomb are kept secret for the sake of national security. But it should be clear that once pure uranium 235 or plutonium is obtained, the rest of the problem is relatively simple.

Uranium-graphite pile and the production of plutonium. You might suspect that we produced plutonium by separating uranium 238 from the other uranium isotopes and then bombarding it with neutrons in an atom-smashing machine. Instead, a more ingenious device was used. The U^{235} and the U^{238} were left together, and neutrons from the U^{235} were used to bombard the U^{238}. When the plutonium was formed,

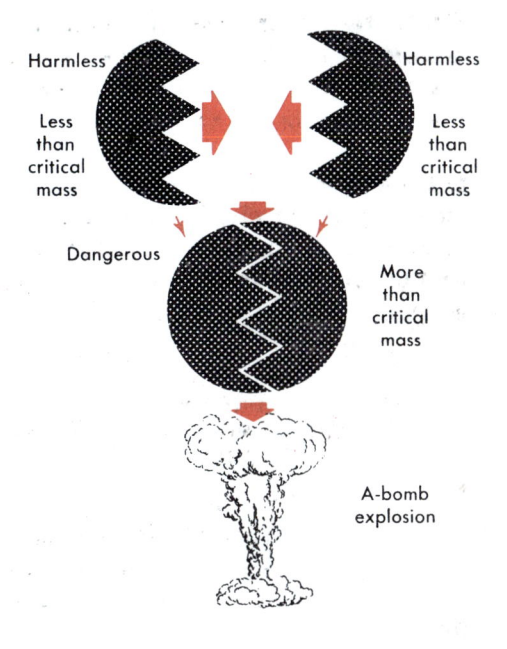

Fig. 3. When two masses of fissionable material each slightly less than the critical mass are suddenly brought together, an atomic explosion occurs.

NUCLEAR PHYSICS (ATOMIC ENERGY)

as explained above, it was separated chemically from the pile.

The problem in using this method was to keep the U^{235} chain reaction going. For, as you may recall, U^{238} readily captures the neutrons from U^{235} so that normally the chain reaction stops quickly. It was found, however, that if the neutrons emitted by U^{235} could be slowed down, then the U^{238} atoms had little tendency to capture them, whereas the U^{235} atoms readily captured them. See Fig. 4.

Carbon (graphite), heavy water, and several other substances can be used to slow down the neutrons. For example, if blocks of graphite are put into the natural uranium, neutrons from U^{235}, in passing through the carbon block, are slowed down enough so that they produce fission in U^{235} on the other side of the block. By increasing or decreasing the amount of carbon in the pile, the U^{235} reaction can be sustained and controlled.

As shown in Fig. 5, a somewhat similar arrangement, known as a *uranium-graphite pile,* was set up first at the University of Chicago in 1942. In operation, the chain reaction in natural uranium diluted with graphite (carbon) produces plutonium, which is removed from the pile. Besides producing plutonium, the pile liberates a tremendous amount of heat, powerful gamma rays, protons, neutrons, and alpha and beta particles.

Uranium-graphite pile as a source of power. Because an enormous amount of heat is produced by a uranium pile, it is obvious that it would make a good source of power which could be substituted for coal, gas, and oil.

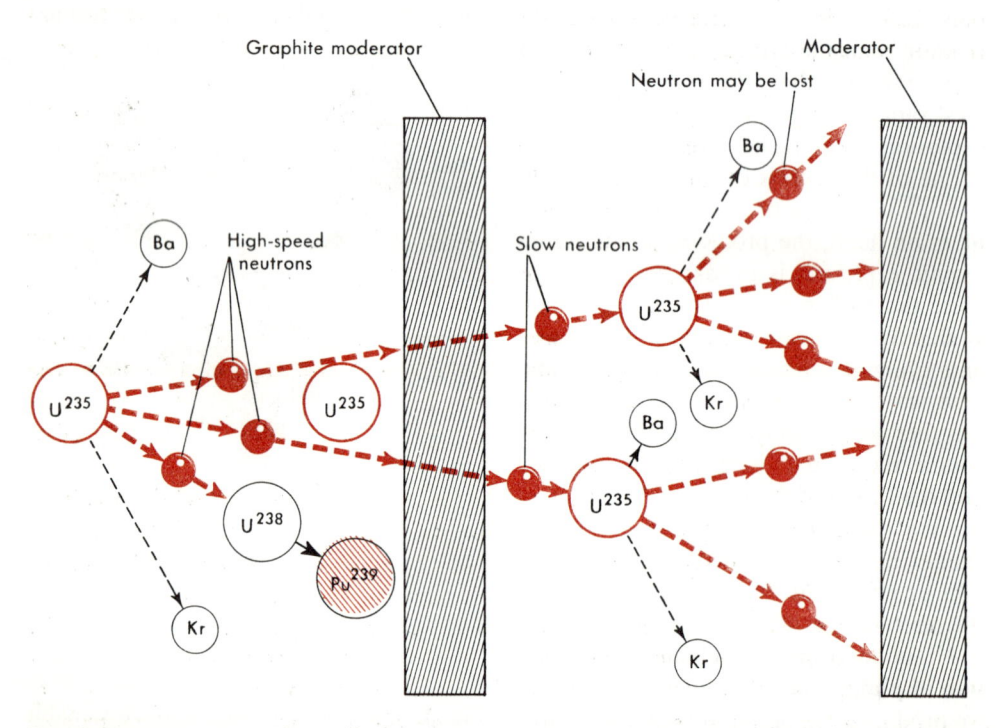

Fig. 4. In natural uranium ore, a chain reaction can be kept going provided that the high-speed neutrons released by exploding atoms of U^{235} are slowed down enough by the moderator so that a sufficient number can be captured by other U^{235} atoms.

Courtesy Argonne National Laboratory

Fig. 5. (a) The first nuclear reactor in which the first self-sustaining chain reaction was achieved on December 2, 1942. The reactor consisted of uranium and uranium oxide lumps placed in a cubic lattice imbedded in graphite.

Courtesy North American Aviation

Fig. 5. (b) Nuclear physicists measure the background radiation level around a water-boiler type of atomic reactor. The concrete blocks used to shield the reactor have been removed to reveal the tanklike housing for the graphite reflector and core.

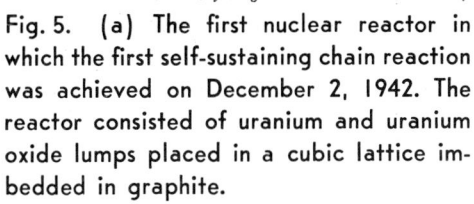

The advantage of atomic power is that it creates no smoke and leaves little or no ash to dispose of. As a result, the black pall of smoke which hangs over our coal-powered cities could be eliminated. Then, too, because of the enormous amount of heat produced by a pile, heat could be sold as a utility in cities, as water and electricity are now sold. This would do away with the necessity for coal furnaces and coal bins, and with all the dirt and grief that accompany this type of heating. Also, no state or nation that lacks coal and oil would need to go power-hungry. The graphite-uranium pile would take care of this.

The disadvantages of an atomic power plant are that it is expensive and very bulky. A pile, like a bomb, must reach the critical size before it will go. The bulkiness is caused by the fact that about five feet of concrete are necessary to prevent the deadly neutrons and other particles and rays from escaping. Because of this needed protection, atomic power for automobiles and similar forms of transportation is most unlikely. Atomic power for ocean-going vessels, however, is already a reality, and giant aircraft, as well as high-speed rockets capable of reaching the moon, are conceded to be possible. The long distances that nuclear-driven vessels can travel without refueling give them many advantages over vessels powered by other types of fuel.

Isotopes—a by-product of the uranium-graphite pile. We have already learned that isotopes are a group of atoms of the same element, all of which have the same number of planetary electrons, the same atomic number, and the same chemical properties, but differ in atomic weight due to having different numbers of neutrons in their nuclei. All told, the chemical elements known have several hundred isotopes.

Many of these isotopes exist in nature;

others can be produced by the bombardment of atoms in an atom-smashing machine. See page 622 for an example of such a reaction. This method is very expensive. However, after a uranium-graphite pile is set up, we can produce isotopes very inexpensively in almost undreamed-of quantities by placing the atoms to be bombarded in the pile. The isotopes of the lighter elements in general are quite unstable and are radioactive. It is because of this latter characteristic that they find many of their uses in medicine, agriculture, and industry.

Uses of isotopes in medicine. It has long been known that certain elements have a strong affinity for certain animal tissues, glands, and organs. For example, iron has a strong affinity for the blood; calcium and phosphorus, for the teeth and bones; and iodine, for the thyroid gland. A number of elements are contained in the tissues and other animal parts and are carried by the

Fig. 6. The Geiger counter is aimed at the "X" on the patient's throat to measure the amount of radioactive iodine that remains in the patient's thyroid gland. Radioactive iodine is absorbed by properly stimulated thyroid cancer tissue and retards or destroys the surrounding cancer growth.

Courtesy Brookhaven National Laboratory

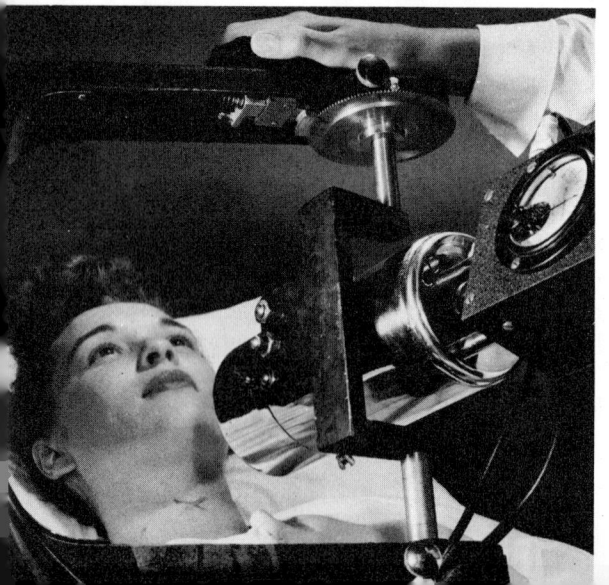

blood to these parts. Since the isotopes used are radioactive, they can be traced with a Geiger counter and are sometimes called *tagged atoms*.

As an example of the use of isotopes in medicine, radioactive phosphorus is used in the study of the flow of blood, some blood diseases, and the use of fat and protein in the body. Sodium in ordinary table salt is used in the study of blood clots; radioactive gold, in the study of leukemia (cancer of the blood); and iodine, in the study of the thyroid gland, which is the seat of a disease known as goiter. Radioactive carbon is used in the study of cancer. Already many astonishing results have been uncovered and more startling findings are made every day.

The use of tagged atoms in agriculture. Plants, like animals, are composed of certain elements which are carried by the circulatory system of the plants somewhat as in animals. Radioactive fertilizers placed in solution at the roots of a plant are found within a few minutes in the leaves, as shown by a Geiger counter or a charged sensitive electroscope. As a result, the part that certain fertilizers play in the growth of plants and whether they are of any value in the growth of certain plants can be determined. Already discoveries have been made which will save millions of dollars' worth of fertilizer every year.

The use of tagged atoms in industry. It is in industry that tagged atoms are being used particularly as tracers. We can mention only a few uses. When radioactive iodine or calcium is dropped into an oil well, it can be followed above ground as it seeps through oil-bearing layers of rock and sand. In this way it aids in locating underground sources of oil.

Another important use is the control of the thickness of films of different kinds. A piece of radioactive carbon 14 is placed

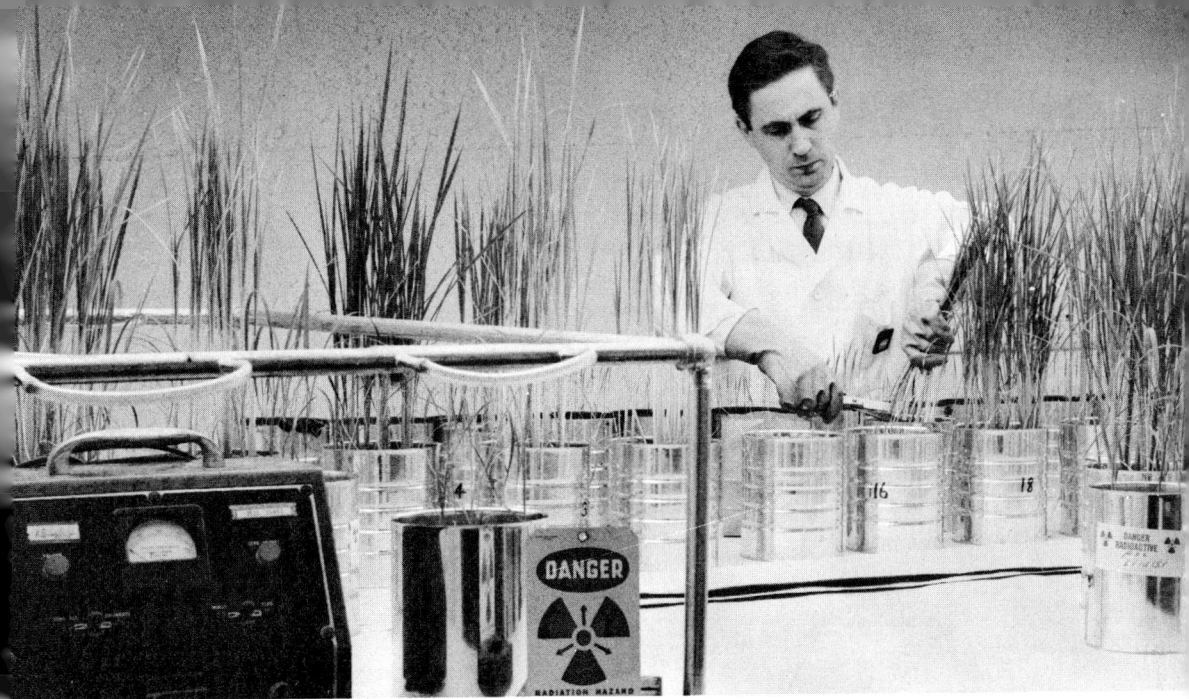

Fig. 7. Radioactive tracer techniques are employed in agriculture to determine how and where plants use various nutrients. After a period of growth under controlled conditions, a soil scientist cuts off the tops of the plants and measures the amount of radioactive nutrient absorbed with an ionization chamber.

under the film, and above the film is placed a Geiger counter. The carbon emits a steady stream of electrons. The thicker the film, the fewer electrons pass through it to the Geiger counter. When properly calibrated, the Geiger counter indicates the thickness of the film. Accuracies as close as one hundred-thousandth of an inch have been obtained by such methods, and it is probable that accuracies as close as a millionth of an inch will eventually be obtained.

Another use of radioactive isotopes is in the study of lubricants. When two substances are rubbed together, some of the one substance rubs off onto the other. By means of radioactivated metals, the rub-off can be ascertained to a very, very small amount. As a result, metals which wear the best when rubbed together, and lubricating oils that prevent wear, can be discovered.

Half lives of radioactive isotopes. The reason that most radioactive isotopes are not found in nature is that their half lives are relatively short. Radioactive gold has a half life of 2.7 days; potassium has a half life of 12.4 hours. One carbon isotope, on the other hand, has a half life of 5000 years.

Handling isotopes. Since these isotopes are radioactive, they must be handled with extreme care if any quantity is being used. In most of the experiments described, the quantities that are used are very small and are usually worked with for only a short time. In this way, danger to the patient and the experimenter can be avoided. The strides that have been made in protecting workers from the radioactive materials which they use are almost as sensational as the harnessing of the atom.

The hydrogen bomb. We learned on page 613 that the vast quantity of heat and light radiated by the sun is due to the union of hydrogen nuclei to form helium

Courtesy Argonne National Laboratory

Fig. 8. Radioisotopes must be handled by remote control to protect the technicians from dangerous radiations.

nuclei. In the process a certain amount of matter is converted to energy in accordance with the equation, $E = mc^2$.

Early atomic workers were unable to duplicate the sun's high temperatures needed to bring about the reaction, so they turned their attention to other possible solutions. Not until July 16, 1945, when the first A-bomb was exploded at Alamogordo, New Mexico, was the needed high temperature attained. At the heart of the bomb, the temperature was estimated to be about 70 million degrees centigrade, compared with the estimated 20 million degrees at the interior of the sun. It was at that time that it became possible to build a hydrogen bomb.

Designing a hydrogen bomb is not easy. Whereas the high temperature in the sun is maintained continually, the high temperature in the bomb lasts but a very small fraction of a second, during which all the ingredients must react. This means that they must all react simultaneously. If they do not do this, the explosion will not take place or will do so only partially.

The ingredients and the proportions in which they are used are a military secret. An H-bomb might be created in several different ways, all of which are known to trained physicists everywhere. Theoretically, if an A-bomb were surrounded by hydrogen and then exploded, helium would be produced from the fusion of hydrogen atoms, with the release of about eight times as much energy as an equal weight of uranium. But unlike the ingredients of the A-bomb, which explode spontaneously when more than the critical mass is assembled, hydrogen can be assembled in any quantity. Several H-bombs, many times more powerful than any A-bomb that can be made, have already been detonated.

Although hydrogen may be the ideal

ingredient, the reaction is most difficult to keep going to completion. Most likely the key ingredient is tritium, a radioactive isotope of hydrogen, (H^3), whose nucleus consists of one proton and two neutrons, as shown in Fig. 3 of Chapter 31. When the tritium nucleus is struck by a proton, a hydrogen nucleus, the two combine into helium and in the process yield energy. Tritium can be made rather cheaply by the bombardment of lithium 6, an isotope of lithium, with neutrons in a uranium pile. The reaction yields tritium and helium. The tritium is then separated chemically from the helium.

Deuterium, whose nucleus contains one proton and one neutron, might be used as a source of the protons needed to react with the tritium. See Fig. 9a. Lithium, whose nucleus contains three protons and four neutrons, might be another ingredient used. When its nucleus is joined with a proton, two helium nuclei are produced and energy is released.

Since the hydrogen isotopes, deuterium and tritium, are gases, it is difficult to "package" them. It is therefore probable that they are used in combination with another element in solid form. Lithium hydride is such a compound; either deuterium or tritium will unite with lithium to form this solid.

All these ingredients, perhaps along with others, are probably arranged around the uranium bomb. When the uranium is set off, its temperature rises to several million degrees, and the whole mass of ingredients turns into a turmoil of high-speed, zigzagging particles. The end result is a terrific and destructive explosion at temperatures surpassing that of the interior of the sun. Deadly neutrons, protons, electrons, and helium nuclei are spread for miles in every direction. These cause the air and other materials in the area, particularly the heavy metals such as gold, silver, mercury, and any compounds of them, to become highly radioactive. And such regions may become uninhabitable for months.

Estimates are that an H-bomb is quite capable of wiping out a large share of the inhabitants and buildings of any large city in the world. Thus, the explosion of a few bombs in the strategic cities of any modern nation could completely paralyze

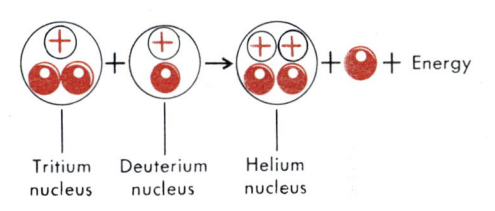

Tritium nucleus   Deuterium nucleus   Helium nucleus

Fig. 9. (a) A fusion reaction in which a helium nucleus and a neutron are formed.

Fig. 9. (b) A thermonuclear reaction or a hydrogen bomb detonation can only take place in the high temperatures produced by a fission bomb explosion. This photograph was taken at a height of approximately 12,000 feet at a distance of 50 miles from the detonation site.

Courtesy U.S. Air Force

Courtesy Westinghouse Electric Corp.

Fig. 10. An artist's sketch of the nation's first central station atomic power plant at Shippingport, Pennsylvania. The atomic reactor which provides the heat and the heat exchangers to generate the steam will be located underground in concrete and steel structures. In the central underground structure, water under pressure is pumped through the pressure vessel which surrounds the reactor itself. Then the water is heated as a result of controlled nuclear chain reactions and pumped to the four heat exchangers where steam is produced to power the turbo-generator. This pioneer nuclear power plant will produce a minimum of 60,000 kilowatts of electricity.

most of its production of manufactured goods and much of its transportation system, along with its power production. Because a vast number of people in modern nations are completely dependent upon these facilities for their day-to-day living, starvation, disease, and general chaos would soon follow.

Is it necessary that modern civilization perish? It is shocking to think that atomic energy, which scientists worked so long and patiently to produce for peacetime purposes, may be used to wipe out the civilization which produced it.

It tends to show that something is wrong with the methods used in solving problems in fields outside of science. At this point, we would like to have you reread Chapter 2, especially the latter part. Then we would like to have you recall the general method which has been used to solve problems, time and time again, in this course.

You should recall that we always began with a problem; that, in general, tentative solutions (hypotheses) were then set up; that the reasoned consequences of these hypotheses were then considered; that these reasoned consequences were then tested by experiment or observation, or by checks against our past experience; and that the hypothesis whose reasoned consequences met the experimental tests was the one chosen as the conclusion. But this conclusion was held to be true only as long as no evidence was found which disagreed with it. That is, all truth was considered to be tentative and subject to change as new discoveries were made which disagreed with it.

Unfortunately, the scientific method is rarely used in other fields. Radio commentators, newspaper editors, columnists, and advertisers seldom present all sides of a given question. Only data favoring their pet theories and prejudices are presented, with the result that the public is often misled on important issues of the day.

Most of the problems confronting the people of the world would be simple to solve, compared to the problems scientists have already solved, provided men of good will and honest minds would approach them in a scientific manner. We are not too stupid to solve the problems which face us; we are just not intellectually honest enough.

The challenge to students today is to bring harmony into a chaotic world. Since the method of science has worked such wonders in doing this whenever it has actually been tried, we believe it should be tried elsewhere. Science points the way, and furnishes the method and tools by which modern civilization can possibly save itself. Whether modern civilization is destined to reach dazzling heights, as science did during the first half of the twentieth century, or whether it is to sink back into the state of ignorance and superstition from which it has been trying for centuries to extricate itself, will depend much upon whether or not the students of today honestly and scientifically face the social and economic problems of tomorrow.

SUMMARY AND CONCLUSIONS

1. Only about 1 per cent of natural uranium is U^{235}, which is fissionable. The other 99 per cent is chiefly U^{238}, which is not fissionable. When the two are together, chain reaction dies out.
2. U^{238}, when bombarded with neutrons, forms U^{239}, which is unstable. Upon the emission of an electron (beta particle) from its nucleus a new element, neptunium, $_{93}Np^{239}$, is formed. Neptunium is likewise unstable. Upon the emission of an electron, plutonium, $_{94}Pu^{239}$, is formed. This is a fairly stable element and is fissionable.
3. The uranium or A-bomb can be built of either plutonium or uranium 235. It is detonated by the bringing together of more than the critical mass of either of these elements. The critical mass is the amount in which fission is barely maintained.
4. The uranium pile is built of the natural uranium. A chain reaction is kept going among the U^{235} atoms by dilution of the uranium ore with carbon or heavy water. This slows down the neutrons, which cause the chain reaction, so that they are not captured by the U^{238} atoms. As a result, the U^{235} atoms are able to capture enough neutrons to keep the reaction going.
5. A uranium pile can be used to produce heat that can be used for large-scale power production. It can also be used to form isotopes of practically all the different elements. Many of these isotopes are radioactive. They find hundreds of uses in medicine, industry, and agriculture.

QUESTIONS FOR REVIEW

1. What is a chain reaction?
2. About what percentage of ordinary uranium is U^{235}? U^{238}?
3. Explain why ordinary uranium is not fissionable.
4. Explain how U^{238} can be made into a product which is fissionable. Write the reactions.
5. Explain a uranium pile and how the chain reaction is maintained and controlled.
6. What are the chief uses of the uranium pile?
7. Why is it not probable that atomic energy will be used to power automobiles, small airplanes, and similar vehicles?

PROJECTS

1. If you can obtain a Geiger counter and some radioactive fertilizer, put some of the fertilizer in water and then put the stem of a cutting from some plant, such as a geranium, in the water. Test a leaf of the geranium with the Geiger counter before the plant is put in the solution. Then test another leaf every ten minutes after the plant is put in the solution. Also, investigate how radio-

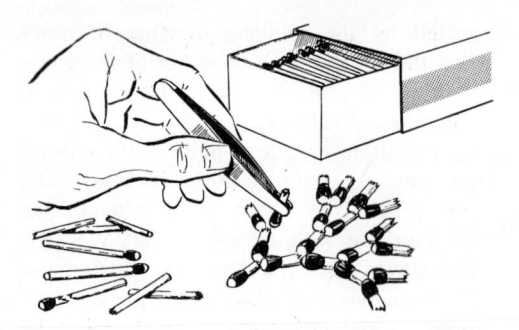

Fig. 11. Demonstrating a chain reaction.

active fertilizers are being used in the study of plant growth. Note: both Geiger counters and Wilson cloud chambers are now being manufactured as toys and can be bought rather cheaply.

2. Test stones, sands, and ores found in your community for radioactivity and report your findings to the class.

3. Make a study of the use of radioisotopes in industry and report to your class. Write to the Atomic Energy Commission in Washington, D. C., for information.

4. Make a study of the use of radioisotopes in medicine.

5. Make a study of the effect of radioactivity on the genes of plants and animals and report to your class.

6. Using paper matches with stems cut to about half the ordinary length, make a chain reaction. Pile the matches so that, when one match is ignited, it sets off two more matches, and so on. See Fig. 11.

7. Plan and invite the public to an Atomic Energy Night. The following activities are suggested:

(a) Display in the halls leading to your auditorium the Life Magazine Charts on Atomic Energy, along with other charts that you may make or obtain.

(b) Display, and demonstrate the use of, an electroscope, Geiger counter, and Wilson cloud chamber as each is used in the study of radioactivity.

(c) Give ten-minute talks or show motion pictures on each of the following subjects:

(1.) Production of atomic energy.
(2.) Use of atomic energy as a source of heat and power.
(3.) Radioisotopes in medicine.
(4.) Radioisotopes in agriculture.
(5.) Radioisotopes in industry.
(6.) The consequences of atomic energy in peace and war. Preferably, students should organize the program, make the demonstrations, and give most of the talks.

READING YOU WILL ENJOY

1. Baxter, J. P., *Scientists Against Time*. Little, Brown and Company, Boston, 1946. Story of the development of the atomic bomb by the U.S. Office of Scientific Research and Development.

2. Glasstone, Samuel, *Sourcebook on Atomic Energy*. New York, D. Van Nostrand Co., Inc., 1950.

3. Korff, Serge A., *Electron and Nuclear Counters*. D. Van Nostrand Co., Inc., New York, 1946. Explains devices and methods of detecting and counting nuclear radiations.

4. United States Atomic Energy Commission, *Laboratory Experiments with Radioisotopes for High School Demonstrations*. U.S. Government Printing Office, Washington, D.C., 1953. These experiments can be performed by high school students.

Appendix

Unit Analysis. When we measure any quantity, it is not sufficient merely to record the numerical size (absolute value) of the quantity. We must use the number in connection with a unit, such as pounds, yards, watts, or gallons. The unit of a quantity tells us the standard measurement to which the quantity is being compared. Thus, all measurements, to be precise and complete, must include:

(a) a number that tells us "how many" and
(b) a unit that tells us which standard measurement is being used.

In working with units in problems, it is important to recognize that answers must be expressed in consistent units. For example, the equation for computing the distance, D, covered in time, t, at a velocity, V, is expressed as follows:

$$D = Vt$$

If D is to be expressed in miles and V is given in miles per hour, t will have to be expressed in hours. If t is expressed in any other unit of time, the unit of the answer will be inconsistent. Similarly, if the distance in feet is to be found, the velocity, which is equal to $D \div t$, must be expressed in feet per min.

Undoubtedly, these conversions could be accomplished by long arithmetic multiplications and divisions, but the method of unit analysis makes it much easier to attain a properly expressed answer.

Problem 1: How many *feet* can an automobile travel in 2 *minutes* at an average speed of 30 *miles per hour*?

$$D = Vt$$
$$D = \frac{30 \text{ mi.}}{\text{hr.}} \times 2 \text{ min.}$$

To change the miles to feet, we must multiply 30 miles per hour by a conversion factor which has *miles* in the denominator and *feet* in the numerator. The conversion factor is the number of feet per mile, or $\frac{5280 \text{ ft.}}{\text{mi.}}$.

$$D = \frac{30 \text{ mi.}}{\text{hr.}} \times \left[\frac{5280 \text{ ft.}}{\text{mi.}}\right] \times 2 \text{ min.}$$

Our solution is not satisfied, because *minutes* cannot cancel *hour*. We need a conversion factor that will cancel minutes from the numerator and hour from the denominator. Such a conversion factor must, therefore, have *hour* in the numerator and *minutes* in the denominator. This is 1 hour per 60 minutes, or $\frac{1 \text{ hr.}}{60 \text{ min.}}$.

$$D = \frac{30}{\text{hr.}} \times \left[5280 \text{ ft.}\right] \times 2 \text{ min.} \times \frac{1 \text{ hr.}}{60 \text{ min.}}$$

$$D = 30 \times 5280 \text{ ft.} \times \frac{2}{60} = 5280 \text{ ft.}$$

Problem 2: If water weighs 62.4 lb. per cubic foot, how many pounds does each cubic inch weigh?

$$62.4 \frac{\text{lb.}}{\text{ft.}^3} \times \frac{1 \text{ ft.}}{12 \text{ in.}} \times \frac{1 \text{ ft.}}{12 \text{ in.}} \times \frac{1 \text{ ft.}}{12 \text{ in.}}$$

$$62.4 \frac{\text{lb.}}{\text{ft.}^3} \times \frac{1 \text{ ft.}^3}{1728 \text{ in.}^3} = \frac{62.4 \text{ lb.}}{1728 \text{ in.}^3}$$

Dividing, we get $.036 \frac{\text{lb.}}{\text{in.}^3}$ (See page 46.)

Now, let us consider some of the sample problems in the text to determine how the unit portion of the answer was obtained.

Total Force
(Page 44)

$$F = Ahd$$

$$F = \text{cm.}^2 \times \text{cm.} \times \frac{\text{g.}}{\text{cm.}^3} = \text{g.}$$

Pressure
(Page 45)
$$P = hd$$
$$P = \text{cm.} \times \frac{\text{g.}}{\text{cm.}^2} = \frac{\text{g.}}{\text{cm.}^2}$$
$$P = \text{ft.} \times \frac{\text{lb.}}{\text{ft.}^2} = \frac{\text{lb.}}{\text{ft.}^2}$$
$$\frac{\text{lb.}}{\text{ft.}^2} \div \frac{\text{in.}^2}{\text{ft.}^2} = \frac{\text{lb.}}{\text{ft.}^2} \times \frac{\text{ft.}^2}{\text{in.}^2} = \frac{\text{lb.}}{\text{in.}^2}$$

(Page 46)
$$P = \text{in.} \times \frac{\text{lb.}}{\text{in.}^2} = \frac{\text{lb.}}{\text{in.}^2}$$

Sidewise Force
(Page 51)
$$F = \frac{hd}{2} \times A$$
$$\frac{F = \text{ft.} \times \frac{\text{lb.}}{\text{ft.}^3} \times \text{ft.}^2}{2} = \text{lb.}$$

Specific Gravity of Solids
$$\text{Sp. gr.} = \frac{\text{Weight in air}}{\text{Weight of water displaced}}$$
(Page 57)
$$\text{Sp. gr.} = \frac{\text{g.}}{\text{g.}} = \begin{array}{c}\text{pure number}\\\text{(no units used)}\end{array}$$

Specific Gravity of Liquids
$$\text{Sp. gr.} = \frac{\text{Loss of weight in brine}}{\text{Loss of weight in water}}$$
(Page 58)
$$\text{Sp. gr.} = \frac{\text{g.}}{\text{g.}} = \begin{array}{c}\text{pure number}\\\text{(no units used)}\end{array}$$

Boyle's Law
$$P_1 V_1 = P_2 V_2$$
(Page 92)
$$\frac{\text{lb.}}{\text{in.}^2} \times \text{ft.}^3 = \frac{\text{lb.}}{\text{in.}^2} \times V_2$$
$$V_2 = \frac{\text{lb.}}{\text{in.}^2} \times \text{ft.}^3 \times \frac{\text{in.}^2}{\text{lb.}}$$
$$V_2 = \text{ft.}^3$$

Average Velocity
$$S = \overline{V} t$$
(Page 134)
$$S = \frac{\text{ft.}}{\text{sec.}} \times \text{sec.} = \text{ft.}$$

Acceleration
$$V = at \quad (V = gt)$$
$$a = \frac{V}{t}$$
(Page 135)
$$a = \frac{\text{ft.}}{\text{sec.}} \div \frac{\text{sec.}}{1} = \frac{\text{ft.}}{\text{sec.}} \times \frac{1}{\text{sec.}} = \frac{\text{ft.}}{\text{sec.}^2}$$

Solving for t,
$$t = \frac{V}{g}$$
$$t = \frac{\text{ft.}}{\text{sec.}} \div \frac{\text{ft.}}{\text{sec.}^2}$$
$$t = \frac{\text{ft.}}{\text{sec.}} \times \frac{\text{sec.}^2}{\text{ft.}} = \text{sec.}$$

Average Velocity for Accelerated Motion
$$\overline{V} = \frac{V}{2}$$
(Page 136) $\quad \overline{V} = \dfrac{\text{ft.}}{\text{sec.}}$

Distance, Acceleration, and Time
$$S = \frac{1}{2} at^2 \quad (S = \frac{1}{2} gt^2)$$
$$S = \frac{1}{2} \times \frac{\text{ft.}}{\text{sec.}^2} \times \frac{\text{sec.}^2}{1} = \text{ft.}$$
(Page 137)

Solving for t
$$t^2 = \frac{2S}{a}$$
$$t^2 = \text{ft.} \div \frac{\text{ft.}}{\text{sec.}^2} = \text{ft.} \times \frac{\text{sec.}^2}{\text{ft.}}$$
$$t^2 = \text{sec.}^2$$
$$t = \sqrt{\text{sec.}^2} = \text{sec.}$$

Velocity, Acceleration, and Distance
$$V^2 = 2aS$$
Solving for S,
$$S = \frac{V^2}{2a}$$
$$S = \left(\frac{\text{ft.}}{\text{sec.}}\right)^2 \div \frac{\text{ft.}}{\text{sec.}^2}$$
$$S = \frac{\text{ft.}^2}{\text{sec.}^2} \times \frac{\text{sec.}^2}{\text{ft.}} = \text{ft.}$$

APPENDIX

Motion of a Freely Falling Body

$$V^2 = 2aH$$

Solving for a,

$$a = \frac{V^2}{2H}$$

$$a = \left(\frac{ft.}{sec.}\right)^2 \div ft. = \frac{ft.^2}{sec.^2} \times \frac{1}{ft.}$$

$$a = \frac{ft.}{sec.^2}$$

(Page 145)

Period of a Pendulum

$$t = 2\pi\sqrt{\frac{l}{g}}$$

Solving for l,

$$l = \frac{t^2 g}{4\pi^2}$$

(Page 150)

$$l = \frac{sec.^2 \times \dfrac{cm.}{sec.^2}}{constants} = cm.$$

Newton's Second Law of Motion

$$f = kma$$

Solving for k,

$$k = \frac{f}{ma}$$

$$k = \frac{lb.}{lb. \times \dfrac{ft.}{sec.^2}} = \frac{1}{\dfrac{ft.}{sec.^2}}$$

(Page 159)

Solving for a,

$$a = \frac{f}{km}$$

$$a = lb. \div \frac{1}{\dfrac{ft.}{sec.^2}} \times \frac{lb.}{1}$$

$$a = lb. \times \frac{ft.}{sec.^2} \times \frac{1}{lb.} = \frac{ft.}{sec.^2}$$

(Page 160)

$$f = \frac{1}{\dfrac{ft.}{sec.^2}} \times lb. \times \frac{ft.}{sec.^2} = lb.$$

(Page 161)

$$f = \frac{1}{\dfrac{cm.}{sec.^2}} \times \frac{g.}{1} \times \frac{\dfrac{cm.}{sec.^2}}{1}$$

$$f = g.$$

Momentum

$$Mv = mV$$

Solving for v,

$$v = \frac{mV}{M}$$

(Page 166)

$$v = \frac{lb. \times \dfrac{ft.}{sec.}}{lb.} = \frac{ft.}{sec.}$$

Centrifugal Force

$$F = \frac{k m v^2}{r}$$

$$F = \frac{1}{\dfrac{ft.}{sec.^2}} \times lb. \times \frac{ft.^2}{sec.^2} \div \frac{ft.}{1}$$

(Page 173)

$$F = \frac{sec.^2}{ft.} \times lb. \times \frac{ft.^2}{sec.^2} \times \frac{1}{ft.}$$

$$F = lb.$$

Projectile Motion

$$H = \frac{1}{2} gt^2$$

Solving for t,

$$t^2 = \frac{2H}{g}$$

$$t^2 = ft. \div \frac{ft.}{sec.^2} = ft. \times \frac{sec.^2}{ft.}$$

$$t^2 = sec.^2$$

$$t = \sqrt{sec.^2} = sec.$$

(Page 181)

Range of a Horizontal Projectile

$$R = Vt$$

(Page 182)

$$R = \frac{ft.}{sec.} \times sec. = ft.$$

APPENDIX

$$R = \frac{V^2}{g}$$

$$R = \left(\frac{\text{ft.}}{\text{sec.}}\right)^2 \div \frac{\text{ft.}}{\text{sec.}^2}$$

$$R = \frac{\text{ft.}^2}{\text{sec.}^2} \times \frac{\text{sec.}^2}{\text{ft.}} = \text{ft.}$$

(Page 185)

Horsepower

$$\text{H.P.} = \frac{F \times S}{33{,}000 \times t}$$

(Page 197)

$$\text{H.P.} = \frac{\text{lb.} \times \text{ft.}}{\frac{\text{ft.-lb.}}{\text{min.}} \times \text{min.}} = \frac{\text{ft.-lb.}}{\text{ft.-lb.}}$$

$$\text{H.P.} = \begin{array}{c}\text{a pure number}\\ \text{(no units used)}\end{array}$$

Kinetic Energy

$$\text{K.E.} = \frac{k\,m\,V^2}{2}$$

$$\text{K.E.} = \frac{\text{lb.} \times \frac{\text{ft.}^2}{\text{sec.}^2}}{\frac{\text{ft.}}{\text{sec.}^2} \times 2} = \text{ft.-lb.}$$

(Page 200)

$$\text{K.E.} = \frac{g \times \frac{\text{cm.}^2}{\text{sec.}^2}}{\frac{\text{cm.}}{\text{sec.}^2} \times 2} = \text{g.-cm.}$$

(Page 200)

Ideal Mechanical Advantage

$$\text{I.M.A.} = \frac{D_E}{D_R}$$

$$\frac{D_E}{D_R} = \frac{\text{ft.}}{\text{ft.}} = \text{a ratio (no units)}$$

(Page 206)

Actual Mechanical Advantage

$$\text{A.M.A.} = \frac{R}{E} = \frac{\text{lb.}}{\text{lb.}} = \text{a ratio (no units)}$$

(Page 206)

Efficiency

$$\text{Efficiency} = \frac{\text{work output}}{\text{work input}}$$

$$\text{Efficiency} = \frac{\text{ft.-lb.}}{\text{ft.-lb.}} = \begin{array}{l}\text{a ratio expressed}\\ \text{as a per cent}\\ \text{(no units)}\end{array}$$

(Page 207)

Efficiency of a screw

$$E = \frac{R \times p}{2\pi r}$$

(Page 211)

$$E = \frac{\text{lb.} \times \text{in.}}{\text{in.}} = \text{lb.}$$

$$\text{Efficiency} = \frac{\text{A.M.A.}}{\text{I.M.A.}} = \begin{array}{l}\text{a ratio expressed}\\ \text{as a per cent}\\ \text{(no units)}\end{array}$$

(Page 211)

Coefficient of Linear Expansion

$$e = k\,l\,t$$

$$e = \frac{\text{ft.} \times °}{°} = \text{ft.}$$

$$e = \frac{\text{ft.}}{1} \times \frac{12\text{ in.}}{\text{ft.}} = \text{in.}$$

(Page 240)

Relation between Absolute Temperature and Pressure

$$\frac{P_1}{P_2} = \frac{T_1}{T_2}$$

Solving for P_2,

$$P_2 = P_1 \times \frac{T_2}{T_1}$$

$$P_2 = \frac{\text{lb.}}{\text{in.}^2} \times \frac{°A}{°A} = \frac{\text{lb.}}{\text{in.}^2}$$

(Page 245)

Charles' Law

$$\frac{V_1}{V_2} = \frac{T_1}{T_2}$$

Solving for V_2,

$$V_2 = V_1 \times \frac{T_2}{T_1}$$

$$V_2 = \text{cc.} \times \frac{°A}{°A} = \text{cc.}$$

(Page 246)

Solving for T_2,

$$T_2 = T_1 \times \frac{V_2}{V_1}$$

$$T_2 = °A \times \frac{\text{cc.}}{\text{cc.}} = °A$$

(Page 247)

APPENDIX

General Gas Law

$$\frac{V_1 P_1}{T_1} = \frac{V_2 P_2}{T_2}$$

Solving for V_2,

$$V_2 = V_1 \times \frac{T_2}{T_1} \times \frac{P_1}{P_2}$$

$$V_2 = \frac{cc.}{1} \times \frac{\cancel{°A}}{\cancel{°A}} \times \frac{mm.}{mm.} = cc.$$

(Page 248)

Heat Gained or Lost by a Body

$$H = m(t_1 - t_2)$$

$$H = g - C° = cal.$$ (See definition of calorie, page 251.)

(Page 252)

Horsepower of a Steam Engine

$$H.P. = 2\frac{PLAN}{33,000} =$$

$$\frac{\frac{\cancel{strokes}}{\cancel{rev.}} \times \frac{lb.}{\cancel{in.^2}} \times \frac{ft.}{stroke} \times \frac{\cancel{in.^2}}{} \times \frac{\cancel{rev.}}{min.}}{\frac{ft.\text{-}lb.}{min.}}$$

$$H.P. = \frac{\cancel{ft.\text{-}lb.}}{\cancel{ft.\text{-}lb.}} = \text{a pure number (no units)}$$

(Page 280)

Resonance

$$n = \frac{V}{4(0.4d + l')}$$

$$n = \frac{ft.}{sec.} \div \frac{ft.}{1} = \frac{\cancel{ft.}}{sec.} \times \frac{1}{\cancel{ft.}}$$

$$n = \frac{(vibrations)}{sec.}$$

(Page 331)

Quantity of Electricity

$$Q = It$$

Solving for I,

$$I = \frac{Q}{t}$$

$$I = \frac{coulombs}{sec.} = amperes$$

(Page 360)

Law of Electrolysis

$$M = ZIt$$

$$M = \frac{g.}{\cancel{amp. \times hr.}} \times \cancel{amp.} \times \cancel{hr.}$$

$$M = g.$$

(Page 403)

Cost of Electrical Energy

$$C = \frac{watts \times time\ (hr.) \times \frac{\cancel{¢}}{K.W.H.}}{1000}$$

$$C = watts \times hr. \times \frac{¢}{K.W.H.} \div \frac{watts}{Kw.}$$

$$C = \cancel{watts} \times \cancel{hr.} \times \frac{¢}{\cancel{K.W.H.}} \times \frac{\cancel{Kw.}}{\cancel{watts}} = ¢$$

(Page 421)

Resistance of a Wire

$$R = \frac{KL}{d^2}$$

$$R = ohms \times \frac{mils}{ft.} \times ft. \div mils$$

$$R = ohms \times \frac{\cancel{mils}}{\cancel{ft.}} \times \cancel{ft.} \times \frac{1}{\cancel{mils}}$$

$$R = ohms$$

(Page 432)

Computing Answers. In solving problems in this book, the question naturally arises as to how many decimal places should be used in the answers. Since the data usually result from measurements, some inaccuracy is always involved. However, it is customary to accept the data given in the problems without questioning the degree of precision. Nevertheless, without knowledge of the accuracy of the original measurements, we must follow certain precautions so that the values obtained from performing arithmetical operations with the data are not of greater accuracy than the original measurements.

You will save yourself much time and unnecessary computation if you observe the following rule:

The result of an arithmetical operation (addition, subtraction, multiplication, or division) should not have more significant figures in it than the least accurate measurement given in the data.

Each of the following measurements has three significant figures (digits that express the number of units of measurement): 3.53 ft., 10.6 mm., .0308 m. and 3.20 cm. Note that zeros between non-zero digits are significant, but that zeros preceding the first nonzero digit are not significant. In the measurement of 3.20 cm. the zero is significant because the measurement was made to a hundredth of a centimeter.

The decimal point has nothing to do with the number of significant figures. For example, the length 3.58 cm. may be written 35.8 mm., or 0.0358 m., or 0.0000358 km., yet each measurement contains three significant figures. Therefore, we can see that changing the unit of measurement does not change the number of significant figures.

Now let us apply the above rules to a typical problem.

PROBLEM: Find the density of a liquid that weighs 206 g. and occupies 21 cc. (Note that the least accurate measurement has only 2 significant figures.)

$$D = \frac{M}{V} = \frac{209 \text{ g.}}{21 \text{ cc.}} = 9.85 \text{ g./cc.} = 9.9 \text{ g./cc.}$$

To round off our result to the correct number of significant figures, we must examine the first dropped digit. If the figure is 5 or more, we drop the figure but raise the preceding figure by 1. If the first dropped figure is less than 5, we merely drop it and do nothing else.

PROBLEM: Find the pressure in pounds per square foot on the bottom of a tank of water 13.55 feet high.

$$P = h\,d$$

$$P = 13.55 \text{ ft.} \times 62.4 \frac{\text{lb.}}{\text{ft.}^3} = \frac{846 \text{ lb.}}{\text{ft.}^2}$$

```
   13.55
  ×62.4
  ─────
   5420
   2710
   8130
  ─────
 845.520
```

Table on PROPERTIES OF COPPER WIRE

Gauge No.	Diam. (mils)	Ohms per 1000 ft. at 0°C	Ohms per 1000 ft. at 20°C	Feet per ohm at 20°C
10	101.9	.9203	.9989	1,001
12	80.81	1.463	1.588	629.6
14	64.08	2.327	2.525	396.0
16	50.82	3.700	4.016	249.0
18	40.30	5.883	6.385	156.6
20	31.96	9.355	10.15	98.5
22	25.35	14.87	16.14	61.95
24	20.10	23.65	25.67	38.96
26	15.94	37.61	40.81	24.50
28	12.64	59.80	64.90	15.41
30	10.03	95.08	103.2	9.691
32	7.950	151.2	164.1	6.095

INDEX

A page reference in bold type (**15**) indicates that a term is defined, an important principle is stated, or a formula is given on that page. A page reference in italic type (*15*) indicates that an illustration, either a line drawing or photograph, will be found on that page.

Absolute humidity, 291-292; and dew point, **293**-294, *293*; problems, 307; project, 307
Absolute units of force, 161
Absolute zero, 245
A.C. generators (alternators), 445, *445*
A.C. motors, 451; *see also* Motors
A.C. transformer, principle of, **459**-460
Acceleration, 134-135, 151, 167-168; and air resistance, 148, *148*; of body thrown straight upward, 147-148, *147*; experimental study of, 137, *138*; formulas, **136**-137, *147*; of freely falling bodies, 144-**147**, *145*, *146*, *147*, *148*, 151; and impulse, 161-164, *162*, *163*, *164*; on inclined planes, 138-139, *145*; and inertia, 154-156, *155*, 167; Newton's second law of motion, **158**-159, *159*; poundals and dynes, **160**-161, *160*; problems, 142, 152, 168-169; of projectiles, 180-184, *181*, *183*; projects, 143, 152; uniform, positive, and negative **135**-136; velocity and unbalanced forces, 156-161, *155*, *156*, *157*, *159*, *160*
Accommodation, 542
Acoustics, architectural, **322**
Action and reaction, 164-166, *165*, *166*
Adhesion, 222
Agonic line, 377
Agriculture, use of radioactive isotopes in, 632, *633*
Air: as conductor of heat, 267; convection currents in, 264-265, *265*; density of, **77**, 87; friction of, 103-105, **104**, *104*; and Mach number, **104**-105, *105*; as matter, 77, 78, 89; moisture capacity of, 291-292; pressure, 77-89; resistance of, 2-3, *3*, 148, *148*; lapse rate of, **296**; shock waves, 105, *105*; sound transmitted by, 312-316, *314*, *315*, *316*
Air brakes, 95
Airplane: and air friction, 103-104, *104*; center of gravity in, 127, *126*; drag of, **116**; icing of, 297; jet engines, 286, *286*; jets, **165**, *166*; lift, 103, *103*, **116**, *116*; projects, 106; rocket, *187*; and supersonic speed, 104-105, *105*; thrust of, **116**
Alpha particle, 615
Alternating current (A.C.), 445, 467-480; capacitive reactance, **473**; capacitive reactance and current lead, 473, *471*; changing to D.C., 477, 590, *591*; condenser in circuit, 472, *472*; cycle of, 467, *468*; effective current, **467**-468, *468*; effective voltage, **468**; frequency of, 445; generators (alternators) of, 447; impedance, **468**-469, 471-474, *471*, *474*, *475*; inductive reactance, 470-**471**, *470*, *471*; measuring, 467, *468*; Ohm's Law, applied to, **468**; oscillations in, 475-476, *476*; phase, 471, *471*, 473; power factor, **474**-475, *475*; problems, 479; projects, 479-480; resonance, **476**; tuned circuits, 476-477, *476*
Altimeter, 83; project, 89
Ammeter, 415-416, *415*; connecting in circuit, 415-416, *416*; hot-wire, 416, *416*
Ampere: 360, *360*; hours, **408**; international, **403**; Ohm's Law, 417, **418**
Ampere turns, 390
Amplification factor, 592
Amplitude, of sound wave, **314**-**315**, *316*, 317-318
Amplitude modulation (AM), 588, *588*
Analyzer, in polarization, **500**
Aneroid barometer, 83-84, *83*, *84*; project, 89
Anode, 400-401
Angstrom, 567-574
Anticyclone, 304
Antinode, 333
Archimedes' Principle, 56; applications of, 61-62, 96; problems, 63-64
Area, English units of measurement, 16
Aristotle: on vacuum, 79; and speed of falling bodies, 1-2, 9; and speed of light, 502
Armature, 443-444, *443*; construction of, 447; eddy currents in, 462, *463*; force for turning, 452; problems, 453-454; stator, 449, *449*
Artists' colors, 564-565
Astigmatism, 545, *545*, *546*
Atmospheric pressure, 77-89; effect of altitude on, 81, 84-86, *85*; machines using, 86-87; on Magdeburg hemispheres, 84-85; modern means of measuring, 82-84, *83*, *84*; problems, 88; project, 89; proving existence of, 78-80, *78*, *79*; standard, **81**-**82**, *82*, 87; Torricelli's barometer, **80**, *80*; units

of, 304, *305*; at varying altitudes, 80-81, *81*, 87
Atmospheric refraction, 492-493, *492, 493, 494*
Atomic energy, 613-638; bomb, 628-629, *629*; atomic power plant, *636*; Einstein's equation, 581-582, 613; electron volt, 621-622; hydrogen bomb, 633-636, *635*; instability of nuclei and emission of, 622-623, *623*; plutonium, discovery of, 627- 628, *628*; projects, 637-638; from radioactive elements, 617-621, *619, 620*; radioactive isotopes produced with, 622, 631-632; radioactive isotopes, applications of, 632-633, *632, 633, 634*; radioactivity, **614**-617, *616*; uranium fission, 623-**624**, *624*, 627; uranium-graphite pile, 629-631, *630, 631*
Atomic number, 354, 355, *356*
Atomic theory of matter, 219-221, *220, 221*, 351-356, 360, 354-356; atomic number, **354**, 355, *356*; chemical properties, 353; charge on nucleus, 354; energy levels, 577-579, *577, 578*; isotopes, **354**; magnetism of atoms, 388-389, *389*; mass number, **353**-354, 355, *356*; relative weights, 354; structure of atoms, 352-353, *352, 353*; *see also* Electron theory
Atomizer, 100-101, *100*
Audio-frequency (a.f.), 588
Automobile jack, 115, *115*
Automobile: clutch and gear system, 69, 212-213, *212*; engines, 282-283, *282, 283*; gas turbine, *285*; fluid drive in, 69-71, *70, 212*; headlights, **512**; hydraulic brakes, 68-69, *69*; problems, 287-288; project, 106; spark plugs, 458

Bach, Johann Sebastian, 328
Back e.m.f., 451
Balloons: "lighter than air," 96; in varying atmospheric pressure, 90, *91*
Barograph, 83-**84**, *84*
Barometers: aneroid, altimeter, and barograph, 83-**84**, *83, 84*; effect of altitude on, 81, *81*; modern mercury, 82-83, *82*; problems, 88; project, 89; Torricellian, **80**-81, *80*
Baseball, pitching curve with, 101-102, *101, 102*
Battery: lead storage, 408-409, *408*; nickel-cadmium, 409, *409*; problem, 411; charging with Tungar rectifier, 590, *591*; *see also* Voltaic cells
Beats, 331; 331; law of, 331-**332**
Becquerel, Edmond, and ultraviolet waves, 574
Becquerel, Henri, and radioactivity, 614
Bell, Alexander Graham, 318
Bernoulli's Principle, 99-100, *100*, 106; atomizer and paint gun, 100-101, *100*; in pitching and golf, 101-102, *101, 102*; projects, 106
Beta particle, 615
Betatron, 620
Binoculars, prism, **535**-536, *535*
Binocular vision, 545-547, **546**, *546*
Block and tackle, 208-209, *209*
Blood pressure, 71-72; diastolic, **71**; project, 73; systolic, **71**
Boiling, 257-258; laws of, 258-**259**, *258*; project, 263; and vaporization, 258
Boiling point, 259

Bourdon gauge, 47, *46*; 77
Boyle, Robert, 90; and transmission of sound, 313; vacuum pump of, 93
Boyle's Law, 90-93, **91**, *91*, 96; and atmospheric pressure, 92-93, *92*; and Charles' Law, combined, **247**; and gauge pressure and absolute pressure, **92**; problems, 97
Brakes, hydraulic, 68-69, *69*
Breathing, process of, 92, *92*
British thermal unit (btu), 251
Broad jump and high jump, 186, *186*
Brownian movement, 225, *225*
Bunsen photometer, 553, *554*
Buoyancy, 48-49, *48*, **51**-52, *50, 52*; Archimedes' Principle, **56**; laws of, **60**-62, *61, 62*; problems, 63-64; projects, 64
Buzzers, electric, 394, 406

Calorie: small, **351**; large, **351**
Calorimeter, 253, *253*
Cam, in controlling valve action, 283
Camera images, 531, 532, 538; developing, 531-532, *532*; and human eye image, 541-542, *541*; in motion pictures, 601; pinhole, 486, *486*, 507; project, 495; stereoscopic, 547, *547*; of ultraviolet region of solar spectrum, 574
Candle power, 551
Capacitance, 365-366; and alternating current lead, 473, *471*; problems, 479; and resistance in A.C. circuit, 473-474, *474*
Capacitive reactance, 473
Capacitor, electric. *See* Condenser
Capillarity, 222, *223*
Carrier current, 587-588
Cartesian diver, 64, *64*
Cathode, 400
Cathode ray tube, 580-581, *581*; for color TV, 607; iconoscope, **603**-604, *604*; image orthicon, **604**-605, *605*
Center of gravity, 123-128, **124**, *123*; applications of, 126-127, *126*; finding, 124-125, *124, 125*; problems, 129; projects, 129-130; in rotating bodies, 127, *126*; and stability, 125-**126**, *125*; and weight of lever, 123-124, *123*
Center of oscillation, 150-151
Center of percussion, 150, *151*
Centigrade scale, 235-236, *235*; conversion rule, 235-236
Centrifugal force, 170-173, *171*, 178; formulas for, **171**-172, *172*; measuring, 172-173, *173*; offsetting, 173, *173*
Centrifugal governor, 278, *279*
Centrifuge, and ultracentrifuge, **171-172**, *172*
Centripetal force, 170, *170*, 178
Chain hoist, 213, *213*
Chain reaction, 623-**624**, *624*
Charles' Law, 246
Chemical effects of an electric current, 399-411; dissociation, **401**-402, *401*; dry cell, 406, *406*; electrolysis of water, 400-401, *401*; electroplating, 402-403, *402*; laws of electrolysis, **403**; liquid conductors and voltaic cells, 400, *400*;

INDEX 647

problems, 410-411; projects, 411; storage cells and batteries, 406-409, *407*, *408*, *409*; voltaic cell, **400**, *400*; voltaic cell, action of, 403-406, *404*, *405*

Chromatic aberration, 528, *528*

Circular and rotary motion, 170-179; banking of roadways, 173, *173*; centrifugal force, **170**-172, *171*; centripetal force, **170,** *170*; gyrocompass, 174-176, *175*, *176*; gyroscope, 173-174, *174*; gyrostabilizer, 176; problems, 178-179; projects, 179; velocity of rotating bodies, 177, *177*

Climate, 291, 306; high specific heat of water, effect of, 254-255, *254*; solar radiation, effect of, 295-296, *295*; *see also* Weather

Clinical thermometer, 236-237, *236*

Clouds, 296-298, *297*, 306; cirrus, **297**; cumulus, **298**; mare's tails, **304**; nimbus, **298**, 306; seeding, 305-306, *306*

Coefficient of friction, 37

Coefficient of linear expansion, 239-240, *240*

Cohesion, 221-222

Coil, inducing current in, 455-457, *456*; left-hand rule for, **388**, *388*; Lenz's Law, **457**; primary and secondary, 457, *457*; self-induction, 469-**470**, *470*

Cold-front storms, 299-300, *299*

Color, 559-570; chromatic aberration, **528,** *528*; complementary, 560-**561**; filters, 563, 564; mixing, in pigment, 564-565; discovery of spectrum, 559-560, *560*; of objects, 561-563, *562*; primary, **561**; primary, in pigment, **564**; printing, 565-566, *565*; projects, 570; proper and improper use of, 566-567; rainbow, 567-569, *568*; spectra, 571-574, *573*, *574*; stage effects, 563; triangle, 561; and wave length, table of, 567

Color blindness, 567

Color television, 606-607, *607*

Columbus, Christopher, and compass, 376

Combustion, heat of, **276**-277, 286

Commutator, 445

Compass, magnetic, **375**-378, *376*; declination or variation of, 377-378, *378*; earth's magnetic poles, 377, *377*; project, 395

Compensation pendulum, 242

Complementary colors: in light, 560-**561**; in pigment, 564

Composition of forces, 110-112

Compound, 221

Compound-wound generators, 449, *448*

Compound-wound motors, 453

Compression and expansion in gases, 90-98, 244-248; absolute and gauge pressure, 92; Boyle's Law, 90-**91**, 92-93, *91*, *92*; Charles' Law, 245-**246**; general gas law, **247**-248; "lighter than air" machines, 96; pressure and absolute temperature, 245; pressure coefficient, 244-**245**; problems, 97, 249; projects, 97; uses of compressed air, 95-96; vacuum and compression pumps, 93-94, *93*, *94*; vacuum cleaner, 94-95, *94*

Concave (diverging) lenses, 520-522, *521*, *522*, 529; in Galileo's telescope and opera glasses, 534-535, *535*; image formation by, 525, *525*; power of, **526-527,** *526*, *527*; project, 539

Concave mirror, 509-510, *510*, *511*, 512-514, *512*, *513*, *514*, 517; formula for, **516**-517; magnification with, **515**-516, *515*; Pepper's Ghost, 515, *515*; principal focus, **510**, *510*; problems, 518; projects, 518-159; uses of, *512*, 514, *515*

Condensation: 260, *260*; dew and frost, 293; heat of, **258**; problems, 262; in refrigerator, 260, *260*

Condensations in sound waves, 314, *314*, 315

Condensers (capacitors), electric, 363-366, **365,** *366*, 370; in A.C. circuit, 472-473; in A.C. circuit, capacitive reactance of, **473**-474, *474*; capacitance of, **365**-366; early storage bottle, 363-364, *364*; fixed and variable, **366,** *366*; Leyden jar, **364**-365, *364*, *365*; oscillating current in, 475-476, *476*; problems, 479

Conduction, electrostatic, 344-**345,** *345*

Conduction of heat, 265-267; applications of, 270-271; *271*, 273; by liquids and gases, 266-267, *266*; problems, 273; table of conductivities, 266, *266*

Conductors of electric current, 352, *352*, 356, *356*, 357; ions produced in, 357, *357*; liquid, and voltaic cells, 400, *400*; resistance of, 417, 431-**432**

Constant, 25

Continuous spectrum, 571

Convection, 264-265, *265*, 273; project, 274; use of, in heating, 269-270, *269*, *270*

Convex (converging) lenses, 520-521, *521*, *522*, 529, *528*; in Galileo's telescope, 534-535, *535*; images formed by, 522-525, *523*, *524*; magnification with, 524-525, *524*, 533, *533*; in microscopes, 536, *536*; in opera glasses, 534-535; in photography, 531; power of, **526**-527, *526*, *527*; in prism binoculars, 535-536, *535*; problems, 530; in projectors, 532, *533*; projects, 539; in telescopes, 533-534, *534*

Convex mirror, 509-512, *510*, *511*, 517; formula for, **516**-517; problems, 518

Coolidge tube, 579, *579*

Cooling, Newton's Law of, **268**

Corpuscular theory of light, 483-484, *484*; and Einstein's formula, **581**-582; photoelectric effect explained by, 576; reflection explained by, *488*; refraction explained by, 493, *494*; *see also* Light

Cosmic rays, 618

Coulomb, 358, 418

Coulomb's Law, 343

Couple, 122

Critical angle, 491, *491*

Critical mass, 628-**629**

Crookes radiometer, 268, *268*

Curie, Marie and Pierre, 615

Curvature, center of: of lenses, **520**; of spherical mirror, **509**

Cyclonic storms, 300-304, *302*, *303*

Cyclotron, 620-621, *620*

Cylindrical lenses. *See* Lenses

Dalton, John, and atomic theory, 615-616

D'Arsonval galvanometer, 412-413, *414*

Davy, Sir Humphry, 232
D.C. ammeter, **415**-416, *415*, *416*
D.C. generators, 445-447, **446**, *445*, *446*, *447*, *448*, *449*
D.C. motors, 451, *451*, 452-453
Decibel, 319
Decimal system, 15
Declination, magnetic, 377-**378**, *378*
Dees, of cyclotron, **620**
DeForest, Lee, and triode tube, 590-591
Density, **34**, 39; of air, 77, 87; of gases, 96; problems, 40; project, 40; and specific gravity, 60-62, *61*, *62*; tables of, 35, 60; of water, **34**, *35*, *45*, 243-244; *see also* Pressure
Detector, 590-591
Deuterium, **352**-354, *353*, 621, 635
Deuteron, **621**
Dew point, **293**-294, *293*; problems, 307
Diamonds, reflection of light by, 492, *491*
Dielectric, 357
Diesel engines, **284**-286, *284*, *285*, 287
Differential expansion, **241**, *241*; in compensation pendulum, 242, *242*; in thermostat, 241-242, *242*
Differential pulley, 213, *213*
Diffusion, of gases, 226-**227**; of light, **489**, *488*; of liquids, **225**-226, *226*
Diode, 590, *591*; as detector, 592
Diopter, **527**
Dipping needle, 377, *377*
Direct current (D.C.): changing A.C. to, 477, 590, *591*; condenser in circuit, 472, *472*; and equivalent A.C., 467; generators of, 445-449, *445*, *446*, *447*, *448*, *449*; pulsating, **446**
Direct variation, **25**-27, *25*; shown by graph, 26-27, *25*; written as proportion, 26
Dirigibles, 96
Discus, and javelin throw, 186, *186*,
Dissociation, **401**-402, *401*
Dissonance, 332
Distance: in acceleration formulas, 136-137; and average velocity, 133-134; judging, 547-548, *548*; problems, 141-142
Distillation, **259**, *259*
Diverging lens. *See* Concave lens
Diving bells and suits, 95, *95*
Doldrums, 295
Doppler Effect, in sound, **329**, *329*
Dry cells, 406, *406*; in parallel, 434-435, *435*; in series, 434, *435*; electromotive force (e.m.f.) of, 433-434, *434*; problems, 438
Dry ice, 255-256; in rainmaking, 305-306, *306*
Dyne, **160**-161, *160*
Dyne-centimeters. *See* Ergs

Earth: calculating age of, 617; declination, 377-**378**; magnetic poles of, 377, *377*; magnetism of, 376-377
Earth satellite, *181*, *188*
Eccentric, 279
Echo, **321**
Eclipse, solar, **487**, *487*
Eddy current, **462**-463, *463*

Edison, Thomas A., 219; storage cell of, 409; vacuum tube developed by, 590
Efficiency of machines, **207**-211, *207*
Einstein, Albert, 6, 7, 23, 483; equation for energy and matter, **581**-583, 613, 619-620; General Theory of Relativity, 582-583; special theory of relativity, **505**
Elastic limit, **30**, *31*
Electric bell, batteries for, 406; principle of, 393-394, *393*
Electric circuits, 427-438; cells in series, 434, *435*; fuses, 432-433, *433*; parallel, **427**, *428*, 428-431, *429*; problems, 437-438; resistance of wire, 431-432; series, **427**-428, *428*, *429*; series-parallel connection, 435-436, *435*; terminal voltage of cell, **433**-434, *434*; tuned, 476-477, *476*; voltage distribution in, 431, *431*; Wheatstone bridge, 436, *436*
Electric current, **351**, *352*; ampere, **360**, *360*; cells in series and in parallel, 434-435, *435*; conductors and insulators, 351-**352**, *352*, 356-357, *357*; cost of, **420**-421, *421*; direction of flow, 360; electron theory of, 356-357; heating effect of, 412, *413*; magnetic effect of, 412, *413*; magnetic field surrounding, 386-388, *386*, *387*, *388*, *389*; in parallel circuit, 428-430, *429*; potential, difference of, 357-359, **358**; power, **420**; problems, 361-362, 371, 437-438; rate of flow and quantity, 359-360, *360*; in series circuit, 427-428, *429*; volts, **358**, *358*; work done by, **418**-420; *see also* Electric circuits; Electrical measurements
Electric machines, 441-464; eddy currents, **462**-463, *463*; generators, **443**-449, *443*, *444*, *445*, *446*, *447*, *448*, *449*; induced electromotive force, **441**-443, *442*, *443*, 455-457, *456*, *457*; induction coils, **457**-458, *457*, *458*; motors, **449**-453, *450*, *451*, *452*; telephone, 461-462, *462*; transformers, 458-461, *459*, *461*
Electrical measurement, 412-424; ammeters for direct current, **415**-416; for consumer, 420-421, *421*; D'Arsonval galvanometer, 412-413; heating effect in, 419-420; of large currents, 415; potential, unit of, 417; power, **420**; problems, 422-423; projects, 423-424; of resistance, 418; resistance, unit of, 417; tangent galvanometer, **412**; voltmeters, **417**-418; Weston galvanometer, 413-415; work done by electricity, 418-419
Electricity, static, **341**-350, 363-372; attraction and repulsion, 341-343, *342*, *343*; charging by conduction, 344-345, *345*; charging by induction, 344, 345, 347-348, *348*, *349*; condenser, 365-366, *366*; conductor, effect of induction on, 357, *357*; Coulomb's law, **343**; detecting charge and determining kind, 344; discharging body by grounding, 359, *359*; early storage bottle, 363-364, *364*; electron theory of, **346**-347; fields of force, **343**, *343*; Franklin's theory of, 345-346, *346*, 360; instruments for determining kind of charge, 344-345, *344*, *345*; Leyden jar, **364**-365, *364*, *365*; lightning, 366-368, *367*, *368*; lightning rods, 368-370, *369*, *370*; lines of force, **343**; and magnetism, 385-386, *386*; neutral bodies,

INDEX 649

343, 345, *346*; neutral bodies, attraction of, by charged bodies, 347, *347*; potential of body, 357-358, *358*; potential, unit of, **358**-359, *358*; projects, 350, 371; Von Guericke's electrostatic machine, 363, *364*

Electrochemical equivalents of elements, table of, **403**

Electrolysis, 401; of copper (electroplating), 402-403, *402*; Faraday's laws of, **403**; problems, 410; of water, 400-402, *401*

Electrolyte, 400, *400*

Electromagnet, 388-394; electric bells, 393-394, *393*; factors affecting strength of, 389-390; left-hand rule for, **388**, *388*; for lifting, 391, *390*; problems, 395; producing permanent magnets with, 391; projects, 395-396; relays, **392**-393; telegraph, 391-392, *391*, *392*, *393*

Electromagnetic energy, 576-578

Electromagnetic theory of light, 574-575

Electromotive force (e.m.f.), 441-449, 453; in A.C. transformer, 459-460; back, **451**; in coil, 455-457, *456*, *457*, 463; direction of induced current, 441-443, *443*; Faraday's discovery of, 441, *442*; generators, 443-449, *444*, *445*, *446*, *447*, *448*, *449*; and impedance, in A.C. circuit, 469-470, *470*; by induction coil, 458; Lenz's Law, **457**

Electromotive force of cell, 433-434, *434*

Electron gun, of cathode ray tube, **580**-581, *581*

Electron microscope, 537-538, *537*, *538*

Electron theory, 346, 349, 352-362; and atomic structure, 352-353, *352*, *353*, 354-356; and charged bodies, 346-347, *346*, *347*; charging by induction, 347-348, *348*, *349*; chemical properties of atoms, 353; discharging charged body, 359, *359*; and electric current, 356-357, *357*, 360; charge on nucleus, 354, 355, *356*; electrical potential of body, 357-359, *358*; and emission of light, 577-579, *577*, *578*; ions, 357, *357*; isotopes, **354**; and Leyden jar, 364-365, *364*; magnetism of atoms, 388-389, *389*; mass number, **353**-354, 355, *356*; relative weights of atoms, 354

Electron volt, 621-622

Electronics: radar, 607-608, *607*, *609*; radio, 587-600; sound-motion pictures, 601-602; television, 602-607

Electrons, 346; high-speed, 581; mass of, 348-349; in photoelectric effect, 575-576, *576*

Electroplating, 402-403, *402*, problem, 410

Electroscopes, 344-345; charging by contact, 344-345, *345*; charging by induction, 344, *349*; project, 350; types of, 344, *344*

Elements, 221, 351; analysis by spectroscope, 571-574; electrochemical equivalents of, table, 403; electromotive series of, table, 400; electron distribution in, table, 355; transmutation of, **615**-617, 619; *see also* Atomic theory of matter

Energy, 197-204; atomic, 613-638; computing kinetic, **199**-200; conservation of, law of, 201-202, *202*; electric, 358-359, *358*; electric, commercial unit of, 420; electric, and e.m.f. induced in coil, 455-456; electric, and heat, 419-420, *419*, *420*; electric, measuring for consumer, 420-421, *421*; electric, and mechanical, 418-419; electromagnetic, 576-578; of electrons, 577-578; in food, 277; heat, **232**-233, 275-276; kinetic, **197**; kinetic and potential, 197-199, *197*, *198*; potential, **198**; and matter, 581-583, 613; problems, 204, 287-288; project, 238; sound, **312**, *312*, 315, 322; sound, transmission of, 311-314, *312*, *313*, *314*; transformation of, 200-201, *201*, 275

Energy levels, 355-356; and emission of light, 577-578

Engines. *See* Heat engines

English system of measurement, 16; and metric system, conversion table, 19

Equator, magnetic, **377**, *377*

Equilibrant, 109

Equilibrium, first condition for, **36**, 39, 119, *119*, **122**; second condition for, 120-**122**, *120*, *121*; *see also* Forces in equilibrium

Erg, 195, *195*

Ether, theory of, 267, **485**, 504-505

Evaporation, 257, *257*; cooling by, 292-293; project, 262-263

Even-tempered scale, 328

Expansion, 239-250, *240*; differential, **241**-242, *241*, *242*; of gas, 90-93, 244-248; of gas, 286; linear, **239**-241; problems, 249; projects, 250; volumetric, **239**; of water, 242-244, *242*, *243*, *244*

Experiment, in method of science, 2, 9-11

External combustion engine, 277-278

Eyeglasses: for astigmatism, 545, *546*; bifocal, 543; for farsightedness, 544-545, *545*; for nearsightedness, 544, *544*

Eyesight, 540-550; astigmatism, **545**, *546*; binocular vision, 545-547, *546*, *546*; color perception, 566; eye as living camera, 541-542, *541*; farsightedness, **544**-545, *545*; focusing of eye, **542**, *542*; impaired, 540; improper muscle balance, 548-549; and intensity of illumination, 554-556, *554*; lens of eye, accommodation, near point, and far point, **542**-543, *542*; near points, table of, 543; nearsightedness, **543**-544, *544*; presbyopia, **543**; projects, 549-550

Fahrenheit scale, 234-235; conversion rule, 235-236

Falling bodies, 1-5, 144-147, 155; acceleration and unbalanced force, **156**-161, *155*, *156*, *157*, *159*, *160*; and acceleration on inclined planes, 144-147, *145*, *146*; and air friction, 148, *148*; Aristotle on, 1, 9, 144; and inertia, 154-156, *155*; Galileo's experiments, 1-2, *2*, *10*, 144-145; guinea-and-feather experiment, 2-3, *3*; hitting force, 161-164, *162*, *163*, *164*; and motion of body thrown straight upward, 147-148, *147*; Newton's second law of motion, **158**-159, *159*; and projectile motion, 181, *181*, 182-183, *183*; projects, 5

Farad, 365-366, 472

Faraday, Michael, and electric motor, 449-450; and induced e.m.f., **441**; laws of electrolysis, **403**; and liquefying of gases, 260

Farsightedness (hyperopia), 544-545, *545*

Film, photographic, 531-532, *532*, 574

Fission, 623-**624**, *624*

650 INDEX

Fizeau, Armand, and speed of light, 503
Fleming, Joseph, and vacuum tube detector, 590
Floating bodies, 48-49, *48*; and center of gravity, 127; laws applying to, **60**-62, *61*, *62*; *see also* Submerged objects
Fluorescence, 579, *578*
FM radio, 588, *588*
Focal length, of lens, **521**; of mirror, **510**
Food, fuel values of, table, 277
Foot-candle, 551
Foot-candle meter, 553, *555*
Foot-pound, 194
Foot-poundal, 194
Force, 30-32, **39**; of friction, **36**-38; of gravity, **31**-32; Hooke's Law, **31**, *31*; measurement of, 30-31; of moving body, 161-164, *162*, 163, *164*; problems, 40; unbalanced, 156-161, *155*, *156*, *157*, *159*, *160*, 164, 167
Force pumps, 86, *86*
Forces, 109-118; 110-111, *110*; angle for maximum resultant, 113, *112*, *113*; components of, **113**-114; equal, acting at right angles, 111-112, *111*, *112*; equilibrant, **109**; parallelogram method, **111**; problems, 117-118; projects, 118; resolution of, 113-116, **114**, *113*, *114*, *115*, *116*; resultant, **109**; two forces acting in same direction, 109, *110*; unequal, acting at right angles, 112, *112*
Forces in confined liquids (Pascal's Law), 67-68; applications of, 68-74, *67*, *68*, *69*, *70*, *71*, *72*
Forces in equilibrium, 119-130, *119*; center of gravity, 123-125, **124**, *123*, *124*, *125*, *126*; couple, **122**, *120*; lever principle, **120**-122, *120*, *121*; problems, 128-129; projects, 129-130; stability, 125-**126**, *125*
Forces in gases, measurement of, 77-78; *see also* Atmospheric pressure; Compression and expansion in gases; High-speed liquids and gases
Forces in liquids in open vessels, 43-54; apparent loss of weight in submerged body, **51**-52, *50*, *52*, 56-57, *57*; measuring pressure, 47-48, *46*, *47*; pressure, 44-46, **45**, *44*, *45*, *46*; problems, 53; projects, 53-54; sidewise pressure, 49-51, *49*; total force, 43-**44**, *44*, 65-67, *65*, *66*; upward, 48-49, *48*; *see also* Hydraulic machines
Formulas. *See* Mathematical formulas
Foucault, Jean, and speed of light, 503
Fractional distillation, 259
Franklin, Benjamin, experiments with Leyden jars, 364, 365; lightning rod of, 368; kite experiment of, 367, *367*; theory of electricity, 345-346, *346*, 360
Fraunhofer lines, 571-572
Free fall, 3; formulas for, **147**
Freezing and melting of water, 243-244, 255-257; heat of fusion, **255**-256; regelation, 256-**257**, *256*
Frequency of alternating current, 445; of tuned circuits, **477**
Frequency of light waves, 567
Frequency of sound waves, 314-**315**, *316*, 318, 337; and beats, 331-332, *331*; in Doppler Effect, 329, *329*; fundamental and overtones, 333-335, **334**, *334*, *335*; in major diatonic scale, 326; and musical intervals, 327; and pitch, 326; problems, 338; and resonance, 330-331, *330*; of standard pitch, 328-329; and sympathetic vibrations, 329-330, *330*; ultrasonics, **336**, *336*; of vibrating air columns, 333-335, *333*, *334*, *335*; of vibrating strings, laws of, **332**, *332*; wave length formula, 319-**320**, *319*; *see also* Radio broadcasting; Radio reception
Friction, 36-38, *37*, *39*; coefficient of, **37**; and efficiency of machines, 207-208, *207*; electrostatic charge produced by, 341, 346-347; factors affecting, 37; fluid, 103-105, **104**, *104*, *105*, 148, *148*; and heat, 232; kinds of, 37, 38; problems, 40; and transformation of energy, 200-201
Fuels, heat of combustion table, 277
Fulcrum, 119
Fundamental, 334
Fuses, electric, 432-433, *433*
Fusing point of substances, table of, 255

G, 145-147; and period of pendulum, 150; units of centrifugal force, 171-172, *172*
Galileo, and accelerated motion, 138; and atmospheric pressure, 79; and cohesion, 222; compound microscope of, 536, *536*; and experiments with falling bodies, 1-2, *2*, 9-10, 144-145; and pendulum experiments, 149; and speed of light, 502; and surface tension, 223, 224; telescope of, 534-535, *535*; thermoscope of, 233-234, *233*
Galvani, Luigi, electrical experiments of, 399
Galvanometers, 412-418, 422; ammeters, **415**-416, *415*, *416*; D'Arsonval, 412-413, *414*; increasing range of, 415, *415*; problems, 422; project, 423-424; tangent, **412**, *413*; voltmeters, **417**-418, *417*, *418*; Weston, 413-415, **414**, *414*
Gamma rays, 615, *616*
Gas: analyzed by spectroscope, 571-572; combustion of, 276-277, 286; as conductor of heat, 266-267; in "lighter than air" machines, 96; liquefying of, 259-260, *260*; general law, **247**-248; pressure of, 227, *227*; pressure coefficient of, **245**; pressure and temperature, 244-245, *244*; pressure and volume, 90-91; problems, 249; project, 262; refrigerant, 260, *260*; visible light emitted by, 578-579, *578*; volume and temperature, 245-247, *246*
Gasoline engines, 282-284; four-stroke-cycle, 282-283, *282*; formula for determining horsepower, **283**; multiple-cylinder, **283**, *283*; problems, 287-288; two-stroke-cycle, **282**, 284, *284*, 287
Gay-Lussac's Law, 246
Gears, 211-214, *211*, *212*, *213*, *214*
Geiger counter, 621, *621*
General gas law, 247
Generators, electric, **443**-449, 453; alternating current (A.C.), 447; armatures, **443**, 447, *447*, *448*; commercial, large, 449, *449*; compound-wound, **449**, *448*; direct-current (D.C.), 445-447, **446**, *445*, *446*, *447*; field magnets, 447; principles of, 443-445, *443*, *444*, *445*; left-hand rule for, **443**, *443*; problem, 453; self-excited (D.C.), **447**-449;

INDEX

series-wound, **448**, *448*; shunt-wound, **448**-449, *448*
Gilbert, William, and earth's magnetism, 376-377
Glare, 501, 556, *557*
Goethe, Johann W. von, and light, 560
Gram-centimeter, 195
Graphs, 26; direct variation, 26-27, *25*; inverse variation, 27; Mach numbers and horsepower requirements, *105*; parallelogram method, 111, *111*; resultant of two forces shown by, 109-110, *110*
Gravity, 31-32, 39; community water system based on, 72, *72*; measurement of, 31, 32-33, *33*, *36*; Newton's law of universal gravitation, **32**; problems, 40; project, 40; and projectiles, 181, *181*, 183, *183*; and velocity of falling bodies, 154-159, *155*, 167; *see also* Center of gravity
Grid, **590**-591; bias, 592; leak, 592-593
Guericke, Otto von, electrostatic machine of, 363, *364*; Magdeburg hemispheres of, 84
Gyroscope, 174, *174*; applications of, 174-176, *175*, *176*

Hail, formation of, **298**
Harmony, in musical sounds, 332
Head of water, 48
Heat, 231-233, **232**, 251-263; boiling, laws of, 258-259, *258*; boiling, process of, 257-258; of combustion, 276-277; of condensation, 258; and distillation, 259, *259*; as energy, 232-233, 275-276; and evaporation, **257**, *257*; exchange, law of, **252**; and expansion of water, 242-243; of fusion, **255**-256; and linear expansion, 239-242, 248; and liquefying of gases, 259-260, **260**; lost or gained by water, measuring, 251-252; problems, 262, 287; produced by electrical energy, **419**-420, *419*, *420*; projects, 238, 262-263; regelation, 256-**257**, *256*; in refrigerator, 260, *260*; specific, **252**; specific, measuring, 253-254, *253*; specific, table of, 253; specific, of water, effect on climate, 254-255, *254*; units for measuring, 251; of vaporization, **258**, *258*; and work, 275-276, *276*, 286; *see also* Temperature
Heat engines, 277-288; diesel, **284**-286, *284*, *285*; experimental gas turbine, *285*; external combustion and internal combustion, 277-**278**; gasoline, 282-284, *282*, *283*, *284*; jet, 286, *286*; multiple-expansion, **280**; problems, 287-288; projects, 288; steam, 278-280, *278*, *279*; steam turbine, 280-282, *281*
Heat pump, 272-273
Heat transference, 264-274; by conduction, **265**-267, *265*, *266*; by convection, **264**-265, *265*; cooking by conduction, 270; heat pump, 272-273, *272*; house-heating systems, ·269-270, *269*, *270*; preventing, 271-272, *271*; problems, 273; projects, 274; by radiation, **267**-269, *268*; radiation, laws of, **268-269**; water heater using convection, 269, *269*
Heating systems: "fireless furnace," 272-273, *272*; hot-air, 269-270, *270*; hot-water, 269-270, *270*; radiant, **270**; steam, 269, *269*

Helium, 353-354, *353*, 356; discovery of, 572; in nuclear fusion, 613-614, *614*, 615-616, 633-635
Helmholtz, Hermann von, on sound, 336
Henry, 470
Henry, Joseph, electromagnet of, 390
High-speed liquids and gases, 99-106; Bernoulli's Principle; **99**-103, *100*, *101*, *102*, *103*; fluid friction 103-105, *104*, *105*; projects, 106
Hitting force of moving body, 161-164, *162*, *163*, *164*
Hooke's Law, 30-**31**, *31*
Horse latitudes, 295, *295*
Horsepower, 196-197
Humidity, 291-295, 306; absolute, **291**-292; and dew point, **293**-294, *293*; problems, 307; project, 307; relative, **292**-293; relative, measuring, 294-295, *294*
Hurricanes, 300-302, *301*
Huyghens, Christian, "ether," theory of, 267, 485; and microscope, 536; refraction explained by, 493-494, *494*; and speed of light, 502; wave theory of light, **484**-485, *484*, 494
Hydraulic machines, 43, 65-74; brakes, 68-69, *69*; fluid drive, 69-71, *70*; measuring blood pressure, 71-72, *71*; Pascal's Law, **67**; press, 68, *67*, *68*; principle of, 68; problems, 73; project, 74
Hydrogen, isotopes of, 352-354, *352*, *353*; in nuclear fusion, 613, *614*, 618, 621, 622-623, *623*, 633-635
Hydrogen bomb, 633-636, *635*
Hydrometer, 57-60, *59*
Hydrostatic paradox, 65-67, *65*, *66*
Hygrometer, 294
Hyperopia (farsightedness), 544-545, *545*
Hypothesis, 2; and experiment, 9-11, *10*

Ice. *See* Water
Ice storms, 298
Iconoscope, 603-604, *604*
Illumination, 551-558; distribution of light, 556; foot-candle meters, 553-554, *555*; glare, 556, *557*; intensity of, **552**, 554-556, *554*; measuring, 551-552, *552*; photometry, **552-553**, *553*, *554*, *555*; problems, 558; projects, 558
Image formation, 507-539; by cameras, 486, *485*, 507, 531; characteristics of, 509; by eye, 541-545; by lenses, 520-530, *521*, *522*, *523*, *524*, *525*, *527*, *528*; by mirrors, 507-517, *508*, *509*, *510*, *511*, *512*, *513*, *514*, *515*; by optical instruments, 531-539; projects, 539; virtual and real, **508**-509
Image orthicon, 604-605, *605*
Impedance, in A. C. circuit, **468**-470, 478; problems, 479; with resistance and capacitance, 473-474, *474*; formula for, 471-**472**, *471*; with resistance, coil, and condenser, 474, *475*
Impulse, 164, *164*; and law of action and reaction, 165-166
Incandescence, 571-572
Incidence, angle of: in reflection, **487-488**, *488*; in refraction, 490
Inclination, angle of, **377**
Inclined plane, 209-210, *210*; motion on, 138-139, 145-147, *145*, *147*

INDEX

Index of refraction, 491, *490*, 492, 495, **504**; for various substances, table of, 491
Induced electromotive force. *See* Electromotive force
Induced magnetism, 378-379, *379*
Inductance, in A. C. circuit, **470**, *470*; and current lag, 471, *470*, *471*; problems, 479; project, 479; reactance caused by, 470; units of, 470; resistance, and impedance, 471-473, *471*
Inductance coil, 457-458, *457*, *458*; in transformer, 458-459, *459*
Induction coil, **457**-458
Induction of electrostatic charge, **344**, 345, 347-348, *348*, *349*
Induction motor, 451
Industry, radioactive isotopes in, 632-633
Inertia, 154-156, **155**, *155*, 167; Newton's first law of motion, **164**, 167
Infrared rays, 574
Insulation, heat, 271-272, *271*; project, 274
Insulators of electric current, **352**, *352*, 356-357, *356*
Interference of waves: of light, 496-497, *497*, *498*; of light, project, 506; of sound, beats, 331-332, *331*; of sound, constructive and destructive, **320**-321, *320*, *321*
Internal combustion engine, 277-**278**
International candle, **551**
Intervals, musical, 327
Inverse-square law, applications of, 317
Inverse variations, **27**-28, *27*; written as proportion, 28
Ion, **357**, *357*
Ionization, in electrolysis and electroplating, 401-402; in Geiger counters, 621; lightning, 368
Iron atoms, 622-623, *623*
Isobar, 304
Isotherm, 304
Isotopes, **354**; radioactive, 622, 631-632; radioactive, applications of, 632-633, *632*, *633*, *634*; radioactive, half lives of, 633; radioactive, handling, 633, *634*

Jack screw, 210, 211, *210*
Jeans, Sir James, 11
Jet aircraft. *See* Airplanes
Jet engines, 286, *286*
Joly photometer, **553**, *553*
Joule, 195, **276**, *276*
Kilowatt, 420
Kilowatt-hour, 420-421
Kinescope, 605-606
Kinetic energy, **197**-201, 203; formula for, **199**-200; heat as, 232-233; and potential energy, 198-199, *198*; problems, 204; of sound medium, 315; of sound producer, 312, *312*; and potential energy, 200-202, *201*
Kirchhoff, Gustav R,. 572, 573

Lead storage batteries, **408**-409, *408*
Leeuwenhoek, Anton van, microscope of, 536
Length: conversion table of measures, 19; English units of measurement, **16**, **17**; metric units of, **16**-**17**, *17*

Lenses, 520-530; achromatic, **528**; for astigmatism, 545, *546*; bifocal, for eyeglasses, 543; chromatic aberration, **528**, *528*; converging (convex), **520**, *521*, *522*; converging, location of image, 522-525, *523*, *524*; diverging (concave), **520**, *521*, *522*, 525, *525*; in Galileo's telescope, 534-535, *535*; for hyperopia, 545, *545*; lens equation, **525**-526; magnetic, **538**, *537*; magnifying, 533, *533*, 536-537; of microscopes, 536, *536*; for myopia, 544, *544*; in opera glasses, 534-535; optical center, 522; passage of light through, 520-522, *521*, *522*; photographic, 531; power of, **526**-**527**, *526*, *527*; principal focus and focal length, **521**; of prism binoculars, 535-536, *535*; problems, 530; in projectors, 532, *533*; projects, 539; refracted image, **522**; spherical aberration, **527**-528, *527*, *528*; spherical and cylindrical, 520, *521*; telescopic, 533-534, *534*; *see also* Eyesight
Lenz's Law, 457
Lever, 119-122, **205**-207, *205*; class of, **122**, *123*; couple, **122**, *120*; efficiency of, 207-208, *207*; in equilibrium, 119-122, *119*, *120*, *121*; fulcrum, **119**; I.M.A. and A.M.A. of, 206-207, *206*; principle, **120**-122, *120*, *121*, 205; problems, 129; weight of, 123-124, *123*, *124*, 127-128, *127*
Leyden jar, **364**-365, *364*, *365*; Franklin's experiments with, 365, 367; oscillating current of, 475-476, *476*; problem, 479
Liebig condenser, 259, *259*
Lift pump, **86**, *86*
Light, 267, 483, 506; ancient Greek theory of, 483; and camera images, 486, *486*; diffusion, **489**, *488*; eclipses, **487**, *487*; Einstein's formula for energy and matter, **581**-582; Einstein's special theory of relativity, **505**; electromagnetic theory of, 574-575, *575*; emission of, 577-579, *577*, *578*; ether, theory of, *485*, 504-505; Huyghens' wave theory of, **484**-485, *484*, *494*; infrared, **267**, 574; interference, 496-497, *497*; luminous intensity of, **551**; mirages, **492**-493, *492*, *493 494*; Newton's corpuscular theory of, 483-484, *484*, *494*; photoelectric effect, **575**-576, *576*; photoelectric cell, 579-580, *580*; polarized **500**-501, *500*, *501*; projects, 495, 506; reflection of, **487**-489, *488*; refraction of, **489**-491, *489*, *490*; refraction explained by Newton and Huyghens,, 493-494, *494*; speed of, 501-504, **503**, *502*, *503*; straight-line path of, 485-486, *485*, *486*; total reflection, 491-492, *491*, *492*; ultraviolet, **574**; umbra and penumbra of, **486**, *486*; wave length, 497-498, *498*; wave theory proved, 496-497; waves, nature of, 498-500, *499*, *500*; X-rays, 579; *see also* Camera images; Color; Illumination; Mirror images
Light year, **504**
Lightning, 366-370; causes of, 367-368, *368*; Franklin's kite experiment, 367, *367*; path of, 368; protection against, 368-370, *369*, *370*
Linear expansion, 239-241, 248; coefficient of, **239**-240, *240*; differential, **241**-242, *241*, *242*; problems, 249; projects, 250; table of coefficients of, 241

INDEX

Liquefying of gases, 259-260, *260*; project, 262
Liter, 17
Lithium atoms, 354, 635
Local action, 405
Lucretius, atomic theory of, 219
Luminous intensity, 551

Mach number, **104**-105, *104*, *105*
Machines, 205-216; automobile transmission, 212-213, *212*; block and tackle, 208-209, *209*; differential pulley, **213**, *213*; efficiency of, **207**-208, *207*; I.M.A. and A.M.A. of, **206**-207, *206*; inclined plane, 209-210, *210*; lever, 205-207; problems, 215; project, 216; pulleys, 208, *208*; pulleys, belts, and gears, 211-212, *211*; screw, **210**-211, *210*; wedge, 210, *210*; wheel and axle, **209**, *209*; worm gear, **214**, *213*, *214*
Magdeburg hemispheres, 84-85
Magnetism, 375-396; attraction of magnet, 375; compass, **375**-376, *376*; of earth, 376-378, *377*, *378*; and electricity, 385-386; electromagnets and applications, 388-394; induced, 378-**379**; left-hand rule for a coil, 387-**388**, *388*; left-hand rule for a current-carrying conductor, 386-**387**, *387*, *388*; lines of force and magnetic field, 380-382, **381**, *381*, *382*; magnetic field about current-carrying conductor, 386, *386*; measuring electric current by, 412-416, *413*, *414*, *415*, *416*; molecular theory of, 380; permanent, **379**, 388-389, *389*; permeability, **382**-383, *383*; poles of magnet, 375, *375*; poles, 376, *376*, 379-380, *380*; problems, 394-395; projects, 384, 395-396; saturation of, **380**; *see also* Electric machines
Magneto, 447
Magnets: field, in D. C. motors, 452-453; field in generators, 447; keeper, 382; line of force of, **381**; permanent, **379**, 391; retaining strength of, 382-383, *383*; temporary, **379**
Magnification: with concave lens, 524-525, *524*, 536-537; with concave mirror, **515**-516, *515*; with convex lens, **533**; of electron microscope, 537-538, *537*, *538*; *see also* Optical instruments; Telescopes
Magnifying glass, **533**, *533*
Major diatonic scale, **326**-327, *327*, project, 338
Manometer, open-tube, **47**, *47*; for measuring fluid pressure, 71, *71*, 77-78
Mariotte, and Boyle's Law, **91**
Mass, **18**, **32**, 39; conversion table for, 19; English units of, 16, *19*; measurement of, 33-34, *34*; metric units of, 18, *19*, problems, 40; project, 40; and weight, units of, **34**
Mass number, 353-354, 355, 356
Mathematical formulas, 23-29; definitions as, 24; proportions as, 24-25; ratios as, 24; variations as, 25-28
Matter, **3**, 219-228; adhesion of, **222**; Brownian movement, **225**, *225*; capillary action, **222**, *223*; cohesion, **221**-222; diffusion of gases, 226-**227**; diffusion of liquid, **225**-226, *226*; early theories of, 219-221, *220*, *221*; elements, **221**; and energy, Einstein's formula, **581**-583, 613, 619-620; gas pressure, 227, *227*; molecular theory of, 221; osmosis, **226**, *226*; projects, 228; surface tension, **223**-225, *223*, *224*
Maxwell, James Clerk, electromagnetic theory of light of, 574-575, *575*, 577
Measurement, 14-22, **15**; conversion table for metric and English units, 19; English system of, **16**, *17*; international system of, **19**; metric system of, **16**-18; projects on, 22; scientific, 15-**16**; square and cubic, *16*; time, units of, **19**-20, *20*, *21*
Mechanical advantage, 68; actual, **206**; ideal, **206**, *206*
Mechanical equivalent of heat, 275
Medicine, radioactive isotopes in, 632, *632*
Mercury barometers, modern, 82-83, *82*; Torricellian, **80**-81, *80*
Meson, 618
Metals: as conductors of electric current, 356; testing purity of, 55-56; project, 64
Meter, **16**-17
Metric system, 16-19; and English system, conversion table, 19; units of length, 16-17, *17*; units of volume, 17-18, *18*; units of weight and mass, 18, *19*
Michelson, Albert A., and ether, 504; and speed of light, 503, *503*
Microscopes, 536, *536*; compound, **536**-537; electron, 537-538, *537*, *538*; project, 539
Microwatt, unit of sound intensity, 317
Millibars, 304
Mirages, **492**-493, *492*, *493*, *494*; project, 495
Mirror images, 507-519; characteristics of, 509, 512-515, **517**; concave, 509, 512-514, *510*, *511*, *512*, *513*, *514*; concave, magnification with, 515-516, *515*; concave, Pepper's Ghost, 515, *515*; concave, used in telescope, 514, *515*; convex, **509**, 510-512, *510*, *511*; curved, 509-510, *510*, *511*; formula for, **516**-517; plane, location of, **509**, *508*; principle of, 507-508, *508*; problems, 518
Molecular theory of matter, **221**-228, 351; adhesion, **222**; and Brownian movement, 225, *225*; and capillarity, 222, *223*; cohesion, **221**-222; and diffusion of fluids, 225-227, *226*; and gas pressure, 227, *227*; and magnetism 380; and osmosis, 226, *226*; projects, 228; and surface tension, 223-225, *223*
Moments of force, 120-**122**, *120*, *121*, 128; and center of gravity, 123-124, *123*, 124; of couple, 122, *120*; problems, 129; and weight of lever, 123-124, *123*, *124*, 127-128, *127*
Momentum: 164, *164*; and law of action and reaction, **165**-166; Newton's second law of motion on, **158**-159, *159*
Morse code, 392
Motion, **3**; Newton's first law, **164**, 167; Newton's second law, **158**-159, *159*, 167; Newton's third law, 164-166, **165**, *165*, *166*, 167; perpetual, project on, 216; *see also* Acceleration; Circular and rotary motion; Projectile motion
Motion pictures, 542; projector for, 533; sound, 601-602, *602*; 3D, 547, *547*
Motors, electric, 449-453; back e.m.f. in, **451**;

INDEX

D.C., action of, 451, *451*; D.C., windings for, 452-453; essentials of, 450-451, *451*; Faraday's invention of, 449-450; force to turn armature, 452; problems, 453-454; right-hand rule for, **450**, *450*; rheostat, 451-**452**, *452*

Musical sounds, **325**-338; beats, **331**, *331*; beats, law of, 331-**332**; black keys on pianos and organs, 327-328, *328*; dissonance, 332; Doppler Effect, **329**, *329*; even-tempered scale, **328**; harmony, **332**; major diatonic scale, **326**-327, *327*; musical intervals, 327; nature of, 325, *326*; overtones, 333-335, **334**; on oscilloscope screen, 336, *336*; wind instruments, 333, *333*; pitch, 325-**326**; problems, 338; project, 338; quality, 335-**336**, *335*; resonance, **330**-331, *330*; standard pitch, 328-**329**; sympathetic vibrations, 329-**330**, *330*; vibrating strings, laws of, **332**, *332*

Myopia (nearsightedness), 543-**544**, *544*

Nautical mile, 14
Nearsightedness (myopia), 543-**544**, *544*
Neptunium, 628
Neutrons, **353**; mass of, 614; *see also* Atomic theory of matter; Nuclear physics
Newcomen, Thomas, steam engine of, 278, *278*
Newton, Sir Isaac, 31-32; color experiment of, 559-561; corpuscular theory of light, 483-485, *484*, 494; first law of motion, **164**, 167; Law of Cooling, **268**; law of universal gravitation, 32-33; project on laws of, 169; refraction explained by, 493, *494*; second law of motion, **158**-159, *159*, 167; and speed of light, 502; third law of motion, 164-166, **165**, *165*, *166*, 167
Nickel-cadmium storage batteries, 409, *409*
Node, 333
North pole, magnetic, 377, *377*
Nuclear physics, 613-638; atomic bomb, 628, 629, *629*; fission of uranium, 623-624, *624*, 627; Geiger counter, 621; hydrogen bomb, 633-636, *635*, packing factor (binding energy) of nucleus, **622**-623; plutonium, discovery of, 627-628, *628*; projects, 637-638; radioactive isotopes, 622, 631-632, *632*, *633*, *634*; radioactivity, discovery of, 614-617, *616*; releasing atomic energy, 617-621, *619*, *620*; uranium-graphite pile, 629-631, *630*, *631*

Oersted, Hans Christian, and magnetic field of current-carrying conductor, 385-**386**, *386*
Ohms, 417
Ohm's Law, **418**; in A.C. circuit, 468-469
Opera glasses, **534**-535
Optical instruments, 531-539; cameras, 531-532, *532*; magnifying glass, **533**, *533*; microscope, **536**, *536*; opera glasses, **534**-535; prism binoculars, **535**-536, *535*; projecting lanterns, **532**, *533*; projects, 539; refracting telescope, 533-**534**, *534*
Organs: black keys on, 327-328, *328*; fundamental and overtones on, 334-335, *334*, *335*, pipes of, 333, *333*; problems, 338
Oscillation, center of, 150-151, *151*
Oscilloscope: radar, 608, *609*; sound waves shown on, 316, *318*, 336, *336*; *see also* Cathode ray tubes
Osmosis, **226**, *226*
Overtones, 333-335, **334**; project 338; harmonics, **334**

Packing factor, **622**-623, *623*
Paint gun, principle of, 100-101, *100*
Parallel circuits, **427**, *428*, 428-430, *429*; laws of, **430-431**
Pascal, Blaise: barometric pressure tested by, 80-81; and compression and expansion of gas, 90; solution of hydrostatic paradox, 65, *65*, *66*
Pascal's Law, **67** 68, *67*; applications of, 68-74, *67*, *68*, *69*, 70, *71*, *72*
Pendulum, 148-**150**, *149*; laws of, 149-**150**
Pendulum clock, 242, *242*
Pentode, 597
Penumbra, **486**, *486*; in solar eclipse, 487, *487*
Pepper's Ghost, **515**, *515*; project, 518
Percussion, center of, 150-151, *151*
Period of vibration: of baseball bat, 150-151, *151*; of pendulum, 149-**150**, *149*; projects, 152-153
Phase in A.C. circuits, **471**, *471*, 473; power factor, 474-475, *475*
Photoelasticity, 500-501, *501*; project, 506
Photoelectric effect, **575**-576, *576*
Photoelectric tube or cell, **579**-580, *580*; project, 584; and sound films, 601-602, *602*
Photography. *See* Camera images
Photometry, **552**-553, *553*, *554*, *555*; project, 558
Photons, 577-579
Physics, 3, **202**
Pianos: black keys on, 327-328, *328*; problems, 338; strings of, 332, *332*
Pipe organ: fundamental and overtones on, 334-335, *334*, *335*; principle of, 333, *333*; problems, 338
Pitch, **325**-326; standard, 328-**329**; in Doppler Effect, 329, *329*
Planck, Max, quantum theory of, 576-577
Plutonium, 627-628, *628*; produced by uranium-graphite pile, 629-630, *630*
Pneumatic dispatch, 95
Pneumatic lift, 95, *96*
Polar front and polar highs, 296, *295*
Polarization of voltaic cell, 405-406, *405*
Polarized light, **500**, *500*, *501*; projects, 506; uses of, 500-501, *501*
Polarizer, **498**-500, *499*, *500*
Polonium, 615
Positron, 618
Potential energy, 197-199, **198**, *197*, *198*, 203; formula for, **199**; heat as, 232-233; and kinetic energy, 198-199, *198*, 200-202, *201*; problems, 204; of sound medium, 315; of sound-producer, 312, *312*
Poundal, **160**, *160*
Power, 195-197, **196**, 203; electric, 420, 468; electric, of out-of-phase current, 474-475, *475*; electric, units of, **420**; problems, 204; units of, 196-197, *196*, *197*
Power factor in A.C. circuit, **474**-475, *475*

INDEX

Presbyopia, 543
Pressure, 44-51, **45**, *49*; absolute and gauge, **92**; Bernoulli's Principle, **99**-103, *100*, *101*, *102*, *103*; formulas for computing, 44-**46**, *44*, *45*, *46*; of gas, critical, **260**; of gas, and absolute temperature, 244-245, *244*; of gas, and volume, 90-92, *91*; hydrostatic paradox, **65**-67, *65*; measuring, 47-48, *46*, *47*, 77-78; Pascal's Law, **67**-74, *67*, *68*, *69*, *70*, *71*, *72*; problems, 53; projects, 53-54; sidewise, 49-51, *49*; on submerged body, 51-52, *50*, *52*; units, 46; upward, 48-49, *48*; *see also* Atmospheric pressure
Primary colors, in light, **561**; in pigment, *564*
Principal axis, of lens, **520**; of mirror, **509**
Principal focus, of lens, **521**; of mirror, **510**
Prism binoculars, 535-536, *535*
Problem-solving: by appeal to authority, 7-8, *8*; by hypotheses and experiment, 9-11, *10*; by observation, 8-9, *9*; by reasoning, 8, *9*; scientific, steps in, 10
Projectile motion, 180-190; angle for maximum range, 184, *184*; application in sports, 186, *186*; finding range, 184-186, *185*; horizontal velocity, 182-184, *182*, *183*; path of projectile fired horizontally, 181, *181*; path of projectile not fired horizontally, 182-184, *183*; problems, 189; projects, 189-190; trajectory, **180**
Projecting lanterns (projectors), 532, *533*; for 3D motion pictures, 547, *547*
Proportion, 24-25
Protons, 346; mass of, 348-349, 614
Psychrometer, sling, 294, *294*; project, 307
Pulleys, 208, *208*, 211-214, *211*, *212*, *213*, *214*
Purity, testing, by specific gravity, 55-56; project, 64
Pycnometer, 57-58, *58*

Quality of sounds, 335-336
Quantum theory, 576-577; and emission of light, 577-579, *577*, *578*, *579*; and interference, 581

Radar, 607-609, **608**, *608*, *609*
Radiation, solar, effect on weather, 295-296, *295*
Radiation, thermal, **267**-269, 273; applications, 270; demonstrations of, 258, *268*; laws of, **268**-269; project, 274
Radiator, heating with, 269, *269*
Radio broadcasting, 587-589, **588**, 599; amplitude modulation (AM), 588, *588*; audio frequency (a.f.), **588**; cycle, frequency, and wave length defined, **588**-589; frequency modulation (FM), **588**, *588*; projects, 599-600; radio frequency (r.f.), **588**, *587*; triode as oscillator, 594-595, *594*
Radio reception, 589-600; "B" and "C" batteries, 406; crystal detector, 589, *589*, 590, *590*; diode as detector, 592, *589*; filter (pi) circuit, 595-597, *595*, *596*; full-wave rectifier, **596**-597, *596*; half-wave rectification, 590, **595**, *595*; modern vacuum tubes, 597, *597*; projects, 599-600; transistors, **597**-598, *598*; triode tube, 590-592, *591*, *592*; triode as detector and amplifier, 592-594; tuning in, 476-477, *476*, 589, *589*; vacuum tube detector, **590**-591, *591*

Radio waves, 575, *575*, 599; generation of, 587
Radioactivity: alpha, beta, and gamma rays, **615**, *616*; controlling atomic energy released by, 617-621, *619*, *620*; discovery of, 614-615; half life, **617**, *617*; Geiger counter for measuring, **621**, *621*; projects, 637-638; radium discovered, 615; and transmutation of elements, 615-617, 619
Radioisotopes, 622, 631-632; applications of, 632-633, *632*, *633*, *634*; half lives of, 633; handling, 633, *634*; projects, 638
Radium, 615-617; shooting nuclei with, 618
Rain, cause of, 296; making, by seeding clouds, 305-306, *306*
Rainbows, 567-569, *568*
Rarefactions, in sound waves, **314,** *314*, *315*
Ratio, 24
Reactance, in electric circuit, 474, *475*; capacitive, **473,** *471*; inductive, **470,** *471*; problems, 479; *see also* Capacitance; Inductance
Rectification, half-wave, **595**; full-wave, **596**
Rectifier: crystal detector, 590, *590*; Tungar, 590, *591*
Reflecting telescope, 514, *515*; *see also* Telescopes
Reflection of light, 487-489, *488*, 494; angle of, **488**; diffuse, **489**; laws of, **488**; regular, **489**; polarization by, 500; total, 491-492, *491*, *492*; *see also* Camera images; Mirror images
Refracting telescopes, 533-534, *534*; *see also* Telescopes
Refraction, 489-491, *489*, 495; atmospheric, and mirages, 492-493, *492*, *493*, *494*; critical angle of, **491**-492, *491*, *492*; explained by Huyghens, 493-494, *494*; explained by Newton, 493, *494*; index of, **491**, *490*, 492, 504; laws of, **490**; projects, 495; *see also* Lenses
Refrigerants, 255-256
Refrigerator, 260, *260*; problem, 273
Regelation, 256-257, **262**; project, 262
Relativity: Einstein's General Theory of, 582-583; Einstein's special theory of, **505**
Relays, telegraphic, 392-393
Resistance, in electric circuits, 417, 421-422; and electromotive force of cell, 433-434, *434*; factors affecting, 431-432; and heat energy, 419-420, *419*; measuring, 418, *417*, *418*; in parallel circuit, law of, 428-431, **430,** *429*; problems, 422-423, 437-438; in series circuit, law of, 427-**428,** *429*; in series-parallel circuit, 435-436, *435*; specific, **432**; and temperature, 432; unit of, 417; variable starting, 451-452, *452*; and wattage, 420, *421*; of a wire, formula for, **432**
Resistance in electric A.C. circuits: and capacitive reactance, 473-474, *474*; of coil, 468-469, *468*; with coil and condenser, 474, *475*; of condenser, 473; and current and wattage, 468, inductance, and impedance, 471-472, *471*; inductive, ·**470,** *470*; problems, 479
Resolution of forces, 113-114
Resonance: of sound, **330**-331, *330*; of electric circuits, **476**
Resultant, 109
Reverberations of sound, avoiding, 321-322

Rheostat, 451-**452**, *452*
Rockets, 186-188, *187*, *188*; principle of, 165, *166*
Roemer, Olaus, speed of light found by, 502-503, *502*
Roly-poly dolls, 126-127, *126*
Rotating bodies, center of gravity in, 127, *126*; see also Circular and rotary motion
Rotation of earth, 295-296, *295*
Rumford, Count (Benjamin Thompson), heat theory of, 231-232
Rutherford, Ernest, atomic research, 615, 618-620, *619*

Sailboats, 116, *116*
St. Elmo's fire, 369
Scanning, **606**, *606*
Scientific method, 6-13, **10**; hypothesis and experiment, **2**, 9-11, *10*; projects on, 12; steps in, 10; unsound methods of solving problems, 7-9
Screw, 210-211, *210*
Searchlights, concave mirror used in, *512*
Seeing. See Eyesight
Series circuits, **427**-428, *428*, *429*; cells in, 434, 435; laws of, **428**
Series-parallel connection of resistors, 435-436, *435*
Series-wound generators, **448**, *448*
Series-wound motors, 452
Short-wave broadcasting, 588-589
Shunt resistor, 415
Shunt-wound generators, **448**-449, *448*
Shunt-wound motors, 452
Sine of angle, 491
Siphon, 86-87, *87*
Siren disk, 325, *326*
Sleet, formation of, **298**
Sling psychrometer, 294
Snellen chart, to test myopia, 544, *544*
Solar battery, 580
Solar furnace, *512*
Solar radiation, 295-296, *295*
Solar spectrum, 571-572; infrared region of, 574; ultraviolet region of, 574
Sound, 311-324, **312**; absorption of, to avoid reverberations, 321-322; amplitude, **315**, *316*; condensations in, 314, *314*, *315*; directing, 322; Doppler Effect in, 329, *329*; energy relations in medium carrying, 315; frequency, **315**; intensity of, 317-319, **318**, *318*; interference, 320-321, *320*, *321*; loudness of, 317; problems, 323; producer, **312**, *312*; producing, force required in, 311-312; projects, 323; rarefactions in, 314, *314*, *315*; reflection of, 321, *321*; threshold of feeling, **319**; threshold of hearing, **318**; transmission of, by air, 312-313; transmission of, by liquids and solids, 313, *313*; transmission of, 313-314, *314*; velocity of, 104, 316-317, *319*; velocity through various substances, table, 317; wave length, **314**; wave length, formula for, 319-**320**, *319*; as transverse waves, 315-**316**, *316*; see also Musical sounds; Supersonic speeds
Sound motion pictures, 601-602, *602*
Sounder, telegraphic, 392, *392*

Spark plugs, 458
Specific gravity, 55-60, 62-64; and density, 60-62, *61*, *62*; of floating body, 57, *57*; of liquids, 57-60, *58*; of liquids, bottle method, 57-58, *58*; of liquids, hydrometer method, 58-60, *59*; of liquids, sinker method, 58, *58*; of solids, 56; problems, 63-64; projects, 64; tables of, 60
Specific heat. See Heat
Spectroscope, 571, *573*; chemicals analyzed by, 573-574; helium discovered by, 572; stars studied by, 573
Spectrum, color, 559, *560*; bright-line, **571**; bright-line, and electron theory, 577-578; continuous, **571**; dark-line or absorption, **571**-572, *574*; of stars, 573; of sun, 572-573, *574*; used for analysis, 572-574
Speed, of fluids, and friction, 103-104; of fluids, and pressure, 99-103, *100*, *101*, *102*, *103*; see also Velocity
Spherical aberration, **527**-528, *527*, *528*
Spherical lenses. See Lenses
Spherical mirrors, 509-517, *510*; center of curvature, **509**; concave, **509**-510, *510*, *511*, 512-515, *512*, *513*, *514*, *515*; convex, 510-512, *511*; magnification with, 515-516, *515*; mirror equation, 516-517; problems, 518; projects, 518-519
Sports: baseball, pitching curves in, 101-102, *101*, *102*; baseball bat, center of percussion of, 150-151, *151*; hitting force of moving bodies, 161-164, *162*, *163*, *164*; projectile motion applied to, 186, *186*
Stability: and center of gravity, 125-126, *125*; ways of increasing, **126**
Static electricity, 341; see also Electricity, static
Steam engines, 278-282, 287; centrifugal governor in, 278-279, *279*; condensing, 280; Hero's, 278, *278*; measuring power of, 280; multiple expansion, 280; Newcomen's, 278, *278*; problems, 287-288; projects, 288; reciprocating, 278-279, *279*; turbines, 280-282, *281*
Stereoscope, 546-547; camera, 547, *547*
Storage batteries, 406-408, *407*; charging with Tungar rectifier, 590, *591*; Edison, 409; lead, 408-409, *408*; nickel-cadmium, 409, *409*; problem, 411; projects, 411
Stratosphere, 86, *85*
Streamlining, 104
Stress patterns, 500-501, *501*; project, 506
String instruments: fundamental and overtones in, 333-334, *334*; principle of, 332, *332*; problems, 338
Sublimation, 257
Submarines: principle of, 61-62; use of compressed air in, 96
Submerged objects: apparent loss of weight of, 51-52; Archimedes' Principle, 56; laws applying to, 60-62, **61**, *61*, *62*; projects, 64; see also Specific gravity
Suction pump, principle of, 79-80, *79*
Supersonic speeds, 104-105, *104*, *105*
Surface tension, **223**-224, *223*, *224*; reducing, 224-225, *224*

INDEX

Sympathetic vibrations, 329-330, *330*; resonance, 330-331, *330*

Tangent galvanometer, **412**, *413*
Telegraph, 391-393, *391*, *392*, *393*
Telephone, 461-462, *462*; receivers, 590, *590*
Telescopes: field, 523; Galileo's, 534-535, *535*; projects, 518-519, 539; reflecting, **514**, *515*; refracting, 533-534, *534*
Television, 602-607, 609; channels, 606; color, 606-607, *607*; iconoscope, **603**-604, *604*; image orthicon, **604**-605, *605*; kinescope, 580-581, **606**, *605*, *606*; projects, 610; range of broadcasting, 602, *603*; video signals, 604
Temperature, 232-237; absolute, 245; of gas, critical, 259-260; of gas, and pressure, 244-245, *244*; of gas, and volume, 245-248, *246*; problems, 249; projects, 238; and resistance of electric wire, 432; thermometers for measuring, 233-237; *see also* Heat
Temperature, atmospheric, 295-296, *295*, 306; and humidity, 291-295, *293*, *294*; and precipitation, 296-299, *297*, *298*; problems, 317, 323; and sound velocity, 316-317
Tetrode, 597
Thermometers, 233-238; centigrade, 235-236, *235*; Fahrenheit, 235-236, *235*; fixed points of, **234**-235, *234*; Galileo's, 233-234, *233*; problems, 238; projects, 238; scales for, fixing, 234-235, *234*; special types of, 236-237, *236*, *237*; wet-and-dry bulb, 294
Thermostat, **241**-242, *241*
Thomson, Sir J. J., 590
Threshold: of feeling, **319**; of hearing, **318**
Thunderstorms, 298-299, *298*
Time: civilian and military methods of reckoning, 20, *21*; distance, and acceleration, relationship among, 136-137; and force of moving body, 161-164, *162*, *163*, *164*; standard, 20, *20*; units of, **19-20**
Tornadoes, 300, *300*
Torque, 69, 70
Torricellian (mercurial) barometer, **80**-81, *80*
Total force, formula for, 43-**44**
Transformers, 458-464; A.C., **459**-460, *459*; construction of, 458-459; currents in, 462; problems, 464; step-down, uses of, 460-461, *461*; step-up, 460; in telephones, 461-462, *462*; in transmission of electrical power, 460, *461*
Transistor, **597**, *598*
Triode, 590-595, **591**, *591*; as detector and amplifier, 592-594, *593*; as oscillator, 594-595, *594*
Tritium, 353-354, *353*, 635
Troposphere, 86, *85*
Truss, 115-116, *115*
Tuned electric circuits, **476**, *476*; project, 479; in radios, 476-477; *see also* Radio reception
Tungar rectifier, 590, *591*
Typhoons, 300-302, *301*

Ultrasonics, **336**, *336*

Ultraviolet light, **574**; photoelectric effect of, 575-576, *576*
Umbra, 486, *486*; in solar eclipse, 487, *487*
Unbalanced force and laws of motion, 156-161, *155*, *156*, *157*, *159*, *160*, 164, 167
Units, solving problems in, 34-35; section on analysis of, 639-642
Uranium, 614, 617, 623, *623*; atom of, 354, 356; critical mass of, 628-629, *629*; fission of, 623-624, *624*; plutonium manufactured from, 627-628, *628*; scarcity of fissionable isotopes, 627, *628*
Uranium-graphite pile, 628-630, *630*, *631*; radio-active isotopes from, 631-633, *632*, *633*, *634*

Vacuum: Aristotle on, 79; Magdeburg hemispheres, 84; partial, **94**; Pascal's conclusion, 81; sound in, 313
Vacuum bottle, **271**-272, *271*
Vacuum cleaner, 94-95, *94*
Vacuum pump, 93-94, *93*, *94*
Vacuum tubes, 590-595, 599; amplification factor, 592; development of, 590, *591*; diode, 590, *591*; diode as detector, 590, 592, modern types of, **597**, *597*; projects, 600; triode, 590-592, *591*, *592*; triode as detector and amplifier, 592-594, *593*; triode as oscillator, 594-595, *594*; Tungar rectifier, 590, *591*
Vaporization: application of, 260, *260*; heat of, 258; problems, 262
Variable, 25
Variation, 25-28; direct, **25**-27, *25*; inverse, **27**-28, *27*,
Vectors: combining forces by means of, 110, *110*; finding impedance with, 471-472, *471*
Velocity, 133-143, **134**, 151, 167-168; acceleration, 134-136; acceleration, and distance, relationship among, *137*; acceleration, and unbalanced force, 156-159, *155*, *156*, *157*, *159*; acceleration and inertia, 154-156, *155*; average, and distance, 133-134; average, of uniformly accelerated motion, **136**; of body thrown straight upward, 147-148, *147*; combined, 139-140, *139*, *140*, *141*; of freely falling bodies, 1-5, 144-147, *145*, *146*, *147*, 148, *148*, 151; and hitting force of moving body, 161-164, *162*, *163*, *164*; on inclined planes, 138-139, *145*; and inertia, 164; of light, 501-504, *502*, *503*; problems, 141-142, 152, 168-169; of projectiles, 165-166, 180, 182-184, *182*, *183*; projects, 142-143, 169, 189-190; of rotating bodies, 177, *177*; of sound, 104, 316-317, *319*; terminal, **148**, *148*; units of, **134**
Vertical motion: of body thrown straight upward, 147-148, *147*; of projectiles, 180-181, *181*, 182-184, *183*, 184
Vibrations: of air columns, **333**-335, *333*, *334*, *335*; fundamental and overtones, 333-335, *334*, *335*; and intensity of sound, 317-318, *318*; of musical sounds, 325, 337; project, 338; resonance, 330-331, *330*; of sound-producers, 312, *312*; of strings or wires, laws of, **332**, *332*, 333-334, *334*;

sympathetic, 329-**330**, *330*; ultrasonics, 336; *see also* Frequency of sound waves
Vision. *See* Eyesight
Volt, 358, *358*
Volta, Alessandro, and voltaic cell, 399-400, *400*
Voltage, 417-419, 421-422; A.C., effective, 468; A.C., out of phase with current, 471, *471*, 473, 474-475, *475*; of A.C. transformer, 459-460; distribution of, in circuit, 431, *431*; measuring, 417-418; problems, 422-423; parallel circuit, law of, 428-430; problems, 438, 464, 479; of series circuit, law of, 427-428; terminal, of cell, **433**-434, *434*; in transmission of electrical power, 460, *461*; and work done, 418-419
Voltaic cells, 400-411, *400*; action of, 403-405, *404*; connected in parallel, 434-435, *435*; connected in series, 434, *435*; dry cells, 406, *406*; electrolytic cells, 400-403, *400*, *401*, *402*; electromotive force (e.m.f.) of, 433-434, *434*; local action, **405**, *405*; polarization, **405**-406, *405*; problems, 410, 438; projects, 411; series-parallel connection of resistors with, 435-436, *435*; storage cells, 406-409, *407*, *408*, *409*; Wheatstone bridge, 436, *436*
Voltmeters, 417-418, *417*, *418*; connecting in circuit, 418
Volume: conversion table of measures, 19; English units of measurement, **16**, *18*; of gas, and pressure, 90-92, *91*; of gas, and absolute temperature, 245-248, *246*; of irregularly shaped body, finding, 35-36, *36*; metric units of, **17**-18, *18*

Warm front, 303, *303*
Water: boiling, laws of, 258-259; boiling, process of, 257-258; boiling point of, 259; as conductor of heat, 266-267, *266*; convection currents in, 264-265, *265*; density of, 34, *35*, *45*; electrolysis of, 400-402, *401*; evaporation of, 257, *257*; expansion of, 242-244, *242*, *243*; freezing and boiling points of, 234-235, *234*; heat exchange, law of, 251-252; heat of fusion of, 255-256; high specific heat of, 254-255, *254*; problems, 262; projects, 250, 262-263; supercooled, **243**, 297; vaporization of, 258; *see also* Forces in water and other liquids; Humidity; Hydraulic machines; Specific gravity
Water head, 48
Water systems, 72, *72*
Watt, James, and horsepower, 196; steam engine of, 278
Watt-hour meter, 420-421, *421*
Watts, 420; of A.C. circuit, 468
Wave theory of light, 484-485, *484*; and Einstein's formula for energy and matter, 581-582; photoelectric effect explained by, 575-576; proved by Young, 496-497; reflection explained according to, 489, *489*; refraction explained according to, 493-494, *494*; shaken by Einstein's special theory of relativity, 505; *see also* Light
Waves, light: and Fraunhofer lines, 572; infrared, **574**; length of, 497-498, *498*; length of, and color, 567; nature of, 498-500, *499*, *500*; ultraviolet, 574
Waves, radio (electromagnetic), 574-575, *575*, 587, 599
Waves, sound, 313-314, *314*, 322-323; absorption of, 321-322; in air columns of pipe organs or wind instruments, 333-335, *333*, *334*, *335*; amplitude of, **315**; condensations and rarefactions, 314, *314*, 315; directing, 322; in Doppler Effect, 329, *329*; formula for wave length, 319-**320**, *319*; frequency of, **315**; interference, constructive and destructive, 320-321, *320*, *321*; project, 324; reflection of, 321, *321*; as transverse waves, 315-**316**, *316*; wave length, **314**-315, *314*, *316*; *see also* Sound
Weather, 291-308; anticyclone, 304; cloud formation and lapse rate, 296-297; cold front, 296; cold-front storms, 299-300, *299*; cold squall, **299**; cyclonic storm, 302-304, *302*, *303*; forecasting, 304; hail, **298**; highs, 296, 304, *305*; humidity, 291-295; hurricanes or typhoons, 300-302, *301*; ice storms, 298; icing, 297; lows, 302-303, 304, *305*; maps of, making, 304, *305*; orographic precipitation, **299**; problems, 307; projects, 307-308; rain, 296; rainmaking, 305-306, *306*; sleet, **298**; snow, 297-298, *298*; thunderstorms, 298-299, *298*; tornadoes, **300**, *300*; warm front, 303, *303*; winds, 295-296, *295*
Wedge, 210, *210*
Weight, 31, 39; conversion table of, 19; definition of, 31, *36*; English units of, **16**; and mass, units of, distinguished, 34; metric units of, **18**; problems, 40; variations in, 32-33, *33*
Welding, transformer set-up for, 460-461, *461*
Weston-movement galvanometer, 413-415, *414*
Wet-and-dry bulb thermometer, 294
Wetting agents, 224-225
Wheatstone bridge, 436, *436*
Wheel and axle, 209, *209*
Wheels, belts, and gears, 211-214, *211*, *212*, *213*, *214*
Wilson cloud chamber, 618, *619*
Wind instruments: fundamental and overtones on, 334-335, *334*, *335*; principle of, 333, *333*
Winds, 295-296, *295*, 306; cold-front storms, 299-300, *299*; cyclonic storms, 300-304, *302*, *303*; hurricane or typhoons, 300-302, *301*; tornadoes, 300, *300*
Wire, resistance of, 431-**432**
Work, 193-195, **194**, *194*, 203; combustion, heat of, 276-277, 286; and heat, 275-276, *276*, 286; problems, 204; units of, 194-195, *194*, *195*; *see also* Energy; Force
Worm gear, 214, *213*, *214*

X-axis, in graphs, 26
X-rays, 579, *579*; gamma rays, 615, *616*

Y-axis, in graphs, 26
Young, Thomas, and wave theory of light proved by, 496-497

GIVEN

$t_o = t_u = 4.5$ sec ; $t_u = 4.5 - t_o$

$t = 11°C$

$g = 32'/sec^2$

$V_o = 1088$ '/sec

$H = \frac{1}{2} g t_o^2$

$V_x = V_o + 2t$

$D_o = D_u$

$D_o = \frac{1}{2} g t_o^2$

$D_u = V_t \times t_u$

$\frac{1}{2} g t_o^2 = V_t \times t_u$

$V_t = 1110$ '/sec

$$\Delta t_D = \frac{-b \pm \sqrt{b^2 - 4ac}}{2a}$$

Rubber rod, + cob, Sur
Glass rod + silk
plastic rod